The National Historical Publications Commission is charged by Congress with responsibility for planning and recommending the publication of historical documents and for collecting and preserving such documents. To further these aims the Commission has prepared a complete guide to all depositories of archives and manuscripts in the United States, with summary descriptions of their holdings.

The *Guide* covers more than thirteen hundred depositories and twenty thousand collections of personal papers and archival groups, located in all fifty states, the District of Columbia, Puerto Rico, and the Canal Zone, and ranging in time from Babylonian clay tablets to 1960.

Some of the important types of records briefly described are business account books, diaries, sermons, church registers, war documents, personal correspondence, memoirs, municipal transactions, and legal records. There is a 132-page index and full citations to all pertinent inventories, guides, and published accounts of the various categories and individual subjects.

A GUIDE TO ARCHIVES AND MANUSCRIPTS

IN THE UNITED STATES

A Guide to Archives and Manuscripts

in the United States

Compiled for the

National Historical Publications Commission

PHILIP M. HAMER, Editor

New Haven, Yale University Press

NATIONAL HISTORICAL PUBLICATIONS COMMISSION

PREFACE

The National Historical Publications Commission was established by act of Congress in 1934 and reconstituted by the Federal Records Act of 1950 (44 U.S.C. 393). It has been directed by Congress to cooperate with and encourage other agencies, both governmental and nongovernmental, in collecting, preserving, and publishing papers important for an understanding and appreciation of the history of the United States. This volume is the result of the cooperation of the Commission and its staff with more than one thousand archival agencies, historical societies, libraries, and other organizations in providing, within the compass of one volume, a guide to the archives and manuscripts that these organizations have collected and are preserving. These materials consist of hundreds of millions of individual items. Together they constitute a tremendously rich array of source materials for the study of the history of the United States and its relations with other nations and peoples.

This Guide has been produced under the editorial direction and supervision of the Commission's Executive Director, Philip M. Hamer, with the able assistance of Mrs. Elizabeth H. Buck and other members of his staff.

> Wayne C. Grover
> Archivist of the United States
> and Chairman, National Historical
> Publications Commission

CONTENTS

INTRODUCTION

For many years historical societies, libraries, archival agencies, and other organizations in the United States have properly considered it one of their important functions to collect and preserve manuscripts and archival materials, as well as books, newspapers, and other printed matter, in which those who wish to do so may follow the advice inscribed on the National Archives Building in Washington: "Study the Past." Need for a guide to the vast accumulations of such materials, for the most part unpublished, has long been recognized; and the present volume, prepared by the staff of the National Historical Publications Commission, represents an attempt to provide such a guide in convenient form for ready reference within the compass of one volume.

The volume here presented is not, and is not intended to be, a union catalog or a complete listing of all groups of archives and manuscripts in all depositories throughout the United States. As its name indicates, it is intended to be a guide that will assist a searcher in finding the particular groups of archives or manuscripts that contain the information he desires. It supplements and brings up to date earlier guides that were incomplete in their coverage or dealt only with the holdings of one depository, and, within the limits necessarily prescribed for one volume of convenient size, it provides also a more extensive coverage than any earlier guide.

In the present guide there is information about the archival and manuscript holdings of some 1300 depositories in the 50 States of the United States, the District of Columbia, Puerto Rico, and the Canal Zone. This information is organized in terms of entries for the individual depositories, and these entries are arranged alphabetically by States (or other major governmental units), within such units alphabetically by city or town where the depositories are located, and within cities and towns alphabetically by name of each depository concerned. For each depository the name and address are given, together with the names and titles of persons to whom communications regarding the holdings should be addressed. For each depository there is usually a general statement of its field of special interest and some indication of the size of its holdings. This is followed by specific mention of groups of papers considered to be of special interest.

The papers of individuals are named, as a general rule, when the person concerned has been of sufficient importance to have had a biographical sketch included in the Dictionary of American Biography or, for recent years, in Who's Who in America, or in comparable sources of biographical information, and when the quantity of papers amounts to some fifty items. Each individual is usually identified in terms of the State or States, or foreign country, in which he resided for substantial portions of his productive life, and his major occupation or the most important positions that he held. When available, the inclusive dates and some indication of the quantity of each group of papers are given. The papers of a total of more than 7,600 persons are identified, as well as the records of numerous business, political, social, and other organizations. Some attempt is made also to indicate special subjects covered by the papers of particular depositories.

At the end of the entry for each depository there is provided, when con-

veniently available, a reference to printed sources containing additional information about the holdings of that depository. No attempt is made to list unpublished indexes, catalogs, and the like that may facilitate the work of a person
visiting a depository, nor is there information about the times when a depository is open to the public. A prospective searcher, moreover, should remem-
ber that there may be restrictions on the use of certain papers. Before visiting
any depository he should communicate with an appropriate official regarding the
availability of papers he may wish to examine.

Every reasonable effort has been exerted to make this Guide as comprehensive and up-to-date as circumstances and the decision to limit it in size to one
volume have permitted. Requests for information have been sent to a large
number of libraries, historical societies, museums, archival agencies, and
other organizations. On the basis of information provided in response to this
request, and in published guides, lists, directories, and other sources that
were examined by the Commission's staff, draft entries were prepared in the
office of the National Historical Publications Commission in Washington and
submitted to the depositories concerned for approval or revision. As a result
many depositories submitted extensive lists of information to be added, and
this frequently required extensive rewriting of draft entries. About the end of
1959 depositories were requested to review the entries that had been prepared
for publication and bring them up to date as of January 1960. As a result,
there was a considerable amount of last-minute revising of copy. The volume
as published may be considered reasonably complete in coverage to the beginning of 1960.

Inevitably, some depositories (chiefly small or newly established ones)
have been unknowingly omitted and the information about the holdings of others,
for one reason or another, is not as complete as ideally one would like to have
it. Information that may be useful for future supplements to or revised editions of this Guide, if the Commission decides to have them prepared, will be
welcomed. Communications should be addressed to the Executive Director,
National Historical Publications Commission, National Archives Building,
Washington 25, D. C.

The production of the Guide would not have been possible without the fine
cooperation of officials and staff of many depositories. They are too numerous
to mention here, but grateful thanks are due all of them. In the Commission's
office, Mrs. Marian Rice Andersen was most helpful with suggestions in the
initial planning of this volume. At various stages, Mr. Fred L. Miller, Mrs.
Anne Harris Henry, and Miss F. Helen Beach provided valuable assistance in
the form of information and first drafts of entries. Mrs. Mary Darnall was
highly efficient in maintaining the files and typing copy with remarkable accu-
racy. As Administrative Assistant to the Commission's Executive Director,
Miss Maude Lyles has often been of the greatest assistance far beyond the call
of duty. And the contribution of Mrs. Elizabeth H. Buck, in preparing many of
the more difficult entries and in reviewing professionally much of the final
copy, has been invaluable.

                                            Philip M. Hamer

September 29, 1960

NOTE ON BIBLIOGRAPHICAL GUIDES

In addition to the numerous sources of information about the holdings of particular depositories that are cited later in this volume, many other published sources have been consulted in the course of its preparation. Only some of the more helpful ones can be specifically mentioned here. Diligent searchers, looking for materials on a particular subject, may find it profitable to examine them and to follow leads to still other sources that they suggest.

There are several general bibliographical guides from which helpful information may be gleaned. Still useful for twentieth-century publications is Edmund C. Burnett, "A List of Printed Guides to and Descriptions of Archives and Other Repositories of Historical Manuscript," in American Historical Association, Annual Report, 1896, I (1897), 481-512. Numerous guides to archives and manuscripts are listed in Henry P. Beers, Bibliographies in American History (rev. ed., 1942). The annual volumes of Writings on American History for the years 1902-1953, with gaps, contain useful entries for archives and manuscripts. Beginning in 1943 the American Archivist has contained annual bibliographies of "Writings on Archives and Manuscripts." Scattered information may be found in Robert B. Downs, American Library Resources: A Bibliographical Guide (1951); and Rose L. Vormelker, Special Library Resources (1941-47), 4 vols. The Harvard Guide to American History provides helpful guidance to information about archives and manuscripts. The most complete compilation of recent years is Ray Allen Billington, Guides to American History Manuscript Collections in Libraries of the United States (1952), reprinted from Mississippi Valley Historical Review (Dec. 1951).

Numerous specialized guides have been prepared. Regional in their coverage are such studies as Robert B. Downs (ed.), Resources of Southern Libraries: A Survey of Facilities for Research (1938); Charles W. Smith, A Union List of Manuscripts in Libraries of the Pacific Northwest (1931); and John Van Male, Resources of Pacific Northwest Libraries (1943). Even more restricted as regards the area of its coverage, but especially notable for the detailed and valuable information it contains, is Evarts B. Greene and Richard B. Morris, A Guide to the Principal Sources of Early American History in the City of New York (2d ed., 1953).

Several guides attempt, with notable success, to provide information about manuscript materials pertaining to particular subjects. Among these, with the subjects indicated by the titles, are William H. Allison, Inventory of Unpublished Material for American Religious History in Protestant Church Archives and Other Repositories (1910); Samuel F. Bemis and Grace G. Griffin, Guide to the Diplomatic History of the United States, 1775-1921 (1935); Henrietta M. Larson, Guide to Business History: Materials for the Study of American Business History and Suggestions for Their Use (1948); and Waldo G. Leland and Newton D. Mereness, Introduction to the American Official Sources for the Economic and Social History of the World War (1926). The Forest History Foundation, Inc., has published Forest History Sources of the United States and Canada, compiled by Cloudaugh M. Neiderheiser (1956); Edward Lurie has assembled valuable information in "Some Manuscripts in the History of Nineteenth Century American Natural Science," in Isis (Dec. 1953); and Whitfield J. Bell, Jr., has provided helpful guidance to manuscripts in the same field in his Early American Science, Needs and Opportunities for Study (1955).

Guides to particular kinds of manuscripts are illustrated by H. I. Poleman, A Census of Indic Manuscripts in the United States and Canada (1938), and Seymour de Ricci and W. J. Wilson, Census of Medieval and Renaissance Manuscripts in the United States and Canada (1935-40), a revision of which is being prepared.

During the early years of the twentieth century the Public Archives Commission of the American Historical Association sponsored the preparation of studies descriptive of the archives of all except a few of the states of the United States. These studies were published from time to time in Annual Reports of the Association; although they are now outdated to a large extent, many contain information still useful to students.

An early attempt at a nation-wide guide to manuscript collections was the publication by the Library of Congress of its Check List of Collections of Personal Papers in Historical Societies, University and Public Libraries, and Other Learned Institutions in the United States (1918). In revised form, with information about manuscripts in the possession of 130 depositories, this was issued a few years later as Manuscripts in Public and Private Collections in the United States (1924).

A most ambitious effort to provide guidance to the tremendous archival and manuscript resources of the United States was made by the Historical Records Survey, a unit of the Work Projects Administration, during the late thirties and the early forties of the twentieth century. It produced many volumes of inventories or other descriptions of state archives, county archives, municipal and town archives, church archives, federal archives outside the District of Columbia, and manuscripts. The published results of the Survey's activities are set forth in detail in its Bibliography of Research Projects Reports: Check List of Historical Records Survey Publications (1943). (In the present Guide no attempt has been made to describe county, church, business, or other archives except when they are known to be noncurrent and to have been transferred to a separately maintained archival establishment or manuscript depository; nor has it been considered advisable to attempt to describe manuscripts in private possession.)

Much scattered information about manuscript materials can be found in articles and news notes in local, state, and national publications. The American Historical Review, the Mississippi Valley Historical Review, the Journal of Southern History, the Library Quarterly, and the American Archivist are especially helpful. Manuscripts, and its predecessor Autograph Collector's Journal, has a special interest in autographs. The Directory of the Manuscript Society lists the special fields of interest of the Society's members.

Of great potential value to persons seeking information about manuscripts is the National Union Catalog of Manuscript Collections now in preparation at the Library of Congress according to rules comparable to those used for book cataloging. Catalog cards are prepared and are available for purchase as they are printed. Also of interest to users of the present Guide is a special guide to photographic reproductions of manuscripts that is expected to be published soon for the American Historical Association.

SHORT TITLES

Hist. Records Survey, <u>Guide</u> for Calif.

Historical Records Survey, <u>Guide to Depositories of Manuscript Collections in the United States: California</u> (1941. 75 p. Processed).

Hist. Records Survey, <u>Guide</u> for Fla.

Historical Records Survey, <u>Guide to Depositories of Manuscript Collections in the United States: Florida</u> (1940. 28 p. Processed).

Hist. Records Survey, <u>Guide</u> for Ill.

Historical Records Survey, <u>Guide to Depositories of Manuscript Collections in Illinois</u>. Preliminary Edition (1940. 55 p. Processed).

Hist. Records Survey, <u>Guide</u> for Iowa

Historical Records Survey, <u>Guide to Depositories of Manuscript Collections in the United States: Iowa</u> (1940. 47 p. Processed).

Hist. Records Survey, <u>Guide</u> for La.

Historical Records Survey, <u>Guide to Depositories of Manuscript Collections in Louisiana</u> (1941. 48 p. Processed).

Ring, <u>Reference List</u> for Maine, index

Elizabeth Ring, <u>Index to A Reference List of Manuscripts Relating to the History of Maine</u>, Vol. III (1941. 211 p.).

Hist. Records Survey, <u>Guide</u> for Mass.

Historical Records Survey, <u>Guide to Depositories of Manuscript Collections in Massachusetts, Preliminary Edition</u> (1939. 160 p. Processed).

Hist. Records Survey, <u>Guide</u> for Mich.

Historical Records Survey, <u>Guide to Depositories in the United States: Michigan</u> (1940. 75 p. Processed).

Hist. Records Survey, <u>Guide</u> for Minn.

Historical Records Survey, <u>Guide to Manuscript Depositories in the United States: Minnesota</u> (1941. 84 p. Processed).

Hist. Records Survey, _Guide_ for Mo.

Historical Records Survey, _Guide to Depositories of Manuscript Collections in the United States: Missouri_, Preliminary Edition (1940. 17 p. Processed).

Hist. Records Survey, _Guide_ for Nebr.

Historical Records Survey, _Guide to Depositories of Manuscript Collections in the United States: Nebraska_, Preliminary Edition (1940. 43 p. Processed).

Hist. Records Survey, _Guide_ for N. H.

Historical Records Survey, _Guide to Depositories of Manuscript Collections in the United States: New Hampshire_ (1940. 44 p. Processed).

Hist. Records Survey, _Guide_ for N. J.

Historical Records Survey, _Guide to Manuscript Depositories in the United States: New Jersey_, Preliminary Edition (1941. 62 p. Processed).

Hist. Records Survey, _Guide_ for N. C.

Historical Records Survey, _Guide to Manuscript Depositories in the United States: North Carolina_ (1940. 18 p.).

Hist. Records Survey, _Guide_ for Pa.

Historical Records Survey, _Guide to Depositories of Manuscript Collections in Pennsylvania_ (1939. 126 p.).

Hist. Records Survey, _Guide_ for Oreg.- Wash.

Historical Records Survey, _Guide to Depositories of Manuscript Collections in the United States: Oregon-Washington_ (1940. 42 p. Processed).

Hist. Records Survey, _Guide_ for Wis.

Historical Records Survey, _Guide to Manuscript Depositories in Wisconsin_ (1941. 36 p. Processed).

Hist. Records Survey, _Guide_ for New York City

Historical Records Survey, _Guide to Manuscript Depositories in New York City_ (1941. 150 p. Processed).

Hist. Records Survey, _Guide_ for N.Y. State

Historical Records Survey, _Guide_

to Depositories of Manuscript
Collections in New York State
(Exclusive of New York City)
(1941. 512 p.).

[and its] Supplement   Supplement (1944. 23 p.).

Hist. Records Survey, 100 Sample Entries   Historical Records Survey, Guide
to Depositories of Manuscript Col-
lections in the United States: 100
Sample Entries (1938. 134 p.
Processed).

Allison, Inventory   William H. Allison, Inventory of
Unpublished Material for Ameri-
can Religious History (1910).

Forest History Sources   Forest History Sources of the
United States and Canada, com-
piled by Clodaugh M. Neiderheiser, published by Forest History Foundation, Inc., Saint Paul,
1956. 140 p.

Ill. Libraries   Illinois Libraries, published by
the Illinois State Library.
(Monthly, except in July and
August.)

Greene and Morris, Guide   Greene and Morris, A Guide to
the Principal Sources for Early
American History (1600-1800)
in the City of New York (1953.
400 p.).

De Ricci, Census   Seymour De Ricci and W. J. Wil-
son, Census of Medieval and
Renaissance Manuscripts in the
United States and Canada (1935).

ALABAMA

AUBURN

Auburn University Libraries. Clyde
H. Cantrell, Director of Libraries.

Holdings: Included are papers of
William L. Yancey (Ala.; U.S. Rep.,
Confed. Sen.), 1845-65 (45 pieces).

BIRMINGHAM 3

Birmingham Public Library. Fant
Hill Thornley, Director.

Holdings: 74 vols. and 278 pieces,
1818-1941, in the library's Southern
Collection. They relate chiefly to Birmingham and Jefferson County, Ala.,
and, in less degree, to the South. Included are papers of Erskine Ramsay
(Ala.; mining engineer, industrialist),
1889-1953 (a large quantity not yet ful-
ly examined and not included in total
holdings shown above); papers of Edmund Rucker (Ala.; railroad pres., industrialist), 1864-1924 (110 pieces); a
collection of autograph letters of Alabama Governors and Senators, 1818-
1941 (55 pieces); some plantation and
other account books, minutes of several local societies and associations,
and records of an iron company; and
the Hill Ferguson Collection of letters,
memoirs, and other materials assembled by the Birmingham Historical Society.
    See Sarah A. Maxwell, "Tutwiler
Collection of Southern History and Literature," in Special Libraries, 33:367-
369 (Dec. 1942).

BIRMINGHAM 9

Howard College Library. F. Wilbur
Helmbold, Librarian.

Holdings: A considerable collection, relating chiefly to Baptists in
Alabama, the early history of Howard
College, and other aspects of Alabama
history. Included are papers of
James H. Devotie (Ala., Ga.; Baptist
minister), 1835-83 (7 vols. and 190
pieces), consisting of Bible notes,
correspondence, and minutes of the
Alabama Baptist State Convention,
1848-52, records of the Georgia Home
Mission Board, 1877-81, and correspondence about the founding of Howard
College in Marion (Ala.); prescrip-
tions used in a Marion hospital, 1863-
64 (2 vols.); letters and business records of members of the Heflin family,
including James Thomas Heflin (Ala.;
lawyer, U.S. Rep. and Sen.), 1830-
1911 (63 pieces); and papers of Joseph J. Willett (Ala.; lawyer) and his
family, 90,000 pieces, centering
around the activities of 3 generations
of lawyers in Anniston and Carrollton, Ala., and having important political relationships with the Democratic Party.

MAXWELL AIR FORCE BASE

Archives Branch, USAF Historical
Division, Air University. Marguerite K. Kennedy, Chief.

Holdings: 14,500 cubic ft.,
chiefly 1907 to date, consisting for
the most part of monthly and semi-
annual AAF/USAF histories, with supporting documents, prepared by both
lower- and higher-echelon units in ac-
cordance with the AAF/USAF historical program, which was begun in 1942
and continued after the establishment
of the United States Air Force in 1947.
There are also a collection of early
material (including a chronology of
United States military aeronautics,

dating back to the Civil War), translations of certain captured German and
Japanese documents of World War II,
a considerable amount of material furnished by the British Air Ministry, and
special collections given to the Archives by men prominent in military
aeronautics or their heirs.

See Marguerite K. Kennedy, "The
Archives of the Historical Division,
USAF," in Am. Archivist, 17:123-134
(Apr. 1954).

MONTGOMERY 5

Department of Archives and History,
State of Alabama. Peter A. Brannon,
Director; (Mrs.) Virginia Jones, Man-
uscripts Archivist.

Holdings: (1) Noncurrent official
records of the Territory and State of
Alabama, 1818 to recent date, held by
the Department as the State's archival
agency; and (2) other papers of historical value, relating chiefly to Alabama.

Papers of political leaders include
those of John H. Bankhead (Ala.; Confed. Army officer, planter, U.S. Rep.
and Sen.), 1891-1943 (20 drawers);
John H. Bankhead, Jr. (Ala.; pres. of
coal company, U.S. Sen.), 1917-46 (3
drawers); William B. Bankhead (Ala.;
lawyer, U.S. Rep.), 1896-1940 (32
file boxes); Clement Comer Clay (Ala.;
U.S. Rep. and Sen.) and Clement Claiborne Clay (Ala.; U.S. Sen., Confed.
Sen. and diplomat), 1818-66 (3 vols.,
typed); Jabez Lamar Monroe Curry
(Ala., Va.; U.S. and Confed. Rep.,
pres. of Howard College, Ala., prof.
at Richmond College, Minister to
Spain), 1786-1903 (2,500 pieces); Jefferson Davis (Miss.; U.S. Rep. and
Sen.; Sec. War, Confed. Pres.), a
large collection; Stanley H. Dent, Jr.
(Ala.; lawyer, U.S. Rep.), 1908-20 (6
folders); Bolling Hall (Ga., Ala.;
planter, lawyer, U.S. Rep.) and his
descendants, 1786-1905 (1,178 pieces);
Andrew Jackson (Tenn.; U.S. Army of-

ficer and Pres.), 1775-1828 (200
pieces relating to East Florida); Thomas G. Jones (Ala.; Gov., U.S. dist.
court judge), 1881-1943 (4 drawers);
William Rufus King (N.C., Ala.; U.S.
Rep. and Sen., Minister to France,
U.S. Vice Pres.) and his family, 19th
century ($1\frac{1}{2}$ drawers); John Tyler
Morgan (Ala.; Confed. Army officer,
U.S. Sen.), 50 pieces; Lewis Parsons (Ala.; lawyer, Gov.), 1830-91
($\frac{1}{2}$ drawer); Benjamin F. Perry (S.
C.; lawyer, journalist, Gov.), 1818-
79 (1 drawer); Israel Pickens (N.C.,
Ala.; U.S. Rep. from N.C., Gov. of
and U.S. Sen. from Ala.), 1805-84
(20 folders); Charles Tait (Ga., Ala.;
planter, U.S. Sen. and dist. court
judge), 1768-1874 (1,000 pieces); Os-
car W. Underwood (Ala.; U.S. Rep.
and Sen.), 1895-1930 (30 drawers);
John Williams Walker (Ala.; lawyer,
U.S. Sen.), 1820-38 (15 folders); Leroy Pope Walker (Ala.; Confed. Sec.
War), 1861-65 (200 pieces); Thomas
H. Watts (Ala.; Confed. Attorney
Gen., Gov.), 1818-92 (150 pieces);
John A. Winston (Ala.; planter, Gov.,
Confed. Army officer), 125 folders
constituting a personal collection; and
William L. Yancey (Ala.; U.S. Rep.,
Confed. Sen.), 1846-63 (1,000 pieces).

Papers of other persons include
those of William Wirt Allen (Ala.;
Confed. Army officer), 1863-65 (545
items); William C. Avery (Ala.; physician, naturalist), 1875-1919 (275
items); Richard A. Blount (Ga.;
chairman of Georgia-Alabama Boundary Commission), 1816-60 (25 folders); John Coffee (Tenn., Ala.; Creek
War and War of 1812 officer, survey-
or), 1796-1887 (1,500 pieces); John
Witherspoon Du Bose (Ala.; planter,
author), 1857-1917 (3 drawers); Peter J. Hamilton (Ala.; historian, Federal judge in Puerto Rico), 1564-1888
(21 folders), including a collection
assembled by him; William Joseph
Hardee (Ga., Ala.; U.S. and Confed.

Army officer), 1862-65; Arthur Fort Harman (Ala.; educator), 1902-46 (4 drawers); Juliet Ann Opie Hopkins (Ala.; administrator of Confed. hospitals), 1861-67 (425 pieces); James Marion Jones (Ala.; City Commissioner of Birmingham), 1913-40 (3 drawers); Thomas C. McClellan (Ala.; State supreme court justice), 1903-23 (25 folders); Robert McKee (Ky., Ala.; journalist), 1860-99 (538 items); Colin J. McRae (Ala., Honduras; merchant, Confed. financial agent in Europe), 1837-66 (200 items); Basil Manly, Sr. (S.C., Ala.; Baptist minister, Univ. of Ala. pres.), 1827-1930 (22 folders); Alexander B. Meek (Ala.; author, State attorney gen., promoter of public school system) and his family, 1814-1903 ($^1/_2$ drawer); John Turner Milner (Ga., Ala.; civil engineer, industrialist) and his family, 1776-1936 (175 items); Thomas M. Owen (Ala.; historian, archivist), 1901-21 (42 file boxes); Albert J. Pickett (Ala.; planter, historian), 1800-66 (1,000 pieces), including notes and letters relating to the history of Alabama; Reuben Saffold (Ala.; State supreme court justice), 1854-57 (4 folders); and Earl Van Dorn (Miss.; U.S. and Confed. Army officer), 1842-1915 (200 pieces).

Records of organizations include those of the Alabama Anthropological Society, 1908-19, and of the Alabama Historical Society, 1824-1919 (10 drawers). The Department has on deposit and administers a quantity of records collected by the Alabama Conference Historical Society and relating chiefly to the Methodist Church in central and southern Alabama; included are record books of districts and circuits and records of several local churches. The Department also has other records of the Methodist Church, dating from 1836; extensive records of Baptist, Episcopal, and Presbyterian churches in Alabama; and typed copies of birth, marriage, and other records of the [Catholic] Cathedral of the Im-

maculate Conception, Mobile, dating from 1704. There are also numerous diaries, scrapbooks, and maps and a collection of autograph letters of U.S. Presidents.

TALLADEGA

Savery Library, Talladega College. Margaret H. Scott, Librarian.

Holdings: 22 linear ft., 1867-1954, consisting chiefly of the archives of the College. There are also minutes of the Alabama State Teachers' Association, 1882-1912; and reports of the Congregational Conference of Alabama Churches, 1871-1920.

TUSKEGEE

Department of Records and Research, Tuskegee Institute. (Mrs.) Jessie P. Guzman, Director.

Holdings: Over 150 file drawers of manuscripts, 1887-1959, relating chiefly to the progress and education of the American Negro. There are extensive records of the administration of Tuskegee Institute and the national and regional activities of Robert Russa Moton (Va., Ala.; commandant at Hampton Institute, pres. of Tuskegee), 1916-35 (111 file drawers). Included also are papers of George Washington Carver (Iowa, Ala.; botanist, agricultural scientist at Tuskegee), 1887-1943 (16 file drawers); Clinton J. Calloway (Tenn., Ala.; director of extension dept., Tuskegee), 1916-30 (3 file drawers), relating to the rural school program in Alabama financed in part by the Julius Rosenwald Fund; Albon L. Holsey (Ga., Ala.; asst. to the pres. of Tuskegee, and sec. of National Negro Business League), 1904-47 (16 file drawers), relating chiefly to the work of the league; and William

Taylor Burwell Williams (Ind., Ala.; field director of Hampton Institute, dean and vice pres. of Tuskegee), 1902-40 (4 file drawers), concerning particularly his work with the Anna T. Jeanes and John F. Slater educational funds. One large collection, chiefly of news clippings and magazine articles relating to the social problems and history of the Negro, 1910-59 (482 file drawers), contains an undetermined amount of correspondence relating to the Negro carried on by Monroe Nathan Work (N.C., Ala.; sociologist, director of dept. of records and research, Tuskegee), 1908-38. (Note: Only the last collection is at present open to the public for research purposes.)

UNIVERSITY

University of Alabama Library. (Mrs.) Sarah A. Verner, Librarian, Rare Book Room.

Holdings: In the Rare Book Room there are 85 vols. and 665,000 manuscript items, 1797-1952, relating chiefly to the South and to Alabama in particular.

Papers of individuals include those of James Bowron (Tenn., Ala.; iron and steel manufacturer), 1874-1928 (428 items), comprising diaries, correspondence, and industrial records; Iveson Brookes (Ga., S.C.; Baptist minister), 1811-1911 (3,505 items), chiefly Civil War; Henry De Lamar Clayton (Ga., Ala.; lawyer, Confed. Army officer, Univ. of Ala. pres.), 1840-89 (1,931 items), containing battle reports, muster rolls, and a diary; Henry De Lamar Clayton, Jr. (Ala.; lawyer, U.S. Rep. and dist. court judge), 1882-1930 (46,433 items); Landon Cabell Garland (Ala.; Univ. of

Ala. pres.), 1862-64 (2 letter books); Josiah Gorgas (Ala.; U.S. and Confed. Army officer), 1821-1942 (681 items); William Crawford Gorgas (sanitarian, U.S. Army Surgeon Gen.), 1875-1927 (2,000 items); James Thomas Heflin (Ala.; lawyer, U.S. Rep. and Sen.), 1903-31 (12,951 letters, 223 scrapbooks, and 7,000 miscellaneous items) [restricted]; Sam (Samuel Francis) Hobbs (Ala.; U.S. Rep.), 1887-1952 (36,269 items); Robert Jemison (Ala.; businessman, Confed. Sen.), 1797-1916 (1,500 items), containing information on stagecoach lines, saw and flour mills, and early railroads; Basil Manly (S.C., Ala.; Baptist clergyman, Univ. of Ala. pres.), 1821-1930 (3,000 items); Henry Clifton Pannell (Ala.; Univ. of Ala. prof.), 1923-46 (700 items); John Gill Shorter (Ala.; jurist, Confed. Rep., Gov.), 1861-63 (65 items); Oliver Day Street (Ala.; U.S. dist. attorney for Northern Dist. of Ala.), 1888-1942 (21,423 items); and Julia Strudwick Tutwiler (Ala.; educator, prison reform advocate), 1873-1910 (25 items).

Other papers include records of the Alabama Industrial and Scientific Society, 1890-1900 (4 vols.); Brierfield (Ala.) Iron Works, 1864-74 (9 vols.); Shelby (Ala.) Iron Works, 1859-1915 (494,212 items); and a country store, 1907-36 (111 items). There are also papers on the mining industry in Birmingham, 1889-1940 (298 items); on cock fighting and game chickens, 1892-1901 (176 items); and on plantation operations, including the emancipation of slaves.

See James F. Doster, "The Shelby Iron Works Collection," in Business Historical Society, Bulletin, 26: 214-217 (Dec. 1952).

ALASKA

COLLEGE

University of Alaska Museum. Ivar Skarland, Director.

Holdings: A few manuscripts relating to Alaska, including a manuscript by a Jesuit priest on the language of the Tanana Indians.

JUNEAU

Alaska Historical Library and Museum. Edward L. Keithahn, Librarian and Curator.

Holdings: 277 vols., 1821-1926, relating chiefly to Alaska. Included are an account of the flight of the dirigible Norge over the North Pole, 1926, by Riiser Larsen, navigator; papers of Father Veniaminoff (Bishop Innocenti), 1821-40) (3 vols.); and diaries of missionaries at Gambell, St. Lawrence Island, 1898-1906. There are also Alaska customs records, 1867-1914 (263 vols.); a volume labeled "American Occupation 1867," consisting of copies of reports and letters of the collector of customs at Sitka, 1867-69; a volume labeled "Consent Government of Sitka, Alaska," 1867, containing the charter and organic act of Sitka, ordinances, and tax and license records; a volume of the proceedings of the Sitka city council, 1867-73; and police dockets and a municipal court docket of Nome, 1899-1900 (3 vols.).

—oOo—

Office of the Secretary of Alaska.

Holdings: Alaska does not have a central depository for its archives, but in 1955 reports of the Governor, from 1885, Territorial election returns, from 1918, and session laws, 1913-55, were kept in the vault of the Secretary of Alaska. Other noncurrent records were kept by various Territorial agencies.

GRAND CANYON

Grand Canyon National Park. Superintendent.

Holdings: 4 vols. and a quantity of other pieces, 1871-1955, relating to the Park and the Colorado River. Included are unsorted notes and other papers of François Emile Matthes (Mass., D.C., Calif.; topographer, geologist), on the topographical mapping of the Grand Canyon, 1902-3; journals of W. P. Powell, nephew and companion of John Wesley Powell on the Colorado River navigation, 1871-72 (3 vols., restricted); a copy of a report by Robert Brewster Stanton (Ohio, N.Y.; civil and mining engineer) on a preliminary survey, 1889-90, for a route for Denver, Colorado Canyon, and Pacific Railroad Co.; a journal of a Colorado River trip from Wyoming to Arizona, 1896; typescripts of other Colorado River journals, 1871-1955; and packets of unsorted letters, 1890-1910, on mining and the hotel business in the area.

PHOENIX

Department of Library and Archives. 309 State House. Mulford Winsor, Director.

Holdings: Documents occupying 4,000 sq. ft. of floor space and consisting chiefly of (1) noncurrent official records held by the Department as the State's archival agency; and (2) a few diaries of Arizona pioneers and copies of diaries of pioneer Mormon families. In the former group are Territorial records, 1864-1912, chiefly institutional and county records; and

a large quantity of State, county, and municipal records, 1912-49.

PRESCOTT

Sharlott Hall Historical Museum of Arizona. Elsie M. Knight, Curator.

Holdings: A collection of manuscripts, 1850-1905, relating chiefly to Arizona. Included are a few diaries, some reminiscences of pioneers, and papers on such subjects as missions, explorations, Mormon colonization, the Civil War period, and Indian wars. (The depository was formerly known as the Prescott Historical Society.)

TUCSON

Arizona Pioneers' Historical Society. 949 East Second St. (Mrs.) Yndia S. Moore, Historical Secretary.

Holdings: 7,000 collections relating chiefly to Arizona and the Southwest. Included are papers of Will C. Barnes (Ariz.; author, political leader, cattleman), 1901-36 (36 pocket diaries and 4 folders); Leon Kneipp (Ariz.; author, forester); and Frank C. Lockwood (Ill., Ariz.; author). There is biographical and other material prepared by members of the society. The W. J. Holliday Collection includes manuscripts, photographs, and maps, as well as rare books.

—oOo—

Special Collections Division, University of Arizona Library. Phyllis Ball, Special Collections Librarian.

Holdings: A quantity of manuscripts pertaining chiefly to Arizona. Included are correspondence of Henry

Fountain Ashurst (Ariz., D.C.; lawyer, U.S. Sen.), 1913-53 (1 box), chiefly relating to the U.S. Senatorial election of 1940; letters, reports, and other papers of Howard Judson Hall (Ariz.; prof. of English and librarian at Univ. of Ariz.), 1892-1904 (1 box); letters and legal papers of Eugene Semmes Ives (Ariz.; lawyer, State legislator), 1901-16 (38 vols. and 8 boxes); papers of Charles D. Poston (Ariz.; explorer, Terr. Delegate to Cong.), consisting of a manuscript on the Apache Indians and lectures on religion and education; and unpublished manuscripts and other papers of Mary Kidder Rak (Calif., Ariz.; social worker, cattle raiser, author), 20th century (2 boxes). There are also records of the office of the president of the University, 1891-1914, including official correspondence and other papers of presidents Theodore B. Comstock, Howard Billman, Millard M. Parker, F. Yale Adams, and Arthur H. Wilde. Other holdings include records of a merchandise store and various banking concerns in Tucson and Tombstone, Ariz., 1867-1909 (100 vols. and 11 boxes); papers relating to the United Verde Copper Co., 1886-89 (1 portfolio); papers relating to the establishment of Saguaro National Monument, 1930-37 (1 portfolio); and archives of Pima County, Ariz., 1864-1923 (53 containers of various kinds).

CONWAY

Hendrix College Library. (Mrs.) Raylene M. Steelman, Librarian.

Holdings: Manuscripts, from 1845, relating to the Methodist Church in Arkansas. Some belong to the Methodist Historical Society of the Little Rock Conference (Rev. Kenneth L. Spore, Custodian, Monticello, Ark.), among them journals of the Little Rock Conference, 1854-81, several district conference journals, and some personal papers of men prominent in the early days of the conference. Other papers belong to the Methodist Historical Society of the North Arkansas Conference (Rev. N. Lee Cate, Secretary, Jacksonville, Ark.), 1845-1947, among them journals of a few district conferences, treasurer's books of the North Arkansas Conference Woman's Society of Christian Service, 1916-43, and records of several churches. Belonging to the College Library are "Ten Years Recollections, 1859-1869," of a member of the Arkansas Conference and one volume of brief life stories and pictures of more than 100 members of the Woman's Society of Christian Service.

FAYETTEVILLE

University of Arkansas Library. Georgia Clark, Reference Librarian.

Holdings: 22,289 items, 1823-1959, relating chiefly to Arkansas. Included are papers of Charles H. Brough (Ark.; Gov.), 1895-1935 (9,531 pieces); Cyrus Byington (Mass., Miss.; missionary to the Choctaw), 1819-61 (31 pieces); James S. Deas (Ark.; planter), 1830s-50s (50 pieces), con-

sisting of maps, deeds, and other papers dealing with property in Southwest Arkansas; John Gould Fletcher (England; poet), consisting of correspondence, original manuscripts of poems, journals, and other items (not yet arranged or counted); Thomas C. McRae (Ark.; U.S. Rep., Gov.), 1879-1929 (1,538 pieces); Tom P. Morgan (Ark.; humorist), 1864-1929 (116 pieces); Harvey Parnell (Ark.; Gov.), 1929-31 (88 pieces), consisting principally of speeches; Nathaniel M. Ragland (Ark.; clergyman), 1860-1933 (90 pieces); Harmon L. Remmell (Ark.; industrialist, Republican leader), 1879-1925 (7,304 pieces); Daniel H. Reynolds (Ark.; Confed. Army officer), 1861-66 (131 pieces); David Y. Thomas (Ark.; political scientist), 1914-38 (415 pieces); Jesse Turner (Ark.; State supreme court judge), 1831-87 (31 pieces); and David Walker (Ark.; State supreme court judge), 1841-79 (93 pieces).

The University's folklore project, covering Arkansas and the Ozark Mountain region, has made 309 reels of recording tape, with transcriptions, of folk songs, sayings, tales, fiddle tunes, etc. Present also are letters, ledgers and account books, and church records, chiefly relating to Arkansas and the Presbyterian church in Arkansas, and to the University of Arkansas, 1872-1953 (1,014 pieces arranged, and many more yet to be arranged).

—oOo—

Washington County Historical Society. P.O. Box 225. Tom Feathers, Secretary.

Holdings: Materials relating to the county, since 1830, including records of several churches, a few business records, copies of inscriptions in cemeteries, and genealogies.

LITTLE ROCK

Arkansas History Commission. Department of Archives and History. Ted R. Worley, Executive Secretary.

Holdings: (1) 1,020 vols., 1823-1937, of noncurrent official records of the Territorial and State governments and of many counties, held by the Department as the State's archival agency; and (2) 47 vols., 13,634 items, and 2 cu. ft. of other manuscripts, 1815-1911, relating chiefly to Arkansas.

Among papers of individuals are those of Calvin Comins Bliss (Ark.; newspaper editor), 1841-80 (600 items); Elbert H. English (Ark.; State supreme court justice), 1844-69 (295 items), many of them papers of or relating to the Masonic Order; Harris Flanagin (Ark.; Gov.), 1846-74 (30 items); James M. Keller (Ky., Tenn., Ark.; physician, Confed. Army surgeon), 1860-1905 (96 items); John E. Knight (Ark.; newspaper editor), 1815-57 (102 items); Asa Morgan (Ark.; Confed. Army officer), 1842-65 (152 items); James Parrott (Ark.; Confed. Army officer), 1827-74 (120 items); R. Minor Wallace (Ark.; lawyer, U. S. Rep.), 1900-12 (2 cu. ft.); Samuel W. Williams (Ark.; Confed. Army officer, State supreme court justice), 1814-69 (203 items); and William E. Woodruff (Ark.; newspaper editor, State treasurer, land agent and specu-lator), 1820-82 (10,000 items).

Other holdings include U.S. Census returns for Arkansas on agriculture, manufactures, mortality, and defective, dependent, and delinquent classes, 1860-80 (25 vols.); a collection of autograph letters of Arkansas Governors and U. S. Senators, 1839-1910 (41 items); 6 vols. of Civil War diaries; and a collection of business papers, 1830-70, chiefly of merchants but including 2 vols. of steamboat accounts. There are also some papers of a planter, 1854-81, and a few personal journals and account books.

See Ark. History Commission, Bulletins of Information, Nos. 2 and 5 (June 1912, Mar. 1913), William E. Woodruff Papers; Index (1955. 24 p. Processed), Catalogue of the Papers of Calvin Comins Bliss (1955. 7 p. Processed), and Catalogue of the Robert Wilson Trimble Collection (1955. 8 p. Processed); and the Department's processed list of its principal nonarchival manuscript holdings (1955. 4 p.).

—oOo—

Arkansas Library Commission, 506½ Center St. (Mrs.) Margaret Yost, Reference Librarian.

Holdings: Archives of and manuscripts belonging to the Authors and Composers Society of Arkansas (organized in 1914). Included are 3 vols. of biographical material on Arkansas writers and musicians for the period since about 1865.

CALIFORNIA

ANGWIN

Pacific Union College Library. Lois J. Walker, Librarian.

Holdings: 3 boxes of mimeographed records of Japanese war crime trials (held after World War II), collected by an interpreter during the trials.

BERKELEY 4

Bancroft Library, University of California. George P. Hammond, Director.

Holdings: 3,500,000 items, 1500-1955, relating chiefly to western North America and especially to California and Mexico. The basic part of the collection was assembled by Hubert Howe Bancroft (Calif.; historian) and was acquired by the University of California in 1905.

Papers of political leaders include those of Sir John Bowring (Hawaii; diplomat), 1842-70 (8 vols.); Mason Brayman (Ill.; lawyer, editor, Gov. of Idaho Terr.), 1876-81 (150 items); William M. Gwin (Calif.; U.S. Sen.), 1857-85 (100 items); George J. Hatfield (Calif.; U.S. dist. attorney, Lt. Gov., State sen.), 1917-53 (80,000 items); Hiram W. Johnson (Calif.; Gov., U.S. Sen.), 1910-45 (collection unsorted); Robert W. Kenny (Calif.; judge, State sen., State attorney gen.), 1920-47 (40,000 items); Franklin K. Lane (Calif.; Interstate Commerce Commissioner, Sec. Interior), 1908-19 (250 items), consisting of speeches and press releases; Thomas O. Larkin (Calif.; merchant, U.S. consul at Monterey, naval agent), 1822-56 (36 vols. and 181 folders); Anne Martin (Nev.; feminist, political leader), 1915-40 (10,000 items); Frank F. Merriam

(Calif.; State sen., Gov.), 1898-1947 (collection unsorted); Culbert L. Olson (Calif.; lawyer, State sen., Gov.), 1912-49 (5,000 items); George C. Pardee (Calif.; mayor of Oakland, Gov.), 1898-1912 (53,000 items); James Duval Phelan (Calif.; Mayor of San Francisco, U.S. Sen.), 1906-30 (25,000 items); Gaspar de Portola (Spain; 1st Gov. of Upper Calif.), 1769-85 (15 items); second Count of Revilla Gigedo (Mexico; Viceroy), 1789-94 (37 vols.); Chester H. Rowell (Calif.; editor, political leader), 1887-1946 (16,000 items); Mariano Guadalupe Vallejo (Mexico, Calif.; military and political leader), 1780-1875 (36 vols. and 2,000 items); and John D. Works (Calif.; judge, U.S. Sen.), 1910-20 (1,500 items).

Papers of men in the armed services of the United States include those of Christopher Carson, known as Kit Carson (N. Mex.; trapper, Indian agent, U.S. Army officer), 1847-67 (500 items); John C. Frémont (D.C., Calif.; explorer, U.S. Army officer, U.S. Sen.), 1847-90 (50 items); Robert Bradford Marshall (Calif.; geographer, U.S. Army engineer), 1889-1949 (8,000 items); and Charles F. Pond (Calif.; U.S. naval officer), 1876-1929 (collection unsorted).

Papers of literary and newspaper figures include those of Gertrude Atherton (Calif.; novelist), 1917-48 (3,400 items); Mary Austin (Calif., N. Mex.; novelist, dramatist), 1903-32 (75 items); Ambrose Bierce (Calif.; short-story writer, journalist), 1893-1913 (100 items); Gelett Burgess (Calif.; author), 1873-1951 (4,000 items); Ina Donna Coolbrith (Calif.; poet), 1906-28 (3,000 items); Dane Coolidge (Calif.; novelist, naturalist), 1903-31 (7,000 items);

Charles Caldwell Dobie (Calif.; author), 1905-40 (30,000 items); Francis Bret Harte (Calif., N.Y.; short-story writer), 1863-1901 (366 items); Wallace Irwin (N.Y., Calif.; author), 1915-58 (600 items); Joseph Henry Jackson (Calif.; journalist, author), 1937-55 (3,000 items); Charles F. McGlashan (Calif.; journalist, historian), 1870-1925 (500 items); Cincinnatus Hiner Miller, known as Joaquin Miller (Oreg., Calif.; poet, playwright), 1872-1913 (75 items); Frank Norris (Calif.; novelist), 1885-1903 (300 items); Fremont Older (Calif.; newspaper editor), 1907-35 (1,500 items); Blanch Partington (Calif.; journalist), 1882-1946 (800 items); and George Sterling (Calif.; poet), 1901-26 (420 items).

Other personal papers include those of Herbert E. Bolton (Calif.; historian), 1906-52 (290,000 items); William A. Carter (Wyo.; trader), 1860-84 (900 items); Marcel E. Cerf (Calif.; judge), 1863-1916 (14,900 items); George Davidson (Calif.; scientist), 1846-1911 (41,000 items); John T. Doyle (Calif.; lawyer), 1858-1906 (34 vols.); Carl Ewald Grunsky (Calif.; civil engineer), 1880-1930 (500 items); Robert Underwood Johnson (N.Y.; editor, author, conservationist, Ambassador to Italy), 1889-1924 (1,243 items); William Keith (Calif.; artist), 1850-1911 (collection unsorted); Thomas J. Mooney (Calif.; labor leader, prisoner), 1906-42 (44,600 items); Jackson Harvey Ralston (Calif., D.C.; lawyer, author); William Henry Smythe (Calif.; engineer, writer), 1869-1936 (4,000 items); Adolph Sutro (Nev., Calif.; mining engineer, mayor of San Francisco), 1860-95 (13,000 items); August Vollmer (Calif.; criminologist, police administrator), 1898-1945 (7,600 items); Lorenzo G. Yates (Calif.; naturalist), 1852-1909 (200 items); and Henry M. Yerlington (Nev.; rail-road administrator), 1863-1940 (9,500 items).

The Library has some national, State, and city records, among them records of the customhouses at Monterey, Calif., 1847-65 (500 items), and at San Francisco, 1849-70 (10,560 items); the Archives of California (63 vols.), copies made before the originals were destroyed in the fire of 1906; and records of the California Geological Survey, 1860-84 (900 items), the San Francisco board of aldermen, 1852-55 (25 vols.), the San Francisco graft prosecution, 1906-10 (101 vols.), and the Panana Pacific International Exposition, 1913-16 (773,000 items). Included also are records of the Pacific Coast Committee on American Principles and Fair Play, 1942-45 (3,500 items), relating largely to the treatment of the Japanese during World War II. Included, too, are many collections of papers of early California families of the Spanish and Mexican eras; and extensive copies (transcripts, photostats, and microfilms) of papers relating to missions in Mexico, California, the southwestern United States, and Alaska and to Spanish and Mexican land grants in California.

Records of industry and business include papers of three mining companies, 1854-1921 (20,000 items); a lumber company, 1886-1940 (54 vols.); a ranch at Fresno, 1888-1940 (50,000 items); a sugar refining company, 1886-1948 (15,000 items); and a water supply company at San Francisco, 1903-41 (10,000 items). Among the larger collections of papers of business firms are those of the Albert Dibblee [commercial] Enterprises, 1849-95 (350 vols.); John Kentfield and Co. (lumbering and shipping), 1853-1923 (174,000 items); and the Miller and Lux Co. (ranching), 1900-20 (890,000 items).

The Bancroft Library Foreign Microfilm Project, begun in 1948, has yielded more than 2,725,000 frames of microfilmed materials in foreign archives relating to the history of the Pacific Coast, including Central America and Mexico. Filming was done in England and Scotland (1,340,000 frames), France (26,372 frames), Mexico (865,000 frames), the Netherlands (95,095 frames), Portugal (101,540 frames), and Spain (300,000 frames).

See Hubert Howe Bancroft, Works (1883-90. 39 vols.), especially the "Authorities Quoted" and footnotes; Herbert I. Priestley, "Manuscript Collections in the Bancroft Library," in Archives and Libraries: Papers Presented at the 1939 Conference of the American Library Association, p. 64-70 (1939. Processed); George P. Hammond, "Manuscript Collections in the Bancroft Library," in Am. Archivist, 13:15-26 (Jan. 1950); S. George Ellsworth, A Guide to Utah Manuscripts in the Bancroft Library (n. d.), a reprint of two articles from the Utah Hist. Quarterly, 22:99-124 and 197-247 (Apr. and July 1954, respectively); Mary Ann Fisher, Preliminary Guide to the Microfilm Collection in the Bancroft Library (1955. 28 p. Processed); Doris Marion Wright, A Guide to the Mariano Guadalupe Vallejo documentos para la historia de California, 1780-1875 (1953. 264 p. Processed); Bancroftiana (occasional publication of the Friends of the Bancroft Library, 1950 to date); Lawrence Kinnaird, Spain in the Mississippi Valley, 1765-1794, in Am. Hist. Assn., Annual Report for 1945, vols. 2-4; and Forest History Sources, pp. 3-6.

BERKELEY 9

Historical Society of the California-Nevada Annual Conference of the Methodist Church. Pacific School of Religion. B. J. Morris, President.

Holdings: The archives of the Conference, 4,000 items, 1853-1954, including conference minutes, early church records, sermons, diaries, and biographies of leading churchmen. The Conference archives are physically divided between this School and the College of the Pacific, another Methodist educational center at Stockton, Calif.

—oOo—

Pacific School of Religion Library. 1798 Scenic Ave. Stillson Judah, Librarian.

Holdings: 1,000 items, 1845-75, relating chiefly to Congregational and Methodist churches and ministers in early California. Included are some papers of the Spanish and Mexican periods in California; records of missionary work among the Chinese and Japanese in California; correspondence of ministers and minutes of church meetings; and diaries of missionaries, including that of William Taylor (Calif.; Methodist evangelist, missionary, Missionary Bishop for Africa). On deposit and not open for research are 24 linear ft. of papers of John Muir (Calif.; naturalist, explorer).

See Hist. Records Survey, Guide for Calif., p. 1.

BERKELEY 4

University of California General Library. Donald Coney, University Librarian.

Holdings: A large amount of manuscript material consisting of (1) the archives of the University and its predecessor, the College of California, 1855-1960, uncounted; (2) papers of university officials and faculty members; and (3) important materials of more general interest. The holdings of the Bancroft Library, which is a department of the General Library, are described in a separate entry.

Among the General Library's holdings are 56 medieval and Renaissance manuscripts, 12th-16th centuries; 20 Indic manuscripts, 14th-19th centuries; approximately 4,000 papyri, ca. 200 B. C. — ca. 200 A. D., Greek and demotic official archives and personal correspondence relating to the town of Tebtunis; and a hieratic medical manuscript of ca. 2,000 B. C. In the East Asiatic Library, a department of the General Library, are approximately 6,000 vols. of Chinese, Japanese, and Korean manuscripts on all subjects, including some famous authors' manuscripts of published and unpublished works. Over 5,000 of the manuscripts are Japanese, mostly from the 18th-19th centuries.

One of the most important groups in the General Library consists of papers of and relating to Samuel L. Clemens, better known as Mark Twain (Mo., Calif., Conn., N. Y.; novelist, humorist). One part, on deposit as a bequest to the University, comprises 523 literary manuscripts, 45 notebooks, 4 file drawers of letters written by Twain (of which 260 are in manuscript and the rest in typescript or photocopy), 34 vols. with marginalia by Twain, and 12 file drawers of letters to Twain. The other part, owned by the University, includes among other items 2,129 letters of Mark Twain and members of his family, 209 of which are by Twain himself; 10 scrapbooks containing biographical information and newspaper clippings of previously undiscovered publications by Twain; microfilm copies of 300 letters to Twain from William Dean Howells (Ohio, N. Y.; journalist, novelist); 45 vols., some with marginalia, from Twain's library; and some correspondence of two successive editors of the Mark Twain es-

tate, Bernard DeVoto, 1938-47, and Dixon Wecter, 1947-50.

Other papers of or pertaining to literary figures include those of Julian Hawthorne (Mass., N. Y., Calif.; author, son of Nathaniel Hawthorne), 1861-1930 (107 literary manuscripts, 8 diaries, and 256 letters to him), and a few papers of members of his family; a collection of Roger Ingpen (England; author, editor), containing uncounted copies of letters and manuscripts of Percy Bysshe Shelley (England; poet) and 400 letters concerning Shelley and notes and papers relating to Ingpen's editions of Shelley's poems; 375 manuscripts, including letters, of David H. Lawrence (England; poet, novelist), 1908-30; preliminary and final manuscripts of 15 novels by Wright Morris (Nebr., France, Pa.; novelist), 1936-59; papers of Edward Rowland Sill (Conn., Calif.; poet, English prof. at Univ. of Calif.), 1865-82 (21 literary manuscripts and 180 letters); 5 diaries of Amelia Keyser Stein (mother of Gertrude Stein, author), 1878-86; papers of George Rippy Stewart (Pa., Calif.; novelist, English prof. at Univ. of Calif.), 1928-52 (4 folders and 4 literary manuscripts); 132 manuscripts of Walt Whitman (N.Y., D.C., N.J.; poet), including one travel diary and working manuscripts of sections of Specimen Days; and smaller amounts of papers of other distinguished writers.

Papers of musicians include those of Ernest Bloch (Switzerland, N. Y., Ohio, Calif., Oreg.; composer, conductor, music prof. at Univ. of Calif.), 1901-25 (correspondence and 10 vols. of musical compositions); Alfred Hertz (Germany, N. Y., Calif.; conductor), 1887-1941 (correspondence, autobiography, documents, and musican compositions); Lilly Hertz (Germany, Calif.; opera singer, wife of Alfred), 1912-45 (correspondence,

biography of Alfred Hertz, documents);
Alfred Einstein (Germany, N.Y., Calif.; musicologist), 1920-50 (research
notes and transcriptions on the Italian
madrigal, early instrumental music);
Manfred Bukofzer (Germany, Calif.;
musicologist, music prof. at Univ. of
Calif.), 1944-55 (correspondence, re-
search notes, and transcriptions);
Sigmund Romberg (Hungary, N.Y.,
Calif.; light opera composer), 1919-
36 (19 operettas, some in photostat);
and individual manuscript scores by
the following contemporary composers:
Sir Arthur Bliss, William D. Denny,
Randall Thompson, Roger Sessions,
Igor Stravinsky, and Ralph Vaughan
Williams.

Manuscripts of early music include
16 compositions in the autograph of Sir
William Herschel (Germany, England;
astronomer, composer); a collection
of late 18th-century Italian instrumental music in parts (1,200 compositions
by some 80 composers); a collection
of late 18th-century vocal music (400
compositions); a collection of 18th
century Italian opera excerpts, compiled for Lord Clive of India (25 vols.);
a volume of the madrigals of Michel-
angelo Rossi in score (early 17th cent.);
a volume of early 17th-century English
organ music; and 7 vols. of early liturgical music, 11th-16th centuries.

Papers of University of California
officials include those of David Prescott Barrows (Ill., Philippine Islands,
Calif.; political science prof. and
pres. of Univ. of Calif., Calif. Nat.
Guard officer), 1898-1950 (25,000 letters from prominent persons, 12 boxes of manuscripts of books, lectures,
addresses, radio talks, and diaries);
Daniel Coit Gilman (Conn., Calif.,
Md.; pres. of Univ. of Calif. and
Johns Hopkins Univ.), 1870-75 (2 vols.
of letters relating to the Univ. of Calif.); Frank Holman Probert (England,
Calif.; dean of the University's College of Mining), 1917-40 (2 bundles of

addresses); Joseph Cummings Rowell
(Calif.; librarian of the University),
1878-1938 (21 vols. and many pieces);
Robert Gordon Sproul (Calif.; pres. of
Univ. of Calif.), 1930-58 (100 manuscripts of articles and speeches);
Benjamin Ide Wheeler (Mass., R.I.,
N.Y., Calif.; pres. of Univ. of Calif.), 1898-1925 (28,000 letters and 8
vols. of addresses and articles); and
Samuel Hopkins Willey (N.H., Calif.;
clergyman, vice pres. and acting
pres. of the college that became the
Univ. of Calif.), 1849-1910 (7 vols.
of letters, sermons, diaries, and documents.

There are also papers of University of California professors, in addition to some of those mentioned above.
Because many of these papers have not
yet been examined and arranged, the
dates used in this paragraph are those
of service on the faculty. The papers
include those of Frank Adams (Ill.,
Calif.; irrigation investigator of the
U.S. Dept. of Agriculture, irrigation
prof.), 1916-45 (5 boxes); Frederic
Theodore Bioletti (England, South Africa, Calif.; viticulture prof.), 1894-
1935 (8 correspondence file boxes);
Florian Cajori (Switzerland, Wis.,
La., Colo., Calif.; mathematics
prof.), 1918-30 (10 bundles); John
Bell Condliffe (New Zealand, Switzerland, Calif.; economics prof., sec-
retariat of League of Nations), from
1940 (24 filing drawers and 9 boxes);
John Fryer (England, China, Calif.;
oriental languages and literature
prof.), 1896-1914 (4 boxes); Richard
Benedict Goldschmidt (Germany, Calif.; zoology prof.), 1936-58 (1,394
letters written since 1900 by prominent biologists and zoologists); Eugene Woldemar Hilgard (Germany,
Miss., Calif.; dean, College of Agriculture), 1874-1916 (30,000 pieces);
George Holmes Howison (Md., Mass.,
Calif.; philosophy prof.), 1884-1916
(5 file drawers); Robert Joseph Ker-

ner (Mo., Calif.; history prof.), 1928-57 (28,000 pieces and 15 boxes); Yoshi Saburo Kuno (Japan, Calif.; asst. prof. Japanese), 1911-35 (2,500 pieces and 4 boxes); George Davis Louderback (Calif., Nev.; geologist and geology prof.), 1906-57 (23,000 pieces and 4 boxes); Robert Harry Lowie (N. Y., Calif.; anthropology prof.), 1921-57 (23 boxes); John Campbell Merriam (Calif., D. C.; paleontology and historical geology prof., pres. of Carnegie Inst. of Washington), 1894-1920 (12,000 pieces); Bernard Moses (Conn., Calif.; history and political science prof., member U. S. Philippine Commission), 1876-1911 (8 bundles); Henry Morse Stephens (Scotland, England, Calif.; history prof.), 1902-19 (3,000 pieces, 11 vols., and 1 bundle of material relating to Rudyard Kipling (England, India; author); and George Malcolm Stratton (Calif., N. J.; psychology prof.), 1891-1957 (7 boxes).

Papers of other individuals include those of James Graham Cooper (Wash., Calif.; physician, naturalist, author), 1861-70 (8 vols. on the zoology of the Pacific Coast); Stephen Johnson Field (N. Y., Calif.; justice of State supreme court and U. S. Supreme Court), 1840-96 (111 items); John Henry Nash (Canada, Calif.; printer), from 1895 (3,000 items); and George Bishop Sudworth (Wis., D. C.; dendrologist, U. S. Forest Service), ca. 1900 (11 vols.), pertaining to an extensive survey of California forests.

There are also a photostat copy of the Cecil Sharp collection of English folk-songs and folk dances (original in 51 vols. at Clare College, Cambridge Univ.); the Rebecca Godchaux collection of authograph letters of French literary figures, actors, and musicians, 1886-1937 (80 items); and a collection of autograph letters received by the Overland Monthly, 1869-75 (147 items). Included also is a microfilm copy of documents in the Ger-

man Foreign Ministry Archives, 1867-1920, pertaining to German relations with China, England, Russia, the United States, and other countries.

Materials concerning labor include a record of cases before the National War Labor Board (10th Region), 1943-45 (78 file drawers and 36 notebooks); the National Longshoremen's Labor Board proceedings before the arbitrators for the ports of San Francisco, Los Angeles, and Seattle, 1934 (8 vols.); correspondence and files of the executive secretary, California State Federation of Teachers, 1953-58 (5 file drawers); minutes of weekly meetings of the Marine Cooks and Stewards Association of the Pacific Coast, 1910-31 (1 file drawer); arbitration records, including transcripts of hearings and texts of awards and exhibits, 1931-49 (38 file drawers); correspondence and questionnaires returned to the California Industrial Union Council (C. I. O.) by candidates for state and national offices in the 1952 and 1954 elections (1 file drawer); microfilmed transcripts of hearings conducted by C. I. O. investigating committees, 1950 (3 reels); verbatim transcripts of proceedings of the first five conventions of the California State Industrial Union Council (C. I. O.), 1938-42 (5 reels and 1 vol.); a collection of contracts covering all major U. S. industries, 1920-43 (5 file drawers); documents relating to merger negotiations between the California State Federation of Labor and the California Congress of Industrial Organizations (1 file drawer); a stenographic transcript of the Senate subcommittee hearings on the manpower problems of the longshore industry of the Pacific Coast, 1943 (1 vol.); and a microfilm copy of a stenographic transcript of a conference, 1936, between the Governor of California, the Growers-Shippers Vegetable Association, and the California State Feder-

ation of Labor on the Salinas-Watson-
ville district strike (1 vol.). Court
proceedings in the case of Federal Reserve Board vs. Transamerica Corp.,
1952, are represented by 15 vols. of
transcripts.

CAMARILLO

Edward Laurence Doheny Memorial
Library. St. John's Seminary, P.O.
Box 38. Rev. Patrick O'Brien, Li-
brarian.

Holdings: 3,000 items, 1490-1937,
in Estelle Doheny Collection, consisting chiefly of several autograph collections. These include autographed papers of the signers of the Declaration
of Independence, Presidents of the
United States, and other persons of
prominence in the United States and
Europe. There are also a collection
of autographs of California pioneers,
1769-1848, and a collection of 70 literary manuscripts (holograph and corrected typescript), 1832-1932, of
James Fenimore Cooper, Ralph Waldo
Emerson, Henry James, Walt Whitman, and others.
See Hist. Records Survey, Guide
for Calif., p. 4; and Robert O. Schad,
"The Estelle Doheny Collection," in
New Colophon, 3:229-242 (1950).

CLAREMONT

Honnold Library. 222 East Ninth St.
David W. Davies, Librarian.

Holdings: This building houses the
libraries of both Pomona College and
Claremont College. Manuscripts in
the former consist of 3 Revolutionary
War items and a 1911 diary. The
Claremont College library has records
of 19 Pacific Coast steamship companies, 1900-25 (2 tons); and a collection of materials on the water problem of southern California and the
Southwest, 1890-1934.

See Hist. Records Survey, Guide
for Calif., p. 6; and Rolland C. Thompson, Calendar of Archives and Records of Certain Pacific Coast Steamship Companies, Preserved in and the
Property of Claremont College Library, Claremont, California (1940-41.
22 p.).

FRESNO

Fresno State College Library. Henry
M. Madden, Librarian.

Holdings: 5 vols. and 1,650 letters, 1874-1911, relating chiefly to
the Credit Foncier Co., an American
cooperative colony founded at Topo-
lobampo and Los Mochis, Sinaloa,
Mexico; and approximately 200 official U.S. and Mexican documents.
There are also 50 contemporary maps
and plans and 200 photographs of the
colony taken by an official photographer.

—oOo—

Monterey-Fresno Diocesan Chancery
and Academy of California Church
History. P.O. Box 1668.   Msgr.
James H. Culleton, Chancellor.

Holdings: Bound records and
other manuscripts pertaining chiefly
to the Catholic Church in California,
1770-1955. Included are all extant
original bound vital records and pa-
tentes of the missions of San Luis
Obispo, San Antonio, Soledad, Car-
mel, and Santa Cruz, 1770-1850 (42
vols.); and, on microfilm, vital records for San Miguel and San Juan
Bautista. There are also the extant
bound and unbound vital and other records of all Catholic churches and
most Catholic institutions in central
California, 1850-1955, either in the
original (220 vols. and 47 filing drawers) or on microfilm; and some 8,000
photostats of documents relating to
Junipero Serra (Spain, Mexico, Cal-

if.; Franciscan missionary). Records and manuscripts of published books of the Academy of California Church History, 1946-55, and a few other papers, 1836-70, are deposited in the Chancery (4 filing drawers).

Aside from church materials there are legal documents pertaining to the San Joaquin Valley, 1850-70 (100 pieces); also the complete collection made by George Van Namee (N. Y.; manager of Al Smith's campaigns), of ephemeral material relating to the governorship campaigns of Alfred E. Smith (N. Y.; Gov.) and containing manuscripts, 1918-26 (16 vols.).

GOLETA

Santa Barbara College Library, University of California. Donald C. Davidson, Librarian.

Holdings: Included in the Wyles Collection of Lincolniana and Americana are a few journals and other manuscripts relating chiefly to the Civil War and to Santa Barbara.

LOMA LINDA

Vernier-Radcliffe Memorial Library of the College of Medical Evangelists. Leroy W. Otto, Librarian; Margaret R. White, Historical Records Librarian.

Holdings: 7,500 pieces, 1900-59, relating in general to the medical work of the Seventh-day Adventist Church and in particular to the development of the College of Medical Evangelists at Loma Linda and Los Angeles, and containing a special collection of letters and manuscripts of Ellen G. White (Mich., D. C., Calif.; one of the founders of the Seventh-day Adventist Church). Also housed in Historical Records (but not included in the above figure) are pictures, museum objects, and minutes of faculty, board,

and various administrative and executive bodies of the College of Medical Evangelists.

LONG BEACH 2

Long Beach Public Library. Ocean at Pacific Ave. Edwin Castagna, Librarian.

Holdings: A few items of miscellaneous character. Included are a Ceylonese manuscript; a diary of overland travel to California, 1849; and some local material.

See Hist. Records Survey, Guide for Calif., p. 8.

LOS ANGELES 24

American Mathematical Society. University of California. J. W. Green, Secretary.

Holdings: 24 filing drawers, 1920-59, consisting of the noncurrent correspondence and other records of the Society. Included are 5 filing drawers of correspondence concerned with such special activities of the Society as the International Congress of Mathematicians held in Cambridge, Mass., 1950. A fire in 1920 destroyed earlier archives of the Society.

LOS ANGELES 7

Los Angeles County Museum Library. Exposition Park. (Mrs.) Dorothy E. Martin, Librarian.

Holdings: A small quantity of manuscripts, 1774-1916, relating chiefly to California and the Southwest. Included are papers of Antonio Franco Coronel (Calif.; pioneer, political leader), 1850-93 (5 pamphlet cases); papers of William E. Satterlee (Rev. War officer), 1774-1832 (1 loose leaf binder); papers of a Michigan officer in the Civil War (150 pieces); and papers collected by the Historical Society of Southern California, 1815-1900 (2 vols., 10 bundles, 5 pieces), containing transcripts of records of old Spanish families in Southern California and other papers concerning California and the Southwest.

See Hist. Records Survey, Guide for Calif., p. 10.

LOS ANGELES 17

Los Angeles Public Library. 630 West 5th St. Harold Hamill, City Librarian.

Holdings: 2,000 items, 1770-1959, relating chiefly to California and the West. Included are the "Mercury Case," a collection of original letters and proceedings concerning contraband trade on the California coast, 1806-16, and the confiscation of the Mercury; autobiographical sketches of prominent citizens of Los Angeles (1,275 items); transcripts of diaries of pioneers; 2 literary manuscripts and 30 letters of Theodore Dreiser (Mo., N.Y.; editor, novelist); and a collection of autograph letters of prominent Americans, from 1870 (311 items).

See Hist. Records Survey, Guide for Calif., p. 11.

LOS ANGELES 12

Municipal Reference Department, Los Angeles Public Library. City Hall. Ruth E. Palmer, Librarian.

Holdings: 3 vols., consisting of a chronological record of Los Angeles city officials, 1850-1938, compiled by a project of the Works Progress Administration.

LOS ANGELES 41

Occidental College Library. 1600

Campus Rd. Tyrus G. Harmsen, Librarian.

Holdings: Included are many personal papers of William Jennings Bryan (Nebr.; U.S. Rep., Sec. State); and letters, literary manuscripts, and other papers of or relating to Robinson Jeffers (Calif.; poet), 1905-55 (200 items). Among the correspondents of Jeffers were Lawrence Clark Powell (Calif.; librarian) and Albert M. Bender (Ireland, Calif.; businessman).

See Hist. Records Survey, Guide for Calif., p. 13; Occidental College Library; an Appreciation of the Founders and Donors (1953. 24 p.); and Robinson Jeffers at Occidental College; a Check List (1955. 23 p.).

LOS ANGELES 24

School of Law Library, University of California.

Holdings: 44 tons of briefs of cases and other records of California courts, 1900-59, some of which were formerly in the University of San Francisco. Briefs are currently received from the California Supreme Court.

LOS ANGELES 42

Southwest Museum Library. Highland Park. (Mrs.) Ella Robinson, Librarian.

Holdings: 1,250 items, 1598-1930, relating chiefly to the history, ethnology, and archeology of the Western Hemisphere, especially the southwestern United States. Included are papers of or relating to John Charles Frémont (D.C., Calif.; U.S. Army officer, explorer, U.S. Sen., Pres. candidate), 1838-1907 (60 items); papers of Charles Fletcher Lummis (Calif.; author, editor, promoter of restoration of Calif. missions and betterment of Calif. Indians), 1898-1928 (500 items); the George Byrd Grinnell Collection of journals, field notes, and other materials on the Plains Indians, 1870-1930 (450 items); and original Spanish documents, letters, and other historical material relating to California, New Mexico, and Mexico, 1598-1900 (240 items).

See Hist. Records Survey, Guide for Calif., p. 15.

LOS ANGELES 24

University of California Library. Lawrence Clark Powell, Librarian; Wilbur J. Smith, Head, Department of Special Collections.

Holdings: 153,397 pieces, 1500-1956, relating chiefly to California and the American West but containing much of wider interest. The William Andrews Clark Memorial Library and the School of Law Library are separately described elsewhere under Los Angeles.

Papers of individuals include those of Cornelius Cole (Calif.; U.S. Sen.), 1840-1940 (36 linear ft.); Edward A. Dickson (Calif.; newspaper publisher and editor), 1893-1956 (5,000 pieces); Norman Douglas (England; author), 1916-52 (3 linear ft.); Clarence A. Dykstra (Ohio, Wis., Calif.; city manager, university pres. and provost), 1923-50 (5,000 pieces); John Fiske (Mass.; philosopher, historian, author), 1865-1917 (63 pieces); Archibald H. Gillespie (U.S. Marine Corps officer), 1845-60 (900 pieces); Frederick Webb Hodge (D.C., N.Y., Calif.; anthropologist, ethnologist), 1890-1956 (100 pieces); John Percival Jones (Calif., Nev.; U.S. Sen. from Nev.), 1873-1903 (16 linear ft.); D. H. Lawrence (England; poet, novelist), 1910-48 (300 pieces); William Gibbs McAdoo (N.Y., Calif.; Sec. Treas., U.S. Sen. from Calif.),

1902-41 (14 linear ft.); Llewelyn Powys (N.Y., England; author), 1907-39 (185 pieces); Rodman McCamley Price (N.J., Calif.; U.S. naval officer, U.S. Rep. from N.J., Gov. of N.J.), 1847-84 (1 linear ft.); William S. Rosecrans (Ohio, Calif.; U.S. Army officer, engineer) and his family, 1841-1910 (25,000 pieces); Ferdinand Canning Scott Schiller (England, Calif.; philosopher, prof. at Univ. of Southern Calif.), 1886-1937 (7,000 pieces); Arthur Schnitzler (Austria; physician, playwright, novelist), 1874-1930 (41 reels of microfilm); Jonathan Drake Stevenson (Army officer in the Mexican War and the Civil War), 1840-92 (1 linear ft.); Irving Stone (Calif.; author), 1934— (38 linear ft.); Jim Tully (Calif.; author), 1916-35 (26 linear ft.); Gideon Welles (Conn.; newspaper editor, Sec. Navy), 1803-61 (90 pieces); Franz V. Werfel (Austria; poet, dramatist, novelist), 1920-40 (10 linear ft.); James Alexander Williamson (Iowa; Civil War officer, U.S. General Land Office Commissioner, railroad pres.), 1861-1902 (2 linear ft.); and John D. Works (Calif.; judge, U.S. Sen.), 1911-17 (160 pieces).

Business and organizational records include those of the Pinal Dome Oil Co., Santa Maria, Calif., 1895-1922 (160 linear ft.); Townsend Plan, Inc., 12th Regional District, 1938-52 (54 linear ft.); the Halleck (Henry Wager), Peachy (Archibald), Billings (Frederick) and Yale (Gregory) law firm, San Francisco, 1830-75 (5 linear ft.); the Society for the Propagation of the Gospel, London, 1680-1901 (184 reels of microfilm); and the U.S. War Relocation Authority, 1942-45 (75,000 pieces). Other important holdings are the Robert E. Cowan collection on California and the American West, 1830-1900 (6,000 items); papers relating to the citrus industry in Southern California, from 1890 (50 linear ft.); and

miscellaneous manuscripts, chiefly
small quantities of letters of each of
numerous prominent Americans, from
1700 (40 linear ft.). There are also
collections documenting the history of
the American Colonies and the Revolution; Central America and the Caribbean; the Civil War; Great Britain and
the Empire; Europe; and literature in
America and Great Britain.

See the Library's Guide to Special
Collections in the Library of the University of California at Los Angeles
(1958. 76 p. Processed).

LOS ANGELES 7

University of Southern California Library. Lewis F. Stieg, Librarian.

Holdings: 16,600 pieces, chiefly
from 1850 to date, relating for the
most part to philosophy and literature.

In the American Literature Collection there are literary manuscripts and
letters of American authors, 1850 to
date (15,000 pieces), among them papers of Irving Bacheller (N. Y.; journalist, novelist), 147 pieces; Ambrose
Bierce (Calif.; journalist, short-story
writer), 52 pieces; Phillips Brooks
(Mass.; Episcopal bishop, author), 89
pieces; Henry Blake Fuller (Ill.; novelist), 323 pieces; Hamlin Garland
(Mass., Ill., Calif.; novelist), 13,000
pieces; James A. Herne (N. Y., Calif.;
actor, playwright), 82 pieces; William
Dean Howells (Mass., N. Y.; novelist,
literary critic, editor of Atlantic
Monthly), 192 pieces; Jack London
(Calif.; novelist), 185 pieces; Edwin
Markham (Calif., N. Y.; poet, lecturer), 62 pieces; James Brander Matthews (N. Y.; prof. of dramatic literature at Columbia Univ., author), 63
pieces; Albert Bigelow Paine (Kans.,
N. Y.; author, editor), 62 pieces; Theodore Roosevelt (N. Y.; U. S. Pres.),
60 pieces; Augustus Thomas (Mo., N.
Y.; dramatist), 59 pieces; and Stewart
Edward White (Ill., N. Y.; novelist),

142 pieces. There are about 50 book
manuscripts of contemporary authors,
including the Barrymore family; 10
letters of Herbert Hoover (Calif.; U.S.
Pres.); and 5 cases of Hamlin Garland's notebooks, correspondence,
and other source materials for his
study of Ulysses S. Grant (U. S. Army
officer, U. S. Pres.).

In the Rare Book Collection there
are about 100 pieces of manuscripts,
including papers of the master of a
steamboat on the Mississippi River
during the Civil War; letters and orders of Union officers (69 pieces); and
one or two letters by each of several
political leaders of national importance.

The Hoose Library of Philosophy
contains 1,500 pieces, chiefly letters
and literary manuscripts of modern
philosophers, as well as about 10
manuscripts of the 13th to 15th centuries. Included are letters by Borden Parker Bowne (N. Y., Mass.;
philosopher, prof. at Boston Univ.),
and Herbert Wildon Carr (England,
Calif.; philosophy prof.); letters to
Theodor Gomperz (Germany; philologist), 394 pieces, and to his son
Heinrich Gomperz (Germany; prof.
of philosophy), 132 pieces, many from
European writers and philosophers,
and some manuscripts of Theodor and
Heinrich Gomperz; letters to William
Torrey Harris (Mo., Mass., D. C.;
philosopher, author, U. S. Commissioner of Education), 848 pieces; and
the unpublished "Ethics of Pessimism"
and lecture notes of Ferdinand Canning Scott Schiller (England, Calif.;
philosopher, prof. at Univ. of Southern Calif.).

LOS ANGELES 18

William Andrews Clark Memorial Library, University of California.
2205 West Adams Blvd. Lawrence
Clark Powell, Director.

Holdings: 6,300 pieces, 17th-20th centuries, relating chiefly to English and American literature. One important collection, designated as "Wilde, Wildeiana and the 'Nineties,'" includes letters and literary manuscripts of Oscar Wilde (England; poet, novelist, playwright), 1872-1900 (463 pieces), and letters and other papers, 1875-1953, of other figures of Wilde's circle or prominent in the 1890's (2,462 items). There are also papers of Francis Bret Harte (Calif., N.Y.; short-story writer), 1864-1902 (264 pieces); and of a trader in Indian Territory, 1851-61 (305 pieces). Other collections include one of letters, literary manuscripts, and other papers of English and a few American authors, 17th-19th centuries (670 pieces); an autograph collection of letters and other papers of "rulers and statesmen," 1614-1924 (114 pieces); letters and manuscript scores of prominent musicians, 1789-1926 (37 pieces); and a graphic arts collection, 1908-53 (1,000 pieces), chiefly letters from California printers but including numerous letters from Eric Gill (England; sculptor, engraver). Manuscripts in the Montana Collection, 1833-1934 (549 pieces), include papers of a resident of Helena, 1899-1928 (422 pieces), a few papers of U.S. Senators, some legal papers relating to mining claims, and journals and memoirs of pioneers.

See H. Richard Archer, "Literary and Historical Manuscripts in the Clark Memorial Library," in Autograph Collectors' Journal, 3 (no. 2): 7-13 (Jan. 1951); the Library's Oscar Wilde and His Literary Circle; a Catalog of Manuscripts (1957); and the following processed publications of the Hist. Records Survey: Guide for Calif., p. 18; a list of the letters and manuscripts of musicians in the Library (1940. 12 p.); a list of the letters and documents of rulers and statesmen (1941. 16 p.); a calendar of the Montana papers (1942. 103 p.); and a calendar of the Bret Harte letters (1942. 35 p.).

MARYSVILLE

Marysville City Library. Fourth and C Sts. Thelma G. Neaville, Librarian.

Holdings: Several volumes, 1851-1908, relating to Marysville. Included are minutes of a local vigilante group, 1851 (1 vol.); a business account book, 1856-72; and records of a fire engine company, 1859-1906 (1 vol.), and of the city fire department, 1887-1908 (3 vols.).

OAKLAND 13

Mills College Library. (Mrs.) Mary Manning Cook, Reference Librarian.

Holdings: A considerable quantity of papers, from the 15th century to the present but largely of the 19th and 20th centuries, relating chiefly to literature. They constitute an important part of the Albert M. Bender Collection of Rare Books and Manuscripts. Included are a few leaves of medieval manuscripts, a 15th-century Flemish Book of Hours, a 17th-century Spanish missal, a collection of music for the cittern dated about 1600, a collection of 200 English songs and dance tunes of the 18th century; literary manuscripts of California and other American writers and of English authors; and a substantial collection of autographs and letters of literary and other world figures. There are 70 letters by Ina Donna Coolbrith (Calif.; poet, librarian, journalist), and 35 by Edwin Markham (Calif., N.Y.; poet, lecturer). Correspondence of Albert M. Bender (Ireland, Calif.; businessman), 1920-41 (1 filing cabinet), contains sizable files of letters from Mary Austin (Calif., N. Mex.;

novelist, dramatist) and William Butler Yeats (Ireland; poet). There are
60 boxes of typescripts of stories and
books by Dane Coolidge (Calif.; novelist, naturalist). The Lillie Hitchcock
Coit Collection of some 3,000 letters
and personal diaries, from the American Revolution to recent years, includes papers of the James Hunter
family of Virginia, journals relating
to life in San Francisco, 1851-80, and
letters from persons important in the
literary life of San Francisco.
   See Hist. Records Survey, Guide
for Calif., p. 22-23.

OAKLAND 12

Oakland Public Library. 125 14th St.
Peter T. Conmy, Librarian.

   Holdings: 37 pieces, chiefly letters
of California writers.

PALOS VERDES ESTATES

Palos Verdes Public Library. 2400
Via Campesina.

   Holdings: The Bixby Records Collection, consisting of 226 items, 1840-
84, relating to the legal history of the
Rancho Palos Verdes, with some information on the lives of its various
owners.
   See Hist. Records Survey, Guide
for Calif., p. 23, and the Survey's Inventory of the Bixby Records Collection (1940. 43 p. Processed).

PASADENA

California Institute of Technology Library. Roger Stanton, Director of
Libraries.

   Holdings: 10 file drawers of papers,
1920-53, of Robert A. Millikan (Ill.,
Calif.; physicist), consisting of extensive correspondence, drafts of his autobiography, and manuscripts of many
speeches and scientific papers.

PASADENA 1

Pasadena Art Museum. 46 North Los
Robles Ave. Thomas W. Leavitt, Director.

   Holdings: Letters and other manuscripts of or concerning the following modern German painters: Lyonel
C. A. Feininger, Alexei Jawlensky,
Wassily Kandinsky, and Paul Klee.

Pasadena Public Library. 285 East
Walnut St. Marjorie Donaldson, City
Librarian.

   Holdings: 2 vols., 1 containing
autograph letters and other manuscripts of Mexican governors and other officials and of American pioneers
in and near San Francisco, 1840-54;
the other containing letters of San Diego pioneers, 1850-55, many to William Heath Davis (Calif.; U. S. customs officer at San Francisco).
   See Hist. Records Survey, Guide
for Calif., p. 24.

SACRAMENTO 9

California State Library. Library
and Courts Bldg., Capitol Ave.
(Mrs.) Carma Russell Zimmerman,
Librarian; Allan R. Ottley, California Section Librarian.

   Holdings: Some 400 vols. and
9,000 pieces dating from 1826 and relating chiefly to California, especially
in the pioneer period. Included are
papers of and relating to John A. Sutter (Calif.; colonist), 1840-61 (145
original letters and 175 transcripts);
diaries, many of the gold-rush period
(100 vols.); a collection of account
books, other commercial documents,
and letters of California businessmen,
1826-90 (41 vols., 3,000 business papers, and hundreds of letters), among
them letters of a businessman in Honolulu; other account books, 1846-
1900 (200 vols.), chiefly of the 1850's;

a collection relating chiefly to southern California and its first railroad company (3,000 pieces); and records of one of the major silver mining companies of the Comstock lode, 1859-85 (46 vols.). There are also a collection containing letters from pioneers and papers concerning the California Battalion in the conquest of California; and many record books of early courts and social, medical, and business organizations.

See Hist. Records Survey, Guide for Calif., p. 26.

SACRAMENTO 14

State Archives and Central Record Depository. Office of the Secretary of State. 1020 O St. Paul J. O'Brien, State Archivist.

Holdings: Chiefly archives, 1784-1959, of the State of California. Included are Spanish land-grant documents, 1784-1847 (20 vols.), consisting of translations and transcriptions of land-grant papers, diseños, and maps and surveys; deeds to State property, 1850-1959; and the State constitutions of 1849 and 1879 (2 vols., with related loose papers) and the journal of the constitutional convention of 1849, with related loose papers.

Records of the executive branch of the State government include oaths of office of constitutional and appointive officials, 1849-1959, and the bonds of such officials, 1871-1959; letter books of State officials, including a few of the early Governors, 1851-80; Governor's registers of proclamations, executive appointments, pardons, commutations, and reprieves, 1850-1959; diaries, account books, journals, ledgers, registers, and reports of the Governor and other State officials, 1850—early 1900's; and minute books of various State boards, commissions, and districts, 1850—early 1900's. There are also election papers, 1849-1959; military records relating to In-

dian wars, the militia, and the National Guard, 1849-1940; California Selective Service records, 1940-48; articles of incorporation and amendments, 1850-1959; a series called Trade Marks and Change of Names, 1860's-1959; and maps (railroad, irrigation, swamp and overflow, tidelands, and schools), 1850's—early 1900's.

Records of the legislative branch consist of volumes of laws and journals, with appendixes, 1849-1959; and drafts of bills, amendments, minutes, petitions, and reports, 1849-1959. Records of the judicial branch include those of the State supreme and appellate courts, 1850's-1950.

The Depository has also the private papers of Earl Warren (Calif.; State attorney gen. and Gov.), 1939-53 (650 cu. ft.), under seal until 1963; and Goodwin J. Knight (Calif.; lawyer, Gov.), 1953-59 (153 cu. ft.), under seal until 1969. Other records of special importance include certain selected material from the files of several members of the California Congressional Delegation, 83rd thru the 86th Congresses (200 cu. ft.); and a beginning collection of early judicial records from several of the California counties, 1850-79 (300 cu. ft.).

SACRAMENTO 16

Sutter's Fort State Historical Monument. 2701 L St. C. D. Hall, Monument Supervisor.

Holdings: A small miscellaneous collection of letters and several diaries relating to the gold-rush period of California history. There are a few letters of John A. Sutter (Calif.; colonist), and numerous letters and business records relating to John Bidwell (Calif.; U. S. Rep.) and to the Donner Party, 1846-47.

SAN ANSELMO

San Francisco Theological Seminary
Library. Clifford M. Drury, Curator
of Rare Books and Manuscripts.

Holdings: A quantity of manuscripts,
1833-1955, consisting of (1) records
held by the seminary as the official
archival depository of the Presbyterian
Church, U.S.A., on the Pacific Coast,
and (2) papers of or relating to Presbyterian missionaries and ministers in
the area.

Church archives include the records
of seven synods in California, Oregon,
and Utah, 1852-1939, two of which are
of the Cumberland Presbyterian Church.
There are also records of 16 California
presbyteries, 1850-1941; of 10 Oregon
presbyteries, 1851-1942; and of 9 presbyteries elsewhere in the area, 1851-
1951, including Alaska, Arizona, Texas, Utah, and Washington. Six of the
above 35 presbyteries are those of the
Cumberland Presbyterian Church. Included too are sessional records of 150
churches, from 1849, chiefly in California; of the women's Occidental
Board of Foreign Missions, 1906-23;
and of the Woman's North Pacific Presbyterian Board of Missions, 1911-22,
some of which are printed.

Papers of individuals include those
of Timothy Dwight Hunt (Hawaii, Calif.; missionary and pioneer minister),
1845-56 (marriage records, journals,
and personal papers); Kate McBeth
(Oreg.; missionary to the Nez Percé
Indians), 1890-1915 (journal and several boxes of letters); Edward Marsden (first native Presbyterian minister
in Alaska), 1897-1921 (4 letter books);
William Anderson Scott (La., Calif.;
Presbyterian minister, founder of San
Francisco Theological Seminary), from
1854 (boxes of journals, letters, and
sermons); Clarence Thwing (Alaska;
missionary at Fort Wrangel), 1892-95
(1 letter book); Marcus Whitman (N.Y.,
Oreg.; physician, missionary, pioneer)

and his wife Narcissa, 1835-46 (original overland diary and 6 letters);
Samuel H. Willey (Calif.; pioneer
Presbyterian minister, founder at
Berkeley of the academy that became
Calif. College, vice pres. and acting
pres. of Calif. College, later the
Univ. of Calif.), from 1849 (marriage
records, notebooks, and other pieces); and many more pioneer Presbyterian ministers in the West.

SAN BERNARDINO

San Bernardino County Free Library.
Court House.

Holdings: 321 pieces, chiefly of
the 19th century, relating mainly to
San Bernardino County. Included are
excerpts from a diary concerning a
wagon road and railroad; the diary of
a ferryman, 1855-58; and reports of
the county water commissioners,
1864-68.

See Hist. Records Survey, Guide
for Calif., p. 29.

SAN DIEGO 3

Junipero Serra Museum. 2727 Pre-
sidio Dr.   G. F. MacMullen, Director.

Holdings: Many vols. and about
40,000 pieces, some dating from the
18th century, of material relating to
the Spanish, Mexican, and American
periods for the locality and region.
The Museum is operated by the San
Diego Historical Society.

Included are 18th- and 19th-cen-
tury mission records, consisting of a
death register of the Mission San
Francisco de Borja and a baptismal
register of the Mission Santa Gertru-
dis (both in Lower California); and
English transcripts of baptismal,
marriage, and death records of the
Mission San Diego de Alcalá. There
are also various documents and ac-

counts of early settlers, merchants, civic leaders, and pioneer physicians, among them Henry D. Fitch (Calif.; first storekeeper of San Diego and surveyor of its pueblo lands); and the Kerr Collection (21 vols.) of notes on early California ranchos. Other holdings include assessor's tax declarations, 1850-80; school records, 1850-1920; 20 vols. of historical photographs, and some mounted and framed photographs; some maps; and extensive biographical files on local families.

See Hist. Records Survey, Guide for Calif., p. 31.

SAN DIEGO 1

San Diego Natural History Museum. Balboa Park.   Mildred H. Meeder, Librarian.

Holdings: 200 pieces, 1870-1935, consisting chiefly of letters from botanists, paleontologists, and geologists.

See Hist. Records Survey, Guide for Calif., p. 30.

—oOo—

San Diego Public Library.   820 E St. Clara E. Breed, City Librarian.

Holdings: 146 items, 1849-1903, being mostly transcripts of diaries, memoirs, and accounts of explorations relating to California and the West.

See Hist. Records Survey, Guide for Calif., p. 31.

SAN FRANCISCO 18

California Academy of Sciences Library.   Golden Gate Park.

Holdings: 4 file drawers and 27 notebooks, 1853-1940, relating chiefly to natural history, especially ornithology and entomology, and to the marine life of the Pacific Ocean. In-

cluded are field notes and other papers of Barton Warren Evermann (Calif.; ichthyologist, author).

See Hist. Records Survey, Guide for Calif., p. 32.

SAN FRANCISCO 4

California Genealogical Society Library.   926-928 De Young Bldg.

Holdings: 25 boxes, chiefly 20th century, consisting of reminiscences of or about California pioneers and genealogies and genealogical data.

See Hist. Records Survey, Guide for Calif., p. 33.

SAN FRANCISCO 9

California Historical Society. 2090 Jackson St.   Donald C. Biggs, Director; James de T. Abajian, Librarian.

Holdings: 100,000 pieces, mainly of the 19th and 20th centuries, relating chiefly to California.

There are substantial quantities of papers of Joseph L. Folsom (N.H., Calif.; U.S. Army officer, collector of customs at San Francisco, capitalist), 1841-74; Andrew Smith Hallidie (Calif.; engineer, inventor, builder of suspension bridges and city cable-car systems), 1852-1900; Asbury Harpending (Calif.; mining speculator, capitalist), 1872-1918 (8,000 pieces); John Coffee Hays (Calif.; Mexican War officer, surveyor-gen. of Calif., capitalist), 1847-74; Milton Slocum Latham (Calif.; lawyer, banker, U.S. Rep., Gov., U.S. Sen.), 1842-85; James Rolph (Calif.; mayor of San Francisco Gov.), 1911-18 (40,000 pieces); and Adolph Sutro (Nev., Calif.; mining engineer, mayor of San Francisco), 1853-99.

Also included are business papers of several San Francisco firms, notably the Alaska Commercial Co.,

1868-1918; the Crim Real Estate Co.,
1846-1904; and Spreckels Enterprises,
1879-1936, representing the sugar,
transportation, and other business interests of John D. and Adolph B.
Spreckels (Calif.; capitalists). There
are also records of the Traders' Association of the City and County of San
Francisco, 1862-96; papers of California general stores, mining companies,
and other businesses; logs or journals
of 9 ships, 1821-67; papers of New England companies organized for emigration, 1849; many diaries and other papers of the gold-rush period; and records of a regiment of California volunteer cavalry, 1863-64, a woman
suffrage association, 1869-72, and a
homeopathic medical society, 1898-
1908; and records of the League of
Women Voters of California, 1922-55
(12,000 pieces).

See James de T. Abajian, "Preliminary Listing of Manuscript Collections
in Library of California Historical Society," in Calif. Hist. Society Quarterly, 33:[372]-376 (Dec. 1954).

SAN FRANCISCO 18

M. H. de Young Memorial Museum.
Golden Gate Park.

Holdings: A small collection, 1849-
1921, relating chiefly to finance and
commerce in California. Included are
a few papers of some California pioneers and State Governors; account
books of a railroad company, 1851-64;
and ships' logbooks.
See Hist. Records Survey, Guide
for Calif., p. 36.

Msgr. Joseph M. Gleason Memorial
Library, San Francisco College for
Women. K. Cassidy, Librarian.

Holdings: Manuscripts relating
chiefly to the history of religion, some
of them dating from the 12th century.
Included are some Civil War documents;

papers of Joseph M. Gleason (Calif.;
Catholic priest), 1869-1942 (several
cartons), not yet available for use;
and papers of George Lacombe (Calif.; Catholic priest, medievalist),
1886-1934.
See Hist. Records Survey, Guide
for Calif., p. 37.

SAN FRANCISCO 5

Pacific Telephone and Telegraph
Company. 140 New Montgomery
St. W. H. Topham, Corporate
Supervisor.

Holdings: 386 file drawers of records, from November 1879, consisting of company archives of permanent value, including articles of
incorporation, bylaws, and other corporate records; franchises, licenses,
and permits; leases, deeds, and bills
of sale; contracts, agreements, and
rights of way; and records relating to
mergers of companies, company's
stock and debentures, and taxes.
See W. H. Topham, "Pacific Telephone's Records Management Program," in Am. Archivist, 17:111-121
(Apr. 1954).

SAN FRANCISCO 17

Richard A. Gleeson Library, Univer-
sity of San Francisco. Golden Gate
Ave. at Parker. Rev. John B. Mc-
Gloin, S.J., Archivist.

Holdings: Official records of St.
Ignatius College, 1855-1930, and of
the University of San Francisco, 1930
to date; and manuscripts containing
materials concerning the American
period of Roman Catholicism in California, 1846 to date. Included are
extensive filmed transcripts from European ecclesiastical archives, especially those of the Vatican Archives
and the Congregation "de Propaganda
Fide" Archives in Rome.

SAN FRANCISCO 2

Society of California Pioneers. 456 McAllister St. Elliot Evans, Curator; Hester Robinson, Librarian; Hazel M. Ball, Office Manager.

Holdings: 25,000 items, 1840-1940, relating chiefly to California. Included are correspondence of Thomas Starr King (Mass., Calif.; Unitarian minister), 1861-64, which contains letters from Jessie Benton Frémont (D.C., Calif.; writer); the Jacob Rink Snyder Collection (295 items), consisting largely of documents pertaining to the California Battalion; diaries kept by pioneers and "forty-niners," 1842-52 (over 200 vols.); and reminiscences of pioneers (8 vols.). There are also many business records, dating from 1850 and including records of businesses in old mining towns and stock certificates in early mining companies; a list of vessels arriving in San Francisco in 1849-50; a music collection, containing sheet music from as early as 1840, early theatrical posters, and biographical sketches of California musicians; and 20,000 photographs of San Francisco and California.

—oOo—

Sutro Library, California State Library. Public Library Bldg. Richard H. Dillon, Sutro Librarian.

Holdings: 75 vols., 150 folders, 207 folios, 149 boxes and bundles, and 49 linear ft. Included are 14th-16th century Hebrew and Arabic manuscripts (160 items); a collection of 12 Arabic and Persian manuscript books; medieval Latin and Italian Renaissance documents (200 items); the Halliwell-Phillips Collection relating to Shakespeare and Stratford-on-Avon (85 pieces); a collection of 17th-19th century Spanish and Mexican manuscripts (100 items); papers of Sir Joseph Banks (England; scientist), 1780-1820 (10,000 pieces); reports, drawings, and other manuscripts on English engineering, 1820's-1830's (6 vols.), in the John Murray Collection; the McCabe Journal, which provides information about the theater and other public entertainment in San Francisco, 1849-82 (11 vols.); the Theodore H. Hittell Manuscripts Collection (41 pieces), some being book-length unpublished manuscripts; a collection of 42 manuscripts of David Starr Jordan (Ind., Calif.; naturalist, pres. of Ind. and Stanford Univs.); and a collection of letters and memorabilia of Adolph Sutro (Nev., Calif.; mining engineer, mayor of San Francisco). There are also several log books, various collections of Western Americana manuscripts, literary or historical; and some Midwestern Americana manuscripts, such as the Clayton Collection of Illinois-Wisconsin letters.

See Helen M. Bruner, "Possibilities for Research in the Sutro Collection," in Library Journal, 60:787-789 (Oct. 15, 1935); Hist. Records Survey, Guide for Calif., p. 38; De Ricci, Census, pp. 26-28; and Richard H. Dillon, "A Peek at Sutro Library," in Book Club of Calif., Quarterly News Letter, 7:27-32 (spring 1952), "Random Notes on Sutro Library's Autographs and Manuscripts," in Autograph Collectors' Journal, 4 (no. 4):49-51 (summer 1952), and "A San Francisco Research Library," in Library World, 54:89 (Dec. 1952).

SAN FRANCISCO 22

University of California Medical Center Library. 3rd and Parnassus Ave. (Mrs.) Carmenina Tomassini, Administrative Librarian.

Holdings: In the Historical Collection there are several thousand items, 1539-1959, relating to various medical subjects. Included are several

Mexican manuscripts, 17th-19th centuries; a 16th-century Latin manuscript; and 2 Ola (Palm leaf) manuscripts, 18th century, one in the Pali language. There are also a modern collection of several hundred pieces on the history of anesthesia, a collection relating to the history of medicine in California, some biographical sketches of early California physicians, and a large collection of letters of outstanding medical men. In the "archive collection" are records of the Office of the Dean of the University of California School of Medicine, early 20th century (40 boxes); papers of Chauncey Leake (Wis., Calif.; prof. of pharmacology), 20th century, largely about various aspects of the history of medicine; and papers of Esther Rosencrantz (Calif.; physician, assoc. prof. of medicine), 20th century, concerning her teaching, her work on tuberculosis, and her gathering of a collection on Sir William Osler (Canada, Md., England; physician, prof. at Johns Hopkins and Oxford Univs.).

SAN FRANCISCO 20

Wells Fargo Bank History Room. Market at Montgomery. Irene Simpson, Director.

Holdings: A collection of records of the Wells Fargo banking and express firm, reminiscences of former employees and their descendants, and other papers relating to California and the West, 1852-1906.

SAN LUIS REY

San Luis Rey College. Rev. Anthony Soto, Librarian.

Holdings: 2 vols., 2 boxes, and 130 pieces, 1893-1912, relating exclusively to the establishment and conduct of an "Apostolic College" conducted by the Franciscan Fathers of

Mexico at San Luis Rey Mission. Included are official documents, letters, and reports. The documents relate exclusively to the ecclesiastical training of the candidates. All are in the Spanish language, except for a few in Latin and in English. There are also 2 vols. of records relating to the government of the College, 1893-1908.

SAN MARINO

Henry E. Huntington Library and Art Gallery. John E. Pomfret, Director; Robert Ormes Dougan, Librarian; Herbert C. Schulz, Curator of Manuscripts.

Holdings: 1,500,000 pieces (in 450 collections), 11th-20th centuries, relating chiefly to English, Latin-American, and United States history and literature. Besides some Indic manuscripts, there are substantial holdings of medieval and Renaissance manuscripts, some of which are identified specifically below.

Several very large and important groups provide information about many aspects of English history, and in less degree about other parts of the British Empire. Among these are records of the Abbey of St. Martin, founded by William the Conqueror and commonly called Battle Abbey, 1077-1780 (3,000 pieces); papers of the Hastings family, Earls of Huntingdon, Marquesses of Hastings, and Countesses of Loudoun, 1100-1892 (50,000 pieces); papers of the Egerton family, Earls of Ellesmere and Dukes and Earls of Bridgewater, and manuscripts from the Bridgewater House library, 1150-1800 (12,000 pieces); the Stowe Collection, 1175-1925 (525,000 pieces), consisting of papers of the interrelated Brydges, Grenville, Nugent, O'Conor, and Temple families; and papers of the Campbells, Earls of Loudoun, 1510-1839 (16,000 pieces), relating chiefly to Scotland and to America.

Papers of persons in Great Britain who were prominent in literary and closely related fields include correspondence and frequently literary manuscripts of the following: William Harrison Ainsworth (novelist, editor), 1828-73 (94 pieces); Thomas Bewick (wood engraver, book illustrator), 1796-1828 (55 pieces); Richard Doddridge Blackmore (novelist), 1860-99 (74 pieces); Charlotte Brontë (novelist), 1832-54 (125 pieces); Elizabeth Barrett Browning (poet), 1827-58 (79 pieces); Robert Browning (poet), 1833-89 (200 pieces); Edward Bulwer-Lytton (novelist), 1827-72 (130 pieces); Rosina Doyle Bulwer-Lytton (novelist), 1838-61 (66 pieces); Robert Burns (poet), 1786-96 (43 pieces); Richard Francis Burton (explorer, Orientalist, author), 1885-92 (120 pieces); Thomas Campbell (poet), 1795-1844 (50 pieces); Thomas Carlyle (essayist, biographer), 1835-70 (135 pieces); Frances Power Cobbe (writer on religious and social subjects, philanthropist), 1855-1902 (854 pieces); Samuel Taylor Coleridge (poet), 1795-1829 (67 pieces); John Payne Collier (journalist, Shakespearean critic), 1874-81 (40 pieces); Thomas Frognall Dibdin (bibliographer), 1807-45 (693 pieces); Charles Dickens (novelist), 1832-70 (1,250 pieces); Charles Lutwidge Dodgson, known as Lewis Carroll (mathematician, author), 1848-97 (88 pieces); and Edward Gordon Duff (librarian), 1889-1924 (1,250 pieces).

Other papers of British origin that concern literature and closely related fields are those of Alfred Henry Forrester (artist, book illustrator), 1850-70 (330 pieces), letters and sketches addressed to him; James Anthony Froude (historian, prof. at Oxford Univ.), 1861-92 (80 letters); Frederick James Furnivall (philologist, editor), 1843-1910 (982 pieces), including correspondence with many prominent writers; Louise Imogen Guiney (poet, essayist), 1884-1914 (201 pieces), including 127 letters to James T. Fields (Mass.; author, publisher); Henry Rider Haggard (novelist), 1880-1925 (215 pieces); George Payne Rainsford James (novelist), 1826-40 (43 pieces); Edward Jerningham (poet, dramatist), 1760-1812 (1,194 pieces); Charles Lamb (essayist, poet, critic), 1796-1834 (228 pieces); Walter Savage Landor (poet, author), 1813-58 (164 pieces); Charles James Lever (novelist, British consul at Spezzia and Trieste), 1841-72 (328 pieces); George Meredith (novelist, poet), 1849-1901 (70 pieces); Mary Russell Mitford (novelist, dramatist), 1847-54 (64 pieces); Elizabeth Robinson Montagu (author, leader of bluestocking literary circles), 1732-1800 (6,923 pieces); Thomas Moore (poet), 1812-45 (40 pieces); William Morris (poet, artist), 1860-90 (65 pieces); Amelia Alderson Opie (novelist, poet), 1794-1854 (364 pieces); Thomas Percy (bishop, antiquarian, poet), 1694-1801 (100 pieces); James Robinson Planché (playwright, antiquarian), 1794-1880 (282 pieces); and John Poole (dramatist), 1817-37 (75 pieces).

Still other papers of British origin that concern literature and closely related fields are those of Charles Reade (novelist, dramatist), 1863-76 (106 pieces); Dante Gabriel Rossetti (poet, painter), 1846-85 (53 pieces); John Ruskin (critic, author, reformer), 1839-86 (626 pieces); William Raymond Sams (publisher), 1847-70 (69 pieces), consisting chiefly of letters from actors, playwrights, composers, and singers; Sir Walter Scott (poet, novelist), 1803-31 (111 pieces); William Sharp (poet, promoter of Celtic revival), 1890-97 (49 pieces); Mary Wollstonecraft Shelley (novelist), 1817-49 (167 pieces), including

42 letters to John Howard Payne (N. Y.; playwright, actor); Charlotte Turner Smith (poet, novelist), 1784-1806 (46 pieces); Robert Southey (poet), 1798-1839 (1,391 pieces); Herbert Spencer (philosopher, author), 1864-94 (41 letters); Robert Louis Stevenson (novelist, essayist, poet), 1852-94 (160 pieces); Jonathan Swift (satirist), 1725-39 (70 pieces); Algernon Charles Swinburne (poet), 1866-84 (85 pieces); Sir Thomas Noon Talfourd (judge, dramatic poet, editor), 1835-44 (194 pieces); William Makepeace Thackeray (novelist), 1830-61 (316 pieces); Philip Thicknesse (Lt. Gov. of Landguard Fort, author), 1770-85 (218 pieces); William Upcott (antiquary, autograph collector and dealer), 1802-45 (735 pieces); William Wordsworth (poet), 1795-1848 (175 pieces); and William Butler Yeats (poet), 1887-1929 (76 pieces). Other papers of British literary importance include a Middle English Collection of the works of Chaucer, Lydgate, and others, 14th-16th centuries (50 vols.); letters from literary clients to the London publishing firm of Cadell and Davies, 1769-1832 (496 pieces); and letters of members of the Pre-Raphaelite Brotherhood, 1840-1920 (88 pieces).

Papers of other persons of importance in Great Britain include those of Richard Carlile (reformer, freethinker), 1819-1900 (620 pieces); Thomas Clarkson (philanthropist, antislavery advocate), 1787-1847 (210 pieces); Henry Green (Presbyterian clergyman, bibliographer), 1869-70 (150 pieces); William Hamilton (philosopher), 1769-1801 (87 pieces), correspondence with Charles Greville (clerk of Privy Council, diarist); John Hollingshead (journalist, manager of the Gaiety Theatre, London), 1860-91 (308 pieces); Richard Howe (naval officer), 1776-99 (408 pieces), correspondence relating to the British Navy; Dorothy Jordan (actress), 1810-12 (565 pieces), letters to William

IV; Sir Robert Murray Keith (British Ambassador to Austria), 1776-92 (102 pieces); Zachary Macaulay (philanthropist, abolitionist, editor) and his family, 1793-1888 (1,014 pieces); Robert Saunders Dundas Melville (1st Lord of the Admiralty), 1812-14 (42 pieces), concerning the British and American Navies; Horatio Lord Nelson (naval officer), 1777-1805 (280 pieces); Edmond Sexton Pery (Speaker of the Irish House of Commons), 1749-98 (350 pieces); Edward F. Pigott (Examiner of Plays in the Lord Chamberlain's Office), 1818-79 (70 letters received); Sir George Pocock (naval officer), 1733-93 (1,170 pieces), chiefly official and private correspondence concerning the British expedition against Cuba; John Rickman (statistician), 1798-1839 (1,278 pieces), containing correspondence with Robert Southey (poet); Cloudesley Shovell (naval officer), 1690-1705 (85 pieces); Queen Victoria, 1830-61 (65 pieces); Arthur Wellesley, Duke of Wellington (army officer, Ambassador to France, Prime Minister), 1800-47 (100 pieces); Sir David Wilkie (genre and portrait painter), 1815-36 (53 pieces); and Sir George Yonge (Sec. for War), 1750-1814 (850 pieces).

Latin-American materials include records from the archives of the Holy Office of the Inquisition in Mexico, 1525-1824 (2,000 pieces); the Pizarro-La Gasca papers, 1540-80 (1,000 pieces), consisting chiefly of papers of Pedro de La Gasca concerning the rebellion led by Gonzalo Pizarro in Peru, 1544-48, together with papers of Gonzalo's that wer seized by La Gasca; papers of Eusebio Francisco Kino (Mexico; Jesuit missionary, explorer), 1680-87 (33 pieces); correspondence and other official papers of Pierre de Rigaud, Marquis de Vaudreuil (France; Colonial Gov. of La.), 1740-53 (383 pieces); papers of José de Gálvez (Spain; Visitador Gen. of Mexico), 1763-94 (734 pieces); some Spanish documents concerning Florida and the West Indies, 1783-95 (86 pieces); a group of letters and other documents dealing with the Spanish expedition to Nootka Island, 1789-93 (148 pieces); and papers of Ephraim George Squier (N.Y.; journalist, archeologist, diplomat), 1852-58 (489 pieces), relating to his project for the Honduras Interoceanic Railroad.

Papers relating to British colonies in America form a part of the Hastings, Ellesmere, Stowe, and Loudo Collections mentioned above. The Stowe Collection contains papers, 1680-1789 (650 pieces), relating to exports to America, land speculation in the early colonial period, plantations in the West Indies, and the American Revolution. The manuscripts in the Loudoun Collection, 1682-1780 (8,000 pieces), are especially important for the papers of John Campbell, Fourth Earl of Loudoun (British commander in chief in North America), 1756-58; and for records of the Board of Trade, valuable for their information concerning the commercial status of the colonies. Other papers important for this period are those of James Abercromby (British commander in chief in North America), 1674-1787 (1,000 pieces), relating chiefly to the French and Indian War; William Blathwayt (England; Sec. of the Lords of Trade and Plantations, Sec. at War), 1657-1770 (461 pieces); and Charles Spencer, Third Earl of Sunderland (England; statesman, bibliophile), 1704-10 (87 pieces), concerning political disturbances in New Jersey and New York. For this period also there are the holograph autobiography of Benjamin Franklin (Pa.; printer, scientist, diplomat), and letters and sermons of Increase, Cotton, and Richard Mather (Mass.; Congregational clergymen), 1645-1760 (76 pieces).

Among papers relating to the American Revolution and the early national period of United States history are a journal of John André (England; Army officer); and papers of Jacob Barker (Mass., N.Y.; merchant, financier), 1813-63 (163 pieces), relating chiefly to the raising of a war loan in 1814; Aaron Burr (N.Y.; Rev. War officer, U.S. Sen. and Vice Pres.), diary; Charles René Dominique Destouches (France; Rev. War naval officer), 1754-1804 (117 pieces); William Eaton (Mass.; U.S. Army officer, consul at Tunis, naval agent to Barbary States), 1792-1829 (555 pieces); Pierpont Edwards (Conn.; Member Continental Cong., U.S. dist. court judge) and his family, 1753-1876 (45 pieces); Nathanael Greene (R.I., Ga.; Rev. War officer), 1775-86 (107 pieces); Ebenezer Huntington (Conn.; Rev. War officer, U.S. Rep.), 1774-1830 (79 pieces); John Jay (N.Y.; Pres. of Continental Cong., diplomat, U.S. Chief Justice), 1779-82 (1 letter book); Thomas Jefferson (Va.; Member Continental Cong., Gov., Minister to France, Sec. State, U.S. Pres.), 1764-1826 (800 pieces), including architectural drawings and surveys; John Paul Jones (Rev. War naval officer), 1776-92 (41 pieces); Rufus King (Mass., N.Y.; Member Continental Cong., U.S. Sen. from N.Y., Minister to Great Britain), 1782-1830 (599 pieces); the Marquis de Lafayette (France; American Rev. War officer), 1779-1835 (100 pieces); James McHenry (Md.; Rev. War officer, Member Continental Cong., Sec. War), 1776-1815 (161 pieces); James Madison (Va.; U.S. Rep., Sec. State, U.S. Pres.), 1815-16 (104 pieces), consisting of correspondence with Alexander James Dallas (Pa.; Sec. Treas.); Robert Morris (Pa.; financier, Member Continental Cong., U.S. Sen.), 1774-1837 (320 pieces), including correspondence with Nathanael Greene (see above) on the subsistence of the Southern Army; Andrew Pickens (S. C.; Rev. War officer, U. S. Rep.), 1785-1835 (51 pieces), relating chiefly to his activities while Indian commissioner in the Carolinas; Timothy Pitkin (Conn.; lawyer, U. S. Rep.), chiefly early 19th century (336 pieces); and George Washington (Va.; Rev. War commander in chief, U. S. Pres.), 1749-1806 (450 pieces), chiefly correspondence with his wife. There is a collection of Revolutionary War orderly books, 1775-83 (55 vols.), among them 3 vols. of British Army orders. Included also are other papers, in smaller quantity, of many other important men of the period.

Papers of individuals who were important for their military or civilian service during the Civil War, in addition to some named elsewhere, include those of Frank Dwight Baldwin (U. S. Army officer), 1861-1921 (3,075 pieces); Samuel Ryan Curtis (Ohio, Iowa; engineer, Mexican and Civil War officer, U. S. Rep. from Iowa), 1828-66 (79 pieces); Thomas Haines Dudley (N. J.; U. S. consul at Liverpool), 1841-1900 (5,000 pieces), relating chiefly to blockade running; David Glasgow Farragut (U. S. naval officer), 1863-80 (102 pieces); Ulysses S. Grant (U. S. Army officer, U. S. Pres.), 1864-65 (345 pieces); Joseph Eggleston Johnston (Va.; Confed. Army officer, U. S. Rep.), 1861-65 (523 pieces); Ward Hill Lamon (Ill., Colo., D. C.; lawyer, partner of Lincoln, Civil War officer), 1848-89 (2,409 pieces); and Abraham Lincoln (Ill.; lawyer, U. S. Rep. and Pres.), 1832-65 (241 pieces), chiefly an assemblage of "collectors' items" rather than a homogeneous group. Concerning Lincoln, there are some papers of Daniel Fish (Minn.; lawyer, collector of Lincolniana), 1901-8 (77 pieces); and Charles Henry Hart (Pa.; lawyer, art expert, author), 1866-71 (245 pieces), relating chiefly to his Bibliograph-

ica Lincolniana. Papers of other Civil War leaders include those of David Dixon Porter (Pa., D. C.; U. S. naval officer), 1861-66 (750 pieces); Benjamin Franklin Scribner (Ind.; Civil War officer), 1831-1911 (1,100 pieces); William Tecumseh Sherman (U. S. Army officer), 1862-90 (52 pieces); James Ewell Brown Stuart, known as Jeb Stuart (Va.; U. S. and Confed. Army officer), 1855-64 (266 pieces), including over 100 letters by Robert E. Lee (Va.; U. S. and Confed. Army officer); and Gideon Welles (Conn.; newspaper editor, Sec. Navy), 1846-1902 (600 pieces). There are also records of the U. S. Army Paymaster for the Department of the Northwest, 1861-65 (5,000 pieces); records of the quartermaster of a regiment of U. S. Army colored troops, 1864-54 (392 pieces); and three collections of autographs of Civil War leaders, notably one containing letters of most important military and political figures on both sides, 1845-1900 (15,000 pieces).

Papers of political leaders in addition to some mentioned elsewhere include those of Thomas Robert Bard (Calif.; pioneer, U. S. Sen., oil co. pres.), 1890-1922 (5,000 pieces), business papers; Lincoln Clark (Ala., Iowa; circuit court judge, U. S. Rep.), and his family, 1758-1942 (690 pieces); Henry Clay (Ky.; U. S. Rep. and Sen., Sec. State), 1825-29 (425 pieces); George Mifflin Dallas (Pa.; U. S. Sen., Minister to Russia and to Great Britain, U. S. Vice Pres.), 1847-59 (45 pieces); Charles Fernald (Calif.; oil co. pres., industrial leader in southern Calif., U. S. Sen.), 1852-1904 (8,160 pieces), including 600 letters from Thomas R. Bard (see above); George Harrington (D. C., N. Y.; Asst. Sec. Treas., Minister to Switzerland), 1849-91 (64 pieces); John Milton Hay (Ill., D. C.; biographer of Lincoln, poet, diplomat, Sec. State), 1880-1904

(52 pieces); Sherman Otis Houghton (Calif.; lawyer, Civil War officer, U. S. Rep.), 1832-1907 (265 pieces); John Percival Jones (Calif., Nev.; miner, U. S. Sen. from Nev.), 1819-1936 (5,000 pieces); Lewis Charles Levin (Pa.; lawyer, newspaper editor, U. S. Rep.), 1849-50 (89 pieces); Henry Harrison Markham (Wis., Calif.; lawyer, U. S. Rep., Gov. of Calif.), 1867-99 (2,494 pieces); Tasker Lowndes Oddie (Nev.; miner, Gov., U. S. Sen.), 1863-1928 (5,725 pieces); Rodman McCamley Price (N.J., Calif.; U. S. naval officer, prefect and alcalde of Monterey, Calif., U. S. Rep. from N. J., Gov. of N. J.), 1842-81 (252 pieces); Samuel Jackson Randall (Pa.; U. S. Rep.), 1856-61 (81 pieces); John Arnold Rockwell (Conn., D.C.; jurist, U. S. Rep.), 1791-1871 (3,000 pieces), including correspondence on land development and land grants to railroads; Joseph D. Taylor (Ohio; lawyer, U. S. Rep.), 1863-81 (69 pieces); and Zachary Taylor (Ky.; U. S. Army officer, U. S. Pres.), 1846-48 (41 pieces), chiefly personal letters from Mexico. There are also papers relating to litigation concerning debts of Aaron Burr (N. Y.; lawyer, U. S. Vice Pres.), 1797-1826 (73 pieces); and miscellaneous autographs of New York Governors, chiefly colonial, 1683-1793 (190 pieces).

The Library has impressive holdings of papers of American authors, usually including literary manuscripts, among them papers of Thomas Bailey Aldrich (N. Y., Mass.; poet, short-story writer, editor of Atlantic Monthly), 1855-1906 (118 pieces); Horatio Alger (Mass., N. Y.; writer of books for boys), 1870-98 (88 pieces); Mary Austin (Calif., N. Mex.; novelist, dramatist), 1861-1950 (11,000 pieces); Ambrose Bierce (Calif.; short-story writer, journalist), 1871-1913 (380 pieces); William Cullen Bryant (Mass., N. Y.; poet, newspaper editor), 1806-77 (40 pieces); John Burroughs (N. Y.,

D. C.; poet, author), 1893-1921 (40 pieces); William Bliss Carman (Canada, N. Y., Conn.; poet), 1893-1927 (170 pieces); Willa Cather (Nebr., N. Y.; novelist), 1909-46 (91 pieces), consisting of letters and telegrams to Zoe Akins (Mo., N. Y.; poet, playwright); Thomas Holley Chivers (Ga.; poet), 1827-85 (92 pieces); Samuel L. Clemens, better known as Mark Twain (Mo., Calif., N. Y., Conn.; humorist, novelist), 1867-95 (140 pieces); Ina Donna Coolbrith (Calif.; poet, librarian, journalist), 1876-1932 (950 pieces); Mary Elizabeth Mapes Dodge (N. Y.; author, editor of St. Nicholas Magazine), 1866-91 (65 pieces); Ralph Waldo Emerson (Mass.; essayist, poet), 1821-72 (72 pieces); Eugene Field (Mo., Ill.; journalist, poet), 1872-94 (77 pieces); James Thomas Fields (Mass.; publisher, author, editor of Atlantic Monthly), 1850-1914 (5,374 pieces); John Fiske (Mass.; philosopher, historian, author), 1850-1901 (1,455 pieces); Ford Madox Ford (England, N. Y.; poet, critic, novelist), 1901-33 (305 pieces); and Robert Frost (N. H., Mass.; poet, lecturer), 1891-1929 (56 pieces).

Papers of other American authors include those of Francis Bret Harte (Calif., N. Y.; short-story writer), 1869-1901 (113 pieces); Nathaniel Hawthorne (Mass.; novelist), 1819-1921 (300 pieces); Lafcadio Hearn (Ohio, La., Japan; author), 1883-89 (41 pieces); Oliver Wendell Holmes (Mass.; poet, essayist, physician), 1830-94 (209 pieces); William Dean Howells (Mass., N. Y.; novelist, literary critic, editor of Atlantic Monthly, 1860-1915 (278 pieces); Washington Irving (N. Y.; author, Minister to Spain), 1819-59 (40 pieces); Helen Hunt Jackson (Mass., R. I., Colo.; poet, novelist, philanthropist), 1852-87 (169 pieces); Florence R. Keene (Calif.; poet), 1896-1950 (2,800 pieces); Lucy Larcom (Mass.; author, teacher), 1859-

90 (51 pieces); Jack London (Calif.; novelist), 1888-1932 (15,000 pieces); Henry Wadsworth Longfellow (Maine, Mass.; poet), 1825-81 (205 pieces); Benson John Lossing (N. Y.; wood engraver, author, editor), 1848-90 (1,000 drawings and 80 pieces); James Russell Lowell (Mass.; poet, essayist, Minister to Spain and to Great Britain), 1849-91 (152 pieces); Edgar Lee Masters (Ill., N. Y.; poet, dramatist), 1923 (40 pieces), chiefly poems; Henry Louis Mencken (Md.; author, editor, critic), 1916-48 (139 pieces); Cincinnatus Hiner Miller, known as Joaquin Miller (Oreg., Calif.; poet, playwright), 1869-1909 (264 pieces); and William Vaughn Moody (Ill., N. Y.; poet, playwright, Univ. of Chicago English prof.), 1901-9, 1935-36 (302 pieces).

Still other papers of American authors include those of Thomas Bird Mosher (Maine; publisher and editor of belles-lettres), 1894-1923 (146 pieces), consisting of letters to his life-long friend, W. Irving Way; Albert Bigelow Paine (Kans., N. Y.; author, editor), 1890-1934 (1,950 pieces); John Howard Payne (N. Y.; actor, playwright, U. S. consul at Tunis), 1813-50 (49 pieces); Edgar Allan Poe (Va., Md., Pa., N. Y.; poet, critic, short-story writer), 1829-49 (40 pieces); Eugene Manlove Rhodes (N. Mex., Calif.; cowboy, author), 1940-48 (620 pieces); James Whitcomb Riley (Ind.; poet), 1879-1904 (140 pieces); Upton Sinclair (N. J., Calif.; author), 1905-25 (64 pieces); Edmund Clarence Stedman (N. Y.; poet, anthologist, stockbroker), 1863-1901 (94 pieces); James King Steele (Calif.; journalist, newspaper editor, author), 1909-36 (590 pieces); George Sterling (Calif.; poet), 1895-1927 (885 pieces); Charles Warren Stoddard (Calif.; author), 1878-1909 (391 pieces); Harriet Beecher Stowe (Ohio, Mass., Conn.; author, abolitionist), 1853-88 (210 pieces); Bayard Taylor (Pa., N.Y.; author, traveler), 1840-1903 (460 pieces); Hen-

ry David Thoreau (Mass.; essayist, poet), 1836-76 (86 pieces); Anna Strunsky Walling (N. Y.; social economist, author), 1899-1948 (160 pieces); Charles Dudley Warner (Conn.; essayist, novelist, newspaper editor), 1883-99 (72 pieces); Walt Whitman (N. Y., D. C., N. J.; poet), 1857-90 (40 pieces); and John Greenleaf Whittier (Mass.; poet, abolitionist), 1832-91 (351 pieces).

Papers relating largely to science and scientists, chiefly in the United States, include papers of and collected by William Jones Rhees (D. C.; bibliographer, chief clerk of the Smithsonian Institution), 1744-1906 (4,700 pieces). In this collection are papers of Louis Agassiz (Switzerland, Mass., S. C.; zoologist, prof. at Harvard and Medical College of S. C.), 41 pieces; Alexander Dallas Bache (Pa., D. C.; physicist, Girard College pres., Supt. of U. S. Coast Survey), 1827-67 (1,898 pieces); and Henry Rowe Schoolcraft (N. Y., Mich.; explorer, ethnologist, supt. of Indian affairs for Mich.), 1815-74 (129 pieces). Also in this collection are papers concerning the National Institution for the Promotion of Science, 1816-58 (316 pieces); and papers relating to the Smithsonian Institution, 1831-1906 (1,624 pieces), including some correspondence of Joseph Henry (N. J., D. C.; physicist, Sec. of the Institution, Pres. of National Academy of Sciences). The Library has also papers of John Casper Branner (Ind., Ark., Calif.; geologist, pres. of Stanford Univ.), 1881-1925 (100 pieces); Charles Robert Darwin (England; naturalist, author), 1858-82 (65 pieces); Clarence King (D. C.; geologist, head of U. S. Geological Survey), 1859-1902 (525 pieces); Theodore P. Lukens (Calif.; conservationist, U. S. forester in southern Calif.), 1869-1942 (3,600 pieces); John Muir (Calif.; naturalist, explorer), 1874-1913 (116 pieces); William

Robert Prince (N. Y., Calif.; horticulturist), 1841-54 (65 pieces); and George Suckley (U. S. Army surgeon, naturalist), 1846-86 (97 pieces), containing letters of Spencer F. Baird (Pa., D. C.; zoologist, Sec. of Smithsonian Institution, U. S. Commissioner of Fish and Fisheries).

Papers of clergymen and educators include those of George Allen (Vt., Del., Pa.; Episcopal clergyman, languages prof. at Del. College and Univ. of Pa.), 1858-97 (47 pieces); George Henry Atkinson (Oreg.; Congregational clergyman, community builder), 1841-87 (126 pieces); Samuel Cooper (Mass.; Congregational clergyman), 1718-98 (270 pieces); Thomas Wentworth Higginson (Mass.; Unitarian clergyman, abolitionist, Civil War officer, author), 1841-92 (133 pieces); Francis Lieber (S. C., N. Y.; political scientist, prof. at Univ. of S. C. and Columbia Univ.), 1815-88 (6,000 pieces); Ferdinand Canning Scott Schiller (England, Calif.; philosopher, prof. at Univ. of Southern Calif.), 1887-1936 (357 pieces); John Martin Vincent (Md.; prof. of history and political science at Johns Hopkins Univ.), 1831-1929 (3,500 pieces); and Elkanah Walker (Oreg.; missionary, pioneer), 1837-71 (84 pieces). Also included are some records of the Society of Friends in Ohio, 1798-1853 (72 pieces); papers of a mental healer who practiced in the Midwest, 1845-1921 (200 pieces); a collection of Mormon diaries and other papers, 1815-1948; and papers, 1885-1932 (1,800 pieces), concerning Moravian missionaries in Alaska and among the Indians of southern California.

Papers of other persons include those of Emilio Aguinaldo Y Famy (Philippine Islands; rebel leader against Spain and U. S.), 1883-99 (63 pieces); Samuel Austin Allibone (Pa., N. Y.; librarian, literary lexicographer), 1841-87 (401 pieces); John Sherman Bagg (Mich.; editor of Detroit

Free Press, 1835-76 (482 pieces); Joseph Bonaparte (France; King of Naples and of Spain, resident in U. S.), 1825-39 (43 pieces); Fredrika Bremer (Sweden; novelist), 1849-65 (40 pieces); Simon Bolivar Buckner (Ky.; U. S. and Confed. Army officer, editor of Louisville Courier, Gov.), 1830-1912 (2,150 pieces); John Vance Cheney (Calif., Ill.; poet, author, librarian), 1885-95 (218 pieces); John Williams Gunnison (U. S. Army engineer), 1832-71 (61 pieces); Ida Husted Harper (Ind., N. Y.; journalist, suffrage leader), 1841-1910 (235 pieces), consisting of letters on the woman-suffrage movement gathered by her; George Archibald McCall (U. S. Army officer), 1831-53 (49 pieces), relating to Indian wars in Florida and the Southwest; Francisco Xavier Monteiro (Portugal; sec. of commissariat at Lisbon, deputy in Portuguese Congress), 1813-41 (100 pieces); Ely Samuel Parker (N. Y., Ill.; Seneca sachem, civil engineer, Civil War officer), 1802-94 (125 pieces), relating chiefly to the Seneca Indians; John Henry Hobart Peshine (N. J.; U. S. naval and Army officer, military attaché at Madrid), 1849-1903 (850 pieces); Charles Henry Ray (Ill.; physician, editor of Chicago Tribune), 1826-1904 (437 pieces); Walter Scribner Schuyler (N. Y., Calif.; U. S. Army officer, Indian fighter, military science prof. at Cornell Univ.), 1817-1932 (175 pieces); Richard Shackleton (Ireland; headmaster of Ballytore School), 1658-1808 (401 pieces); and Henry Ellsworth Wood (Colo.; mining engineer), 1854-1932 (537 pieces).

The library's substantial holdings of papers relating especially to Virginia and Virginians consist largely of papers collected by Robert Alonzo Brock (Va.; newspaper editor, historian), 1582-1914 (50,000 pieces). Included are many groups of family papers of individuals, among them papers of Joseph Reid Anderson (Va.; iron manufacturer, Confed. Army officer), 1847-96 (90 pieces); James Garland (Va.; lawyer, U.S. Rep.) and his family, 1762-1870 (300 pieces); Benjamin Harrison (Va.; Member Continental Cong., Gov.) and his family, 1701-1910 (195 pieces); Fitzhugh Lee (Va.; U.S. and Confed. Army officer, Gov.), 1863-89 (78 pieces); Robert E. Lee (Va.; U.S. and Confed. Army officer, pres. of Washington College) and his family, 1722-1892 (150 pieces); James Lyons (Va.; lawyer, State legislator, Confed. Rep.) and his family, 1772-1886 (882 pieces); Matthew Fontaine Maury (Va.; U.S. and Confed. naval officer, Naval Observatory Supt., oceanographer) and Dabney Herndon Maury (Va.; U.S. and Confed. Army officer, prof. at U.S. Military Academy) and their family, 1755-1900 (165 pieces); and Thomas Hicks Wynne (Va.; business executive, antiquarian), 1848-1901 (680 pieces). There are also papers of Virginia's Board of Trade, Board of War, Land Office, and War Office, 1779-81 (495 pieces), and some county records. Business records include a portion of the records of the Proprietors Office of the Northern Neck of Virginia (Fairfax Proprietary), 1690-1843 (350 pieces); a collection on railroads in Virginia, 1821-94 (1,950 pieces); records of a fire insurance company, 1795-1878 (575 pieces); and records of several mercantile and other business firms, for the late colonial period and the 19th century. Other papers in the Brock collection include records of the Washington National Monument Society, 1833-67 (85 pieces); letters to the editors of a Baptist periodical in Richmond, 1846-93 (110 pieces); various religious and fraternal records; some literary material; and many miscellaneous items.

In recent years the Library has given special attention to the acquisition of manuscripts important for the history of California and the West. Particularly important are papers of members of the stagecoach firm of Russell, Majors and Waddell (originator of the Pony Express mail service), 1839-68 (508 pieces); papers relating to Fort Sutter, 1845-62 (270 pieces), chiefly concerning the Bear Flag Revolt and the conquest of California, 1846-47; a collection of gold-rush journals, 1841-60 (68 vols.); papers dealing with the development of overland mail service, 1850-98 (166 pieces); records of the San Francisco Committee of Vigilance, 1853-58 (3,750 pieces); legal documents dealing with western railroads, 1860-79 (41 pieces), including 14 vols. on litigation, 1876, involving the Central Pacific Railroad Co.; and narratives and letters, 1870-1932 (550 pieces), concerning the Death Valley party of 1849.

Papers of men who were prominent in the settlement and/or development of California include those of Lynden Ellsworth Behymer (impresario, founder and manager of the Los Angeles Symphony), 1881-1947 (3,990 pieces); Amos Parmalee Catlin (State legislator, superior court judge), 1849-71 (2,600 pieces); James Clyman (Mo., Ill., Calif.; trapper, pioneer settler, chronicler), 1827-81 (52 pieces); George Ezra Dane (author) and his family, 1849-1934 (1,030 pieces), chiefly concerning California and the gold-rush period and his writings on that and related subjects; William Heath Davis (merchant, U.S. customs officer at San Francisco), 1843-1906 (634 pieces); Jackson A. Graves (lawyer, bank pres.), 1878-1930 (14,000 pieces); James Duncan Hague (Calif., N.Y.; mining engineer), 1855-1918 (18,000 pieces), including papers of Clarence King (D.C., N.Y.; geologist, head of U.S. Geological Survey); Henry Huntley Haight (lawyer, Gov.), 1846-85 (436 pieces); George Wharton

James (lecturer and writer on the Southwest), 1887-1909 (140 pieces); Louis Janin (mining engineer), 1828-1910 (876 pieces); Charles Augustus Keeler (author, director of Museum of Calif. Academy of Sciences), 1895-1944 (1,700 pieces); William Leidesdorff (sea captain, merchant, U.S. vice consul), 1840-67 (502 pieces); and James Wylie Mandeville (pioneer, State legislator), 1848-60 (700 pieces).

Papers of other men who were prominent in the settlement and/or development of California include those of William Moore (surveyor), 1851-91 (33 vols. and 67 pieces); Horatio Nelson Rust (nurseryman, U.S. Indian agent, archeological collector), 1799-1906 (1,229 pieces), including materials of and relating to John Brown (Pa., N.Y., Kans.; abolitionist); William Andrew Spalding (journalist, sec. of Los Angeles civil service commission), 1861-1941 (1,493 pieces); Abel Stearns (pioneer, rancher, merchant), 1806-1935 (12,500 pieces); Marshall Stimson (lawyer, civic leader), 1893-1951 (820 pieces); Adolph Sutro (Nev., Calif.; mining engineer, mayor of San Francisco), 1871-94 (208 pieces); Edward De Witt Taylor (printer, painter, etcher, poet), 1909-50 (4,954 pieces); David Smith Terry (State supreme court chief justice, Confed. Army officer), 1849-1933 (260 pieces); Mariano Guadalupe Vallejo (military and political leader), 1833-88 (257 pieces); George Clinton Ward (N.Y., Calif.; civil engineer, pres. of the Southern California Edison Co.), 1887-1936 (624 pieces); James Perry Worden (N.Y., Calif.; journalist, U.S. consul at Bristol, England, lecturer, author), 1821-1936 (550 pieces); Charles Erskine Scott Wood (Oreg., Calif.; U.S. Army officer, lawyer, author), 1887-1950 (1,200 pieces); and Thomas Lee Woolwine (district attorney of Los Angeles), 1914-22 (600 pieces).

Other records of importance for California history include those of the Prefecture of Los Angeles, 1823-50 (900 pieces); El Dorado County, 1842-1906 (1,600 pieces); the San Francisco Branch of the U.S. Mint, 1856-99 (62 pieces), consisting chiefly of letters containing instructions from the U.S. Treasury Department; the Business Women's Legislative Council of California, 1927-43 (150 pieces); and Ojai Festivals, Ltd., an organization for the production of annual music, theater, and dance festivals, 1946-53 (9,110 pieces). Records of California businessmen and organizations include those of the Pacific Mail Steamship Co., 1853-1917 (550 vols. and 190,000 pieces); a harness and saddlery firm in Los Angeles, 1854-1925 (59 vols.); a general storekeeper, postmaster, and Wells Fargo express agent in Kernville, 1856-96 (100 vols. and 2,656 pieces); a Napa bank president, 1859-1928 (78 vols. and 507 pieces); a director of the California Stage Co., 1860-66 (67 pieces); the president of the Indiana Colony (later called the San Gabriel Orange Growers Association) relating to the founding of Pasadena, 1873-74 (140 pieces); a rancher prominent in the development of the citrus and wine industries, 1877-97 (6,500 pieces); the Los Angeles Railroad Corp., 1888-1913 (175 pieces); the Duarte-Monrovia Fruit Exchange, 1892-1937 (21,000 pieces); and a fruit growers' association, 1896-1927 (350 pieces).

There are many papers relating to mining in California and other parts of the West, ranging from letters of prospectors to reports of mining engineers, and including papers of a firm of land attorneys and mineral surveyors of Weaverville, Calif., 1856-1929 (12,481 pieces); the Sierra Nevada Silver Mining Co. of Virginia City, Nev., 1859-80 (53 pieces); and a U.S. deputy mineral surveyor for

California, 1875-1909 (330 pieces). Representative of groups of manuscripts dealing with land claims and surveying is a collection of field books, maps, and other papers of Hansen, Solano, and Reeve, surveyors of Los Angeles County, 1849-1900 (1,400 pieces).

Among manuscripts important for the history of parts of the West other than California, there are papers dealing with official life in New Mexico, 1539-1890 (2,274 pieces), particularly the years 1840-84, covering the American occupation, the Civil War, and Indian affairs; papers of two Oregon pioneers, 1831-1925 (442 pieces), relating chiefly to military protection of the Territory during the Civil War period and the development of the Oregon Central Railroad; papers concerning the activities of the Hudson's Bay Co. and the Puget Sound Agricultural Co. in and around Fort Nisqually, Wash., 1833-1901 (2,600 pieces, including 111 vols.); official records from Forts Dalles, Simcoe, and Vancouver and other Army posts, principally in Oregon, 1850-80 (3,070 pieces); account books and other records of an Oregon lawyer and newspaperman, 1856-68 (274 pieces), dealing with settlement of claims against the Government for services in defense of the frontier in the Rogue River Indian troubles; and legal records relating to the Mountain Meadows (Utah) massacre, 1857-1912 (63 pieces).

Miscellaneous other manuscripts include papers relating to Canada, 1642-1900 (257 pieces); some relating to Indians east of the Mississippi River, chiefly the Seneca, 1642-1913 (265 pieces); papers and photographs chiefly concerning the Custer Massacre (300 pieces); papers, largely correspondence, relating to the U.S. Navy, 1732-1915 (539 pieces); records of the British Army Paymaster General's Office, 1767-1827 (181 pieces), concerning forces stationed out of Eng-

land; letter books, contracts, reports, and other papers relating to railroads, chiefly in England, Ireland, Scotland, Australia, and India, 1812-84 (200 pieces); papers relating to the Anti-Masonic Party in Massachusetts, 1829-34 (51 pieces); and notes and manuscripts on Gaelic mythology (1,735 pieces).

See the Annual Reports of the Henry E. Huntington Library and Art Gallery, since 1927, for brief notes on accessions; and the following detailed descriptions in the Huntington Library Bulletin (Huntington Library Quarterly beginning in Oct. 1937): "Huntington Library Collections," 1:33-106 (May 1931); "Loudoun Papers," by Stanley M. Pargellis and Norma B. Cuthbert, 3:97-107 (Feb. 1933); "Papers of Francis Lieber," by Charles B. Robson, 3:135-155 (Feb. 1933); "Summary Report on the Hastings Manuscripts," 5:1-67 (Apr. 1934); "California Books and Manuscripts in the Huntington Library," by John C. Parish, 7:1-58 (Apr. 1935); and "The Research Facilities of the Huntington Library: Americana," by Robert G. Cleland, 3:135-141 (Oct. 1939). See also De Ricci, Census, pp. 35-146; H. I. Poleman, A Census of Indic Manuscripts in the United States and Canada, passim (1938. 542 p. Processed); R. B. Haselden, "Manuscript Collections in the Huntington Library," in Archives and Libraries; Papers Presented at the 1939 Conference of the American Library Association, pp. 71-79 (1939. Processed); and Norma B. Cuthbert, American Manuscript Collections in the Huntington Library for the History of the Seventeenth and Eighteenth Centuries (1941. 93 p.).

SAN MATEO

San Mateo County Historical Association. College of San Mateo.

Holdings: 1,400 items from 1769, consisting of maps, photographs, and other materials relating chiefly to San Mateo County and vicinity.

SAN RAFAEL

Dominican College Library.   Sister Mary Marguerite, Librarian.

Holdings: Medieval and Renaissance manuscripts (6 vols.), including 3 antiphoners, 1 gradual, 1 psalter, and a book of collects, of the Dominican rite.
See De Ricci, Census, p. 147; and Innocenzo Taurisano, O. P., I Domenicani in Lucca, pp. 158 ff. (1914).

SANTA ANA

Charles W. Bowers Memorial Museum.   2002 North Main St.   (Mrs.) F. E. Coulter, Curator-Director.

Holdings: 1,000 pieces, 1746-1955, relating chiefly to the history of Orange County and Southern California. Spanish documents, the earliest from 1746, include early padres' marriage investigations and dispensations for notable Spanish families, baptismal records, and letters concerning both religious and economic aspects of the early missions. Other papers in Spanish include rancheros' day books and journals, deeds, plats, abstracts of title, wills, and genealogies. There are also early maps of Southern California. Civil War papers include some documents and original pencil drawings of rivers, bridges, and terrain, done by a delineator for the armed forces, 1860-65. There are also papers of Helena Modjeska (Poland, U. S.; actress), including some correspondence and original designs, in water color, for her costumes.

SANTA BARBARA

Santa Barbara Mission Archives. Rev.

Maynard J. Geiger, Archivist.

Holdings: 4,961 items, 1640-1925, relating chiefly to the work of the Franciscans in California. Included are a collection relating to Junipero Serra (Spain, Mexico, Calif.; Franciscan missionary), 1713-84 (961 items); the archives of and papers relating to Santa Barbara Mission and other missions in California; and records of the College of Our Lady of Sorrows at Santa Barbara.
See Hist. Records Survey, Guide for Calif., p. 43; and Maynard J. Geiger, Calendar of Documents in the Santa Barbara Mission Archives (1947. 291 p.).

SOUTH SAN FRANCISCO

Federal Records Center, GSA. Box 708. Chief.

Holdings: A large quantity of noncurrent or semicurrent records, chiefly of recent date, of nonmilitary agencies of the U. S. Government in northern California and Nevada. Because of the wide jurisdiction of regional offices, especially those located in San Francisco, many of the records deal with affairs in all the Western states. Most of the papers have been appraised for disposal after specified periods of time, but some will be preserved because of their enduring value. Included in the latter category are records of the Bureau of Customs, from 1851; Coast Guard, from 1877; Bureau of the Mint, from 1853; Bureau of Indian Affairs, from 1864; National Park Service, from 1927; Geological Survey, from 1901; Bureau of Land Management and its predecessor, the General Land Office, from 1873; Immigration and Naturalization Service, from 1877; Bureau of Agricultural Engineering, from 1889; Forest Service, from 1905; Soil Conservation Service and predecessors, from 1903; and Philippine War Damage Commission, from 1946.

STANFORD UNIVERSITY

Hoover Institution on War, Revolution, and Peace. C. Easton Rothwell, Director; Philip T. McLean, Librarian; Thomas T. Thalken, Archivist of the Herbert Hoover Archives.

Holdings: A large collection of manuscript records and archives supplementing the Library's printed documentation of the 20th-century political, economic, and social evolution, with emphasis on the periods of the two World Wars and their political and social consequences.

Records of or pertaining to international organizations and conferences include those of the Conference on the Limitation of Armament, Washington, D. C., 1921-22 (10 ft.); the Institute of Pacific Relations, 1925-39 (12 ft.); the Inter-Allied Rhineland High Commission, 1919-22 (15 vols.); the International Military Tribunal, Nuremberg, 1945-49, and the 12 American trials, Nuremberg, 1946-49 (325 ft.); the International Military Tribunal of the Far East, 1946-48 (65 ft.); the Paris Peace Conference, 1919 (115 ft.); the Reparations Commission, 1920-24 (25 ft.); and the office of the Supreme Commander of the Allied Powers, consisting of press translations and summaries, 1945-49 (30 ft.), and papers of its Natural Resources Section, 1945-52 (12 ft.).

Among materials pertaining to the United States, as regards both domestic and international interests, are personal papers of Robert D. Burhans (U. S. Army officer), 1942-44 (6 cases), consisting of records of the First Service Force; Edwin F. Gay (Mass., N. Y.; Harvard Univ. economist, member of the War Industries Board), 1917-19 (10 boxes); George D. Herron (Iowa,

N. Y., Italy; unofficial adviser to Pres. Woodrow Wilson), 1917-19 (13 vols.); Jay Calvin Huston (Calif.; U. S. consul in China), 1917-31 (18 boxes), concerning Sino-Russian relations; David Starr Jordan (Ind., Calif.; naturalist, pres. of Ind. and Stanford Univs., peace leader), 1910-25 (5 scrapbooks and 25 ft.); Thomas C. Lonergan (U. S. Army officer), maps and documents on the American Expeditionary Forces in World War I (13 boxes); Gino Speranza (N. Y.; lawyer, attaché at the U. S. Embassy in Rome), 1914-18 (3 ft.), relating to Italy in World War I; Joseph W. Stilwell (U. S. Army officer), 1941-44 (18 vols. and 10 boxes), including diaries relating chiefly to the China-Burma-India theater in World War II; George Sylvester Viereck (N. Y.; journalist, Nazi propagandist), 1903-42 (33 vols.), personal scrapbooks covering his political and literary career; and Brand Whitlock (Ohio; Ambassador to Belgium, author), 1914-18 (17 boxes). There are also records of the following American organizations and governmental bodies: the America First Committee, 1940-41 (60 ft.); the Military Order of the World Wars, 1914-45 (12 ft.); the National Council for Prevention of War (22 boxes); the National Japanese American Student Relocation Council, Philadelphia, 1942-46 (18 filing cabinets); the Near East Relief, 1915-25 (10 ft.); the Northern California Service Board for Conscientious Objectors (3 boxes); and the U. S. Office of Naval Intelligence, 1940 (2 filing cabinets), containing cross cultural survey files on the western and central Pacific islands.

Materials pertaining to Western Europe include papers of Wilfrid Bade (Germany; official in the Ministry of Propaganda), 1933-44 (12 boxes); correspondence and diaries of Alfred Fried (Austria; jurist, pacifist), 1915-

19 (18 vols.); the diary of Josef Goebbels (Germany; Minister of Propaganda), 1942-43 (6,800 pages); correspondence of Konrad Haenisch (Germany; Social Democratic Party leader), 1907-15 (177 items); diaries of Franz Halder (Germany; Army officer), 1939-43 (7 vols.); and photostatic copies of the files of the Reichsführer S. S. Personlicher Stab (Heinrich Himmler), 1942-44 (60 folders), and Himmler diaries, 1914-24 (6 notebooks). Included also are the Grace Davis Booth Collection of German proclamations in occupied Belgium, 1914-18 (18 ft.); the H. A. Dorten Collection on the separatist movement in the Rhineland, 1919 (3 vols.); records of the Deutsche Kongress Zentrale (German center for participation in international congresses), 1936-38 (171 ft.); records of the Gesamtverband Deutscher Anti-kommunistischen Vereinigungen (also called the Antikomintern), 1933-45 (200 folders); proceedings of the Finnish war guilt trials, Helsinki, 1945-46 (20 folders), in Finnish; microfilm of selected files from Ernst Reuter (Germany; Mayor of Berlin) Archives, 1918-53 (39 reels); N. S. D. A. P. Hauptarchiv (National Socialist Party Archive, microfilmed at the Department of State Document Center, Berlin), 129 reels; and photoblowups of selected frames (organized by serial number) of the German Foreign Ministry Archives [1936-44].

Among materials pertaining to Russia are archives and papers of the following White Russian generals of the Civil War period: Feodor F. Abramov, 1918-27 (70 folders); Nicholas N. Golovine, 1904-21 (32 folders); Boris V. Heroys, 1919-20 (34 folders) Pavel A. Kussonsky, 1918-25 (49 folders); A. A. von Lampe, 1919-26 (57 folders); Eugene K. Miller, 1917-24 (45 folders); Dimitri Shcherbachev, 1917-20 (64 folders); Peter N. Wrangel, 1918-23 (350 folders); and Nicholas Yudenich, 1919-20 (150 folders).

There are also diplomatic records and correspondence of three army officers who served Russia as military attachés: Vladimir B. Fredericks (in Paris), 1835-76 (25 folders); and M. P. Podtiagin (in Tokyo), 1906-22 (70 folders). Archives and papers of Russian statesmen and civilian leaders include those of Michel de Giers (statesman, ambassador), 1919-26 (131 folders); V. A. Maklakov (lawyer, diplomat), 1917-26 (87 folders); Serge P. Melgunov (historian, editor), 1918-20 (42 boxes); V. I. Moravsky (statesman), 1917-34 (300 folders), relating to anti-Soviet activities of Russian emigrés in the Far East; and Serge N. Paleologue (plenipotentiary for the settlement of Russian refugees in Yugoslavia), 1920-33 (51 folders). There are also files of the Paris headquarters of the Czarist secret police, 1883-1917 (16 large packing cases), pertaining especially to counter-intelligence activities in Central and Western Europe. The Library has other Russian archives some of which are restricted from use at the present time.

The Herbert Hoover Archives include the personal files of Herbert Hoover relating to the period of his service as Secretary of Commerce and U. S. President, and to personal interests preceding and following this period (150 file cases); the personal files of Herbert Hoover as U. S. Food Administrator and personal files of important members of the Food Administration, 1917-19 (25 file cases); records of European operations of the American National Red Cross, 1917-20 (12 file cases); papers of the American Relief Administration relating to the relief and rehabilitation of Europe (including minutes of the Supreme Economic Council and records of European technical advisers), 1919-21, and relating to famine relief in Russia, 1921-23 (90 file cases); records

of the Commission for Relief in Belgium, 1914-20 (25 file cases), relating
to the care and feeding of German-oc-
cupied Belgium and Northern France
during World War I; papers of the Finnish Relief Fund, relating to American
aid to Finland following the Russian in-
vasion, 1939-40; material relating to
inter-Allied shipping and supplies controls, 1917-19 (2 file cases); and records of the [U. S.] National Committee
on Food for the Small Democracies,
1931-43 (7 file cases), relating to A-
merican famine relief in Belgium, the
Netherlands, Norway, Finland, and
Poland. The Archives will not be open
for general use until certain indexing
and processing projects have been
completed.

See Nina Almond and H. H. Fisher,
Special Collections in the Hoover Li-
brary on War, Revolution, and Peace
(1940. 111 p.); Suda L. Bane, "The
Dedicatory Exercises of the Hoover
Library," in Am. Archivist, 5:179-
184 (July 1942); Philip T. McLean,
"The Hoover Institute and Library,"
in Library Quarterly, 19:235-249 (Oct.
1949); Gerhard L. Weinberg, Guide to
Captured German Documents (1952.
90 p.), and Supplement (1959. 69 p.);
C. Easton Rothwell, "Resources and
Research in the Hoover Institute and
Library," in Am. Archivist, 18:141-
150 (Apr. 1955); Witold S. Sworakow-
ski, The Hoover Library Collection on
Russia (1954. 42 p.); and Hildegard R.
Boeninger, The Hoover Library Collection on Germany (1955. 56 p.).

—oOo—

Stanford University Libraries. R. C.
Swank, Director.

Holdings: A variety of manuscripts
in several major collections and special libraries, described below in alphabetical order. The Hoover Institution on War, Revolution, and Peace is
on the Stanford University campus but
is not one of the University Libraries,
and it is separately described above.
See Hist. Records Survey, Guide
for Calif., pp. 45-49.

Borel Collection, Stanford University
Library. J. Terry Bender, Chief,
Division of Special Collections.

Holdings: 37 file drawers, 2 boxes, and 60 linear ft., 1820-1951, relating chiefly to politics. Included are
papers of Thomas V. Cator (Calif.;
Populist leader), 1895-98 (145 items);
John P. Irish (Calif.; journalist), 1876-
1922 (460 items), relating to Japanese
immigration; Francis V. Keesling (Calif.; lawyer, active in the Republican
State Central Committee and the Gold-
en Gate Bridge and Highway Dist.),
1906-51 (16 file drawers); Meyer Liss-
ner (Calif.; lawyer, active in the Lin-
coln-Roosevelt Republican League in
Calif. and the Progressive National
Committee), 1903-21 (40,000 items);
James C. Needham (Calif.; U.S. Rep.),
1899-1908 (24 vols.); Stephen M.
White (Calif.; lawyer, U. S. Sen.), 1881-
1901 (106 vols.); and John D. Works
(Calif.; U. S. Sen.), 1911-26 (200
items). There are also several diaries of pioneers.

Branner Geological Library. School
of Mineral Sciences. (Mrs.) Kathryn Nell Cutler, Mineral Sciences
Librarian.

Holdings: 300 items, consisting
of letters, photographs, reports, and
other papers relating to the San Francisco earthquake of 1906, collected by
the California State Earthquake Investigation Commission.

Division of Special Collections, Stanford University Library. J. Terry
Bender, Chief.

Holdings: Included are 11 illuminated medieval manuscripts; 26 Peruvian documents, 1617-1892, and other Hispanic American papers; European and American historical and literary letters and documents dating from the 16th century.

Papers of individuals include those of Ambrose Bierce (Calif.; journalist, short-story writer), 1871-1914 (620 items, largely letters to Bierce); Bernard A. De Voto (Mass.; author, editor), 40,000 items; John Galsworthy (England; novelist), 1921-32 (142 items); James Huneker (Pa., N.Y.; musical critic), 15 manuscripts; Collis Potter Huntington (Calif., N.Y.; capitalist, railroad builder), 1863-87 (14 vols.), consisting of correspondence with his partner Mark Hopkins (Calif.; capitalist, railroad builder), relating to the Central Pacific, Western Pacific, and Southern Pacific Railroads; Aldous Huxley (England; novelist), 1920-34 (575 items); David Jacks (Calif.; Monterey County landowner), 1845-1909 (1 file drawer); Elisha Kent Kane (U.S. naval officer, physician, explorer), 1854-55 (1 journal), relating to Arctic exploration; Thomas Leiper Kane (Pa.; abolitionist, Civil War officer), 1845-82 (42 items, including 2 diaries), illustrative of Mormon conditions; D. H. Lawrence (England; poet, novelist), 1915-29 (61 items); Jack London (Calif.; novelist), 1902-13 (154 items); Achille Murat (France, Fla.; author), 1820-45 (1 file drawer and 1 letter book); Sir Isaac Newton (England; mathematician, natural philosopher), 8 manuscripts and 8 vols.; Edward Lee Plumb (N.Y., D.C.; Sec. of U.S. Legation in Mexico, consul gen. at Havana), 1860-1905 (2 file drawers), relating largely to the Mexican International Railway; William Rufus Shafter (U.S. Army officer), 1876-98 (3 file drawers), relating chiefly to the Cuban campaign of 1898; Upton Sinclair (N.J., Calif.; author), 1910-13 (235 items); George Sterling (Calif.; poet), 1923-26

31 items and 19 literary manuscripts); and George M. Wheeler (U.S. Army officer, topographical engineer), 1872 (344 vols. and field books), relating to the U.S. Geographical Surveys West of the 100th Meridian.

Other holdings are the Ames Family papers, including a group of letters written by Fisher Ames (Mass.; lawyer, U.S. Rep.), 50 items; the Elmer E. Robinson Collection of American historical documents and correspondence (200 items); Cobden-Sanderson Papers regarding the Doves Press (100 items); 1 volume of presidential autographs; Daingerfield Family papers (100 items); and manuscript copies of the novels of Janet Lewis (Calif.; writer).

There are also conchological drawings, 1810-50 (17 solander boxes and 9 vols.); a collection of American autograph letters, 1683-1840 but largely 18th century (154 items); a transcript of arbitration proceedings in a dispute, 1927, between a California ferryboatman's union and certain railroads; and papers relating to seismology.

Jackson Library. Graduate School of Business. (Mrs.) Marion M. Smith, Director.

Holdings: Chiefly account books and other records relating to business activities in California. Included are business papers of Adolph Sutro (Nev., Calif.; mining engineer) and of the Alaska Commercial Co.; Donohoe Kelly Banking Co.; Geary St. Park and Ocean R.R. Co.; IONE Coal and Iron Co.; D.R. McMillan Co.; McNear and Co.; Northern Commercial Co.; Pacific Improvement Co.; Rocky Mountain Coal and Iron Co.; Union Fuel Co.; and El Verando Villa Assn.

Lane Medical Library. Clara Manson,

Librarian.

Holdings: 17 vols., chiefly Oriental manuscripts relating to medical and other scientific subjects.

Memorial Library of Music.

Holdings: 516 musical manuscripts of great composers and many autograph letters of musicians. The collection of original manuscripts of European composers is the second largest in the United States.

See Nathan van Patten, Catalogue of the Memorial Library of Music, Stanford University (1950. 310 p., with facsimiles).

Stanford Collection. Ruth Scibird, Curator.

Holdings: Papers relating especially to the University. Included are papers of John Casper Branner (Ind., Calif.; geologist, pres. of Stanford Univ.), 1882-1921 (49 vols. and 83 boxes); David Starr Jordan (Ind., Calif.; naturalist, pres. of Stanford Univ.), 1891-1929 (88 boxes); and Leland Stanford (Calif.; railroad builder, Gov., U. S. Sen., founder of Stanford Univ.), 1850-93 (1 vol.).

STOCKTON 4

College of the Pacific Library. Allan P. Laursen, Librarian; (Mrs.) Grace D. Stuart, Curator of collection.

Holdings: A collection of several thousand items, 1850-1900, consisting of letters, account books, and other business papers of grocery, hardware, and other stores in early towns of California and Oregon.

STOCKTON 3

San Joaquin Pioneer Museum. Pershing Ave. and Rose St. Earl Row-

land, Director.

Holdings: A small collection, chiefly of 19th-century materials relating to California. Included are logbooks and journals of voyages, 1842-64 (4 vols.); diaries, 1849-78 (7 vols.), including 2 Civil War diaries and 3 journals of overland travel to California; and miscellaneous groups of letters. There are also some illuminated manuscripts and some manuscript music.

See Hist. Records Survey, Guide for Calif., p. 53.

THREE RIVERS

Ash Mountain Headquarters, Sequoia and Kings Canyon National Parks. The Superintendent.

Holdings: 6 file boxes containing letters, stenographic copies of interviews, and other papers relating to the Kaweah Colony, travels into the Sequoia National Park area before 1900, and contacts of pioneers with Yokuts Indians living within what are now the park boundaries.

VENTURA

Ventura County Free Library. 651 Main St. (Mrs.) Mildred S. Spiller, Librarian.

Holdings: 12 vols., 1870-1920, relating chiefly to Ventura County. Included are a diary of an overland journey to California in 1849 and reminiscences of early settlers.

See Hist. Records Survey, Guide for Calif., p. 55.

WILMINGTON

Federal Records Center, GSA. 2401 East Pacific Coast Highway. Chief.

Holdings: Noncurrent records,

chiefly of the 20th century, of nonmilitary agencies of the U.S. Government in southern California and Arizona. Most of the papers have been appraised for disposal after specified periods of time, but some will be preserved because of their enduring value. Materials in the latter category include records of U.S. district courts, from 1887; Bureau of Customs, from 1883; Bureau of Indian Affairs, from 1875; General Land Office and Bureau of Land Management, from 1853; Geological Survey, from 1889; Forest Service, from 1904; and Weather Bureau, from 1932.

YOSEMITE NATIONAL PARK

Yosemite Museum. The Superintendent.

Holdings: 1,006 manuscripts and other material relating to the human and natural history of the Sierra Nevada region of California. Included are letters and reports written during U.S. Army administration of Yosemite, 1891-1914. Biographical material includes some papers of John Muir (Calif.; naturalist, explorer) and others who contributed importantly to the history of Yosemite.

CANAL ZONE

BALBOA HEIGHTS

Canal Zone Library-Museum. Eleanor D. Burnham, Librarian-Curator.

Holdings: 38 vols., 1 box, 18 portfolios (quarto), and 194 pieces, 1417-1958, relating chiefly to the Panama Canal and the Canal Zone. Included are the originals and copies of maps showing the exploration and colonization of the Isthmus of Panama and Central America and the construction of the Panama Railroad and the Panama Canal, 1417-1947 (158 pieces); diaries and reminiscences, including a diary of William H. Sidell (N.Y., surveyor and chief engineer for the Panama Railroad), 1849 (2 vols.), and reminiscences of men engaged in the construction of the Panama Canal, recorded on tape and transcribed in 1958 (50 pages); annual reports of the Board of Directors of the Panama Railroad Co., 1852-1951 (30 vols., the first 24 of which are in manuscript); archives of the Compagnie Universelle du Canal Interoceanique, 1881-98 (1 vol., 10 portfolios, and 12 pieces), including inventories, engineering studies, and hospital, personnel, and labor recruitment records; papers of or pertaining to societies that flourished during the Canal construction period and later (Society of the Inca, Society of the Chagres, Knights of Pythias, etc.), 1910-38 (1 box, 1 portfolio, and 24 pieces).

COLORADO

BOULDER

University of Colorado Western Historical Collections. Ralph E. Ellsworth, Director; Lucile Fry, Librarian.

Holdings: 55,000 items, from 1858, relating chiefly to Colorado and the Rocky Mountain region. Included are papers of John C. Bell (Colo.; lawyer, U.S. Rep.), 1886-1922 (100 items); William Carey Brown (U.S. Army officer in Philippines and World War I), 1873-1938 (4,000 items, including 34 diaries); Edward P. Costigan (Colo.; lawyer, U.S. Sen., U.S. Tariff Commissioner), 1900-28 (10,000 items, many concerning the Tariff Commission); James A. Owenby (Colo., N. Mex.; mining lawyer), consisting of correspondence and legal briefs, 1895-1920 (500 items); and Henry M. Teller (Colo.; lawyer, U.S. Sen., Sec. Interior), 1863-1908 (500 items). There are also business papers of Leopold Guldman (Colo.; merchant), 1900-35 (1,000 items); and of the J. Sidney Brown Mercantile Co. (wholesale grocery business), 1861-1938 (2,000 items); a collection of papers on the gold rush, 1858-61 (1,000 items); a collection of papers on the "colony towns," established during the Territorial period as cooperative or semi-cooperative enterprises, 1869-90 (1,000 items); and a collection concerned with western trails, assembled by Margaret Long (Colo.; physician, author), 1917-55 (5,000 items), that contains manuscripts as well as books, maps, and photographs.

COLORADO SPRINGS

Colorado College Library. Ellsworth Mason, Librarian.

Holdings: 400 items, including 200 manuscripts and letters of English poets; 50 autographs and letters of prominent 19th-century Americans; and 50 letters and documents pertaining to the French Revolution, the U.S. Revolution, the U.S. Civil War, and the American Founding Fathers.

Pioneers' Museum. 25 West Kiowa St. Dorothy E. Smith, Curator.

Holdings: 25 vols. and 1,000 pieces, 1540-1920, relating chiefly to Colorado and neighboring States. Included are papers of William Jackson Palmer (Pa., Colo.; Civil War officer, railroad executive), 1858-1907 (40 diaries and notebooks); notes, made about 1900-10, of personal interviews with descendants of Christopher Carson, known as Kit Carson (N. Mex.; trapper, Indian agent, U. S. Army officer) and many other explorers and pioneers (20 notebooks); and a collection of photographs and hand-drawn diagrams.

DENVER 10

Colorado Methodist Historical Society. Iliff School of Theology. Martin Rist, Librarian.

Holdings: Papers concerning the Methodist Church, particularly in Colorado. Included are parts of the diary of Jacob Adriance (Colo.; pioneer Methodist preacher); letters and other papers of Henry White Warren (Mass., Pa., Ga., Colo.; Methodist bishop, founder of the Iliff School of Theology); minutes of the Rocky Mountain (later Colo.) Conference of the

Methodist Episcopal Church; and records of a number of individual
churches.

DENVER 3

Division of State Archives and Public
Records. 332 State Services Bldg.,
1525 Sherman St. Dolores C. Renze,
State Archivist.

Holdings: 25,000,000 documents,
1840-1956, consisting largely of noncurrent public records of the State of
Colorado (and the preceding Territory) and its counties, municipalities,
and other political subdivisions that
have been transferred to the State Archivist for permanent custody and administration. Included are all types
of documents and other records common to the conduct of the business of
government, among them maps, photographs, microfilms, motion pictures, wire recordings, paintings,
plans, correspondence, and record
books. Included in the holdings are
papers of the Governors, 1864-1956
(2,500,000 items), records of other
constitutional officers, and records
of 165 other State agencies. With the
many county and municipal records
are inventories made in 1939-40, and
there are also inventories of church
records in 62 counties. Among the
larger manuscript collections having
a direct bearing on service in public
office are papers of John Evans (Ind.,
Ill., Colo.; physician, founder of
Northwestern Univ. and Univ. of
Denver, railroad builder, Gov. of
Colo. Terr.), 1834-1952 (10,000 pieces), and of Roland G. Parvin (Colo.;
mining and real estate promoter,
State Fish and Game Commission
member), 1900-39 (3,000 pieces).
There is also a microfilm copy of
records of the Chicago, Burlington,
and Quincy Railway covering 101
years.

DENVER 25

Federal Records Center, GSA. Bldg.
48, Denver Federal Center. Chief.

Holdings: A large quantity of noncurrent and semicurrent records,
chiefly of recent date, of nonmilitary
agencies of the U. S. Government in
Colorado, New Mexico, Utah, and
Wyoming. Some of these records
have been appraised for disposal after specified periods of time, but
some will be preserved because of
their enduring value. Records in the
latter category include those of U. S.
district courts and predecessor circuit courts, from 1861; Forest Service, from 1887; Bureau of Indian Affairs, from 1865; Bureau of Land Management, from 1854; Bureau of the
Mint, from 1863; Bureau of Reclamation, from 1889; Internal Revenue Service, 1863-69 (1 cu. ft.); Geological
Survey, chiefly topographic maps,
from 1884; and Soil Conservation Service, from 1936.

DENVER 3

Denver Public Library. 1357 Broad-
way. John T. Eastlick, Librarian;
(Mrs.) Alys Freeze, Head, Western
History Department.

Holdings: 12,250 items in the
Western History Department and the
Genealogy Division, including letter
books, journals, boxes of personal
papers, and transcribed church records, relating chiefly to Colorado
and the exploration and development
of the West. There are also three
Arabic manuscripts and one Mameluke inscription.
Included in the Western History
Department manuscripts are papers
of Jacob Adriance (Colo.; pioneer
Methodist preacher), 1854-64 (10
journals and 1 box); William Newton

Byers (Colo.; pioneer, surveyor, newspaper editor), 1852-1903 (42 journals, 3 letter books, and 266 letters); Farrington R. Carpenter (Colo., D. C.; lawyer, director of grazing in U. S. Interior Dept.), 1934-38 (2 boxes), on activating the Taylor Grazing Act; John Wallace Crawford (N. Mex., N. Y.; "the poet scout"), 1877-1911 (some literary manuscripts and 250 letters received); John L. Dailey (Colo.; newspaper publisher in Denver), 1857-67 (diaries); David C. Dodge (Ill., Colo.; railroad official, capitalist), 1870-71 (555 letters); Grenville M. Dodge (Iowa; Civil War officer, civil engineer, U. S. Rep.) and his family, 1852-1902 (415 letters and some diaries); Eugene Field (Mo., Ill.; journalist, poet), 1885-95 (manuscripts of several poems); Aaron E. Gove (Ill., Colo.; Civil War officer, supt. of Denver schools, founder of the National Education Association), 1877-1912 (9 letter books and 12 boxes); Horace Greeley (N. Y.; editor of New York Tribune, political leader), 1870-72 (46 letters); Irving Hale (Colo.; U. S. Army and Spanish-Am. War officer, manager and electrical engineer of General Electric Co., Denver), 1881-1930 (68 boxes); Frank Hall (Colo.; miner, journalist, sec. of Colo. Terr.), 1834-1917 (200 letters), photostats; Henry M. Teller (Colo.; lawyer, U. S. Sen. and Sec. Interior), 1877-78 (571 letters); James B. Thompson (Colo.; Indian agent for the Utes), 1871-80 (7 letter books); Joel F. Vaile (Colo.; lawyer), 1887-1911 (13 letter books); and William N. Vaile (Colo.; lawyer, U. S. Rep.), 1902-16 (5 letter books and 14 boxes). There are also ledgers of several Colorado business firms; minutes of Pioneer Men and Women of Colorado (Society), 1885-1940; and a collection of material on William Frederick Cody, known as Buffalo Bill (Kans., Wyo.; scout, showman, U. S. Army officer) made by a

manager for Cody's Wild West Shows, 1855-1903 (13 scrapbooks, 1 filing drawer of pictures and photo albums, 1 filing drawer of programs and miscellaneous items).

Papers in the Genealogy Division include 220 genealogical manuscripts; wills of the Green and Greene families of Rhode Island; transcripts of church baptismal and membership records of a Congregational church in Cheyenne, Wyo., and a Presbyterian church in Denver; and records of 6 Colorado cemeteries, chiefly 19th century, in transcript and on microfilm.

See articles on the Arabic manuscripts and the Mameluke inscription by Charles D. Matthews in Moslem World, 30:269-279 (July 1940), and in Am. Oriental Society, Journal, 60:370-382 (Sept. 1940).

DENVER 11

Regis College Library. West 50th St. and Lowell Blvd.

Holdings: 16 vols. of diaries, 1878-1910, and 300 photographs relating to the Catholic Church in the Southwest, particularly St. Patrick's Church in Pueblo, Colo.

See Library Quarterly, 10:182 (Apr. 1940).

DENVER 2

State Historical Society of Colorado. State Museum Bldg. Maurice Frink, Executive Director; Agnes W. Spring, State Historian; Glenn H. Johnson, Jr., Librarian.

Holdings: Over 100,000 items, 1805 to date, relating to Colorado and the West, in addition to a larger quantity of material in special collections.

Personal papers include those of Andy Adams (Colo.; author of Western stories and plays), 35 literary manuscripts; Frank Dwight Baldwin (Civil War and U.S. Army officer, Commander of the Dept. of the Colo.); 100 letters and reports; William Abraham Bell (Ireland, Colo.; physician, capitalist, organizer of the Denver and Rio Grande R.R. and the Colo. Coal and Iron Co.), 1868-1926 (10,000 pieces); James Joseph Brown (Colo.; capitalist), records of his mining interests chiefly in the Leadville area; James Viola Dexter (Ill., Mo.; Civil War officer, capitalist, numismatist, gem collector), 1862-1930 (7,500 pieces); Elbridge Gerry (Colo.; pioneer, trader, rancher), 1853-60 (4 account books); William Henry Jackson (Colo., Mich., N.Y.; official photographer of U.S. Geological Survey, explorer, artist), 1867-1952 (1,000 papers and, in the Picture Collection, 7,000 glass plate negatives of his work west of the Mississippi); Lawrence Lewis (Colo.; lawyer, U.S. Rep.), 1933-41 (9 vols. of diaries); Joseph P. Machebeuf (N. Mex., Colo.; Catholic prelate), 1860-89 (3,000 pieces); Nathan Cook Meeker (Ohio, Colo.; journalist, founder of Union Colony at Greeley, Ute Indian agent), 1824-79 (5,000 pieces), and his wife, Arvilla Delight Smith Meeker, 1843-1904 (300 pieces); Ralph Lovejoy Meeker (Ill., N.Y., Colo.; journalist, foreign correspondent), 1853-1921 (2,500 pieces); William Jackson Palmer (Pa., Colo.; Civil War officer, railroad executive), 1822-1947 (20,000 pieces); James Grafton Rogers (Conn., D.C., Colo.; lawyer, educator, statesman), 1912-21 (1,500 pieces); John Franklin Shafroth (Colo.; lawyer, Gov., U.S. Rep. and Sen.), 1901-22 (3,000 pieces); Horace A. W. Tabor (Kans., Colo.; mining magnate, Lt. Gov., U.S. Sen., postmaster of Denver), 1872-1900 (10,000 pieces), and his wife, Elizabeth McCourt Doe Tabor, 1872-1932 (5,000 pieces); Henry M. Teller (Colo.; lawyer, U.S. Sen. and Sec. Interior), 600 pieces; Charles S. Thomas (Colo.; lawyer, Gov., U.S. Sen.), 4,200 pieces; Davis H. Waite (Wis., N.Y., Colo.; Gov. of Colo., woman suffrage advocate), 4,000 pieces); and J. R. Walker (S. Dak.; resident physician at Pine Ridge Sioux Agency), 1,000 pieces, containing original Lakota manuscripts of customs, legends, and myths.

There are also papers of the Colorado Land and Immigration Co., 1894-95 (250 pieces), relating to the sale of land in the San Luis Valley; the Congregational Church of Central City, 1863-76 (1 vol.); the Longmont Farmers Institute, 1895-1919 (3 vols.); and other company and institutional records.

Special collections include the Civil Works Administration Collection, consisting of field interviews with pioneers in all counties of the State (22 vols.), to which currently tape recorded interviews are being added, and original notes and manuscripts compiled for the Colorado Writers Project; the Picture Collection, containing over 25,000 pictures of Colorado; and the Railroad Collection, including the archives of the Denver and Rio Grande Railroad, 1869-1952 (200,000 pieces). Material assembled by the Western Range Cattle Industry Study consists of manuscript, printed, and reproduced material relating to the development of the range cattle industry in the West from 1865 to 1895. There are photostatic copies of brand books and cattle association records; typed copies of incorporation records of cattle companies in Montana, Colorado, Wyoming, and New Mexico; and original ranch papers of several land and cattle companies. There are also 260 rolls of microfilm copies of materials in Europe as well as in the United States.

FORT COLLINS

Colorado State University Libraries.
Le Moyne W. Anderson, Director of
Libraries.

Holdings: Manuscripts relating to
the University and to forestry and reclamation in Colorado. Included are
a personal file of Charles A. Lory
(Colo.; chairman of the U.S. Reclamation Repayment Commission),
1937-38; and the records, from the
early part of the 20th century, of
the Colorado Forestry Association.
There are also archives of the University.

GOLDEN

Colorado School of Mines Library.
Virginia Lee Wilcox, Librarian.

Holdings: Mining engineers' reports on 150 western mines, 1880-
1935, many accompanied by maps,
diagrams, or sketches.

TRINIDAD

Carnegie Public Library. Ruth A.
Justin, Librarian.

Holdings: A small quantity of personal recollections and other manuscripts of local interest.

CONNECTICUT

BRIDGEPORT 4

Bridgeport Public Library. 925 Broad St. Julian A. Sohon, Librarian.

Holdings: 3,000 vols., 1770-1954, relating chiefly to Connecticut. Included are account books, diaries, and other papers of local families, 1770-1870 (50 vols.); uncataloged papers relating to the Civil War, 1861-65 (2 bundles); town and city common council records, 1800-1915 (68 vols.); and U.S. Custom House records, 1797-1875 (95 vols.).

BRISTOL

Public Library. Marion O'Connor, Reference Librarian.

Holdings: A small quantity of manuscripts, 1742-1897, relating chiefly to local history. Included are records of the Ecclesiastical Society (predecessor of the First Congregational Church of Bristol), 1742-1836, and 5 vols. of photostat records of the society and the church, 1742-1897, the originals of which have been deposited in the State Library at Hartford. There are also personal and business account books, 1797-1890 (7 vols.); a transcript of the diary of a clockmaker's daughter, 1801-6, the original of which is in private hands; and a list of deaths in Bristol, 1793-1859.

CORNWALL

Cornwall Free Library. Emily E. Marsh, Librarian.

Holdings: Manuscripts, 1755-1919, relating chiefly to Cornwall. Included are tax lists, 1754-1800; church records, 1755-1904; papers relating to a foreign mission school, 1818-25; and a diary, 1759. There are also military records (rolls and lists), 1759-1919, including those of Heman Swift (Conn.; Rev. War officer), 1781-82; and materials concerning John Sedgwick (Conn.; Civil War officer).

FAIRFIELD

Fairfield Historical Society. 1335 Post Rd.

Holdings: 50 items, relating chiefly to Fairfield and Connecticut. Included are autograph letters of several notable Americans.

FARMINGTON

Farmington Museum. Mrs. Walter Eyers, Curator.

Holdings: 12 vols. and several hundred pieces, chiefly of the 17th and 18th centuries, pertaining to Farmington and the early days of five nearby "daughter towns," which were separated from Farmington between 1779 and 1830. Included are sermons and church records of the local Congregational church, from 1652; 12 account books, of which the earliest is dated 1694; diaries and letters relating to Revolutionary War soldiers and the early social life of Farmington; and incomplete public and private school records, from 1799.

GLASTONBURY

Historical Society of Glastonbury. William Z. Holman, President. 594 Main St., South Glastonbury, Conn.

Holdings: Deeds, account books, diaries, maps and charts, and other papers relating chiefly to Glastonbury.

HARTFORD 1

Archives of the Episcopal Diocese of Connecticut. P.O. Box 1080. Kenneth Walter Cameron, Archivist and Historiographer.

Holdings: 50,000 pieces, 1727-1955, relating chiefly to the Episcopal Church in Connecticut. They are housed in the library of Trinity College, Hartford.

Papers of the Bishops of Connecticut, 1784-1955 (6,000 pieces), include those of Edward Campion Acheson, 1915-34; Chauncey Bunce Brewster, 1897-1928; Thomas Church Brownell, 1819-65; Frederick Grandy Budlong, 1931-51; Walter Henry Gray, 1940-55; Abraham Jarvis, 1797-1813; Samuel Seabury, 1784-96; and John Williams, 1851-99. There is also a collection of other letters and historical documents relating to the Episcopal Church in Connecticut, 1786-1885 (6,000 pieces), containing some letters of bishops of the Anglican Communion. Among papers in this collection are those of Eben Edwards Beardsley (Conn.; Episcopal clergyman, historian), 1866-85; George Burgess (Conn., Maine; first Bishop of Maine); and Samuel Farmar Jarvis (Conn.; Episcopal clergyman), 1800-50. The depository also has papers of William Agur Beardsley (Conn.; Episcopal clergyman), 1880-1940 (1,000 pieces).

Included also are many early sermons, 1727-1850, by prominent clergymen; records of Christ Church Cathedral, Hartford (500 early pieces); Connecticut parochial archives (4,000 pieces); many parish registers; records of various diocesan associations and societies; papers of standing committees of the diocese, from 1790 (30,000 pieces); and records of the

Episcopal Academy of Connecticut (formerly the Cheshire Academy), 1789-1925 (5,000 pieces), including papers of Eri Davidson Woodbury (Conn.; teacher of classics and principal of the academy).

See Hist. Records Survey, Inventory of the Church Archives of Connecticut; Protestant Episcopal, pp. 25-60 (1940. Processed). Accessions are periodically reported in the Connecticut Churchman and in the Historiographer of the Episcopal Diocese of Connecticut, issued quarterly by the Archivist.

HARTFORD 5

Case Memorial Library, Hartford Seminary Foundation. 55 Elizabeth St. Elizabeth de W. Root, Archivist.

Holdings: Several thousand items relating chiefly to the ecclesiastical and secular history of New England, particularly in Connecticut, but including also a collection of manuscript books in Arabic, 15th-20th centuries (1,171 items), mostly on the Koran and Arabic literature, and some British parchments of the reigns of Queen Elizabeth and King Charles I.

There are papers of Joseph Bellamy (Conn., N.Y.; theologian of the "New Light" School), 1731-88 (426 letters, many relating to the Revolutionary War, and 61 sermons); Edward W. Capen (Conn.; sociologist, dean of Kennedy School of Missions), 1891-1947 (3 filing cases, 10 vols.), including an extensive diary, lecture notes, literary manuscripts, and correspondence; Jonathan Edwards, Jr. (Conn., N.Y.; theologian, pres. of Union College), 1766-1800 (1,115 sermons and a few letters); Lewis Hodous (Conn.; prof. of Chinese at Hartford Theological Seminary), 1917-46 (8 filing drawers); Duncan Black Macdonald (Conn.; orientalist, Semitic lan-

guages prof. at Hartford Theological
Seminary), 1892-1943 (9 filing drawers of literary manuscripts and correspondence); William Douglas Mackenzie (Ill., Conn.; theologian, prof.
at Chicago Theological Seminary and
pres. of Hartford Theological Seminary), 1904-30 (9 filing drawers);
Asahel Nettleton (Conn.; Congregational evangelist), 1817-65 (32 sermons, 1,271 letters, and diaries);
Waldo S. Pratt (Conn.; musician,
Hartford Theological Seminary prof.),
late 19th and early 20th centuries
(over 100 typewritten addresses on
hymns and music); and Augustus C.
Thompson (Mass.; Congregational
minister, author), 1842-1901 (323
vols.).

There are also miscellaneous sermons dating from as early as 1705;
and various account books and diaries,
1762-90. Some of the papers mentioned are among the archives of or
collections relating to the Theological
Institute of Connecticut, the Hartford
Theological Seminary, and the Hartford Seminary Foundation, from 1833.

See the Library's Manuscripts in
the Archives of the Hartford Seminary
Foundation (1951. [18] p. Processed).

—oOo—

Congregational House. 125 Sherman
St. James F. English, General Superintendent.

Holdings: A quantity of manuscripts,
from the late 18th century, relating
chiefly to Congregational churches in
Connecticut. Included are records of
the Missionary Society of Connecticut,
among them reports of Connecticut
missionaries in New York, northern
New England, Ohio, and the upper
Mississippi Valley, late 18th and early 19th centuries; journals of Samuel
Nott (Conn.; Congregational minister
at Franklin for 70 years) and other
ministers; records of the Connecticut
Branch of the American Education So-

ciety, 1826-58; and records of other
State and local Congregational organizations.

See Allison, Inventory, pp. 3-6.

—oOo—

Connecticut Historical Society. 1
Elizabeth St. Thompson R. Harlow,
Director.

Holdings: 1,000,000 pieces, 1635-
1900, relating chiefly to Connecticut
and New England.

Papers of political leaders include
those of O. Vincent Coffin (N. Y.,
Conn.; insurance executive, State sen.
and Gov. of Conn.), 1887-1917 (18 letter books, 9 vols., and 9 boxes), including 3 vols. of records of the Nebraska Real Estate and Livestock
Assn.; Silas Deane (Conn.; Member
Continental Cong., diplomat), 1771-
89 (1,000 pieces); Thomas Fitch (Conn.;
lawyer, Gov.), 1754-66 (1 vol.); the
Holley family, mostly of Alexander
Hamilton Holley (Conn.; cutlery manufacturer, Gov.), 1850-80 (3,376 pieces); Samuel D. Hubbard (Conn.; U. S.
Rep., Postmaster Gen.), 1822-43 (1
box); the Huntington family, 1758-1814
(500 pieces), including Jedediah (Conn.;
Rev. War officer), 1758-1814 (3 vols.),
Jonathan (diary, 1731-32), and Samuel (Conn.; Pres. of Continental Cong.,
Gov.), 1779-92 (50 pieces); William
Samuel Johnson (Conn., N. Y.; colo-
nial agent in England, Member Con-
tinental Cong., U. S. Sen. from Conn.,
pres. of Columbia College), 1765-90
(1,500 pieces,; Jonathan Law (Conn.;
lawyer, Gov.), 1741-50 (650 pieces);
Thomas H. Seymour (Conn.; Gov.,
U. S. Rep., Minister to Russia), 1830-
67 (1,000 pieces); John Cotton Smith
(Conn.; U. S. Rep., Gov.), 1783-1842
(2,100 pieces); Joseph Talcott (Conn.;
Gov.), 1724-41 (271 pieces); Gideon
Tomlinson (Conn.; U. S. Rep., Gov.,
U. S. Sen.), 1840-54 (13 boxes); John
Treadwell (Conn.; Member Continental Cong., Gov.), 1798-1818 (1 box);

Jonathan Trumbull (Conn.; Gov.), 1737-85 (18 account books and 600 pieces); Jonathan Trumbull, Jr. (Conn.; Rev. War officer, Gov., U.S. Rep. and Sen.), 1773-1809 (8 account books and 1,000 pieces); Joseph Trumbull (Conn.; Member Continental Cong., Rev. War commissary gen.), 1760-78 (4 boxes); Jeremiah Wadsworth (Conn.; Rev. War commissary gen., Member Continental Cong., U.S. Rep.); 1777-1803 (5,000 pieces); Gideon Welles (Conn.; newspaper editor, Sec. Navy), 1784-1878 (18 boxes); Roger Wolcott (Conn.; Gov.), 1631-1768 (2 vols.); Oliver Wolcott (Conn.; Member Continental Cong., Rev. War officer, Gov.), 1767-1834 (4 vols.); and Oliver Wolcott, Jr. (Conn.; banker, Sec. Treas., Gov.), 1795-1827 (10,000 pieces).

Papers of military leaders, in addition to those named above, include those of Nathanael Greene (R. I., Ga.; Rev. War officer), 1778-85 (50 pieces); Thomas Knowlton (Conn.; Rev. War officer), 1776 (1 account book); and Israel Putnam (Conn.; French and Indian War and Rev. War officer), 1757-73 (1 journal and a few letters).

Papers of educators and clergymen include those of Henry Barnard (Conn., R. I.; educational reformer, U.S. Commissioner of Education), 1839-40 (200 pieces); Samuel William Johnson (Conn.; agricultural chemist, prof. at Yale, author), 300 pieces; Samson Occom (Conn., N. Y.; Indian clergyman, missionary), 1721-1808 (several pieces, including a diary, 1787); and Thomas Robbins (Conn., Mass.; Congregational clergyman, antiquarian), 1792-1856 (1,300 pieces and a 12-vol. diary).

Papers of other persons include those of James Goodwin Batterson (Conn.; originator of accident insurance and pres. of the Travelers Insurance Co.), relating to the election of 1864 (255 pieces); James Brewster (Conn.; railway promoter, philanthropist), from 1835 (145 pieces); Samuel Colt (Conn.; inventor of first revolving firearm, manufacturer), 1830-61 (3,500 pieces); William Hamersley (Conn.; printer) and his son William Hamersley (Conn.; lawyer, mayor of Hartford), 1855-92 (4,000 pieces); the McClellan family, including papers of Samuel McClellan (Conn.; Rev. War officer) and John McClellan (Conn.; lawyer), 1759-1905 (30 boxes and 100 account books); Calvin Wheeler Philleo (Conn.; lawyer, author), 1849-58 (1,500 pieces), letters and diaries; and Julia Evelina Smith (Conn.; advocate of woman's rights), 1810-42 (1 box), diaries. The Stillman Collection contains miscellaneous papers of the Francis, Welles, Stillman, and Goodrich families of Connecticut and New York, 1684-1912 (2,300 pieces). Papers of the Williams family, 1700-1897 (1,750 pieces and 6 account books), include papers of William Williams (Conn.; Member Continental Cong., judge), Ezekiel Williams (Conn.; sheriff of Hartford County, Rev. War commissary of prisoners for Conn.), and Ezekiel Williams, Jr. (Conn.; marine insurance broker).

There are also acts and other papers of the Connecticut General Assembly, 1650-1800; papers relating to the Separatist movement in New England, 1733-1800; correspondence with agents of the colony of Connecticut while in England, 1742-59; correspondence with other colonies and with Congress, 1753-1809; Mohegan and Pequot Indian papers, 1743-69; sermons and church records; records of Connecticut towns; and records of Connecticut troops in the French and Indian War, the American Revolution, and the War of 1812. Business papers include papers and account books of Elisha, John, and Sidney Babcock (Hartford and New Haven printers), 1792-1809 (2 boxes and 1 vol.); bills, orders, and accounts of Beardsley and Alvord (Conn.; merchants and manufacturers of cutlery), 1839-70

(27 boxes); business papers of Roswell Moore and Sons (Conn.; cement manufacturers), 1834-40 (3 boxes); and fishing papers of Capt. Noah Scoville of Saybrook (338 pieces). There are also records of the Hartford Charitable Society, 1792-1871 (439 pieces).

See Allison, Inventory, p. 1; and Conn. Historical Society, Annual Reports, 1890 to date.

HARTFORD 15

Connecticut State Library. Capitol Ave. Robert C. Sale, State Librarian.

Holdings: Several million papers, 1631-1955, consisting of (1) noncurrent official records held by the Library as the State's archival agency, and (2) other papers relating chiefly to Connecticut and New England.

In the first category are legislative records of the Colony and State, 1636-1933 (50 vols.), including the Fundamental Orders of 1639; other Colony records (13 vols.), including records of the United Colonies; the so-called Connecticut Archives (legislative papers), 1636-1820 (over 400 vols.); the Trumbull Collection of Connecticut Colonial Official Papers, 1631-1784 (29 vols.); voluminous records of colonial and State courts, including probate courts, 1636-1930; New Haven Colony records, 1638-65 (2 vols.); records of the Connecticut constitutional conventions of 1818 and 1902; Newgate Prison accounts and miscellaneous papers, 1790-1838 (4 vols. and 100 pieces); census records, 1790-1880; records of State boundaries revised to date; some town records, including microfilms of all land and probate records to 1850; and records of some State departments.

Papers of men prominent in the colonial and early national periods include those of Eliphalet Dyer (Conn.; Member Continental Cong., chief justice of Conn.), 1763-65 (1 journal);

Samuel Huntington (Conn.; Pres. of Continental Cong., Gov.), official documents and a few miscellaneous papers; William Samuel Johnson (Conn., N.Y.; colonial agent in England, Member Continental Cong., U.S. Sen. from Conn., pres. of Columbia College), 1766-71 (1 letter book and a few pieces); John Pratt (Conn.; Rev. War and U.S. Army officer, magistrate of Middletown), 1778-1824 (2 vols. containing both military papers and personal correspondence); Daniel Putnam (Conn.; militia officer), 1812-32 (100 letters and miscellaneous papers), together with a few papers of his father, Israel Putnam (Conn.; Rev. War officer); Roger Sherman (Conn.; lawyer, Member Continental Cong., U.S. Rep. and Sen.), official documents and a few early writs and other pieces; John Trumbull (Conn., N.Y.; Rev. War officer, historical painter), official documents and family letters, chiefly 1775-81, and 2 maps, 1776; Jonathan Trumbull (Conn.; Gov.), an account book, 1741-71, and many official and family letters and documents, including correspondence with George Washington; Jonathan Trumbull, Jr. (Conn.; Rev. War officer, U.S. Rep. and Sen., Gov.), 1783-1808 (125 letters and some miscellaneous papers); Joseph Trumbull (Conn.; Member Continental Cong., Rev. War commissary gen.), 1775-78 (350 items); Jeremiah Wadsworth (Conn.; Rev. War commissary gen., Member Continental Cong., U.S. Rep.), 1775-98 (many official documents and letters); George Washington (Va.; Rev. War Commander in Chief, U.S. Pres.), 1775-89 (many letters, especially in the Trumbull Collection); William Williams (Conn.; Member Continental Cong., judge), official documents and a few miscellaneous items; Oliver Wolcott (Conn.; Member Continental Cong., Rev. War officer, Gov.), many official documents and some letters, also a few papers of his son Oliver Wolcott, Jr. (Conn.; banker, Sec. Treas., Gov.); and Samuel Wyllys (Conn.; magistrate), 1662-1728 (2 vols. on witchcraft and criminal cases).

Papers of persons prominent in the 19th and early 20th centuries include those of William A. Buckingham (Conn.; Gov., U. S. Sen.), 1850-73 (200 items); Prudence Crandall (Conn., Ill.; educator of Negroes, reformer), 1869-86 (a few letters); William W. Ellsworth (Conn.; lawyer, U. S. Rep., Gov.), 1839-42 (some letters and memoranda), and a few letters of his father Oliver Ellsworth (Conn.; Member Continental Cong., U. S. Sen., Chief Justice of U.S.); Sylvester Gilbert (Conn.; judge, U. S. Rep.), 1818-39, correspondence concerning pensioners; William Gillette (Conn.; actor, playwright), 1884-1931 (40 letters and extensive memorabilia); Samuel Farmar Jarvis (Conn.; Episcopal clergyman), with papers of his son of the same name and others of his family, 1798-1908 (1,900 pieces); James B. Olcott (Conn.; agriculturalist), 1890-95 (16 vols.), including diaries and records of his research and experiments in grass growing at his Manchester turf gardens; Orville H. Platt (Conn.; lawyer, U. S. Sen.), 1880-1903 (22 vols.); Henry Wade Rogers (Mich., Ill., Conn.; dean of Univ. of Mich. and Yale Univ. law schools, pres. of Northwestern Univ.), 1891-1915, a large collection including letters from four U. S. Presidents and correspondence on intercollegiate football; Abby Hadassah and Julia Evalina Smith, known as the Smith sisters (Conn.; abolitionists, feminists), 1796-1819 (23 letters); Isaac Toucey (Conn.; Gov., U. S. Attorney Gen., U. S. Sen., Sec. Navy), 1831-70 (98 pieces), including a diary, 1831-49, and some of his wife's correspondence; Gideon Welles (Conn.; newspaper editor, Sec. Navy), 1829-75 (150 letters, a diary of 1836, and some accounts); and Horace Wells (Conn.; dentist, pioneer an-

esthetist), 1837-53 (50 letters).

There are also, besides the Jarvis family papers mentioned in the preceding paragraph, collections relating to other Connecticut families, among them the Boardman and Seymour families of early Hartford and Wethersfield, 1661-1835 (5,729 documents), and the Sedgwick family of Cornwall, 1742-1856 (150 pieces). The Robert C. Winthrop Collection of Connecticut Manuscripts, 1631-1794 (4 vols.), includes some papers of Gov. John Winthrop. There are several autograph collections; descriptions, photographs, and plans of over 1,000 old Connecticut houses; records of approximately 700 churches, 1639-1930; a number of sermons, 1717-1861; school and tax records; and records of some fraternal and medical and other professional societies. Business papers include records of the Connecticut Land Company and the Western Reserve, 1792-1828 (6 vols. and 700 pieces); and Farmington Canal papers, 1825-50 (500 pieces, with maps); and many account books, diaries, and logbooks, relating to whaling, shipping, railroads, highways, merchants, pedlars, fishing, and manufacturing (especially of clocks and firearms). Military records include papers relating to the Connecticut militia, from 1678, the French and Indian wars, the American Revolution, and all other U. S. wars; and there are many materials relating to the Mohegan, Pequot, and Scatacook Indians. There is a large amount of genealogical material, including collections of Connecticut vital records, cemetery inscriptions, and family Bible records. Included also are the unpublished Historical Records Survey compilations of the holdings, in Connecticut libraries, of American imprints to 1887.

HARTFORD 5

Hartford Medical Society Library.

230 Scarborough St. Harmona R. Potter, Assistant Librarian.

Holdings: 72 manuscripts, 1636-1938, relating chiefly to the medical profession, and consisting largely of letters from Hartford physicians, lecture notes, case books and prescription books, and early records of the medical society. Included are papers of Gershom Bulkeley (Conn., Mass.; clergyman and physician in King Phillip's War), 1636-1713 (17 pieces); and a daybook of Horace Wells (Conn.; dentist, pioneer anesthetist), 1841-45.

HARTFORD 6

Trinity College Library. Donald B. Engley, Librarian.

Holdings: 75 vols. and 10,000 pieces, 1823-1954, relating chiefly to Trinity College, the Protestant Episcopal Church, and the humanities. (The archives of the Diocese of Connecticut, described in a separate entry above, are housed in the Trinity College Library.)

The Trinity College collections include sermons of Samuel J. Andrews (Conn.; Congregational and later Catholic Apostolic clergyman, philosophy prof. at Trinity College), 1748-76; papers of Thomas Church Brownell (Conn.; Episcopal bishop, pres. of Trinity College), 1821-39 (1 vol.); medical notes of Gershom Bulkeley (Conn.; clergyman, physician), late 17th and early 18th centuries (7 vols.); sermons of Timothy Cutler (Conn., Mass.; Episcopal clergyman, rector of Yale College), 1748-1815; and papers of Nathaniel S. Wheaton (Conn., La.; Episcopal clergyman, pres. of Washington College, now Trinity), 1816-36 (9 vols.). Also included are records of the administration of Trinity College and of student organizations, from 1823; some archives of the German Legation at Peking, China, 1868-1904 (580 items); and records of

the De Sibour family, 1612-1917, including letters written by the French Consul in Charleston, S. C. (Jean Antoin Gabriel de Sibour) and his wife Mary depicting the Civil War.

There are also manuscripts in the Watkinson Library, which is now part of Trinity College Library. These include papers of Nathan H. Allen (Mass., Conn.; musician, composer), 1864-1922 (852 pieces); Henry Barnard (Conn., R. I.; educational reformer, U. S. Commissioner of Education), 1825-1900 (506 pieces); James Hammond Trumbull (Conn.; historian, philologist, bibliographer), 1863-95 (184 items), consisting of letters received and notes on the languages and literature of the American Indians; and Charles Dudley Warner (Conn.; essayist, novelist, newspaper editor), 1851-1900 (3,062 items), among them literary manuscripts, journals, and letters received. The Library has also documents concerning genealogy, lands, commerce, the militia, and politics in the Jeffersonian era.

See Public Documents . . . With Archives and Libraries . . . Papers Presented at the 1938 Conference of the American Library Association, pp. 318-320 (1938. Processed).

HARTFORD 3

Wadsworth Atheneum, 25 Atheneum Square, North. Marjorie L. Ellis, Registrar.

Holdings: 500 pieces, dating from the late 18th to the early 20th century and relating chiefly to New England though including a number of papers of national importance. There are papers of Henry Barnard (Conn., R. I.; educational reformer, U. S. Commissioner of Education), 1830-1900 (on deposit in Trinity College Library, Hartford, Conn.); a few papers of Samuel Colt (Conn.; inventor, arms manufacturer), 1830-61, and of John

Trumbull (Conn., N. Y.; historical painter), 1789-1841; letters of Jeremiah Wadsworth (Conn.; Rev. War officer, Member Continental Cong., U.S. Rep.), 1779-85 (55 pieces), and his family, 1793-1848 (38 pieces); other papers of distinguished men, in small quantity for each; and a collection of autograph letters of U.S. Presidents and others prominent in American history, 19th-20th centuries (281 pieces).

KENSINGTON

Peck Memorial Library. Mrs. Thomas Emerson, Librarian.

Holdings: 1 folder, 1712-1914, of records of a local Congregational church.

LITCHFIELD

Litchfield Historical Society. Charlotte M. Wiggin, Curator.

Holdings: A quantity of manuscripts, 1722-1920, relating chiefly to Litchfield County and Connecticut. Included are papers of Bezaleel Beebe (Conn.; Rev. War officer), consisting of an orderly book, 1776, 1780 (60 pages); Julius Deming (Conn.; merchant, Rev. War officer) and his family, 1776-1887 (7 files), including 8 account books pertaining to army commissary, 1776-80; Gideon H. Hollister (Conn.; lawyer, writer, U.S. Minister to Haiti), 1850-81 (3 files), including his history of Santo Domingo, 1492-1803 (24 chapters); Andrew Perkins (Conn.; shipowner, merchant) and his family, 1768-1910 (2 files), including logbooks of a privateer, 1782-83 (2 vols.); Benjamin Tallmadge (Conn.; merchant, banker, Rev. War officer, U.S. Rep.) and his family, 1776-1863 (7 vols.), including 54 pieces of correspondence with George Washington, 1777-83; George Washington (Va.; Rev. War Commander in Chief, U.S. Pres.), general orders, Jan. 1—Apr. 2, 1776

(52 pages); Nathan Whiting (Conn.; French and Indian War officer), orderly book, 1758 (149 pages); Frederick Wolcott (Conn.; judge, manufacturer, Conn. senator), 1648-1834 (270 pieces); Oliver Wolcott (Conn.; Member Continental Cong., Rev. War officer, Gov.); Oliver Wolcott, Jr. (Conn.; banker, Sec. Treas., Gov.), 1799-1814 (65 pieces); and Roger Wolcott (Conn.; colonial Gov.).

Also included are a collection of autograph letters of some U.S. Presidents and other leading Americans, 1770-1905 (106 vols. containing chiefly printed material); papers relating to the Western Reserve, 1795-97 (1 vol. and 1 piece); a "Victorian Lady's Records of Her Life" (Conn., N. Y.), 1865-1920 (20 files); Civil War letters and diaries, 1861-65 (1 vol. and 338 pieces); papers pertaining to the Litchfield Law School of Tapping Reeve (Conn.; jurist, educator), 1770-1829 (41 vols. and 25 pieces); town records, 1785-1903 (23 boxes), including 60 "grand lists"; Litchfield County records, 1722-1902 (75 pieces), including account books; merchant's records, 1819-36 (2 files); and records concerning the "inhabitants of South Farms" (Morris, Conn.), 1720-1892 (431 pages in transcript).

MIDDLETOWN

Middlesex County Historical Society. 151 Main St. Homer C. Hood, President.

Holdings: 25 vols. and several thousand sheets, relating chiefly to Middlesex County. Included are account books and letter books of persons in Middletown and vicinity, 19th century; records of the Middletown Customs House, 1815-23 (1 vol.); letters, bills for sums due from the town of Middletown presented to the selectmen, and some court records, late 1700's through mid-1800's; and

letters and sermons of early 19th-cen-
tury ministers (unclassified and un-
catalogued in 1960).

—oOo—

Wesleyan University Library.   Church
St.

Holdings: 4 boxes, 1831-1920, relating chiefly to Wesleyan University
and the Methodist Church.   Included
are papers of Wilbur Fisk (Conn.;
Methodist minister, pres. of Wesleyan Univ.), 1831-39; Stephen Qlin (Conn.;
Methodist minister, pres. of Wesleyan
Univ.), 1839-51; and Caleb T. Winchester (Conn.; prof. of English literature at Wesleyan Univ., editor), 1873-
1920.

MYSTIC

Marine Historical Association.   Glenn
E. Thompson, Research Associate.

Holdings: 450 ship logs and journals, 400 account books, diaries, and
letter books, and 200 boxes of manuscripts, relating to United States maritime history.   Although 19th-century
materials predominate, the holdings
range from the 18th to the 20th centuries.   Included are papers of shipbuilders and owners, merchants,
whalers, shipmasters, oystermen,
naval officers, yachtsmen, and explorers.   The New England area is
most heavily represented, but the collections are not confined to it.   Individuals and companies extensively represented in the holdings are: J. D.
Beckwith, John H. Brower Co., Amos
Clift, Elam Eldredge, Nathan Fish,
George Greenman Co., Holmes Ship-
yard, Isaac Jeanes Co., Joseph King,
Joseph Lawrence Co., Aaron Lopez,
Charles Mallory, Charles W. Morgan, B. F. Noyes, J. and N. Palmer,
Russell Co., Admiral O. F. Stanton,
L. A. Storrs, A. M. Underhill, and
George B. Wendell.   Subject, sur-

name, and vessel indexes to the collections are available for reference
in the Stillman Library of the Association.

NEW BRITAIN

New Britain Institute.   High and West
Main Sts.   Dotha E. White, Librarian.

Holdings: 65 pieces, 1841-78, consisting chiefly of journals (21 vols.,
1841-59) and other papers of Elihu
Burritt (Conn., Mass.; reformer, advocate of world peace, linguist).

NEW HAVEN 10

New Haven Colony Historical Society.
114 Whitney Ave.   Ralph W. Thomas,
Curator.

Holdings: Included are some papers of Jared Ingersoll (Conn., Pa.;
colonial agent in London, judge of
vice-admiralty court) and Ezra Stiles
(R. I., Conn.; Congregational clergyman, Yale College pres.).   There are
also payrolls, muster rolls, and other papers relating to the Revolutionary War; logbooks and a journal concerning the expedition led by Lt.
Charles Wilkes to the Antarctic,
1839; and other logbooks and diaries
kept on sea voyages, 1795-1850.
See Library of Congress, Manuscripts . . . in the U. S. (1924), p. 11.

NEW HAVEN

Yale University Library.   James T.
Babb, University Librarian.   Inqui-
ries about all collections should be
addressed to D. R. Watkins, Reference Librarian, Sterling Memorial
Library, Yale University, New Haven, Conn.

Holdings: A large and important
body of manuscripts, comprising numerous groups and collections, dat-

ing from some 3000 B. C. to recent years, and relating to many aspects of world history and especially the history of the United States. Most of them are in the physical custody of and are administered by the different units of the Library shown below, but there are also manuscripts, not separately described, in the James Boswell Collection and the Map Collection. Some papers of Othniel C. Marsh are in the Peabody Museum of Natural History.

See Yale University Library Gazette for scattered information about various groups of manuscripts.

Special Collections

Babylonian Collection. Ferris J. Stephens, Curator.

Holdings: 27,200 cuneiform tablets and 800 stone engraved seals and art objects, dating from approximately 3000 B. C. to the 1st century B. C., relating to the entire range of Babylonian history and coming from a large number of ancient sites, principally in southern Babylonia but also in Assyria and Asia Minor. The collection, comprising virtually all types of cuneiform material, includes the Goucher College collection, on permanent deposit, the Pierpont Morgan Library collection, on long-term loan, and other collections donated by Edward Theodore Newell (N. Y.; authority on ancient coins) and James Buchanan Nies (N. Y.; Episcopal clergyman, orientalist).

Edward M. House Collection. Charles Seymour, Curator; H. B. Gottlieb, Librarian.

Holdings: 92 filing drawers and 94 boxes, 1880-1926 but chiefly 1912-20, consisting of the papers of Edward M. House (Tex.; personal representative of President Woodrow Wilson to European nations, member of the American Commission to Negotiate Peace) and

papers of others associated with him during World War I and the Paris Peace Conference.

Included are 383 letters and telegrams to House from Woodrow Wilson (N. J.; U. S. Pres.); carbon copies of over 700 letters from House to Wilson; and House's detailed diary, 1912-26 (18 vols.). There is also substantial correspondence of House with the following foreign and American diplomats: Arthur James Balfour (England; Foreign Sec.), Count Johann-Heinrich Bernstorff (Germany; Ambassador to U. S.), Sir James Bryce (England; author, Ambassador to U.S.), Lord Robert Cecil (England; Minister of Blockade, Asst. Foreign Sec.), Georges Clemenceau (France; Premier), James W. Gerard (N. Y.; lawyer, Ambassador to Germany), Sir Edward Grey (England; Foreign Sec., Ambassador to U. S.), Thomas Nelson Page (Va., D. C.; lawyer, author, Ambassador to Italy), Walter Hines Page (N. C., N. Y.; journalist, Ambassador to Great Britain), Sir Horace Curzon Plunkett (Ireland; agriculturist, M.P., presiding officer of Irish Convention), Frederic C. Penfield (Conn.; diplomat, author, U. S. Ambassador to Austria-Hungary), Lord Reading (England; Lord Chief Justice, special envoy to U. S.), and Brand Whitlock (Ohio; author, lawyer, Ambassador to Belgium).

Besides the House papers there are papers of Gordon Auchincloss (N. Y.; assistant counselor to the State Department, sec. of American War Mission to England and France in 1917, Col. House's sec. at Paris Peace Conference); William Hepburn Buckler (Md.; lawyer, archeologist, special agent attached to U. S. Embassy in London and to American Commission to Negotiate Peace), containing detailed reports on British political opinion; William C. Bullitt (N. Y.; diplomat); Frank Lyon Polk (N. Y.; lawyer, Under Sec. of State, head of U. S. delegation to Paris Peace Conference);

and Sir William Wiseman (England;
World War I chief of British Intelligence in U.S.).

Franklin Collection. Archibald Hanna, Librarian.

Holdings: 1,000 pieces, relating
to Benjamin Franklin (Pa.; printer,
scientist, diplomat). Included are
200 letters by or to Franklin; additional Franklin manuscripts relating
to his literary, political, and scientific interests; other contemporary manuscripts; and a considerable quantity
of letters and family papers of Franklin's grandnephew Jonathan Williams
(assistant to Franklin in France, U.S.
Army engineer, Supt. of U.S. Military
Academy). Present also is the Stuart
Jackson Collection of 400 letters to,
from, and about the Marquis de Lafayette (France; American Rev. War
officer).

Historical Manuscripts Collection.
H. B. Gottlieb, Librarian.

Holdings: Manuscripts, 11th-20th
centuries, chiefly of general American
interest, with special emphasis on Connecticut. Several important groups are
not mentioned below because they have
not yet been processed or because they
are not yet available to the public.
Foreign materials include personal
papers of Sir Joseph Banks (England;
scientist), 1763-1819 (3,500 items), relating to his lands and to English agricultural development; Jean André De
Luc and his nephew of the same name
(Switzerland, England; geologists, paleontologists), 1746-1847 (96 boxes);
Sir Wilfred Grenfell (England; physician,
missionary), 1882-1940 (35 boxes and
44 scrapbooks), concerning the Grenfell Mission in Labrador; John Stuart
Mill (England; economist, reformer),
1812-88 (425 items); and Thomas Turner (England; general storekeeper in

Essex), 1754-65 (111 vols. of diaries).
The James M. Osborn Collection relating to England (70 vols. and 28 boxes) includes materials on the Anglo-
Norman period, compiled in the 17th
century (10 vols.); papers of Sir William Lee (England; Lord Chief Justice), 1588-1793 (28 boxes); letter
books of Sir Thomas Duckworth (England; naval officer), 1793-1812; and
800 folders of and concerning "Victorian worthies." There are also a
collection of miscellaneous English
manuscripts, 1362-1954 (10 vols. and
12 boxes); and logs of British war-
ships (in the Neeser collection), 1808-
39 (69 vols.). There are miscellaneous French manuscripts, late 18th-
20th centuries (5 boxes); correspondence of Louis Maillard, secretary to
Joseph Bonaparte (France; King of
Naples and of Spain, resident in U.S.)
and executor of his estate, with his
heirs in France; Alexis de Tocqueville (France; writer, Premier), manuscripts, transcripts, and reproductions of drawings relating to his travels in America; and materials relating
to the Spanish and Portuguese languages and literature, 1880-1934, collected by Henry Roseman Lang (Conn.;
Yale prof. of Romance languages).
Latin-American manuscripts include
records of civil and criminal cases
in the state of Puebla, Mexico, 1570-
1878 (119 boxes); manuscripts of the
18th and 19th centuries (150 vols.);
and many Peruvian materials.
In the paragraphs that follow, papers of Americans are listed chiefly
by occupation. In some cases papers
of Americans are listed in later paragraphs on family papers.
Papers of political leaders and
government officials include a collection in honor of James Elisha Babb
(Ill., Idaho; lawyer, political leader),
1855-1940 (6 boxes), containing Civil
War letters and papers relating to
Idaho political affairs, with some

correspondence of William Jennings Bryan (Nebr.; U.S. Rep., Sec. State), and William E. Borah (Idaho; U.S. Sen.). Included also are papers of William Henry Bishop (Conn.; author, U.S. consul at Genoa and Palermo), 1902-12 (10 boxes); David Josiah Brewer (Kans.; State supreme court judge), U.S. Supreme Court Justice), 1846-1908 (8 boxes); Wilbur L. Cross (Conn.; English prof. at Yale, Gov.), 1886-1948 (90 boxes); Chauncey M. Depew (N.Y.; lawyer, U.S. Sen.), 23 vols. and 40 boxes; Roger Griswold (Conn.; U.S. Rep., State judge, Gov.), 1783-1812 (2 boxes); Ebenezer J. Hill (Conn.; U.S. Rep.), 1894-1911 (90 boxes); Charles Dewey Hilles (N.Y.; asst. sec. Treas., sec. to Pres. Taft, political leader), 1900-25 (1,000,000 items); William Kent (Ill., Calif.; U.S. Rep. from Calif., member U.S. Tariff Commission), 1890-1928 (26 scrapbooks and 95 boxes); Arthur Bliss Lane (N.Y.; diplomat), 1913-56 (600,000 items); Charles Nagel (Mo.; lawyer, U.S. Sec. Commerce and Labor), 1880-1940 (116 boxes); Francis G. Newlands (Nev.; U.S. Rep. and Sen.), 1890-1917 (120 vols. of letter books and scrapbooks, and 6 drawers); James Rockwell Sheffield (N.Y.; diplomat), 1860-1938 (19 boxes); Roger Sherman (Conn.; lawyer, Member Continental Cong., U.S. Rep. and Sen.), 1766-92 (2 boxes); Henry L. Stimson (N.Y.; lawyer, Sec. War, Sec. State), 1892-1950 (50,000 items), including his diary, 1910-45 (44 vols.), material relating to his New York State political campaigns, his Philippine governorship, his Nicaraguan mission, the London Economic Conference, and his other offices and activities, and a substantial number of letters from Presidents Hoover, Theodore Roosevelt, and Taft, and from Elihu Root (N.Y.; lawyer, Sec. War, Sec. State, U.S. Sen.); Robert A. Taft (Ohio; U.S. Sen.), 68 boxes, consisting of papers on neutral-

ity and lend lease; and Wendell L. Willkie (Ohio, N.Y.; lawyer, Presidential candidate), 1940 (12 boxes), consisting of materials relating to his Presidential campaign.

Papers of clergymen and lawyers include those of Jonathan Lee (Conn.; Congregational clergyman), 1781-1857 (9 boxes); Charleton Thomas Lewis (N.J.; lawyer, philologist), 1750-1940 (3 boxes); Edwards Amasa Park (Mass.; Congregational clergyman, prof. at Amherst College and Andover Theological Seminary), including materials on the seminary, 1771-1903 (11 boxes); Frank Parsons (Kans., Mass.; lawyer, political scientist, reformer, lecturer), 1885-1909 (15 boxes); George Dudley Seymour (Conn.; lawyer, antiquarian), correspondence, including letters from William Howard Taft (Ohio; U.S. Pres., Chief Justice) and collected materials relating to Nathan Hale (Conn.; Rev. War officer), to the Seymour family, and to State and local history (152 vols. and 379 boxes); Newman Smyth (Maine, R.I., Conn.; Civil War officer, Congregational clergyman), 19th and 20th centuries (7 boxes); Anson Phelps Stokes (Conn., D.C.; Episcopal clergyman, sec. of Yale Univ., educationist), 1900-39 (50 boxes, 4 filing cabinets, and 5 packing cases); Benjamin Trumbull (Conn.; Congregational clergyman, Rev. War chaplain, historian), 1755-1820 (32 boxes), including many sermons; and Harold Weinberger (N.Y.; lawyer), 1908-42 (69 boxes), relating to civil liberties cases.

Papers of scientists and physicians include those of William Henry Brewer (Calif., Conn.; Yale prof. of agriculture), 1850-90 (50 boxes); George Jarvis Brush (Conn.; mineralogist, director of Sheffield Scientific School, Yale), 1850-1939 (17 boxes); Daniel Cady Eaton (Mass., Conn.; botanist, Yale prof.), 19th century

(4,513 items), scientific correspondence, including 335 letters from Asa
Gray (N. Y., Mass.; botanist, Harvard
prof.); Asa Fitch (N. Y.; entomologist,
physician), 1821-79 (21 vols. of diaries); William Thompson Lusk (Conn.,
N. Y.; Civil War officer, obstetrician),
1861-63 (3 vols. of Civil War letters);
Othniel Charles Marsh (Conn.; paleontologist, Yale prof.), 1799-1847 (11
boxes); Theophil Mitchell Prudden
(Conn., N. Y.; physician, bacteriologist, public health authority), 1875-
1918 (6 boxes); William C. Redfield
(Conn., N. Y.; saddle and harness maker, meteorologist, transportation promoter) and his son John Howard Redfield (Conn., N. Y., Pa.; businessman,
naturalist, conservator of Philadelphia
Academy of Natural Sciences herbarium), 1831-61 (15 vols. of meteorological journals); and Benajah Ticknor
(U. S. naval surgeon), 1818-54 (9 vols.
and 1 box).

Papers of Yale professors, in addition to those mentioned elsewhere,
include those of George Burton Adams
(Conn.; historian), 1890-1920 (24 boxes); Thomas Sewall Adams (Conn.;
economist, tax adviser), 1900-33 (34
boxes); Charles McLean Andrews (Pa.,
Md., Conn.; American colonial historian, prof. at Bryn Mawr, Johns Hopkins, and Yale), 39 boxes, chiefly
transcripts and notes, with some 20th-
century correspondence; Kwan-Ichi
Asakawa (Conn.; medievalist), chiefly
bibliography and notes, partly in Japanese (100 boxes); Albert Gabriel
Feuillerat (Conn.; prof. of French),
1835-1939 (6 boxes), including materials collected by him, particularly
on Paul Bourget (France; critic, poet, novelist); Irving Fisher (Conn.;
economist), 1890-1930 (30 boxes);
Charles Templeman Loram (South Africa, Conn.; prof. of education, race
relations specialist), 20th century (17
boxes); James Harvey Rogers (Mo.,
Conn.; economist, prof. at Univ. of
Mo. and Yale), 1922-39 (179 boxes);

William Graham Sumner (Conn.; economist, sociologist) and Albert Galloway Keller (Conn.; prof. of science of
society), 16 boxes); James Hammond
Trumbull (Conn.; historian, philologist, bibliographer), 1842-97 (5 boxes); and William Dwight Whitney
(Mass., Conn.; philologist, Sanskrit
prof.), 1800-98 (29 boxes), chiefly
family correspondence.

Papers of others include those of
Paul Moody Atkins (Ill., N. Y.; economist, industrial adviser to governments and corporations), 20th century (9 boxes); Hugh Byas (N. Y., Conn.;
newspaper correspondent, Yale lecturer), 1915-44 (127 folders and 15
scrapbooks), chiefly material on Japan; George Watson Cole (N. J., Calif.; librarian, bibliographer), 20th
century (11 boxes); Richard Ely Dan-
ielson (Mass.; Atlantic Monthly editor), 1931-49 (8 boxes); Thomas Davidson (England, Mo., Mass., N. Y.;
philosopher and wandering scholar),
1866-1900 (49 boxes); Elizabeth Don-
nan (Mass.; historian), 2 boxes,
material on the slave trade; George
Herbert Gray (Conn.; consultant in
architecture and city planning),
1933-40 (5 boxes); John Hays Hammond (Calif., N. Y.; mining engineer),
1893-1936 (3 boxes and letter books);
William Fowler Hopson (Conn.; artist, engraver of book plates), 24
boxes; John LaFarge (N. Y.; painter,
worker in stained glass), 19th and
20th centuries (12 boxes); Walter
Lippman (N. Y.; journalist), 20 boxes,
manuscripts of columns and books;
Katherine Mayo (Conn., N. Y.; author),
1920-35 (10 drawers, not organized);
Charles Gould Morris (Conn.; capitalist), 19th and 20th centuries (4 vols.
and 47 boxes); Edward Luther Stevenson (N. Y., N. Y.; Hispanist, historical geographer and cartographer,
Rutgers Univ. prof.), 1878-1944 (80
boxes); Howard Swiggett (Conn.; auth-
or), 3 boxes, material on Robert Morris; Horace Dutton Taft (Conn.; head-

master of Taft School), 1938-43 (1 box), including material on the League of Nations Association; Dorothy Thompson (N. Y.; journalist), 1939-42 (8 boxes), material on neutrality; John Trumbull (Conn., N. Y.; Rev. War officer, historical painter), from 1750 (16 vols. and 15 boxes); Eli Whitney (Mass., Conn.; inventor) and his son of the same name, 1787-1850 (15 boxes); and Howell Wright (Conn.; author), 1850-1950 (10 boxes and 4 drawers), consisting of material on Rhodesia and South Africa.

Among collections of family papers there are about 25 which contain papers of distinguished men. Papers of the Baldwin family, 1765-1927 (210 boxes), include those of Ebenezer Baldwin Conn.; Rev. War chaplain), Simeon Baldwin (Conn.; U. S. Rep., State supreme court judge), Roger Sherman Baldwin (Conn.; lawyer, Gov., U. S. Sen.), and Simeon Eben Baldwin (Conn.; chief justice of State supreme court, Gov.). There are also papers of the Beecher family (30 boxes), including correspondence of Henry Ward Beecher (Conn., N. Y.; Congregational clergyman); the Bingham family of Hawaii and the United States, 19th and 20th centuries (79 cases, 2 under seal); the Boardman family, 1770-1917 (57 vols. and 106 boxes), including papers of Elijah Boardman (Conn., Ohio; land developer, U. S. Sen. from Conn.), and William Jarvis Boardman (Ohio, D. C.; landowner, lawyer); the Carrington family, 1790-1912 (12 boxes), including papers of Henry Beebe Carrington (Conn., Ohio; Civil War and U. S. Army officer); the Cogswell family, 1741-1902 (8 boxes), including papers of James Cogswell (Conn.; Rev. War surgeon); the Day family, 1760-1900, including papers of Jeremiah Day (Conn.; Yale prof. and pres.), 1797-1867 (15 boxes), Thomas Day (Conn.; lawyer, Conn. sec. of state), 1760-1860 (17 boxes), and Henry Noble Day (Conn., Ohio; Congregational min-

ister, writer of textbooks), 1800-84 (21 boxes); the De Forest family, including papers of David Curtis De Forest (Conn.; merchant, Argentine consul in U. S.), 1798-1825 (20 vols.), and Lee De Forest (N. Y., Ill.; inventor, pioneer in wireless telegraphy and radio), 20th century (5 vols.); the Dwight family, 1797-1885 (7 boxes), including papers of descendants of Timothy Dwight (Mass., Conn.; Congregational minister, Yale pres.); the Farnam family, 19th and 20th centuries (462 boxes), including papers of Henry Farnam (Conn., Ill.; canal and railroad builder), and Henry Walcott Farnam (Conn.; political economist, Yale prof.); and the Goodrich family, 1777-1860 (9 boxes), including papers of Chauncey Allen Goodrich (Conn.; Congregational minister, Yale prof., lexicographer).

Other family papers are those of the Hillhouse family, 1740-1938, including papers of James Hillhouse (Conn.; lawyer, Rev. War officer, U. S. Rep. and Sen.), and James Abraham Hillhouse (Conn.; poet); the Hooker family, 1777-1919 (24 boxes), including papers of Noadiah Hooker (Conn.; Rev. War officer) and Edward Hooker (Conn.; merchant mariner, U. S. naval officer); the Howland family, 1842-1927 (22 boxes), including papers of Charles P. Howland (N. Y., Conn.; lawyer, chairman of Greek Refugee Settlement Commission of the League of Nations, member of General Education Board of the Rockefeller Foundation); the Johnson family, 1790-1875 (90 boxes), including papers of Samuel William Johnson (Conn., N. Y.; land speculator), records of the Johnson Land Co. of Cattaraugus County, N.Y., and 81 letters from William Livingston (N. Y., N. J.; Member Continental Cong., Rev. War officer, Gov. of N.J.) to Noah Welles (Conn.; Presyterian minister), 1742-73; the Kingsley family, 1797-1895 (16 boxes), in-

cluding papers of James Luce Kingsley
(Conn.; Yale librarian and classics
prof.); the Loomis family, 1827-1926
(26 boxes), including papers of Elias
Loomis (Ohio, N.Y., Conn.; mathematician, astronomer, college prof.); the
Morse family, 1779-1900 (32 boxes),
including papers of Jedidiah Morse
(Conn., Mass.; Congregational minister, geographer); the Mulford family,
1850-1903 (66 vols. and 9 boxes),
chiefly papers of Elisha Mulford (N.J.,
Pa., Mass.; Episcopal clergyman, lecturer, writer); the Munger family,
1813-1913 (16 boxes), including papers of Theodore Thornton Munger
(Mass., Conn.; Congregational clergyman, writer); the Palmer family, 19th
and 20th centuries (8 boxes), including
papers of Ray Palmer (N.Y., N.J.;
Congregational clergyman, hymn writer) and Charles Ray Palmer (Mass.,
Conn.; Congregational clergyman); and
the Rice family, 1847-1916 (74 boxes),
including papers of John Pierrepont
Rice (N.Y., Conn.; prof. of Romance
languages).

Still other family papers are those
of the Schwab family, chiefly 19th century (75 vols. and 22 boxes), including
papers of Gustav Schwab (Germany;
poet), his son Gustav Henry Schwab
(N.Y.; merchant), and a grandson John
Christopher Schwab (Conn.; political
scientist, Yale prof.); the Silliman
family, 1750-1900 (20 boxes), including nonscientific correspondence of
Benjamin Silliman (Conn.; chemist,
geologist, Yale prof.) and his son of
the same name (Conn.; chemist, geologist, Yale prof., petroleum research-
er); the Terry family, 1850-1900 (14
boxes), including papers of Alfred
Howe Terry (Conn.; Civil War and U.S.
Army officer); the Wadsworth family,
1775-1885 (3 boxes), including papers
of Jeremiah Wadsworth (Conn.; Rev.
War officer, Member Continental
Cong., U.S. Rep.); the Webb family,
1764-1911 (20 vols. and 58 boxes), including papers of Samuel Blatchley

Webb (Conn.; Rev. War officer),
James Watson Webb (N.Y.; U.S. Army officer, journalist, Minister to
Brazil), and Alexander Stewart Webb
(N.Y.; U.S. Army officer, pres. of
College of City of New York; the Webster family (1,500 items), including
some papers of Noah Webster (Conn.,
N.Y., Mass.; lexicographer, author);
the Whiting family, 1705-1828 (122
items), including papers of Nathan
Whiting (Conn.; French and Indian War
officer); and the Williams family,
1774-1938 (40 boxes), including papers of S. Wells Williams (N.Y.,
Conn.; missionary, diplomat, sino-
logue), and Frederick Wells Williams
(Conn.; oriental history prof. at
Yale).

Included also are collections of
diaries, chiefly 19th century (360
vols.) and whaling logs, 1830-1912
(24 vols.); and transcripts and other
materials on the antebellum South,
1712-1933 but chiefly 1800-61, collected by Ulrich Bonnell Phillips
(Mich., Conn.; historian, Univ. of
Mich. and Yale prof.), including original materials relating to agriculture in Rockbridge County, Va.
Chiefly relating to the Civil War is
the collection made by Anson Conger
Goodyear (N.Y.; manufacturer), 1815-
90 (9 vols.), with the following binder's titles: Political Associates of
Abraham Lincoln; Abraham Lincoln,
North and South; Siege of Fort Sumter (4 vols.); General W.T. Sherman
and his Critics; Andrew Jackson and
John Randolph; and Jefferson Davis
and General P.G.T. Beauregard.
There are also papers relating mainly to the Revolutionary and the Civil
Wars, 1777-1940 (12 boxes), collected by Bernard Knollenberg (N.Y.,
Conn.; lawyer, writer); several small
collections of Civil War letters; World
War II correspondence, 1939-45 (13
boxes); and letters, papers, and drawings (collected by Guy S. Metraux) relating to an International Red Cross

inspection of prisoner-of-war camps in the United States, 1943-44 (7 boxes).

Records of and concerning organizations include a large collection on the Episcopal Church, which contains bishops' letters, late 18th-20th centuries (2,000 items), and papers of Horatio Southgate (Mass.; Episcopal missionary bishop of Constantinople), 1835-86 (18 boxes), Alexander Griswold Cummins (N. Y.; Episcopal clergyman, editor), 20th century (8 boxes), and other clergymen, including a collection by E. Clowes Chorley, church historian, 1763-1941 (11 boxes). There are also records of the Board of Research Associates in American Economic History, 1904-33 (29 boxes), including a number of unpublished monographs; papers of the American Journal of Science; and, among personal papers, materials on the League of Nations Association and its Connecticut branch, the Committee to Defend America by Aiding the Allies, and the Citizens for Victory, 1925-50 (67 boxes).

Groups of business papers include miscellaneous account books, 1720-1920 (600 vols.); records of New York and Connecticut merchants, importers, and general commercial businesses, 1753-1930 (79 vols. and 219 boxes), among them records of the firm of Nathaniel Shaw (Conn.; merchant, Rev. War naval agent for Conn. and the Continental Cong.), 1753-95 (32 vols. and 29 boxes); papers of Bristol, Conn., clockmakers; and records of the National Whaling Bank of New London, 1833-1945 (400 vols. and 50 boxes). Papers relating to transportation include records of Connecticut turnpikes, 1800-54 (4 boxes); and of the Old Colony and Fall River Railroad, 1840-60 (6 boxes). There are also papers of firms manufacturing iron, 19th century (30 boxes); brass, 1857-1947 (1,517 vols. and 1,002 boxes); firearms (the Whitney Arms Co.), 1862-86 (6 vols. and 1 box); hardware, 1864-1925 (759 vols. and 164 boxes); cutlery (55 boxes, 8 packing cases, and 24 filing drawers); clocks, 1857-1947 (230 vols. and 320 boxes); carriages, 1840-96 (48 vols. and 21 boxes); and woolens and other textiles, lumber, and paper, 1829-90 (83 vols. and 44 boxes).

Orientalia Collection. Leon Nemoy, Curator of Hebrew and Arabic Literature.

Holdings: Some 2,000 manuscripts, chiefly Arabic but including important Persian and Hebrew materials and smaller quantities in Indic, Turkish, and other languages. Present also are the Near Eastern manuscripts of the American Oriental Society, which are on permanent deposit. The Arabic manuscripts include works of special literary and historical importance, many of great age, and codices notable for their calligraphy and arabesque decoration. The Persian manuscripts consist chiefly of belles-lettres and history but include also theological, medical, and other pieces. The Hebrew collection includes hymnology, codices, marriage contracts, and several literary manuscripts of Sholem Asch (Poland, N. Y., Conn.; novelist, dramatist) and much of his correspondence.

See Leon Nemoy, Catalogue of Hebrew and Yiddish Manuscripts and Books From the Library of Sholem Asch (1945. 69 p.), his "Hebrew and Kindred Manuscripts in the Yale University Library," in Journal of Jewish Bibliography, vols. 1 and 3 (1939 and 1941), and his Arabic Manuscripts in the Yale University Library ([1956.] 273 p.), issued as vol. 40 of the Connecticut Academy of Arts and Sciences, Transactions. See also Elizabeth Strout, Catalogue of the Library of the American Oriental Society (1930. 308 p.).

Rare Book Room. H. W. Liebert,
Curator; Marjorie Wynne, Librarian.

Holdings: A general collection of
literary and historical manuscripts,
ranging in date from the 9th century
to the present, but chiefly relating to
English literature. Included are classical and medieval texts, especially of
Cicero, Tacitus, and Juvenal; the Zis-
kind Collection of Greek manuscripts;
Bible manuscripts; the James M. Osborn Collection of 17th-century manuscripts; an autograph collection of the
signers of the Declaration of Independence; the David Wagstaff Collection of
sporting manuscripts; the Pequot Library collection of manuscripts (on deposit); papers of the publishing house
of Cadell and Davies; and a varied and
extensive collection of diaries (un-
classed). There are significant quantities of letters and literary manuscripts for the authors and historical
figures listed below.

Richard Aldington (England; poet);
Matthew Arnold (England; poet, essayist) and his family; John James Audubon (Pa., Ky., La., N.Y.; artist, ornithologist); Sir Alfred Austin (England; poet); James M. Barrie (Scotland; novelist, dramatist); Herbert
Ernest Bates (England; novelist); Gustave Beaumont (France; publicist, associate of Tocqueville); William Beck-
ford (England; novelist); Sir Max
Beerbohm (England; critic, humorist); Arnold Bennett (England; novelist); George Borrow (England; novelist); James Boswell (Scotland; biographer); Robert and Elizabeth Barrett Browning (England; poets); George
Gordon, Lord Byron (England; poet);
Thomas Carlyle (England; essayist,
biographer); Sir John Chardin (France,
England; 17th-century traveler and
jewel trader); Samuel Taylor Coleridge (England; poet); Joseph Conrad
(England; novelist); Alfred Edgar Coppard (England; author); Marie Corelli
(England; novelist); George Crabbe

(England; poet) and his son George
Crabbe (England; biographer); Walter
Crane (England; painter, illustrator);
James Dwight Dana (Conn.; mineralogist, geologist, zoologist, Yale
prof.); William De Morgan (England;
artist, novelist); Norman Douglas
(England; author); and John Drinkwater (England; poet, playwright).

Maria Edgeworth (Ireland, Eng-
land; novelist); Jonathan Edwards
(Mass.; Congregational minister, the-
ologian) and his family; George Eliot
(England; novelist); A. Hugh Fisher
(England; artist, writer); Claude Lo-
vat Fraser (England; artist); Josiah
Willard Gibbs (Conn.; philologist,
Yale prof.) and his son of the same
name (Conn.; mathematical physicist,
Yale prof.); George Robert Gissing
(England; novelist); Nathan Hale (Conn.;
Rev. War officer); James Hogg, known
as Ettrick Shepherd (Scotland; poet);
Thomas Hood (England; poet) and his
family; James Joyce (Ireland; author);
Edward Knoblock (England; playwright,
novelist); Walter Savage Landor (Eng-
land; poet); George Henry Lewes (Eng-
land; philosopher, literary critic);
William James Linton (England, N.Y.,
Conn.; wood engraver, reformer,
writer); and Thomas R. Lounsbury
(Conn.; critic, Yale English prof.).

Haldane Macfall (England; novelist); William McFee (England, Conn.;
novelist); Arthur Machen (England;
novelist, essayist); Thomas Mann
(Germany, N.J., Calif.; novelist);
George Meredith (England; novelist,
poet); Mary Russell Mitford (England; novelist, dramatist); Hannah
More (England; religious writer);
Sydney Owen, Lady Morgan (Ireland;
writer); George Augustus Henry Sala
(England; war correspondent, writer); Sir Walter Scott (Scotland; poet,
novelist); Richard Brinsley Sheridan
(England; dramatist); Robert Southey (England; poet); William Buell
Sprague (Mass., N.Y.; Congregational
and Presbyterian minister, autograph

collector; Robert Louis Stevenson (Scotland; author); Ezra Stiles (R. I., Conn.; Congregational clergyman, Yale pres.); André Suarès (France; author); Algernon Charles Swinburne (England; poet); Alfred, Lord Tennyson (England; poet); Henry Major Tomlinson (Engnald; journalist, novelist); Anthony Trollope (England; novelist); Sir William Watson (England; poet); H. G. Wells (England; novelist); and William Wordsworth (England; poet).

Western Americana Collection. Archibald Hanna, William Robertson Coe, Curator.

Holdings: A large collection, chiefly of the first half of the 19th century, relating to the trans-Mississippi and more especially to the trans-Rocky Mountain West. The collection is especially valuable for California, the Pacific Northwest, the New Northwest, and Utah. Included are papers of well known men who played important parts in the early West and papers of obscure individuals who participated in such mass migrations as the gold rush and the Mormon treks.

Papers of officers of the U. S. armed forces include those of Meriwether Lewis Clark (U. S. Army officer, son of William Clark), 1834-47 (1 letter book); Samuel Ryan Curtis (U. S. Army officer, U. S. Rep. from Iowa) and his sons, Henry Z. and Samuel S. Curtis, also Army officers, 1846-66 (416 pieces), with some official materials on the Mexican War and the Civil War; George A. Custer (U. S. Army officer), July-Aug. 1874 (1 vol.), an order and dispatch book of the Black Hills Expedition; Henry Eld (U. S. naval officer), 1832-51 (2 vols. and 100 pieces); George Foster Emmons (U.S. naval officer), 1836-50 (11 vols. and 4,000 pieces); and William Hemsley Emory (U. S. Army officer), 1823-97 (5,000 pieces). Eleven volumes of the Emmons papers contain journals, let-

ters, and sketches relating to the Wilkes Exploring Expedition, 1838-42; other journals kept on this expedition include those of the following naval officers: James L. Blair, 1841-42 (1 vol.), George M. Colvocoresses, 1840 (1 vol.), Silas Holmes, surgeon, 1831-42 (3 vols.), and Joseph A. Underwood, 1831-40 (1 vol.).

Other personal papers include those of George Bent (Arkansas and Platte River Valleys); half-breed son of Col. William Bent), 1904-18 (200 reminiscent letters on Indian life); Ambrose Bierce (Calif.; short-story writer, journalist), 2 journals; David Edwards Blaine (Wash., Oreg.; Methodist minister) and his wife, 1853-58 (200 letters); George Catlin (Pa.; painter, author), mid-19th century (1 literary manuscript, 3 paintings, and 216 drawings); Elwood Evans (Pa., Oreg.; Sec. of Oreg. Terr., historian), 1843-94 (18 vols. and 237 pieces); Andrew Jackson Faulk (Pa., Dak. Terr.; Gov. of Dak. Terr.), 1817-96 (9 vols. and 980 pieces); John White Geary (Kans. Terr., Pa.; Gov. of Kans. Terr., Civil War officer, Gov. of Pa.), 1855-73 (3 vols. and 667 pieces), chiefly his papers as Kansas Territorial Governor; William Huskisson (England; pres. of Board of Trade), 1824-26 (417 pages), papers used in negotiations regarding the U.S. Northwest Boundary; Henry Farrand Livingston (Dak. Terr.; physician, Indian agent), 1866-79 (12 vols. of diaries); Alfred Benjamin Meacham (Oreg.; supt. of Indian affairs), 1869-73 (5 vols.); Henry Miles Moore (La., Mo., Kans.; lawyer, Kans. Terr. and State legislator), 1852-80 (43 vols. and 13 pieces), including records of the Free State Legislature of Kansas and the Leavenworth Association; Silas Reed (Ill., Mo., Wyo. Terr.; U.S. Surveyor-Gen., promoter of mines and railroads), 1833-86 (16 vols. and 2,000 pieces); Isaac Ingalls Stevens (Wash.; U. S. Army officer,

Terr. Gov., Terr. Delegate to Cong.), 1841-59 (265 pieces); James Jesse Strang (N. Y., Wis.; Mormon leader), chiefly 1831-55 (709 pieces), including biographical notes and correspondence about Strang by Milo M. Quaife (Wis., Mich.; historian); Granville Stuart (Mont.; pioneer, Terr. legislator, U. S. Minister to Uruguay and Paraguay), and his brother James, 1854-80 (19 vols. of diaries and 98 pieces); Elkanah Walker and Marcus Whitman (Oreg.; missionaries, pioneers), 1834-72 (533 items), including some records of the Oregon Mission; and Brigham Young (Utah; Mormon leader, Terr. Gov.), 1859-69 (64 pieces), chiefly letters to William H. Hooper (Utah; Terr. Delegate to Cong.).

There are also a number of important maps, including those of William Clark (U. S. Army officer), made on the Lewis and Clark Expedition; several Indian vocabularies; "fort records of the Northwest," 1850-79 (19 vols.), consisting of records of forts in Oregon and Washington Territories; an account book of the post trader at Fort Smith, Ark., and Fort Gibson, Indian Terr., 1823-25 (1 vol.); records of the Nauvoo Legion, 1857-68 (1 vol.); the Maury-Drake papers, consisting of private and official records of an Oregon volunteer cavalry regiment, 1861-65 (675 pieces); and journals, diaries, and letter books of Army officers not mentioned above (14 vols.). Included also are a letter book of the Missouri Fur Co., 1821-23; official and confidential letters received by the Nisqually post of the Hudson's Bay Co., 1841-59 (75 pieces); account books of the Hecla Consolidated Mining Co., Montana, 1876-77, 1879-80, and 1891-1906 (3 vols.); and an account book of a copper mine in Idaho, 1863-64. Besides the sketches, drawings, and paintings mentioned above under personal papers there are some 150 more, in smaller lots, many by well known artists. In addition to the Wilkes Expedition material there are 15 other journals of ship travel and ships' logs, including those of some British ships; and about 85 diaries of overland travel in the West, chiefly to California in the gold rush period but also to Utah and to the Black Hills during the gold rush there. Materials relating especially to Texas and the Southwest are those collected by Henry Raup Wagner (Colo., Mexico, Calif.; author, collector), some 2,000 pieces; and the Thomas W. Streeter Collection on Texas, 1795-1845 (2,100 items).

See Mary C. Withington, A Catalogue of Manuscripts in the Collection of Western Americana Founded by William Robertson Coe; Yale University Library (1952. 398 p.). This catalog also lists some papers relating to the West that are physically housed elsewhere in the Yale University Library, as in the Historical Manuscripts Collection and the Rare Book Room.

Yale Collection of American Literature. Donald C. Gallup, Curator.

Holdings: A large collection, relating especially to American literature in the 20th century. Included are papers (correspondence, except as otherwise noted) of Stephen Vincent Benét (N. Y.; poet, short-story writer), William Rose Benét (N. Y.; novelist, critic, poet), and Elinor Wylie (D. C., N. Y.; poet, novelist), 5,000 pieces, including literary manuscripts and letters; Henry Seidel Canby (Conn.; critic, editor, Yale prof.), 500 pieces; Royal Cortissoz (N. Y.; art critic), 1,000 pieces, including letters; Katherine S. Dreier (N. Y.; artist, social worker, author), 2,200 pieces); Marsden Hartley (Maine; artist, critic, poet), 1,000 pieces), including literary manuscripts and letters; Langston Hughes (N. Y.; poet, librettist, journalist),

5,000 pieces, including literary manuscripts; James Weldon Johnson (Fla., N.Y., Tenn.; author, sec. of Nat. Assn. for the Advancement of Colored People, Fisk Univ. prof.), 10,000 pieces, including literary manuscripts; Sinclair Lewis (Minn., N.Y.; novelist), 1,000 pieces, including literary manuscripts; Mabel Dodge Luhan (N.Y., N. Mex.; author), 2,000 pieces, including literary manuscripts; John Phillips Marquand (Mass.; author), 5 shelves of literary manuscripts; Eugene O'Neill (N.Y.; dramatist, 500 literary manuscripts and letters; William Lyon Phelps (Conn.; critic, author, Yale English prof.), 500 pieces; Gertrude Stein (Calif., France; poet, playwright, critic), 11,500 pieces, including 500 literary manuscripts and 1,000 letters by her; Alfred Stieglitz (N.Y.; photographer, editor), 5,000 pieces, including letters; Carl Van Vechten (N.Y.; novelist, music critic, photographer), 15,000 pieces, including letters; Edith Wharton (N.Y.; novelist), 5,000 pieces, including literary manuscripts and letters; Walter Francis White (N.Y.; author, sec. of Nat. Assn. for the Advancement of Colored People), 1,000 pieces, including manuscripts; and William Carlos Williams (N.J.; physician, poet, essayist), 1,000 pieces, including literary manuscripts.

In a "general collection" of more than 10,000 letters and literary manuscripts there are large amounts of material of Samuel L. Clemens, known as Mark Twain (Mo., Calif., N.Y., Conn.; novelist), 500 pieces, including literary manuscripts and letters; James Fenimore Cooper (N.Y.; novelist) and his family, 2,000 pieces, including literary manuscripts and letters; James Abraham Hillhouse (Conn.; poet, dramatist), 100 manuscripts; Washington Irving (N.Y.; author, Minister to Spain), 600 pieces, including literary manuscripts and letters; Donald Grant Mitchell (Conn.; author), 200 pieces, including literary manuscripts

and letters; James Gates Percival (Conn.; poet), 500 pieces, including literary manuscripts and letters; Walt Whitman (N.Y., D.C., N.J.; poet), 300 pieces, including literary manuscripts and letters; and many other literary figures. The Collection also includes correspondence and other records of the following periodicals: American Review (1,000 files), Blues (500 letters), Bookman (1,000 files), Dial (1,000 files, on deposit), Furioso (1,000 files), Hound and Horn (1,000 files), Southern Review (1,000 files), View (500 letters), and Yale Review (2,000 manuscripts and pieces of correspondence).

Yale Collection of German Literature. Curt von Faber du Faur, Curator.

Holdings: A considerable quantity of 19th- and 20th-century papers, consisting of letters, literary manuscripts, and other materials of and relating chiefly to authors who wrote in the German language.

Included is the Speck Collection of Goetheana (44 inches), representing Johann Wolfgang von Goethe (Germany; poet, dramatist, novelist), his family, friends, associates, and publishers and the composers of musical settings for his works, and containing letters and poems of Goethe himself and letters from Johann Christoph Friedrich von Schiller (Germany; poet, dramatist, novelist), from the Dukes of Saxe-Weimar-Eisenach, and from distinguished foreign contemporaries, including Americans. Another large collection is the Kurt Wolff archive, consisting of correspondence of that Munich publishing firm, 1912-34 (4,100 pieces), and including letters from Max Dauthendey (Germany; dramatist, novelist); Herberg Eulenberg (Germany; dramatist, novelist); Franz Kafka (Austria; poet, novelist); 47 letters; Rainer Maria Rilke (Germany, Austria; poet, novelist); Ernst Toller (Germany, N.Y.; poet, dramatist, social revolutionary leader); Fritz von Unruh (Germany; dramatist, poet, novelist); and Franz Werfel (Austria; poet, dramatist, novelist), 1,000 letters and 35 poems.

There are also papers of Richard Beer-Hofmann (Austria; dramatist, novelist), including letters from Hermann Bahr (Austria; journalist, dramatist, theater manager), 1893-1925 (70 pieces); Hugo von Hoffmannsthal (Austria, Germany; poet, critic, dramatist), 1891-1929 (431 pieces); and Arthur Schnitzler (Austria; physician, playwright, novelist), 1891-1928 (527 pieces). Included also are papers of Hermann Broch (Austria; novelist, dramatist), 62 inches; Gerhart Hauptmann (Germany; poet, dramatist), 1906-7 (48 letters); and Karl G. T. Winkler, known under the pseudonym of Theodor Hell (Germany; poet, dramatist, translator), 207 letters. There are also 23 pieces of music manuscripts.

Yale Papyrus Collection. C. Bradford Welles, Curator.

Holdings: 2,000 papyri, dating from the third century B.C. to the seventh century A.D., chiefly from Egypt but also from Yale excavations in Syria. Included are a number of literary pieces—Homer, Pindar, the New Testament, and others; many nonliterary documents, public and private; and a substantial quantity of Roman military records.

Yale University Archives. Robert F. Metzdorf, University Archivist.

Holdings: 3,017 ft., 1800 to the present, comprising the official archives of Yale University, with personal papers of some graduates and faculty members. Included are official papers of Walter C. Camp (Conn.;

Yale football coach), 150 boxes; Arthur T. Hadley (Conn.; Yale pres.), 37 letter books and 145 boxes; William Lyon Phelps (Conn.; Yale English prof., author), 19 vols. and 20 boxes; Anson Phelps Stokes (Conn., D.C.; Episcopal clergyman, sec. of Yale Univ., canon of Washington Cathedral), 76 letter books; William Graham Sumner (Conn.; economist, sociologist, Yale prof.), 20 vols. and 55 boxes; and John F. Weir (Conn.; dean of Yale School of Fine Arts), 8 boxes. Earlier archives are in the Secretary's office; others remain to be transferred from other collections.

School and Departmental Libraries

Historical Library, Yale University School of Medicine. Frederick Kilgour, Librarian.

Holdings: 100 ft., 13th-20th centuries, relating to medicine and medical history. One of the most important groups consists of the main body of papers of Harvey Cushing (Md., Mass., Conn.; surgeon, prof. at Johns Hopkins, Harvard, and Yale), 1891-1939 (75 vols. and 16 filing drawers), consisting chiefly of diaries, lecture notes, and correspondence, and of papers collected by him. There is substantial correspondence of Cushing with Charles William Eliot (Mass.; chemist, pres. of Harvard Univ.), 1920-25; Fielding Hudson Garrison (D.C., Md.; physician, U.S. Army officer, medical historian), 1912-25; Arnold Carl Klebs (Switzerland, Ill.; physician, public health specialist, medical historian), 1913-39; Silas Weir Mitchell (Pa.; physician, author), 1907-13; Sir William Osler (Canada, Md., England; physician, prof. at Johns Hopkins and Oxford Univs.), 1898-1919; William Henry Welch (Md.; physician, prof. at Johns Hopkins Univ. and director of its School of Hygiene and Public Health), 1897-

1934 (4 vols.); and Leonard Wood (physician, U. S. Army officer, military Gov. of Cuba, Gov. Gen. of the Philippines), 1909-27. Among the papers collected by Cushing are those of Elisha Bartlett (Mass., Ky., N. Y.; physician), 1824-53 (40 items). Also in the Library are papers of William Henry Carmalt (N. Y., Conn.; physician), 1867-1912 (19 vols.); student notes on lectures of Eli Ives (Conn.; physician, prof. at Yale Medical School), 1813-30 (6 vols.); correspondence of Carl Ludwig (Germany; physiologist) with Emil DuBois-Reymond (Germany; physiologist), 1847-95 (120 letters); and many letters and medical reports, in smaller quantities for each man, of other doctors prominent in the development of medical science both in the United States and abroad.

See the Library's Annual Reports, since 1940-41, passim; and its Harvey Cushing Collection of Books and Manuscripts (1943. 207 p.).

Library of the School of Music. Brooks Shepard, Jr., Librarian.

Holdings: Over 1,000 musical manuscripts, 1560-1940. Included are compositions of Yale composers, 1860-1940, principally Gustave Stoeckel, Horatio William Parker, and David Stanley Smith; musical manuscripts of Charles E. Ives (Conn.; composer), 3,000 pieces; the Lowell Mason Collection, 1560-1840 (630 pieces); the Filmer Collection of English music, 1600-1700; and musical manuscripts from continental Europe.

Yale Divinity Library, Yale University Divinity School. Raymond P. Morris, Librarian.

Holdings: 142 file drawers of correspondence and other records of the Student Volunteer Movement; 5 drawers of records of the Student Division of the Young Men's Christian Associa-

tion; 6 drawers of records of the War Emergency Council, Interseminary Commission working under the Young Men's Christian Association (World War II); extensive files of records of the World's Student Christian Federation; 44 drawers of correspondence and papers of John R. Mott (N.Y.; chairman of World's Committee of the Y. M. C. A., gen. sec. of World's Student Christian Federation); extensive files of the following 19th- and 20th-century churchmen and theologians: Horace Bushnell (Conn.; Congregational clergyman); Charles Reynolds Brown (Conn.; Congregational clergyman, dean of Yale Divinity School); Kenneth Scott Latourette (Conn.; Baptist clergyman, Yale prof. of missions, Oriental scholar); and others.

Yale Law School Library. Harry Bitner, Librarian.

Holdings: (1) Archives of the Yale Law School (70 ft.); and (2) other papers of legal interest, 13th-20th centuries (125 ft.).

European legal documents include Italian statuti (municipal laws), 14th-18th centuries (9 ft.); and important collections relating to English law. Among the latter are copies of Magna Charta and other statutes of the late 13th century, chiefly of Edward I; De legibus et Consuetudinibus Angliae, by Henry de Bracton (ecclesiastic, judge), 13th and 14th centuries (2 vols.), and also a collection of other manuscripts of Bracton in photostat; close rolls of 17-26 Edward III, in a 17th-century transcription (670 pages); Liber assisarum, reports of cases, Edward III, a 15th-century copy; Analysis of the Law (1 vol.), by Sir Matthew Hale (Lord Chief Justice), and Hale's commonplace book (2 vols.); and transcripts of proceedings in the House of Commons and of cases in the Court of Common Pleas,

Court of King's Bench, Court of Star Chamber, and Court of Wards and Liveries, various dates (36 vols., many formerly Sir Matthew Hale's). There are also legal instruments, English and American (300 pieces).

American papers of legal interest include those of Roger Sherman Baldwin (Conn.; lawyer, Gov., U.S. Sen.) and Simeon Eben Baldwin (Conn.; chief justice of State supreme court, Gov.), correspondence and legal papers (70 ft.); Charles E. Clark (Conn.; judge, prof. of law), legal papers (23 vols. and 13 boxes); James Hillhouse (N.Y., Conn.; lawyer), briefs (4 boxes); George Chandler Holt (N.Y.. referee in bankruptcy, U.S. dist. judge), opinions, 1899-1904 (2 boxes); Joseph Pierpont (Conn.; justice of the peace of New Haven County), 1784-1808; John M. Woolsey (N.Y.; lawyer, U.S. dist. judge), briefs (12 vols.); and Jasper Yeates (Pa.; State supreme court justice), legal papers and manuscripts (78 pieces). There are also notes of students in the Litchfield (Conn.) Law School, on lectures by Tapping Reeve (Conn.; lawyer, founder of the law school) and James Gould (Conn.; jurist), 1809-24 (12 ft.); notes of a student in the law school of Sylvester Gilbert (Conn.; judge, U.S. Rep.) at Hebron, Conn.; Columbia Law School lecture notes of James Kent (N.Y.; prof. of law, State Chancellor) and others (10 vols.); briefs of the probate court, district of New Haven, 1896-1907 (6 boxes); and a collection of legal association books.

Yale University School of Forestry Library. Frances Bolton, Librarian.

Holdings: Papers of Herman Haupt Chapman (Conn.; forester, prof. at Yale), 1898-1956 (110 vols.), dealing with forestry in Connecticut, Louisiana, and Minnesota; and Henry Solon Graves (Conn., D.C.; Chief of U.S. Forest Service, dean of the Yale School of Forestry), 1899-1950 (7 vols.) and 24 ft.), including his correspondence as dean, 1900-39, and typewritten and published papers.

See Forest History Sources, p. 10.

NEW LONDON

Connecticut College Library. Hazel A. Johnson, Librarian.

Holdings: A considerable and growing manuscript collection, chiefly of the 19th and 20th centuries, consisting for the most part of papers of persons, many of them women, living in Connecticut and neighboring New York. Included are papers of James Montgomery Bailey (Conn.; humorist, journalist), 19th century (17 letters); Ingoldsby Crawford (Conn.; collector of customs at New London), 1824-52 (175 pieces); Frances Perkins (N.Y.; State industrial commissioner, U.S. Sec. Labor), 1928-40 (12 vols. and 326 pieces), resulting chiefly from her official activities, together with addresses, 1933-36, by Daniel W. MacCormack (U.S. Commissioner of Immigration and Naturalization); and Prudence Crandall Philleo (Conn., Ill.; educator of Negroes, reformer) and family, 1831-86 (4 literary manuscripts and 43 letters). There are several small groups of papers of literary personages; an autograph collection containing one or two letters by each of several distinguished persons; and an extensive collection of papers relating to Belle Moskowitz (New York; political adviser to Gov. Alfred E. Smith) and family. There are also court, militia, and other documents of Connecticut local and State interest; a number of account books; some papers relating to French spoliation claims and other aspects of maritime history; and collections of Wadsworth and other Connecticut family papers, some of them relating to the period of the American Revolution.

—oOo—

New London County Historical Society. 11 Blinman St.

Holdings: A small collection of papers dating from 1652 and relating chiefly to New London County. Included are early county and town records and some genealogical material.

See the unpublished records of the Hist. Records Survey in the National Archives.

—oOo—

United States Coast Guard Academy Library. Donald F. Jay, Lt. Com., USCGR, Librarian.

Holdings: 58 pieces of the late 18th and early 19th centuries, relating to the establishment and maintenance of lighthouses and to revenue cutters. These papers contain signatures of the first six Presidents and several cabinet members, particularly the first Secretaries of the Treasury.

NEWTOWN

Cyrenius H. Booth Library. (Mrs.) Sarah B. Mitchell, Librarian.

Holdings: A small quantity of manuscripts, 1733-1863, relating chiefly to Connecticut. Included are a few letters of Luzon B. Morris (Conn.; Gov.); a diary, 1854-63 (4 vols.); some church records and registers of births; and a genealogical and local history collection.

OLD LYME

Phoebe Griffin Noyes Library. Main St.

Holdings: 36 items, 1753-1853, relating chiefly to Old Lyme. Included are minutes of a female reading society, 1816-20 (1 vol.); and some tax lists, school records, and other local archives.

See unpublished records of the Hist. Records Survey in the National Archives.

SEYMOUR

Seymour Public Library. (Mrs.) Peter M. Fryncko, Librarian.

Holdings: A few manuscripts dating from 1813, relating chiefly to Seymour. Included are school registers, 1875-84 (3 vols.); and an account book of a general store, 1813-31 (1 vol.).

SOUTHPORT

Pequot Library. Stanley Crane, Librarian.

Holdings: 2,500 pieces and 400 vols., 1740-1880, relating chiefly to American history, especially that of Connecticut. Included are papers of Joel Barlow (Conn.; poet, diplomat), 1775-1812 (100 pieces); logbooks and crew lists of the brig Augustus, 1841-48; account books of local farmers, 1837-80 (300 vols.), and of local merchants, 1805-80 (80 vols.); and a collection of autograph letters of signers of the Declaration of Independence and other notable Americans (700 pieces). Much of the foregoing material is on long-term loan to the Yale University Library.

SUFFIELD

Kent Memorial Library. Alexina P. Burgess, Librarian.

Holdings: 5,000 items, 1693-1921, relating chiefly to the early history of

Suffield.   Included are muster rolls
and other military records, 1744-81;
personal account books 1764-1877
(100 vols.); a number of church, town,
and school district records; and several diaries.

WALLINGFORD

Wallingford Historical Society.   294 Ivy
St.   G. Sumner Hill, President.

Holdings: A few diaries, sermons,
church records, military commissions,
and other papers relating chiefly to
Wallingford.

WATERBURY

Silas Bronson Library.   (Mrs.) Emelyn
B. Trimble, Librarian.

Holdings: A medieval breviary from
a south German nunnery, 15th century
(1 vol.).

WATERTOWN

Watertown Library.   470 Main St.
(Mrs.) Jeanne G. Shons, Librarian.

Holdings: 100 pieces, from early
18th century to 1892, consisting of
autograph letters and other manuscripts of prominent Americans that
have been tipped or bound in volumes
of a collection of rare books and other
imprints.
See One Hundred Items from the
Benjamin DeForest Curtiss Collection
of Books in the Watertown Library
(1937. 61 p.).

WETHERSFIELD 9

Wethersfield Historical Society.   The
Old Academy Museum, 150 Main St.
John C. Willard, Treasurer.

Holdings: A collection, 17th and
18th centuries, relating chiefly to
Wethersfield and Connecticut.   Included are account books, sermons,
maps, wills, deeds, and logbooks of
several ships.
See unpublished records of the
Hist. Records Survey in the National
Archives.

WOODBURY

Glebe House, Woodbury Center.

Holdings: 9 vols., consisting
chiefly of letters, sermons, and
other papers of or pertaining to Samuel Seabury (Conn., N. Y.; Episcopal
bishop) and his contemporaries.
See Hist. Records Survey, 100
Sample Entries, p. 14.

DELAWARE

DOVER

Delaware Public Archives Commission. Hall of Records. Leon deValinger, Jr., State Archivist.

Holdings: 9,325 cu. ft. of records, 8,030 reels of microfilm, 23,188 photographic negatives and positives, and 1,565 sound recordings, 1674-1959, consisting chiefly of official records held by the Commission as the State's archival depository for State, county, and municipal records.

Included among the State records are the Governor's register, 1674-1905; executive papers, 1776-1850 and 1930-48; records and reports of executive agencies (treasurer, auditor, and Board of Education), 1777-1959 but chiefly 20th century; military records for colonial wars, the Revolutionary War, and all later wars; legislative papers, 1776-1850 and 1927-58; enrolled bills, 1776-1931; minutes of the Assembly, 1739-1810, with gaps; constitutions of the State, 1792-1897; and judicial records. The last include records of colonial courts, 1676-1776; the court of chancery, 1776-1873 and 1914-47; the orphans' court, 1776-1873, including a series of guardian accounts; the court of oyer and terminer, 1776-1868; courts of general sessions, 1776-1873, quarter sessions, 1776-1850, and common pleas, 1726-1860 and 1917-52, supreme court writs and executions, 1798-1831, and superior court writs, 1832-90.

The official county records include levy court minutes, 1775-1872; records of county offices and elected officials (loan offices, coroners, trustees of the poor, rangers, fence viewers, and constables), and tavern licences, election returns, collectors' bonds, escheators' returns, 1728-

1850; records of treasurers, 1728-1850 and 1924-49, assessors, 1728-1950, engineers, 1728-1850 and 1919-34, and tax commissioners, 1728-1850 and 1924-49; apprentice indentures, and manumissions, 1728-1893; assessment and delinquent lists, 1726-1949; land records, principally warrants and surveys, 1640-1860, with gaps; probate records and inventories, 1676-1916; and vital statistics (births, baptisms, marriages, deaths), 1713-1913 passim. There are also official municipal records for the cities of Wilmington, 1769-1949, and Dover, 1920-46.

The Commission also holds papers of private individuals. These include a small group of correspondence of John Middleton Clayton (Del.; U. S. Sen., State chief justice, U. S. Sec. State); official and personal papers of John Dickinson (Pa., Del.; Member Continental Cong., Pres. of Del. and of Pa.); a small group of official and personal papers of George Read (Del.; Member Continental Cong., U. S. Sen., State chief justice); correspondence and papers of Henry M. Ridgely (Del.; lawyer, U.S. Rep. and Sen.), Nicholas Ridgely (Del.; State chancellor), and others of the family, 1742-1899; official and personal papers of Caesar Rodney (Del.; Member Continental Cong., Rev. War officer, Pres. of Del.); a small group of correspondence and personal papers of Caesar Augustus Rodney (Del.; U. S. Rep. and Sen., U. S. Attorney Gen., diplomat); and a small group of correspondence and personal papers of Thomas Rodney (Del., Miss.; Rev. War officer, Member Continental Cong., Del. supreme court justice, U. S. judge for Miss. Terr.).

There are business and some per-

sonal papers, chiefly 19th century, of
Delaware men of less prominence;
these papers largely concern merchandising but there is some material on
banking, agriculture, fruit growing,
and shipping. The last consists of
business correspondence and accounts
of merchant shippers with ship captains, factors, and merchants in the
coastal and foreign trade, 1790-1815.
Among other unofficial records are
originals, transcripts, and photostats
of Delaware church records, 1708-
1940 but principally of the 19th century
(59 vols.); a genealogical collection for
Delaware and DelMarVa peninsula
families (10 file drawers); a collection
of tombstone records throughout the
State, and one of tombstone inscriptions of Sussex County, Del.; and Bible records (6 vols.), compiled by the
D. A. R. in Delaware.

See unpublished records of the
Hist. Records Survey in the National
Archives; Hist. Records Survey, Inventory, County Archives of Delaware,
New Castle County (1941. 325 p. Processed); Delaware Public Archives
Commission, Annual Reports from
1941; and Leon deValinger, Jr., Calendar of Kent County, Delaware, Probate Records, 1680-1800 (1944. 558
p.), and, with Virginia E. Shaw, A
Calendar of Ridgely Family Letters,
1742-1899 (1948-51. 2 vols.).

GREENVILLE

Eleutherian Mills Historical Library.

Holdings: See entries for Eleutherian Mills-Hagley Foundation, Wilmington, Del., and Longwood Library,
Kennett Square, Pa.

NEWARK

University of Delaware Library. W.
D. Lewis, University Archivist.

Holdings: 149 vols., 1702-1930,
relating chiefly to Delaware. Included

are records of or relating to the University, 1833-1916 (8 file drawers);
papers of George Handy Bates (Del.,
Pa.; lawyer, diplomat), 1886-89 (5
portfolios), concerned chiefly with
his activity as special agent of the
State Department to investigate affairs in Samoa; transcripts of records
of nearby Presbyterian and Baptist
churches, 1815-72; minutes of the
Methodist quarterly conference, Newark circuit, 1855-1905 (50 pieces); and
Civil War prisoners' letters from
Fort Delaware (25 pieces).

See William Ditto Lewis, Calendar of the George Handy Bates Samo-
an Papers at the University of Delaware (1942. 41 p.).

WILMINGTON

Eleutherian Mills-Hagley Foundation. Du Pont Bldg. Walter J. Hea-
cock, Director of Research.

Holdings: In the Hagley Museum
Library, a large quantity of material,
1801-1902, consisting chiefly of noncurrent records of E. I. du Pont de
Nemours and Co., powder manufacturer. Included are journals, 1810-
1902 (47 vols.); ledgers, 1801-87 (23
vols.); letter-press books, 1805-57
(40 vols.); workmen's ledgers, 1809-
1902 (75 vols.); incoming correspondence, 1805-90 (250,000 pieces); accounts and correspondence with the
U. S. War and Navy Departments; and
accounts, bills, shipping papers, real
estate records, and miscellaneous
business records (125 boxes). There
are also correspondence, miscellaneous accounts, and other records pertaining to sheep raising, woolen and
cotton mills, a tannery, and other
early 19th-century enterprises in
which members of the du Pont family
were engaged. (It is planned that early in 1961 the Hagley Museum Library
will be consolidated with the Longwood Library, Kennett Square, Pa.,

as the Eleutherian Mills Historical Library, at Greenville, Del.).

WILMINGTON 1

Historical Society of Delaware. Old Town Hall. Mrs. W. Francis Lindell, Librarian.

Holdings: 17,000 pieces, 1680-1951, relating chiefly to Delaware and the surrounding area.

Included are papers of James Brobson (Del.; U. S. marshal, tax commissioner of New Castle County), 1795-1823 (60 items); William P. Brobson (Del.; lawyer, U. S. Marshal, collector of customs), 1810-49 (150 items); John Middleton Clayton (Del.; farmer, U. S. Sen., State chief justice, U. S. Sec. State), 1826-56 (50 items); Thomas Duff (Del.; Rev. War officer), 1749-1807 (50 items), concerned with western lands; Thomas Garrett (Del.; abolitionist) and his family, 1700-1866 (75 items); William Gibbons (Pa., Del.; physician) and his family, 1793-1883 (50 items); John P. Gillis (Del., Ill.; Civil War naval officer), 1847-71 (200 items); Thomas Jefferson (Va.; U. S. Pres.), 1780-1820 (14 items); Allan McLane (Del.; Rev. War officer, U. S. marshal, collector of customs at Wilmington), his son Louis McLane (Del.; U. S. Rep. and Sen., Sec. Treas., Sec. State, Minister to England), and Dr. Allen McLane, 1809-43 (50 items); The William Penn family, 1680-1776 (100 items); Howard Pyle (Del.; artist), 1894-1911 (75 items); George Read (Del.; Member Continental Cong., U. S. Sen., State chief justice) and his family, 1756-1908 (200 items); Caesar Rodney (Del.; Member Continental Cong., Rev. War officer, Pres. of Del.), 1708-90 (257 pieces); Caesar Augustus Royden (Del.; U.S. Rep. and Sen., U. S. Attorney Gen., diplomat), 1772-1824 (700 items); and Thomas Rodney (Del., Miss.; Rev. War officer, Member Continental Cong., Del. supreme court justice, U. S. judge for Miss. Terr.), 1757-1811 (500 items); and papers in small quantity of other distinguished men.

There are also autograph letters, documents, business papers, and deeds of Delaware interest or connection, 1683-1951 (2,000 items); records relating to the Chesapeake and Delaware Canal, 1803-19 (212 items); records of the New Castle Frenchtown Railroad, 1830-35 (500 items); Gilpin family papers concerned with paper mills, 1765-1840 (200 items); Civil War papers, 1861-65 (250 items); and records and copies of records of Delaware churches.

WILMINGTON 6

Wilmington Society of Fine Arts. Delaware Art Center Bldg. 2301 Kentmere Parkway. Rowland Elzea, Curator, Pre-Raphaelite Collection.

Holdings: 40 sonnets of Dante Gabriel Rossetti (England; poet).

WINTERTHUR

Henry Francis du Pont Winterthur Museum. M. Elinor Betts, Manuscript Librarian.

Holdings: Several thousand 17th-19th century manuscripts, all of American origin. Included are household inventories; and inventories and account books of craftsmen, especially artisans producing household furnishings. A few letters of prominent Americans are on exhibit.

WASHINGTON 16

Aaron Burr Association. 6400 Dahlo-
nega Road, Mohican Hills. Samuel
Engle Burr, Jr., President-General.

Holdings: A small collection of pa-
pers of or relating to Aaron Burr (N.Y.;
Rev. War officer, U.S. Sen. and Vice
Pres.).

WASHINGTON 25

Agricultural History Society. Care of
Agricultural Marketing Service, U.S.
Department of Agriculture. Wayne D.
Rasmussen, Secretary-Treasurer.

Holdings: 1 file drawer of early
19th-century diaries, store accounts,
and other documents assembled in
connection with an historical study of
farm prices in Virginia.

WASHINGTON 4

American Military Institute Library.
511 11th St. NW. George J. Stans-
field, Librarian.

Holdings: A small quantity of manuscripts, relating chiefly to military
history. Included is the Order of Indian Wars Collection, 1865-1904 (5 ft.),
consisting of diaries, clippings, maps,
and field notes.

WASHINGTON 6

American National Red Cross Archives.
18th and D Sts. NW. (Mrs.) Hazel
Braugh, Records Officer.

Holdings: 2,000 linear ft., 1881-
1956, consisting of noncurrent records of the Red Cross. Included are
correspondence, reports on war and
disaster relief and other activities of
the Red Cross, minutes and other records of international conventions and
conferences, and records pertaining
to numerous Red Cross societies.
(Permission must be secured for the
use of official records of the organization.)

—oOo—

Columbia Historical Society. 1307
New Hampshire Ave. NW. Elden E.
Billings, Curator.

Holdings: 2,000 pieces, chiefly
1791-1950, relating to the District of
Columbia and its environs. The collection includes documents signed by
George Washington and others relating to the Potomac Co.; correspondence relating to the Territorial Government of the District; account books
of local merchants; record books of
citizens associations; record books of
militia companies; some records of
the Georgetown Customhouse; microfilm copies of the 1798 direct tax of
the District of Columbia; and transcripts of the now missing minutes of
the Board of Aldermen and the Board
of Common Council of the City of
Washington.

—oOo—

Daughters of the American Revolution. 1776 D St. NW. (Mrs.) Mary
T. Walsh, Librarian.

Holdings: In the Library there

are 20,000 manuscripts, 1750-1900, relating chiefly to the American Revolution, with particular reference to the individual participants and their descendants. Included are certified copies of many documents from Bibles, cemeteries, churches, courts, and family records, 1750-1900 (15,000 pieces); and typewritten abstracts of original pension applications, 1818-55 (314 vols.). In the Museum there is a collection of letters of signers of the Federal Constitution. In the Americana Room there are several hundred letters, including a collection of autograph documents of the Members of the Federal Convention, 1770-1818 (1 vol.).

WASHINGTON 17

Department of Archives and Manuscripts, The Catholic University of America. 6th and Michigan Ave. NE. Rev. Dr. Robert Trisco, Archivist.

Holdings: Archives of the University, 1885 to date (400 linear ft. and 75 rolls of microfilm), and historical manuscript collections relating to American Catholic history and to the history of American labor.

Personal papers of clergymen who were members of the University's faculty include those of Thomas J. Bouquillon (Belgium, D. C.; theologian), 1873-1902 (5 in.); John Montgomery Cooper (Md.; anthropologist), 1898-1949 (4 ft.); Peter Guilday (Pa., D.C.; church historian), 1914-47 (38 ft. and 9 rolls of microfilm); Francis J. Haas (Wisc., D. C., Mich.; economist, Bishop of Grand Rapids), 1919-52 (40 ft.); William J. Kerby (Iowa, D. C.; sociologist), 1887-1936 (2 ft.); Edward A. Pace (D. C.; psychologist, editor), 1916-34 (9 ft.); and John A. Ryan (Minn., D. C.; theologian, economist), 1909-45 (24 ft.).

Papers of other men include those of John Carroll (Md.; Catholic Arch-

bishop of Baltimore), 1786-1814 (45 in. and 11 rolls of microfilm and other photocopies), assembled for publication by the American Catholic Historical Association; Charles Warren Currier (Md., D. C.; bishop, Hispanist, author), 1889-1918 (4 ft.); Richard L-G. Deverall (Japan, Europe; labor economist, trade unionist), 1936-59 (10 ft.); Lawrence F. Flick (Pa.; pathologist), 1875-1938 (31 ft.); Louis Aloisius Lambert (N. Y.; priest, journalist), 1863-1909 (5 in.); John Mitchell (Ill.; labor leader, pres. of United Mine Workers), 1898-1919 (32 ft.); William Montavon (D. C.; attorney, writer, lecturer), 1925-54 (4 ft.); Peter J. Muldoon (Ill.; bishop), 1901-26 (3 rolls of microfilm), consisting of his diaries; Philip Murray (Pa., D. C.; head of United Steelworkers of America and Congress of Industrial Organizations), 1943-53 (68 ft.); Terence Vincent Powderly (Pa.; head of the Knights of Labor, U. S. immigration official), 1869-1924 (115 ft.); John Gilmary Shea (N. Y.; historian, author, editor), 1891 (5 in.); and John Martin Spaulding (Ky.; Bishop of Louisville, historian), 1861-65 (1 vol., a journal).

Also included are records of the Fenian Brotherhood (whose members attacked Canada in the late 1860's), 1859-1904 (16 in.); and records of the National Catholic War Council, 1917-32 (100 ft. and 31 rolls of microfilm), relating to participation of Catholics in World War I and to efforts toward reconstruction after the war. Materials on microfilm include some relating to the early history of the Archdiocese of New York, 1785-1866 (7 rolls); manuscripts relating to the history of American Catholicism before 1842, especially manuscripts from foreign archives (8 rolls); and papers of representatives of the American hierarchy in Rome, 1832-1903 (13 rolls).

See Henry J. Browne, "Manu-

script Collections at the Catholic University of America," in Manuscripts,
6:166-168 (spring 1954).

—oOo—

Dominican College. 487 Michigan Ave.
NE. Rev. Charles R. Auth, Librarian.

   Holdings: Medieval and Renaissance manuscripts (2 vols.); historical
records of the Dominican Order (Order
of Friars Preachers) in the United
States; sermons of the Fathers of the
Province of St. Joseph (Dominican Order); and dissertations of the Dominican Fathers and Brothers.

WASHINGTON 7

Dumbarton Oaks Research Library.
1703 32d St. NW. George C. Soulis,
Librarian.

   Holdings: A number of literary
manuscripts and several hundred autograph letters, relating chiefly to
English literature. There are also
some holograph music scores.

WASHINGTON 3

Folger Library. 201 East Capitol St.
Louis B. Wright, Director.

   Holdings: A substantial quantity of
papers relating chiefly to English literature and history of the 16th and
17th centuries but also containing considerable material for later periods.
Among the more important holdings of
British papers are the Loseley manuscripts, which include records of the
Office of Revels during the reigns of
Henry VIII, Edward VI, and Mary and
during the early part of Elizabeth's
reign; papers relating to the several
Blackfriars theaters; and hundreds of

letters of literary and historical importance. There are also many Privy Council letters and other official
records of the British Government; a
long run of manuscript newsletters,
1674-1715, sent by a professional
newswriter from London to the New-
digate family in Warwickshire (4,000
items); and ledgers of the Drury Lane
theatrical group covering a long period in the 18th and 19th centuries. Also included in significant quantity are
papers of Nathaniel Bacon (lawyer,
Puritan, Member of Parliament),
James Burbage (actor), John Donne
(poet, clergyman), John Dryden (poet, dramatist), and Sir Richard New-
digate (chief justice of the King's
bench). There are microfilm copies
of the entire archives of the Cecil
family for the 16th and 17th centuries,
including papers of William Cecil,
Lord Burghley (Member of Parliament, Sec. State, Lord Treasurer),
and Robert Cecil, Earl of Salisbury
(Member of Parliament, Sec. State,
Lord Treasurer, Chief Minister). Papers relating to the American theater
include those of John A. Daly (N. Y.;
playwright, producer) and William
Winter (N. Y.; dramatic critic, historian, poet, essayist). The Library
has also a transcript of significant papers from the archives of the Strozzi
family of Florence, Italy, 16th and
17th centuries (185 vols.).
   See the Library's The Folger
Shakespeare Library: A Brief Description (1957. 16 p.), and The Folger Library: A Decade of Growth,
1950-1960 (1960. 49 p.); Giles E.
Dawson, "The Resources and Policies of the Folger Shakespeare Library," in Library Quarterly, 19:178-
185 (July 1949); and Louis B. Wright,
"The Folger Library as a Research
Institution," in College and Research
Libraries, 13:14-17 (Jan. 1952).

WASHINGTON 17

Franciscan Monastery Library. 14th and Quincy Sts. NE. Brother Henry Demko, Librarian.

Holdings: 2 vols. and 26 leaves of medieval and Renaissance manuscripts, and 2 documents issued by the Latin Patriarch of Jerusalem, 1776-77, to the captains of two vessels permitting them to hoist the flag of the Holy Land in the waters of the Levant.
See De Ricci, Census, p. 463.

WASHINGTON 20

Frederick Douglass Memorial Home. 1411 W St. SE.

Holdings: Papers of Frederick Douglass (Mass., N.Y., D.C.; abolitionist, reformer, journalist), 1845-95 (3 filing cabinets), including correspondence relating to slavery, the Civil War, reconstruction, and woman suffrage. Permission to consult the papers should be obtained from Mrs. Emmett Dixon, President of the Frederick Douglass Memorial and Historical Association, 4917 A, Highland Avenue, St. Louis 13, Mo.
See Hist. Records Survey, Calendar of the Writings of Frederick Douglass in the Douglass Memorial Home, Anacostia, D.C. (1940. 93 p. Processed).

WASHINGTON 7

Georgetown University Archives. 37th and O Sts. NW. Rev. W. C. Repetti, S.J., Archivist.

Holdings: The archives of the University, from 1789, constitute the largest group of material. There are also papers of James G. Blaine (Maine; U.S. Rep. and Sen., Sec. State); John

Carroll (Md.; Catholic Archbishop of Baltimore, founder of Georgetown College), 1764-1815 (225 pieces, mostly transcripts); Tomas Herran (Colombian Minister to the U.S.), 1901-4 (5 boxes), chiefly concerning negotiations for the Panama Canal; Robert G. Ingersoll (Ill., D.C., N.Y.; lawyer, Civil War officer, agnostic lecturer and writer), 200 items; and John Gilmary Shea (N.Y., N.J.; historian, author, editor), including his transcripts relating to the early history of the Catholic Church in the United States and to American Indians. There are collections of autograph letters of the Presidents of the United States, 1791-1953 (33 pieces), and of prominent figures in the Catholic Church (60 pieces); and the literary manuscript of The Adventures of Tom Sawyer by Mark Twain.

—oOo—

Georgetown University Department of History. 37th and O Sts. N.W. Father Joseph Durkin, Professor of American History.

Holdings: Papers of Robert Ferdinand Wagner (N.Y.; lawyer, U.S. Sen.), 1927-48 (250 4-drawer filing cabinets).

WASHINGTON 6

George Washington University Library. 2023 G St. NW. John Russell Mason, Librarian.

Holdings: Included are papers of Chauncey Mitchell Depew (N.Y.; lawyer, U.S. Sen.); and Luther Rice (Mass.; Baptist clergyman and a founder of Columbian College, now George Washington Univ.), 1802-35 (4 vols. and 1 envelope). There are several other small groups of papers, dating from 1825, relating to the University, its faculty, and its student body.

WASHINGTON 25

Historical Branch, Headquarters, U.S.
Marine Corps.

Holdings: A substantial quantity, in
the Marine Corps Historical Archives,
consisting of selected official documents, 1920 to date, relating to the
history of the Marine Corps, personal
papers of a number of Marine officers,
and compiled biographical information
about members of the Corps.

WASHINGTON 17

Holy Name College. 14th and Shepherd
Sts. NE. Rev. Fr. Guardian.

Holdings: Medieval and Renaissance
manuscripts (94 vols.); and 17th- and
18th-century manuscripts (9 vols.),
some from the California area of Mexico.
    See De Ricci, Census, pp. 470-484,
which describes 85 of the manuscripts.

WASHINGTON 1

Howard University Library. 2401 6th
St. NW. Joseph H. Reason, Director
of University Libraries.

Holdings: Several thousand manuscripts, 1798-1959, relating chiefly to
Negro life and history. In the general
library are some papers of and concerning Richard Le Gallienne (England; poet, critic). Papers in the
Moorland Foundation include those of
Blanche K. Bruce (Miss., D.C.; U.S.
Sen.), 1840-1900 (10 boxes); Thomas
Clarkson (England; philanthropist, antislavery advocate), 1791-1887 (50
letters); James A. Cobb (D.C.: municipal court judge), 1917-36 (363 items);
Francis Grimke (D.C.; Presbyterian
clergyman), 1893-1915 (3 shelves of
sermons); Oliver Otis Howard (D.C.,

Vt.; U.S. Army officer, Commissioner of Freedmen's Bureau, pres. of
Howard Univ.), 1853-1907 (4 boxes);
Alain Leroy Locke (D.C.; critic, Howard Univ. philosophy prof.), 1870-1956
(200 boxes); Jesse Edward Moorland
(N.Y.; Congregational clergyman),
1800-1940 (6,000 items); Pinckney Benton Stewart Pinchback (La.; Civil War
officer, Gov.), 1867-1901 (2 boxes);
James T. Rapier (Ala.; newspaper
correspondent, U.S. Rep.), 1856-65
(75 letters); Arthur B. Spingarn (N.Y.;
lawyer), 1900-59 (500 pieces); Joel E.
Spingarn (N.Y.; author, pres. of National Association for the Advancement
of Colored People), 1915-20 (800 pieces); Mary Church Terrell (D.C.; Negro reformer, suffrage leader), 203
items; J. Waties Waring (S.C.; U.S.
dist. court judge), 1947-59 (84 albums and 30 boxes); Daniel Hale Williams (Ill.; surgeon), 1900-40 (5 drawers); and Louis T. Wright (N.Y.; surgeon), 1898-1950 (8 drawers). Also
included are records of Negro troops
in the Civil War (430 vols., formerly
in the National Archives); a collection
of letters and documents relating to
slavery and abolition, 1792-1865 (500
pieces); and music manuscripts by
Negro composers, 1915-35 (200 pieces).

WASHINGTON 25

Library of Congress. L. Quincy
Mumford, Librarian of Congress.

Holdings: 15,700,000 items, 7th-
20th centuries, relating to many aspects of world history but especially
to the history of the United States.
These manuscripts are in the custody
of the following divisions of the Library: (1) Manuscript, (2) Map, (3)
Music, (4) Orientalia, (5) Prints and
Photographs, and (6) Rare Book. In
addition to original manuscripts the
Library has a very large collection

of photographic and other reproductions of manuscripts in archival and other depositories in many countries. The collections of microfilm copies are jointly administered by the Photoduplication Service and the Microfilm Reading Room, the Manuscript Division and the Division of Orientalia. In the entries that follow the holdings of each division are separately described.

See Annual Report of the Librarian of Congress, 1897 to date, and the Library's Quarterly Journal of Current Acquisitions, 1943 to date, for scattered but frequently detailed information about manuscripts and microfilm and other copies of manuscripts in the custody of the several divisions noted below.

Manuscript Division

David C. Mearns, Chief.

Holdings: More than 15,600,000 items relating chiefly to the history of the United States in the national period and extensive transcriptions and photographic copies of documents in British, French, Spanish, and other archives that relate to the colonial and later periods of United States history. The papers of some of the more important political and other leaders are mentioned below in the following order: colonial officials, Presidents, Cabinet officers, Members of Congress, Federal judges, army and navy officers, U. S. diplomatic and consular officials, other U. S. officials, scientists and physicians, clergymen, educators, literary figures, journalists, architects, artists, reformers, and merchants and other businessmen. Then follow other groups: family papers (with mention by name of some of the important members of these families), collections relating to particular subjects, and records of governmental and other organizations.

Papers of persons important in the administration of the British Empire in America, before the American Revolution, include those of John Archdale (England, N. C.; colonial Gov. of N. C.), 1694-1706 (65 items); Jonathan Belcher (Mass., N. J.; colonial Gov.), 1726-48 (1 vol.), letters received; Sir Guy Carleton (England, Canada; Gov. of Quebec, British Army officer), 1774-77 (1 vol.); Spencer Compton, Earl of Wilmington (England; pres. of Privy Council), 1731-43 (96 pieces), chiefly relating to colonial America; Dennys De Berdt (Mass.; colonial agent in London), 1765-70 (1 vol.); Baron Francis Howard Effingham (England, Va.; provincial Gov.), 1684-88 (4 vols.), containing basic documents relating to the royal province of Virginia; Charles Garth (S. C.; colonial agent in London), 1766-74 (1 box), transcripts; Jared Ingersoll (Conn., Pa.; colonial agent in London, judge of vice-admiralty court), 1740-79 (3 boxes); Sir William Johnson (N. Y.; supt. of Indian affairs), 1755-74 (1 vol.); Robert Monckton (British army officer), 1754-63 (1 vol.); and Edward Vernon and Sir Charles Wager (British naval officers), 1654-1773 (16 vols. and 2 boxes), among them materials on British operations in the West Indies, piracy, the slave trade, and the expulsion of Acadians.

Presidents and Cabinet Officers

There are in the Division papers, in varying quantity, of most of the Presidents of the United States. Included are papers of John Adams (Mass.), 1776-1813 (4 boxes); John Quincy Adams (Mass., 1794-1846 (5 vols., 2 boxes, and 2 portfolios); Chester A. Arthur (N. Y.), 1864-86 (5 boxes); James Buchanan (Pa.), 1825-87 (6 vols., 4 boxes, and 1 portfolio), including letters of his niece and official hostess, Harriet Lane Johnston; Grover Cleveland (N. Y.), 1859-1910 (407 vols. and 109 boxes);

Calvin Coolidge (Mass.), 1923-29 (347 boxes), chiefly correspondence of the Executive Office; Millard Fillmore (N.Y.), 1839-59 (1 box); James A. Garfield (Ohio), 1852-81 (318 vols., 20 boxes, and 5 portfolios), including diaries, 1872-81 (10 vols.); Ulysses S. Grant (U.S. Army officer), 1834-85 (95 vols., 6 boxes, and 3 packages), including his Army headquarters records, 1861-69 (76 vols.); Warren G. Harding (Ohio), 1897-1942 (4 boxes), including letters from Harry M. Daugherty (Ohio; U.S. Attorney Gen.), 1916-41; Benjamin Harrison (Ind.), 1758-1931 (290 vols., 179 boxes, and 14 bundles); William Henry Harrison (Ohio), 1735-1860 (9 vols. and 3 boxes); Rutherford B. Hayes (Ohio), 1856-92 (5 boxes and 4 portfolios); Andrew Jackson (Tenn.), 1775-1860 (269 vols. and 58 containers), including military papers, 1781-1832 (14 vols.); Thomas Jefferson (Va.), 1651-1826 (247 vols. and 10 boxes), and extensive reproductions of papers in other depositories and in the hands of individuals; and Andrew Johnson (Tenn.), 1829-91 (244 vols. and 30 boxes), including 2 stenographic notebooks of his secretary, William G. Moore.

The Division has a large and important group of papers of and relating to Abraham Lincoln (Ill.). Included are miscellaneous papers of Lincoln, 1832-65 (2 vols., 13 boxes, 1 package, and 2 portfolios), with many reproductions; and the collection of Lincoln papers preserved by his son, Robert Todd Lincoln (Ill.; Sec. War, Minister to Great Britain). There are also the Albert J. Beveridge Collection of Lincolniana, materials assembled by Beveridge (Ind.; U.S. Sen., historian) for his biography of Lincoln (20 boxes); the Herndon-Weik Collection, 1831-1927 (34 vols. and 7 boxes), including legal papers of Lincoln and his partner, William Henry Herndon (Ill.; lawyer, biographer of Lincoln); the Hertz Collection of Lincolniana (8 boxes), including the manuscript of the biography by

Emanuel Hertz (N.Y.; lawyer); and the papers of John G. Nicolay (Ill.; private secretary and biographer of President Lincoln), 1859-1913 (1 vol. and 16 boxes), including notes, diaries, letters, and scrapbooks relating to Lincoln's administration and correspondence of Nicolay's daughter Helen with Robert Todd Lincoln, 1873-1913. See also the papers of other associates of Lincoln, especially those of John M. Hay, under Cabinet officers, below.

Papers of other Presidents include those of William McKinley (Ohio), 1847-1902 (261 vols. and 156 boxes); James Madison (Va.), 1723-1845 (114 vols., 10 boxes, and 2 containers of microfilm); also papers of his wife, Dolley Payne Madison (Va., D.C.), 1794-1851 (14 vols., 1 box, and 1 portfolio); James Monroe (Va.), 1758-1849 (40 vols., 5 boxes, and 2 reels of microfilm); Franklin Pierce (N.H.), 1820-69 (11 vols. and 14 boxes), including 14 vols. of photostats; James K. Polk (Tenn.), 1775-1891 (148 vols. and 36 boxes), including papers of his wife, Sarah Childress Polk, 1839-91 (3 vols.); Franklin Delano Roosevelt (N.Y.), miscellaneous papers (1 vol., 2 boxes, and 8 portfolios); Theodore Roosevelt (N.Y.), 1870-1940 (266 vols., 904 boxes, and 15 envelopes), also papers of his wife, Edith Kermit Carow Roosevelt, 1901-9 (3 vols. and 3 boxes); William Howard Taft (Ohio), 1810-1921 (1,300 boxes); Zachary Taylor (Ky.), 1814-85 (1 vol. and 2 boxes); Harry S. Truman (Mo.), a small quantity of miscellaneous letters, chiefly copies; John Tyler (Va.), 1710-1861 (8 vols.), including papers of his father, John Tyler (Va.; Rev. War officer, Gov.); Martin Van Buren (N.Y., 1737-1868 (67 vols. and 6 boxes); George Washington (Va.), 1592-1811 (389 vols. and 44 boxes of originals, and 11 vols. and 46 boxes of reproductions, including transcripts and microfilms of papers in private hands);

and Woodrow Wilson (N.J.), 1880-1924 (1,322 boxes). There are also several general collections of Presidential manuscripts, 1770-1899, chiefly photostats of documents in private hands, and photostat copies of the wills of 19 Presidents, 1835-1941.

Papers of Cabinet officers include those of Newton D. Baker (Ohio; lawyer, Sec. War), 1916-37 (254 boxes), including papers relating to the Permanent Court of Arbitration at The Hague; Edward Bates (Mo.; U.S. Rep. and Attorney Gen.), 1859-66 (5 vols.), including notes of Cabinet meetings; Thomas Francis Bayard (Del.; Sec. State, U.S. Sen., Ambassador to Great Britain), 1796-1899 (184 vols. and 107 boxes); Jeremiah Sullivan Black (Pa.; U.S. Attorney Gen., Sec. State), 1813-1904 (73 vols. and 12 boxes); James G. Blaine (Maine; U.S. Rep. and Sen., Sec. State), 1859-92 (3 vols. and 13 boxes); Charles Joseph Bonaparte (Md.; Sec. Navy, U.S. Attorney Gen.), 1874-1921 (163 vols., 320 boxes, and 39 bundles); Benjamin Helm Bristow (Ky.; U.S. Solicitor Gen., Sec. Treas.), 1839-1932 (31 boxes); William Jennings Bryan (Nebr.; U.S. Rep., Sec. State), 1877-1931 (16 vols., 88 boxes, and 5 portfolios); Albert Sidney Burleson (Tex.; lawyer, U.S. Rep., Postmaster Gen.), 1845-1943 (31 vols. and 8 boxes); John C. Calhoun (S.C.; U.S. Rep. and Sen., Vice Pres., Sec. War, Sec. State), 1819-50 (2 boxes); Simon Cameron (Pa.; Minister to Russia, U.S. Sen., Sec. War), 1738-1919 (38 boxes); George Washington Campbell (Tenn.; U.S. Rep. and Sen., Sec. Treas., Minister to Russia), 1793-1886 (1 vol. and 3 boxes); William Eaton Chandler (N.H.; lawyer, U.S. Sen., Sec. Navy), 1862-1917 (166 vols. and 1 box); Zachariah Chandler (Mich.; U.S. Sen., Sec. Interior), 1854-99 (7 vols. and 2 boxes); Henry Clay (Ky.; U.S. Rep. and Sen., Sec. State), 1770-1910 (34 vols. and 5 boxes); John Middleton Clayton (Del.; U.S. Sen., Sec. State), 1798-1865 (12

vols. and 1 envelope); Bainbridge Colby (N.Y.; Sec. State), 1887-1950 (2,500 items); George B. Cortelyou (N.Y.; Sec. Commerce and Labor, Postmaster Gen., Sec. Treas.), 1899-1905 (64 boxes), chiefly relating to his service as private secretary to Presidents William McKinley and Theodore Roosevelt; and Thomas Corwin (Ohio; Gov., U.S. Rep. and Sen., Sec. Treas.), 1850-53 (12 vols.).

Papers of other Cabinet officers include those of William Harris Crawford (Ga.; U.S. Sen., Minister to France, Sec. War, Sec. Treas.), 1813-31 (3 vols. and 1 box); John A. J. Creswell (Md.; U.S. Rep. and Sen., Postmaster Gen.), 1819-87 (17 vols., 8 boxes, and 1 folder); John Jordan Crittenden (Ky.; U.S. Rep. and Sen., U.S. Attorney Gen., Gov.), 1782-1888 (28 vols. and 3 boxes); Caleb Cushing (Mass.; U.S. Rep. and Attorney Gen., diplomat), 1817-79 (49 vols., 530 boxes, and 30 bundles), also the diary of his private secretary, Richard S. Spofford, 1855-57 (2 vols.); Josephus Daniels (N.C.; newspaper editor, Sec. Navy, Ambassador to Mexico), 1813-1948 (66 vols. and 960 boxes); Jefferson Davis (Miss.; U.S. Rep. and Sen., Sec. War, Confed. Pres.), 1840-1913 (6 boxes); James John Davis (Pa.; U.S. Sen., Sec. Labor), 1921-45 (13,000 pieces); George Henry Dern (Utah; Gov., Sec. War), 1933-36 (5 boxes); Donald McDonald Dickinson (Mich.; Postmaster Gen.), 1863-1917 (6 boxes); William Eustis (Mass.; Rev. War surgeon, U.S. Rep., Sec. War, Minister to the Netherlands, Gov.), 1775-1855 (4 vols. and 1 portfolio); William Maxwell Evarts (N.Y.; U.S. Sen., Attorney Gen., Sec. State), 1842-1908 (54 vols. and 8 boxes), including papers relating to the trial of Jefferson Davis (Miss.; Confed. Pres.) and the impeachment of Andrew Johnson (Tenn.; U.S. Pres.); James Aloysius Farley (N.Y.; Postmaster Gen.), 1935-36 (3 boxes); William Pitt Fessenden

(Maine; U.S. Rep. and Sen., Sec. Treas.), 1832-78 (7 vols. and 2 boxes); Hamilton Fish (N. Y.; Gov., U. S. Rep. and Sen., Sec. State), 1804-94 (308 vols. and 188 boxes); Walter Lowrie Fisher (Ill.; Sec. Interior), 1877-1935 (13,000 pieces); John Watson Foster (Ind.; newspaper editor, diplomat, Sec. State), 1872-1917 (1 box); Frederick Theodore Frelinghuysen (N. J.; U. S. Sen., Sec. State), 1881-85 (3 vols.); and Lyman Judson Gage (Ill., N. Y.; banker, Sec. Treas.), 1897-1906 (13 vols.).

Among other papers of Cabinet officers are those of Albert Gallatin (Pa., N. Y.; U. S. Rep. from Pa., Sec. Treas., Minister to France and to Great Britain), 1801-46 (2 vols. and 3 boxes); James Rudolph Garfield (Ohio; Sec. Interior), 1900-48 (62 vols. and 89 boxes); Gideon Granger (Conn., N. Y.; Postmaster Gen.) and his son Francis Granger (N. Y.; U. S. Rep., Postmaster Gen.), 1800-64 (1 vol. and 1 portfolio); Walter Quintin Gresham (Ind.; Civil War officer, U. S. dist. court judge, Postmaster Gen., Sec. Treas., Sec. State), 1857-96 (44 vols., 5 boxes, and 1 portfolio); Thomas Watt Gregory (Tex., D. C.; Rev. War officer, Member Continental Cong., Sec. Treas.), 1749-1849 (132 vols. and 9 boxes); John Milton Hay (Ill., D. C.; sec. of Pres. Lincoln, diplomat, Sec. State, poet), 1859-1914 (15 vols. and 110 boxes); Joseph Holt (Ky.; U. S. Commissioner of Patents, Postmaster Gen., Sec. War, Judge Advocate General), 1817-94 (97 vols. and 25 boxes); Cordell Hull (Tenn.; U. S. Rep. and Sen., Sec. State), 1910-50 (33,000 pieces); Harold L. Ickes (Ill.; Sec. Interior, Public Works Administrator), 1907-52 (150,000 pieces); William M. Jardine (Kans.; Sec. Agriculture, Minister to Egypt, pres. of Wichita Univ.), 1908-55 (1,000 pieces); Reverdy Johnson (Md.; U. S. Sen., Attorney Gen., Minister to Great Britain), 1826-76 (1 box); Jesse Holman Jones (Tex.; financier, Reconstruction Finance

Corporation Director, Sec. Commerce), 1932-45 (60,000 items); Amos Kendall (Ky., D. C.; journalist, political leader, Postmaster Gen.), 1835-80 (2 vols. and 1 box); Horatio King (Maine, D. C.; editor, lawyer, Postmaster Gen.), 1832-93 (13 vols.); William Franklin Knox, known as Frank Knox (Mass., Ill.; newspaper publisher, Sec. Navy), 1898-1944 (7 vols. and 13 boxes); Philander Chase Knox (Pa.; Attorney Gen., U. S. Sen., Sec. State), 1796-1922 (27 vols. and 5 boxes); and Julius Albert Krug (Wis.; public utilities expert, Sec. Interior), 1946-52 (20,000 pieces).

Still other papers of Cabinet officers include those of Daniel S. Lamont (N. Y.; Sec. War, financier), 1871-1906 (80 vols. and 2 boxes), including his papers as private secretary to President Cleveland; Robert Lansing (N. Y.; Sec. State), 1911-28 (62 vols. and 3 boxes); Robert Todd Lincoln (Ill.; Sec. War, Minister to Great Britain), 1790-1916 (194 vols., 2 boxes, and 99 microfilm rolls); William Gibbs McAdoo (N. Y., Calif.; Sec. Treas., U. S. Sen. from Calif.), including his papers as World War I director general of railways; Robert McClelland (Mich.; U. S. Rep., Gov., Sec. Interior), 1856-57 (1 vol.); James McHenry (Md.; Rev. War officer, Member Continental Cong., Sec. War), 1774-1814 (10 vols. of photostats, 7 boxes, and 1 portfolio); Hugh McCulloch (Ind.; Sec. Treas.), 1855-94 (4 vols.); Franklin MacVeagh (Ill.; Sec. Treas.), 1909-28 (17 boxes); Daniel Manning (N.Y.; Sec. Treas.), 1885-1907 (6 vols.); William Learned Marcy (N. Y.; U. S. Sen., Gov., Sec. War, Sec. State), 1806-57 (100 vols., 18 boxes, and 2 packages), including a diary, 1831-57; Return Jonathan Meigs, Jr. (Ohio; U. S. Sen., Gov., Postmaster Gen.), 1772-1885 (2 vols. and 1 portfolio), including papers of his father, Return Jonathan Meigs (Rev. War officer), 1772-85 (1 vol.);

George von Lengerke Meyer (Mass.; Ambassador to Italy and to Russia, Postmaster Gen., Sec. Navy), 1901-17 (10 vols.); Ogden L. Mills (N. Y.; financier, U. S. Rep., Sec. Treas.), 1912-37 (213 containers); Harry S. New (Ind.; newspaper editor, U. S. Sen., Postmaster Gen.), 1887-1929 (2 boxes); Richard Olney (Mass.; Attorney Gen., Sec. State), 1830-1917 (153 vols., 15 boxes, and 3 bundles); Alexander Mitchell Palmer (Pa.; U.S. Rep., Alien Property Custodian, Attorney Gen.), 1910-23 (2 boxes), chiefly letters from Woodrow Wilson (N. J.; U. S. Pres.); and Robert Porter Patterson (N. Y.; U. S. judge, Sec. War), 1940-51 (18 vols.).

Other papers of Cabinet officers are those of Timothy Pickering (Mass.; Rev. War officer, Postmaster Gen., Sec. War, Sec. State, U. S. Rep. and Sen.), 1796-1822 (2 boxes and 1 portfolio), chiefly copies; Joel R. Poinsett (S. C.; U. S. Rep., Minister to Mexico, Sec. War), 1810-41 (1 vol. and 3 boxes), including notes and memoranda on conditions in South America, 1810-12 (2 boxes); Edmund Randolph (Va.; Member Continental Cong., Gov., U. S. Attorney Gen., Sec. State), 1787-95 (2 vols.); Elihu Root (N. Y.; Sec. War, Sec. State, U. S. Sen.), 1898-1937 (73 vols. and 312 boxes); Richard Rush (Pa.; U. S. Attorney Gen., Sec. State, Minister to Great Britain, Sec. Treas.), 1805-58 (1 box); John McAllister Schofield (Mo.; Sec. War, U. S. Army officer), 1853-95 (88 vols.); Carl Schurz (Wis., Mo., N. Y.; Civil War officer, U. S. Sen. from Mo., Sec. Interior), 1842-1906 (187 vols., 70 boxes, and 18 portfolios); Lewis Baxter Schwellenbach (Wash.; U. S. Sen., Sec. Labor), 1935-48 (2,000 pieces); William Henry Seward (N. Y.; Gov., U. S. Sen., Sec. State), 1834-60 (1 box); John Sherman (Ohio; U. S. Rep. and Sen., Sec. Treas., Sec. State), 1846-94 (613 vols. and 12 boxes); Caleb Blood Smith (Ind.; U. S.

Rep., Sec. Interior), 1841-62 (8 vols. and 1 box); Samuel Lewis Southard (N. J.; Gov., U. S. Sen., Sec. Navy), 1809-48 (1 box and 1 portfolio); Edwin M. Stanton (Ohio, D. C.; Attorney Gen., Sec. War), 1818-70 (45 vols. and 5 boxes); Benjamin Stoddert (Md.; Rev. War officer, Sec. Navy), 1784-1812 (1 vol.), also letters of his wife, Rebecca Lowndes Stoddert, 1776-1800 (1 box); Oscar S. Straus (N. Y.; Minister to Turkey, Sec. Commerce and Labor), 1856-1931 (66 boxes); Alexander H. H. Stuart (Va.; U. S. Rep., Sec. Interior), 1790-1868 (1 box); Benjamin Franklin Tracy (N. Y.; Sec. Navy), 1870-1916 (21 vols. and 74 boxes); Robert J. Walker (Pa., Miss.; U. S. Sen. from Miss., Sec. Treas., Gov. of Kans. Terr.), 1815-1936 (9 vols. and 1 roll of maps); Henry A. Wallace (Iowa; Sec. Agriculture, U. S. Vice Pres., Sec. Commerce), 1941-44 (9 scrapbooks, 11 cartons, and 4 transfer cases); Daniel Webster (N.H., Mass.; U. S. Rep. and Sen., Sec. State), 1800-74 (14 vols. and 4 boxes); Gideon Welles (Conn.; Sec. Navy, newspaper editor), 1777-1911 (97 vols. and 21 boxes), including diaries, 1827-69; William C. Whitney (N. Y., Ky.; financier, Sec. Navy), 1757-1904 (182 vols. and 32 boxes); William Wirt (Va.; U. S. Attorney Gen.), 1805-40 (10 vols. and 1 box); and Oliver Wolcott, Jr. (Conn.; banker, Sec. Treas., Gov.), 1792-1829 (1 vol. and 2 boxes). Papers of other Cabinet officers and other Government officials are also to be found in the collections of family papers, treated later in this entry.

Members of Congress

Papers of Members of Congress from New England include those of Nelson Wilmarth Aldrich (R. I.; financier, U. S. Rep. and Sen.), 1762-1915 (13 boxes and 1 portfolio); Elisha Hunt Allen (Maine; U. S. Rep., diplomat, chancellor and chief justice of Hawaii), 1846-82 (13 boxes); Josiah Bartlett, Jr. (N. H.; physician, U.S. Rep.), 1790-1838 (47 boxes); Stephen Row Bradley (Vt.; Rev. War officer, U.S. Sen.), 1777-1881 (2 boxes); Edmund Burke (N.H.; U.S. Rep., Commissioner of Patents), 1821-81 (4 vols. and 1 box); Benjamin Franklin Butler (Mass.; Civil War officer, U.S. Rep., Gov.), 1831-96 (67 vols. and 308 boxes); Henry Laurens Dawes (Mass.; U.S. Rep. and Sen.), 1857-1903 (14 vols. and 113 boxes); Edward Everett (Mass.; Unitarian clergyman, Gov., Minister to Great Britain, pres. of Harvard College, U.S. Rep. and Sen., Sec. State), 1857-64 (2 vols., 3 boxes, and 1 portfolio); John Fairfield (Maine; Gov., U.S. Rep. and Sen.), 1828-67 (4 vols. and 6 boxes), including correspondence relating to the Northeastern boundary question; Elbridge Gerry (Mass.; Member Continental Cong., U.S. Rep., Gov., U.S. Vice Pres.), 1744-1836 (2 vols. and 7 boxes); Nicholas Gilman (N.H.; Member Continental Cong., U.S. Rep. and Sen.), 1780-1804 (1 box); Frank Lester Greene (Vt.; newspaper editor, U.S. Rep. and Sen.), 1890-1930 (78 boxes); Artemas Hale (Mass.; U.S. Rep.), 1846-48 (2-vol. journal); Joseph Roswell Hawley (Conn.; newspaper editor, Gov., U.S. Rep. and Sen.), 1842-1905 (24 vols., 33 boxes, and 3 packages); Samuel Holten (Mass.; physician, Member Continental Cong., U.S. Rep., jurist), 1744-1842 (5 containers); Thomas Allen Jenckes (R.I.; lawyer, U.S. Rep.), 1836-78 (72 boxes), including papers relating to his work as patent attorney; William Samuel Johnson (Conn., N.Y.; Member Continental Cong., U.S. Sen. from Conn., pres. of Columbia College), 1745-90 (1 vol.); and Rufus King (Mass.; N.Y.; Member Continental Cong., U.S. Sen. from N.Y.), 1784-1800 (1 box).

Papers of other New England Members of Congress are those of Levi Lincoln, Jr. (Mass.; Gov., U.S. Rep.), 1807-63 (1 box); Henry Cabot Lodge (Mass.; U.S. Rep. and Sen.), 1892-1911 (1 box); Brien McMahon (Conn.; Asst. Attorney Gen., U.S. Sen.), 1943-52 (11 boxes); Justin Smith Morrill (Vt.; U.S. Rep. and Sen.), 1825-1923 (59 vols. and 21 boxes); William Plumer (N.H.; Gov., U.S. Sen.), 1759-1844 (7 vols., 1 box, and 11 folders); Roger Sherman (Conn.; Member Continental Cong., U.S. Rep. and Sen.), 1746-1810 (1 vol. and 2 boxes); James Fowler Simmons (R.I.; manufacturer, U.S. Sen.), 1830-61 (79 boxes); Albert Smith (Maine; U.S. Rep.), 1817-49 (1 box), including papers relating to the Northeast boundary; Israel Washburn (Maine; U.S. Rep., Gov.), 1838-1908 (3 vols.); George Peabody Wetmore (R.I.; Gov., U.S. Sen.), 1846-1921 (6 boxes and 26 scrapbooks), chiefly relating to the U.S. Commission of Fine Arts; William Whipple (N.H.; Member Continental Cong.), 1774-89 (2 vols.); Wallace Humphrey White, Jr. (Maine; U.S. Rep. and Sen.), 1919-44 (8 file drawers, 5 packing cases, and 14 scrapbooks); and Henry Wilson (Mass.; U.S. Sen. and Vice Pres.), 1851-78 (1 vol.).

Papers of Senators and Representatives from the Middle Atlantic States include those of James A. Bayard (Del.; U.S. Rep. and Sen.), 1797-1855 (7 vols. and 2 boxes), including his diary as Commissioner at Ghent, 1813-15, and some papers of his son, Richard Henry Bayard (Del.; lawyer, U.S. Sen.); Aaron Burr (N.Y.; Rev. War officer, U.S. Sen. and Vice Pres.), 1792-1808 (4 boxes, 1 portfolio, and 1 package); Charles Carroll (Md.; Member Continental Cong., U.S. Sen.), 1684-1829 (4 vols. and 5 boxes), including papers of his father and of the family's iron works; Joseph Ripley Chandler (Pa.; newspaper editor, U.S. Rep.), 1850-51 (1 letter book); William Clark (Pa.; U.S. Rep., War of 1812 officer), 1812-56 (3 boxes); Roscoe Conkling (N. Y.; U. S. Rep. and Sen.), 1769-1895 (1 box); John Covode (Pa.; U. S. Rep.), 1854-71 (1 box); Edward Curtis (N. Y.; U. S. Rep., collector of customs at New York), 1839-53 (1 box); William Darlington (Pa.; physician, botanist, U. S. Rep.), 1801-34 (1 vol.); Charles Augustus Foote (N. Y.; U. S. Rep.), 1751-1871, 60 items among the papers of his father, Ebenezer Foote (1 box); Francis Burton Harrison (N. Y.; U. S. Rep., Gov. Gen. of the Philippines), 1812-1944 (72 containers); John Philip Hill (Md.; U. S. Rep.), 1908-38 (134 vols.); William Maclay (Pa.; U. S. Sen.), 1789-91 (3 vols. of journal and 1 box); George B. McClellan, Jr. (N. Y., N. J.; U. S. Rep. from N. Y., mayor of New York, Princeton Univ. prof.), 1886-1922 (4,600 pieces); Edward McPherson (Pa.; newspaper editor, U. S. Rep.), 1715-1936 (46 vols. and 72 boxes); Gouverneur Morris (N. Y.; Member Continental Cong., U. S. Sen., diplomat), 1789-1816 (53 vols.), including diaries, 1789-1816 (14 vols.); Robert Morris (Pa.; financier, Member Continental Cong.; U. S. Sen.), 1778-98 (19 vols., 3 boxes, and 2 folders), including his official diary and letter books as Supt. of Finance, 1781-84; William Vans Murray (Md.; U. S. Rep., diplomat), 1784-1805 (4 vols. and 3 boxes); Joseph Hopper Nicholson (Md.; U. S. Rep.), 1789-1827 (7 vols.); Amasa J. Parker (N. Y.; U. S. Rep.), 1836-44 (1 box); Philip John Schuyler (N. Y.; Member Continental Cong., Rev. War officer), 1776-87 (2 memorandum books); Daniel E. Sickles (N. Y.; Civil War officer, Minister to Spain, U. S. Rep.), 1861-1906 (4 boxes); Samuel Smith (Md.; Rev. War and War of 1812 officer, U. S. Rep. and Sen.), 1772-1869 (18 boxes); and Thaddeus Stevens (Pa.; lawyer, U. S. Rep.), 1813-69 (16 vols. and 2 boxes).

Papers of Members of Congress from Southern States include those of John Bell (Tenn.; Sec. War, U. S. Rep. and Sen.), 1849-61 (1 vol.); James Brown (La.; U. S. Sen., Minister to France), 1765-1867 (5 vols.), including letters of his brother, John Brown (Ky.; Member Continental Cong.); William Armisted Burwell (Va.; sec. to Pres. Jefferson, U. S. Rep.), 1804-13 (1 box); John F. H. Claiborne (Miss., La.; lawyer, journalist, historian, U. S. Rep. from Miss.), 1818-85 (5 vols., 2 boxes, and 2 packages); Duncan Lamont Clinch (Ga.; U. S. Army officer, U. S. Rep.), 1834-59 (1 vol. and 1 box); Jabez Lamar Monroe Curry (Ala., Va.; U. S. and Confed. Rep., pres. of Howard College, Ala., prof. at Richmond College, Minister to Spain), 1809-1939 (54 vols. and 4 boxes), including correspondence concerning the Peabody fund; Joseph Desha (Ky.; U. S. Rep., Gov.), 1783-1857 (2 vols. and 3 boxes), including correspondence of his son John Randolph Desha (Ky.; physician), 1827-57; Franklin Harper Elmore (S. C.; bank pres., U. S. Rep. and Sen.), 1795-1858 (10 vols. and 6 boxes); George Eustis, Jr. (La.; U. S. Rep., Confed. diplomat), 1659-1884 (3 boxes); Henry De La Warr Flood (Va.; U. S. Rep.), 1870-1921 (2 vols. and 82 boxes); Joseph Smith Fowler (Tenn.; U. S. Sen.), 1865-1903 (3 boxes); James H. Hammond (S. C.; Gov., U. S. Rep. and Sen.), 1823-75 (33 vols., 17 boxes, and 2 packages); Robert Goodloe Harper (S. C., Md.; U. S. Rep. from S. C. and Sen. from Md.), 1796-1823 (1 box); Ralph Izard (S. C.; Member Continental Cong., U. S. Sen., diplomat), 1792-1814 (5 vols.); Richard Mentor Johnson (Ky.; U. S. Rep. and Sen., Vice Pres.), 1808-47 (1 vol.); Richard Bland Lee (Va., D. C.; U. S. Rep. from Va., judge of D. C. orphan's court), 1700-1825 (1 vol.), including family papers; William Lowndes (S. C.; U. S. Rep.), 1787-1842 (1 vol. and 1 box); John McKee (Ala.; U. S. Rep. and Indian agent), 1794-1829 (5 boxes); Willie Person

Mangum (N. C.; U. S. Rep. and Sen.), 1810-97 (18 vols. and 4,000 pieces); James Murray Mason (Va.; U. S. Rep. and Sen., Confed. diplomat), 1838-70 (9 vols.); and John Tyler Morgan (Ala.; Confed. Army officer, U. S. Sen.), 1865-1907 (48 vols., 12 boxes, and 16 packages).

Papers of other Southern Members of Congress include those of Hugh Nelson (Va.; jurist, Minister to Spain, U. S. Rep.), 1808-33 (1 vol.); Wilson Cary Nicholas (Va.; Gov., U. S. Rep. and Sen.), 1765-1831 (7 vols.); Philip Phillips (S. C., Ala., D. C.; U. S. Rep. from Ala.), 1836-93 (52 vols., 13 boxes, and 2 packages); Francis Wilkinson Pickens (S. C.; U. S. Rep., Gov.), 1837-64 (3 vols.), including papers of Milledge Luke Bonham (S.C.; U. S. Rep., Confed. Army officer, Gov.); John Randolph of Roanoke (Va.; U. S. Rep. and Sen.), 1742-1835 (3 vols. and 2 boxes); William Cabell Rives (Va.; Minister to France, U. S. Rep. and Sen., Confed. Rep.), 1756-1939 (205 vols., 202 boxes, and 2 chests); William Loughton Smith (S. C.; Minister to Portugal and Spain, U. S. Rep.), 1792-1806 (1 vol.); William Russell Smith (Ala.; U. S. and Confed. Rep., Confed. Army officer), 1813-64 (80 pieces); Alexander Hamilton Stephens (Ga.; U. S. Rep., Confed. Vice Pres., Gov.), 1784-1886 (115 vols. and 5 boxes); Andrew Stevenson (Va.; U.S. Rep., Minister to Great Britain), 1756-1882 (47 vols., 5 folders, 2 boxes, and 1 bundle), including papers of his son, John White Stevenson (Ky.; Gov., U. S. Rep. and Sen.), 1849-82 (9 vols.); Henry Tazewell (Va.; judge, U. S. Sen.), 1796-98 (1 vol.); Waddy Thompson (S. C., Fla.; U. S. Rep. from S. C., Minister to Mexico), 1826-59 (1 box); Thomas Tudor Tucker (S. C.; Rev. War officer, Member Continental Cong., U.S. Rep., Treasurer of U. S.), 1791-1824 (1 box); David Rogerson Williams (S. C.; Gov., U. S. Rep.), 1793-1816 (1 portfolio); John Sharp Williams (Miss.; U. S. Rep. and Sen.), 1906-23 (190 boxes); and Henry Alexander Wise (Va.; Gov., U. S. Rep., Minister to Brazil), 1840-57 (2 boxes and 1 package).

Papers of Members of Congress from the Middle West include those of William Allen (Ohio; U. S. Rep. and Sen., Gov.), 1825-77 (21 vols. and 3 boxes); Albert J. Beveridge (Ind.; U. S. Sen., historian), 1890-1927 (406 boxes), including papers concerning the Progressive Party and notes for Beveridge's biographies of Lincoln and John Marshall; Henry Pelham Holmes Bromwell (Ill., Colo.; U. S. Rep.), 1845-65 (10 boxes); William Dallas Bynum (Ind.; U. S. Rep.), 1896-1905 (1 vol. and 2 boxes); Schuyler Colfax (Ind.; U. S. Rep., Vice Pres.), 1839-80 (2 boxes and 1 folder); James Rood Doolittle (Wis.; U. S. Sen.), 1860-1913 (1 box); Joseph Benson Foraker (Ohio; Gov., U. S. Sen.), 1885-1918 (1 vol. and 1 package); Joshua Reed Giddings (Ohio; U. S. Rep., abolitionist, consul gen. in Canada), 1839-96 (3 boxes), including correspondence of his son-in-law, George W. Julian (Ind.; U. S. Rep., abolitionist), 1845-96; Gilbert M. Hitchcock (Nebr.; U.S. Rep. and Sen., newspaper editor), 1919-30 (2 vols. and 1 box); Robert Marion La Follette (Wis.; Gov., U. S. Rep. and Sen.), a large collection, including materials on his presidential campaign of 1924 (8 boxes); Robert Marion La Follette, Jr. (Wis.; publisher, U. S. Sen.); and John A. Logan (Ill.; Civil War officer, U. S. Rep. and Sen.), 1848-87 (50,000 pieces).

Papers of other Midwestern Congressmen include those of Duncan McArthur (Ohio; War of 1812 officer, U. S. Rep., Gov.), 1784-1839 (50 vols. and 7 boxes); James Robert Mann (Ill.; U. S. Rep.), 1897-1922 (38 vols.), chiefly of clippings but including some letters; William Medill (Ohio; Gov., U.S. Rep., Commissioner of Indian Affairs, Comptroller of the Treasury), 1828-64 (11 boxes); George W. Norris (Nebr.; U.S. Rep. and Sen.), 1885-1944 (747 boxes, 103 vols., and 11 bundles); Henry Thomas Rainey (Ill.; U.S. Rep.), 1899-1935 (26 boxes); Oliver L. Spaulding (Mich.; Civil War officer, U.S. Rep., Asst. Sec. Treas.), 1838-1928 (2 boxes); John Coit Spooner (Wis.; U.S. Sen.), 1874-1907 (132 vols. and 141 boxes); Robert A. Taft (Ohio; U.S. Sen.), 1939-53 (300,000 pieces); Benjamin Tappan (Ohio; judge, U.S. Sen.), 1788-1900 (22 vols. and 5 boxes), including letters from his brother Arthur Tappan (N.Y.; philanthropist); John Robert Thomas (Ill., Okla.; U.S. Rep. from Ill., U.S. judge in Indian Terr.), 1880-1912 (1 box); Lyman Trumbull (Ill.; State supreme court justice, U.S. Sen.), 1855-72 (77 vols.); Benjamin F. Wade (Ohio; U.S. Sen.), 1832-98 (17 vols. and 3 boxes); Elihu B. Washburne (Ill.; U.S. Rep., Minister to France), 1829-82 (102 vols. and 31 boxes); and Thomas Worthington (Ohio; Gov., U.S. Sen.), 1801-27 (3 boxes).

Papers of Congressmen from other States, chiefly of the Southwest and Far West, include those of William E. Borah (Idaho; U.S. Sen.), 1912-40 (37 vols. and 718 boxes); Thomas Henry Carter (Mont.; U.S. Rep. and Sen.), 1895-1911 (25 vols. and 36 boxes); Thomas Terry Connally (Tex.; U.S. Rep. and Sen.), 1917-53 (100,000 pieces and 42 scrapbooks); Bronson Cutting (N. Mex.; publisher, U.S. Sen.), 1927-35, a large collection, not yet open for research; John E. Erickson (Mont.; U.S. Sen.), 1933-34 (9,000 items); William Ewart Humphrey (Wash.; U.S. Rep.), 1903-36 (2 boxes); Charles Linza McNary (Oreg.; U.S. Sen.), 1921-43 (63 boxes); Robert Latham Owen (Okla.; U.S. Sen.), 1920-41 (17 boxes); Key Pittman (Nev.; U.S. Sen.), chiefly 20th-century papers, not yet open for research; and Thomas James Walsh

(Mont.; U.S. Sen.), 1913-33 (18 vols. and 424 boxes).

Members of the Federal Judiciary

Papers of U.S. judges include those of William Augustus Atlee (Pa.; judge of Pa. supreme court and U.S. dist. court), 1759-1816 (1 box); Salmon Portland Chase (Ohio; Gov., U.S. Sen., Sec. Treas., U.S. Chief Justice), 1755-1874 (114 vols. and 21 boxes), and papers of his secretary, Jacob W. Schuckers, 1836-1900 (2 boxes); Benjamin R. Curtis (Mass.; U.S. Chief Justice), 1831-79 (3 vols. and 1 box); Charles Burke Elliott (Minn.; Philippine Islands supreme court justice), 1910-12 (3 vols. and 3 boxes); George Purnell Fisher (Del., D.C.; U.S. Rep., D.C. supreme court justice), 1865-96 (6 boxes and 1 package); Melville Weston Fuller (Ill.; U.S. Chief Justice), 1902-10 (173 pieces); Learned Hand (N.Y.; U.S. dist. court judge), 1909-24 (25 vols.), consisting of minutes of trials; John Marshall Harlan (Ky.; U.S. Supreme Court Justice), 1866-77 (3,500 pieces); Oliver Wendell Holmes (Mass.; U.S. Chief Justice), 1903-32 (2 boxes and 1 portfolio), chiefly letters to Lewis Einstein (N.Y.; diplomat); Charles Evans Hughes (N.Y.; Gov., Sec. State, U.S. Chief Justice), 57 vols., 16 boxes, 4 packing cases, and 8 filing drawers; Harry Innes (Va., Ky.; commissary agent, U.S. dist. court judge), 1772-1850 (28 vols. and 6 boxes); John Jay (N.Y.; Pres. of Continental Cong., diplomat, U.S. Chief Justice, Gov.), 1776-94 (55 items), microfilm of originals in Windsor Castle; Horace Harmon Lurton (Tenn.; Civil War officer, U.S. Supreme Court Justice), 300 pieces; John McLean (Ohio; U.S. Rep., Postmaster Gen., U.S. Supreme Court Justice), 1828-61 (19 vols. and 10 boxes); John Marshall (Va.; U.S. Rep., Sec. State, U.S. Chief Justice), 1776-

1835 (6 vols. and 1 box), chiefly photostats; William Henry Moody (Mass.; U.S. Rep., Sec. Navy, U.S. Attorney Gen. and Supreme Court Justice), 1879-1916 (16 vols. and 150 pieces); William Paterson (N.J.; U.S. Sen., Gov., U.S. Supreme Court Justice), 1768-1806 (89 pieces); Charles Perley Smith (D.C.; U.S. Tax Court judge), 1920-46 (13 boxes); Harold M. Stephens (Utah, D.C.; Asst. Attorney Gen., judge of U.S. Court of Appeals for D.C.), 1912-55 (162,000 pieces); Harlan Fiske Stone (N.H.; U.S. Attorney Gen. and Chief Justice), 1925-46 (40,000 pieces); Joseph Story (Mass.; U.S. Rep. and Supreme Court Justice), 1804-43 (7 vols. and 1 box); George Sutherland (Utah; U.S. Rep., Sen., and Supreme Court Justice), 20th century (5,000 pieces); Roger Brooke Taney (Md.; U.S. Attorney Gen., Sec. Treas., U.S. Chief Justice), 1829-67 (3 boxes); Smith Thompson (N.Y.; Sec. Navy, U.S. Supreme Court Justice), 1790-1830 (1 box); John Curtiss Underwood (Va.; U.S. dist. court judge), 1856-1905 (1 vol. and 1 box); Morrison Remick Waite (Ohio, D.C.; U.S. Chief Justice), 1858-88 (20,000 items); and Levi Woodbury (N.H.; Gov., U.S. Sen., Sec. Navy, Sec. Treas., U.S. Supreme Court Justice), 1804-97 (60 vols. and 29 boxes).

Army and Navy Officers

Papers of Revolutionary War officers include those of William Alexander, known as Lord Stirling (N.Y., N.J.; Rev. War officer), 1774-82 (2 vols.); John Barry (Pa.; shipowner, U.S. naval officer), 1770-98 (1 box); Ephraim Blaine (Pa.; Rev. War officer), 1766-1805 (10 vols. and 6 boxes), including 1 vol. relating to the Whiskey Rebellion; Elias Boudinot (N.J.; Rev. War officer, Member Continental Cong., U.S. Rep., Director of Mint), 1773-85 (6 boxes); George Clinton (N.Y.; Rev. War officer, Gov.,

Member Continental Cong.), 1777-83 (1 box), including papers of his brother James Clinton (N.Y.; Rev. War officer); John Davis (Pa.; Rev. War officer), 1755-83 (11 vols., 1 box, and 1 folder); Nicholas Fish (N.Y.; lawyer, Rev. War officer, U.S. supervisor of revenue for N.Y. dist.), 1776-1845; John Fisher (N.Y.; Rev. War officer), 1777-1802 (10 vols.), relating chiefly to army supplies; Mordecai Gist (Md.; Rev. War officer), 1776-79 (1 vol. and 1 box); Henry Glen (N.Y.; Rev. War officer), 1777-80 (1 vol.), transcripts relating to commissary affairs; Nathanael Greene (R.I., Ga.; Rev. War officer), 1775-83 (4 vols. and 7 boxes); Edward Hand (Pa.; physician, Rev. War officer, Member Continental Cong.), 1775-84 (4 vols. and 1 box); William Heath (Mass.; Rev. War officer), 1774-1808 (3 vols. and 2 boxes); John Paul Jones (Rev. War naval officer), 1775-89 (15 vols., 5 boxes, and 2 portfolios); the Marquis de Lafayette (France; American Rev. War officer), 1025-1834 (7 vols. and 6 boxes); Samuel Holden Parsons (Conn., Ohio; Rev. War officer), 1769-1871 (1 box); Jonathan Potts (Pa.; Rev. War medical officer), 1776-80 (1 vol.); the Comte de Rochambeau (France; commander of French Army in Am. Revolution), 1763-94 (16 vols.); Charles Simms (Va.; Rev. War officer, mayor of Alexandria), 1731-1822 (7 vols. and 1 box); Thomas Sumter (S.C.; Rev. War officer, U.S. Rep. and Sen.), 1761-1838 (3 vols.); Adam Stephen (Va.; colonial wars and Rev. War officer), 1750-1834 (1 vol.); and Charles Stewart (N.J.; Rev. War officer, Member Continental Cong.), 1777-82 (1 vol.).

Papers of other Army and Navy officers include those of Fred C. Ainsworth (U.S. Army officer), 1901-28 (1 box); Edward Porter Alexander (Ga.; U.S. and Confed. Army officer), 1854-65 (1 vol. and 1 box), including papers on the Battle of Gettysburg;

Henry T. Allen (U. S. Army officer) and his family, 1806-1938 (15,000 items); Robert Anderson (Ky.; U. S. Army officer), 1819-1919 (16 vols. and 4 boxes); Pierre G. T. Beauregard (La.; U. S. and Confed. Army officer, railroad pres.), 1844-83 (51 vols. and 5 boxes), including dispatch books for the Mexican and Civil Wars; James Biddle (U.S. naval officer), 1825-32 (1 box); John Bigelow, Jr. (U. S. Army officer), 1886-1927 (104 boxes); Tasker Howard Bliss (U. S. Army officer), 1870-1937 (273 vols. and 221 boxes), including correspondence relating to the Paris Peace Conference; Mark L. Bristol (U. S. naval officer, High Commissioner to Turkey), 1887-1928 (162 boxes), including official documents concerning his service in Turkey and the Far East; Jacob Brown (U. S. Army officer), 1814-28 (3 vols.), including materials concerning the Niagara campaign; Robert Lee Bullard (U. S. Army officer), 1899-1944 (1,450 pieces); Joshua Lawrence Chamberlain (Maine; Civil War officer, Gov., educator), 1862-71 (4 boxes); James Chesnut (S. C.; U. S. Sen., Confed. Army officer), 1776-77, 1862, including papers relating to the Provisional Government of South Carolina, 1776-77; David Conner (U. S. naval officer), 1817-47 (3 vols.); Henry Clark Corbin (U. S. Army officer), 1865-1905 (18 vols. and 9 boxes), including materials on the Spanish-American War, Philippine affairs, and the Boxer Rebellion in China; Samuel Wylie Crawford (U. S. Army officer), 1860-88 (6 vols. and 39 letters), including a diary kept at Fort Sumter; George Croghan (Ky.; U. S. Army officer) and his family, 1789-1853 (3 boxes); Oscar Terry Crosby (N. Y., D. C.; U. S. Army officer, explorer, author), 1878-1944 (2,550 pieces), including 100 letters from Lord David Davies (Wales; pres. of Univ. College of Wales); John Adolphus Bernard Dahlgren (U. S. naval officer, commandant of Washington Navy Yard, chief of Bureau of Ordnance), 1820-70 (48 vols., 35 boxes, and 2 portfolios); George Dewey (U. S. naval officer), 1880-1917 (65 vols., 64 boxes, and 5 wooden cases); William F. Draper (Mass.; Civil War officer, U. S. Rep.), 1861-64 (1 vol. and 1 box); Jubal Anderson Early (Va.; lawyer, Confed. Army officer), 1829-1911 (15 vols. and 4 boxes); and Richard Stoddert Ewell (U. S. and Confed. Army officer), 1838-96 (5 boxes).

Papers of other Army and Navy officers include those of Thomas Flournoy (U. S. Army officer), 1812-46 (1 box and 1 folder); Andrew Hull Foote (U. S. naval officer), 1822-68 (30 vols.); William Buel Franklin (U.S. Army officer), 1861-65 (1 vol.); George Washington Getty (U. S. Army officer), 1818-1902 (18 boxes), including family papers; Edward Settle Godfrey (U. S. Army officer), 1863-1933 (4 vols. and 5 boxes), including documents relating to the Custer massacre; George Washington Goethals (N. Y.; engineer, U. S. Army officer, Gov. of Canal Zone), 1890-1927 (8 vols. and 91 boxes); Louis M. Goldsborough (U. S. naval officer), 1817-74 (35 vols., 2 boxes, and 4 packages); William Crawford Gorgas (U.S. Army officer, pioneer in tropical medicine), 1880-1920 (14 vols., 67 boxes, and 3 packages); Henry Wager Halleck (U. S. Army officer), 1862 (230 pieces); James Guthrie Harbord (U. S. Army officer), 1886-1916 (41 vols.); James Allen Hardie (U. S. Army officer), 1844-86 (1 box); Samuel Peter Heintzelman (U. S. Army officer), 1822-85 (11 vols. and 11 boxes), including diaries; John Leonard Hines (U. S. Army officer), 1896-1944 (5 vols. and 70 boxes); Ethan Allen Hitchcock (U.S. Army officer, author), 1810-1922 (11 boxes); Henry Hitchcock (Mo.; lawyer, Civil War officer), 1864-65 (2 vols. and 34 pieces), describing Sherman's march to the sea; Richmond Pearson Hobson

(Ala.; U.S. naval officer, U.S. Rep., author), 1890-1937 (122 boxes), including documents relating to naval construction and equipment; Jedediah Hotchkiss (Va.; cartographer, Confed. Army officer), 1847-99 (57 vols. and 81 boxes), including papers relating to the Virginia geological survey and to Confederate Army maps; Everett S. Hughes (U.S. Army officer), 1903-49 (3,000 items); Thomas Jonathan Jackson, known as Stonewall Jackson (Va.; prof. at Va. Military Institute, U.S. and Confed. Army officer), 1845-63 (2 containers), chiefly photostats; Thomas Sidney Jesup (U.S. Army officer), 1780-1907 (16 vols. and 8 boxes); and Albert Sidney Johnston (Tex.; U.S. and Confed. Army officer), 1792-1896 (2 boxes), including some papers of William Preston Johnston (Va., La.; Confed. Army officer, pres. of La. State and Tulane Univs.).

Papers of other Army and Navy officers include those of August Valentine Kautz (U.S. Army officer), 1857-95 (6 boxes), including his Civil War journal; Benjamin King (U.S. Army surgeon), 1825-63 (1 portfolio); Jacob Kingsbury (U.S. Army officer), 1727-1856 (3 vols.); Emory S. Land (U.S. naval officer, U.S. Maritime Commission Chairman), 1901-54 (5,000 items); Daniel R. Larned (Conn.; Civil War officer, private sec. to Gen. A. E. Burnside), 1861-65 (4 vols. and 2 boxes); Thomas Lawson (U.S. Army officer), 1811-64 (1 box); Henry Ware Lawton (U.S. Army officer, military Gov. of Cuba), 1861-1902 (3 boxes), relating chiefly to the Apache Indian campaign of 1886; William D. Leahy (U.S. naval officer, Ambassador to France, Chief of Staff to the Commander in Chief), 1897-1952 (15 vols.), diaries; Robert E. Lee (Va.; U.S. and Confed. Army officer, pres. of Washington College), 1749-1870 (12 boxes); Mansfield Lovell (N.Y., Ga.; civil engineer, U.S. and Confed. Army officer), 1860-69 (1 box); Charles Oscar Maas

(U.S. naval officer), 1917-19 (1 box), relating to his service as assistant naval attaché at the American Embassy in Paris; Thomas Macdonough (U.S. naval officer), 1815-25 (1 vol.); George Brinton McClellan (U.S. Army officer), 1847-85 (199 vols. and 48 boxes); Frank Ross McCoy (U.S. Army officer), 1847-1949 (95 boxes), relating chiefly to his service in the Philippines, on the Mexican border, and in Europe during World War I; James Birdseye McPherson (U.S. Army officer), 1848-64 (2 boxes); Alfred Thayer Mahan (U.S. naval officer, historian), 1824-1914 (2 vols., 21 boxes, 1 portfolio, and 2 packages); Peyton Conway March (U.S. Army officer), 1897-1955 (6 boxes and 5,000 pieces); Matthew Fontaine Maury (Va.; U.S. and Confed. naval officer, Naval Observatory Supt., oceanographer), 1825-95 (64 vols. and 26 boxes); Edgar Alexander Mearns (N.Y.; U.S. Army officer, naturalist), 1880-1910 (31 boxes, 4 portfolios, and 2 packages), including material concerning the African expedition of Theodore Roosevelt; Montgomery C. Meigs (engineer, U.S. Army officer), 1849-89 (35 vols., 8 boxes, 1 portfolio, and 2 packages), including diaries, chiefly in shorthand, relating to construction projects around Washington, D.C.; William Mitchell (U.S. Army officer, aviator), 1917-42 (5 vols., 65 boxes, and 5 bundles), including diaries and papers relating to his court-martial; Alfred Mordecai (Pa.; U.S. Army officer, civil engineer), 1790-1946 (15 vols. and 2 boxes), including letters concerning the Mexico and Pacific Railroad; John Singleton Mosby (Va.; Confed. ranger, lawyer), 1861-86 (1 vol.), photostats of letters in private hands; George Van Horn Moseley (U.S. Army officer), 1899-1954 (21,000 papers); and Albert James Myer (U.S. Army officer), 1851-1933 (4 boxes), including papers relating to the U.S. Weather Bureau.

Papers of other Army and Navy officers include those of Matthew C. Perry (N. Y.; U. S. naval officer, diplomat), 1838-85 (3 boxes), chiefly relating to negotiations with Japan; John J. Pershing (U. S. Army officer, World War I Commander in Chief), a large quantity, including materials on the Apache Indian campaigns, Cuba, the Philippines, Japan, and Mexico, and on his service in World War I and his work as Chief of Staff, together with papers of two of his World War I subordinates, Paul H. Clark (Chief of American Military Mission with the French Army), 1918-19 (2 boxes), and John McAuley Palmer (aide-de-camp to Pershing), 24 boxes); John T. Pickett (Confed. Army officer and diplomatic agent), 1849-84 (8 vols. and 1 box); Orlando Metcalfe Poe (U. S. Army officer, engineer), 1861-87 (2 boxes); Leonidas Polk (Tenn., La.; Episcopal bishop, Confed. Army officer), 1856-68 (1 vol.); David Porter (U. S. naval officer, Minister to Turkey), 1799-1843 (8 vols.), and his son David Dixon Porter (U. S. naval officer), 1812-99 (12 vols. and 62 boxes); Fitz-John Porter (N. Y.; U. S. Army officer, police and fire commissioner of New York City), 1830-1914 (96 vols. and 26 boxes); Horace Porter (N. Y.; U. S. Army officer, military sec. to Pres. Grant, railroad executive, Ambassador to France), 1785-1912 (9 boxes); Richard Henry Pratt (U. S. Army officer), 1840-1923 (1 vol.), an unpublished autobiography; Edward Preble (U. S. naval officer), 1630-1809 (56 vols. and 1 box), including family papers (1 vol.); Samuel Chester Reid (Conn., N. Y.; War of 1812 naval officer, designer of American flag), 1807-60 (33 pieces, photostats); George C. Remey (U. S. naval officer), 1855-1930 (36 vols. and 6 boxes); William Cattron Rigby (Ill., D. C.; lawyer, U. S. Army officer), 1935-42 (300 papers), chiefly relating to his duties as counsel for the Government of Puerto Rico; Isaac Ro-

berdeau (Pa.; U. S. Army officer, engineer), 1818-29 (1 vol.), an unpublished treatise on canals; Henry Martyn Robert (U. S. Army office, parliamentarian), 1853-1927 (10 boxes), including notes relating to his Rules of Order; Paul McD. Robinett (Mo., D. C.; World Wars I and II Army officer), 1943-57 (1,100 pieces); Almon Ferdinand Rockwell (U. S. Army officer), 1854-98 (3 vols. and 13 boxes); John Rodgers (U. S. naval officer, head of Board of Navy Commissioners), 1775-1855 (33 vols. and 25 boxes), including family papers; John Loyall Saunders (U. S. naval officer), 1844-47 (3 vols.); Charles Lewis Scott (U. S. Army officer), 1905-54 (5,000 pieces); Hugh Lenox Scott (U. S. Army officer), 1870-1934 (130 boxes and 6 bundles); and Raphael Semmes (U. S. and Confed. naval officer), 1848-58 (1 vol.).

Papers of other Army and Navy officers include those of Frederick Dummer Sewall (U. S. Army officer), 1834-1904 (11 boxes), among them papers of his father, Joseph Sewall (Maine; collector of customs at Bath), 1834-35; Philip Henry Sheridan (U. S. Army officer), 1853-88 (122 vols. and 73 boxes); William Tecumseh Sherman (U. S. Army officer), 1820-96 (105 vols. and 16 boxes); George Sherwin Simonds (U. S. Army officer), 1895-1938 (51 boxes); Charles Stillman Sperry (U. S. naval officer), 1863-1911 (17 vols., 20 boxes, and 2 bundles); Thomas Stockton (Del.; U. S. Army officer, Gov.), 1783-1829 (3 vols.); Charles Pelot Summerall (S.C.; U. S. Army officer, pres. of The Citadel), 1917-53 (10,000 papers); Charles Crooke Suydam (U. S. Army officer), 1861-64 (1 box); Theodore Talbot (U. S. Army officer), 1845-61 (2 boxes); John R. Thomas (U. S. Army officer), 1898-99 (1 container), a collection of letters concerning relations with the insurrectionist government of the Philippines; Joseph C.

Thomas (Ill.; Civil War chaplain), 1863-68 (2 portfolios), relating chiefly to libraries established by the U.S. Christian Commission; Hoyt Sanford Vandenberg (U.S. Army officer, Air Force Chief of Staff), 20th century (21,000 pieces); Cadmus Marcellus Wilcox (U.S. and Confed. Army officer), 1861-65 (4 boxes); Charles Wilkes (U.S. naval officer, explorer), 1817-1910 (53 boxes and 3 portfolios); James Wilkinson (U.S. Army officer, Gov. of La. Terr.), 1792-1824 (1 vol. and 1 box); Edward Willis (S.C.; Confed. Army officer), 1860-65 (19 vols. and 1 box), including material on blockade running; James Harrison Wilson (U.S. Army officer, civil engineer), 1861-1920 (13 vols. and 76 boxes), including materials on railroad construction in the Mississippi Valley; Leonard Wood (physician, U.S. Army officer, military Gov. of Cuba, Gov. Gen. of the Philippines), 1825-1933 (42 vols., 246 boxes, and 4 rolls of maps), including diaries, 1873-1927 (25 boxes), and scrapbooks, 1898-1921 (37 vols.); and Clark H. Woodward (U.S. naval officer), 1926-50, consisting of copies of speeches, 1926-50, and weekly news commentaries on diplomatic and military developments, 1940-45. Papers of some Army officers who were members of the Air Corps or the U.S. Army Air Forces are in the Aeronautics Collection, described separately below.

Other United States Officials

Papers of U.S. diplomatic or consular officials include those of John Barrett (Vt., D.C.; Minister to Siam and 3 South American countries, Director Gen. of Pan-American Union), 1861-1938 (236 boxes); James Leander Cathcart (Pa.; consul and diplomatic agent), 1785-1817 (7 vols.); Charles Chaillé-Long (Md., Egypt, France; explorer, Egyptian Army officer, U.S. consular official), 1865-1915 (3 vols., 4 boxes, and 2 bundles); William P.

Chandler (Del.; consul at Tunis), 1854-56 (5 vols.), letter book of correspondence with other consuls and a 4-vol. diary; Joseph H. Choate (N.Y.; lawyer, Ambassador to Great Britain), 1861-1917 (39 vols. and 42 boxes); Charles D. Coxe (Pa., N.J.; consul at Tunis), 1806-9 (1 letter book); William S. Culbertson (Pa., D.C.; lawyer, economist, diplomat), 1906-58 (35,000 pieces); John Chandler Bancroft Davis (N.Y.; Asst. Sec. State, Minister to Germany, judge of U.S. Court of Claims), 1851-1903 (82 vols. and 7 boxes); Norman H. Davis (Cuba, N.Y.; financier, U.S. delegate to various international bodies), 1918-42 (93 boxes); Silas Deane (Conn.; Member Continental Cong., diplomat), 1775-84 (6 vols. and 1 box); Charles Monroe Dickinson (N.Y.; consul gen. in Turkey, diplomatic agent to Bulgaria), 1886-1924 (4 boxes); William E. Dodd (Va., Ill.; historian, prof. at Randolph-Macon College and Chicago Univ., Ambassador to Germany), 1900-40 (54 boxes); Andrew Jackson Donelson (Tenn.; sec. to Pres. Jackson, Minister to Prussia, newspaper editor), 1780-1943 (18 vols., 3 boxes, and 1 folder); William Eaton (Mass.; consul at Tunis, naval agent to Barbary States), 1801-8 (1 box); Benjamin Franklin (Pa.; printer, scientist, diplomat), 1726-90 (42 vols., 6 boxes, and 5 portfolios, including records of negotiations in London and of the U.S. Legation in Paris, 1777-82 (16 vols.); Harry F. Guggenheim (N.Y.; diplomat, business executive), 1920-33 (100 items), relating to aviation and his ambassadorship in Cuba; Florence Jaffray Harriman (N.Y.; Minister to Norway, international peace advocate), 1912-50 (10,000 items); Leland Harrison (N.Y.; Minister to Switzerland and other countries, Asst. Sec. State), 1915-47 (123 boxes), much relating to the Versailles Peace Conference (66 boxes); Edward M. House (Tex.; personal representative of Pres. Woodrow Wilson to European nations, member of the American Commission to Negotiate Peace), 1880-1921 (90 letters); Nelson Trusler Johnson (D. C.; Minister to China and Australia), 1916-50 (45 vols. and 2 boxes); William Beach Lawrence (N. Y., R. I.; Chargé d' Affaires in London), 1826-30 (4 vols.); Tobias Lear (N. H.; sec. to Pres. Washington, consul at Algiers), 1797-1813 (2 boxes); Charles William LeGendre (N. Y., Japan, Korea; consul at Amoy, China, adviser to Emperor of Japan and to King of Korea), 1868-92 (23 vols. and 11 boxes); and Breckinridge Long (Mo.; lawyer, Asst. Sec. State, diplomat), 1775-1944 (130 vols. and 86 boxes), including diplomatic reports, 1917-20 (62 vols.), and an autograph collection, 1775-1903 (2 boxes).

Among other papers of consular and diplomatic officials are those of John Mitchell (Pa.; U.S. consul in Cuba and Martinique, American agent at Halifax during War of 1812), 1810-99 (4 vols.); John Bassett Moore (N.Y., D. C.; international lawyer, Columbia Univ. Prof., diplomat), 1886-1947 (9 boxes and 100,000 items); Benjamin Moran (Pa., England; sec. to Pres. Buchanan, diplomat), 1851-86 (44 vols. and 1 box), including diaries (43 vols.); Roland Sletor Morris (Pa.; Univ. of Pa. prof., diplomat), 1910-43 (17 boxes); Thomas Henry Nelson (Ind.; Minister to Chile and Mexico), 1861-66 (2 vols.), letter books of the Legation in Chile; Nathaniel Niles (Mass., N. Y.; Sec. of Legation at Paris), 1802-80 (2 vols.); Walter Hines Page (N. C., N.Y.; journalist, Ambassador to Great Britain), 1885-1918 (4 boxes); James Shepherd Pike (Maine; journalist, author, Minister to the Netherlands), 1849-69 (1 box), chiefly letters to William Pitt Fessenden (Maine; U. S. Rep. and Sen., Sec. Treas.); Edward Lee Plumb (N. Y., D. C.; Sec. of Legation in Mexico, consul gen. at Havana), 1825-90 (22 vols. and 5 boxes); William P. Preble (Maine; diplomat, U. S. dist. attorney, railroad pres.), 1800-60 (1 box); William B. Reed (Pa.; lawyer, Minister to China), 1857-59 (1 vol. and 1 piece); Whitelaw Reid (Ohio, N. Y.; Minister to France and Great Britain, journalist), 1861-1912 (101 vols. and 179 boxes); Edmund Roberts (N. H.; merchant, diplomatic agent in the Far East), 1805-36 (10 vols. and 5 boxes); Jeremy Robinson (Mass.; U. S. agent at Lima and other South American ports), 1806-32 (7 vols. and 4 boxes); William Short (Va., Pa.; sec. to Pres. Jefferson, diplomat), 1778-1849 (53 vols. and 3 boxes); William Henry Trescot (S. C.; diplomat, historian), 1851-70 (1 box); Nicholas P. Trist (Va.; consul at Havana, special agent in Mexico), 1783-1873 (44 vols. and 11 boxes); David Bailie Warden (N. Y.; consul at Paris, author), 1800-43 (22 vols. and 12 boxes); John H. Wheeler (N. C.; Minister to Nicaragua, historian), 1854-1901 (12 boxes); Henry White (N. Y., D. C.; diplomat), 1857-1925 (14 vols. and 144 boxes), including materials on the Paris Peace Conference, 1919 (34 boxes); Brand Whitlock (Ohio; author, Ambassador to Belgium), 1900-34 (58 vols., 172 boxes, and 33 packages); and John Russell Young (N. Y., D. C.; journalist, Minister to China, Librarian of Congress), 1854-98 (34 vols. and 3 boxes).

Papers of U.S. officials not already mentioned include those of Alexander Dallas Bache (Pa., D. C.; physicist, Girard College pres., Supt. of U. S. Coast Survey), 1843-67 (12 vols. and 2 boxes); George F. Becker (Calif., D. C.; mining engineer, physicist, U.S. Geological Survey official), 1814-1928 (35 boxes); Wendell Berge (D. C.; Chief of Antitrust Division of Justice Dept.), 1930-47 (15 cartons); Samuel W. Boggs (N. Y., D. C.; State Dept. geographer), 1912-54 (6,000 items); Daniel Dodge Brodhead (Mass.; naval agent at Boston), 1821-52 (13 vols.); Charles Albert Browne (Mass., D.C.; Agriculture Dept. research chemist), 1895-1945 (37 boxes); Pierce Mason Butler (S. C.; Gov., Indian agent), 1843-45 (1 box), concerning his service as Cherokee agent; Frank Wigglesworth Clarke (Mass., Ohio; Univ. of Cincinnati prof., chief chemist of U.S. Geological Survey), 1865-1931 (7 boxes); William Edmund Curtis (N.Y.; lawyer, Asst. Sec. Treas.), 1885-1908 (11 vols. and 2 boxes); George Stanton Denison (Vt., La.; U.S. Treasury agent, surveyor of customs at New Orleans), 1851-84 (4 vols. and 1 box); Ernest G. Draper (N.Y.; Asst. Sec. Commerce, member of Federal Reserve Board), 1920-53 (3 containers); Samuel F. Emmons (Mass., Colo.; mining engineer, geologist), 1860-1911 (11,500 papers), including materials on the exploration of the 40th parallel, the "King Survey," 1867-77; Albert Kenrick Fisher (D.C.; U.S. Biological Survey zoologist, ornithologist), 1879-1943 (7,500 pieces); Benjamin B. French (N.H.; clerk of U.S. House of Rep., Commissioner of Public Buildings, promoter of the telegraph), 1826-70 (15 vols.); Emanuel Alexander Goldenweiser (D.C.; Federal Reserve Board economist), 1919-52 (1,500 papers), including correspondence pertaining to the Bretton Woods Conference and the British loan of 1945; Charles Summer Hamlin (Mass.; Asst. Sec. Treas., member of Federal Reserve Board), 1871-1950 (345 vols. and 3 boxes); William Torrey Harris (Mo., Mass., D.C.; philosopher, U.S. Commissioner of Education), 1865-1907 (49 boxes); Eugene Gano Hay (Ind., Minn.; U.S. dist. attorney, U.S. general appraiser), 1810-1933 (52 vols. and 38 boxes), including materials relating to tariff reciprocity with Canada; Ebenezer Hazard (N.Y., Pa.; editor of historical documents, Postmaster Gen.), 1643-1814 (17 boxes); Frank Lamson-Scribner (Tenn., D.C.; botanist, prof. at Univ. of Tenn., Agriculture Dept. official), 1888-1937, including some

letters, 1901-4, as Chief of Insular Bureau of Agriculture in the Philippine Islands; and Robert R. Livingston (N.Y.; Member Continental Cong., Sec. of Foreign Affairs, Minister to France), 1732-1823 (2 boxes and 1 folder).

Among papers of other U.S. officials are those of William John McGee (Iowa, D.C.; anthropologist and geologist), 1853-1916 (19 vols. and 52 boxes), including papers concerning his service with the Geological Survey and Bureau of American Ethnology, and papers of his wife, Anita Newcomb McGee, 1814-1929 (10 boxes), among them a collection pertaining to 19th-century communistic experiments in America; Clinton Hart Merriam (N.Y., D.C., Calif.; naturalist, Chief of U.S. Biological Survey), 1873-1938 (73 boxes), including journals, 1873-1938 (125 vols.), and manuscript Indian vocabularies; David Hunter Miller (N.Y., D.C.; international lawyer, author, special asst. to State Dept.), 1918-19 (20 transfer cases and 18 card trays), documents pertaining to the Paris Peace Conference and printer's copy of his diary; Frederick Haynes Newell (Pa., D.C., Ill.; engineer with the Geological Survey and Reclamation Service, Univ. of Ill. prof.), 1885-1931 (20 boxes); Theodore S. Palmer (D.C.; ornithologist, official of U.S. Biological Survey), 1887-1954, correspondence and diaries; Leo Pasvolsky (N.Y., D.C.; author, economist), 4,000 pieces relating to his work as Special Assistant to Secretary of State during World War II; Gifford Pinchot (Pa.; Chief of U.S. Forest Service, forestry prof. at Yale Univ., Gov.), 1872-1946 (3,301 boxes); Oliver Pollock (Pa.; U.S. commercial agent at New Orleans and Havana), 1767-88 (2 vols.); Henry Fowles Pringle (N.Y.; journalist, Columbia Univ. prof.), 1 packing box, relating to his World War II service with the Office of Facts and Figures and Office of War Information; John Robert Proctor (Ky.; geologist, U. S. Civil Service Commissioner), 1867-1903 (15 vols., 2 boxes, and 1 package); Donald Randall Richberg (Ill., D. C.; lawyer, National Recovery Administration Chairman), 2,500 items; Theodore Roosevelt, Jr. (N. Y.; author, Asst. Sec. Navy, Gov. Puerto Rico, Army officer in World Wars I and II), a large collection; Ainsworth R. Spofford (D. C.; Librarian of Congress), 1843-1909 (2 boxes); Charles Thomson (Pa.; Sec. Continental Cong.), 1765-1845 (5 vols. and 1 box); William Lee Trenholm (S. C.; U. S. Civil Service Commissioner, Comptroller of the Currency), 1865-1931 (3 vols. and 1 box); Joseph Sanford Wade (D. C.; Agriculture Dept. entomologist), 1913-54 (10 boxes); George Watterston (D. C.; publisher, Librarian of Congress), 1809-66 (3 vols. and 2 boxes); Harvey W. Wiley (Ind., D. C.; Purdue Univ. prof., chief chemist of Agriculture Dept.), 1854-1930 (239 boxes), including materials relating to his crusade for a pure food law; Walter Francis Willcox (N.Y., D. C.; statistician, Cornell Univ. prof., special agent with U. S. Census Bureau), 1886-1934 (35 boxes), including papers of Joseph Camp Griffith Kennedy (Pa., D. C.; superintending clerk of Census of 1850); Robert W. Woolley (Ky.; lawyer, Director of Mint, member of Interstate Commerce Commission), 1912-58 (3 vols. and 46 boxes); and George Wunderlich (Germany, D. C.; special counsel to U. S. State Dept.), 1904-51 (11 boxes), including materials on the German Empire, the Republic, and the Third Reich.

Scientists, Inventors, and Members of Learned Professions

Papers of physicians, scientists, and inventors include those of John James Audubon (Pa., Ky., La., N. Y.; artist, ornithologist), miscellaneous autograph letters; Evelyn Briggs Baldwin (Mo., D. C.; arctic explorer, meteorologist), 1883-1933 (36 boxes and 2 portfolios), including journals of the Wellman Polar Expedition, 1898-99 (3 vols.); James McKeen Cattrell (Pa., N. Y.; psychologist, prof. at Univ. of Pa. and Columbia Univ.), 1880-1940 (15,000 pieces); Lee De Forest (N. Y., Ill.; inventor, pioneer in wireless telegraphy and radio), 1891-1949 (23 diaries and 50 letters); Andrew Ellicott (Pa., N. Y.; surveyor, mathematician), 1777-1829 (1 vol. and 4 boxes), including reports on the Canadian boundary survey; John Ericsson (England, N. Y.; engineer, inventor, designer of the Monitor and other naval vessels), 1821-88 (11 boxes); John Fitch (N. J., Pa.; inventor), 1781-1826 (10 vols. and 1 package); Robert Fulton (N. Y.; civil engineer, inventor, artist), 1786-1814 (1 box), including a treatise on submarine navigation; Lewis R. Gibbes (S. C.; physician, scientist), 1793-1894 (15 vols., 1 box, and 1 package); Sigmund Freud (Austria, England; physician, psychoanalyst), a sealed collection of papers of and relating to Freud, deposited by the Sigmund Freud Archives; Irving Langmuir (N. Y.; chemist), 20th century (15,000 pieces); Crawford W. Long (Ga.; physician), 1835-1930 (1 box), concerning his use of anesthesia in surgical cases; Mahlon Loomis (Mass., Va.; dentist, pioneer in wireless telegraphy), 1858-86 (2 boxes), including notebooks and drawings; Waldo Lee McAtee (D. C.; ornithologist, U. S. Biological Survey official), 1842-1952 (1 vol., 83 boxes, 1 portfolio, and 22 envelopes), including his journals and diaries and letters from eminent American and European entomologists; and James MacBride (S. C.; physician, botanist), 1808-17 (1 vol.).

Among other papers of physicians, scientists, and inventors are those of Edward Maynard (D. C.; dental surgeon, inventor), 1845-58 (1 box), including papers relating to his improvements in firearms; John Campbell

Merriam (Calif., D. C.; paleontologist, Univ. of Calif. prof., pres. of Carnegie Institution), 1913-38 (50 cartons), including materials on the National Research Council; Harriet Mann Miller, known as Olive Thorne Miller (N.Y., Ill., Calif.; ornithologist, author), 1891-1909 (3 boxes); Merrill Moore (Tenn., Mass.; psychiatrist, poet), 20th century (30,000 pieces); Samuel F. B. Morse (Mass., N.Y.; artist, inventor of the telegraph), 1793-1877 (54 vols., 46 boxes, and 1 portfolio); Simon Newcomb (D. C., Md.; astronomer, prof. at Johns Hopkins Univ.), 1850-1935 (95 vols. and 246 boxes); Joseph N. Nicollet (France, Mo., D.C.; astronomer, explorer, cartographer), 1832-41 (8 vols. and 5 boxes), including reports on his surveys in the Mississippi and Missouri valleys; Joseph Priestley (England, Pa.; chemist, Unitarian theologian), 1789-1802 (68 letters in photostat); Frederick Ward Putnam (Mass., N.Y.; curator of Peabody Museum and the American Museum of Natural History), 1898-1932 (1 box); Henry Rowe Schoolcraft (N.Y., Mich.; explorer, ethnologist, supt. of Indian affairs for Mich.), 1809-79 (59 vols., 61 boxes, and 2 portfolios), including letters of his wife, 1870-78 (9 boxes); Richard Halstead Ward (N. Y.; physician, microscopist), 1852-1943 (12 boxes), including papers of his son Henry Baldwin Ward (Ill.; prof. of zoology at Ill. Univ.); and Harry B. Weiss (N.J.; entomologist), 1910-27 (300 letters). In the Toner collection, 1730-1912 (147 vols., 175 boxes, 1 roll, and 1 envelope), are volumes on medical matters and biographical materials on medical men, 1730-1890 (100 vols.), many volumes of miscellaneous Americana, 1745-1885, and the personal correspondence of Joseph Meredith Toner (D. C.; physician, writer, collector), 1856-1912 (54 boxes).

Papers of clergymen include those of Samuel John Baird (Ohio, Va.; Presbyterian minister, author), 1834-92 (5 vols.); Henry Ward Beecher (Ind., N. Y.; Congregational minister), 1838-85 (23 boxes), including letters concerning the status of Negroes, conditions at Andersonville prison, and the readmission of the seceded States to the Union; James Petigru Boyce (S.C., Ky.; Baptist minister, pres. of Southern Baptist Theological Seminary), 1854-88, 1907 (1 box); Charles Henry Brent (N. Y., Philippine Islands; Episcopal bishop), 1886-1929 (62 boxes), including material on the International Opium Commission, 1901-21; Samuel Warren Dike (Conn., Vt.; Congregational minister, reformer), 1885-1913 (26 boxes); Charles Hodge (N. J.; Presbyterian theologian, prof. at Princeton Theological Seminary), 1854-55 (3 vols.), lectures; Moses Hoge (Va.; Presbyterian minister, pres. of Hampden-Sydney College), 1752-1820 (1 vol. and 1 portfolio); Mercer Green Johnston (Episcopal clergyman, director of People's Legislative Service), 1887-1953 (32,000 pieces); Joshua Leavitt (Mass., N. Y.; Congregational minister, reformer, abolitionist), 1812-71 (1 box); Alexander J. McKelway (N. C.; Presbyterian minister), 1860-1932 (15 boxes), including his correspondence as secretary for the Southern States of the National Child Labor Committee, 1905-12 (5 boxes); James Madison (Va.; Episcopal Bishop of Va., pres. of William and Mary College), 1803-28 (1 box), copies; William Meade (Va.; Episcopal Bishop of Va.), 1822-62 (1 vol.); John Philip Newman (N. Y., D. C.; Methodist Episcopal bishop), 1869-1901 (1 box); Theodore Parker (Mass.; Unitarian minister, abolitionist), 1832-63 (1 box and 150 pieces); Matthew Simpson (Pa., Ill.; Methodist bishop), 1830-87 (34 boxes), including diaries; Hezekiah Smith (S.C., R. I., Mass.; Rev. War chaplain, Baptist minister), 1762-1805 (1 box and 1 portfolio); Samuel Francis Smith (Mass.; Baptist minister), 1883-98 (1 vol. and 1 box); Thomas De Witt

Talmage (N. Y., D. C.; Dutch Reformed clergyman, editor of the Christian Herald), 1865-1910 (2,500 pieces); Moses Waddel (S. C., Ga.; Presbyterian clergyman, educator), 1791-1829 (2 boxes); and George Whitefield (England, Ga.; Methodist minister), 1736-69 (2 vols.).

Papers of lawyers not already mentioned in some other capacity include those of Chandler Parsons Anderson (Conn.; lawyer, international mediator, editor of American Journal of International Law), 1914-29 (101 boxes); Harman Blennerhassett (Ohio; lawyer, associate of Aaron Burr), 1755-1866 (6 vols., 1 box, and 2 folders); John Leeds Bozman (Md.; lawyer, historian), 1669-1887 (3 vols. and 7 boxes), including papers of his nephew, John Leeds Kerr (Md.; U. S. Rep. and Sen.), and family papers relating to Baltimore trade with Philadelphia and London, 1711-22; Boris Brazol (Russia, N. Y.; lawyer, author, lecturer, criminologist), 1919-52 (1 vol. and 63 boxes); John D. Caton (Ill.; State chief justice), 1826-95 (40 boxes); Clarence S. Darrow (Ill.; lawyer, 1910-30 (1 vol. and 57 boxes), including drafts of his jury pleas and speeches; James William Denver (Calif.; lawyer, U. S. Rep., Gov. of Kans. Terr.), 1868-84 (5 vols.); Philip R. Fendall (D. C.; lawyer, author), 1806-60 (1 box); James Kent (N. Y.; State Chancellor, Columbia Univ. prof.), 1779-1847 (26 vols. and 1 package); Louis Theodore Michener (Ind.; lawyer, political manager of Benjamin Harrison), 1880-1924 (2 boxes); Alton Brooks Parker (N. Y.; State supreme court justice, Democratic nominee for Pres. in 1904), 1880-1924 (6,000 items); James Louis Petigru (S. C.; lawyer, Union Party leader), 1812-68 (2 vols.); Amos R. E. Pinchot (N. Y.; publicist), 1863-1943 (11 vols. and 260 boxes); José Ignacio Rodriguez (Cuba; lawyer, librarian, translator), 1840-1900 (183 boxes), including documents relating to claims filed with the

Spanish Treaty Claims Commission; Moorfield Storey (Mass.; lawyer, author, publicist), 1876-1929 (26 vols. and 17 boxes); Oliver P. Temple (Tenn.; lawyer, author), 1830-73 (2 boxes); and Peter Van Schaack (N.Y.; lawyer), chiefly 1792-1800 (1 box).

Papers of educators not already mentioned include those of Charles Butler (N. Y.; lawyer, philanthropist, pres. of Union Theological Seminary), 1819-94 (1 vol. and 5 boxes); Frances Joseph Campbell (Mass., England; educator of the blind, musician), 1876-1931 (35 boxes), including correspondence relating to the education of the blind in England; Edward Miner Gallaudet (Conn., D. C.; educator of the deaf) and his father, Thomas Hopkins Gallaudet (Conn.; educator of the deaf and dumb); Harry A. Garfield (Ohio; lawyer, pres. of Williams College, U. S. Fuel Administrator), 1884-1942 (76 boxes); William James Ghent (N.Y., D. C.; author, pres. of Rand School of Social Science), 1876-1942 (60 boxes); Julius Goebel (Calif., Ill.; prof. of Germanic philology and literature at Stanford Univ. and Univ. of Ill.), 1873-1930 (7 boxes); George Frederick Holmes (Va.; prof. of history and literature at Univ. of Va., writer), 1785-1893 (2 vols.); and Samuel Guy Inman (N. Y.; author, Columbia prof. of international law, lecturer), 1902-52 (42 boxes), including diaries. There is also the Kraus-Boelté collection, 1904-13, relating chiefly to the work of John Kraus and his wife Maria Kraus-Boelté (Germany, N. Y.; pioneers in kindergarten education and teacher-training).

Among other papers of educators are those of Francis Lieber (S. C., N. Y.; political scientist, prof. at S. C. College and Columbia Univ.), 1841-71 (3 vols. and 1 portfolio), also 1 vol. of Lieber's letters in the papers of James A. Garfield (Ohio; U. S. Pres.); Myrtilla Miner (N. Y., D. C.; founder of school for Negro

girls), 1839-1946 (5 boxes), dealing
with the operation of her school, 1839-
86, and including materials on Negro
education collected by Lester Grosve-
neur Wells (N. Y.; curator of special
collections at Syracuse Univ.); Samuel
C. Mitchell (S. C., Del., Va.; pres. of
Univ. of S. C. and Del. College, history prof. at Richmond Univ.), 1908-
13 (14 boxes and 4 bundles); Blaine
Free Moore (Kans., P. I., D. C.; political scientist, school official in Philippine Islands, prof. at Univ. of Kans.,
U. S. Gov't official), 1901-6 (50 letters
and 1 diary), written while he was in
Philippines; David Murray (N. J.; prof.
of mathematics and astronomy at Rutgers College, adviser on education in
Japan), 1870-79 (8 boxes and 2 portfolios), including papers concerning
conditions in Japan; Charles Eliot Norton (Mass.; editor, fine arts prof. at
Harvard Univ.), 1880-97 (2 vols.), including letters from Frederick Law
Olmsted (N. Y.; landscape architect);
William Orr (Mass.; director of education for the International Y. M. C. A.,
State deputy commissioner of education), 1900-36 (9 boxes); Ezra Stiles
(Conn., R. I.; Congregational clergyman, Yale College pres.), 1758-90 (4
vols.), transcripts of diary and miscellaneous papers; Ellery C. Stowell
(D. C.; prof. of international law at
American Univ.), 1802-1949 (14 vols.,
37 boxes, and 1 folder); James Strong
(N. Y., N. J.; Methodist layman, Biblical scholar, prof. at Drew Theological Seminary), 1867-1922 (1 box); Robert Heberton Terrell (D. C.; Negro
teacher, lawyer, jurist), 1889-1925;
Lester Frank Ward (D. C., R. I.; sociologist, prof. at Brown Univ.), 1883-
1906 (15 boxes); Booker T. Washington
(Ala.; founder of Tuskegee Institute),
1884-1922 (108 vols. and 1,215 boxes),
including official correspondence of the
Institute and correspondence of the National Negro Business League; and John
Witherspoon (Scotland, N. J.; Presbyterian minister, Member Continental

Cong., Princeton College pres.),
1758-83 (1 vol. and 1 box).

Papers of others working in intellectual fields include those of Victor
S. Clarke (Hawaii, D. C.; economist,
editor), 1930-39 (16 boxes), including
miscellaneous correspondence of or
relating to the Institute of Current
World Affairs; John Fiske (Mass.;
philosopher, historian), 1868-96 (2
boxes); John C. Fitzpatrick (D. C.; librarian, historical editor), 1928-39
(1 vol. and 32 boxes), chiefly relating
to George Washington (Va.; U. S. Pres.);
Peter Force (D. C.; historian, editor),
1812-68 (36 vols., 7 boxes, 7 portfolios, and 3 folders), chiefly relating
to his activities in compiling his American Archives, also the Force transcripts, 1756-1829 (44 vols., 416 boxes, and 37 folders), some of which are
noted elsewhere; Worthington C. Ford
(N. Y., Mass., D. C.; editor, historian), notes relating to his researches
(17 boxes); Count Adam de Gurowski
(Poland, D. C.; translator, historian),
1850-86 (2 vols. and 5 portfolios);
Dorsey W. Hyde, Jr. (N. Y., D. C.;
librarian, archivist), 1900-55 (42,000
pieces), including materials concerning his service with the National Archives, 1935-42; John Franklin Jameson (Md., R. I., Ill., D. C.; historian,
editor), 1867-1921 (181 boxes); William Dawson Johnston (D. C., Minn.;
librarian), 1880-1924 (16 boxes),
chiefly relating to the history of the
Library of Congress and the library
movement in the United States; Friedrich Kapp (Germany, N. Y.; German
revolutionist in 1849, historian), 1842-
84 (1 box); George Charles Keidel (Md.,
D. C.; author, editor, librarian) and
his family, 1863-1914 (4 vols., 5 boxes, and 1 package), including Civil
War letters received from Union prisoners, 1863-65; Edmund B. O'Calla-
ghan (Canada, N. Y.; historical editor), 1830-68 (21 vols.); James A.
Robertson (D. C., Fla., Md.; librarian, American history prof. at John B.

Stetson Univ., Md. State archivist), 1898-1939 (85 boxes), including materials on Hispanic-American history; and Benjamin Franklin Stevens (Vt., England; bookdealer, antiquarian), 1763-83 (181 vols.), his "Catalogue-Index" of manuscripts in foreign archives relating to America.

Persons Prominent in Literature, Journalism, and the Arts

Papers of literary figures include those of Gertrude Atherton (Calif.; novelist), 1889-1943 (2 boxes and 2 portfolios); Ray Stannard Baker, also known as David Grayson (Mass., Ill.; journalist, author), 1875-1948 (208 boxes and 2 portfolios), including documents relating to his biography of Woodrow Wilson, 1925-39 (78 boxes); Robert Browning (England; poet), 1851-1904 (2 boxes and 1 portfolio); Lyman Bryson (N.Y.; author, lecturer, educator), 20th century (3,900 pieces); Lewis Nathaniel Chase (Maine, N.Y.; critic, prof. of literature and poetry), 1895-1937 (224 boxes); John Vance Cheney (Calif., Ill.; poet, librarian), 1862-1928 (13 boxes and 1 portfolio); Samuel Clemens, better known as Mark Twain (Mo., Calif., N.Y., Conn.; humorist, novelist), 1859-1901 (1 portfolio), and a collection of letters by well known writers, referring to Clemens and to the International Mark Twain Society (2 boxes); John Esten Cooke (Va.; novelist), 1846-86 (3 boxes); Douglas Southall Freeman (Va.; newspaper editor, biographer), 1930-52 (50,000 pieces); Harold Frederic (N.Y., England; journalist, novelist), 1890-98 (4 boxes); Maxim Gorky (U.S.S.R.; short-story writer), 1922-38 (1 box), chiefly correspondence with Vladislav Khodasevich (U.S.S.R.; poet, literary critic); Louise Imogen Guiney (Mass., England; poet, essayist); 1885-1921 (8 boxes); Herman Hagedorn (N.Y.; critic, novelist, poet), 1860-1931 (33 boxes), including

notes relating to Leonard Wood (physician, U.S. Army officer) and William Boyce Thompson (Mont., N.Y.; mining operator); Lafcadio Hearn (Ohio, La., Japan; author, lecturer), 1877-1935 (11 boxes), including papers of George Milbry Gould (Pa.; physician, author), 1900-35; Oliver Wendell Holmes (Mass.; poet, essayist, prof. of anatomy at Harvard), 1846-94 (9 vols. and 2 boxes), and his letters to Esther Bernon Carpenter (R.I.; author), 1869-91 (1 box); Marquis James (N.Y.; journalist, biographer), 1921-55 (16,000 pieces); MacKinlay Kantor (Iowa, Calif.; journalist, novelist), 1912-57 (460 literary manuscripts and 2,000 letters); Charles Lanman (N.Y., Mich., D.C.; journalist, author), 1820-80 (2 vols.); James Russell Lowell (Mass.; poet, essayist), 1881-90 (34 pieces), plus some in the Ticknor Collection; Edwin Markham (Calif., N.Y.; poet, lecturer), 1879-1941 (30 boxes); John Masefield (England; poet laureate), 1932-34 (46 letters); James Albert Michener (Colo., Pa.; prof. of education, novelist, journalist), 1945-54 (24 boxes); George Pope Morris (N.Y.; journalist, poet), 1832-62 (1 folder); and Ellen Louis Chandler Moulton (Mass.; poet), 1880-1908 (51 vols.), including papers (2 vols.) of Philip B. Marston (England; poet).

Other papers of literary figures include those of Albert Jay Nock (N.Y.; author, editor), 1911-45 (5 boxes); Elizabeth Madox Roberts (Ky.; novelist, poet), 1912-40 (15 boxes and 1 portfolio); Kenneth Roberts (Maine; novelist, journalist), 1919-57 (15 boxes); Edwin Arlington Robinson (Maine, N.Y.; poet), 3 boxes, consisting of manuscript poems, and 47 letters; Edward Payson Roe (N.Y.; novelist, Presbyterian clergyman), 1869-87 (1 box); George Bernard Shaw (England; playwright, novelist, critic), 1892-1928 (1 box), photostats of letters to Ellen Terry (England; actress); Logan Pearsall Smith (N. J.; essayist, critic), 1883-1938 (3 vols. and 3 boxes); Margaret Bayard Smith (D.C.; author, society leader), 1789-1850 (16 vols. and 3 boxes); Edmund Clarence Stedman (N. Y.; poet, anthologist, stockbroker), 1871-1923 (1 box and 2 portfolios); Burton E. Stevenson (Ohio; author, anthologist, librarian), 1904-56 (8 containers), including biographical material on other authors and papers relating to Stevenson's service as European director of library war service in World War II; Albert Payson Terhune (N. Y.; novelist, short-story writer), 1894-1941 (18 boxes); Benjamin Ticknor (Mass.; publisher), 1805-1935 (25 vols., 2 boxes, and 1 portfolio), including literary manuscripts of prominent authors of the 19th century; Richard Henry Wilde (Ga.; lawyer, poet, U.S. Rep.), 1842 (6 boxes), consisting of literary manuscripts; and Owen Wister (Pa.; novelist, short-story writer), 1890-1930 (44 boxes and 1 portfolio).

In the Division's Poetry Archive, 19th and 20th centuries (21 vols., 45 boxes, and 42 portfolios), which was assembled by Joseph Auslander (Mass., N.Y.; poet, lecturer) as consultant in poetry at the Library of Congress, there are papers of William Blake (England; poet, artist), 1804-80 (1 box); Alfred Edward Housman (England; poet), 1910-39 (8 vols., 3 boxes, and 1 portfolio); Henry James (Mass., England; novelist), 1882-1915 (3 vols. and 1 box), including transcripts of letters to Sir Edmund William Gosse (England; literary critic, poet); George Sterling (Calif.; poet), 1916-42 (6 boxes); Henry David Thoreau (Mass.; essayist, poet), 1836 (1 vol. and 1 box); and Walt Whitman (N.Y., D.C., N.J.; poet), 1838-1941 (5 vols., 35 boxes, and 6 portfolios).

Papers of journalists and newspaper and magazine editors include those of Frederick Lewis Allen (Mass., N.Y.; editor of Harper's Magazine), 1913-54 (6,500 pieces), among them diaries,

1933-54; John Lloyd Balderston (N.Y.; war correspondent, editor of the Outlook), 1915-50 (2 boxes); James Gordon Bennett (N. Y.; editor and publisher of New York Herald), 1861-63 (1 box), chiefly letters to the editor from correspondents with McClellan's army; Francis Preston Blair (Ky., D. C.; journalist) and his partner, John Cook Rives (D. C.; journalist), 1815-88 (7 vols.), chiefly relating to the Washington Globe; Richard Rogers Bowker (N. Y.; editor, publisher), 1842-1931 (10 vols. and 5 boxes), including papers pertaining to international copyright; Matthew Heywood Campbell Broun, known as Heywood Broun (N.Y.; journalist, lecturer), 1912-38 (1 box); William Conant Church (N. Y.; journalist, author), 1862-1917 (2 boxes), chiefly relating to the Army-Navy Journal; Raymond Clapper (Kans., D. C.; journalist), 1910-44 (261 boxes), including diaries; Herbert Corey (Ohio, N. Y., D. C.; journalist, author), 20th century; George Creel (Mo., Colo., Calif.; newspaper editor, publicity director, author), 1896-1953 (31 boxes), including letters from Woodrow Wilson (N. J.; U.S. Pres.) and papers relating to Creel's services as Chairman of the Committee on Public Information during World War I; William Augustus Croffut (Conn.; author, newspaper editor), 1859-1930 (76 boxes), including papers relating to the Anti-Imperialistic League, 1890-1916 (5 boxes); Charles Anderson Dana (N. Y.; editor of New York Sun, Asst. Sec. War), 1859-82 (2 boxes and 1 portfolio), including dispatches to Edwin M. Stanton (Ohio; Sec. War), 1863-65; Elmer Davis (D. C.; journalist, radio news analyst, Office of War Information Director), 1893-1957 (7,800 items); Frederick Dixon (England, Mass., N. Y.; editor of the Christian Science Monitor), 1897-1923 (2 boxes), including correspondence as European manager of the Monitor; Finley Peter Dunne, known as

Mr. Dooley (Ill.; newspaper editor, humorist), 1889-1936 (1 box); Jonathan Elliott (D. C.; editor and publicist), 1822-25 (1 box); William Dudley Foulke (Ind.; newspaper editor, author, lawyer), 1885-1924 (16 boxes), including correspondence relating to the National Civil Service Reform League, 1923-24; Joseph Gales, Jr. (D. C.; journalist), 1806-67 (1 box), including papers of his partner, William Winston Seaton (D. C.; journalist), relating to the National Intelligencer; Horace Greeley (N. Y.; editor of New York Tribune, political leader), 1839-77 (10 vols. and 5 boxes); and Duff Green (Mo., D. C., Ga.; journalist, political leader, industrial promoter), 1716-1879 (2 vols., 3 boxes, and 2 portfolios).

Other papers of journalists and editors include those of William D. Hassett (D. C.; correspondent for Washington Post, White House sec.), 1930-45 (3 vols. and 160 pieces), including his diary, 1942-45; George Kennan (N. Y., D. C.; explorer, journalist, author, Russian scholar), 1867-1937 (100 boxes), including manuscripts relating to Russia, Japan, and China; Judson King (Tex., Ohio, D. C.; editor, lecturer, writer), 20th century (20,000 items); Hamilton Wright Mabie (N. Y.; editor and critic), 1871-1916 (1 vol.); Manton Malone Marble (Mass., N. Y.; newspaper editor, author, publisher), 1852-1916 (97 vols. and 14 boxes); George Fort Milton (Tenn., D. C.; editor, historian), 1927-45 (15,000 pieces); Louis F. Post (N. Y.; lawyer, newspaper editor), 1864-1928 (400 pieces); Joseph Pulitzer (Mo., N. Y.; newspaper editor and publisher, U. S. Rep. from N. Y.), 1870-1924 (25 vols. and 4 boxes); Thomas Ritchie (Va., D. C.; newspaper editor), 1824-54 (2 boxes); Anne N. Royall (Va., D. C.; journalist, author), 1817-22 (2 boxes); Charles Edward Russell (N. Y.; journalist, author), 1864-1941 (24 vols., 45 boxes, and 2 chests), including diaries kept in England, 1914-19; Franklin Benja-

min Sanborn (Mass.; abolitionist, journalist, biographer, philanthropist), 1857-79 (1 vol.); Eric Sevareid (Minn., Va.; radio news commentator, journalist, author), 1946-58 (10,000 items); George Washburn Smalley (Mass., N. Y.; journalist, war correspondent), 1895-1902 (1 vol.), letters to Millicent, Duchess of Sutherland; Ephraim George Squier (N.Y.; journalist, archeologist, diplomat), 1840-70 (11 vols. and 5 boxes), including materials relating to archeology in Central and South America; Nathaniel Wright Stephenson (Ohio; newspaper editor, author), 1810-64 (55 boxes, 6 bundles, and 4 envelopes); Mark Sullivan (D. C.; journalist, author), 20th century (200 items); Horace Traubel (N. J., Pa.; journalist, newspaper publisher, author), 20th century (2,700 items), including 1,700 cartoons assembled by Traubel covering both national and international affairs, 1899-1903; Stanley Washburn (Ill., N. J.; war correspondent, lecturer, author), 1912-45 (2 boxes); Henry Watterson (Ky.; newspaper editor, U. S. Rep.), 1863-1920 (34 vols. and 9 boxes); Charles Henry Webb, known as John Pol (N. Y., Calif.; journalist, publisher), 1839-1924 (3 vols.); Thurlow Weed (N. Y.; newspaper editor, political leader), 1823-94 (3 boxes), including letters from Francis Granger (N. Y.; U. S. Rep., Postmaster Gen.); and William Allen White (Kans.; newspaper editor, author), 1899-1944 (324 boxes).

Papers of architects include those of Benjamin Henry Latrobe (Pa., D.C.; architect, engineer), 1803-17 (3 vols. and 1 portfolio), including papers concerning the building of the U. S. Capitol; Pierre Charles L'Enfant (France, N. Y., D. C.; Rev. War officer, engineer, architect), 1791-1888 (2 boxes), among them reports, 1791-1805, on plans for the Federal city and letters, 1887-88, relating to efforts to erect a L'Enfant memorial, and the Digges-

L'Enfant-Morgan Collection, 1778-1912
(4 vols., 2 boxes, and 1 portfolio), containing papers of L'Enfant and documents relating to the planning of Washington; Charles F. McKim (N. Y.; architect), 1810-1928 (10 vols. and 23 boxes), including papers relating to the
American Academy in Rome; Robert
Mills (S. C., Pa., D. C.; architect, engineer), 1804-62 (2 vols. and 1 box);
Charles Moore (Mich., D. C.; Chairman of U. S. Fine Arts Commission,
writer), 1745-1937 (6 vols., 32 boxes,
2 folders, and 9 bundles), including
letters of James McMillan (Mich.; U.S.
Sen.), 1901-2 (1 vol.), and letters relating to the Senate Park Planning Commission, 1901-3 (1 vol.); Frederick Law
Olmsted (N. Y.; landscape architect),
1819-1923 (7 vols. and 65 boxes); and
William Thornton (Pa., D. C.; inventor,
architect), 1741-1858 (18 vols., 5 boxes, and 1 portfolio), relating in part to
the development of the steamboat and
the design of the Capitol in Washington.

Papers of persons notable in the
theater and other artistic fields include
those of Paul Wayland Bartlett (France,
N. Y., D. C.; sculptor), 1879-1925
(10,000 items); Gutzon Borglum (N. Y.;
sculptor), 1896-1945 (101 boxes); Henry Kirke Brown (Mass., N. Y.; sculptor);
John Singleton Copley (Mass., England;
painter), 1767-99 (1 box); Charlotte S.
Cushman (Mass.; actress), 1839-76 (21
vols., 4 boxes, and 1 package); Jo Davidson (N. Y.; sculptor), including pencil sketches and photographs of finished
works; Pierre Eugene Du Simitiere (Pa.;
portrait painter, antiquary, naturalist),
1738-84 (6 vols.); Mary H. Greenewalt
(N. Y.; pianist, manufacturer of light
and color players), 1919-51 (4 boxes);
Vinnie Ream Hoxie (D. C.; sculptor),
1850-1914 (12 boxes and 1 portfolio);
Anthony Lauck (Ind.; artist, clergyman); Lee Lawrie (Mass., Md.; sculptor), 1919-53 (3,000 pieces), relating
in part to the Century of Progress Exposition in Chicago and the New York

World's Fair, 1939; Richard Mansfield (N. Y., Mass.; Shakespearean actor), 1890-1900 (7 boxes); Joseph Pennell (Pa., England, N. Y.; etcher),
19th century (2 vols.); May Robson
(N. Y., Calif.; actress), 1882-1942 (39
vols., 22 boxes, and 2 portfolios); Augustus Saint-Gaudens (N. Y., N. H.;
sculptor), 1891-1917 (1 vol.), including correspondence with Daniel H.
Burnham (Ill.; architect), John Trumbull (Conn., N. Y.; historical painter),
1786-1836 (2 vols. and 2 boxes); and
Marshall Pinckney Wilder (N. Y.; humorist, entertainer), 1880-1910 (1 vol.
and 10 boxes).

Other Individuals

Papers of reformers not previously mentioned include those of Susan B.
Anthony (N. Y.; suffragist, reformer),
1848-1934 (9 boxes and 2 portfolios),
including materials pertaining to the
woman-suffrage movement; Clara Barton (Mass., D. C.; philanthropist,
founder of American Red Cross), 1834-
1918 (30 vols., 42 boxes, and 2 portfolios); James Gillespie Birney (Ky.,
Ala., N. Y., Mich.; antislavery leader), 1830-50 (1 box), diary and notes;
Mabel Thorp Boardman (Ohio, D. C.;
sec. of American Red Cross), 1853-
1935 (16 boxes and 1 portfolio), including letters from William Howard
Taft (Ohio; U. S. Pres.); Sophonisba
Preston Breckinridge (Ky.; social
worker), 1750-1949 (1 vol. and 38
boxes); John Brown (N. Y., Kans.,
Mass.; abolitionist), 1851-1928 (2 boxes), including letters, relating to
Brown, written to Henry Alexander
Wise (Va.; Gov., U. S. Rep.); Anna
Elizabeth Dickinson (Pa.; feminist,
author, lecturer), 1860-1932 (66 boxes and 1 portfolio); Olivia B. Hall
(Mich.; suffragist), 1869-1905 (300
pieces), including 70 letters from Susan B. Anthony; Ida Husted Harper
(Ind., N. Y.; suffrage leader, journalist), 1916-18 (7 boxes); Julia Ward

Howe (Mass.; abolitionist, feminist, author), 1861-1917 (11 boxes); John A. Kingsbury (N. Y.; social worker, commissioner of charities and correction), 1902-35 (12,000 pieces); Benjamin B. Lindsey (Colo., Calif.; juvenile court judge in Denver, judge of Calif. superior court), 1890-1944 (352 boxes); Benjamin C. Marsh (Pa., N. Y., D. C.; sec. of the People's Reconstruction League and the People's Lobby), 1910-50 (6 boxes); Jacob A. Riis (N. Y.; journalist, author, reformer), late 19th and early 20th centuries (2,500 items); Margaret Sanger (N. Y.; leader of birth-control movement), 1910-50 (271 boxes); Elizabeth Cady Stanton (N. Y.; reformer, suffrage leader), 1814-1901 (11 vols. and 9 boxes); Lewis Tappan (Mass., N. Y.; merchant, abolitionist), 1809-70 (13 boxes); Mary Church Terrell (D. C.; Negro reformer, suffrage leader), 1897-1954 (14,000 pieces), including her autobiography and diaries; Elizur Wright (Ohio, Mass.; reformer, editor of abolitionist periodicals, actuary), 1817-95 (25 vols., 5 boxes, and 1 package); and Frances Wright (England, N. Y.; reformer, lecturer), 1843-96 (1 box).

Papers of merchants include those of Thomas Amory (S. C., Mass.; merchant, trader, shipbuilder) and his family, 1711-1804 (9 boxes), with materials on the West Indian trade; Seth Barton (Md.; Baltimore merchant), 1781-1876 (1 box), including papers of Daniel Jenifer (Md.; U. S. Rep., Minister to Austria); Samuel Blodget, Jr. (N. H., Pa., D. C.; merchant, economist, architect), 1758-1813 (1 box); Sylvanus Bourne (Mass.; merchant, U. S. consul at Amsterdam), 1775-1859 (39 vols. and 1 box); Levinus Clarkson (S. C.; Negro merchant), 1772-93 (1 box and 1 portfolio); Edward Dixon (Va.; merchant at Port Royal), 1743-96 (37 vols.); Neil Jamieson (Va., N. Y.; Norfolk merchant, loyalist), 1757-89 (23 vols. and 2 envelopes); John Lloyd (Va.; Alexandria merchant), 1794-1888 (52 vols. and 12 boxes); Abiel Abbot Low (Mass.; merchant), 1829-73 (7 boxes), including correspondence of his firm relating to the Chinese and Japanese trade; Nicholas Low (N. Y.; merchant, land speculator), 1783-1865 (12 vols. and 167 boxes), including papers of his brother, Isaac Low (N. Y.; merchant, Member Continental Cong., loyalist); Jonathan Meredith (Md.; Baltimore merchant), 1795-1859 (34 vols., 5 boxes, and 2 folders), relating to South American trade; Robert Curtis Ogden (Pa.; merchant, pres. of Southern Education Board), 1843-1923 (5 vols. and 40 boxes); and William Taylor (Md.; Baltimore merchant), 1775-1856 (67 vols., 29 boxes, and 3 packages). There are also many other papers of merchants and mercantile firms, particularly for the late 18th and early 19th centuries. Some of these are mentioned among family papers, below.

Papers of bankers, financiers, and industrialists include those of William Waldorf Astor (N. Y., England; financier, journalist), 1904-10 (1 box); Wharton Barker (Pa.; banker, financial agent for Russia), 1870-1920 (12 vols. and 27 boxes), including correspondence on investments in China and Russia; Nicholas Biddle (Pa.; statesman, financier), 1655-1933 (119 vols. and 2 boxes), including his correspondence as president of the Second Bank of the United States; Alexander Brown (Md.; banker, merchant, shipowner), 1796-1884 (266 vols.), chiefly records of the Baltimore banking firm he founded; George William Burton (Wis.; banker), 1908-30 (2 vols. and 1 box), including correspondence with William Howard Taft (Ohio; U. S. Pres.); Andrew Carnegie (Pa., N. Y.; industrialist, philanthropist), 1803-1930 (244 vols. and 133 boxes), relating in part to the American steel industry and to international peace; William Wilson Corcoran (D. C.; financier, philanthropist, founder of

Corcoran Art Gallery), 1791-1888 (101 vols. and 2 boxes); William Gregg (S. C.; cotton manufacturer), 1847-1927 (2 boxes and 1 portfolio), also microfilm copies of papers in possession of the Graniteville Co., Graniteville, S. C., 1847-65; George F. Peabody (Ga., N. Y.; banker, director of General Education Board, philanthropist), 1894-1936 (75 boxes), including correspondence concerning his service as director of the Federal Reserve Bank in New York City, 1914-21 (3 boxes); William Polk (N. C.; Rev. War officer, pres. of N. C. State bank), 1767-1868 (106 pieces); Alexander R. Shepherd (D. C.; investor, Terr. Gov. of D. C.), 1847-1943 (3 vols. and 13 boxes), including papers relating to mining in Mexico; Daniel Augustus Tompkins (S.C., N.C.; industrial leader, newspaper publisher), 1889-1920 (12 boxes); and George A. Trenholm (S. C.; cotton broker, financier, Confed. Sec. Treas.), 1853-97 (4 vols.).

Papers of foreigners, not mentioned elsewhere, who have played an important part in the history of the United States include those of Philippe Jean Bunau-Varilla (France, Panama; engineer, Minister from Panama to U. S.), 1884-1940 (59 boxes), including papers relating to the Panama Canal and the creation of the Republic of Panama; Sir George Cockburn (England; naval officer), 1788-1847 (82 vols.), including logbooks, journals, and fleet orders for the War of 1812; Michel-Guillaume Jean de Crèvecoeur (France; essayist, consul at New York), 1783-88 (1 box), transcripts and microfilm; Charles William Frederick Dumas (Holland; agent for Continental Cong.), 1775-93 (2 vols.), including letters from John Adams (Mass.; U. S. Pres.) and his wife Abigail, and from Thomas Jefferson (Va.; U. S. Pres.); Augustus John Foster (England; British Minister to U.S.), 1794-1844 (8 vols. and 7 boxes), including diaries, 1798-1844; Christopher French (British Army of-

ficer), 1756-76 (3 vols.), relating to the French and Indian War and the American Revolution; Edmond Charles Genêt (France, N. Y.; French Minister to U. S.), 1750-1832 (10 vols., 92 boxes, and 11 bundles), including official and private manuscripts of his father, Edmé Jacques Genêt of the French Foreign Office; John Holker (France; French consul at Philadelphia), 1777-1822 (40 vols.); Andrault, Comte de Langeron (France; Army officer), 1761-89 (5 vols.), correspondence and documents showing French participation in the American Revolution; Philip Mazzei (Va., Poland; horticulturist, agent for Va. in Europe), 1773-1817 (1 vol. and 2 boxes); Charles Jules, Comte de Menou (France; Chargé d'Affaires in Washington), 1821-26 (1 box); John de Neufville and Son (Holland; merchants), 1779-85 (2 vols.); Marquis Phillippe Henri de Segur (France; Minister of War), 1780-87 (3 portfolios); and Anne Louis de Tousard (U. S. Army officer, vice consul of France at New Orleans and other cities), 1810-28 (1 box).

Papers of other individuals include those of Leonard Porter Ayres (D. C., Ohio; director of education and statistics of the Russel Sage Foundation, War Dept. statistician in World War I), 1919-44 (200 items), including journals dealing with his work on the Dawes Commission on German Reparations (1924); Daniel Carter Beard (N. Y.; organizer of Boy Scout movement in U. S., painter, author), 1808-1941 (3 vols., 435 boxes, 4 packages, 2 chests, and 1 trunk), including correspondence with Boy Scout headquarters and files of his outdoor school and camp; Otto Sternoff Beyer (Kans., Va.; consulting engineer), 1915-48 (30,000 papers), many relating to labor-management relations; Christopher Carson, known as Kit Carson (N. Mex.; trapper, Indian agent, U. S. Army officer), 1863-64 (1 box), including a letter book of the

Navajo expedition; Robert "councillor" Carter (Va.; planter), 1774-1805 (16 vols.); Cyrus B. Comstock (Mass.; Civil War officer, civilian engineer), 1855-1909 (9 vols., 1 box, and 1 portfolio), chiefly concerning engineering operations around Vicksburg and postwar improvements on the Mississippi; Laura Dreyfus-Barney (D. C., France; lecturer, member of League of Nations committees, author), 1931-54 (15,000 items); Albert Fink (Ky., Ga.; engineer, "father of railway economics"), 1875-85 (6 boxes), including materials on railroad bridges; John P. Frey (Minn., Ohio; labor leader), 1903-51 (27 boxes), concerning the American Federation of Labor and Frey's work as labor adviser on Government committees; Hugh Gaine (N. Y.; printer and bookseller), 1779-81 (1 vol.), concerning the British occupation of New York City; Joseph Galloway (Pa., England; colonial statesman, loyalist), 1758-81 (2 vols.); Rebecca Gratz (Pa.; philanthropist), 1797-1860 (1 box); Lewis M. Haupt (Pa.; engineer), 1863-1924 (8 boxes), including papers relating to his work on the Nicaragua Canal project; and Edith B. Helm (D. C.; White House social sec.), 1918-53 (25 boxes), including materials relating to the Peace Conference, 1918-19, and scrapbooks concerning social functions at the White House, 1933-53.

Among papers of still other individuals are those of John Henry (Mass., Vt.; Canadian secret agent in New England), 1809-12 (1 vol.); Irwin Hood Hoover (D. C.; White House chief usher), 1909-33 (11 boxes), consisting of memorabilia of White House affairs, memoranda concerning President Wilson's visit to France, 1918-19, and notebooks and diaries with observations on the Presidents from Benjamin Harrison to Herbert Hoover; Henry Hotze (Confed. consul gen. in London), 1861-65 (1 vol. and 2 boxes); Robert C. Ingersoll (Ill., D.C., N. Y.; lawyer, Civil War officer, agnostic lecturer and writer), 1858-1939 (135 boxes and 2 portfolios); Helen Keller (Conn.; deaf and blind author, lecturer), 1921-54 (2 boxes); Frederick West Lander (Mass., Vt.; civil engineer, Civil War officer, explorer), 1849-62 (10 vols. and 1 box), and his wife, Jean Margaret Davenport Lander (England, Mass., D. C.; actress), 1836-69 (3 boxes); George Mason (Va.; planter, Rev. War statesman), 1763-91 (1 vol.); John Purroy Mitchel (N. Y.; lawyer, mayor of New York City), 1882-1932 (55 boxes and 16 scrapbooks), chiefly relating to municipal reform, 1906-17; John Nicholson (Pa.; State comptroller gen., land-company promoter), 1786-1865 (3 boxes), relating in part to the Pennsylvania Land Co.; Nathaniel Brown Palmer (Conn.; sea captain, Antarctic explorer), 1797-1906 (18 boxes), including logs of Antarctic cruises, 1820-43; Phineas P. Quimby (Maine; pioneer in mental healing), 1861-65 (6 boxes), including papers of Mary Baker Eddy (Mass.; founder of the Christian Science Church); Kermit Roosevelt (N. Y.; businessman, explorer, engineer, writer), 1920-38 (87 boxes), including correspondence concerning steamship lines, the merchant marine, and the U. S. Shipping Board; Andrew Talcott (Va., N. Y.; U. S. Army officer, civil engineer), 1865-66 (1 box); Nicholas Van Dyke (Del.; Member Continental Cong., Pres. of Del.), 1780-93 (1 vol.); Meschech Weare (N. H.; chief justice and Pres. of N. H.), 1169-1807 (3 vols. and 1 box); and David Ames Wells (Conn.; free-trade economist, author), 1795-1899 (23 vols. and 1 box).

Family Papers

Among the papers of notable families, many of whom were prominent in commerce, and of a few business firms are the Bancroft-Bliss papers, 1802-1928 (1 vol. and 37 boxes), in-

cluding papers of George Bancroft
Mass.; historian, Sec. Navy, diplomat) and Alexander Bliss (Mass.; lawyer); the Barnard family of Connecticut and New York, 1757-1890 (5 boxes), including papers relating to Washington's army in Virginia and trade
with the West Indies; the Blair and allied families, 1785-1923 (80 vols., 157
boxes, and 30 bundles), including papers of Francis Preston Blair (Ky.,
D. C.; banker, journalist), his sons,
Francis Preston Blair, Jr. (Ky.; U.S.
Rep. and Sen.), and Montgomery Blair
(Mo., Md.; lawyer, Postmaster Gen.),
and Levi Woodbury (N. H.; Gov., U.S.
Sen., Sec. Navy, Sec. Treas., U.S.
Supreme Court Justice); the Bradley
family of Vermont, including Stephen
Row Bradley (Vt.; Rev. War officer,
U.S. Sen.), William Czar Bradley (Vt.;
State legislator, U.S. Rep.), and Mark
Richards (Vt.; U.S. Rep., Lt. Gov.);
the Breckinridge family, 1752-1934
(637 vols., 429 boxes, 63 bundles, and
2 chests), including papers of John
Breckinridge (Ky.; U.S. Sen., Attor-
ney Gen.), his sons, John Breckinridge, Jr., and Robert Jefferson
Breckinridge (Ky.; Presbyterian ministers), and his grandsons, William
Campbell Preston Breckinridge (Ky.;
U.S. Rep.) and John Cabell Breckinridge (Ky.; U.S. Rep. and Sen., Vice
Pres., Confed. Sec. War); the Burlingame family, 1810-1922 (5 boxes),
including papers of Anson Burlingame
(Mass.; U.S. Rep., Minister to China)
and his son Edward Livermore Burlingame (N. Y.; editor of Scribners
Magazine); and the Campbell-Preston
families of Virginia, 1741-1925 (11
vols. and 6 boxes). There is also the
Causten-Pickett Collection, 1777-1937,
records of and assembled by a law
firm established to handle French
spoliation claims of American citizens.

Other family and business papers
include those of the Clay family, 1737-
1928 (33 vols. and 39 boxes), includ-

ing papers of Henry Clay (Ky.; U.S.
Rep. and Sen., Sec. State) and his son
James Brown Clay (Ky.; U.S. Rep.);
Stephen Collins and Son (Philadelphia
merchants), 1749-1857 (90 vols. and
86 boxes); the New Jersey manufacturing firm of Cooper, Hewitt and Co.,
1840-1902 (218 vols. and 374 boxes),
including papers of Peter Cooper (N.Y.;
inventor, philanthropist) and Abram S.
Hewitt (N. Y., N. J.; manufacturer,
philanthropist, U.S. Rep. from N. Y.),
relating to the management of their
iron works and glue factory; the Cranch
family, 1758-1882 (1 vol. and 1 box),
including letters of William Cranch
(Mass., D. C.; U.S. circuit court judge);
the Decatur House, 2,000 items, consisting largely of the papers of Edward
Fitzgerald Beale (D. C., Calif.; U.S.
naval officer, pioneer, Minister to
Austria-Hungary), and Truxtun Beale
(Calif., D. C.; rancher, diplomat), but
containing some papers of Stephen Decatur (Pa.; U.S. naval officer) and
Thomas Truxton (Pa.; U.S. naval officer), and other members of the family; Dutilh and Wachsmuth (Pa.; Philadelphia merchants), 1784-97 (2 boxes and 1 portfolio), including material
on the African slave trade; the Ellis-
Allan papers, of the firm of John Allan (Va.; merchant at Richmond, un-
cle of Edgar Allan Poe), 1795-1889
(615 vols., 2 portfolios, and 11 packages); the Ewing family of Ohio, 1769-
1949 (159 vols. and 350 boxes), including papers of Thomas Ewing (Ohio;
U.S. Sen., Sec. Treas., Sec. Interior) and his son, Thomas Ewing, Jr.
(Ohio, Kans., N. Y.; chief justice of
Kans., Civil War officer, U.S. Rep.
from Ohio); the Fleetwood family,
1797-1903 (4 boxes and 2 portfolios),
including war letters and diaries of
Christian Abraham Fleetwood (Md.;
Negro Civil War sergeant); the Gal-
loway-Maxcy-Markoe family of Maryland, 1658-1888 (79 vols. and 12 boxes), including papers of Samuel and
John Galloway (Md.; merchants),

1738-1820, and of Vergil Maxcy (Md.; U. S. Solicitor of the Treasury), 1815-36; and the Garrett family, Baltimore merchants, 1820-80 (10 vols. and 178 boxes), including papers of John Work Garrett (Md.; banker, railroad pres.), relating to the Baltimore and Ohio Railroad and mercantile affairs in Baltimore. There are also the Gregg Collection, 1716-1916 (4 vols. and 3 boxes), including papers of Andrew Gregg (Pa.; U. S. Rep. and Sen.), his grandson David McMurtrie Gregg (U. S. Army officer), and Frederick Augustus Conrad Muhlenberg (Pa.; Lutheran clergyman, Member Continental Cong., U. S. Rep.); and papers of the Hale family of Massachusetts, 1843-1914 (15 boxes), including papers of Nathan Hale (Mass.; newspaper editor, railroad pres.) and his son Edward Everett Hale (Mass.; Unitarian minister, author); Patrick Henry (Va.; lawyer, Member Continental Cong., Gov.), 1762-1881 (1 box), and his family; the Hopkinson family, 1762-1876 (6 portfolios, 1 package, and a scrapbook), including correspondence of Francis Hopkinson (N. J., Pa.; Member Continental Cong., judge of Pa. admiralty court) and many others; William Henry Hunt (La., D. C.; jurist, Sec. Navy, Minister to Russia), and his son Gaillard Hunt (D. C.; State Dept. official, Chief of Manuscript Div., Library of Congress, historical writer), 500 items on microfilm; and the Jones family of Virginia, 1662-1890 (35 vols. and 6 boxes), including papers of Thomas Jones (Va.; planter, merchant, large landowner), dating from 1702, and a second Thomas Jones (Va.; merchant, Northumberland County clerk), 1750-1800.

Among other family papers are those of the Latimer family, 1679-1892 (7 vols. and 43 boxes), chiefly relating to American trade with China; the Lee family, 1753-1927 (4 boxes), including papers pertaining to ciphers used, 1776-79, by Arthur and Richard Henry Lee; the McCook family of Ohio, 1861-72 (1 vol., 19 boxes, and 1 portfolio), including papers of Anson George McCook (Ohio, N. Y.; Civil War officer, U. S. Rep. from N. Y., newspaper editor); and the Morgenthau family, 1834-1941 (39 vols. and 48 boxes), including papers of Henry Morgenthau, Sr. (N. Y.; financier, Ambassador to Turkey and Mexico). There are also the Morris-Popham Collection, 1667-1872 (4 boxes), including papers of Richard Morris (N.Y.; State supreme court chief justice), 1760-1808, and his son-in-law William Popham (N. Y.; Rev. War officer), 1810-49, and papers of the Peckham family, 1857-1909 (4 containers), including papers of Wheeler Hazard Peckham (N. Y.; U. S. dist. attorney) and his brother Rufus Wheeler Peckham (N. Y.; U. S. Supreme Court Justice); the Pinckney family, 1694-1866 (5 vols. and 52 boxes), including papers of Charles Cotesworth Pinckney (S. C.; Rev. War officer, Minister to France), and his brother Thomas Pinckney (S. C.; Rev. War officer, Gov., Minister to Great Britain, U. S. Rep.), and of Charles Pinckney (S. C.; Member Continental Cong., Gov., U.S. Rep. and Sen.) and his son Henry Laurens Pinckney (Ky.; U. S. Rep.); the Polk family of North Carolina, 1767-1859 (2 vols.), including letters to William Polk (N. C.; Rev. War officer); the Randolph family, 1742-1869 (5 vols. and 42 boxes), including papers of John Randolph of Roanoke (Va.; U. S. Rep. and Sen.); the Redington family, 1820-60 (1,500 pieces), including papers concerning the Northern Railroad; the Read family, 1568-1906 (6 vols. and 2 boxes), including papers of John Read (Pa., N. J.; lawyer, director of the Philadelphia Bank); and the Redfield family, 1821-1932 (3 boxes), including papers of William C. Redfield (Conn., N. Y.; saddle and harness maker, meteorologist, transportation promoter), 1821-56, and his grandson

William Cox Redfield (N.Y.; manufacturer, U.S. Rep., Sec. Commerce),
1882-1932.

Still other family papers include
those of the Riggs family, 1813-1944
(240 vols. and 322 boxes), including
records of the Riggs banking interests
in Washington, D.C., and papers of
the allied Corcoran family; Thomas
Rodney (Del., Miss.; Member Continental Cong., State supreme court
justice, U.S. judge for Miss. Terr.),
1771-1824 (2 vols., 11 boxes, and 2
folders), including papers of Caesar
Rodney (Del.; Member Continental
Cong., Pres. of Del.) and Caesar Augustus Rodney (Del.; U.S. Rep. and
Sen., U.S. Attorney Gen.); the Shaw
family of Massachusetts, 1768-1857
(2 boxes), including letters of Abigail
Adams (Mass.; wife of Pres. John Adams) and William Smith Shaw (Mass.;
sec. to Pres. John Adams, librarian
of Boston Athenaeum); the Shelby family, 1738-1863 (8 vols.), including papers of Evan Shelby (Va.; Rev. War officer) and his son Isaac Shelby (Va.,
Ky.; Rev. War and War of 1812 officer, Gov. of Ky.); the Shippen family,
1693-1936 (2 vols., 31 boxes, and 2
portfolios); the Short, Harrison,
Symmes, and allied families, 1784-
1862 (1 vol. and 61 boxes), including
papers of Charles Wilkins Short (Ky.;
physician, botanist), William Short
(Va., Pa.; diplomat), William Henry
Harrison (Ohio; U.S. Rep. and Sen.,
U.S. Pres.), and John Cleves Symmes
(N.J., Ohio; Member Continental Cong.,
Northwest Terr. judge); and the Singleton family of South Carolina, 1758-1860
(4 boxes). There are also the J. Henley Smith Collection, 1686-1903 (4 vols.,
2 boxes, and 1 portfolio), including papers of Jonathan Bayard Smith (Pa.;
Member Continental Cong.) and his son
Samuel Harrison Smith (Pa., D.C.;
journalist, banker, author), with many
papers of Tobias Lear (N.H.; sec. to
Pres. Washington, consul at Algiers)
among the papers of the elder Smith;

papers of the Walsh-McLean family,
1870-1940 (87 boxes and 10 file drawers), including papers of Thomas F.
Walsh (Colo.; mining operator) and
his daughter Evelyn Walsh McLean
(D.C.; hostess); the Wigfall family of
South Carolina, 1858-1909 (7 boxes),
including papers of Louis Trezevant
Wigfall (Tex.; Confed. Army officer
and Sen., U.S. Sen.), 1858-68 (1 box);
and the Willard family, 1851-1924 (83
boxes and 5 bundles), including records relating to the Willard Hotel
and other business ventures in Washington and papers of Joseph Edward
Willard (Va.; lawyer, Spanish-Am.
War officer, Ambassador to Spain).

Subject Collections and Organization-al Records

Among the Division's many collections on special subjects is the extensive Aeronautics Collection. Included are papers of Maxwell Frank
Andrews (U.S. Air Force officer),
1920-42 (8,000 items); Henry Harley
Arnold (U.S. Air Force officer),
1930-50 (10 footlockers); Octave Cha-
nute (Ill., Kans.; civil engineer, aerial navigator), 1860-1910 (25 vols. and
18 boxes); Alfred Hildebrandt (Germany), 1900-45 (24 vols. and 438 envelopes); Frank Samuel Lahm (Ohio;
businessman, aeronaut) and his son
Frank Purdy Lahm (U.S. Army officer), 1906-44 (3 boxes and 1 portfolio); Charles Augustus Lindbergh
(Nebr., N.Y., Conn.; aviator, author),
1930-50 (36 boxes), including charts
and logs used in his transatlantic
flight, manuscripts of his book, and
literary manuscripts of his wife, Anne
Morrow Lindbergh (Mass., Conn.; author); Grover C. Loening (N.Y., Fla.;
aircraft engineer), 20th century; Elwood R. Quesada (U.S. Air Force officer), 1927-51 (6 boxes and 1 package); Igor I. Sikorsky (Russia, Conn.;
designer and engineer of airplanes
and helicopters); Carl Spaatz (U.S.

Air Force officer), 1922-48 (56 filing drawers); Oscar Ursinus (Germany; editor of aeronautical journal), 1909-43 (14 boxes); and Orville and Wilbur Wright (Ohio; pioneers in aviation), 1881-1948 (95 boxes and 3 portfolios), including detailed notes of experiments. There are also records of the President's Aircraft Board (the Morrow Board), 1924-46 (2 boxes); records of the Daniel Guggenheim Fund for the Promotion of Aeronautics, Inc., 1926-30 (100 folders); and a collection of French documents earlier than 1900, made by Albert and Gaston Tissandier (France; aeronauts), 700 items.

Other collections are a collection on forestry, 1902-36 (10 boxes), including papers of several members of the U.S. Forest Service; a collection on Indians, 1724-1900 (10 vols., 19 boxes, and 2 portfolios), including Indian vocabularies and documents relating to rock cuttings of the Sioux and Chippewa Nations and to various other tribes; a Marine Miscellany, 1710-1937 (20 vols. and 25 boxes), including journals of voyages to the South Seas, Antarctica, and India, and logbooks of whaling vessels; a group of "Negro papers," 1734-1944 (22 boxes), including materials collected by Carter Godwin Woodson (Va.; author, editor of Journal of Negro History) relating to the Negro in the United States, 1804-1927; and some miscellaneous "slave papers," 1719-1860 (2 boxes and 4 portfolios). Among collections relating to church organizations are a "religion miscellany," 1067-1941 (25 vols., 15 boxes, 3 portfolios, and 3 bundles), including articles and confessions of faith, sermons, notes on church history, and a history of Mormonism by William H. Whitsitt (Tenn., Ky., Va.; pres. of Southern Baptist Theological Seminary); transcriptions of Mormon diaries and journals, 1830-70 (18 boxes), the originals of which are in various towns in Utah; and a collection relating to Shakers, 1797-1893 (84

boxes), the larger part of which consists of records of Shaker communities in Ohio, 1805-93 (57 boxes). A "science miscellany," 1559-1922 (52 vols., 25 boxes, and 1 portfolio), includes manuscript and published copies of treatises (many with hand-colored plates dealing with alchemy, astronomy, mathematics, and logic) and letters, memoranda, and notebooks, relating to applied science.

There are also collections of account books, 1717-1894 (303 vols. and 18 boxes), including those of a succession of Scottish merchants in Maryland and Virginia, 1753-1834 (181 vols.), and of other merchants in Virginia, 1833-84 (21 vols.); orderly books, 1759-1917 (160 vols.), including records of various expeditions, regiments, and companies, 1759-1800 (110 vols.); and a collection of journals and diaries, 1640-1920 (300 vols.), including diaries of individuals and journals of military and naval operations, exploring expeditions, voyages, and overland trips. Among the journals are those of Anna Maria Brodeau Thornton, wife of William Thornton (Pa., D.C.; architect, inventor), 1793 (7 vols.); John Fell (N.J.; Member Continental Cong.), 1778-79 (2 boxes); and Edmund Ruffin (Va.; agriculturist, Confed. leader), 1856-65 (14 vols.). Ten autograph collections, 1491-1923 (8 vols., 8 boxes, 4 portfolios, and 510 pieces), contain autographs of Europeans and Americans prominent in politics, literature, science, art, and religion, among them the J. Pierpont Morgan collection of prints, portraits, and documents of the signers of the Declaration of Independence (1 vol.); a collection of the American Academy of Arts and Letters, including letters written by 19th-century American and European literary figures, scientists, and statesmen (435 documents); the Simon Gratz autograph collection of American clergymen, 1719-1873 (1 box);

and the Library's own collection of miscellaneous autograph documents of
Americans and Europeans, 1742-1900
(4 boxes, 1 vol., and 4 portfolios).
There is also a collection of facsimiles
of British and American public documents and of personal papers of notable
individuals, 1742-1900 (1 vol., 4 boxes, and 4 portfolios). "Miscellaneous
Personal Papers" is a collection of six
or fewer pieces for each of hundreds
of persons.

The Naval Historical Foundation
Collection, 1790-1950 (321 boxes and
3 portfolios), which contains official
and private papers of a number of men
connected with the U.S. Navy and Navy
Department, is on long-term deposit
in the Manuscript Division. Included
are papers of the following Navy officers: Washington I. Chambers (pioneer in naval aviation), 1871-1934 (20
boxes); Freeland William Fullam,
1883-1926 (8 boxes); Albert Gleaves,
1879-1939 (9 boxes); Stanford C. Hooper, 1916-52 (10,000 pieces and 156
reels of magnetic tape on which Hooper
and other pioneers in the field traced
the "naval history of radio-radar-so-
nar"); Dudley Knox (historian), 1896-
1950 (17 boxes); S. P. Lee, 1861-65
(20 boxes); Charles O'Neil (Chief of
Bureau of Ordnance), including 40
vols. of diaries, 1872-1927; Daniel
Todd Patterson, 1832-35 (3 boxes);
Arthur Stanley Riggs (N. Y., D. C.;
editor, author), 1946-52 (17 containers); John Rodgers and his son John
Rodgers, 1804-1929 (27 boxes); Thomas Oliver Selfridge and his son
Thomas Oliver Selfridge, 1816-1919
(16 boxes); David Foote Sellers, 1898-
1947 (13 boxes); Robert W. Shufeldt,
1864-84 (22 boxes); Montgomery Meigs
Taylor, 1917-26 (10 boxes); and Harry
Ervin Yarnell, 1936-39 (11 boxes). Also in this collection are some records
of the Naval Observatory, 1830-1900
(29 boxes).

The Division has the records of a
number of American societies and
other organizations. Included are
those of the American Antislavery
Society, 1833-40 (1 box), and the
Western Antislavery Society, 1845-
57 (2 vols.); the American Colonization Society, 1816-1908 (626 vols.,
32 boxes, and 4 bundles), including
materials on the colony in Liberia;
the American Council of Learned
Societies, 1926-36 (156 boxes), relating to the compilation of the Dictionary of American Biography; the
American Historical Association,
1882-1945 (463 boxes, 41 packages,
and 8 filing drawers); the American
Ornithologists Union, 1883-1946,
including its minutes (1 vol.), and
papers of Charles Bendire (U. S. Army officer), 1890-96 (4 boxes); the
American Peace Society, 1825-96,
1928, including letters of William
Ladd (N.H.; founder of the Society)
to Samuel J. May (Mass., Conn.;
Unitarian clergyman, reformer),
1827-39, and proceedings of the Conference on International Justice, 1928;
the American Press Association,
1890-99 (3 boxes), including correspondence with contemporary writers;
the American Public Relations Association, 1947-55 (167 containers); the
Drama League of America, 1915-21
(1 box), relating to the Washington
Center of American Drama; the publishing firm of Harper and Brothers,
1869-1955 (a large quantity of selected materials); the Joint Committee on
Materials for Research of the American Council of Learned Societies and
the Social Science Research Council,
1930-39 (18 transfer cases); and the
League of Women Voters of the United States, 1920-50 (966 boxes and 28
bundles), including records of the
predecessor National League of Women Voters, 1920-30 (109 boxes and
28 bundles).

Records of other organizations
include those of the National Association for Universal Military Training,
1917-23 (39 boxes); the National Board

for Historical Services, 1917-21 (33 boxes and 19 card trays), including correspondence with the National Association of State War History Associations (6 boxes); the National Child Labor Committee, 1904-45 (23 vols. and 52 boxes), including 14 vols. of minutes; the National Committee on Atomic Information, 1945-48 (16 file drawers); the National Consumers' League, 1899-1946 (6,000 items); the National Policy Committee, 1933-47 (26 boxes); the National Society of the Daughters of Founders and Patriots of America (37 vols., 5 boxes, and 8 packages); the National Society for Vocational Education, 1906-18 (41 boxes), including records of the National Society for the Promotion of Industrial Education; the National Woman's Party, 1912-21 (302 boxes, 9 portfolios, and 12 card trays), including original cartoons pertaining to the suffrage movement; the National Women's Trade Union League of America, 1903-50 (29 boxes), including headquarters files, Washington office files, and proceedings of international conventions; the New York Society for the Suppression of Vice, 1872-1950 (4 vols.), dockets of arrests with notations by Anthony Comstock (N. Y.; sec. of the Society); Allan Pinkerton's National Detective Agency, Inc., 1861-83 (7 vols.); the President's Research Committee on Social Trends, 1924-36 (11 vols., 33 boxes, and 2 portfolios); the Social Democratic Workingmen's Party (Philadelphia), 1873-1944; and the Society of the Cincinnati, 1783-1938 (2 vols., 24 boxes, and 4 portfolios).

Besides the personal papers of many participants in U.S. wars and collections of orderly books and journals, there are a number of other collections relating to the armed forces and to the major wars in which the United States has engaged. There are some U.S. Army records, 1776-1917 (45 vols., 33 boxes, 11 portfolios, and 1 package), including letter books, payrolls, and other records of the Quar-

termaster's Department, 1791-1848 (20 vols. and 4 boxes), the Commissary Department, 1809-63 (2 vols. and 2 boxes), and the Commissary of Prisoners, 1813-18 (3 vols.); records of the U. S. War Department, 1790-1919 (38 vols., 92 portfolios, 36 envelopes, 15 packages, and 3 chests), including records concerning the Cumberland Road; papers pertaining to the U. S. Military Academy, 1790-1834 (3 vols., 1 box, and 2 portfolios), including the report of the board of appraisers, 1790-97; and U. S. Navy records, 1775-1898 (34 vols., 17 boxes, and 6 portfolios), including logbooks and journals kept by officers on board naval vessels. For the Civil War, there is a miscellaneous collection of records of or about the Confederate States (79 vols., 104 boxes, 8 portfolios, and 6 packages). There are also records of the U. S. Christian Commission, 1863-68 (5 boxes), and papers of its president, George Hay Stuart (Pa.; philanthropist), 1792-1930 (2 vols. and 2 boxes); and papers of and relating to the U. S. Sanitary Commission, 1863-65 (1 vol. and 1 box).

The World War I Collection, 1914-25, includes the personal diary of a U. S. military attaché with the British Army (2 vols.); reports on the battle participation of American units in France; and mimeographed material pertaining to the Paris Peace Conference. There are also transcripts and mimeographed documents from the library of the American Commission to Negotiate Peace, 1918-19, chiefly documents of The Inquiry; the Ford Peace Ship Collection, 1915-16 (14 boxes); and records of the War Service Office of the American Library Association (15 containers). Papers pertaining to World War II include records of Food for Freedom, Inc., and the predecessor Reconstruction Service Committee, 1942-46 (24 boxes); the Stars and Stripes, service

newspaper, 1943-45 (29 boxes), including letters and poems submitted by ser-
vicemen overseas; and the Writers' War
Board, 1942-45 (143 boxes), including
correspondence concerning the dissemi-
nation of information and propaganda.
A collection by Maurice F. Neufeld
(N. Y.; Cornell Univ. prof. of industrial labor relations) contains 2,000
papers relating to Allied military government in Italy and to World War II.
There are also captured German papers, 1800-1945 (778 containers), including records of the Deutsches Aus-
land Institute, 1917-33 (350 containers), some of the archives of the
Nazi Party, personal and semiofficial
papers of Adolph Hitler (Germany;
Chancellor, Führer), his personal adjutant, Fritz Wiedemann, and other
Nazi leaders, and documents concerning German military forces and Ger-
man-Japanese technical cooperation;
and captured Italian papers, 1932-45
(7 boxes and 3 portfolios), including
records pertaining to the Supreme Command, 1943.

Among many other collections of
records of or relating to U.S. Government agencies are the "U.S. Finance"
collection, 1748-1926 (34 vols., 25 boxes, 5 portfolios, and 8 bundles), including records of the Treasury Department, 1761-1897 (18 vols., 9 boxes,
and 2 portfolios), and documents relating to the U.S. Lottery, 1748-99 (4
vols. and 9 boxes), and to the Bank of
the United States, 1774-1856; the "U.S.
Executive Mansion" collection, 1799-
1909 (40 vols., 29 boxes, and 1 portfolio), including a record of letters
received, 1889-1909 (21 vols.), and
materials on White House receptions;
the "U.S. Executive Miscellany," 1791-
1925 (5 vols., 6 boxes, and 2 portfolios), including letters of U.S. Presidents to Commissioners of the District
of Columbia, 1791-1869 (1 vol.); the
"U.S. Miscellany," 1789-1924 (1 vol.
and 16 boxes); records, transferred
from the State Department, of appli-

cations for appointments to Federal
posts during the administrations of
George Washington; the "U.S. Treasury" collection, 1801-1919 (19 vols.,
9 boxes, and 1 roll), including records of collectors of customs, 1801-
1909, and of the Office of Internal
Revenue, 1862-65, and ledgers of accounts of claims of individuals kept by
the Third Auditor of the Treasury,
1789-1858; and the archives of the Library of Congress, 1800-1946 (several thousand containers).

Other special collections in the
Division are based on geographic
areas. Papers relating to States and
Territorial possessions of the United
States include collections on Alaska,
1915-24 (12 boxes), including papers
of the Alaskan Engineering Commission and the Alaska Railroad and River Boat Service, with records of the
Russian Orthodox Church in Alaska,
1774-1917 (7 vols. and 978 boxes);
Connecticut, 1637-1836 (23 vols. and
3 boxes), including transcripts of colonial records, 1637-1787, receipts
of the Continental Loan Office, 1781-
1804, and papers relating to religious
affairs, 1781-1836; Delaware, 1684-
1865 (4 vols., 4 boxes, and 1 package),
including original messages of the
Presidents of Delaware, 1770-1800,
and other State papers; District of
Columbia, 1790-1940 (a very large
collection), including records of the
Board of Aldermen and the Corporation of Georgetown, the City Council
of Washington, and other governing
agencies of the District, 1751-1881
(5 vols., 19 boxes, and 4 packages),
records relating to the site and the
building of the Federal City, 1790-
1828 (17 vols., 5 boxes, and 1 portfolio), and records of several private
and semi-official organizations; Florida, 1493-1938 (14 vols., 14 boxes,
and 1 portfolio), including copies of
Spanish documents, with East Florida
papers, 1777-1821 (119 vols. and 751
boxes), comprising Spanish archives

transferred to the United States with the cession of the territory, and West Florida papers, 1763-1827 (10 vols. and 3 boxes), including records of the colony under British control; Georgia, 1732-1869 (13 vols. and 6 boxes), including Force transcripts of miscellaneous correspondence and proceedings of the Executive Council, 1749-89 (3 boxes) and of records relating in part to Indiana, 1751-89 (3 vols.); Louisiana, 1491-1933 (17 vols., 20 boxes, and 2 folders), including materials on the French and Spanish regimes; Maryland, 1632-1918, including records of the Council of Safety, 1773-77 (4 vols.) and of the Baltimore Branch of the United States Bank, 1795-1855 (11 boxes); Massachusetts, 1620-1931, including various bound volumes from the Force Collection, 1631-1780 (18 vols.), and Force transcripts, 1731-83 (44 vols.); New Hampshire, 1629-1918 (21 boxes and 31 vols.), including Force transcripts, 1697-1788 (17 vols.), and other items from the Force Collection, 1651-1774 (10 vols.); New York, 1623-1942 (67 vols. and 14 boxes), including Force transcripts, 1775-78 (40 vols.) and original records from the Force Collection, 1664-1810 (20 vols.); the Pacific Islands, 1653-1923 (6 vols., 71 boxes, and 1 portfolio), including records of Guam, 1762-1896 (5 vols. and 43 boxes), and papers relating to the history of the Philippines, 1653-1914 (4 vols. and 10 boxes); Pennsylvania, 1650-1925 (17 vols. and 19 boxes), including records of the Continental Loan Office and the Commissioner of Loans, 1786-91 (4 vols.), and papers relating to the Whiskey Rebellion, 1792-96 (1 vol.); Rhode Island, 1587-1890 (13 vols. and 4 boxes), including proceedings of the General Assembly, 1653-1747 (4 vols. and 4 boxes), and records of the Commissioner of Loans, 1790-99 (7 vols.); Vermont, 1744-1936 (46 vols. and 5 boxes), including Force transcripts, 1744-83 (9 vols. and 1 box), and photostats of pa-

pers relating to Ira Allen (Vt., Pa.; Rev. War officer, political leader), 1774-1800 (36 vols.); and Virginia, 1606-1925 (35 vols. and 32 boxes), including some papers originally part of the library of Thomas Jefferson (Va.; U.S. Pres.), 1606-1737 (9 vols., 5 boxes, and 4 portfolios), and correspondence of William and Thomas Dawson (Va.; clergymen, presidents of the College of William and Mary). There are also smaller collections for other States and geographic areas.

The Division has many collections relating to Latin America. Among materials on Mexico and Central America are papers on Mexico, 1590-1910 (19 vols., 53 boxes, and 13 portfolios), including documents relating to the Inquisition in Spanish America, 1631-1848, and papers of Luis Berlandier on exploration in upper Mexico (and Texas) and the Mexican War, 1826-46 (5 boxes); papers of Augustin de Iturbide (Mexico; revolutionist, Emperor), 1799-1876 (26 boxes), including his military diaries, official and personal correspondence, papers of his associates, and documents relating to his estate; a collection on Indian languages of Mexico and Central America (25 vols. and 228 boxes), including dictionaries, vocabularies, and some English translations of Aztec dramas; another collection of manuscripts (38 boxes), copied by the ethnologist Rudolph R. Schuller, concerning archeology, ethnography, and the languages of Central and South America; a collection on Central America, 1670-1931 (6 vols., 15 boxes, and 7 packages), including volumes written in ancient Central American dialects and papers of Ephraim George Squier (N.Y.; journalist, archeologist, diplomat), relating to the Honduras Interoceanic Railroad, 1853-70; and papers of the Nicaragua Canal Construction Co., 1886-91 (8 boxes), including field notes and maps. A collection of

Guatemalan documents, 1944-54 (60 reels of microfilm and 35,000 photoprints of selected portions of the film) includes correspondence, minutes, and financial accounts of labor unions, political organizations, and government agencies. For South America there are two general collections: "America, Spanish Colonies," 1493-1829 (31 vols. and 23 boxes), including the collection made by Edward Stephen Harkness (N.Y.; capitalist, trustee of the Metropolitan Museum of Art), with material particularly on Peru, but with some on Mexico; and "South America," 1568-1943 (20 vols., 20 boxes, and 10 portfolios), including documents relating to Argentina, 1772-1938, Brazil, 1568-1861, Chile, 1808-1943, Colombia, 1862-1904, Ecuador, 1854, Peru, 1579-1942, and Venezuela, 1806-1926; also grammars and vocabularies of Indian languages, 1595-1835 (5 vols. and 2 boxes). There are also papers of the Women's Auxiliary Conferences of the Pan-American Congresses, 1915-27 (10 boxes), including minutes and correspondence.

The West Indies miscellany, 1494-1821 (28 vols., 10 boxes, and 1 portfolio), contains materials relating to the British West Indies, including Barbados, 1756-67 (7 vols.), Crooked Island, 1795-1805 (1 vol.), and Grenada Island, 1777-95 (6 vols.); another West Indies miscellany, 1591-1938 (15 vols., 30 boxes, and 20 portfolios), includes manuscripts and transcripts relating to Cuba, 1762-1938 (1 vol., 5 boxes, and 4 portfolios), Haiti, 1776-1912 (2 vols., 4 boxes, and 8 portfolios), and Puerto Rico, 1591-1899 (12 vols., 21 boxes, and 8 portfolios). Included also are the Del Monte Collection, 1500-1848 (3 vols., 14 boxes, 1 portfolio, and 1 folder), historical manuscripts pertaining to the Spanish colonies in the West Indies; and papers of d'Ossier Roune (France; administrative agent in Santo Domingo), 1791-1802 (1 box), among them correspondence with Toussaint l'Ouverture (Haiti; Negro gen. and liberator). A collection of Bermudiana, 1690-1893 (9 boxes), includes extracts from Bermuda newspapers, 1704-1893, and notes from colonial court records, 1704-64, and from manuscript laws, 1690-1735, collected by Winslow Manley Bell (Bermuda; antiquary).

For European nations also there are several collections, the largest of which are noted here. A collection on Great Britain, 1591-1939 (146 vols., 147 boxes, and 2 portfolios), includes manuscripts from the library of George Chalmers (Md., England; antiquary, chief clerk to the Privy Council), 1660-1772 (36 vols.), papers of Spencer Compton, Earl of Wilmington (pres. of the Privy Council concerning colonies), 1731-43 (2 portfolios), and papers concerning the establishment of the Royal African Co., 1735-44 (2 vols.). Other English papers are those of the Frewen family of Great Britain, 1823-1934 (1 vol., 67 boxes, and 1 portfolio), including correspondence of Moreton Frewen (England; world traveler, cattle rancher, financier); the Marlborough papers, 1706-1926 (5 vols. and 2 boxes), including papers of Charles Richard John Spencer-Churchill, 9th Duke of Marlborough, from the archives of Blenheim Palace; photostats (10 vols.) of Geoffrey of Monmouth's "Historia de Gestis Regum Britanniae"; and the Wakefield Collection, 13th-19th centuries (71 boxes), of parchments and papers referring to lands and estates in England. For Ireland there is a collection, 1776-1916 (82 vols. and 6 boxes), including stenographic notes and manuscript reports of debates in the Irish Parliament, 1776-89 (82 vols.). There are also collections on France (50 vols., 21 boxes, and 3 portfolios), including records of the baronies of St. Désiré, 1380-1784 (12 vols. and 69 pieces), de Vaux, 1511-1780 (14 vols., and 69 pieces), and Bourbonnais, 1401-44 (1 vol.); Spain, 1480-1939 (4 vols., 25 boxes, and 8 portfolios), including the Harkness collection of Spanish manuscripts, 1529-1651 (17 boxes), records relating to the Inquisition and to the Canary Islands, 1479-1779 (2 vols.), and papers relating to Loyalists, 1936-39; and Portugal, 17th-19th centuries (215 vols., 80 boxes, 7 portfolios, and 2 packages), including a manuscript volume of the 16th century concerning the kings of Portugal from A. D. 68, manuscripts pertaining to the Inquisition, copies of Papal bulls, and copies of diplomatic despatches from Miguel Martins d'Antas (Portugal; Minister to U. S.), 1867-69. Also of European interest are papers of the Argenteau (Mercy-Argenteau) family, 1428-1880 (109 boxes), including materials relating to the Silesian War and the Seven Years War; and "Estonian archives," archives of Estonian displaced persons organizations in Germany and of the Estonian Central Committee.

Other special collections in the Manuscript Division include a few medieval manuscripts; a collection of photocopies (1 vol., 2 boxes, 9 file drawers, and 2 bundles) of medieval Latin and vernacular manuscripts in European repositories that were published in facsimile, 1832-1932, together with an index compiled by Elias Avery Lowe (D. C.; paleographer with the Institute of Advanced Study at Princeton and with the Carnegie Institution); an Orientalia collection, dating from the 10th century (98 vols., 73 boxes, 12 file drawers, and 15 bundles), including Sanskrit manuscripts collected by Albrecht Friedrich Weber (Germany; prof. of Sanskrit at Univ. of Berlin) and his correspondence with many outstanding orientalists, 1881-83 (62 vols., 4 unbound manuscripts, and 4 folders of letters), Tibetan manuscripts collected by William Woodville Rockhill (Pa.; diplomat, orientalist), and manuscripts in Arabic, Persian,

Greek, and Ethiopian, including illuminated copies of the Koran; and a collection concerning Christopher Columbus (Spain, Portugal; discoverer of America), 1485-1515 (15 boxes, 5 portfolios, and 15 notebooks), including copies of grants and privileges awarded him by the King and Queen of Spain and reproductions of letters and documents, the originals of which are in private collections.

See the Library's Handbook of Manuscripts in the Library of Congress (1918. 750 p.); Curtis W. Garrison, List of Manuscript Collections in the Library of Congress to July 1931 (1932. [126] p.); and C. Percy Powell, List of Manuscript Collections Received in the Library of Congress July 1931 to July 1938 (1939. 33 p.). See also the Library's Annual Report and the Quarterly Journal of Current Acquisitions for lists of accessions and descriptions of particular groups, and the Manuscript Division's Registers (processed) providing detailed information about particular collections.

Map Division

Arch Gerlach, Chief.

Holdings: 3,000 manuscript maps and atlases, relating chiefly to America but including other maps exemplifying the art of cartography.

Included are a number of rare Chinese maps and atlases dating from the Ming dynasty; numerous tracings and reproductions of rare maps, the originals of which are in European archives, from pre-Columbian times to 1836; 12 charts drawn by Italian, Spanish, and Portuguese cartographers, 15th-17th centuries, depicting parts of the Mediterranean coast and areas of Central and South America; and manuscript atlases representing the work of Joao Teixeiro (Portugal; cos-

mographer of the King), 1612-70, and
of Battista Agnese (Italy; cartographer).
There are also a series of maps and
charts from the Royal School of Navigation, chiefly maps of America and
the West Indies, 1712-1824 (375 items);
18th-century maps of South America
relating chiefly to the boundaries between Spanish and Portuguese possessions fixed by the Treaty of 1777; and
maps and charts collected by Richard
Howe (England; naval officer), 1776-77
(72 items), depicting areas along the
Atlantic coast and the coasts of the
West Indies and the Philippine Islands.

Relating more specifically to the
United States are maps and plans concerning the Braddock expedition, other aspects of the French and Indian
War, and colonial America (101 items);
a series of military and topographic
maps drawn by French Army engineers
during the American Revolution (38
items); maps relating to Andrew Jackson's military activities along the Gulf
coast (11 items); Civil War maps, chiefly of areas in Virginia and West Virginia, 1862-64 (340 items); and photostats
of maps made under the direction of Albert U. Campbell (Va.; chief of Topographical Dept. of the Army of Northern Va.), the originals of which are in
the Virginia Historical Society, the
U. S. Military Academy, and the College of William and Mary.

Music Division

Harold Spivacke, Chief.

Holdings: A collection of music,
music literature, and sound recordings
totaling more than two and a quarter
million items. It is the largest and
most comprehensive collection in the
country and perhaps in the world, covering the development of Western music from medieval times to the present.
In this vast collection are thousands of
composers' original manuscripts, mu-

sicians' autograph letters, and miscellaneous documents that have unique
value as primary resources for research.

Three foundation collections are
particularly noteworthy for their
wealth of holograph scores. The
Whittall Foundation Collection contains significant original manuscripts
of J. S. Bach, Beethoven, Brahms,
Haydn, Mendelssohn, Mozart, Schoenberg, Schubert, and Weber. The Coolidge Foundation Collection has autograph scores of modern composers
receiving commissions from the Foundation itself and from Mrs. Coolidge
personally, including Alfano, Bartók,
Bax, Bliss, Bloch, Bridge, Britten,
Casella, Copland, Eichheim, Farwell,
Finney, Hanson, Harris, Hidenmith,
Honegger, Lajtha, Loeffler, Malipi-
ero, Martinů, Milhaud, Piston, Piz-
zetti, Prokofieff, Ravel, Respighi,
Riegger, Roussel, Schoenberg, Schumann, Sessions, Sowerby, Strawinsky,
Tansman, Toch, Villa-Lobos, Webern, Weiner, and Wellesz. In the
Koussevitzky Foundation Collection,
also assembled through commission-
ing activities, important holographs
of the following are found: Barber,
Bartók, Bergsma, Bernstein, Blitz-
stein, Bloch, Britten, Carter, Cha-
vez, Copland, Dallapiccola, Foss,
Guarnieri, Harris, Honegger, Ibert,
Kay, Kirchner, Lopatnikoff, Martinů, Mennin, Messiaen, Milhand,
Moore, Petrassi, Phillips, Piston,
Riegger, Schoenberg, Strawinsky, and
Villa-Lobos. The foundations formed
by Elizabeth Sprague Coolidge and
Serge Koussevitzky also contain a
large accumulation of the personal papers of these founders, amounting to
thousands of letters, documents, photographs, etc.

The general manuscript collections
of the Division are likewise rich in
holograph scores and letters. Important representations include J. S. Bach,
Beethoven, Berg, Brahms, Delibes,

Haydn, Kreisler, Liszt, Loeffler, Medtner, Rachmaninoff, Schumann, and Wagner. Special emphasis is placed on the work of American composers, extensive manuscript sources of the following being specially important: Bloch, Carpenter, Chadwick, Converse, Cowell, Gershwin, Heinrich, Herbert, Loomis, Rodgers, Smith, Sonneck, Sousa, Sowerby, and Taylor.

A number of "unit collections," formed by one individual or family or organization, provide unique opportunities for research and investigation. Among such holdings are the Rachmaninoff Archives, the Geraldine Farrar Collection, the archives of the National Federation of Music Clubs, the archives of the Arthur P. Schmidt Co., the Arnold Volpe Collection, the Harold Bauer Collection, and the Dayton C. Miller Collection. Each of these collections contains exceedingly important documents reflecting the careers of the persons and organizations concerned.

In addition to holograph material the Division has thousands of manuscripts running from the medieval period through the Renaissance, baroque, and classical centuries. These include liturgical music, secular part-songs, instrumental ensembles, and opera scores. The opera collections of the Division, incidentally, are probably the strongest in existence, their wealth being equally distributed among full scores, piano-vocal scores, and librettos.

The collection of musicians' autograph letters includes the correspondence of celebrated artists as well as composers, and affords invaluable comment on and criticism of the musical experience of their authors. Prominent individuals represented by collections of letters (from several to several hundred) include: Beethoven, Berg, Bloch, Brahms, Bülow, Busoni, Cherubini, Engel, Foote, Godowsky, Grainger, Henselt, Kiesewetter, Lehmann, Liszt, MacDowell, Medt-

ner, Moor, Paganini, Rachmaninoff, Schlesinger, Sonneck, Wagner, Webern, and Wieniawski.

A huge amount of unique source material is embraced in the Archive of Folk Song. This exists predominantly in sound recordings (cylinders, discs, tapes), but a large collection on documents is a valuable supplement. The folk music collection is international in scope, although the greatest strength is American in its essence, origin, location, or antecedents.

A constantly growing collection of microfilms enhances the Division's supply of original sources and research materials. Approximately 400 reels now contain several thousand manuscripts, treatises, and scores in European or in private hands.

See Otto E. Albrecht, A Census of Autograph Music Manuscripts of European Composers in American Libraries, pp. 319-320 (1953); Autograph Musical Scores in the Coolidge Foundation Collection (1950. 30 p.); Edward N. Waters, Autograph Musical Scores and Autograph Letters in the Whittall Foundation Collection (rev. 1953. 19 p.); Julia Gregory, Catalogue of Early Books on Music (1913. 312 p.); Hazel Bartlett, Catalogue of Early Books on Music, Supplement (1944. 143 p.).

Orientalia Division

Horace I. Poleman, Chief.

Holdings: Included are manuscript writings in pictographic symbols of an aboriginal tribe of southwest China; a collection of manuscripts ranging from the 15th to the 19th century from the Tientsin region; 9 Buddhist manuscripts; 41 handwritten vols. of an 11,095-volume encyclopedia compiled in 1403-8, of which less than 400 vols. are known to exist today; and 1,070 reels of microfilm of Chinese manuscripts and early printed books dating from the 9th to the 15th century, reproduced from originals deposited for safekeeping in the Library of Congress by the Chinese National Library in 1941. There are also some manuscripts relating to Indic culture; 1,400 manuscripts assembled in the Al-Azhar University at Cairo relating to Muslim learning; a collection of works in old Turkish written in Arabic script; and a number of manuscripts in Hebrew script.

See the Library's Quarterly Journal of Current Acquisitions, vol. 11, no. 2 (Feb. 1954).

Prints and Photographs Division

Dr. Edgar Breitenbach, Chief.

Holdings: A large number of original drawings and prints documenting various aspects of American life from the late 18th century to the early 20th century, as well as extensive collections of photographs. Among architectural drawings of importance are original plans, elevations, cross sections, and details for the U.S. Capitol at Washington and other public buildings, made during the late 18th and early 19th centuries (200 large drawings and several sketchbooks) by Benjamin Henry Latrobe (Pa., D.C.; architect, engineer), Etienne Sulpice Hallet, also known as Stephen Hallet (France, D.C.; architect), Charles Bulfinch (Mass.; architect), and Thomas Ustick Walter (Pa., D.C.; architect). Of related interest are other original Latrobe drawings and plans for public and domestic buildings proposed for erection in Virginia, Pennsylvania, and New York, 1795-1818 (83 sheets and 3 pages); and original pencil drawings of early American architecture by Milton Smith Osborne (Canada, Penn.; architect, prof. Penn. State Univ.), 1924-34 (137 draw-

ings). There is also a collection of original measured drawings of 2,800 buildings in the United States constructed before 1870; these drawings were made between 1933 and 1941 (25,600 sheets) by the Historic American Buildings Survey in cooperation with the National Park Service and the American Institute of Architects and are accompanied by 29,200 photographs and negatives and 7,600 pages of typed data. The papers of Frances Benjamin Johnston (D.C.; pioneer woman photographer, author, lecturer) include extensive correspondence and photographs of buildings, especially in the region from Maryland to Louisiana.

The Division has a collection of original political and humorous cartoons, 1880 through the 1940's, including those of Clifford Kennedy Berryman (D.C.; staff artist on Washington newspapers), 1890's-1940's (1,150 drawings). Other cartoons are in the "Cabinet of American Illustration," a collection of more than 4,000 drawings and watercolors representing 200 illustrators of the period 1880-1910 with an accompanying file of correspondence between William Patten (N.Y.; art editor of Harper's Magazine) and various artists invited to contribute to the cabinet.

Among other original illustrations are the pencil drawings and color "cartoons" of American Indians prepared by George Catlin (Pa.; artist, author), 1860-70 (29 drawings); pencil drawings, etchings, and paintings of Civil War battles and camp scenes by Edwin Forbes (N.Y.; staff artist for Leslie's Illustrated Weekly Newspapers), 1862-68 (300 drawings, 40 etchings, and 12 oil paintings); pen, pencil, and crayon drawings and photographs of scenic areas around Washington, D.C., by Robert Eaton Dickinson (D.C.; artist, photographer), 1918 (125 items). In the field of fine arts there is the extensive collection of Whistleriana, 1836-1908, including original letters of James McNeill Whistler (Mass., France, England; painter, etcher) to Ignace Henri Joseph Théodore Fantin-Latour (France; painter) and of his mother, Anna Mathilda McNeill Whistler, together with prints, sketches, and other materials assembled by Joseph Pennell (Pa., England, N.Y.; etcher, author) and his wife, Elizabeth Robins Pennell (Pa.; author) in writing their biography of the artist. The J. and E. R. Pennell Collection also includes manuscripts and letters written to Pennell (61 boxes), and numerous watercolors and drawings by him.

See Guide to the Special Collections of Prints and Photographs in the Library of Congress, comp. by Paul Vandenbilt (1955. 200 p.).

Rare Book Division

Frederick R. Goff, Chief.

Holdings: Included are medieval and Renaissance manuscripts and early manuscript books (100 items); and letters and literary manuscripts of Hans Christian Andersen (Denmark; writer of fairy tales), 1833-75 (110 items); William Blake (England; poet, artist), 1757-1827 (1 vol. and 1 folder); Sinclair Lewis (Minn., N.Y.; novelist); Somerset Maugham (England; novelist, playwright); Hugh Walpole (England; novelist); and James McNeill Whistler (Mass., France, England; painter, etcher). There are collections containing autograph documents of famous poets, lawyers, and scientists; and of French notables, European sovereigns, and other famous persons, chiefly Italian, 1422-1881 (2,000 items). The Division also has custody of some early copyright records originally kept by U.S. district courts, 1790-1870 (304 vols.), and correspondence relating to copyrights, 1871-90.

See De Ricci, Census, pp. 179-266;

the Library's Rare Books Division; a Guide to Its Collections and Services (1950. 57 p.); and Martin A. Roberts, The Library of Congress; Records in the Copyright Office Deposited by the United States District Courts Covering the Period 1790-1870 (1939. 19 p., with facsimiles).

WASHINGTON 9

Library of the Supreme Council, Scottish Rite of Freemasonry. 1733 16th St. NW. R. Baker Harris, Librarian.

Holdings: 50,000 pieces, 1801-1955, relating to Freemasonry. Included are papers of Albert Pike (Mass., Ark., D.C.; lawyer, author, Confed. Army officer, exponent of Freemasonry), 1830-91 (89 vols. and 192 pieces), consisting of letters, manuscripts of his translations from Sanskrit and ancient Hebrew, and other papers. Also included are an autograph collection of letters of U.S. Presidents, and one of letters of prominent men who were Masons (250 pieces).

See Ray Baker Harris, ed., Bibliography of the Writings of Albert Pike, pp. 56-60 and 102-107 (1957).

WASHINGTON 4

Lincoln Museum. 511 10th St. NW. Randle B. Truett, Chief, National Memorial and Historical Sites Section.

Holdings: 60 pieces, 1861-65, relating to Abraham Lincoln and the Civil War, with particular reference to the assassination of Lincoln.

WASHINGTON 25

National Archives and Records Service. Wayne C. Grover, Archivist of the United States.

Holdings: Chiefly (1) noncurrent and semicurrent official records of the United States Government, dating for the most part from 1774, and amounting to many millions of pieces, and (2) personal papers in two Presidential libraries. The official records are administered, under the direction of the Archivist of the United States, by the two offices described separately below. For the Presidential libraries, which are also administrative units of the National Archives and Records Service, see entries for the Franklin D. Roosevelt Library, at Hyde Park, N.Y., and the Harry S. Truman Library, at Independence, Mo.

Office of Records Management. Everett O. Alldredge, Assistant Archivist of the United States.

Though not itself a custodial agency, this Office has central responsibility for the administration of records in the several Federal Records Centers of the General Services Administration and their annexes. In these depositories are kept chiefly noncurrent and semicurrent field records of the Government, most of which are scheduled for destruction after the expiration of specified periods of time but some of which are scheduled for indefinite preservation. The holdings of 16 of these depositories are briefly described in the present volume under the following cities or towns: Chicago, Clearfield (Utah), Denver, Dorchester (Mass.), East Point (Ga.), Fort Worth, Honolulu, Kansas City (Mo.), Mechanicsburg (Pa.), New Orleans, New York, Philadelphia, St. Louis, Seattle, South San Francisco, and Wilmington (Calif.). A 17th depository, at Alexandria, Va., administers semicurrent records from agencies in the Washington, D.C., area before disposal or transfer to the National Archives, and hence its holdings are

described below with those of the National Archives.

National Archives. Theodore R. Schellenberg, Assistant Archivist of the United States.

Holdings: 800,000 cu. ft. of records, dating chiefly from the period of the American Revolution to recent years and consisting of most of the records created or formerly maintained by Federal agencies in the Washington area that are not in current use and need to be preserved indefinitely because of their value for research or other purposes. The holdings comprise over 300 record groups, each of which usually consists of the records of a single agency (and its predecessors) at the bureau level; and they are administered by divisions of the National Archives having responsibilities for diplomatic, legislative, judicial, and fiscal records; for industrial records; for records relating to the exploitation and management of natural resources; for military and naval records; for cartographic records; and for audio-visual records. These records document importantly the manifold activities of the Government itself; they provide information about Presidents, Cabinet officers, Members of Congress, and many other persons; and they constitute a mine of information about many varied aspects of the development of the United States.

The oldest records of the Government are the Papers of the Continental Congress, 1774-89 (formerly in the Library of Congress). Records of the legislative branch include records of the Senate, the House of Representatives, joint committees of Congress, and the General Accounting Office. Records of the judicial branch include records of the Supreme Court of the United States, the U.S.

Court of Claims, and a few district courts, especially complete for those of the District of Columbia, the Southern District of New York, and the Eastern District of Pennsylvania. Among the records of the executive branch are records of all the executive departments—State, Treasury, Defense (including War, Navy, and Air Force Departments), Justice, Post Office, Interior, Agriculture, Commerce, Labor, and Health, Education, and Welfare—including records of their predecessors and their bureaus and other organizational units.

Among the important correspondence series of the executive agencies of the 18th and 19th centuries are the diplomatic and consular correspondence of the State Department dating from 1789; correspondence of the Secretary of War from 1800, the Office of the Paymaster General from 1799, the Office of the Judge Advocate General from 1812, the Office of the Chief of Engineers from 1813, the Office of the Chief of Ordnance from 1815, the Office of the Commissary General of Subsistence from 1818, the Office of the Surgeon General from 1818, the Headquarters of the Army from 1825, the Office of the Chief Signal Officer from 1860, and the Office of the Inspector General from 1863; correspondence of the Secretary of the Navy from 1794, the Board of Navy Commissioners from 1825 to 1842, the Naval Observatory from 1840, the Bureau of Yards and Docks from 1842, the Bureau of Ordnance from 1842, the Bureau of Medicine and Surgery from 1842, and the Hydrographic Office from 1862; correspondence of the Secretary of the Treasury from 1789, the Treasurer of the United States from 1813, the Bureau of Navigation from 1814, the Steamboat Inspection Service from 1852, and the Supervising Surgeon General from 1860; correspondence of the Attorney General from 1818; fragmentary correspondence of

the Postmaster General from 1789; correspondence of the Secretary of the Interior from 1849, the Bureau of Indian Affairs from 1824, Indian superintendencies from 1801, the Commissioner of Education from 1870, the Commissioner of Fish and Fisheries from 1871, and the Geological Survey from 1879; correspondence of the Commissioner and Secretary of Agriculture from 1879, the Division of Entomology from 1883, the Division of Chemistry from 1886, the Division of Botany and Pomology from 1886, the Division of Forestry from 1886, the Bureau of Animal Industry from 1887, and the Office of Experiment Stations from 1888.

Other major bodies of records in the National Archives for the 19th century and earlier are domestic loan accounts from 1774, the Revolutionary War collection from 1775, treaties with foreign governments and Indian tribes from 1778, military service records from 1784, records of the administration of the Territories from 1787, amnesty and pardon records from 1789, records of foreign-service posts from 1789, marine documents and cargo manifests from 1789, records of the establishment of post offices and appointment of postmasters from 1790, schedules of population censuses from 1790, Presidential proclamations and Executive orders from 1791, passport applications from 1791, records of boundary and claims commissions and arbitrations from 1794, records of surveys of public lands from 1796, land-entry papers from 1796, court-martial case files from 1799, pension files from 1800, records of Army commands from 1813, meteorological records from 1819, passenger lists of vessels entering United States ports from 1820, and patent case files from 1836.

There are also voluminous bodies of records for the 20th century. In addition to continuations of many of the series mentioned above, they include records of many independent agencies established since 1900, among them emergency agencies of World Wars I and II. There are also records of the Office of the Secretary of Defense and associated boards and staffs; headquarters agencies of the Departments of the Army, Navy, and Air Force; combined operational headquarters of World War II; war crimes tribunals and commissions; allied military government headquarters; and the Army historical program.

Records of other governments that have been acquired by the United States Government include records of the Danish Government of the Virgin Islands, 1672-1915; the Spanish Governors of Puerto Rico, 1750-1898; the Russian-American Company, which administered Alaska, 1802-67; the Confederate States of America, 1861-65; and various agencies of the Philippine Government during the period of the Philippine Insurrection, 1898-1903. As a result of World War II many German records were acquired either in original or microfilm form. A few collections of private papers that were either acquired separately or embodied in other files are found in the National Archives. Included among them, for example, are the papers of Cleveland Abbe, Sr., early American meteorologist, 1863-1916, and the journals and letter books of many officers of the U.S. Navy, 1776-1908.

Records of Federal agencies operating in the District of Columbia, Maryland, and Virginia, chiefly of later date and in continuation of those described above, are housed and serviced at Alexandria, Va., as if they were in the National Archives Building. While most of the holdings date from 1900, they include some important 19th-century records of the Bureau of Entomology and Plant Quarantine, the Bureau

of the Census, the Coast and Geodetic Survey, the Weather Bureau, the Patent Office, the Bureau of Accounts (Treasury Department), the Public Health Service, the Bureau of Customs, the Bureau of Internal Revenue, the Interstate Commerce Commission, the Veterans Administration, and the Post Office Department. Also at Alexandria are records of the judicial branch of the Government that merit special mention, among them those of the Administrative Office of the U.S. Courts, 1922-52; U.S. Court of Appeals for the District of Columbia, 1891-1953, and for the Fourth Circuit, 1891-1943; and U.S. District Courts for the District of Maryland, 1798-1949, for the District of Puerto Rico, 1899-1949, and for the Eastern District of Virginia, 1867-1938.

See the following publications of the National Archives: List of Record Groups in the National Archives and the Federal Records Centers (1956. 34 p. Processed); Guide to the Records in the National Archives (1948. 684 p.), supplemented by National Archives Accessions, beginning with No. 31; Handbook of Federal World War Agencies and Their Records, 1917-1921 (1943. 666 p.); Federal Records of World War II (1950-51): Vol. 1, Civilian Agencies (1,073 p.), and Vol. 2, Military Agencies (1,061 p.), which describes records not only in the National Archives but elsewhere; and these publications, which are issued from time to time: Preliminary Inventories, which describe the record groups series by series; Special Lists, which describe in detail certain record series; and Reference Information Papers, which describe materials relating to various geographical areas, economic topics, and other subjects.

—oOo—

Naval Historical Foundation. Room

1080, Main Navy Bldg. Secretary.

Holdings: A considerable quantity of manuscripts relating chiefly to the maritime history of the United States. The bulk of this material is on long-term loan to the Library of Congress and is described in the entry above for the Manuscript Division of that Library, but the Foundation has retained in its immediate custody the papers of several naval officers of high rank and some manuscripts of books on naval history.

—oOo—

Naval History Division, Office of the Chief of Naval Operations, Navy Department. Rear Adm. E. M. Eller, USN (Ret.), Director of Naval History.

Holdings: 3,500,000 items, consisting chiefly of operation plans, war diaries, action reports, and other operational records of the U.S. Navy during and following World War II through the Korean War. Included also are 320 volumes of unpublished administrative narratives of various organizational units of the U.S. Naval Establishment during World War II; and certain German and Japanese naval records of the same war period.

WASHINGTON 6

Pan American Sanitary Bureau Library. 1501 New Hampshire Ave. NW. Janeiro B. Schmid, Chief Librarian.

Holdings: Archives of the Pan American Sanitary Bureau, 1902 to date, including records of the director, executive committee and directing council, and conferences; financial reports and budgets; and monthly reports. The archives relate chiefly to the Americas with respect to public health and sanitation, communi-cable and tropical diseases, vital statistics, maternal and child welfare, parasitology, medicine, and pharmacy.

—oOo—

Pan American Union. Arthur E. Gropp, Librarian.

Holdings: In the Division of Laws and Treaties there are the original drafts of treaties, conventions, and agreements among the American nations, accompanied by the instruments of ratification by the countries concerned; in the Division of Conferences and Organizations there are papers concerning the Organization of American States and its specialized councils and agencies; and in the Archives Collection, Columbus Memorial Library, there are record copies of the proceedings of the Council (formerly Governing Board) of the Organization of American States, the reports of the Secretary General (formerly Director General), and the documents of the general and special conferences, of the Meetings of Consultation of the Ministers of Foreign Affairs, and of the specialized council meetings (Juridical, Economic and Social Affairs, Cultural) as well as of the conferences coming within the province of the specialized agencies.

WASHINGTON 25

Smithsonian Institution. Leonard Carmichael, Secretary.

Holdings: A quantity of manuscripts and archives chiefly resulting from and relating to the scientific and cultural activities of the Institution and its subordinate units: The U.S. National Museum (with its departments of Anthropology, Botany, Geology, and Zoology), the Museum of History and Technology, the Bureau of American Ethnology, the

Astrophysical Observatory, the National Collection of Fine Arts, the Freer Gallery of Art, the National Air Museum, the National Zoological Park, and the National Gallery of Art. The greater part of these materials is in the administrative units specifically described below. Others are scattered among several units of the National Museum and elsewhere.

Smithsonian Institution Archives. Louise M. Pearson, Administrative Assistant to the Secretary.

Holdings: Records relating to the organization and history of the Institution, since 1846; official correspondence of the Institution, since 1863; private correspondence and scientific papers of Joseph Henry (N.Y., N.J., D.C.; physicist, prof. at College of N.J., Sec. of Smithsonian Institution, Pres. of National Academy of Sciences), 1831-78; and Spencer F. Baird (Pa., D.C.; zoologist, Dickinson College prof., U.S. Commissioner of Fish and Fisheries, Sec. of Smithsonian Institution), 1850-87; and correspondence and records of Samuel P. Langley (Pa., D.C.; astronomer, Sec. of Smithsonian Institution, pioneer in aviation), 1890-1907, regarding aircraft experiments.

Smithsonian Institution Library. Natural History Bldg. Ruth Blanchard, Librarian.

Holdings: 210 ft. of records, since 1760, relating to natural history—including anthropology, archeology, botany, conchology, embryology, entomology, ethnology, geology, ichthyology, ornithology, and zoology—and radio and electronics.

Papers of individuals include those of Spencer F. Baird (Pa., D.C.; zoologist, U.S. Commissioner of Fish and Fisheries, Sec. of Smithsonian Institution), 1836-51 (1 vol. and 1 package); William D. Brackenridge (D.C., Md.;

botanist, landscape architect), 1833-75 (117 pieces and 1 diary); James Graham Cooper (Wash., Calif.; physician, naturalist, author), 1853-70 (1 vol. and 2 packages); Charles Hallock (Canada, N.Y., D.C.; author, scientist, editor), 1860-1912 (200 pieces); Oliver Perry Hay (N.Y., D.C.; paleontologist, museum curator, Carnegie Institution research associate), 1911-30 (6 packages); Otis Tufton Mason (D.C.; curator of ethnology and of anthropology in the Smithsonian Institution), undated literary manuscripts (5 packages); Edward Maynard (D.C.; dental surgeon, inventor), 1852-90 (1 package); Fielding B. Meek (N.Y., D.C.; paleontologist), 1848-76 (22 vols. and 1 box); Constantine S. Rafinesque (Ky., Pa.; botanist, ichthyologist, prof. at Transylvania Univ.), 1818-26 (10 notebooks); Charles Rau (N.Y., D.C.; archeologist, curator in National Museum), 1839-81 (1 vol., 9 folders, and 7 envelopes); William Stimpson (D.C., Ill.; naturalist, director of Chicago Academy of Sciences), 1853-56 (2 packages); and John Xántus (Calif.; ornithologist, U.S. consul at Manzanillo, Mexico), 1857-64 (1 vol.).

The records of the Western Union International Telegraph Expedition, 1865-67 (1 box), include many letters of William Healey Dall (Ill., D.C.; naturalist, curator of mollusks in the National Museum, author) and Robert Kennicott (Ill.; naturalist, explorer, founder and director of Chicago Academy of Sciences). Also in the Library are papers concerning various exploring expeditions, including records of the U.S. Exploring Expedition commanded by Capt. Charles Wilkes, 1838-42 (48 vols. and 5 envelopes); and journals, 1849-61 (4 vols.), of a surgeon who accompanied the overland exploring expedition, 1853-56, for a northern railway route to the Pacific, commanded by Gov. Isaac Stevens. There are also statistics of the exportation and importation of fishery products, 1731-1880 (5 vols.); records of the Northwestern Boundary Survey, 1859-60 (8 vols.), relating chiefly to natural history; papers concerning the Philadelphia International Exposition, 1876 (1 package), including letters of Spencer F. Baird on the exhibit illustrating mineral resources of the United States; and the George H. Clark collection of manuscripts on the history of radio and electronics (180 linear ft.).

Bureau of American Ethnology Archives. (Mrs.) Margaret C. Blaker, Archivist.

Holdings: 4,500 files covered by an indexed card catalog, consisting of 550 cu. ft. of materials, 1848 to date, dealing with the ethnology, history, archeology, and languages of the American Indian, especially of North America, that have been submitted by staff members, collaborators, and correspondents of the Bureau of American Ethnology and its predecessors. Data collected by anthropologists and by other observers, such as travelers and military men, include the following types of records: materials on Indian languages (vocabularies, texts, grammatical notes, comparative data); ethnological and archeological field notes and drafts of reports; photographs supplementing such reports (exclusive of the Bureau's major collection of about 17,000 negatives, consisting of portraits showing physical types and costumes, and views illustrating other aspects of the culture of North American Indians); transcripts of native historical and other accounts; transcriptions of native music; Indian drawings and paintings on paper, including autobiographical and mnemonic accounts (e. g. autobiographies of Sitting Bull), and illustrations made at the request of ethnographers; ethnological extracts from published and archival historical sources; and manuscript maps and maps with manuscript annotations.

The materials are primarily cataloged by tribe and region, for the convenience of anthropological, historical, legal, and other researchers using them; however, the card index also locates all records by and about a given individual. Among the contributors are Franz Boas (N. Y.; anthropologist, philologist, prof. at Columbia Univ.), Charles Upson Clark (Conn., N. Y.; prof. languages at College of City of N. Y., research investigator for Smithsonian Institution), Frances Densmore (Minn.; student of American Indian music), James Owen Dorsey (Md.; ethnologist, Episcopal minister), Philip Drucker (D. C.; anthropologist), Alice Cunningham Fletcher (D. C.; student of American Indian music, ethnologist), Albert Samuel Gatschet (N. Y., D. C.; linguist, ethnologist), George Gibbs (N. Y., Oreg.; geologist, ethnologist), John Peabody Harrington (D. C.; linguist, ethnologist), John Napoleon Brinton Hewitt (N. Y., D. C.; ethnologist), Alfred L. Kroeber (N. Y., Calif.; anthropologist), Truman Michelson (N. Y., D. C.; ethnologist, prof. Geo. Wash. Univ.), James Mooney (D. C.; ethnologist), John Wesley Powell (Ill., D. C.; geologist, Director of Geological Survey and Bureau of American Ethnology), Hugh Lenox Scott (U. S. Army officer, negotiator with various Indian tribes), Frank G. Speck (Pa.; anthropologist, prof. Univ. of Pa.), John Reed Swanton (D. C.; ethnologist), and Cyrus Thomas (Tenn., Ill.; ethnologist, entomologist).

See James C. Pilling, "Catalogue of Linguistic Manuscripts in the Library of the Bureau of Ethnology," in the Bureau's First Annual Report, pp. 553-577 (1881); and Pilling's linguistic bibliographies in the Bureau's Bulletins 1, 5, 6, 9, 13, 14, 15, 16, and 19 (1887-94). Information about new accessions appears in the Annual Reports of the Bureau of American Ethnology.

Freer Gallery of Art. 12th St. and Jefferson Dr. SW. (Mrs.) Bertha M. Usilton, Librarian.

Holdings: Manuscripts from the 3rd century are representative of the arts of bookmaking, calligraphy, illumination, and illustration. The Greek (which include the "Washington MSS. "), Syriac (Aramaic), Coptic, and Armenian manuscripts, 3rd-13th centuries, are Christian; most of the Muslim manuscripts, 8th-16th centuries, are Koranic; the Persian manuscripts, 13th-16th centuries, represent works of science, history, and poetry; and the Indian manuscripts, 13th-19th centuries, are Buddhist and Jain scriptures, and secular poetry.
See H. I. Poleman, A Census of Indic Manuscripts in the United States and Canada, p. 287 (1938. Processed); De Ricci, Census, pp. 464-469; and University of Michigan Studies, Humanistic Series (1917-27), vols. 8 (Old Testament), 9 (New Testament), 10 (Coptic manuscripts), 12 (Early Christian and Roman art), 13 (Arabic [Judeo-Arabic]), and 21 (Minor Prophets).

WASHINGTON 7

Volta Bureau Library. 1537 35th St. NW. Librarian.

Holdings: 5,000 pieces, 1887-1936, relating chiefly to the problems of teaching speech to the deaf. Included are papers of Alexander Graham Bell (Mass., D. C.; inventor of the telephone, founder of the Bureau), 1871-1922 (236 items); John Hitz (Swiss consul gen. in U. S., and first supt. of the Bureau), 1887-1907; Gardiner Greene Hubbard (Mass., D. C.; promoter of

education of the deaf, founder and pres. of National Geographic Society) and his daughter, Mabel G. Hubbard (Mrs. Alexander Graham Bell); and Harriet Burbank Rogers (Mass.; pioneer oral teacher of the deaf). Included also are noncurrent records of the Bureau.
See Hist. Records Survey, 100 Sample Entries, p. 19, and Calendar of Alexander Graham Bell Correspondence in the Volta Bureau (1940. 41 p. Processed).

WASHINGTON 16

Washington Cathedral Library. John L. Lord, Library Consultant.

Holdings: Archives of the Protestant Episcopal Diocese of Washington (comprising the District of Columbia and four nearby counties of Maryland), 22 vols., 1848-1935, chiefly parish registers, account books, and vestry minutes (District of Columbia parishes only); Protestant Episcopal bishops' letters, 1790-1870 (2 vols.); and various pieces relating to the foundation and early construction of the Washington Cathedral.

—oOo—

Wesley Theological Seminary Library. 4400 Massachusetts Ave. NW. Roland E. Kircher, Librarian.

Holdings: A small collection relating chiefly to Methodism, and especially to the former Methodist Protestant Church. Included are sermons of Nicholas Snethen (early Methodist Protestant leader), and letters of John Wesley (England; founder of

Methodism) and Francis Asbury (U.S. Methodist bishop). The collection also contains conference journals of the Methodist Protestant and the Methodist Episcopal Churches, in manuscript form.

FLORIDA

GAINESVILLE

Florida Historical Society. University of Florida. Merlin G. Cox, Secretary.

Holdings: 1,800 items, 1764-1893, relating chiefly to Florida. Included are a journal and miscellaneous papers of Richard Keith Call (Fla.; Terr. Gov., Terr. delegate to Cong.), 1819-66 (160 items); a letter book of John Milton (Fla.; Gov.), 1861-63 (50 items); and Confederate muster rolls and other papers of Francis P. Fleming (Fla.; Gov.), 1880-93 (150 items). There are also records of the Confederate commissary supply department for Florida, 1863-65 (600 items); records of the Indian trading firm of Panton, Leslie and Co., 1764-1832 (500 items); and miscellaneous plantation records, 1833-66 (300 items).

See Hist. Records Survey, Guide for Fla., pp. 6-8.

—oOo—

P. K. Yonge Library of Florida History, University of Florida Libraries. Margaret L. Chapman, Librarian.

Holdings: A large number of manuscripts or copies of manuscripts, relating chiefly to Florida and the South. Except as otherwise shown, estimates of quantities are in cubic feet.

Papers of political leaders include those of Charles O. Andrews (Fla.; U.S. Sen.), 1936-46 (25 ft.); Napoleon B. Broward (Fla.; Gov.), 1880-1909 (8,000 items); Millard F. Caldwell (Fla.; U.S. Rep., Gov.), 1933-49 (6 ft.); Charles Dougherty (Fla.; U.S. Rep.), 1877-1912 ($\frac{1}{2}$ ft.); William H. Gleason (Fla.; Lt. Gov., radical leader, pioneer developer), 1866-93 (4 ft.);

Robert A. Green (Fla.; U.S. Rep.), 1925-44 (30 ft.); Joseph E. Hendricks (Fla.; U.S. Rep.), 1937-49 (1,000 items); James B. Hodges (Fla.; legislator, member State Board of Control of Educational Institutions), 1909-21 (5 ft.); Spessard Lindsay Holland (Fla.; State sen., Gov., U.S. Sen.), 1932-45 (a large quantity); William S. Jennings (Fla.; Gov.), 1901-5 (3 ft.); James H. Peterson (Fla.; U.S. Rep.), 1933-51 (20 ft.); Thomas A. Yon (Fla.; U.S. Rep.), 1927-33 (1 ft.); Chandler C. Yonge (Fla.; State sen., U.S. and Confed. dist. attorney), 1843-65 (3 ft.); and David L. Yulee (Fla.; U.S. Sen., railroad builder), 1841-86 (10,000 pieces).

Papers of other individuals include those of T. Fred Davis (Fla.; historian), 1909-46 (4 ft.); Arthur E. Morgan (Ohio, Tenn.; civil engineer, pres. of Antioch College, chairman of Tenn. Valley Authority), 1912-28 (2 ft.); Samuel A. Swann (Fla.; land developer, railway official), 1853-1907 (40 ft.); Thomas E. Will (Fla.; pioneer, engaged in reclamation of the Everglades), 1910-35 (10 ft.); and P. K. Yonge (Fla.; educator), 1905-33 (20 ft.).

Business records include those of Panton, Leslie and Co., 1776-1806 (6,000 sheets of copies and translations); the Fernandina [Fla.] Dock and Development Co., 1844-1939 (6 ft.); and the Florida East Coast Railway, 1889-1912 (750 items on microfilm). Included also are records of the U.S. District Land Office for Florida, 1826-1931 (120 ft.); the Florida Flood Control Association, 1924-40 (1 ft.); and photostats and other copies of British, Spanish, and Mexican archives relating to Florida, 1518-1821 (144,700 pages), among which are the copies formerly owned by the defunct Florida State Historical Society.

—oOo—

University of Florida Libraries. Stanley L. West, Director of Libraries.

Holdings: In the general Library are the Austin Cary Memorial Forestry Collection, 1918-36 (103 vols. of notebooks and 433 other items), containing 196 items by Cary (Maine; forester on U.S. Forest Service staff); papers of Robert Dunbar (Va.; merchant) and William Dunbar (Va.; lawyer), 1773-1829 (510 pieces); papers of Donatien de Rochambeau (France; army officer), 1764-1803 (2,500 items), concerning the French in Haiti and the Haitian War for Independence; and archives of the University of Florida, 1853-1953 (100,000 pieces). The holdings of the P. K. Yonge Library of Florida History, a unit of the University of Florida Library, are separately described below.

JACKSONVILLE

Jacksonville Historical Society. Jacksonville Public Library. James C. Craig, President, P.O. Box 4343.

Holdings: 1 filing cabinet of papers, relating chiefly to northeastern Florida. Included are 75 letters dated soon after the Civil War.

—oOo—

Jacksonville Public Library. 101 East Adams St. Audrey Broward, Reference Department.

Holdings: 100 pieces, 1740-1884, relating to Florida. Included are letters, materials on early orange groves, an 1869 diary, and travel notes made in 1874 and 1884.

See Hist. Records Survey, Guide for Fla., p. 8.

LAKELAND

Park Trammell Public Library. City Librarian.

Holdings: A collection of papers relating to Spanish-American War encampments in Lakeland, 1898; and the papers (not yet cataloged) of Park Trammell (Fla.; Gov., U.S. Sen.), including clippings, letters, and photographs, and amounting to several thousand items.

MIAMI 4

Historical Association of Southern Florida. 1340 DuPont Bldg. Virginia Wilson, Corresponding Secretary.

Holdings: 750 pieces, 16th to 20th centuries, consisting of a collection of manuscripts on south Florida and the Caribbean area, 16th century to 1925 (430 pieces); 20 letters by William P. Duval (Fla.; Terr. Gov.), 1822-30; and letters by south Florida pioneers, 1880-1920 (300 pieces).

MIAMI 32

Miami Public Library. (Mrs.) Helga H. Eason, Head of Department of Community Relations.

Holdings: A small collection of manuscripts of books and short stories by Florida authors.

ST. AUGUSTINE

Castillo de San Marcos National

Monument.   The Superintendent.

Holdings: 5,000 feet of microfilm
and many photostats, on which are reproduced 34 vols., 31 bundles, 2,600
pieces, and 241 maps, 1513-1925, relating mainly to colonial Florida history, and especially to Spanish fortifications in the St. Augustine vicinity.
The originals of these documents are
in the Library of Congress, the North
Carolina State Department of Archives,
the William L. Clements Library, and
other depositories.   Included are Spanish archival and military papers, 1566-
1763, 1783-1821 (9 vols. and 2,600
pieces); British Colonial Office and military correspondence, 1763-83 (25 vols.
and 31 bundles); and maps and plans,
mostly relating to Castillo de San Marcos and other fortifications in the Southeast, 1513-1925 (241 pieces).

—oOo—

St. Augustine Historical Society.
22 St. Francis St.   Albert C. Manucy,
Librarian.

Holdings: 7,000 pieces, relating
chiefly to Florida.   Included are photostats of 15 vols. of records of the parish of St. Augustine, 1594-1763 (from
originals in the custody of the Bishop
of the Diocese of St. Augustine); numerous photographic and other copies of
papers in the Library of Congress, the
Spanish archives, and elsewhere, and
an index to selected Spanish and other
manuscripts relating to Florida history during the period 1512-1764 (10,000
entries); a medical officer's account
of experiences in the Second Seminole
War; and miscellaneous papers pertaining to slavery, Indian relations,
land transactions, and the War of 1812.
   See Hist. Records Survey, Guide
for Fla., pp. 12-14.

ST. LEO

St. Leo Abbey Library.   Rev. Fidelis

J. Dunlap, Librarian.

Holdings: 200 vols. and 1 folder,
relating chiefly to the Catholic Church
in Florida.
   See Hist. Records Survey, Guide
for Fla., p. 15.

ST. PETERSBURG

St. Petersburg Historical Society.
335 Second Ave. NE.   (Mrs.) Oma M.
Cross, Curator; Alfred E. Newman,
Historical Research Secretary.

Holdings: 2,500 items, from
1689, but chiefly 19th century, relating for the most part to Florida
and Floridians.   Included are the
journal of a Massachusetts clergyman
and daguerreotypist, 1832-72; letterpress copies of correspondence about
the construction of a railroad from
Oakland to St. Petersburg, 1886-89
(2 vols.); and other scattered manuscripts used for exhibit purposes in
the Society's museum.
   See Hist. Records Survey, Guide
for Fla., p. 15.

SANFORD

Henry S. Sanford Memorial Library.
115 West 5th St.   (Mrs.) Sara M.
Driggers, Librarian.

Holdings: Papers of Henry S.
Sanford (Conn., Fla.; Minister to Belgium, founder of Sanford, Fla.), 1838-
91 (10,000 pieces).

TALLAHASSEE

Field Note Division, State Department of Agriculture.   Nathan Mayo,
Commissioner of Agriculture.

Holdings: Records transferred

in 1908 from the Office of the U. S. Surveyor-General of Florida to the State Commissioner of Agriculture, consisting of records of the Board of Commissioners for Ascertaining Claims and Titles to Lands in East Florida, 1781-1846 (10 linear ft.); records of the Board of Commissioners for Ascertaining Claims and Titles to Lands in West Florida, 1775-1846 (2 linear ft.); and records of the Office of the U. S. Surveyor-General of Florida, 1799-1908 (65 linear ft.). There are also "Briefed Translations of Spanish Land Grants in Florida," prepared by the Historical Records Survey (5 vols.).

See Survey of Federal Archives, Inventory of Federal Archives in the States, Series VIII, Fla., pp. 3-12 (1941. Processed).

—oOo—

Florida State Library. Dorothy Dodd, State Librarian.

Holdings: 260 linear ft., comprising (1) noncurrent official records of the State, including some records of the Territory of Florida, 1822-45, and (2) personal papers and other materials that are not part of the State's archives (7,000 pieces). The latter group includes papers relating to Achille Murat (France, Fla.; author), 1826-46 (150 pieces); business records, including papers on the Florida Coast Line Canal and Transportation Co., 1891-1912 (4,500 pieces); a collection of Civil War letters; some county records (200 pieces); Florida Historical Records Survey "typoscripts" of diaries, letters, and other manuscripts, chiefly 1784-1900 (93 items); and photostats and microfilms of documents pertaining to Florida now in the National Archives and elsewhere.

See Hist. Records Survey, Guide for Fla., pp. 18-20; and a list of "typoscripts" in Fla. Hist. Quarterly, 18:216-224 (Jan. 1940).

Florida State University Library. N. Orwin Rush, Director of Libraries.

Holdings: 217 items, relating chiefly to Tallahassee, British West Florida, and Florida. Included are a diary of an Alabama farmer, 1836-38; a soldier's journal kept during the Florida War, 1837-39; 103 land grants issued at Pensacola, 1770-80; and 53 items relating to British possessions in East and West Florida, 1767-1801.

WINTER PARK

Mills Memorial Library, Rollins College. (Mrs.) Alice McBride Hansen, Librarian.

Holdings: One Pali manuscript on the Burmese religion and two 17th-century breviaries; the Jessie B. Rittenhouse Collection of 1,479 autographed letters, 1890-1947, of American and British poets, among which are 99 from Sara Teasdale (Mo., N.Y.; poet), 1911-32; 28 manuscripts of Irving Bacheller (N.Y.; journalist, novelist), typed with the author's revisions; 1 filing case drawer of undated manuscripts of William Sloane Kennedy (Conn., Pa., Mass.; anthologist, literary biographer); letters, miscellaneous papers, and 124 manuscripts of Henry Nehrling (Wis., Fla.; botanist, ornithologist); 2 large trunks of letters, account books, and miscellaneous papers of horticultural interest, 1866-1930, of Theodore Luqueer Mead; 11 filing case drawers and 19 scrapbooks of papers of Hamilton Holt (N.Y., Fla.; editor, international peace advocate, pres. of Rollins College), 1899-1942; and a few miscellaneous items. The Library maintains a Union Catalog of Floridiana, which includes information about manuscripts in Florida libraries.

GEORGIA

ATHENS

University of Georgia Libraries. William Porter Kellam, Director of Libraries.

Holdings: A substantial body of papers, in the Special Collections Division, 1732-1955, relating chiefly to the University, to Georgia, and to the South.

For the colonial period there are the Egmont Papers, 1732-52 (21 vols.), including records of the Trustees of the Colony of Georgia, the journal of William Stephens (Secretary of the Colony), and the journal of John Wesley (England; founder of Methodism). In the Telamon Cuyler Collection, 1735-1945, are colonial items, as well as materials for later periods (15,077 items). The Keith Read Manuscript Collection, 1732-1865 (3,625 items), consisting of maps, letters, diaries, letter books, autographs, and deeds, is especially rich for the colonial period.

Papers of persons who held high public offices include those of Joseph M. Brown (Ga.; railroad administrator, Gov.), 1865-1930 (961 items); Howell Cobb (Ga.; Gov., U.S. Rep. and Sec. Treas., Confed. Army officer), 1861-65 (8 letter books); Rebecca Latimer Felton (Ga.; writer, lecturer, first woman U.S. Sen.), 1835-1929 (4,000 items); William Henry Fleming (Ga.; lawyer, U.S. Rep.), 1875-1912 (102 items); E. Stevens Henry (Conn.; merchant, U.S. Rep.), 1896-1913 (5 letter books); Joseph Rucker Lamar (Ga.; U.S. Supreme Court Justice), 1911-16 (several hundred letters and other items); Wilson Lumpkin (Ga.; Gov., U.S. Rep. and Sen.), 1828-65 (43 personal letters);

and Hoke Smith (Ga.; newspaper editor, Gov., U.S. Sen. and Sec. Interior), 1879-1931 (30 vols. and 24,313 items).

Papers of other persons include those of Godfrey Barnsley (Ga.; English consul, cotton merchant) and family, 19th century (several hundred items); Corra May Harris (Ga.; author), 1908-39 (17,400 items), including letters and literary manuscripts; and Joseph N. LeConte (Ga.; educator) and family, colonial period through the 1930's (several thousand items). There are also numerous papers of other Georgia individuals and families, containing information about education, railroads, plantations, and business operations generally.

Records of organizations include those of the Odd Fellows (of Georgia), 1904-8 (5,973 items); the Georgia Psychological Association, 1946-54 (345 items); and the Georgia State Democratic Committee, 1948-54 (36 vols.), consisting of letters, reports, minutes, and other papers.

The University archives include official records of the University and some of its administrative units, 1785-1955 (100 vols.), and records of various student organizations (several hundred volumes). Among the papers of faculty members, 1870-1950 (several thousand items), are those of David Crenshaw Barrow (chancellor, 1906-25), Harmon W. Caldwell (pres., 1935-48), Walter Barnard Hill (chancellor, 1899-1905), Patrick Hues Mell (chancellor, 1878-88), 528 items and 8 scrapbooks, Jonathan Clark Rogers (Pres., 1949-50), several hundred items, Charles Mercer Snelling (chancellor, 1926-32), and Andrew McNairn Soule (pres. of College of Agriculture, 1907-33).

ATLANTA   9

Atlanta Historical Society, Inc. 1753
Peachtree St. NE. Col. Allen Phelps
Julian, USA (Ret.), Director.

Holdings: Several thousand letters
and other manuscripts, relating chiefly to Atlanta; and 20,000 pictures of
the Atlanta area.

ATLANTA

Atlanta University Library. Andrew
J. McLemore, Librarian, Special
Services.

Holdings: A collection relating
chiefly to Negro history and culture.
Included are 49 letters of John Brown
(Pa., N.Y., Kans.; abolitionist), 1826-
59; papers of Horace Bumstead (Ga.;
Congregational minister, pres. of Atlanta Univ.), 1875-1907 (1 box); papers
of Thomas Clarkson (England; antislavery advocate), 1785-1839 (19 letters);
and a ledger of contracts between freedmen and employers, 1867. There are
also the records of the Commission on
Interracial Cooperation, 1919-44 (40
file drawers).

ATLANTA   9

Department of Archives and History.
Mary Givens Bryan, Director.

Holdings: 90,000 vols. and 4,000,000
pieces, 1732 to date, consisting of (1)
noncurrent official records, many dating from the colonial period, held by
the Department as the State's archival
agency, and (2) other papers relating
chiefly to Georgia.

In the first category are transcripts
of papers pertaining to colonial Georgia
from the British Public Record Office
(39 vols.); correspondence of the Governors, 1786-1897; executive department minutes, 1793-1930; the State
constitutions of 1789 and 1861; journals of the constitutional conventions
of 1787-89 and 1795; legislative journals, 1777 to date; Georgia laws,
1764 to date; and judicial records, including those of the court of appeals
and the supreme court. Of particular importance are land grant records
and maps and plats of the surveyor
general's office; the adjutant general's records relating to the Revolutionary War, the War of 1812, and
Indian wars and to the militia in the
Civil War (other Confederate records
have not yet been transferred); and
records concerning the State-owned
Western and Atlanta Railroad, 1836-
70 (1,502 vols. and many pieces).
Some original county records, including wills, land grants, deeds, and tax
digests, are in the Department; and
other county records are being microfilmed for deposit in it.

In the second category are papers
of organizations, including churches,
educational institutions, and some pa-
triotic and local historical societies.
There are also unknown quantities of
the papers of Joseph E. Brown (Ga.;
Gov., U.S. Sen.), 1861-65; Howell
Cobb (Ga.; Gov., U.S. Rep., Sec.
Treas., Confed. Army officer); Lucian Lamar Knight (Ga.; State historian, organizer and director of the
Department of Archives); James
Longstreet (Ala., La., Ga.; U.S. and
Confed. Army officer, U.S. Railroad
Commissioner); James E. Oglethorpe
(England; philanthropist, founder of
the colony of Ga.); and Harman Ver-
elst (Ga.; sec. to the trustees of the
colony), 1732-54 (1 vol.).

See Maud B. Cobb, "Check List
of the Georgia Archival Material in
Certain Offices of the Capitol," in Ga.
Hist. Assn., Proceedings, 1917, pp.
49-63; Lucian L. Knight, Shall Our
Records Be Lost? Georgia's Most
Vital Need: a Department of Archives
(1917. 34 p.); and Mary Givens Bry-

an, A Report by the Georgia Department of Archives and History on Archival, Historical and Museum Activities in Georgia (1955. [65] p. Processed).

ATLANTA 22

Emory University Library. Thomas
E. Crowder, Chief, Special Collections.

Holdings: 179,300 pieces, 1750-
1940, relating chiefly to (1) the history of Methodism and (2) the history
of the South, particularly in the Confederate period.

In the former field the Thursfield
Smith Wesleyana Collection, 1750-
1900 (3,000 pieces), contains a diary
and numerous letters of John Wesley
(England; Methodist clergyman and
hymn writer) and other members of
the family; letters and other papers
of Methodist bishops and ministers in
America; records of individual churches and conferences and Indian missions;
and other manuscripts on Methodism
from its beginning to the 20th century.
Also in this field are papers of Young
J. Allen (Methodist missionary to China), 1857-1907 (700 pieces); Warren
A. Candler (Ga.; Methodist bishop,
author, chancellor of Emory Univ.),
1898-1938 (30,000 pieces); Atticus
Greene Haygood (Ga.; Methodist bishop, author, pres. of Emory College),
1880-1910 (2,000 pieces); and John
McClintock (Pa., N. Y.; Methodist
clergyman, Dickinson College prof.,
author), 1825-75 (1,600 pieces).

Other holdings include papers of
Joseph M. Brown (Ga.; railroad administrator, Gov.), 1891-98 (9,614
letters in 17 letter books); Henry W.
Grady (Ga.; journalist, orator), 1875-
85 (1,000 pieces); Joel Chandler Harris (Ga.; journalist, author), 1855-
1925 (4,000 pieces); Mary Noailles
Murfree, known as Charles Egbert

Craddock (Tenn.; novelist), 1870-
1900 (260 pieces); and Augustus M.
Toplady (England; Calvinist clergyman, author, hymn writer), 1762-
76 (234 pieces).

Relating particularly to the South
are manuscripts in the Keith Read
Confederate Collection, 1850-75
(9,000 pieces), which include papers
of Godfrey Barnsley (Ga.; English
consul, cotton merchant), 1826-1923
(1,000 pieces), Jefferson Davis (Miss.;
U. S. Rep. and Sen., Sec. War, Confed. Pres.), 1846-85 (68 pieces); J.P.
Hambleton (Ga.; journalist and surgeon), 1857-93 (275 pieces); John H.
Hewitt (Md., Va., Ga.; journalist,
playwright, musician), 1830-1901
(2,000 pieces); and James Chesnut
(S. C.; U. S. Sen., Confed. Army officer), 1864-65 (425 letters in 1 military letter book). Included also are
various papers relating to Confederate armies, particularly the quartermaster and medical departments of
the Army of the Tennessee (4,000
pieces). Closely related to this collection are papers of Alexander Hamilton Stephens (Ga.; U. S. Rep., Confed. Vice Pres., Gov.), 1837-82
(1,900 pieces); records of the Savannah Squadron of the Confederate Navy
(600 pieces); some Confederate medical records, including a volume of
records of the Georgia Relief and
Hospital Association and the papers
of Samuel H. Stout (Tenn., Ga., Tex.;
physician, medical director of Confed. hospitals), 1847-1903 (673 pieces).
Scattered among various collections
are 150 letters by Robert Toombs
(Ga.; U. S. Rep. and Sen., Confed.
Sec. State).

The Library also has records of
the Stone Mountain Confederate Mon-
umental Association, 1914-35 (3,000
pieces), including more than 100 letters of Gutzon Borglum (N. Y.; sculptor); a number of small collections of
Civil War soldiers' letters (both
Northern and Southern); a number of

Civil War diaries; and business records of the firm of Harrold Brothers, Americus, Ga., factors, 1859-1940 (100,000 pieces).

See Downs, Resources of Southern Libraries, p. 69; Richard B. Harwell, "A Brief Calendar of the Jefferson Davis Papers in the . . . Emory University Library," in Journal of Miss. History, 4:20-30 (Jan. 1942), and "The Emory Library: Its Collections," in Antiquarian Bookman, 4:305-307 (Aug. 13, 1949); and James H. Young, "Alexander H. Stephens Papers in the Emory University Library," in Emory Univ. Quarterly, 2:30-37 (Mar. 1946).

ATLANTA 3

Georgia State Library. Jane Oliver, State Librarian.

Holdings: Letters of Francis Robert Goulding (Ga.; Presbyterian clergyman, author), 1862-81 (112 items), principally to his son.

—oOo—

Sheppard W. Foster Library. Emory University School of Dentistry. 106 Forrest Ave. NE. (Mrs.) Kathleen M. Barron, Librarian.

Holdings: 8 vols., 1869-1906, chiefly minutes of the Georgia State Dental Society, 1869-79; the Southern Dental Association, 1869-97; the National Association of Dental Faculties, 1884-1902; the Southern Branch of the National Dental Association, 1897-1905; and the Atlanta Dental College faculty, 1893-95.

EAST POINT

Federal Records Center, GSA. 221 St. Joseph Ave. Chief.

Holdings: A large quantity of non-current and semicurrent records, chiefly of recent date, of nonmilitary agencies of the U. S. Government in Alabama, Florida, Georgia, Mississippi, North Carolina, South Carolina, and Tennessee. Most of these records have been appraised for disposal after specified periods of time, but some will be preserved because of their enduring value. Records in the latter category include those of the British admiralty court and its successor State admiralty court in Charleston, S. C., 1716-89 (9 ft.); U.S. district courts and predecessor circuit courts, including some records of the courts of the Confederate States of America, from 1789; and semiofficial records of Xenophon Hicks (Tenn.; U. S. dist. court and circuit court of appeals judge), 1923-52 (48 ft.). Also scheduled for preservation are records of the Bureau of Customs, from 1837; Post Office ante bellum and Spaulding indemnity claims, 1861-1942 (26 ft.); and Internal Revenue agents' correspondence, 1867-1910 (13 ft.). There are also records of the Mixed Claims Commission, United States and Germany, and of the Tripartite Claims Commission, United States, Austria, and Hungary, 1922-37 (488 ft.).

MILLEDGEVILLE

Georgia State College for Women College and Regional Archives. Elizabeth G. Ferguson, Reference Librarian.

Holdings: Archives of the College, 1887 to date (47 ft.), and 1,292 other items, 1791 to date, relating chiefly to Georgia. Included are a collection of autographs of early Georgia governors (23 items); a letter collection containing one or a few letters by each of several 19th-century Southerners; some ledgers, account books, plantation records, and other business documents; a number of indentures and land grants; a diary kept while visiting schools from Georgia to New England, 1849-51; a War Between the States collection, 1861-70 (65 items); and minutes of the Thalian Society of Oglethorpe University, 1859-63.

SAVANNAH

Georgia Historical Society.   501 Whitaker St.   Mrs. L. M. Hawes, Director.

Holdings: A substantial quantity of manuscripts, 1748-1955, relating chiefly to Georgia. Personal papers include those of Samuel Elbert (Ga.; Rev. War officer, Gov.), 1776-86 (1 vol. and 2 pieces); Benjamin Hawkins (N.C.; Member Continental Cong., U.S. Sen., Indian agent), 1796-1813 (11 vols.); James Jackson (Ga.; U.S. Rep. and Sen.), 1781-98 (1 vol. and 25 pieces); and Lachlan McIntosh (Ga.; Rev. War officer), 1774-99 (1 vol. and 71 pieces). There is also a diary of John J. Zubly (Ga.; Member Continental Cong., Presbyterian clergyman, pamphleteer), 1770-81 (1 vol.).   The Wayne-Stites-Anderson family papers, 1791-1875 (25 vols. and 11 boxes), contain papers of Richard Wayne (S.C., Ga.; commission merchant), James Moore Wayne (Ga.; U.S. Rep. and Supreme Court Justice), Richard M. Stites (Ga.; lawyer), and George W. Anderson (Ga.; Confed. Army officer, cotton factor, planter).   The Gordon family papers, 1810-1939 (36 vols. and 25 boxes), containing correspondence, diaries, notebooks, scrapbooks, and business papers of Gordon and Co., cotton factors, includes papers of William Washington Gordon (Ga.; lawyer, railroad pres.) and his son William Washington

Gordon (Ga.; Confed. Army and Spanish-Am. War officer, cotton merchant), Juliette Magill Kinzie (Ill.; author), and Juliette Gordon Low (England, Scotland, Ga.; founder of Girl Scouts of America).   Another large collection of family papers is that of the Telfair family of Georgia, 1772-1875 (7 vols. and 25 boxes), including papers of Edward Telfair (Ga.; planter, Member Continental Cong., Gov.), Thomas Gibbons (Ga.; lawyer, politician, steamboat operator), and William Gibbons (Ga.; lawyer, Member Continental Cong.).

Also included are journals of the Georgia Council of Safety and Executive Council, 1777 (1 vol.); minutes of the Royal Governor and Council of Georgia, 1774-75 and 1779-80 (2 vols.); the Georgia Society of Colonial Dames Collection, 1768-1909 (20 boxes), consisting of family papers, genealogical records, deeds, plantation accounts, and maps; a minute book of the commissioners of pilotage, Port of Savannah, 1800-15 (1 vol.); daybooks of two physicians, 1804-7 and 1810-12 (3 vols.); minutes of the faculty of the Savannah Medical College, 1853-62 (1 vol.); a collection of Confederate Army muster rolls and payrolls, 1863-65 (14 boxes); and records of several local military units, notably Chatham Artillery and Irish Jasper Greens. Other holdings include records of business firms, diaries, census records, land lottery records, plantation records, and personal account books.

See Lilla M. Hawes, "A Profile of the Georgia Historical Society," in Ga. Hist. Quarterly, 36:132-136 (June 1952); and occasional notes in the Ga. Hist. Society, Collections (1840-1955. 11 vols.) and Ga. Hist. Quarterly (1917 to date).

HAWAII

HONOLULU

Federal Records Center Annex, GSA. P. O. Box 673. Chief.

Holdings: A quantity of noncurrent or semicurrent records of nonmilitary agencies of the U. S. Government in Hawaii. Most of them have been appraised for disposal after specified periods, but some will be retained because of their enduring value. Among the latter are records of the U. S. district court, from 1900; U. S. attorneys, from 1917; Coast Guard, from 1900; Immigration and Naturalization Service, from 1908; and Geological Survey, from 1895. (This Annex is under the jurisdiction of the Federal Records Center, San Francisco.)

HONOLULU 14

Gregg M. Sinclair Library. University of Hawaii. Carl Stroven, Librarian; Janet E. Bell, Librarian in charge of Hawaiiana.

Holdings: 38 vols., 1 box, 5 filing cases, several pieces, and some unsorted and uncounted groups of papers, 1824-1934, relating chiefly to Hawaii.

Papers of individuals include those of Francis T. Bishop (England; ship's surgeon), 1832-35 (4 vols. and 8 pieces), pertaining to Pacific whaling, Hawaii, and Tahiti; Lady Jane Franklin (England; widow of arctic explorer Sir John Franklin) and some of her associates, 1861-81 (1 box), relating to her visit to Hawaii and her interest in the Church of England there; David L. Gregg (Ill., Hawaii, Nev.; U. S. Commissioner to the Hawaiian Kingdom, Minister of Finance of the Hawaiian

Kingdom), 1853-62 (9-vol. diary and 15 letter books); Thomas A. Jaggar (Hawaii; volcanologist), 1907-53 (2 filing cases); Lawrence M. Judd (Hawaii; Gov.), 1929-34 (2 filing cases); Elisha Loomis (Hawaii; printer, early missionary), 1824-26 (1 vol.); John Rae (Canada, Hawaii; teacher, economist), 1853-72 (700 pages); Gregg M. Sinclair (Hawaii; Director of Oriental Institute, pres. of Univ. of Hawaii), 1936-55 (1 filing case); Charles Warren Stoddard (Calif.; author), 1882-83, Hawaiian diary (9 vols.), a few letters, and several of his published books with marginal annotations by him; and Thomas George Thrum (Hawaii; specialist in Hawaiian culture), undated [1880-1920 ?] translations of Hawaiian legends, short stories, etc., and drafts of some of his published works; and several small groups of letters of other persons important in Hawaiian life.

There are also a journal of a voyage from Astoria, Oreg., to Honolulu, 1872-73; a study of volcanic phenomena, 1887 (1 vol.); letter books and other business papers of the manager of Koloa plantation, oldest sugar plantation in the islands, 1837-39; and business correspondence of the W. G. Irwin Co., sugar factors, 1890-1910.

HONOLULU 3

Hawaiian Historical Society. P. O. Box 2596. (Mrs.) Willowdean C. Handy, Librarian.

Holdings: 4 filing drawers, 1828-1912, relating chiefly to the Hawaiian Islands and Polynesia and including papers of several missionaries under

the American Board of Commissioners
for Foreign Missions. There are papers of William Dewitt Alexander (Hawaii; historian, linguist, Surveyor-
Gen.), 1890-1912 (250 pieces); Hiram
Bingham, Jr. (Hawaii, Gilbert Islands;
missionary), 1856-57 (1 vol.), journal
of a voyage from Boston to Micronesia;
Sereno Edwards Bishop (Hawaii; missionary, surveyor, editor, writer),
1900-5, 73 letters to G. D. Gilman
(see below); Samuel Northrup Castle
(N. Y., Hawaii; missionary, merchant,
member Privy Council, House of Reps.,
and House of Nobles, Hawaiian Kingdom), 1839-41 (1 vol. and 3 pieces);
Titus Coan (Conn., Hawaii; missionary), 1844-82, shipping lists (82 pages); Gorham Dummer Gilman (Mass.,
Hawaii; consul general for Hawaii at
Boston), 1843-48 (598 pages), concerning travel in the Hawaiian Islands (see
also S. E. Bishop above); David L.
Gregg (Ill., Hawaii, Nev.; U. S. Commissioner to the Hawaiian Kingdom),
1853-54 (1 vol.); Joseph Jackson (Postmaster Gen., Hawaiian Kingdom), 1856-
59 (1 vol. and 20 pieces); Alexander Li-
holiho (Hawaii; King Kamehameha IV),
1849-50 (1 vol.), a journal of voyages
made to the United States, England, and
France; William Charles Lunalilo (Hawaii; King), 1847-53 (110 pages), including diaries, letters, poems, music, and drawings; Henry Obookiah
(Hawaii; pupil at mission school in
Conn.), 1817 (1 vol.), an elementary
grammar and vocabulary of the Hawaiian language; William Cooper Parke
(N. H., Hawaii; Marshal of the Hawaiian
Kingdom), 1859-60 (1 vol.), journal;
and Joel Turrill (N. Y.; U. S. Rep., U. S.
consul to Hawaiian Islands), 1850-60
(103 pieces), correspondence with prominent men of the Islands.

HONOLULU 13

Hawaiian Mission Children's Society
Library. 560 Kawaiahao St. Bernice

Judd, Librarian.

Holdings: 65 vols. and 33 file
drawers, 1819-1946, relating to American missionaries and the American
Mission in Hawaii. Included are journals of 32 missionaries, 1820-94 but
chiefly 1820-60 (65 vols.); and a mass
of material (33 file drawers), 1819-
1946, concerning the American Mission in Hawaii (sponsored and sup-
ported by the American Board of Commissioners for Foreign Missions) and
its successor, the Hawaiian Evangelical Association.

HONOLULU 14

Hawaii War Records Depository (Uni-
versity of Hawaii Library). Carl
Stroven, Librarian; Janet E. Bell,
Librarian in charge of depository.

Holdings: A large amount of
material relating to Hawaii in World
War II. Included are 17 filing cases
that contain (in addition to books,
pamphlets, articles, and Federal,
Territorial, and municipal documents)
an undetermined amount of manuscript
material. There are letters, memoranda, cablegrams, personal diaries
and narratives, and transcripts of interviews and radio broadcasts.

HONOLULU 13

Public Archives. Iolani Palace
Grounds. Agnes C. Conrad, Archivist.

Holdings: 3,250 ft., 1824-1959,
consisting of (1) noncurrent official
records held by the depository as
Hawaii's archival agency and (2) other papers relating chiefly to the Hawaiian Islands. The quantity of documents is given in terms of linear
feet.

In the first category are records of the Kingdom, provisional government, Republic, and Territory. Among the most important files for the period before annexation are records of the Privy, Cabinet, and Executive Councils, 1846-1900 (6 ft.); the Executive and Foreign Office, 1840-1900 (105 ft.); the Interior Department, including land records, 1830-1900 (120 ft.); the Department of Public Instruction, 1846-1900 (35 ft.); and the Attorney General, 1844-1900 (150 ft.). There are also legislative records, 1840-1900 (115 ft.), and immigration and naturalization records, 1845-1900 (30 ft.). Records of the Territory include files of the Governor, 1900-57 (215 ft.); the Attorney General, 1900-6 (50 ft.); the Department of Public Instruction, 1900-25 (120 ft.); the Department of Public Works, 1900-13 (50 ft.); the Office of Civilian Defense, 1941-45 (300 ft.); and the Hawaii Statehood Commission, 1937-59 (40 ft.). There are also legislative records, 1900-59 (800 ft.); and election records, 1900-59 (100 ft.).

In the second category are papers of Liliuokalani (Hawaii; Queen), 1833-1924 (4 ft.); Emma (Hawaii; Queen Consort), 1853-83 (2 ft.); Robert C. Wyllie (Hawaii; Minister of Foreign Affairs), 1844-65 (1 ft.); Henry A. P. Carter (Hawaii; merchant, Minister to the U. S.), 1891-1910 (1 ft.); and papers of six Delegates to the U. S. Congress from the Territory of Hawaii, 1902-56 (90 ft.). Included also are copies of British Foreign Office records pertaining to Hawaii, 1824-71 (1 ft.); and copies of logs, journals, and letters relating to Captain Cook and the discovery of the Hawaiian Islands (50 pieces).

IDAHO

BOISE

Idaho Historical Society. 610 Parkway Dr. Merle W. Wells, Historian and Archivist.

Holdings: A growing collection consisting of (1) noncurrent official records in the Idaho State Archives and (2) other papers relating chiefly to Idaho and the Pacific Northwest.

In the former group are nearly all surviving territorial records (except the original legislative journals and session laws preserved by the Secretary of State), the entire correspondence of the Governor's office to 1950, and the State treasurer's records to 1928. There are also significant papers relating to several important Carey Act irrigation projects.

In the Division of Manuscripts there are more than 50 collections. Personal papers include diaries of William Judson Boone (Idaho; Presbyterian minister, pres. of the College of Idaho), 1891-1936; papers of William E. Borah (Idaho; lawyer, U.S. Sen.), 1896-1907 (28 ft.); papers of Calvin Cobb and his daughter Margaret Cobb Ailshie (Idaho; newspaper publishers), 20th century, relating substantially to forest history; the autobiography of Fred Thomas Dubois (Idaho; U.S. Sen.); and papers of James Henry Hawley (Idaho; lawyer, Gov.), late 19th and early 20th centuries (80 ft.). Included also are letters sent from the Lapwai Indian Agency (Nez Perce Reservation), 1871-76, 1880-83 (6 vols.); the records of a department store in Boise, about 1880-1920 (24 ft.); and papers pertaining to missionaries, mining, fur trading, and pioneer settlements.

IDAHO FALLS

Idaho Falls Public Library. (Mrs.) Dorothy Coffin Hickey, Librarian.

Holdings: Reminiscences of pioneers and miscellaneous papers relating chiefly to Idaho Falls and its vicinity.

See John Van Male, Resources of Pacific Northwest Libraries, p. 170 (1943).

MOSCOW

University of Idaho Library. L. F. Zimmerman, Librarian.

Holdings: A quantity of papers consisting of (1) the archives of the University from 1889; and (2) other papers relating chiefly to Idaho. The archives include papers of the presidents of the University, 1897-1917, and 7,500 photographs. Other holdings are a collection relating to William E. Borah (Idaho; U.S. Sen.), 1904-40 (5 scrapbooks and 450 pictures, cartoons, and miscellaneous items); papers of Weldon B. Heyburn (Idaho; U.S. Sen.), 1897-1912 (4 letterpress books and 5,200 letters); and papers of George L. Shoup (Idaho; Gov., U.S. Sen.), 1861-1901 (1,200 items), including personal business records and letters.

POCATELLO

Idaho State College Museum. Earl H. Swanson, Director.

Holdings: 123,000 items, dating

from 1836 and relating chiefly to Idaho. Included are papers of Fred Thomas DuBois (Idaho; Terr. Delegate to Cong., U. S. Sen., member of U. S.–Canada International Joint Commission), consisting of both public and private correspondence (100,000 items); personal correspondence of Ethel E. Redfield (Idaho; State Supt. of public instruction); and a few letters of George L. Shoup (Idaho; Gov., U. S. Sen.). There are also records of the Lemhi Indian agency, 1886-1911 (10,000 items); statements by Indians on their history (169 items); and other materials on Idaho Indians (4,078 items). Also included are a number of volumes of diaries and reminiscences of pioneers, the earliest, 1836-40; doc-

uments pertaining to Fort Hall, 1877-1942 (289 items); records of a pioneer store in Salmon City, 1869-79 (901 items); a ledger, 1875-1907, of a trading post at Silver City; historical materials on the Mormons, 1922-37 (83 items and 842 pages); documents relating to Pocatello, 1915-40 (164 items); and documents pertaining to an Illinois volunteer company in the Civil War (43 items). There are also Idaho materials compiled by the WPA (2,937 items).

See Harold C. Vedeler, "Historical Materials at the Southern Branch of the University of Idaho" (i. e., Idaho State College), in Pacific Northwest Quarterly, 27:174 (Apr. 1936).

AURORA

Aurora College Library. Ethel W. Tapper, Librarian.

Holdings: 2,000 items relating chiefly to the Advent Christian Church. Included are correspondence, 1814-49 (on microfilm), sermons, and other papers of William Miller (Vt., N. Y.; leader of the Adventist movement); and some letters and papers of other important Adventist leaders.
See Ill. Libraries, 40:369 (Apr. 1958).

BLOOMINGTON

Illinois Conference Historical Library. 201 East University Ave. Charles P. Lotz, Director; Rodney J. Ferguson, Librarian.

Holdings: 500 items, 1824-1955, relating chiefly to Methodism in Illinois and the Central West. The collection is housed in the library of Illinois Wesleyan University. Included are sketches of early ministers, laymen, schools, circuits, and camp meetings, 1809-74. There are also minutes of annual conferences, quarterly conference records, sermons, manuscripts, and pictures of Illinois annual conferences, 1866-1948; histories of central Illinois churches and institutions related to the Methodist Church; and letters written by and about pioneer Methodist figures.
See Hist. Records Survey, Guide for Ill., p. 1.

—oOo—

McLean County Historical Society. 201 East Grove St.

Holdings: 600 items relating chiefly to pioneer settlers, Indians, industrial and agricultural developments, schools, and other aspects of local history.
See Hist. Records Survey, Guide for Ill., p. 1.

CAIRO

Cairo Public Library.

Holdings: 30 items, 1837-1933, mainly of local interest. Included are a Cairo steamboat register, 1853; the register of a wharfboat, 1853-55; cash books of a showboat, 1882-1922 (3 vols.); and records of a Grand Army of the Republic post, 1855-1915 (3 vols.).
See Hist. Records Survey, Guide for Ill., p. 2.

CARBONDALE

Southern Illinois University Library. Ralph E. McCoy, Director.

Holdings: Scattered official records of some southern Illinois counties, especially Gallatin County; archives of the University, 1885 to date; several collections of personal papers, among them papers of James Joyce (Ireland; author), Michael K. Lawler (Ill.; Mexican War and Civil War officer) and his family, and papers of a Presbyterian minister in Illinois, Kansas, Nebraska, and Oklahoma, 1882-1941; and miscellaneous manuscripts relating to various business and professional pursuits.
See Ill. Libraries, 40:333-339 (Apr. 1958).

CHICAGO 11

American College of Surgeons Library. 40 East Erie St. Kathleen Worst, Librarian.

Holdings: 6 linear ft. of x-ray films and 30 linear ft. of manuscript case histories, 1900-16, by John Benjamin Murphy (Ill.; pioneer in abdominal surgery, prof. of surgery at Rush Medical College and Northwestern Univ. Medical School).

CHICAGO 3

Art Institute of Chicago. Michigan Blvd. at Adams St. Ruth E. Schoneman, Librarian.

Holdings: 61 vols., 615 pieces, 25 rolls of microfilm, and many architectural drawings and blueprints, relating chiefly to art and architecture in the Chicago area. Included are a collection, in the Institute's Department of Prints and Drawings, of illuminated medieval and Renaissance manuscripts (13 books and 122 pieces); and, in the Ryerson Library, the minutes of the Society for the Advancement of Truth in Art, 1863-65 (1 vol.).

The Burnham Library contains the papers of Daniel H. Burnham (Ill.; architect, city planner), 1890-1912. These include Burnham's diaries, 1895-1909 (15 vols.); his letter books, 1890-1912 (20 vols., of which 3 contain private letters); and working drawings for 10 buildings designed by his firms. There are also materials relating to the World's Columbian Exposition of 1893, including a volume of photographs of the grounds and buildings under construction, 1891-92; Burnham's final report as Director of Work, 1894 (8 vols.); and a letter book of McKim, Mead, and White, 1890-93, concerning the exposition. Included also are 353 drawings by Walter Burley

Griffin (Ill., Australia; architect, city planner, developer of Canberra, manager of the Greater Sydney Development Association) and his wife, Marion Mahoney Griffin; and a business letter book, 1896-1901, of Howard Van Doren Shaw (Ill.; architect). Also in the Burnham Library are papers of Louis Henri Sullivan (Ill.; architect), 1868-1922 (3 vols., 53 manuscript pieces, 56 sketches, 20 drawings, and 9 sheets of working drawings of ornaments); these include Sullivan's manuscript of his "System of Ornament," with 20 drawings; and correspondence, 1922-24 (52 pieces) between Sullivan and his friend Charles H. Whitaker. The Chicago Architectural Archive in this library consists of many original working drawings and blueprints, and 23 rolls of microfilm containing over 6,500 frames of architectural drawings of early buildings in the Chicago area and documents concerning them.

See De Ricci, Census, pp. 513-518, and Ill. Libraries, 40:380 (Apr. 1958).

CHICAGO 14

Chicago Historical Society. North Ave. at Clark St. Paul M. Angle, Director; Margaret Scriven, Librarian.

Holdings: 300 linear ft., 1480-1960 but chiefly of the 19th century, relating to Chicago and the Old Northwest.

Papers of Presidents and other officials of the executive branch of the Federal Government include those of John Cabell Breckinridge (Ky.; U.S. Rep. and Sen., Vice Pres., Confed. Sec. War), 1799-1865 (60 pieces); John C. Calhoun (S.C.; U.S. Rep. and Sen., Sec. War, Vice Pres., Sec. State), 1818-50 (30 pieces); Henry Clay (Ky.; U.S. Rep. and Sen., Sec.

State), 1813-52 (65 pieces); Schuyler
Colfax (Ind.; U.S. Rep., Vice Pres.),
1845-85 (45 pieces); Henry Dearborn
(Mass.; U.S. Rep., Sec. War, War of
1812 officer), 1807-13 (150 pieces);
Henry A. S. Dearborn (Mass.; U.S.
Rep., political leader, author, collector of customs at Boston), 1805-51
(325 pieces); Zebina Eastman (Ill.;
journalist, abolitionist, U.S. consul
at Bristol), 1840-83 (286 pieces and
32 account books); Ulysses S. Grant
(U.S. Army officer, U.S. Pres.), 1851-
85 (125 pieces); Andrew Jackson (Tenn.;
U.S. Rep. and Sen., U.S. Army officer, U.S. Pres.), 1786-1845 (450 pieces);
Abraham Lincoln (Ill.; U.S. Rep., U.S.
Pres.), 1826-65 (50 pieces); Henry C.
Morris (Ill.; lawyer, U.S. consul at
Ghent), 1881-1918 (1,500 letters and a
12-vol. diary); and George Washington
(Va.; Rev. War Commander in Chief,
U.S. Pres.), 1732-99 (150 pieces). All
other Presidents are represented in
small quantities.

Papers of Members of Congress not
mentioned above include those of Isaac
Newton Arnold (Ill.; lawyer, author,
U.S. Rep.), 1840-85 (110 pieces); David
Davis (Ill.; U.S. Supreme Court Justice,
U.S. Sen.), 1815-1921 (9 linear ft. of
transcripts); John J. Hardin (Ill.; Black
Hawk War officer, U.S. Rep.) and Mar-
tin D. Hardin (Ky.; U.S. Sen.), 1754-
1929 (10 linear ft.); Elias Kent Kane
(Ill.; Terr. judge, Ill. sec. state, U.S.
Sen.), 1816-35 (250 pieces); William
Ralls Morrison (Ill.; Civil War officer,
U.S. Rep., Interstate Commerce Com-
missioner), 1858-72 (50 pieces); and
William McKendree Springer (Ill.; U.S.
Rep., judge in Indian Terr.), 1861-1904
(1,000 pieces). See also Ninian Ed-
wards, below.

Papers of other political leaders
include those of Mason Brayman (Ill.;
lawyer, editor, Civil War officer, Gov.
of Idaho Terr.), 1820-95 (3,700 pieces);
William Butler (Ill.; State treasurer),
1839-63 (75 pieces); Edward Coles (Ill.;
Gov., abolitionist), 1812-58 (100 pieces);

William Emmett Dever (Ill.; mayor of
Chicago), 1884-1929 (7 vols. and
12,000 pieces); Ninian Edwards (Ky.,
Ill.; chief justice of Ky., Gov. of Ill.,
U.S. Sen.), 1793-1833 (2,000 pieces);
Joseph Gillespie (Ill.; judge, member
of State legislature), 1809-85 (161
pieces); Madison Y. Johnson (Ill.; lawyer, railroad executive, Peace Demo-
crat), 1807-1904 (1,100 pieces);
Pierre Menard (Ill.; fur trader, merchant, Lt. Gov.), 1748-1850 (1,500
pieces); William B. Ogden (Ill.; pioneer, railroad executive, mayor of
Chicago), 1835-50 (500 pieces); and
Logan Uriah Reavis (Ill.; editor, political leader), 1844-88 (70 pieces).

Other papers include those of John
Brown (Pa., N.Y., Kans.; abolitionist),
1842-59 (90 pieces); Will J. Davis (Ill.;
theater manager), 1846-1901 (400
pieces); Melville Weston Fuller (Ill.;
Chief Justice of U.S.), 1833-1910 (8
linear ft. of transcripts); Charles J.
Guiteau (Ill.; Pres. Garfield's assas-
sin), 1852-82 (41 pieces); Jacob Kingsbury (U.S. Army officer), 1803-13
(300 pieces, chiefly transcripts); Mary Eliza McDowell (Ill.; head Univ.
of Chicago Settlement), 1894-1944
(850 pieces); Harold Fowler McCormick (Ill.; manufacturer, philanthropist, son of the inventor, C. H. Mc-
Cormick), 1880-1907 (465 pieces);
Charles Mears (Mich., Ill.; lumber
dealer), 1849-1895 (7 vols. and 1,100
pieces); Agnes Nestor (Ill.; international labor leader), 1896-1954 (6,000
pieces); Richard Parker (Va.; judge at
John Brown's trial), 1796-1879 (60
pieces); Jeremiah Porter (Ill.; pioneer
Presbyterian preacher), 1831-46 (18-
booklet journal); George Mortimer
Pullman (N.Y., Ill., Colo.; inventor,
designer of Pullman cars), 1865-1957
(3 vols. and 100 pieces); Baron Friedrich von Steuben (Prussia, N.Y.; Rev.
War officer), 1776-1822 (1,000 pieces,
chiefly transcripts); Lorado Taft (Ill.;
sculptor), 1889-1938 (200 pieces); and
James Wilkinson (U.S. Army officer,

Gov. of La. Terr.), 1779-1823 (650 pieces).

Of general interest for American history are collections on the Indians of the Chicago region (1,000 pieces); French activities in the Mississippi Valley, 1642-1800 (2,500 pieces); the American Fur Co. and other fur-trading enterprises (5,000 pieces); the Revolutionary War (a sizable amount); the Louisiana Purchase (a small but important lot); the American Colonization Society, 1820-58 (115 pieces); the gold rush (150 pieces); the Civil War (500 letters, 100 diaries, and several military rosters); the Spanish-American War, 1898 (600 pieces); the Military Order of the Loyal Legion of the United States, 1879-1924 (23 vols. and 1,300 letters); and the Naval Order of the United States, 1894-1928 (250 pieces). There is also an autograph collection of papers by signers of the Declaration of Independence.

Important for regional and State history are records relating to the English settlement in Illinois, of the early 19th century (3 diaries and 100 letters); and the Mormons in Illinois, 1836-90 (200 pieces). Materials relating to the economic growth of the Middle West include records of the Illinois and Michigan Canal (6,500 pieces); papers relating to the Galena and Chicago Union Railroad and the Illinois Central and the Burlington Railroads and to the establishment of railway mail service in Illinois; records of the White City Construction Co. (Chicago Amusement Park), 1905-12 (500 pieces); 50 collections concerning real estate; and 150 business account books. There are also papers relating to the Haymarket Riot, 1886 (9 linear ft.); the World's Columbian Exposition, 1893 (15 linear ft.); and the American Legion of Illinois, 1919 (50 pieces).

See "The Gold Rush," in Chicago History, 2:33-41 (winter 1948-49); Charles B. Pike, "Chicago Historical Society," in Business Hist. Society,

Bulletin, 8:37-41 (May 1934); Margaret Scriven, "The Chicago Historical Society," in Antiquarian Bookman, 1:802-804 (May 15, 1948), and in Ill. Libraries, 40:287-288 (Apr. 1958); and George B. Utley, "Source Material for the Study of American History in the Libraries of Chicago," in Bibliographical Society of America, Papers, 16: 30-38 (1922).

CHICAGO 37

Chicago Theological Seminary Library. 5757 University Ave. Harvey Arnold, Librarian.

Holdings: A large body of papers, 1825-1929, relating chiefly to Congregational Church history. Included are correspondence files of the American Home Missionary Society, 1825-1907 (85 filing drawers), containing letters and reports of missionaries especially those in Illinois, Indiana, Wisconsin, Michigan, and New York, but also in other parts of the United States, Canada, Hawaii, and Panama, 1825-95, and 191 letter books of the Secretary of the Society, 1826-1907; 21 letter books of the American Board of Commissioners for Foreign Missions, 1871-1906; correspondence of the Congregational Church Building Society, 1870-1920; correspondence of Edward Franklin Williams (D.C., Ill.; Congregational minister), relating to the U.S. Christian Commission and missionary education in Washington, D.C., 1850-1919 (4 filing drawers); files of the Chicago Congregational Association; and minute books and other records of various Congregational churches and other organizations.

CHICAGO 1

De Paul University Library. 64 East

Lake St. Virginia B. Goult, Librarian.

Holdings: 9 facsimiles of letters of Napoleon and associates and some papers of Robert M. La Follette (Wis.; Gov., U. S. Rep. and Sen.).

CHICAGO 25

Evangelical Mission Covenant Church of America Archives. North Park College and Theological Seminary. 3225 Foster Ave.   E. Gustav Johnson, Archivist.

Holdings: Uncataloged archives of the Church and other materials relating to it. Included are diaries of Swedish pioneers, sermons and autobiographies of early ministers, records of churches, and correspondence. Almost all of these documents are in the Swedish language.

CHICAGO 38

Federal Records Center, GSA. 7201 South Leamington Ave. Chief.

Holdings: A large quantity of noncurrent or semicurrent records, chiefly of recent date, of nonmilitary agencies of the U. S. Government in Illinois, Wisconsin, Michigan, Ohio, Kentucky, and Indiana. Most of these records have been appraised for disposal after specified periods of time, but some will be preserved because of their enduring value. Records in the latter category include records of U. S. district courts and predecessor circuit courts, from 1802; Coast Guard, from 1820; Bureau of Customs, from 1867; and Bureau of Indian Affairs, from 1869.

CHICAGO

Field Museum Library. Grant Park.

Holdings: Some Tibetan, Manchurian, and Mongolian documents pertaining to anthropology, botany, geology, and zoology and some English documents in the last three fields.

CHICAGO 90

First National Bank of Chicago Library. 38 South Dearborn St.

Holdings: Chiefly noncurrent records of the Bank. Included are personal and official papers of James B. Forgan (Ill.; banker), 1900-25 (40 ft.), containing information about the currency reform movement and the establishment of the Federal Reserve System.

CHICAGO 15

George Williams College Library. 5315 South Drexel Ave.

Holdings: 6,000 items, constituting the personal and business papers of Robert Weidensall (Ill.; Y. M. C. A. leader), including Civil War correspondence concerning the United States Military Railroad and various aspects of army life, diaries (42 vols.), and letters concerning the Young Men's Christian Association, especially in the Middle West.
    See Hist. Records Survey, Calendar of the Robert Weidensall Correspondence, 1861-1865 (1940. 34 p. Processed).

CHICAGO 16

Illinois Institute of Technology Library. 3300 South Federal St. William H. Hyde, Librarian.

Holdings: 3 vols. of medieval and

Renaissance manuscripts, a small autograph collection containing letters of some political and literary figures, and a collection of letters and other papers of famous inventors and scientists. (The Institute was formerly known as the Armour Institute of Technology.)

See De Ricci, Census, p. 512; and Hist. Records Survey, Guide for Ill., p. 2.

CHICAGO 1

John Crerar Library. 86 East Randolph St. Herman H. Henkle, Librarian.

Holdings: Several small collections relating chiefly to science, technology, and medicine. Included are some papers of Ludwig Hektoen (Ill.; pathologist, prof. at Univ. of Chicago, director of the John McCormick Institute for Infectious Diseases); James B. Herrick (Ill.; physician, prof. at Rush Medical College of Univ. of Chicago); and Nicholas Senn (Wis., Ill.; surgeon), 1868-1907 (176 manuscripts). There are also papers of a New Orleans cotton factor, 1842-63.

CHICAGO 14

McCormick Theological Seminary Library. 2330 North Halsted St. Calvin H. Schmitt, Librarian.

Holdings: 5,000 pieces, 1840 to to date, consisting chiefly of account books, letters, sermons, and other papers pertaining to the Presbyterian Church in the Middle Western States. (Some of these were transferred from the former Lane Theological Seminary, Cincinnati, Ohio.)

See Hist. Records Survey, Guide for Ill., p. 18; and Allison, Inventory, p. 143.

CHICAGO 37

Meadville Theological School Library. 5701 Woodlawn Ave.

Holdings: 110 items, 19th century, relating chiefly to the Unitarian Church in America. Included are sermons by William Ellery Channing (Mass.; Congregational minister, organizer of the American Unitarian Association), and letters from prominent 19th-century Americans.

See Hist. Records Survey, Guide for Ill., p. 14.

—oOo—

Midwest Inter-Library Center. 5721 South Cottage Grove Ave. Gordon R. Williams, Director.

Holdings: A substantial collection of papers, chiefly of modern interest. Included are records and briefs filed with the U. S. Courts of Appeals for the Second, Third, Fourth, Sixth, Ninth, and District of Columbia Circuits, and similar records filed with the Wisconsin supreme court, 1930's to date (2,300 ft.); microfilm copies of transcripts and records of 23 important recent trials involving the issue of communism (170,000 pages); nearly complete records of the Nuremberg war crimes trials (1,343 pamphlet boxes) and many of the Far East war crimes trials, 1944-47; manuscript annual reports of insurance companies, submitted to the insurance commissioner of Illinois, 1930's to date (15,000 reports); foreign radio broadcast scripts, 1931-45, as monitored by the Columbia Broadcasting System (63 pamphlet boxes); papers, studies, and maps relating to Chicago, assembled in 1912-15 by a committee investigating smoke abatement and electrification of railway terminals (418 vols.,

43 packages, 6 portfolios, and 89 map
cases); orders, opinions, hearings, and
reports of the National War Labor Board
Regional Directive Boards, 1940's (24
filing drawers); and records of the Sixth
Regional Office of the National War Labor Board, 1940's (30 filing drawers).

See Ill. Libraries, 40:382 (Apr.
1958).

CHICAGO 10

Moodyana Exhibit, Moody Bible Institute. 820 North LaSalle St. Bernard
R. DeRemer, Archivist.

Holdings: Several thousand pieces
relating to evangelical campaigns in
the United States and abroad, the founding and work of the Institute and of
Moody Church, and book publication
and distribution. Included are letters
and a few other papers of Dwight L.
Moody (Mass., Ill.; evangelist), 1854-
99 (800 pieces), among them 41 copies
of letters of Moody to F. G. Ensign, an
early co-worker, and Moody's notes
for 15 of his famous sermons. There
are also papers and personal correspondence of the Moody family dating
from 1830; the constitution and bylaws
of the Chicago Evangelization Society,
predecessor of the Moody Institute; and
many early photographs and other papers relating to the Institute and Moody's evangelistic activities. These
last include correspondence with and
reference to such well known men as
John V. Farwell (Ill.; wholesale dry-
goods merchant), Cyrus Hall McCormick (Va., Ill.; inventor and manufacturer of the reaper), and his son Cyrus H., Jr. (Ill.; manufacturer). There
are also 352 sets of sermon notes of
Cyrus Ingerson Scofield (Kans., Tex.,
Mass.; Congregational minister, editor of the Scofield Reference Bible)
and 214 outlines made by him for his
lectures and writings; and some letters and diaries of D. W. Whittle (Ill.,

Mass.; Civil War officer, evangelist),
1862-84.

See Wilbur M. Smith, An Annotated Bibliography of D. L. Moody
([1948]. 221 p.), which reproduces a
few of Moody's papers.

CHICAGO 40

Mundelein College Library. 6353
Sheridan Rd. Sister Mary Clara,
Librarian.

Holdings: A small collection of
autograph letters and other documents
of signers of the Declaration of Independence and of various other persons.

See Hist. Records Survey, Guide
for Ill., p. 15.

CHICAGO

Museum of Jewish Antiquities. 32
West Randolph St.

Holdings: 70 items, chiefly Hebrew religious writings, 9th-20th
centuries.

See Hist. Records Survey, Guide
for Ill., p. 8.

CHICAGO 37

Museum of Science and Industry Library. East 57th St. and Lake Michigan.

Holdings: Records of a flour mill
at Nashville, Ill., 1850-75 (30 cu. ft.).

See Hist. Records Survey, Guide
for Ill., p. 16.

CHICAGO 10

Newberry Library. 60 West Walton
Pl. Stanley Pargellis, Librarian.

Holdings: 3,800,000 pages, occupying 4,300 ft. of shelf space, dated from about 800 to 1954, and relating to numerous aspects of world history and literature. Included are a Medieval and Renaissance Collection, 9th-16th centuries (about 170 vols.); a Music Collection, 13th-20th centuries; an Oriental Collection (chiefly Arabian, Indian, and Turkish), 15th-19th centuries (about 25 vols.); and a miscellaneous collection, 16th-20th centuries, containing diaries, letters, and other papers on a variety of subjects.

Manuscripts in the Edward E. Ayer Collection, 15th century—1880 (about 155,000 pages), relate chiefly to the archeology and ethnology of the Indians in North and South America and their relations with the whites, to many aspects of exploration and frontier history in the Americas, and to the inhabitants of the Philippine Islands. Among the larger groups of papers of individuals in this collection are those of William Bollaert (England; scientist), papers and sketches on Texas, 1837-49 (11 vols. and some sketches); Benjamin Henry Grierson (U. S. Army officer, commander of the Departments of Tex., N. Mex., Ariz.), 1868-80 (656 pieces); David Brydie Mitchell (Ga.; Gov., U.S. agent to the Creek Indians), 1809-21 (200 pieces); John Howard Payne (N. Y.; actor, playwright), 1826-41 (14 vols.), chiefly concerning the Cherokee Indians; Eleazer Williams (N. Y., Wis.; Episcopal missionary to the Indians), 1804-6 (about 500 pages); and Charles Williamson (England, N. Y.; land promoter, British agent in America), 1775-1808 (750 pieces). There are copies of many documents in the archives of Spain, Cuba, Mexico, Matamoros, and Nacogdoches, relating especially to Texas, New Mexico, and California. There are transcripts of records of the American Board of Commissioners for Foreign Missions, 1830-78 (6,976 pages), consisting of letters from missionaries to the Indians in Minnesota, Dakota Territory, and Oregon. There are transcripts also of minutes and other records of the (U. S.) Board of Indian Commissioners, 1869-1919 (1,484 pages). Many diaries and journals of travels and explorations are in the collection, and a large number of manuscript maps.

The Library's holdings of the papers of individuals engaged primarily in publishing and editing newspapers and periodicals include those of Edward Price Bell (Ind., Ill.; foreign correspondent for the Chicago Daily News, author), 1890-1943 (10,000 pieces); Francis Fisher Browne (Ill.; editor of the Dial), 1860-1946 (1,895 pieces); Ralph W. Cram (Iowa; newspaper editor, banker), 1906-51 (202 pieces); Charles H. Dennis (Ill.; editor of the Chicago Daily News), 1868-1942 (463 pieces); Victor F. Lawson (Ill.; publisher of the Chicago Daily News, pres. of Associated Press), 1873-1925 (160,000 pieces); William Morton Payne (Ill.; associate editor and chief literary critic of the Dial), 1866-1919 (1,759 pieces); and Hermann Raster (Ill.; editor of the Illinois Staats Zeitung), 1859-1940 (3,900 pieces).

Papers of authors, chiefly of the Middle West, include those of Sherwood Anderson (Ill., Va.; novelist, poet), 1904-41 (16,309 pieces); Mary Hartwell Catherwood (Ill.; novelist), 1860-1945 (150 pieces); Malcolm Cowley (Pa.; critic, author), 1918-48 (2,525 pieces); Floyd Dell (Ill., N. Y.; novelist, playwright, literary editor), from 1908 (3,571 pieces); Alice French (Iowa; novelist), 1892-1934 (684 pieces); Henry Blake Fuller (Ill.; novelist), 1878-1929 (600 pieces); Joseph Kirkland (Ill.; Civil War officer, novelist, literary editor), 1870-90 (121 pieces); Eunice Tietjens (Ill.; novelist, poet, lecturer), 1905-42 (4,200 pieces); and Henry Kitchell Webster (Ill.; novelist), 1911-32

(4,936 pieces).

Papers of other individuals include those of Orville E. Babcock (D.C.; Civil War officer, engineer, Pres. Grant's private secretary), 1849-1947 (1,283 pieces); Eliphalet W. Blatchford (Ill.; manufacturer, pres. of Newberry Library), 1835-1919 (1,695 pieces); Carter Harrison (Ill.; mayor of Chicago), 1769-1953 (2,077 pieces); Charles Lawrence Hutchinson (Ill.; banker, civic leader, first pres. of Chicago Art Institute), 1866-1934 (708 pieces); William V. Judson (U.S. Army officer, engineer with Panama Canal Commission, Chief of Am. Military Mission to Russia in World War I), 1907-19 (783 pieces); John Tinney McCutcheon (Ill., Ind.; cartoonist, world traveler), 1885-1949 (10,703 pieces); William F. Poole (Mass., Ohio, Ill.; librarian, bibliographer, historian), 1858-94 (5,175 pieces); Platt Rogers Spencer (Ohio; teacher of penmanship, originator of the Spencerian Hand), 1836-1952 (7,300 pieces); Graham Taylor (Conn., Ill.; Congregational clergyman, sociologist, prof. at Chicago Theological Seminary), 1862-1938 (10,000 pieces); Christian F. Theodore Thomas (N.Y., Ill.; musician, conductor of the New York Philharmonic Society and the Chicago Symphony Orchestra), 1860-1926 (631 pieces); and Lambert Tree (Ill.; Cook County judge, U.S. Minister to Belgium and Russia, civic leader), 1821-1948 (1,467 pieces).

Business records include two major groups of railroad records. The first consists of central office and land office records of the Chicago, Burlington and Quincy Railroad Co., 1851-1901 (1,000,000 letters, 1,500 bundles, and 2,000 vols.). The second consists of central office records of the Illinois Central Railroad, 1851-1906 (400,000 letters, 126 bundles or boxes, and 2,000 vols.). Included in both groups are papers of predecessor and subsidiary railroads and other corporations.

See Hist. Records Survey, Guide for Ill., p. 16; Ill. Libraries, 40:314-320 (Apr. 1958); Clara A. Smith, List of Manuscript Maps in the Edward E. Ayer Collection (1927. 101 p. Processed); Ruth Lapham Butler, A Checklist of Manuscripts in the Edward E. Ayer Collection (1937. 295 p.); Elisabeth C. Jackson and Carolyn Curtis, Guide to the Burlington Archives (1949. 374 p. Processed); Carolyn C. Mohr, Guide to the Illinois Central Archives (1951. 210 p. Processed); Paul Lietz, Calendar of Philippine Documents in the Ayer Collection (1956. 259 p.); and notes and articles in the Newberry Library Bulletin (since July 1948). Special articles in the Bulletin contain information about the papers of Sherwood Anderson, Orville E. Babcock, Edward Price Bell, Ralph W. Cram, Floyd Dell, Alice French, William V. Judson, Joseph Kirkland, William Morton Payne, Platt Rogers Spencer, Graham Taylor, Eunice Tietjens, and Lambert Tree.

CHICAGO 25

North Park College and Theological Seminary Library. Betty Jane Highfield, Librarian.

Holdings: In a collection on Jenny Lind (Sweden; singer), some letters, portraits, and memorabilia.

CHICAGO 12

Northern Baptist Theological Seminary Library. 3040 West Washington Blvd. Ruth M. Gray, Librarian.

Holdings: 100 items relating to the Norwegian Baptists.

See Ill. Libraries, 40:376 (Apr. 1958).

CHICAGO 11

Northwestern University Medical School Library. 303 East Chicago Ave. Elizabeth F. Carr, Librarian.

Holdings: 25 vols. and some 150 pieces, 1400-1945, relating chiefly to medicine, medical biography, and related subjects. Included are 4 Arabic medical manuscripts, 18 Burmese medical manuscripts, and 25 book-manuscripts ("olas") from Ceylon, in Pali or Singhalese, 1400-1700, comprising medical charms and incantations, student notebooks, and medical treatises. Papers of physicians include those of J. M. Bates (Maine; Civil War surgeon), 1862-64 (1 order and letter book); William Cullen (Scotland; physician, prof. at the Univs. of Glasgow and Edinburgh), 1760 (59 lectures); Nathan Smith Davis (N.Y., Ill.; physician, sanitarian, co-founder of the American Medical Association and of Northwestern Univ. and its medical department), 1837-86 (12 account books); George Fordyce (England; physician, lecturer on medicine), 1781-82 (250 p. of lectures); Edwin James (U.S. Army surgeon, explorer, naturalist), miscellaneous manuscripts and letters; and Sir William Lawrence (England; surgeon), 1825 (3 vols. of notes for lectures on the eye). There are also minutes of meetings of the Northwestern University Medical School faculty, 1859-1902 (3 vols.).

—oOo—

Northwestern University School of Dentistry Library. 311 East Chicago Ave. Minnie Orfanos, Librarian.

Holdings: A small quantity of manuscripts relating to dentistry and allied subjects. Included are letters and other papers of Greene Vardiman Black (Ill.; dentist, dean of Northwestern Univ. School of Dentistry).

CHICAGO 22

Archives and Museum of the Polish Roman Catholic Union. 984 Milwaukee Ave. George C. Walter, Curator.

Holdings: Several collections, 16th-20th centuries, relating chiefly to Polish culture and to the history of Poles in America. Included are some papers of Thaddeus Kosciuszko (Poland; American Rev. War officer), 1775-1816 (78 pieces); Helena Modjeska (Poland, U.S.; actress); Ignace J. Paderewski (Poland, U.S.; pianist, composer, statesman); Casimir Pulaski (Poland; Polish patriot, American Rev. War officer); and single or small numbers of letters of various prominent Americans of the Revolutionary and later periods. There are also a collection of letters and other documents of Polish Kings, 16th-18th centuries; and the archives of the Polish National Department, 1912-25, the Polish Army in France, 1916-20, and American Relief to Poland, 1939-50.

See Anderson Galleries, Memorial Exhibition, Thaddeus Kosciuszko ([1927.] 72 p.).

CHICAGO 2

Public Library. Gertrude E. Gscheidle, Librarian.

Holdings: Civil War collections include two diaries; telegrams sent by Daniel Ruggles (Mass., Va.; U.S. and Confed. Army officer), 1862 (1 vol.); and a record of military endorsements by Pierre G. T. Beauregard (La.; U.S. and Confed. Army officer, railroad pres.), 1861 (1 vol.). There is also some correspondence of Ulysses S. Grant (U.S. Army officer, U.S. Pres.), 1862-71 (10 pieces).

See <u>Ill. Libraries</u>, 40:355 (Apr. 1958).

CHICAGO 5

Roosevelt University Library. 430 South Michigan Ave. (Mrs.) Marjorie C. Keenlyside, Librarian.

<u>Holdings</u>: 85 holograph letters and other documents, chiefly 19th century, by German composers and writers and other important persons of continental Europe.
See <u>Ill. Libraries</u>, 40:377-379 (Apr. 1958).

CHICAGO 37

University of Chicago Library. Herman H. Fussler, Director; Robert Rosenthal, Curator of Special Collections.

<u>Holdings</u>: 1,500,000 pieces consisting of (1) medieval and Renaissance and other early manuscripts; (2) modern European and American manuscripts, principally of historical and literary interest; and (3) records of the University of Chicago. All manuscripts belonging to the University of Chicago are in the Library's Department of Special Collections with the exception of some 200 Arabic and Persian manuscripts and collections of papyri in the Oriental Institute.

The Library's grouping of "General" holdings includes papyri grain receipts from Karanis, 2d century (91 pieces); the Edgar J. Goodspeed Collection of New Testament Manuscripts, 6th-17th centuries (60 vols.); and "Miscellaneous manuscripts," including medieval and Renaissance manuscripts, 13th-20th centuries (1,100 vols. and 5,000 pieces).

Papers relating to England and Ireland include those of Sir Nicholas Bacon (statesman), among them documents concerning his estates in Norfolk and Suffolk and records of the manorial lands formerly in the possession of the Abbey of Bury St. Edmunds, 13th-18th centuries (1,600 deeds, 750 court and compotus rolls, and 2,000 letters, inventories, receipts, and other documents); the Bowes family, 1696-1728 (107 pieces); Sir Percy Bunting (editor of the <u>Contemporary Review</u>), 1836-1911 (2,500 pieces); Adam Clarke (Methodist minister, classical and Biblical scholar), 1799-1828 (59 pieces); Geoffrey Chaucer (poet), photostats of all extant manuscripts of the <u>Canterbury Tales</u> (61 boxes), with scholarly apparatus for their editing, and "Chaucer Life Records," containing transcripts and reproductions of documents from English depositories revealing Chaucer's life and times (25,000 pieces); George Gordon Coulton (historian), 1858-1947 (271 notebooks and 1,200 pieces); John D'Alton (Irish historian), 1792-1867 (150 vols.); Charles Wentworth Dilke (antiquary, critic), 1789-1864 (54 pieces); Welbore Ellis, Baron Mendip (political leader), 1734-1817 (54 pieces); Charles Godolphin (political leader), letters to Richard Bulstrode (diplomat), 1680-82 (102 pieces); Henry Hunt (political leader), 1773-1835 (100 pieces); Charles J. P. Mahon (Irish political leader), 1800-91 (3,000 pieces); James Payn (novelist), 1830-98 (60 vols.); Richard John Smith (actor), 1786-1855 (200 pieces); and Sir Robert Walpole (statesman), 1701-9 (76 pieces).

Papers representing modern continental Europe include those of Immanuel B. Bekker (Germany; philologist), 1806-39 (220 pieces); Cecilia Böhl de Faber, known as Fernan Caballero (Spain; novelist), 1856-76 (850 pieces); André Gide (France; author), 1891-1931 (50 pieces), letters to Francis Viele-Griffin (French-American poet); and the Marquis de

Lafayette (France; American Rev. War officer), 1774-1834 (250 pieces). There are also 150,000 photostats of German folksongs from the Deutsches Volkslied Archiv in Freiburg.

Papers of prominent Americans include those of William E. Barton (Ill.; Congregational clergyman, author), 1899-1932 (14 boxes); William Beaumont (Wis., Mo.; surgeon, physiologist), 1834-79 (127 pieces); Henry Northrup Castle (Hawaii; newspaper editor), 19th century (8 boxes); Stephen A. Douglas (Ill.; U.S. Rep. and Sen.), 1833-61 (16,000 pieces), chiefly letters to Douglas; William H. English (Ind.; U.S. Rep., historian), 1671-1884 (23 boxes), comprising material collected by him on early organization of the State of Indiana, including letters of early Governors; Elijah Grant (Ohio, Kans.; social reformer), 1843-71 (3 boxes); John Gunther (Ill., N.Y.; journalist), 20th century (a large quantity); Salmon O. Levinson (Ill.; lawyer, pacifist), 1914-43 (40,000 pieces); Fielding Lewis (Va.; plantation owner), 1790-1834 (1,500 pieces); Frank Orren Lowden (Ill.; lawyer, U.S. Rep., Gov., agriculturist), 1895-1943 (200,000 pieces); Charles Henry MacDowell (Ill.; adviser to American Commission to Negotiate Peace), 1919 (8 boxes); Wyndham Robertson (Va.; Gov., Confed. Army officer, author) and his family, 1750-1913 (21 boxes), including papers of the Loyal Company of Virginia, 1752-1844 (3 boxes), and of John Robertson (Va.; U.S. Rep.), 1818-72 (1 box); Julius Rosenwald (Ill.; merchant, philanthropist), 1862-1932 (30,000 pieces), not including business records; John Morgan Walden (Kans., Ohio; newspaperman, Methodist bishop), 1854-1914 (6 boxes); and Delos Franklin Wilcox (Mich., N.Y.; public utility expert), 20th century (46 boxes).

Two special collections include papers of other prominent Americans. The Lincoln Historical Collection (4 boxes), includes 40 manuscripts of Abraham Lincoln (Ill.; lawyer, U.S. Rep. and Pres.), others relating to his family and career, and papers of leaders and participants in affairs preceding and following the Civil War as well as during the war itself. The Reuben T. Durrett Collection, 1674-1913 (2,800 pieces), consists of originals and transcripts of papers relating to Kentucky and the Ohio Valley, chiefly in the late 18th and early 19th centuries, and including letters of important men interested in the region or active in it, and journals and letters of less prominent early western pioneers. The larger groups of personal papers in the collection are those of Mann Butler (Ky.; historian), 1806-45 (3 boxes); Richard H. Collins (Ky.; historian), 1870-90 (2 boxes); Joel Tanner Hart (Ky.; sculptor, poet), 1823-76 (19 vols.); Harry Innes (Va., Ky.; U.S. dist. court judge), 1774-1804, including some of Edmund Lyne's estate (1 box); George Nicholas (Va., Ky.; political leader, State attorney gen.), 1789-99 (1 vol.); and Joshua Lacy Wilson (Ohio; Presbyterian minister, philosophy and logic prof. at Cincinnati College), 1807-46 (11 vols. and 12 boxes). Among the transcripts in the collection are dispatches of Diego de Gardoqui (Spanish commissioner and Chargé d'Affaires in the U.S.), 1784-99 (6 vols.), from Spanish archives, and miscellaneous transcripts from the Haldimand Papers in the Canadian Archives.

Two other collections in the Library are the Ethno-History Collection, relating to the early contact between white men and Indians of the Mississippi Valley, 1670-1840 (50,000 pages), consisting of reproductions of manuscripts from depositories in the United States, Canada, and Europe; and the American Church History Collection, consisting of transcripts of records relating to religion on the frontier, including minutes of church organizations and journals of ministers (45 vols.).

Among 20th-century American papers are the files of Poetry: a Magazine of Verse, 1912-54, including correspondence and manuscripts submitted to editors, particularly Harriet Monroe, 1912-36, from modern poets (70,000 pieces); the Library also has the personal papers of Harriet Monroe (Ill.; editor, poet), 1880-1936 (28 boxes). Other manuscripts relating particularly to modern poetry are the personal papers of Mary Aldis (Ill.; poet), 1919 (1 box); Amy Bonner (N.Y.; business representative of Poetry), 1937-47 (2 boxes); Ronald Latimer (N.Y.; publisher of Alcestis Press), 1932-38, which include letters and manuscripts of modern poets (2 boxes); and Harriet Moody (Ill.; literary patron), 1914-34 (3 boxes).

Other groups of papers in the Library include records of the Emergency Committee of Atomic Scientists, 1946-51 (45 boxes); the Atomic Scientists of Chicago, 1945-49 (28 boxes); the Association of Oak Ridge Engineers and Scientists, 1945-48 (21 boxes); the Committee to Frame a World Constitution, 1945-51 (56 boxes); and the World Citizens Association, 1940-53 (11 boxes); and Elizabeth Mann Borgese's papers of the World Movement for World Federal Government, 1947-51 (29 boxes).

The University of Chicago Archives consist of official records, personal correspondence of persons associated with the University, records of related organizations, and other materials of University interest. The following collections in the Archives are papers of the persons named which contain manuscripts external to the work of the University: Edith and Grace Abbott (Ill.; social workers, educators), 1876-1957, 1878-1939 (20 boxes); Ernest DeWitt Burton (Ill.; theologian, educator), 1890-1925 (35 boxes); Thomas C. Chamberlin (Wis., D.C., Ill.; geologist, pres. of Univ. of Wis.), 1880-1928 (6 boxes); John Dewey (Ill., N.Y.; philosopher, educator), 1896-1906 (100 pieces); Enrico Fermi (N.Y., Ill.; physicist), 1940-54 (44 boxes); John C. M. Hanson (Ill.; librarian), 1900-30 (4 boxes); Samuel Northrup Harper (Ill.; historian), 1900-43 (30,000 pieces); William Rainey Harper (Ill.; theologian, univ. pres.), 1870-1906 (10,000 pieces); Robert Herrick (Ill.; novelist, Government Sec. for the Virgin Islands), 1893-1938 (43 boxes); Hermann Eduard von Holst (Germany, Ill.; historian), 1867-1900 (15 boxes); Robert Maynard Hutchins (Ill.; univ. pres.), 1926-50 (65 boxes); Robert Morss Lovett (Ill.; English prof., author, reformer, Government Sec. for the Virgin Islands), 1876-1950 (3 boxes); Andrew C. McLaughlin (Mich., Ill.; historian), 1899-1938 (8 boxes); John M. Manly (Ill.; English prof., cryptographer), 1900-40 (11 boxes); George Herbert Mead (Ill.; philosopher), 1920-30 (11 boxes); William Vaughn Moody (Ill., N.Y.; playwright, poet), 1891-1930, including correspondence of his wife (6 boxes); John Ulric Nef (Ill.; chemist), 1893-1915 (2 boxes); Howard Taylor Ricketts (Ill.; bacteriologist), 1904-10 (10 boxes); John D. Rockefeller (N.Y.; capitalist, philanthropist), 1880-1915 (300 pieces); Albion W. Small (Maine, Ill.; sociologist, educator), 1854-1926 (2 boxes); Thomas V. Smith (Ill.; philosopher, U.S. Rep.), 1934-45 (11 boxes); Marion Talbot (Ill.; home economist, dean of women), 1854-1948 (22 boxes); and James H. Tufts (Ill.; philosopher), 1911-17 (5 boxes).

See Edgar J. Goodspeed, A Descriptive Catalogue of Manuscripts in the Libraries of the University of Chicago (1912. 128 p.); Hist. Records Survey, Guide for Ill., pp. 19-21; De·Ricci, Census, pp. 552-600; Roscoe R. Hill, American Missions in European Archives, p. 112 (1951); and Ill. Libraries, 40:340-348 (Apr. 1958).

CHICAGO 12

University of Illinois Library of Medical Sciences. 1853 West Polk St. Wilma Troxel, Librarian.

Holdings: 143 items, 1804-1927, many written in German, some of which contain information on medical schools and research; and a commentary in Latin, 1465 (1 vol.), on Aristotle and Thomas Aquinas.
See Hist. Records Survey, Guide for Ill., p. 21.

EDWARDSVILLE

Madison County Historical Society. Jessie E. Springer, Secretary.

Holdings: 130 items, consisting of letters, account books, and papers chiefly about various aspects of Madison County history.
See Ill. Libraries, 40:385-388 (Apr. 1958).

ELMHURST

Elmhurst College Library. (Mrs.) Mary G. Henley, Librarian.

Holdings: 1,000 items relating to the Evangelical and Reformed Churches and to Elmhurst College.

EVANSTON

Evanston Historical Society. 1703 Orrington Ave.

Holdings: 3,500 pieces, dating from 1835, and relating chiefly to Evanston and its vicinity. Included are papers, 1850-55, pertaining to the establishment of Northwestern University, and some Civil War, Spanish-American War, and World War I

materials.
See Hist. Records Survey, Guide for Ill., p. 21.

—oOo—

Frances E. Willard Memorial Library for Alcohol Research, National Woman's Christian Temperance Union. 1730 Chicago Ave. (Mrs.) Alice Weaver, Librarian.

Holdings: 125 vols., 1 filing cabinet, and several pieces, 1855-96, relating to the temperance movement chiefly in the United States. Included are journals of Frances E. Willard (N.Y.; reformer) and her sister Mary, 1855-96 (55 vols.); her correspondence (1 filing cabinet); and the manuscript of her autobiography. There are also minutes of annual meetings of the National Woman's Christian Temperance Union, 1874-81 (3 vols.); several sermons; and addresses by some prominent temperance workers.

—oOo—

Garrett Biblical Institute Library. Sheridan Rd.

Holdings: 3,847 pieces, largely of the 18th and 19th centuries, relating chiefly to the Methodist Church. Included are some correspondence of Francis Asbury (Methodist bishop); and papers of Ezekiel Cooper (pioneer Methodist minister), 1785-1839 (24 vols.), and Richard Whatcoat (Methodist bishop). There are also some 20 vols. of letters, journals, and sermons of prominent Methodist ministers; a collection with John Wesley in 1736; archives of the Rock River (Ill.) Conference of the Methodist Church, including records of individual churches; papers relating to the history of McKendree College, Lebanon, Ill. (5 vols.); and letters from diplomats, scientists, U.S. Presidents, and other individuals relating to the campaign of John Lee (Methodist minister) for religious freedom in South American republics, 1882-1920 (2,500 pieces).

See Allison, Inventory, p. 8; Hist. Records Survey, Guide for Ill., p. 22; and the Survey's Calendar of the Ezekiel Cooper Collection of Early American Methodist Manuscripts, 1785-1839 (1941. 97 p. Processed).

—oOo—

Northwestern University Library.
Edward Doro, Curator of Rare Books.

Holdings: 100,000 pieces, of miscellaneous character. Included are diaries, sermons, correspondence, and other papers of Manasseh Cutler (Mass.; Congregational minister, botanist, physician, colonizer, U.S. Rep.), 1762-1820 (76 vols.), among them papers relating to the Ohio Co. and the Northwest Territory; the main body of correspondence, diaries, and other papers of Charles G. Dawes (Nebr., Ill., D.C.; lawyer, banker, World War I Army officer, U.S. Vice Pres., Ambassador to Great Britain), a large collection (chiefly 20th century); 433 original cartoons by John T. McCutcheon (Ill.; cartoonist, author); letters by Charles Camille Saint-Saens (France; composer), 1902-15 (132 items); correspondence and other papers of Lew Sarett (Ill.; prof. of oral interpretation at Northwestern Univ., poet), 20th century (1,350 pieces); and correspondence of Ralph Straus (England; novelist, biographer, bibliophile), 700 letters (20th century). The papers of James B. Pinker (England; literary agent with headquarters in London and New York), 1900-34 (50,000 pieces), include 435 letters about Hugh Walpole (England; novelist), 2,000 letters about Arnold Bennett (England; novelist), 500 letters about Ford Madox Ford (England; poet, critic, novelist), 125 letters from

Phyllis Bottome (England; novelist, short-story writer), and 180 letters from Perceval Gibbon (England; journalist).

There are also manuscripts of Hispanic-American interest (66 vols.), chiefly relating to Bolivia, 1682-1880, among them papers concerned with the sale of lands, 1682-1833, military affairs, 1826-36, colleges and public libraries, 1829-42, the proceedings of the Bolivian Congress, 1832-80, the revolutions of 1843 and 1870, and Jose Ballivián (Bolivia; Army officer, Pres.), 1841-52. Other holdings include a small collection of First French Republic documents in manuscript (50 pages); a "general letter collection" (1,000 pieces) containing more than 50 holograph letters exchanged between John Stuart Mill (England; reformer, economist) and Herbert Spencer (England; philosopher, author), and smaller quantities of letters of many other prominent persons in Europe and America; and a number of medieval and Renaissance manuscripts.

(The manuscripts in the Northwestern University Medical School Library and the Northwestern University School of Dentistry are described under Chicago.)

See Ill. Libraries, 40:321-322 (Apr. 1958).

GALESBURG

Knox College Library. L. W. Elder, Curator of Memorabilia.

Holdings: 3,500 items, 1773-1954, relating chiefly to the college and its vicinity. Included are records and other papers relating to Knox, Lombard, and Amity Colleges; records of student societies; and talks on education by Newton Bateman (Ill.; State supt. of public instruction, pres. of Knox College), 1875-96 (380 items).

There are also sermons of Samuel A. W. Duffield (Ill., Mich., Pa., N.J.; Presbyterian clergyman) and others of his family; records of Presbyterian and Congregational churches in Galesburg and of the Peoria Synod; letters and business records of early settlers; and an autograph collection.

See Hist. Records Survey, Guide for Ill., p. 24.

JACKSONVILLE

Illinois College Library.   D. C. Ritter, Librarian.

Holdings: 1,100 items, 1822-1930, relating chiefly to the College and its faculty and alumni. Included are correspondence of Theron Baldwin (Ill., N.Y.; missionary, promoter of higher education in the Middle West), 1829-69 (50 items); the manuscript of an unpublished novel by Edward Beecher (Mass., Ill.; Congregational minister, first pres. of Ill. College); and papers of Julian M. Sturtevant (Ill.; Congregational minister, pres. of Ill. College), 1829-85 (60 items).

See C. H. Rammelkamp, Illinois College; a Centennial History, 1829-1929 (1928. 605 p.).

—oOo—

MacMurray College Library.   Victoria E. Hargrave, Librarian.

Holdings: A small collection, 1839-1925, relating chiefly to the College and the Methodist Church in the area. Included are letters and essays of students and reminiscences of alumnae, from 1863 (44 pieces); and autobiographies, letters, and other papers of former presidents of the college, 1858-1925 (300 pieces), including papers of Joseph R. Harker (England, Ill.; teacher, Methodist minister), 1893-1925 (250 pieces). There are also papers

on William Henry Milburn (Ill.; Methodist Episcopal clergyman, chaplain of Cong.), collected in 1940-42 for an uncompleted biography.

—oOo—

Morgan County Historical Society. 201 West College Ave.

Holdings: 60 vols. and 900 pieces, relating chiefly to the history of Morgan County from 1823. Included are Jacksonville weather reports; and records of the Old Settlers Society and the public library.

See Hist. Records Survey, Guide for Ill., p. 26.

LINCOLN

Lincoln College Library.   Mrs. William J. Stigall, Jr., Librarian.

Holdings: 300 items of miscellaneous character, including a collection of letters signed by all U.S. Presidents, and several papers relating to Abraham Lincoln (Ill.; U.S. Pres.).

See Ill. Libraries, 40:374 (Apr. 1958).

MOUNT CARROLL

Shimer College Library. (Mrs.) Margaret McBride, Librarian.

Holdings: Some 50 vols. and 1,000 letters, 1848-1917, chiefly papers relating to the college, and cashbooks and other records of flour milling and whisky distilling establishments of the locality, 1853-1917.

See Hist. Records Survey, Guide for Ill., p. 28.

NAPERVILLE

North Central College and Evangelical
Theological Seminary Library. Ruth
Kraemer, Director.

Holdings: A small quantity of manuscripts, chiefly translations of journals, diaries, and letters written in
German by 19th-century Evangelical
clergymen. These include a journal,
1820-59, of John Seybert (Pa.; bishop
of the Evangelical Association).
See Ill. Libraries, 40:376 (Apr.
1958).

NORMAL

Illinois State Normal University Library. Dr. R. Hertel, Director of
Libraries.

Holdings: A substantial collection,
mainly 19th century, relating chiefly
to the University and to education.
Included are papers of John Williston
Cook (Ill.; prof. at and pres. of Ill.
State Normal), 1890-99; David Davis
(Ill.; U.S. Supreme Court Justice,
U.S. Sen.), 10 reels of microfilm of
papers privately owned; Richard Edwards (Ill.; pres. of Ill. State Normal) and his family; Raymond W.
Fairchild (Ill.; prof. at and pres. of
Ill. State Normal), 2 file drawers;
David Felmley (Ill.; mathematics
prof., pres. of Ill. State Normal),
1 file drawer; Minnie Saltzman-
Stevens (Ill.; operatic soprano); and
Ella Flagg Young (Ill.; feminist,
pres. of Ill. State Normal, Chicago
school supt.). There are also a
number of diaries, including one
western travel diary, 1837; and one
or two letters by each of several
prominent persons, chiefly in the
field of American literature.
See Ill. Libraries, 40:370-373
(Apr. 1958).

PEORIA

Peoria Historical Society, Inc. 226
North Western Ave. Gerald T.
Kelsch, President.

Holdings: 7,588 sheets and 50,000
cards, produced in the 20th century
but reproducing or dealing with records chiefly of the 19th century that
relate to the locality. Included are
an index of Peoria newspapers, 1837-
63 (50,000 cards); copies of court records, 1825-50 (1,470 sheets); copies
of marriage licenses, 1826-83 (1,146
sheets); WPA manuscripts on all
phases of Peoria history, 1837-1936
(3,096 sheets); and 125 other historical manuscripts on Peoria (1,876
sheets).

PEORIA 3

Peoria Public Library. 111 North
Monroe St. William W. Bryan, Librarian.

Holdings: 17 vols., 1849-86. Included are the diary of a local insurance agent, 1850-86 (15 small vols.);
a copy of the diary of Allen L. Fahn-
stock (Ill.; Civil War officer), 1862-
66 (1 vol.); and a travel diary from
Peoria to San Diego, 1849 (1 vol.).

QUINCY

Historical Society of Quincy and
Adams County. 1261½ Kentucky
St. (Mrs.) Edna Williams, Curator.

Holdings: 2,100 items, of the 19th
century, relating chiefly to Quincy
and its vicinity. Included are papers
of James Dada Morgan (Ill.; Mexican
War and Civil War officer, banker),
1846-96 (323 items); a Civil War diary, 1864-65 (6 vols.); letters of a

Civil War nurse, 1861-65; sermons by a local clergyman, 1843-47 (200 items); and lectures and other papers on anti-vivisection (276 items).

See Hist. Records Survey, Guide for Ill., p. 29.

ROCK ISLAND

Augustana College Library. 3500 Seventh Ave. Librarian.

Holdings: 102,000 items, of the 19th and 20th centuries, relating chiefly to the Augustana Synod of the Evangelical Lutheran Church (now named the Augustana Evangelical Lutheran Church) and to Swedish immigrants to the United States. Included are daybooks, journals, and some 400 or 500 miscellaneous letters of leaders of the church and of early Swedish settlers; and minutes of the synod from 1860, of the successor church, and of the subsidiary Illinois Conference (some 400 items yearly are now received from the church and the conference). The Library also has custody of some permanently valuable records of the College.

See Ill. Libraries, 40:279-286 (Apr. 1958).

SPRINGFIELD

Illinois State Archives. Theodore J. Cassady, Assistant State Archivist.

Holdings: 41,000 cu. ft., 1722-1959, consisting chiefly of noncurrent official records held by the State's archival agency. (There are also 68,000 cu. ft. of permanent records in the Archives Building still under the jurisdiction of the departments of origin.) Territorial and State records in the Archives include those of the General Assembly, 1812-1959, among them over 100 documents in the handwriting of Abraham Lincoln, 1834-41; the Governors, 1809-1900 and 1917-52; the constitutional conventions of 1818, 1847, 1862, 1869-70, and 1922; the secretary of state, 1809-1957; the auditor of public accounts, including U.S. and State land records, 1722-1959; the adjutant general and service recognition boards, 1812-1953, including all service records except those of the Illinois National Guard; and the Illinois and Michigan Canal, 1819-1933. There are also noncurrent records of a few counties, including records of French, British, and American authorities at Cahokia, from 1737, and at Kaskaskia, from 1722 (on microfilm). Several counties are depositing security microfilm copies of their records; these are not open for research. The Archives has custody also of transcripts and descriptions of many county archives, prepared by the Historical Records Survey. It also has originals of Territorial and State censuses of population, 1818-65; original schedules for Illinois of the U.S. censuses of agriculture, manufacturing, mortality, and social statistics, 1850-80, and population, 1880; and microfilm copies of the population schedules for Illinois of the Federal censuses, 1820-80. Records of the State supreme court, of teacher certification, and of vital statistics (birth and death records from 1916) are in departmental vaults under the jurisdiction of the clerk of the supreme court, the Superintendent of Public Instruction, and the Department of Public Health, respectively.

See general descriptions by Margaret C. Norton, "The Resources of the Illinois State Archives," and Theodore J. Cassady, "Record Holdings of Illinois State Archives," in Ill. Libraries, 36:33-41 (Jan. 1954), and 40:295-304 (Apr. 1958);

and detailed information about the Lincoln items, the canal records, the land
records, and other accessions in other
issues of this periodical, including the
Illinois State Archives Issue (Apr.
1959).

—oOo—

Illinois State Historical Library. Centennial Building, Capitol Grounds.
Clyde C. Walton, Jr., State Historian.

Holdings: A large quantity of manuscripts, 1731-1951 but mostly dating
from 1819, relating chiefly to Illinois
and the Midwest. Some of these papers
have been collected by the Illinois State
Historical Society.

There are many papers of and relating to Abraham Lincoln (Ill.; lawyer,
U.S. Rep. and Pres.), of his political
and personal associates, and of his bi-
ographers. These materials include
papers of Lincoln himself, 1809-65
(1,200 originals and 5,000 photostats);
Mary Todd Lincoln, his wife, 1848-80
(128 pieces); Albert J. Beveridge (Ind.;
U.S. Sen., Lincoln biographer), 1924-
26 (60 pieces concerning his biography);
John Milton Hay (Ill., D.C.; Lincoln's
secretary and biographer, poet, diplomat, Sec. State), 1856-1905 (700
pieces), as well as notes and other
products of his collaboration on a Lincoln biography with John G. Nicolay,
1886-90 (5,800 pieces); Anson J. Henry (Ill., Wash. Terr.; physician to
Lincoln and his wife, surveyor), 1852-
65 (23 pieces including an overland
journal); William Hayne (Ill., Dakota
Terr.; physician, friend of Lincoln),
1855-1911 (60 pieces); John T. Stuart
(Ill.; law partner of Lincoln, Black
Hawk War officer, U.S. Rep.) and
Milton Hay (Ill.; legislator, lawyer),
1817-91 (500 pieces); Leonard Swett
(Ill.; lawyer, friend of Lincoln), 1847-
90 (100 pieces); Jesse W. Weik (Ind.;
Lincoln biographer), 1828-1929
(1,000 pieces); and Gideon Welles

(Conn.; newspaper editor, Sec. Navy),
1860-61 (26 pieces and manuscript
recollections). Other papers that
contain Lincoln material include the
Sangamon County (Ill.) Commissioners' Court records, 1821-40 (4 vols.),
which cover the period of Lincoln's
residence in New Salem; the files of
the Abraham Lincoln Association,
1909-52 (5,000 pieces), which include
correspondence about Lincoln with
collectors, writers, and artists and
the recollections of persons associated with Lincoln; and the records of
the National Lincoln Monument Association, concerning the erection of
the Lincoln Monument at Springfield,
1865-95 (1 vol. and 3,000 pieces).
Included also is the Frank E. Stevens
collection on the Black Hawk War,
Lincoln, and Douglas, 1821-70 (400
pieces).

Papers of political leaders other
than those mentioned above include
those of John P. Altgeld (Ill.; Gov.),
1890-1902 (100 pieces); Nathaniel P.
Banks (Mass., Ill.; Gov. of Mass.,
U.S. Rep., railroad executive, Civil
War officer), 1840-94 (2,300 pieces);
Sidney Breese (Ill.; U.S. Sen., judge
of State supreme court), 1731-1896
(250 pieces); Orville H. Browning
(Ill.; U.S. Sen., Sec. Interior), 1850-
81 (23 diaries and 125 pieces); Joseph G. Cannon (Ill.; U.S. Rep.,
Speaker of the House), 1872-1925
(5,000 pieces); Shelby M. Cullom
(Ill.; Gov., U.S. Sen.), 1881-1914
(4 vols. and 600 pieces); Charles S.
Deneen (Ill.; Gov., U.S. Sen.), 1905-
30 (24 vols. and 1,500 pieces); Stephen A. Douglas (Ill.; U.S. Rep. and
Sen.), 1836-61 (120 pieces); Joseph
W. Fifer (Ill.; Gov.), 1868-1940 (500
pieces); Augustus C. French (Ill.;
Gov.), 1841-53 (3,250 pieces, many
of them formerly in the McKendree
College Library); Ulysses S. Grant
(U.S. Army officer, U.S. Pres.),
1844-85 (200 pieces), including 70
letters to Elihu B. Washburne (Ill.;

U.S. Rep., Minister to France); Ozias M. Hatch (Ill.; State legislator and sec. state), 1818-75 (6 vols. and 775 pieces); Elias Kent Kane (Ill.; Terr. judge, Ill. sec. state, U.S. Sen.) and William H. Bissell (Ill.; U.S. Rep., Gov.), 1815-58 (200 pieces); John A. McClernand (Ill.; lawyer, U.S. Rep., Civil War officer), 1823-96 (9 vols. and 10,000 pieces); William Ralls Morrison (Ill.; Civil War officer, U.S. Rep., Interstate Commerce Commissioner), 1858-98 (250 pieces); John M. Palmer (Ill.; Civil War officer, Gov., U.S. Sen.), 1839-1902 (2,500 pieces); Jesse B. Thomas (Ill.; Terr. judge, U.S. Sen.), 1785-1862 (225 pieces); George W. Wall (Ill.; politician, circuit judge), 1869-95 (650 pieces); and Richard Yates (Ill.; Gov., U.S. Rep. and Sen.), and Richard Yates, Jr. (Ill.; Gov., U.S. Rep.), 1789-1910 (10,000 pieces, and photostats of 150 letters to the senior Yates).

Papers of military leaders, in addition to those named above, include those of Jacob Ammen (Ky., Ohio, Md.; college prof., Civil War officer, engineer), 1827-75 (350 pieces); Smith D. Atkins (Ill.; Civil War officer, editor), 1852-87 (50 pieces); Christopher C. Augur (U.S. Army officer), 1861-67 (200 pieces); John G. Ballance (U.S. Army officer), 1871-1900 (5 vols. and 7 folders, including materials on operations in the Philippines, 1899-1900); John C. Black (Ill.; Civil War officer, lawyer, U.S. Commissioner of Pensions, Civil Service Commissioner), 1830-1951 (24 vols. and 8,500 pieces); William P. Black (Ill.; Civil War officer, lawyer), 1861-1913 (160 pieces); Charles H. Brush (Ill.; Civil War officer), 1837-1909 (5 vols. and 400 pieces); Samuel Ryan Curtis (Ohio, Iowa; Mex. War and Civil War officer, U.S. Rep. from Iowa), 1859-62 (2 vols.); John Watts DePeyster (N.Y.; author, N.Y. militia officer), 1862-65 (7 notebooks and 1,000 pieces); Henry S. Dodge (N.Y., Ill.; War of 1812

officer), 1811-13 (52 pieces); James F. Drish (Ill.; Civil War officer), 1862-65 (175 pieces); Elmer E. Ellsworth (Ill., N.Y.; Civil War officer), 1858-61 (100 pieces); Samuel Gordon (Ill.; Civil War officer), 1862-65 (210 pieces); Benjamin Henry Grierson (U.S. Army officer), 1854-98 (4,000 pieces and autobiography); Douglas Hapeman (Ill.; Civil War officer), 1862-1905 (10 vols. of diaries and 40 pieces); Humphrey H. Hood (Ill.; Civil War surgeon), 1862-65 (400 pieces); John S. Loomis (Ill.; Civil War officer), 1861-66 (74 pieces); Alexander G. McQueen (Iowa; Civil War officer), 1861-1900 (50 pieces); William W. Orme (Ill.; lawyer, Civil War officer), 1853-75 (350 pieces); Lewis B. Parsons (Ill., Mo.; lawyer, agriculturist, Civil War officer in charge of Army transportation, Dept. of Miss.), 1777-1908 (5,000 pieces); Levi A. Ross (Ill.; Civil War officer), 1862-63 (2 vols. and 55 pieces); William R. Rowley (Ill.; Civil War officer), 1862-92 (72 pieces); Francis W. Tupper (Ill.; Civil War officer), 1862-65 (3 vols. and 80 pieces); William H. L. Wallace (Ill.; Civil War officer) and T. Lyle Dickey (Ill.; Civil War officer, Ill. supreme court justice), 1816-1934 (48 vols. and 8,000 pieces); and John S. Wilcox (N.Y., Ill.; Civil War officer), 1852-1920 (550 pieces).

Papers of other individuals include those of John C. Bagby (Ill.; U.S. Rep., Ill. circuit court judge), 1859-86 (161 pieces); Newton Bateman (Ill.; State supt. of public instruction, pres. of Knox College), 1831-96 (2,000 pieces); Greene V. Black (Ill.; dentist, dean of Northwestern Univ. Dental School) and Carl E. Black (Ill.; physician), 1880-1941 (22,300 pieces and 3,000 photographs of Ill. physicians); Philander Chase (Conn., Ohio, Ill.; Episcopal bishop, founder of Kenyon College), 1823-69 (1,500 pieces); David Davis (Ill.; U.S. Supreme Court Justice, U.S. Sen.), 1830-90 (25,000 pieces); Samuel M. Fellows (Ill., Iowa; Latin prof. and pres. of Cornell College, Iowa), 1849-63 (60 pieces); Daniel F. Hitt (Ill.; surveyor, Civil War officer), 1831-65 (760 pieces); Robert G. Ingersoll (Ill., D. C., N. Y.; lawyer, Civil War officer, agnostic lecturer and writer), 1849-1900 (17,000 pieces); Charles H. Lanphier (Ill.; editor),1838-86 (400 pieces); Nicholas Vachel Lindsay, known as Vachel Lindsay (Ill.; poet), 1916-28 (50 pieces); George Marsh, Sr. and Jr. (Ill., D. C.; Civil War preachers), 1820-79 (300 pieces); Edgar Lee Masters (Ill., N. Y.; poet, dramatist), 1924-42 (120 pieces); John Messinger (Ill.; teacher, surveyor, State legislator), 1797-1878 (300 pieces); William H. Powell (Ohio, N. Y.; historical and portrait painter), 1825-99 (1 vol. autobiography); George A. Schilling (Ill.; sec. State Board of Labor Commissioners), 1876-1938 (1,000 pieces), relating to trade unionism and the single tax movement; John F. Snyder (Mo., Ill.; Confed. surgeon, archeologist, author), 1797-1921 (9,000 pieces); Don A. Spaulding (Ill.; U. S. surveyor), 1833-71 (100 letters and many surveys, with notebooks for Ill., Iowa, and Mo.); Jonathan B. Turner (Ill.; Ill. College prof., agriculturist), 1837-95 (500 pieces); Horace White (Ill., N. Y.; journalist, editor, economist), 1888-1915 (350 pieces); Samuel Willard (Ill.; abolitionist, Civil War surgeon, educator), 1840-65 (200 pieces); William Wilson (Ill.; chief justice of State supreme court, farmer), 1810-70 (200 pieces); and John Stephen Wright (Ill.; editor of agricultural papers, Chicago real estate operator), 1840-77 (100 pieces, chiefly copies).

Business records include the Black-Williams papers, relative to a Springfield, Ill., store and to lands, railroads, mines, electric light, and manufacturing, 1828-1905 (200 vols. and 7,500 pieces); records of Bryant and Morrison's store in Kaskaskia,

1805-25 (12 vols.); papers of Pierre Menard (Ill.; fur trader, merchant, Lt. Gov.), 1780-1899 (68 vols. and 1,000 pieces), including letters of Pierre Chouteau, Manuel Lisa, François Vigo, and William Henry Harrison; and papers of Tardiveau, Andrian et Cie. (traders in the Northwest Terr. and Ind. and Ill. Terr.), 1790-1810 (several hundred letters in 4 vols.).

Additional holdings include a collection on the Black Hawk War, 1831-33 (300 pieces); the Illinois and Michigan Canal Commissioners' correspondence, 1836-63 (200 pieces); manuscripts on western travel, pioneer life, and the Mormons in Illinois; Civil War diaries and letters besides those in the personal papers of military leaders listed above; and the Jesse E. Ricks collection of letters of persons prominent in the 19th century (700 pieces), including a manuscript notebook of Theodore Parker (Mass.; Unitarian minister, abolitionist).

See Hist. Records Survey, Guide for Ill., pp. 33-36; Clyde C. Walton, "Manuscripts in The Illinois State Historical Library," in Ill. Libraries, 40:305-313 (Apr. 1958); Donald J. Berthrong, The Civil War Collection of the Illinois State Historical Library (1949. 23 p.); and Harry E. Pratt, "Lewis B. Parsons: Mover of Armies and Railroad Builder," in Ill. State Hist. Society, Journal, 44:349-354 (winter 1951), "Manuscripts in the Illinois State Historical Library," in Autograph Collectors' Journal, 5 (no. 2):38-44 (winter 1953), and Lincolniana in the Illinois State Historical Library (1955. 30 p.).

URBANA

Illinois Historical Survey, University of Illinois. (Mrs.) Marguerite Jenison Pease, Director.

Holdings: A substantial collection, 1600-1948, relating chiefly to Illinois and the West. Included are extensive groups of transcripts and microfilm or other photographic copies of manuscripts in other depositories or, less frequently, in private possession.

Papers of individuals include those of Albert Brisbane (N.Y.; social reformer, author), 1840-90 (11 vols. and several thousand items); Stephen A. Douglas (Ill.; U.S. Rep. and Sen.), 1845-60 (transcripts of 38 letters in private hands); Henry Eddy (Ill.; newspaper publisher, lawyer, legislator), 1822-48 (transcripts of 882 items in private hands); Ulysses S. Grant (Ill.; U.S. Army officer, U.S. Pres.), 1863-73 (27 letters); Pierre Menard (Ill.; fur trader, merchant, Lt. Gov.), 1808-42 (8 vols. and 28 pieces); George Morgan (Ill., Pa.; land speculator, Indian agent, Rev. War officer), 1766-1826 (242 items); Thomas J. Morgan (Ill.; lawyer, labor leader), 1880-1910 (19 vols. and 64 folders); William W. Orme (Ill.; lawyer, Civil War officer), 1855-94 (132 items); and Jonathan B. Turner (Ill.; Ill. College prof., agriculturist), 1834-1910 (95 letters).

Included also are records of the Virginia Military District in Ohio, 1784-1896 (17 vols. and 10,000 items), relating to bounty lands for Revolutionary soldiers; a small collection on Indian languages; several folders on Illinois in World Wars I and II; and an extensive collection of originals and photographic copies of papers on communitarian colonies in the United States, including New Harmony and Brook Farm. There are microfilm copies of the Kaskaskia documents, 1720-90 (the originals of which are in the custody of the county clerk of Randolph County), and of the complete Cahokia and St. Clair County papers, 1722-1809 (the originals of which are in the Archives Division of the Illinois State Library); photostats of letter books of two fac-

tors of the American Fur Co., 1816-25 (2 vols.); microfilm copies of colonial records of South Carolina, 1706-75 (37 cartons); and microfilm and other copies of several thousand items, chiefly 18th century, in British, French, and Spanish archives.

See Marguerite J. Pease, Guide to Manuscript Materials Relating to Western History in Foreign Depositories Reproduced for the Illinois Historical Survey (rev. ed. 1956. 112 p. Processed), and Guide to Manuscript Materials of American Origin in the Illinois Historical Survey (rev. ed. 1956. 115 p. Processed); Arthur E. Bestor, Jr., Records of the New Harmony Community (2d ed., rev. 1951. 17 p. Processed); and Ill. Libraries, 40:289-294 (Apr. 1958).

—oOo—

Journalism Library, University of Illinois. 122 Gregory Hall. Eleanor Blum, Librarian.

Holdings: 8 manuscripts of short stories, novels, and plays by prominent writers associated with Illinois; and 112 other pieces of miscellaneous character, including some autographed cartoons.

—oOo—

University of Illinois Library. Robert B. Downs, Director.

Holdings: Over 900 cu. ft., dating from the Middle Ages to the 20th century, and consisting of (1) archives of the University of Illinois, 1867-1958 (500 cu. ft.); and (2) other papers, many of which relate to English literature.

In this second category are a substantial number of medieval and Renaissance manuscripts and the extensive Cavagna collection of manuscripts on Italian local history and genealogy. Papers of individuals include those of

George Bentley (England; publisher), 1850-95 (a diary and several thousand letters from English writers); Henry Thomas Buckle (England; historian), 19th century (9 vols. and 250 items); Robert Clayton (England; businessman), chiefly 17th century (3,000 items); the Heath family of England, including Sir Robert Heath (attorney-gen., judge), 17th century (a substantial quantity); and Grant Richards (England; publisher), late 19th and early 20th centuries (20,000 letters by and to authors and printers).

There are also some letters and other papers of Robert and Elizabeth Barrett Browning (England; poets), 173 items; 83 letters of William Cobbett (England; journalist, publicist); 239 letters of Mrs. Annie Edwards (U.S.; author); 120 letters of Alfred Edward Housman (England; poet); 122 letters of Frances Anne Kemble, known as Fanny Kemble (England, Pa., Ga., Mass.; actress, author); papers of Albert Howe Lybyer (Turkey, Ohio, Ill.; historian), 20th century; a collection of letters, experimental notes, and other papers of Gregor Mendel (Moravia; monk, geneticist), 19th century; 164 letters of Paul Elmer More (N.Y., N.J.; editor, essayist, literary critic); 600 letters of Marcel Proust (France; author); 109 letters of Rainer Maria Rilke (Germany, Austria; poet, novelist); the main body of papers of Carl Sandburg (Ill.; poet,

Lincoln biographer), including some Lincoln letters; correspondence and literary manuscripts of Stuart Pratt Sherman (Ill.; Univ. of Ill. English prof., literary critic, editor); letters, journals, and unpublished works of Anthony Trollope (England; novelist); and the main body of literary manuscripts and correspondence of H. G. Wells (England; novelist). There are also business records of Illinois firms of the late 19th and early 20th centuries (400 cu. ft.). (The University of Illinois Medical and Dental School Library is described under Chicago.)

See De Ricci, Census, pp. 696-711; Meta M. Sexton, Manuscripts and Printed Documents of the Archivio Cavagna Sanguiliani in the University of Illinois Library (1950. 535, 95 p. Processed); and "University of Illinois Library Manuscript Collection," in Ill. Libraries, 40:349-352 (Apr. 1958).

WHEATON

Wheaton College Library.   Robert A. Golter, Librarian.

Holdings: Letters of Jonathan Blanchard (Ohio, Ill.; Presbyterian minister, abolitionist, pres. of Knox and Wheaton Colleges), 1848-90 (over 200 pieces and photostatic copies of other letters).

INDIANA

BLOOMINGTON

Indiana University Library. Doris M. Reed, Curator of Manuscripts.

Holdings: 1,360,700 pieces, consisting of medieval (185 pieces) and modern manuscripts. The latter, principally 1688-1959, are concerned especially with American history and American and English literature. A considerable quantity of the history manuscripts relate to Indiana, the Middle West, and the Far West.

Papers of Members of Congress and high officials of the Federal Government include those of Montgomery Blair (Mo., Md.; lawyer, Postmaster Gen.), 1843-81 (64 pieces); Henry Clay (Ky.; U. S. Rep. and Sen., Sec. State), 1812-49 (247 pieces); William Cumback (Ind.; U. S. Rep.), 1835-1904 (72 pieces); George Grundy Dunn (Ind.; U. S. Rep.), 1834-50 (1,398 pieces); Richard Nash Elliott (Ind.; U. S. Rep.), 1926-48 (67 pieces); Charles Warren Fairbanks (Ohio, Ind.; lawyer, U. S. Sen. and Vice Pres.), 1858-1918 (150,000 pieces); Courtland Craig Gillen (Ind.; U. S. Rep.), 1930-33 (200 pieces); John Hanna (Ind.; U. S. Rep.), 1853-79 (59 pieces); James Alexander Hemenway (Ind.; U. S. Rep. and Sen.), 1904-21 (111 pieces); Alvin Peterson Hovey (Ind.; Civil War officer, Minister to Peru, U. S. Rep., Gov.), 1841-91 (707 pieces); John George Jackson (Va.; U. S. Rep.), 1781-1825 (143 pieces); Rufus King (Mass. N. Y.; Member Continental Cong., U. S. Sen. from N. Y., Minister to Great Britain), 1815-26 (94 pieces); Henry Smith Lane (Ind.; U. S. Rep. and Sen., Gov.), 1828-81 (791 pieces); Joseph Lane (Ind., Oreg.; Mexican War officer, Gov. of Oreg. Terr., U. S. Sen.),

1835-81 (3,248 pieces); Abraham Lincoln (Ill.; lawyer, U. S. Rep. and Pres.), 1826-65 (215 pieces); Louis Leon Ludlow (Ind.; U. S. Rep.), 1898-1928 (330 pieces); Hugh McCulloch (Ind.; Sec. Treas.), 1833-95 (4,512 pieces); Paul Vories McNutt (Ind., N. Y.; Gov. of Ind., U. S. High Commissioner to Philippine Islands, Chairman War Manpower Commission), 1917-32 (25,000 pieces); Return Jonathan Meigs, Jr. (Ohio; U.S. Sen., Gov., Postmaster Gen.), 1794-1824 (85 pieces); Samuel Moffett Ralston (Ind.; U. S. Sen., Gov.), 1868-1928 (20,000 pieces); George Washington Rauch (Ind.; lawyer, U. S. Rep.), 1911-40 (703 pieces); William Sulzer (N. Y.; U. S. Rep., Gov.), 1917-32 (111 pieces); and Richard Wigginton Thompson (Ind.; U. S. Rep., Sec. Navy), 1837-99 (382 pieces).

Papers of other individuals include those of Amos William Butler (Ind.; zoologist, sociologist), 1835-1937 (10,597 pieces); Philip Dormer Stanhope, 4th Earl of Chesterfield (England; political leader, letter writer), 1740-70 (330 pieces); Joseph Conrad (England; novelist), 1886-1935 (217 pieces); Theodore Dreiser (Mo., N. Y.; editor, novelist), 1896-1931 (78 pieces); Alexandre Dumas, fils (France; playwright, novelist), 1877-90 (307 pieces); Max Eastman (N. Y., Mass.; author), 1896-1959 (252 pieces); Havelock Ellis (England; psychologist), 1925-37 (164 pieces); Powers Hapgood (Ind.; labor leader, 1915-49 (4,286 pieces); Stephen Selwyn Harding (Ind.; Gov. of Utah Terr., chief justice of Colo. Terr.), 1855-91 (86 pieces); Samuel Judah (Ind.; lawyer, political leader), 1827-69 (951 pieces); Nathan Kimball (Ind.; Mexican War and Civil War officer, surveyor gen. of Utah), 1828-98 (510 pieces); Marquis de Lafayette (France; American Rev. War officer), 1737-1834 (3,160 pieces), including many relating to him; Nicholas Vachel Lindsay, known as Vachel Lindsay (Ill.; poet), 1913-57 (167 pieces); David Hervey Maxwell (Ind.; physician, educational leader), 1825-52 (340 pieces); Joel Palmer (Ind., Oreg.; author, supt. of Indian affairs for Oreg. Terr.), 1849-81 (1,181 pieces); Edgar Allan Poe (Va., Pa., N.Y.; poet, critic, short-story writer), 313 pieces; James Whitcomb Riley (Ind.; poet), 6,238 pieces; George William Russell, AE, pseud. (Ireland; writer), 1889-1933 (234 pieces); Upton Sinclair (N.J., Calif.; author), 1892-1959 (260,600 pieces); Hamilton Smith (Ind., Ky.; mining engineer), 1825-75 (775 pieces); William Arnold Stevens (Ohio, N.Y.; Biblical scholar), 1850-1910 (1,401 pieces); Booth Tarkington (Ind.; novelist, playwright), 1895-1930 (50 pieces); Lewis Wallace, known as Lew Wallace (Ind.; soldier, diplomat, author), 1865-1949 (707 pieces); Jonathan Williams (assistant to Benjamin Franklin in France, U.S. Army engineer, Supt. of U.S. Military Academy), 1766-1815 (7,182 pieces); and William Butler Yeats (Ireland; poet), 1889-1954 (50 pieces).

Among the materials for business history are the records of Howard Ship Yards and Dock Co., Jeffersonville, Ind., 1834-1942 (250,000 pieces), of the Cannelton (later Indiana) Cotton Mills, 1850-1947 (7,500 pieces), of the Columbia Conserve Co., Indianapolis, Ind., 1903-53 (56,321 pieces); and of other concerns or individuals engaged in journalism, law, banking, canning, coal mining, merchandising, and railroad operation. There are records of gold mining in California, the flatboat and steamboat trade on the Ohio and the Mississippi, lumbering in Michigan, and hotel keeping in New York.

There is also much material on political history, for instance records of the Willkie Clubs of America, 1940 (65,000 items). The educational history of Ohio and Indiana and the development of religious sects and organizations in Indiana are represented. Military records include a collection of War of 1812 papers (4,405 items). The peace movement is represented by the Archives of the United World Federalists, Inc., 1947-56 (185,500 pieces).

See Doris M. Reed, Indiana University Library Manuscript Collections Relating to Business History (1951. 2 p. Processed), and "Manuscripts in the Indiana University Library," in Ind. Magazine of History, 49:191-196 (June 1953); and Oscar O. Winther, "The Robert S. Ellison Collection," in Ind. Quarterly for Bookmen, 4:7-19 (Jan. 1948).

CRAWFORDSVILLE

Lilly Library, Wabash College. Donald E. Thompson, Librarian.

Holdings: A considerable quantity of papers of the 19th and 20th centuries, relating chiefly to the College. Included are the Wabash College archives, containing materials on students, faculty, and alumni as well as on the College itself; some manuscripts of Meredith Nicholson (Ind.; novelist, poet, Minister to Paraguay and Venezuela); and papers of Joseph Farrand Tuttle (N.J., Ind.; Presbyterian minister, pres. of Wabash College), late 19th century.

EVANSVILLE 8

Evansville Museum of Arts and Sciences. 411 SE. Riverside Ave. Florita Eichel, Registrar.

Holdings: A quantity of papers,

largely of the 19th century, relating chiefly to Evansville and Indiana. Included are many personal letters from early settlers and scattered letters of a number of notable Americans; papers of James L. Orr (Ind.; Civil War commissary officer), 1862-64 (1 trunk and 1 diary); records of a Sons of Temperance group in Illinois, 1862; and records of local businesses, churches, and schools.

FRANKLIN

Franklin College Library. Robert Y. Coward, Head Librarian.

Holdings: 40 vols., 2 boxes, and 150 pieces, 1799-1933, consisting of Indiana Baptist Church records and other materials relating to the Baptist Church in Indiana. Included are papers of Jesse Lynch Holman (Ind.; Baptist minister, U.S. dist. court judge), 1820-42 (150 pieces); minutes and other records of various Baptist churches, 1799-1931 (34 vols.); minutes of Baptist associations, 1826-96 (6 vols.); and letters relating to Indiana Baptist churches, 1913-33 (2 boxes).

See John F. Cady, The Origin and Development of the Missionary Baptist Church in Indiana, pp. 325-329 (1942).

GOSHEN

Archives of the Mennonite Church. Goshen College. Melvin Gingerich, Archivist.

Holdings: 400 linear ft. (500,000 pieces), from the early 19th century to the present, relating chiefly to the Mennonite Church in the United States and Canada. Included are papers of officers, committees, and institutions of the Mennonite General Conference, Board of Missions and Charities, Board of Education, and Board of Publication; records of the Mennonite Publishing Co., Elkhart, Ind.; some records of Mennonite district conferences and local Mennonite congregations; records of the Mennonite Central Committee, Akron, Pa., dated in the 1920's and 1930's, relating to American Mennonite relief work in Russia and the Near East following World War I and to the settlement of Mennonites from Russia in the Paraguayan Chaco; records of other Mennonite organizations; papers of individual Mennonite and Amish Mennonite leaders; microfilms, slides, and recordings. The manuscript collections belonging to the Mennonite Historical Library, Goshen College, are filed in the Archives of the Mennonite Church and are included in this description.

GREENCASTLE

Archives of DePauw University and Indiana Methodism. Roy O. West Library, DePauw University. Eleanore Cammack, Archivist.

Holdings: 308 linear ft., 1807-1959, consisting of (1) archives of the University and (2) archives of the Methodist Church in Indiana. The University archives, 1837-1954 (263 linear ft.), include records of the board of trustees, the presidents and other administrative officials, the faculty committee, departments of instruction, students, and alumni; and records concerning finance and buildings. For the recent period there is at present only a sampling of noncurrent records. The Methodist Church archives, 1807-1959 (45 linear ft.), of which a part consists of rare books), include official minutes and correspondence, 1832-1959, of the three Indiana conferences now in existence and of one that has been terminated, histories of 1,000 Indiana churches, and biographical material on conference ministers. A card index has been compiled of the obituaries for those appearing in the annual Minutes of all conferences in Indiana Methodism, thus totaling to date about 1,200. In the archives there are also records of the earliest Methodist church in Indiana, 1807, many diaries, and records of numerous early Methodist seminaries in the State. Microfilms and movies are being accessioned respectively of historical materials and significant events which occur at the University. Tape recordings of meaningful programs at DePauw are filed in the Archives. The depository has custody of a small but growing collection of letters, reminiscences, genealogies, and other papers belonging to the Putnam County Historical Society and relating to the county.

INDIANAPOLIS 6

American Legion National Headquarters Library. 700 North Pennsylvania St. Thomas V. Hull, Librarian.

Holdings: 814 file drawers, 1919-60, consisting of the archives of the American Legion Headquarters. Included are post histories, records pertaining to national and departmental activities, and extensive information about officials who have held departmental or national office.

See Verna Grimm, "The American Legion National Headquarters Library, Archives and Files," in Special Libraries, 39:3-9 (Jan. 1948), annually revised and distributed by the American Legion Extension Institute, Indianapolis 6, Ind.

INDIANAPOLIS 4

Archives Division, Indiana State

Library. 140 North Senate Ave. Margaret Pierson, Archivist.

Holdings: 15,000 vols. and 3,000 filing drawers and storage boxes, 1790-1956, of noncurrent official records held by the Division as the State's archival agency. (Holdings of the Indiana Division of the Library are described separately.) Included are Territorial court and executive records, 1790-1817 (4 filing drawers); records of the supreme court of Indiana, 1816-1930 (287 vols.); original bills of the General Assembly, 1863-1957 (1,185 vols.); and correspondence of the Governors, 1816-1956 (30 vols. and 169 filing drawers). Records of other executive officials and agencies include those of the adjutant general, 1803-1921 (1,278 vols. and 90 filing drawers, and 201 reels 16 mm. microfilm), containing information on the State militia and the National Guard and their participation in wars of the United States; the attorney general, 1855-1953 (208 vols. and 124 filing drawers); the secretary of state, 1817-1956 (125 vols. and 463 filing drawers); the Department of Education, 1844-1935 (440 vols. and 40 filing drawers); and the State Board of Charities, 1889-1937 (95 vols. and 25 filing drawers). There are also records of the State Bank, 1824-70 (70 vols. and 12 filing drawers); financial records concerning internal improvements, chiefly canals and roads, 1832-82 (130 vols. and 21 filing drawers); records of United States land offices in Indiana, 1805-76 (895 vols. and 25 filing drawers); and 51 vols. of original schedules for Indiana of the United States censuses of agriculture and of industry and manufactures, 1850-80, of social statistics, 1850-70, and of defective, dependent, and delinquent classes, 1880.

—oOo—

Indiana Division, Indiana State

Library. 140 North Senate Ave. (Mrs.) Hazel W. Hopper, Head, Indiana Division.

Holdings: A large quantity of papers, 1778-1952, relating chiefly to Indiana and the Middle West, but including much of national interest.

Papers of men who held Federal office include those of Abraham L. Brick (Ind.; U.S. Rep.), 1901-8 (2 boxes); John Coburn (Ind.; lawyer, Civil War officer, U.S. Rep.), 1850-1904 (9 letter books and 117 pieces); Schuyler Colfax (Ind.; newspaper publisher, U.S. Rep. and Vice Pres.) and his family, 1778-1926 (300 pieces); Jefferson Columbus Davis (Ind.; U.S. Army officer), 1860-70 (5 boxes); Elisha Embree (Ind.; U.S. Rep.), 1786-1860 (4 boxes); Benjamin Harrison (Ind.; U.S. Sen., Pres.), 1855-1901 (1 box), and letters to his law partner and Attorney General William H. H. Miller, 1892-1900 (46 pieces); Will H. Hays (Ind., N.Y.; Chairman Republican Nat'l Committee, Postmaster Gen., business executive), 1896-1954 (200,000 pieces); William S. Holman (Ind.; lawyer, U.S. Rep.), 1838-99 (1 box); George W. Julian (Ind.; lawyer, U.S. Rep., abolitionist), 1819-99 (5 boxes); Thomas R. Marshall (Ind.; lawyer, Gov., U.S. Vice Pres.), 1860-1925 (2,000 pages); William H. H. Miller (Ind.; U.S. Attorney Gen.), 1890-1917 (1 box); Oliver H. P. T. Morton (Ind.; lawyer, Gov., U.S. Sen.), 1825-77 (6 boxes); Harry S. New (Ind.; newspaper editor, U.S. Sen., Postmaster Gen.), 1869-1938 (225 items); Godlove S. Orth (Ind.; U.S. Rep.), 1845-79 (50 pieces); Robert Dale Owen (Ind.; social reformer, author, U.S. Rep.), 1827-77 (1,500 pieces); Daniel D. Pratt (Ind.; lawyer, U.S. Sen.), 1832-77 (20,000 pieces); Thomas Taggart (Ind.; U.S. Sen.), 1874-1929 (550 items); Richard Wigginton Thompson (Ind.; U.S. Rep., Sec. Navy), 1818-99 (400 pieces); John Tipton (Ind.; Indian

agent, U.S. Sen.), 1806-58 (8,000 pieces); Raymond E. Willis (Ind.; newspaper publisher, U.S. Sen.), 1936-50 (3 boxes); and Joseph A. Wright (Ind.; Gov., U.S. Rep. and Sen., Minister to Prussia), 1843-1931 (700 pieces).

Papers of other persons include those of Austin H. Brown (Ind.; publisher of the Ind. State Sentinel), 1830-1901 (600 pieces); Eugene V. Debs (Ind.; labor leader, Socialist), 1895-1922 (5 folders); William G. and George W. Ewing (Ind.; fur traders), 1818-81 (30,000 pieces); William Dudley Foulke (Ind.; author, lawyer, civil service reformer), 1849-1931 (4 boxes); Noah Noble (Ind.; Gov.), 1816-44 (2,000 pieces); Lucius B. Swift (Ind.; lawyer, civil service reformer), 1855-1929 (4 vols. of diary and 1,200 pieces); Robert S. Taylor (Ind.; legislator, patent attorney, member of Miss. River Commission), 1869-1917 (12,000 pieces); Lewis Wallace, known as Lew Wallace (Ind.; soldier, diplomat, author), 1861-85 (1 box); and John T. Wilder (Ind.; Civil War officer), 1858-69 (1 box).

Business records include account books, letters, and other papers relating to early economic conditions in Vincennes and Logansport, the fur trade, trade and other relations with Indians, especially the Potawatomie and Miami, railroads and other forms of transportation, banking, and land sales. There are also numerous Civil War letters.

See Mildred C. Stoler, "Manuscripts in Indiana State Library" and "Manuscript Accessions—Indiana State Library," in Ind. Magazine of History, 27:236-39 (Sept. 1931) and 29:44-77 (Mar. 1933); and Hazel W. Hopper, "Indiana Manuscript Collection," in Library Occurrent, 17:36 (June 1951); and "Indiana State Manuscript Collection," in Library Occurrent, 19:65-67 (Sept. 1957) and 19:114-115 (Mar. 1958).

Indiana Historical Society. 140 North
Senate Ave. Hubert H. Hawkins, Secretary; Caroline Dunn, Librarian.

Holdings: 25,000 pieces, 1741-
1950, relating chiefly to Indiana and
the Old Northwest,
Included are papers of Noble C.
Butler (Ind.; lawyer, clerk U. S. dist.
court), 1850-1925 (5,000 pieces); John
Dowling (Ind.; newspaper editor, legislator), 1827-71 (587 pieces); William
H. English (Ind.; U. S. Rep., historian),
1758-1892 (3,875 pieces, including
1,226 pieces relating to the Hite and
Bowman families, 1741-1871, and other items collected by him); Calvin
Fletcher (Ind.; lawyer, banker), 1817-
66 (2,000 pieces, including a diary,
1820-66); William Henry Harrison
(Ohio; Gov. of Ind. Terr., War of 1812
officer, U. S. Rep. and Sen., U. S.
Pres.), 1794-1864 (300 pieces); Henry
Smith Lane (Ind.; U. S. Rep. and Sen.,
Gov.), 1821-69 (1,000 pieces); Samuel
Merrill (Ind.; banker, railroad promoter), 1813-82 (1,700 pieces); Meredith
Nicholson (Ind.; novelist, poet, Minis-
ter to Paraguay and Venezuela), 1895-
1943 (127 pieces); Robert Dale Owen
(Ind., N. Y.; social reformer, author,
U. S. Rep.), 1829-86 (25 pieces); Wil-
liam Henry Smith (Ohio, Ill.; newspa-
per editor, historian), 1814-96 (7,730
pieces), also material collected by
him, principally transcripts; Elihu
Stout (Ind.; printer) and his family,
1780-1902 (950 pieces); Henry P.
Thornton (Ind.; lawyer), 1819-64 (187
pieces), some relating to the Indiana
Constitutional Convention of 1850;
Samuel C. Vance (Army paymaster at
Cincinnati, founder of Lawrenceburg,
Ind.), 1797-1869 (2,000 pieces); and
Lewis Wallace, known as Lew Wallace
(Ind.; soldier, diplomat, author), 1822-
1916 (2,000 pieces).
Also included are papers relating
to old Vincennes and to Anthony Wayne's
campaigns in the Old Northwest; other
Old Northwest papers, 1749-1838 (500

pieces); papers relating to the Ohio
Co. and the New Harmony community; collections of manuscripts on mills
and covered bridges in Indiana; account books of merchants and other
business records; many letters, diaries, and other papers relating to the
Mexican War and the Civil War; and
an autograph collection containing letters of U. S. Presidents and Cabinet
members.
See the Librarian's reports on
accessions in Proceedings of annual
Indiana History Conferences in Ind.
History Bulletin, 1936-47, and the
separately published reports of the
Librarian, 1948-54; and special articles and notes in Ind. Magazine of
History, 1934-45.

LAFAYETTE

Purdue University Libraries. John
H. Moriarty, Director.

Holdings: 36 vols., 32 filing
drawers, and some 4,500 additional
pieces, 1873-1955, consisting of
(1) some archives of the University
and (2) other papers chiefly of literary
and engineering interest. The archives
include official letter books of presidents and other prominent officials of
the University, 1873-1900 (22 vols.).
Papers of writers include those of
George Ade (Ind.; humorist, novelist,
playwright), 1896-1943 (4,000 letters
sent and received and 170 manuscripts
of plays, stories, fables, and sketches); Archibald J. Cronin (Scotland;
novelist, physician), a manuscript of
The Green Years, with revisions;
George Barr McCutcheon (Ind.; novelist, playwright), 1898-1924 (18 literary manuscripts); John Tinney Mc-
Cutcheon (Ill., Ind.; cartoonist, world
traveler), 1896-1946 (800 cartoons);
and Charles Major (Ind.; novelist),
1896-1912 (30 literary manuscripts
and revisions, and some scrapbooks).

There are also papers of Amelia Earhart (Kans., Ill., N.Y.; aviatrix), part of a logbook and handwritten news stories and cablegrams; Frank B. Gilbreth (Mass., R.I., N.Y.; industrial management specialist), 1910-24 (32 file drawers); and William F. M. Goss (Ind.; engineering prof. and dean at Purdue Univ.), 1884-1907 (14 vols., including 3 letter books and 5 vols. of reports). Business records include those of the Indiana Hardwood Lumbermen's Association, 1899-1955.

See William M. Hepburn, "The Charles Major Manuscripts in the Purdue University Libraries," in Ind. Quarterly for Bookmen, 2:71-81 (July 1946), and his Manual of the William Freeman Myrick Goss Library of the History of Engineering and Associated Collections, pp. 54, 179 (1947).

—oOo—

Tippecanoe County Historical Association. County Museum. Alameda McCollough, Curator.

Holdings: A small quantity of papers, of the 19th century, relating chiefly to the county. Included are a literary manuscript of George Barr McCutcheon (Ind.; novelist); correspondence of B. Wilson Smith (Ind.; Methodist preacher, teacher, State legislator), 1882-96 (7 packages); and watercolor paintings by George Winter (Ind.; pioneer artist), 1837-39, and his journal, 1781.

NEW CASTLE

Henry County Historical Society Museum. 614 South 14th St. (Mrs.) Elsie G. Pickett, Curator.

Holdings: 2,000 vols., 1820-1950, as well as museum pieces, relating chiefly to Henry County and Indiana. Included are papers of Omar Bundy (Ind.; U.S. Army officer in World War I), of a military nature; Arthur Osborn (Ind.; naturalist, botanist), 1870-1920; and Thomas B. Redding (Ind.; lawyer, scientist), 1850-1900. There are also some official records of various county officials, 1820-70 (100 vols.); diaries and scrapbooks of Henry County residents (100 items); and papers relating to meetings of the Society of Friends in the county, 1850-90.

NEW HARMONY

New Harmony Workingmen's Institute Library. (Mrs.) Josephine M. Elliott, Librarian.

Holdings: A quantity of papers, 1821-1938, relating chiefly to the New Harmony Community of Equality and to the town of New Harmony. (These have recently been arranged and many of them microfilmed by the Illinois Historical Survey and the American Philosophical Society, Philadelphia).

Among the New Harmony Community records, from the early years of the 19th century to 1870, are considerable quantities of papers of the following: William Maclure (England, Mexico; geologist, founder of the school of agriculture at the Community), including diaries, drafts of articles, and 400 pieces of correspondence with Marie D. Fretageot, his principal lieutenant at New Harmony; Robert Owen (England; social reformer, founder of the Community) and Robert Dale Owen (Ind., N.Y.; social reformer, author, member of the Community, U.S. Rep. from Ind.); John Heinrich Pestalozzi (Switzerland; educational reformer); Thomas Say (Pa., Ind.; entomologist, conchologist, prof. at Univ. of Pa.); Josiah Warren (Ind., Ohio, N.Y., Mass.; reformer, philosophical anarchist, inventor); and Frances Wright (England, N. Y.; reformer, lecturer). There are also 10 ledgers and other accounts of the Community, a volume containing musical scores and directions for dances, 1826; and correspondence of and concerning the Workingmen's Institute, founded by Maclure in 1838.

Papers relating to the town of New Harmony include records of local justices of the peace, 1835-80; a Methodist church, 1845-1938; several business firms, from 1860 (100 ledgers); and records of the Workingmen's Institute Library, of the later period. The Library has also a substantial collection of papers of the Pelham family, 18th-20th centuries.

See Roger A. Hurst, "The New Harmony Manuscript Collections," in Ind. Magazine of History, 37:45-49 (Mar. 1941); and Arthur E. Bestor, Jr., "Interim Report on the Arrangement, Microfilming, and Cataloguing of the New Harmony Manuscripts," a processed memorandum (Univ. of Ill. Dept. of History, Sept. 14, 1950. 12 p.), and Records of the New Harmony Community (2d ed., rev. 1951. 17 p. Processed).

NOTRE DAME

University of Notre Dame Archives. Rev. Thomas T. McAvoy, Archivist.

Holdings: About 2,000 boxes of papers, largely 19th century, relating chiefly to the University and to the Catholic Church in the United States. (The box used in this depository measures 10 by 14 by $2\frac{1}{2}$ inches.)

Personal papers of Catholic clergymen include those of Peter Baart (Mich.; canonist), 1882-1907 (25 boxes); Frederic Baraga (Mich.; missionary priest and bishop), 1892-1900 (2 boxes of transcripts and 2 rolls of microfilm); Patrick J. Carroll (Ind.; editor of Ave Maria), 1930-37 (3 boxes); Francis S. Chatard (Md., Ind.; Bishop

of Vincennes and Indianapolis), 1855-1912 (9 rolls of microfilm); James Edward Coyle (Ala.; priest), 1878-1918 (4 boxes); Daniel E. Hudson (Ind.; editor of Ave Maria), 1875-1924 (42 boxes); Felix Klein (France; abbé, controversialist, central figure in the Americanist heresy), 1829-1908 (16 boxes); Andrew Arnold Lambing (Pa.; historian, founder of the Ohio Valley Historical Society), 1 box; Philip R. McDevitt (Pa.; Bishop of Harrisburg), 1891-1935 (16 boxes); Joseph H. McMahon (N.Y.; librarian, organizer of the Catholic Summer School of America), 1892 (1 box); Julius Arthur Nieuwland (Ind.; chemistry prof. at Notre Dame), 1904-36 (4 boxes); Denis Joseph O'Connell (D. C., Calif., Va.; Bishop of Richmond), 1912-26 (11 rolls of microfilm); John Mary Odin (Tex., La.; Bishop of New Orleans), 1 roll of microfilm; John Francis O'Hara (Ind., N.Y.; pres. of Notre Dame, Auxiliary Bishop of the Army and Navy during World War II, Bishop of Buffalo), 1940-45 (30 boxes, restricted); Robert Seton (N.J., Italy; Titular Archbishop of Heliopolis), 1903-27 (25 boxes); John Bannister Tabb (Va., Md.; priest, poet, English prof.), 1845-1909 (1 box); and John Augustine Zahm (Ind., D. C.; scientist, author), 1871-1921 (8 boxes).

Papers of laymen include those of Henry F. Brownson (N.Y., Mich.; lawyer, author, editor of his father's works), 1860-1902 (9 boxes); Orestes Brownson (Mass., N.J.; Universalist minister, Catholic convert, author, editor), 1823-72 (41 boxes); Don Carlos Buell (U. S. Army officer), 1853-56 (3 boxes); James F. Edwards (Ohio, Ind.; librarian, founder of Notre Dame Univ. Archives), 1860-1911 (69 boxes); Thomas Ewing (Ohio; U.S. Sen., Sec. Treas., Sec. Interior) and his family, 1815-96 (121 boxes); Austin Ford (N.Y.; editor of the Freeman's Journal), 1885-97 (2 boxes); Edward Lee Greene (Colo., Calif., D. C.; botanist, prof. at Univ. of Calif. and Catholic Univ.), 1843-1915 (36 cu. ft.); Louise Imogen Guiney (Mass., England; poet, essayist), 1 box; Edward N. Hurley (Ill.; manufacturer, financier, Chairman of the U. S. Shipping Board), 1912-33 (122 boxes, restricted); Lawrence Kehoe (N. Y.; editor of the Catholic World), 1870-90 (3 boxes); Frederick P. Kenkel (Ill., Mo.; sociologist, journalist, editor of Amerika and Social Justice Review), 1874-1952 (32 boxes); James Alphonsus McMaster (N. Y.; editor of the Freeman's Journal), 1844-88 (16 boxes); Austin O'Malley (Ind., Pa.; oculist, writer, English prof. at Notre Dame), 1897-98 (1 box); William James Onahan (Ill.; banker, promoter of Catholic laymen's activities), 1862-99 (20 boxes); John Gilmary Shea (N. Y., N. J.; historian, author, editor), 1867-98 (4 boxes); William Tecumseh Sherman (U. S. Army officer) and his family, 1820-91 (30 cu. ft.); Eliza Allen Starr (Mass., Miss., Ill.; author, lecturer on art), 1848-67 (1 box); Charles Warren Stoddard (Calif.; author, prof. at Notre Dame), 1884-85 (3 boxes and 7 vols. of diary); Frank C. Walker (Mont., D. C., Pa.; lawyer, Postmaster Gen.), 1886-1959 (70 boxes, restricted); and Albert F. Zahm (Ind., D. C.; prof. at Univ. of Notre Dame and Catholic Univ., pioneer in aerial navigation), 1862-1954 (48 cu. ft.).

Organizational papers include material on early Notre Dame, 1837-1900 (153 boxes); correspondence of all the University's presidents, 1842-1949 (818 boxes); and 240 boxes of diocesan papers, the use of which is restricted. Among the more important or extensive of the diocesan papers are some from the Archdiocese of Baltimore (16 boxes), including letters of the Carroll and Brent families, papers of Mount St. Mary's College, and papers of Simon W. G. Bruté de Rémur (Md., Ind.; first Bishop of

Vincennes); the Archdiocese of Cincinnati (20 boxes); and the Archdiocese of New Orleans (113 boxes), including personal correspondence of Napoleon Joseph Perché (La.; bishop and archbishop) and a collection of and relating to Adrien Emmanuel Rouquette (La.; missionary priest, poet). The more important papers from dioceses include those of the dioceses of Charleston (3 boxes), with photostats of the diary of John England (Ireland, S. C.; first Bishop of Charleston); Columbus (1 box), with the diary of Sylvester Horton Rosecrans (Ohio; Bishop of Columbus); Detroit (11 boxes); Hartford (3 boxes), including personal letters of Francis P. McFarland (N. Y., Conn.; Bishop of Hartford); Marquette (2 boxes), including materials for the instruction of the Indians used by Ignatius Mrak (Wis., Mich.; Catholic missionary, Bishop of Marquette and Sault Ste. Marie); and Vincennes (13 boxes), including sermons and the diary of Celestine R. L. G. de la Hailandière (Ind.; Bishop of Vincennes). Included also are photostats of material on early Catholic missions in Texas and the Southwest (20 boxes). There are microfilm copies of letters of American missionaries to the Society for the Propagation of the Faith, Lyons, 1822-1900 (15 rolls); letters to the Society for the Propagation of the Faith, Paris, 1830- (30 rolls); letters to Ludwigs Missionverein, Munich, 1850-1912 (5 rolls); and letters to Der Leopoldinen Stiftung, Vienna (8 rolls); Berichte der Leopoldinen Stiftung, vols. 1-45, 1829-92 (2 rolls).

RICHMOND

Earlham College Library. Robert M. Agard, Librarian.

Holdings: 25 vols., 8 boxes, and 35 ft. of other materials, 1821-1954, relating chiefly to the Society of Friends. Included are papers of Charles F. Coffin (Ind., Ill.; banker, Quaker minister) and his wife, 1850-91 (6 ft.); Homer L. Morris (Pa.; economist, American Friends Service Committee official, field supervisor of the Subsistence Homestead Division of the U. S. Interior Dept.), 1905-51 (5 ft.), including material on relief work in Germany and Russia, 1919-23, subsistence homesteads in the 1930's, and Japanese relocation, 1846-48; Marcus Mote (Ind., Ohio; primitive painter), 1838-95 (25 vols.); Elbert Russell (Ind., Pa., N. C.; dean of the School of Religion of Duke Univ.), 1898-1950 (5 ft.); and Walter C. Woodward (Oreg., Ind.; college prof., editor, Society of Friends official), 1917-18 (6 boxes).   There are also archives of the Board of Young Friends Activities, the American Young Friends Fellowship, and the Young Friends Committee of North America, 1909-54; and scattered minutes of some monthly meetings of Friends.

SAINT MEINRAD

Saint Meinrad Archabbey.   Rev. Simeon Daly.

Holdings: Medieval and Renaissance manuscripts (2 vols.); and several thousand letters and other documents relating to the foundation and activities of this monastery. Included is considerable material on Catholic Indian missions in North and South Dakota.
See De Ricci, Census, p. 715.

SHELBYVILLE

Inlow Foundation Library. 103 West Washington St.   H. H. Inlow, M. D., Director.

Holdings: Extensive materials,

1811-1954, relating chiefly to the history of medicine and to Rush and Shelby Counties, Indiana. Included are unpublished manuscripts of William D. Inlow (Ind.; physician), 1925-50 (25 pieces); notebooks of medical students at the University of Pennsylvania, 1811, and Ohio Medical College, 1849; many papers relating to the history of Rush and Shelby Counties, 1821-1954, including letters, interviews, and cemetery records; and manuscript material, 1880-1954, relating to the geology, paleontology, and archeology of Shelby County.

SOUTH BEND

Northern Indiana Historical Society. 112 South Lafayette Blvd.   Mrs. Thomas E. Stanfield, Curator.

Holdings: A small quantity of manuscripts, mainly of the 19th century, relating chiefly to the northern Indiana area. Included are letters and a journal of Schuyler Colfax (Ind.; U. S. Rep., Vice Pres.), 1863-73; letters and other papers of pioneers; several diaries; and some account books of pioneer merchants, 1792-1855.

VINCENNES

Old Cathedral Library. 205 Church St.

Holdings: Papers relating chiefly to Catholic missionary work and other activities in the Vincennes area. Included are accounts of voyages of Pierre F. X. Charlevoix (France; explorer, historian) and Louis Hennepin (France; Recollect missionary, explorer); missionary records, 1660, 1702, and 1707; and parish records dated from

1749. There are also some illuminated manuscripts.

See Special Libraries Association, Special Library Resources, vol. 2, entry 1246
(1946).

IOWA

AMES

Iowa State University of Science and Technology Library.   Robert W. Orr, Director.

Holdings: A small quantity of papers, largely unprocessed.   Included are miscellaneous letters and documents in files of the Iowa State Planning Board assembled for its social studies.   The Iowa State History Collection contains considerable correspondence of Louis Hermann Pammel (Iowa; botanist, conservationist, prof. at Iowa State College), 1889-1931, which includes correspondence with his student, George Washington Carver (Iowa, Ala.; botanist, agricultural scientist at Tuskegee Institute), and papers relative to the Iowa Soil Conservation, Iowa State Park Commission, and Iowa Academy of Science.

BURLINGTON

Free Public Library.   Mary Dugan, Librarian.

Holdings: 700 pieces, 1843-88, chiefly a collection of autograph letters and other documents of prominent Americans.
See Hist. Records Survey, Guide for Iowa, p. 2.

CEDAR RAPIDS

Iowa Masonic Library.   815 First Ave., SE.   Ralph E. Whipple, Grand Secretary and Librarian.

Holdings: An autograph collection of 750 items, containing letters of a number of Americans prominent in literature and politics.
See Hist. Records Survey, Guide for Iowa, p. 3.

COUNCIL BLUFFS

Free Public Library.   Mildred K. Smock, Librarian.

Holdings: 507 items, 1842-1928, including papers of Amelia Jenks Bloomer (N. Y., Iowa; reformer), 1848-88 (16 items), mostly relating to woman's suffrage and temperance; letters and an autobiography of Grenville M. Dodge (Iowa; Civil War officer, civil engineer, U. S. Rep.), 1861-1916 (27 vols.), mostly relating to construction of the Union Pacific Railroad; and a manuscript autobiography of Frank W. Dean (Iowa; physician) relating to the history of Council Bluffs and the advance of medicine.

DAVENPORT

Davenport Public Library.   Elizabeth Martin, Librarian.

Holdings: 112 pieces, consisting of (1) medieval and Renaissance manuscripts (10 vols.), chiefly devotional but including notarial records of the monastery of San Lorenzo, Venice, 1478-1520; and (2) some items of local interest.
See De Ricci, Census, pp. 717-719.

DECORAH

Luther College Library.   O. M.

Hovde, Librarian.

Holdings: 27,000 pieces, 1844-1955, relating chiefly to Norwegian-Americans and the Norwegian Lutheran Church. Personal papers include those of Claus L. Clausen (Wis., Iowa, Minn.; pioneer Lutheran clergyman, editor), 1864-85 (1 box); James Christian Meinich Hanson (Iowa, D. C., Ill., Wis.; librarian), 2 boxes; Ulrik Vilhelm Koren (Iowa; Norwegian Lutheran clergyman), 1853-1910 (4 boxes); Peter Laurentius Larsen (Mo., Iowa; Norwegian Lutheran clergyman, pres. of Luther College, editor), 1859-1911 (14 boxes); Christian K. Preus (Iowa; Lutheran clergyman, pres. of Luther College), 1817-1917 (4 boxes); and Herman Amberg Preus (Wis.; Norwegian Lutheran clergyman, a founder and pres. of Norwegian Synod), 1846-94 (9 boxes). Also included are records of the Synod of the Norwegian Lutheran Church in America, 1872-1921; records of Luther Seminary and Luther College, 1863-1955; and papers relating to the Civil War and World War I.

See Hist. Records Survey, Guide for Iowa, pp. 7-9.

DES MOINES 19

Iowa State Department of History and Archives. Historical Bldg. Jack W. Musgrove, Acting Curator.

Holdings: An unknown quantity of (1) official records held by the Department as the State's archival agency and (2) other papers relating chiefly to Iowa. Personal papers include those of William B. Allison (Iowa; U. S. Rep. and Sen.), 1850-1908 (200,000 pieces); William Worth Belknap (Iowa, D. C.; lawyer, Civil War officer, Sec. War); Albert B. Cummins (Iowa; lawyer, Gov., U. S. Sen.), 1891-1909 (12,000 items); Samuel Ryan Curtis (Ohio, Iowa; Mexican War and Civil War officer,

U. S. Rep. from Iowa), Civil War letters; Horace R. Deemer (Iowa; jurist), 1877-1915 (23,200 items); Grenville M. Dodge (Iowa; Civil War officer, civil engineer, U. S. Rep.), 455 vols., some relating to the Union Pacific Railroad; George W. Jones (Mich., Wis., Iowa; Terr. Delegate to Cong. from Mich. and Wis., U. S. Sen. from Iowa); John A. Kasson (Iowa; diplomat, U. S. Rep.), 1877-1910 (1,200 items); Samuel J. Kirkwood (Iowa; Gov., U. S. Sen., Sec. Interior), 1846-93 (1,950 items); Robert Lucas (Ohio, Iowa; Gov. of Ohio and Terr. Gov. of Iowa), 1838-41 (100 items); Charles Mason (N. Y., D. C.. Iowa; jurist, U. S. Commissioner of Patents), 1804-82; George D. Perkins (Iowa; U. S. Rep., editor), 1878-1912 (1,200 items); George C. Remey (U. S. naval officer), 1867-1919 (300 items); and William Salter (Iowa; Congregational clergyman, Civil War chaplain, author), 1824-1903 (600 items). Also included are records of the Iowa Equal Suffrage Association and other woman-suffrage organizations, 1854-1919; correspondence of the Union League of America; and several large collections pertaining to the Civil War.

See Iowa State Department of History and Archives (previously the Historical, Memorial and Art Department of Iowa), Biennial Report, 1892 to date; Edgar R. Harlan, "Ethics Involved in the Handling of Personal Papers," in Annals of Iowa, 3d ser., 16:610-621 (Apr. 1929); and Hist. Records Survey, Guide for Iowa, pp. 9-13.

—oOo—

Iowa State Medical Library. East 12th St. at Grand Ave. Jeannette Dean-Throckmorton, M. D., Medical Librarian.

Holdings: 15 vols. and over 2,000 pieces, 1849-1917, pertaining to med-

ical societies and subjects. Included
are papers of Oscar Burbank (Iowa;
physician), containing accounts of California during the gold rush; records
of the Second District Medical Society
of Iowa, 1907 (1 vol.); and "One Hundred Years of Iowa Medicine" by the
Iowa State Medical Society.

See Hist. Records Survey, Guide
for Iowa, pp. 13-15.

DUBUQUE

American Lutheran Church Archives.
Wartburg Theological Seminary.
William F. Goetz, Archivist.

Holdings: 200 vols. and 600 ft.,
consisting of the official records and
publications of the American Lutheran
Church, 1930-60, and its antecedent
synods: Buffalo, 1845-1930; Iowa,
1854-1930; Joint Synod of Ohio, 1818-
1930; and Texas, 1851-1930.

See Hist. Records Survey, Guide
for Iowa, p. 21.

—oOo—

Catholic Chancery Office. 1104 Bluff
St.

Holdings: An unknown quantity of
papers, chiefly the business and ecclesiastical archives of the Dubuque
archdiocese. Included are correspondence from Iowa priests with Jean Mathias Pierre Loras (Ala., Wis. Terr., Iowa; Bishop of Dubuque), 1839-60.

See Hist. Records Survey, Guide for
Iowa, p. 15.

—oOo—

Columbia Museum. Alta Vista St.

Holdings: 475 items, relating
chiefly to Iowa and the Catholic Church
in the area. Included are papers of
pioneer settlers, Civil War and World

War I correspondence, records of
Catholic churches, papers of several
clergymen, and an autograph collection.

See Hist. Records Survey, Guide
for Iowa, pp. 18-20.

—oOo—

Loras College Library. Alta Vista
St. Rev. A. V. Manternach, Librarian.

Holdings: 1,500 pieces, including
a collection of 14 medieval and Renaissance manuscripts, 1000-1500,
chiefly Italian, and other Italian documents of the 16th century.

See Hist. Records Survey, Guide
for Iowa, p. 17.

GRINNELL

Grinnell College Library. Henry
Alden, Librarian.

Holdings: A substantial quantity
of materials, 1840-1925, relating
chiefly to Congregationalism in Iowa,
particularly to the activities of the
"Iowa Band," a group of men who
came from Andover Seminary to
found churches and open a school
which is now Grinnell College. Papers of clergymen include those of
Ephraim Adams (Iowa; Congregational clergyman), 1844-1905 (50
letters); Julius A. Reed (Iowa; Congregational clergyman, agent for the
American Home Missionary Society),
1837-88 (1,573 letters, 17 addresses
and papers, 52 sermons, and diaries
covering 19 years); William Salter
(Iowa; Congregational clergyman,
Civil War chaplain, author), 1843-
96 (395 letters). Included also are
records of the Congregational Association of Iowa, 1840-83; and of local Congregational organizations, including the Davenport Association,

1843-1908; the Denmark Association, 1843-89; and the Des Moines River Association, 1849-93. There are also 58 letters relating to early Presbyterian-Congregational relations, and manuscripts containing biographical information about many Iowa ministers.

HARLAN

Danish Baptist Archive. Rev. I. Fredmund, Archivist, Albert Lea, Minn.

Holdings: Chiefly records, from 1856, of the Danish Baptist General Conference in America and its constituent units. Included are record books of individual churches, reports of annual conferences, general correspondence, and papers concerning the Danish Baptist Mission in Canada. There are also pictures of ministers, churches, church groups, and conferences.

IOWA CITY

State Historical Society of Iowa. State University of Iowa. William J. Petersen, Superintendent.

Holdings: A substantial collection of papers of individuals prominent in the history of Iowa, together with records of various organizations and State agencies.

Among the papers of men who held high State or national office are those of Cyrus C. Carpenter (Iowa; Gov., Civil War officer, U. S. Rep.), 1850-98 (4 filing drawers), including correspondence, letterpress books, and diaries; John Chambers (D. C., Ky., Iowa; Gov. of Iowa Terr.), 1828-52 (1 folder); Cyrenus Cole (Iowa; editor, U. S. Rep.), 1893-1936 (1 folder); Albert B. Cummins (Iowa; lawyer, Gov., U. S. Sen.), 1905-15 (1 folder); Augustus Caesar Dodge (Wis., Iowa; U. S. Sen., Minister to Spain), 1838-83 (9

vols. and 8 folders); Jonathan P. Dolliver (Iowa; U. S. Rep. and Sen.), correspondence, including that of members of his family, 1860-1920 (12 vols., 87 boxes, 2 filing drawers, and 2 cases); James Harlan (Iowa; U. S. Sen., Sec. Interior), 1855-95 (5 folders), including correspondence relating to Harlan, 1905-9; Samuel J. Kirkwood (Iowa; Gov., U. S. Sen., Sec. Interior), 1846-1915 (16 letter books, 29 folders, and 1 box), including correspondence of his wife; and Robert Lucas (Ohio, Iowa; Gov. of Ohio and of Iowa Terr.), 1835-52 (3 vols. and 1 filing drawer).

Included also are papers of Charles Aldrich (Iowa; editor, State legislator, curator of State historical department), 1901-7 (1 folder); Leander Clark (Wis., Calif., Iowa; Indian agent), 1866-73 (10 folders); Charles W. Kepler (Iowa; Civil War soldier and lawyer), 1860-1923 (62 vols. and 16 boxes); Lucius H. Langworthy (Iowa; businessman, member of Terr. legislature, sheriff of Dubuque County), 1835-65 (15 folders); Emlin McClain (Iowa; prof. at Univ. of Iowa, chief justice of State supreme court), 1863-1908 (6 folders of miscellaneous material); Thomas McKnight (Mo., Ill., Iowa; businessman and politician), 1805-56 (48 folders); Theodore S. Parvin (Iowa; judge, historian, sec. of the State historical society), 1847-88 (1 folder); Robert Smyth (Iowa; banker, State legislator), 1840, 1854-66 (22 folders); and John P. Wallace (Iowa; World War I Red Cross leader), 1917-19 (11 folders).

There are many records of cities, counties, courts, and schools; a few early State government records; numerous Civil War diaries and company and regimental records; and some records of Universalist, Unitarian, Presbyterian, Episcopalian, and other church groups. The manuscript records for Iowa, of the United States agricultural, social, and other special censuses, 1850-80, are also available.

—oOo—

State University of Iowa Libraries. Leslie W. Dunlap, Director.

Holdings: Several collections of miscellaneous character, 1797-1952. The Leigh Hunt Collection of letters and literary manuscripts, 1797-1929 (1,750 pieces), contains 111 literary manuscripts and 514 letters of Leigh Hunt (England; essayist, poet), and smaller quantities of the papers of other authors, mostly English, chiefly of the first half of the 19th century. The Iowa Historical Manuscripts Collection contains papers of Gilbert Nelson Haugen (Iowa; banker, U. S. Rep.), 1894-1932; and records of the following Iowa organizations: a law firm, 1857-1947 (71,000 pieces), a corn products manufacturing firm, 1866-1941 (124 vols.), an electrical manufacturing firm, 1911-51 (a large quantity), a grain dealers' association, 1920-40, a mutual hail association, 1898-1952, a local of the American Federation of Grain Millers (9 boxes), and a savings bank, 1889-1931. The Iowa Literary Manuscripts Collection consists of 300 drafts of books by contemporary Iowa authors, some of them at times residents also of other States. Another collection consists of notes by Edwin Ford Piper (Nebr., Iowa; prof. at Univ. of Nebr. and State Univ. of Iowa) on western American ballads and other folk expression. The Levi O. Leonard Collection includes material relating to the Union Pacific, the Mississippi and Missouri, and the Chicago, Rock Island and Pacific railroads during the period 1850-1900. The Chatauqua Collection (100,000 items) consists principally of the records of the Redpath Bureau and the Redpath-Vawter Chatauquas. There is also a collection of the official correspondence of

the presidents of the State University of Iowa, 1888-1934.

KEOKUK

Keokuk Public Library. Doris A. Foley, Librarian.

Holdings: 8 vols., 1850-1912, comprising the diary of Joshua M. Shaffer (Iowa; physician, entomologist).

McGREGOR

Effigy Mounds National Monument. Superintendent.

Holdings: 11 vols. and 2 boxes, 1934-40, relating to archeology and historic sites of northeast Iowa. Included are archeological field notes of Ellison Orr (Iowa; field supervisor of the Iowa Archeological Survey) in narrative form, maps, notes, and short descriptive papers on local archeological, geological, and historic sites. There are also files of Orr's correspondence with archeologists and conservationists. Much of the correspondence with the latter relates to the purchase and preservation of archeological and historic sites by the State of Iowa.

PELLA

Central College Library. Mrs. Robert Lautenbach, Curator.

Holdings: 850 pieces, 1830-50, relating chiefly to the separation of church and state in the Netherlands and to the subsequent emigration of the Dutch to America and the founding of the city of Pella. Most of the papers are in the Dutch language. Included are official papers, correspondence, business records, and letters.

SIOUX CITY

Sioux City Public Museum. 2901 Jackson St. Eugene Fugle, Director; (Mrs.) Lillian Smith, Curator.

Holdings: 5,000 pieces, 1857-90, including journals, diaries, letters, reminiscences of pioneers, and Presbyterian church records chiefly concerning northwestern Iowa.
See Hist. Records Survey, Guide

for Iowa, pp. 32-34.

WEBSTER CITY

Kendall Young Library.

Holdings: 1,200 pieces, 1857-1918, chiefly of local interest. Included are a small collection of letters of American authors; Civil War records, maps, and veterans' records; and World War I service records (1,100 pieces).
See Hist. Records Survey, Guide for Iowa, p. 34.

KANSAS

ATCHISON

St. Benedict's Abbey Archives.   Rev.
Peter Beckman, Archivist.

Holdings: 116 vols. and 263 boxes
relating to St. Benedict's College, Atchison, and to Catholic parishes in the
area, from 1856. Included are letters
of Boniface Wimmer (Germany, Pa.;
Roman Catholic archabbot, founder of
the Benedictine Order in the U. S.) to
Innocent Wolf (Pa., Kans.; Roman
Catholic abbot, founder of St. Benedict's Abbey in Atchison), 1868-87
(113 pieces).

—oOo—

St. Benedict's College Library.   Rev.
Colman J. Farrell, Librarian.

Holdings: 140 pieces, 1550-1860,
originating chiefly in Italy. Included
are 19 parchments, chiefly papal documents, 1550-1800; a few unpublished
letters dealing with the Napoleonic
wars; and several passports, hunting
licenses, and the like, 1840-60.

EMPORIA

College of Emporia Library.

Holdings: 24 vols., 9 bundles, and
1 box, 1855-1915, consisting chiefly
of official records of various organizational units in Kansas of the Cumberland Presbyterian Church and the Presbyterian Church in the United States.
  See unpublished records of the
Hist. Records Survey in the National
Archives.

KANSAS CITY 12

History of Medicine Collection,
Clendening Medical Library.
G. S. T. Cavanagh, Librarian.

Holdings: Miscellaneous manuscripts, 14th to 20th centuries, relating to medical history. Included
are a French manuscript, 14th century, on alchemy and medicine; an
illustrated Persian manuscript,
17th century, on anatomy; and a
2-vol. copy of an illustrated Japanese
manuscript of R. Yoshimura, 1784,
on anatomy. There are notes on lectures by Thomas Denman (England;
naval surgeon, London physician) on
midwifery, 1780; by William Cullen
and John Gregory (Scotland; physicians, profs. at Edinburgh Univ.) on
medicine, 1767-68; by William Gibson (Pa., Ga.; surgeon, prof. at
Univ. of Pa.) on surgery, 1820-21;
by David Hosack (N. Y.; physician,
prof. at College of Physicians and
Surgeons) on medicine, 1820; by Alexander Monro (Scotland; anatomist,
prof. at Edinburgh Univ.) on surgery,
1781-72 (2 vols.); and by Philip Syng
Physick (Pa.; surgeon, prof. at Univ.
of Pa.) on surgery. Included also
are correspondence and clinical observations of Joseph Despine (France;
physician), 18th century (20 vols.);
and correspondence of Henry P. Walcott (Mass.; physician, public health
administrator), 1892-1919. A manuscript of Sir Charles Bell (Scotland;
anatomist), "A Drive Into the West
of England and Wales," 1826 (1 vol.),
is in Lady Bell's handwriting, with
36 color sketches by Sir Charles.

KANSAS CITY 1

Public Library. 6th and Minnesota Ave. Esther Norman, Librarian.

Holdings: The Connelley Collection, relating chiefly to the Wyandotte Indians and early local history (3 boxes).

LAWRENCE

University of Kansas Libraries. Robert Vosper, Director.

Holdings: 449 vols., 503 boxes, and 83 pieces, 1841-1954, relating primarily to the history of Kansas and the University. Included are papers of Samuel Johnson Crawford (Kans.; Civil War officer, Gov.), 1889-92 (1 box); Lyman Underwood Humphrey (Ohio, Kans.; Civil War officer, Gov. of Kans.), 1873-1905 (2 boxes); James Henry Lane (Ind., Kans.; Mexican War officer, U. S. Rep. from Ind., U. S. Sen. from Kans.), 1841-66 (4 boxes and 10 pieces); William Clarke Quantrill (Kans.; guerilla leader, outlaw), 1855-1909 (1 box); Charles Robinson (Mass., Kans.; agent of New England Emigrant Aid Co., Gov. of Kans.), 1851-1909 (2 boxes); Francis H. Snow (Kans.; entomologist, chancellor of Univ. of Kans.), 1864-1900 (1 vol., 3 boxes, and 1 piece); Frank Strong (Mo., Nebr., Oreg., Kans.; pres. of Oreg. State Univ., chancellor of Univ. of Kans.), 1899-1916 (1 box); and Jabez Bunting Watkins (Ill., Kans.; land speculator), 1873-1919 (435 boxes and 363 letter books), covering land investment and speculation in Kansas, Iowa, Missouri, and western Louisiana.

See accessions occasionally reported in the depository's quarterly, Books and Libraries.

NORTH NEWTON

Bethel College Historical Library. Cornelius Krahn, Director.

Holdings: 110 linear ft. (957,000 items) in archive boxes, 540 drawers (16" x 9" x 3"), 40 modern filing drawers, and 120,000 frames of microfilm, spanning four centuries and relating to the Anabaptist-Mennonites the world over. The original documents consist of diaries, correspondence, sermons, church records, and other papers concerning Mennonites in Russia and Prussia and particularly in the prairie States and provinces of of the United States and Canada. The documents on microfilm are the archives of the Mennonite Church of Amsterdam, dealing with the Anabaptists and Mennonites of the Low Countries.

See John F. Schmidt, "The Story of a Library," in Mennonite Life, 9: 68 ff. (Apr. 1954); and Cornelius Krahn, "Mennonite Historical Library," in Mennonite Encyclopedia, 3:625.

ST. MARYS

St. Mary's College Archives. Rev. A. C. Wand, Archivist.

Holdings: Materials relating to pioneer Catholicism on the Kansas-Missouri border, 1835-69, especially to Jesuit missions among the Kickapoo and Potawatomi Indians. Included are registers and account books of missions and diaries of three Jesuit missionaries: John Duerinck, Maurice Gailland, and Christian Hoecken. There are also registers, diaries, and miscellaneous papers concerning St. Mary's College, 1870-1931.

ST. PAUL

St. Francis Monastery. Archivist.

Holdings: A small collection of
19th-century papers, relating chiefly
to the Catholic Church in Kansas. Included are records of the Jesuit mission among the Osage Indians of Kansas and Missouri, 1820-93, among
them vital records (5 vols.) of the Big
and Little Osage and of some other Indians, notes on the history of the mission, correspondence about the Osage
with Isidore Robot (Okla.; founder of
Benedictine monastery and mission
among the Potawatomi, Prefect Apostolic of Indian Terr.), and documents
relating to the mission's manual labor
school. Included also are a list of
Catholics in Kansas, 1848, and records concerning the founding of churches at Neodesha, Independence, and Cher-
ryvale, Kans.

TOPEKA

Kansas State Historical Society. Nyle
H. Miller, Secretary.

Holdings: A large collection consisting of (1) noncurrent official records held by the Society as the State's
archival agency and (2) other papers relating chiefly to Kansas and the Middle
West.
    In the first category are records of
the Governors' offices, 1861-1956; the
Board of Agriculture, 1862-1959; the
attorney general, 1882-1905; the secretary of state, 1861-85; the Railroad
Commission, 1880-1905; the Labor Department, 1919-42; the insurance commissioner, 1863-1952; the adjutant
general, 1861-1903 and 1932-45; and
other State officials and agencies.
There are also some county and township archives.
    Papers of persons who served as
Federal officials include those of Jo-

seph L. Bristow (Kans.; newspaper
editor and publisher, U. S. Sen.),
1900-25 (120 boxes); Arthur Capper
(Kans.; newspaper editor and publish-
er, Gov., U. S. Sen.), 20th century
(36 file drawers); William Clark (Ky.,
Mo.; explorer, Gov. of Mo. Terr.,
Indian agent), 1807-38 (included among
the records of the U. S. Indian Super-
intendency, St. Louis, below); Albert
M. Cole (Kans.; U. S. Rep.), 1945-53;
Thomas Ewing, Jr. (Ohio, Kans.,
N. Y.; lawyer, chief justice of Kans.,
Civil War officer, U. S. Rep. from
Ohio), 1857-66 (4 letterpress books,
2 account books, and 250 letters);
James M. Harvey (Kans.; Gov., U. S.
Sen.), 1861-94 (7 boxes); Clifford R.
Hope (Kans.; U. S. Rep.), 20th centu-
ry (156 transfer cases), temporarily
restricted; Walter A. Huxman (Kans.;
Gov., U. S. circuit court judge),
1937-39 (2 boxes); John J. Ingalls
(Kans.; U. S. Sen.), 1863-95 (52
items); Chester I. Long (Kans.; U. S.
Rep. and Sen.), 1889-1917 (54 boxes,
28 letter books, and 4 scrapbooks);
Preston B. Plumb (Kans.; Civil War
officer, U. S. Sen.), 1862-65 (340 mi-
litary papers); Samuel C. Pomeroy
(Kans.; Free-State advocate, U. S.
Sen.), 1857-62 (131 items); Charles
F. Scott (Kans.; newspaper editor,
U. S. Rep.), 1883-1939 (123 pieces);
John Palmer Usher (Ind., Kans.; lawyer, Sec. Interior), 1837-1932 (666
items), including many letters of his
wife and sons; and Harry H. Woodring
(Kans.; Gov., Sec. War), 1931-33 (33
boxes).
    Papers of persons who served as
State officials, in addition to some of
those above, include those of Jess C.
Denious (Kans.; newspaper editor,
publisher, State sen., Lt. Gov.)
(15,000 pieces); Isaac T. Goodnow
(Kans.; pioneer, supt. of public instruction), 1833-94 (a 45-vol. diary
and 6 boxes); Alfred M. Landon (Kans.;
Gov.), 20th century (90 file drawers);
Clyde M. Reed (Kans.; Gov., newspa-

per publisher), 1929-31 (40 boxes); Charles Robinson (Mass., Kans.; agent of New England Emigrant Aid Co., Gov. of Kans.), 1856-94 (23 boxes); Jacob C. Ruppenthal (Kans.; editor, State judge), 1881-88 (diary and miscellaneous items); and John P. St. John (Kans.; Gov., prohibitionist), 1879-1915 (4 letterpress books, 30 boxes, and 16 scrapbooks).

Papers of other persons include those of Daniel Read Anthony (N. Y., Kans.; newspaper publisher, Civil War officer), 1857-62 (122 items); Elam Bartholomew (Kans.; scientist), 1871-1934 (diary, 38 vols.); John Brown (Pa., N. Y., Kans.; abolitionist), 1855-59 (34 items); John S. Brown (Kans.; pioneer Unitarian minister), 1818-1906 (800 items); Augustus Burton (Kans.; Civil War officer), 1862-65 (500 items); Rolla Clymer (Kans.; editor and publisher), 1919-58 (53 letter file cases); Thomas Wentworth Higginson (Mass.; Unitarian clergyman, abolitionist, Civil War officer), 1855-60 (1 box); Cyrus K. Holliday (Pa., Kans.; founder of Topeka, pres. of the Atchison, Topeka and Santa Fe Railroad), 1854-96 (1 box); Jay E. House (Kans.; mayor of Topeka, newspaperman), 1919-26 (3 boxes); Isaac McCoy (Ind., Ky.; Indian agent, Baptist missionary), 1808-54 (39 vols.); Jotham Meeker (Mich., Kans.; Baptist missionary, printer), 1832-55 (4 letter books); John G. Pratt (Kans.; Baptist missionary, printer), 1834-69 (18 boxes); Robert Simerwell (Mich., Kans.; Baptist missionary), 1824-67 (8-vol. diary and 4 boxes); George L. Stearns (Mass.; businessman, Free-Soiler), 1856-67 (1 box); William Allen White (Kans.; newspaper editor, author), 1902-43 (275 items); and Charles Wilkes (U. S. naval officer, explorer), 1837-47 (5 vols., including a journal of the Pacific exploring expedition, 1838-42).

Other papers include records of the U. S. Indian Superintendency, St. Louis, 1807-55 (33 vols.); the New England Emigrant Aid Society, 1854-69 (26 vols. and 9 boxes); the Freedmen's Relief Association, 1879-81 (4 vols. and 1 box); Presbyterian, Baptist, and other churches; business firms, including a stage company's passenger register, 1874-79; and the law department of the Union Pacific Railroad Co., not yet processed (33 boxes). There are also records pertaining to livestock brands, 1855-1937 (21 boxes); records of two Turnvereine, one in Atchison, 1859-1903 (25 vols. and 3 letter books), the other in Topeka, 1904-22 (4 vols.); letters and diaries of Civil War soldiers and muster rolls, payrolls, and other documents; records of detachments of the U. S. Army Hospital Corps at Ft. Riley, 1853-1902 (370 pieces); and journals of overland trips to California in the gold-rush period.

See the successive reports of annual meetings of the Society, printed in Kans. Hist. Quarterly, 1931 to date.

WICHITA 2

Wichita City Library.   Ford A. Rockwell, Librarian.

Holdings: Some literary manuscripts of Charles B. Driscoll (Kans., Ohio, N. Y.; writer on piracy), and of Paul I. Wellman (Kans., Calif.; novelist, historian); and a ship's log, the diary of a Spanish corsair, and a few other papers in the Driscoll Piracy Collection.

WINFIELD

Historical Society of the Central Kansas Conference. Southwestern

College.   W. J. Poundstone, Custodian.

Holdings: A collection of several hundred items relating chiefly to this Methodist conference and its churches.   Included are histories of 75 churches, 1856-1959; and autobiographies or memoirs of 168 Kansas Methodist ministers.

KENTUCKY

BEREA

Berea College Library. Elizabeth Gilbert, Librarian; (Mrs.) Elisabeth S. Peck, College Historian.

Holdings: 18 file drawers and numerous boxes and other containers not yet processed, 1842-1925, relating chiefly to the College and its educational program, and to antislavery in the United States. Included are papers of the following leaders in the movement for the abolition of slavery and the education of Negroes: Cassius Marcellus Clay (Ky.; U.S. Minister to Russia), 53 pieces; Edward Henry Fairchild (Ohio, Ky.; Presbyterian clergyman, Oberlin College official, pres. of Berea College), 58 pieces; and John G. Fee (Ky.; Presbyterian clergyman, founder of Berea College), 774 pieces. There are undetermined numbers of papers of William G. Frost (Ky.; pres. of Berea College); William Goodell (R.I., N.Y.; editor, reformer); John A. R. Rogers (Ohio, Ill., Ky.; Congregational clergyman, teacher at the predecessor of Berea College); Gerrit Smith (N.Y.; philanthropist, U.S. Rep.); and Lewis Tappan (Mass., N.Y.; merchant, abolitionist). There are also minutes and other records relating to the College and the community (74 pieces); and nine collections of old diaries.

BOWLING GREEN

Kentucky Library, Western Kentucky State College. Elizabeth Coombs, Librarian.

Holdings: 9,000 pieces, dating from 1764 but mainly 19th century, relating chiefly to Bowling Green, Warren County, and other nearby Kentucky counties. Included are journals, 1803 and 1807, of Robert Breckinridge McAfee (Ky.; lawyer, War of 1812 officer, State legislator and historian); papers of several Kentucky families; and some Civil War letters and diaries. There are also records of early churches, Methodist and Presbyterian, 1798-1887, and of the South Union, Ky., colony of Shakers, 1804-1916; music manuscripts, including Shaker hymnals; old cipher books for teaching arithmetic; and some business account books and ledgers, including guest registers at Mammoth Cave, 1861-65. Included also are copies of certain records of Warren County, 1796-1878; and of Nelson County, 1784-1820; and manuscripts of some Kentucky authors.

See Mary T. Moore, "The Kentucky Library Collection at Western Kentucky State College," in Ky. Hist. Society, Register, 49:113-132 (Apr. 1951).

FRANKFORT

Kentucky Historical Society. Old State House. George M. Chinn, Secretary-Treasurer.

Holdings: A large collection consisting of (1) public records held by the Society as an official archival depository of the State and (2) papers of Kentuckians and Kentucky organizations.

Included in the archival holdings are acts of the General Assembly, 1792-1955; enrolled bills, 1792-1920 (405 vols.); journals or copies of journals of the House of Representatives, 1792-1958, with gaps, and of the State Senate, 1792-1958, with gaps; papers of the Governors, 1792-1923 (1,180 docket files and 204 executive journals); "Kentucky documents," i. e. reports on State government activities, 1834-1958; and Kentucky geological survey maps (2,000 topographic sheets). Included also are 100 vols. of muster rolls and morning reports of the Civil War period; records of the Civil War period; records of the Kentucky Confederate Pension Department (4,600 folders); and records of the Confederate home at Pee Wee Valley. There are also vital records for 1852-62 and a scattering of other years to 1911 (2,300 vols.); and tax lists, by counties, 1787-1875 (5,000 vols.).

Personal papers include those of James Lane Allen (Ky., N. Y.; short-story writer, novelist), 1890-1924 (71 letters and a literary manuscript); Orlando Brown (Ky., D. C.; newspaper editor, U. S. Commissioner of Indian Affairs), 1819-85 (139 items); Henry Clay (Ky.; U. S. Sen. and Rep., Sec. State), 1800-48 (32 items), plus materials concerning Clay; Philip Slater Fall (Ky.; Disciples of Christ clergyman), 1859-83 (200 items and 1 folder of sermons); William Henry Harrison (Ohio; War of 1812 officer, U. S. Rep. and Sen., U. S. Pres.), 1811-24 (15 letters and photostats of letters); Samuel Hopkins (Va., Ky.; Rev. War officer, U. S. Rep.), 1796-1817 (30 letters); Harry Innes (Va., Ky.; U. S. dist. court judge), 1773-1807 (11 vols., 1 folder, and 4 other items); George M. Johnson (Ky.; Confed. Gov. of Ky.), 300 items; Robert P. Letcher (Ky.; lawyer, U. S. Rep., Gov.), 1844-50 (46 letters); John D. Matthews (Ky.; State supt. of public instruction), 1855-57 (71 letters); Valentine Peers (Va., Ky.; Rev. War officer, salt and cotton manufacturer, judge), 1802-25 (2 vols. and 82 items), chiefly relating to the Maysville-Lex-

ington turnpike and a Maysville factory; D. Howard Smith (Ky.; Confed. Army officer), 1859-83 (2 folders and 29 items), relating chiefly to Morgan's cavalry in the Civil War; Zachary Taylor (Ky.; U. S. Army officer, U. S. Pres.), 1809-50 (17 items), plus material about him and his family; Charles Stewart Todd (Ky.; lawyer, War of 1812 officer, Minister to Russia), 1816-51 (1 folder and 8 items); and James Wilkinson (U. S. Army officer, Gov. of La. Terr.), 1784-1811 (21 letters).

There are also land grants and other papers, 1774-1851 (751 items), including surveys and field notes, for 65 early landowners; Kentucky militia papers, chiefly 1792-94; a number of Civil War letters; various church minute books; abstracts of marriages, wills, deeds, and church records; diaries and journals; and 50 vols. of account books.

See Ky. Secretary of State, Catalog Records, Documents, Papers, etc.; Kentucky Governors, 1792-1926 (1926. 185 p.); G. Glenn Clift, Guide to the Manuscripts of the Kentucky Historical Society (1955. 185 p. Processed); W. R. Jillson, "Kentucky Acts and Legislative Journals, 1792-1800; and a Preliminary Locating Index," in Ky. Hist. Society, Register, 35:196 (Apr. 1937).

LEXINGTON

College of the Bible Library. Roscoe M. Pierson, Librarian.

Holdings: 75 vols. of manuscripts in folio volumes, 31 vols. of church records, and numerous diaries, commonplace books, and unpublished sermons relating to the Disciples of Christ in Kentucky and the southeastern United States, in China, and in the Belgian Congo. Included are papers of Alonzo Willard Fortune (Ohio,

Ky.; Disciples of Christ minister, prof. and dean of College of the Bible), 1920-50 (more than 500 sermons); Andrew F. Hensey (Disciples missionary to Belgian Congo), 1906-30's (5 vols.), correspondence and ethnological writings about the Bantus; John William McGarvey (Mo., Ky.; Disciples of Christ minister, pres. of College of the Bible), sermons, reports, and miscellaneous papers; and Isaac T. Reneau (Ky., Tenn.; Disciples of Christ minister, physician, teacher), 1832-1902 (5 vols. and 1 box). Other papers relating to ministers and churches on the midwestern frontier, 1808-80 (12 standard filing cabinet drawers), include material on Thomas M. Allen (Ky., Mo.; pioneer minister of Disciples of Christ), Walter Scott (Pa., Ohio, Ky.; preacher, religious reformer), and John Smith (Ky., Ala., Mo.; a founder of the Disciples of Christ). All available records of the Kentucky Christian Missionary Society since 1890's are on deposit in this library.

—oOo—

Lexington Public Library. Virginia Hayes, Librarian.

Holdings: A medieval cartulary of Ipswich Priory, England (1 vol.); and papers relating to Constantine S. Rafinesque (Ky., Pa.; botanist, ichthyologist, prof. at Transylvania Univ.) and the establishment in 1825-26 of the botanic garden in Lexington (38 items).

—oOo—

Margaret I. King Library, University of Kentucky. Jacqueline Bull, Archivist.

Holdings: A large collection, 1700-1951, but mainly 19th century, consisting of (1) some Kentucky archives and (2) personal and organizational papers relating chiefly to Kentucky.

State archives include papers of the Bank of Kentucky, 1806-40 (700 vols.); assessment records of Kentucky counties, 1910-36 (350 vols.); and records of the State court of appeals, 1865-1931 (4,000 cu. ft.). There are also photographic reproductions of some records of Lexington and Fayette and seven other nearby Kentucky counties, 1781-1859 (35 rolls of microfilm and 2 vols. of photographs); the circuit court records of Pike County, 1860-67 (5 rolls); and the Kentucky District superior court records, 1783-86 (1 roll).

Papers of political leaders include those of Alben W. Barkley (Ky.; U.S. Rep. and Sen., Vice Pres.), 1912-56 (50 filing drawers, 100 pieces, 100 scrapbooks, and recordings of speeches), including official and personal correspondence and original cartoons, many by Clifford K. Berryman (D.C.; cartoonist); Henry Clay (Ky.; U.S. Rep. and Sen., Sec. State), 1801-43 (85 letters); James Proctor Knott (Ky.; lawyer, U.S. Rep., Gov.), 1885-86 (1 letter book); William Lindsay (Ky., N.Y.; Confed. Army officer, chief justice of Ky. court of appeals, U.S. Sen.), 1867-1932 (14,000 pieces); William Jennings Price (Ky., D.C.; Minister to Panama, law prof. at Georgetown Univ.), 1851-1951 (498 pieces); Charles Scott (Va., Ky.; Rev. War officer, Gov. of Ky.), 1777-1828 (93 pieces); Isaac Shelby (Va., Ky.; Rev. War and War of 1812 officer, Gov. of Ky.) and family, 1781-1899 (851 pieces); Jouett Shouse (Ky., Kans., D.C.; lawyer, U.S. Rep. from Kans., Democratic Party leader), 1915-38 (a large quantity); Augustus Owsley Stanley (Ky., D.C.; lawyer, U.S. Rep., Gov., U.S. Sen.), 20th century (12,000 pieces); Zachary Taylor (Ky.; U.S. Army officer, U.S. Pres.), 1831-84 (40 pieces); and Urey Woodson (Ky.; newspaper editor and publisher, U.S. Alien Property Custodian), 1932-39 (661 pieces).

Papers of Army men other than those mentioned above include those of B. F. Buckner (Ky.; farmer, lawyer, Civil War soldier), 1786-1884 (5 vols. and 2 transfer cases); Thomas Henry Hines (Ky.; Confed. Army officer, chief justice of State court of appeals), 1786-1936 (10 vols. and 212 pieces); John Daniel Imboden (Va.; lawyer, Confed. Army officer, mining promoter), 1833-92 (137 pieces), chiefly business papers; Thomas Walker (Va.; physician, French and Indian War officer, explorer), 1733-64 (25 pieces); and William Woodford (Va.; French and Indian War and Rev. War officer), 1723-37 (1 letter book), concerning tobacco trade between London and Virginia.

Papers of educators include those of Thomas B. Craighead (Tenn.; Presbyterian clergyman, pres. of Cumberland College), 1810-18 (31 pieces); Grant C. Knight (Ky.; author, English prof. at Univ. of Ky.), 1924-49 (3 vols.), letters from literary figures; Frank L. McVey (Minn., N. Dak., Ky.; pres. of Univs. of N. Dak. and Ky.), papers not yet processed; James Kennedy Patterson (Ky.; pres. of Univ. of Ky.), 1859-1919 (9,279 pieces); Robert Peter (Ky.; physician, chemist, college prof.), 1828-1905 (28 vols. and 339 pieces), concerning geological surveys in Kentucky, Arkansas, and Indiana; and Ellen Churchill Semple (Ky., Mass.; geographer, prof. at Clark Univ., author), 1900-32 (1 vol., 82 pieces, and 70 pkgs.).

Papers of other individuals include those of James Lane Allen (Ky., N.Y.; short-story writer, novelist), 1892-1921 (3 boxes, 56 pieces, and 9 microfilmed letters); James Anderson Anderson (Ky., N.Y.; typographer), 1870-1948 (1,860 pieces), concerning typography; Edwin Green Bedford (Ky.; farmer, livestock breeder), 1812-1902 (44 vols. and 324 pieces); John Bradford (Ky.; pioneer printer, civil engineer), 1780-1831 (122 pieces), relating to land claims; Laura Clay (Ky.; reformer, suffragist), 1882-1938 (7,000 pieces), including correspondence with many leaders in the woman-suffrage movement; John William Fox, Jr. (Ky., Va.; novelist), 1888-1948 (5 vols. and 152 pieces, including literary manuscripts); Chauncey Hawley Griffith (Ky., N.Y.; type designer, vice pres. of Mergenthaler Linotype Co.), 1929-54 (2,000 pieces), concerning typographical matters; John W. Hunt (Ky.; merchant) and his family, 1790-1949 (4,500 pieces), including materials on trade with the East and with New Orleans; Harry Innes (Ky.; U.S. dist. court judge), 1785-94 (1 account book); William B. Kinkead (Ky.; lawyer), 1852-85 (31 diary vols.); Henry M. Waite (Ohio, N.Y.; civil engineer), 1909-36 (13 diary vols.), largely dealing with city planning; and Samuel M. Wilson (Ky.; lawyer, historian), 18th century to 1946 (100,000 pieces, plus ancestral papers).

There are also an autograph collection, chiefly single items but including a few small groups, of papers of 50 distinguished Americans; and literary manuscripts of more than 40 authors. Records relating to medicine include case books of a South Carolina physician, 1847-55 (2 vols.); records of a county hospital, 1907-16; and medical account books of two physicians, 1860-91 (20 vols.). Papers relating to farming and allied operations include minutes of the board of the Bourbon County Agricultural Society, 1875-87 (1 vol.); records of the Burley Tobacco Cooperatives, 1904-23 (97 vols.); and papers concerning livestock and horse breeding, 1834-1915 (39 vols. and 1 roll of microfilm). See also Edwin Green Bedford, above.

Business records include those of the Southern Mercantile Collection, covering the southeastern States, 1865-1900 (1,814 vols. and 47,650 pieces); papers relating to business transactions on the Big Sandy River, 1843-98 (25 ft. of microfilm); and records of the Grahamton (Ky.) Manufacturing Co., relating to textile manufacture, 1837-1905 (128 vols. and 3 boxes of letters); an iron furnace and general store, 1817-50 (4 vols. and 42 pieces); a hotel and a tavern, 1797-1832 (2 vols.); and the Lexington Gas Co., 1852-57 (4 vols.).

Records of churches and ministers, 1787-1951, chiefly Baptist and Presbyterian, consist of 7 vols. of original church records; papers of a Baptist minister at Lexington, 1838-91 (5 vols.); 39 rolls of microfilmed records (including 5 rolls of records of Disciples of Christ) and a microfilmed diary, 1801-8, of a Presbyterian preacher. There are also copies of records of Shaker colonies in Kentucky, 1769-1893 (19 rolls and 842 photostats).

Records relating to education include those of a school district in Warren County, 1848-58 (1 vol.); Bourbon Academy, 1799-1855 (16 ft. of microfilm); student societies at the Central University, Richmond, and the University of Kentucky, 1885-1939 (6 vols.); and the Kentucky Association of Deans of Women, 1921-50 (1 vol.). There are also records of the Kentucky Botanic Garden, 1827-50 (1 vol. and 218 pieces); two Masonic chapters, 1851-1913 (5 vols. and 1 roll of microfilm); the Kentucky Academy of Sciences, 1892-1953 (1 vol. and 1,175 pieces); the Democratic Party of Kentucky, 1897-1939 (4,080 pieces); the Democratic Women's Club (1,133 pieces); and a woman-suffrage association, 1917-20 (1 vol. and 10 pieces).

See Jacqueline Bull, "The Samuel M. Wilson Library," in Ky. Hist. Society, Register, 47:52-54 (Jan. 1949), a reprint of which is available free from the King Library, University of Kentucky.

Transylvania College Library. Roemol Henry, Librarian.

Holdings: 10,000 pieces, 1780-1893, relating chiefly to higher education in Kentucky. Included are papers of Charles Caldwell (Pa., Ky.; physician, prof. at Transylvania Univ. and Louisville Medical Institute), 1819-37 (50 pieces); Henry Clay (Ky.; U.S. Rep. and Sen., Sec. State), 1809-49 (200 pieces); Jefferson Davis (Miss.; U.S. Rep. and Sen., Sec. War, Confed. Pres.), 1865-66 (25 letters); Horace Holley (Conn., Mass., Ky.; Unitarian minister, pres. of Transylvania Univ.), 1818-27 (50 pieces); Robert Peter (Ky.; physician, chemist, college prof.), 1828-93 (1,000 items); and Constantine S. Rafinesque (Ky., Pa.; botanist, ichthyologist, prof. at Transylvania Univ.), 1783-1840 (50 pieces). Also included are business records of Transylvania College, 1783-1851 (5,640 pieces); and minutes of the Board of Trustees, 1783-1850 (bound vols.).

LOUISVILLE 3

Filson Club. 118 West Breckinridge St. (Mrs.) Dorothy Thomas Cullen, Curator; Mabel C. Weaks, Archivist.

Holdings: A large quantity of manuscripts, 1734-1944, but largely of the 19th century, relating chiefly to Kentucky, the Ohio Valley, and the Old Northwest.

Papers of political leaders include those of William Taylor Barry (Ky.; chief justice of State court of appeals, U.S. Rep. and Sen., Postmaster Gen., Minister to Spain), 1798-1835 (1 vol., copies); Cassius Marcellus Clay (Ky.; Mexican War officer, abolitionist, Minister to Russia), 1844-1907 (2 boxes); Henry Clay (Ky.; U.S. Rep. and Sen., Sec. State), 1810-52 (32 items); Willis Green (Ky.; merchant,

miller, lumberman, U.S. Rep.), 1818-
62 (3 boxes); John Warren Grigsby
(Va., Ky.; farmer, U.S. consul at
Bordeaux, Confed. Army officer),
1838-77 (10 boxes); James Guthrie
(Ky.; lawyer, Sec. Treas., U.S. Sen.)
1820-69 (49 boxes); John Marshall
Harlan (Ky.; U.S. Supreme Court Jus-
tice), 1888-1911 (114 items); Richard
Mentor Johnson (Ky.; U.S. Rep., Sen.,
and Vice Pres.), 1824-41 (2 boxes);
George Wood Meriwether (Ky.; Louis-
ville councilman), 1808-31 (2 boxes);
John Pope (Ky.; U.S. Rep. and Sen.,
Terr. Gov. of Ark.), 1808-43 (2 vols.
and 9 items); Isaac Shelby (Va., Ky.;
Rev. War and War of 1812 officer,
Gov. of Ky.), 1760-1839 (2 boxes);
Charles Stewart Todd (Ky.; lawyer,
War of 1812 officer, Minister to Rus-
sia), 1810-70 (2 vols. and 2 boxes);
Harry Innes Todd (Ky.; State legis-
lator), 1823-91 (1 box); Albert Shelby Willis (Ky.; lawyer, U.S. Rep.,
Minister to Hawaii), 1893-95 (1 vol.);
and Augustus Everett Willson (Ky.;
lawyer, Gov.), 1873-1921 (13 boxes
and 21 scrapbooks).

Papers of military leaders, in addition to some named above, include
those of James William Abert (U.S.
Army topographical engineer), 1861-
93 (2 boxes); Richard Clough Anderson (Va., Ky.; Rev. War officer, surveyor-gen.), 1777-1887 (2 boxes);
Arthur Campbell (Va.; Rev. War officer), 1752-1811 (1 box); George Rogers Clark (Va., Ky.; Rev. War officer), 1776-1835 (50 vols., of which
49 are photostats); Jonathan Clark
(Va., Ky.; Rev. War officer) and his
family, 1734-1812 (12 boxes); and
James Taylor (U.S. Army dist. paymaster and Quartermaster Gen.) and
his son, 1785-1883 (6 boxes).

Papers of lawyers, in addition to
some named above, include those of
Andrew Jackson Ballard (Ky.; lawyer,
State legislator, clerk of U.S. circuit
and dist. courts), 1848-96 (3 vols.
and 6 boxes); Joseph Barbour (Ky.;

lawyer), 1861-97 (2 boxes); Temple
Bodley (Ky.; lawyer, author), 1614-
1940 (41 vols. and 5 boxes), including transcripts of papers concerning
the history of the West during the
American Revolution and the career
of George Rogers Clark; John B. Bruner (Ky.; lawyer, State legislator),
1848-76 (4 boxes); Joseph Hamilton
Daveiss (Ky.; U.S. attorney for the
Ky. Dist.), 1797-1811 (1 box); Samuel Daveiss (Ky.; lawyer), 1811-55
(1 box); John Harding (Ky.; lawyer,
stock breeder), 1859-1914 (5 boxes);
Arthur Earlle Hopkins (Ky.; lawyer),
1919-44 (5 boxes); and Stephen Fitz-
James Trabue (Ky.; lawyer), 1851-81
(23 vols.).

Papers of clergymen and educators include those of Robert Jefferson
Breckinridge (Ky., Md., Pa.; Presbyterian clergyman, pres. of Jefferson College, prof. at Danville Theological Seminary), 1845-52 (1 box);
Thomas Horace Cleland (Ky.; Presbyterian clergyman), 1841-92 (1 box);
Edward Owings Guerrant (Ky.; Confed. Army officer, physician, Presbyterian clergyman), 1858-1915 (2
boxes); Thomas Henderson (Ky.;
Baptist clergyman, supt. of Choctaw
Academy in Scott County), 1824-41
(2 boxes); Peyton Harrison Hoge (Va.,
Ky.; Presbyterian clergyman), 1882-
1910 (1 vol. and 51 pieces); Edward
Lindsay Powell (Va., Ky.; Disciples
of Christ clergyman), 1878-1932 (10
vols. and 9 boxes); and Charles Wilkins Short (Ky.; physician, botanist,
prof. at Transylvania Univ. and the
Medical Institute of Louisville), 1811-
69 (15 boxes), including correspondence with William Short (Va., Pa.;
diplomat).

Papers of editors and authors include those of Hew Ainslie (Ky.; poet), 1834-78 (1 box); James Lane Allen (Ky., N.Y.; short-story writer,
novelist), 1893-1924 (45 items); Carl
Bernhardt (Ind.; journalist), 1931-36
(3 vols. and 3 boxes); Orlando Brown

(Ky., D. C.; newspaper editor, U. S. Commissioner of Indian Affairs), 1820-67 (8 boxes); Madison Julius Cawein (Ky.; poet), 1888-1912 (3 boxes); Reuben Thomas Durrett (Ky.; lawyer, newspaper editor, historian), 1849-1913 (23 boxes); Joel Tanner Hart (Ky.; sculptor, poet), 1830-82 (2 boxes); Josiah Stoddard Johnston (Ky.; farmer, editor, historian), 1850-1912 (7 vols. and 3 boxes); Cleves Kinkead (Ky.; lawyer journalist, playwright), 1903-39 (5 boxes); and Alfred Pirtle (Ky.; author), 1847-1920 (1 box).

Papers of farmers, in addition to those named above, include those of Isaac Clark (Ky.; farmer of "Mulberry Hill" in Jefferson County), 1807-69 (3 boxes); William Clark (Ky.; physician, farmer, owner of rope walk), 1811-79 (1 vol. and 4 boxes); Henry Miles (Ky.; pioneer, farmer), 1812-49 (6 vols. and 13 boxes); and Alfred Shelby (Ky.; farmer, son of Gov. Isaac Shelby), 2 boxes.

Papers of merchants and businessmen include those of Edmund Clark (Va., Ky.; merchant), 1791-1836 (10 vols. and 5 boxes); John Hite Clark (Ky.; merchant), 1806-33 (2 boxes); George F. Downs (Ky.; merchant, landowner, art collector), 1846-1908 (2 boxes); George W. Erwin (Tenn., Ky.; salt works operator), 1832-74 (1 box); Dennis Fitzhugh (Ky.; merchant), 1802-28 (11 vols. and 1 box); Norvin Green (Ky., N. Y.; physician, commissioner of public schools, pres. of Western Union Telegraph Co.), 1839-92 (6 vols. and 11 boxes); Thomas C. Howard (Ky.; merchant), 1780-1844 (3 boxes); John Wesley Hunt (Ky.; merchant), 1792-1849 (12 boxes); John Jeremiah Jacob (Md., Ky.; merchant, banker, railroad pres., philanthropist), 1806-51 (6 boxes); Alexander Jeffrey (N. Y., Tenn., Ky.; manager of gas works), 1835-99 (9 boxes); George L. Miles (Ky., Tenn.; merchant, Hardin County commissioner), 1818-74 (6 vols. and 13 boxes); John O'Fallon (Ky., Mo.; War of 1812 offi-

cer, merchant, railroad pres., philanthropist), 1806-50 (1 box); Samuel Rose (Ky.; merchant), 1803-12 (1 box); Edmund Haynes Taylor (Ky.; banker, treasurer of Ky. Colonization Society), 1818-73 (6 boxes); Charles William Thruston (Ky.; merchant, owner of rope walk), 1818-65 (2 vols. and 5 boxes); and Jacob F. Weller (Ky.; merchant, pres. of Masonic home), 1853-96 (2 vols. and 2 boxes).

Papers of other individuals include those of Susan Preston Shelby Grigsby (Ky., D. C.; granddaughter of Isaac Shelby), 1842-84 (10 boxes); George Hancock (Ky.; pres. of the Tex. Assn.) and his wife, 1852-1902 (1 box); Jeremiah Ingram (Va., Ky.; pioneer), 1796-1832 (1 box); Harry Innes (Va., Ky.; U. S. dist. judge), 1750-1810 (1 vol.); John Jeffrey (Ky., Ohio, Cuba; architect, gas engineer), 1836-79 (10 boxes); William Jeffrey (N. Y.; agent of estates of John Greig, William Hornby, and Sir Patrick Colquhoun), 1852-76 (1 box); Thomas Joyes (Ky.; surveyor, landowner and speculator, War of 1812 officer), 1806-66 (8 boxes); Robert Breckinridge McAfee (Ky.; lawyer, War of 1812 officer, State legislator and historian), 1813-45 (565 pages); Chiles Terrell (Va., Ky.; pioneer, surveyor, educator), 1799-1865 (1 box); Edwin Porter Thompson (Ky.; Confed. Army officer, compiler of Confed. records, supt. of public instruction and State librarian), 1872-1902 (4 vols. and 4 boxes); and Rogers Clark Ballard Thruston (Ky.; geologist), 1873-1946 (21 vols., 51 boxes, and 1 filing cabinet).

Church records include journals, account books, and other papers of the Shakers of Mercer County, 1815-1905 (24 vols.). Business records include those of C. C. Morgan and Co., Lexington manufacturers of bagging and woolen goods, 1853-80 (2 boxes), and John P. Morton and Co., Louisville publishing company, 1888-

1915 (1 box). There are account books of merchants in Louisville and other Kentucky towns, 1800-90 (50 vols.). Included also are papers relating to the genealogy of the signers of the Declaration of Independence (53 vols.), with some letters of the signers; a collection of autograph letters and other papers of the Governors of Kentucky, 1792-1941 (1 portfolio); journals, orderly books, and other papers relating to Gen. Anthony Wayne's campaign against the Indians, 1792-95; records of a brigade of Confederate volunteer infantry, 1861-65 (1 box); and military service records of Kentuckians who served in the armed forces during World War I, 1917-19 (144 vols.).

—oOo—

Louisville Free Public Library. 301-333 Library Pl. Edna J. Grauman, Head, Reference Department.

Holdings: 60 vols. and 11 pieces, 1775-1951, relating chiefly to Kentucky. Included are a student medical notebook of Theodore S. Bell (Ky.; physician, prof. at Univ. of Louisville), 1830-31; two literary manuscripts of Isabel McLennan McMeekin (Ky.; author); and manuscripts of other Kentucky authors. There are also a volume of letters of men prominent in the 18th and 19th centuries, and several other single letters from such men, 1775-1845; six scrapbooks on the 1895 encampment of the Grand Army of the Republic, including one composed of original letters; and records of the Kentucky Council of Defense in Louisville and Jefferson County, 1917-19 (34 vols.).

LOUISVILLE 2

Louisville Presbyterian Theological Seminary Library. 109 East Broadway. Ernest M. White, Librarian.

Holdings: 33,702 items, dating

from 1783, relating chiefly to the Presbyterian church in Kentucky. Included are manuscript minutes of the Synod of Kentucky, Presbyterian Church; records of various presbyteries and churches, chiefly in Kentucky; records of the Danville Theological Seminary, 1888-1901; and records of the Louisville Presbyterian Theological Seminary, and predecessors, 1894 to date.

See Allison, Inventory, p. 11.

LOUISVILLE 6

Southern Baptist Theological Seminary. 2825 Lexington Rd. Leo T. Crismon, Librarian.

Holdings: 50 linear ft. of vols. and more than 31 filing drawers of papers, chiefly 19th century, relating to the Baptist Church and the Seminary. Included are papers of the following ministers who were professors at the Seminary: James Petigru Boyce (S.C., Ky.), 1827-88 (7 filing drawers); John A. Broadus (Va., N. C., Ky.), 1827-95 (11 filing drawers and several notebooks); Basil Manly, Jr. (Va., S. C., Ky.), 1825-92 (extensive correspondence); John R. Sampey (Ky.), 1863-1946, 1 filing drawer and several notebooks; and William H. Whitsitt (Tenn., Ky., Va.), 1841-1911, several notebooks. There are also extensive papers, chiefly sermons and addresses, of Basil Manly, Sr. (S.C., Ala.; Baptist minister, pres. of Univ. of Ala.), 1798-1868; minutes of the business sessions of Baptist churches, chiefly of the South; minutes of the Board of Trustees of the Seminary, from 1859; several diaries; and many sermons.

See Allison, Inventory, p. 12.

LOUISVILLE 8

University of Louisville Law School

Library.   (Mrs.) Pearl Von Allmen, Librarian.

Holdings: Papers of Louis D. Brandeis (Mass., D.C.; U.S. Supreme Court Justice), 1879-1940 (10,000 pieces), and of John Marshall Harlan (Ky.; U. S. Supreme Court Justice), 1892-1905 (5,000 pieces).

NAZARETH

Sisters of Charity of Nazareth Archives.   Sister Mary Ramond Mattingly, Archivist.

Holdings: 35 letter books and 15 boxes, 1812-1953, relating chiefly to Kentucky but with materials for other Southern States.   Included are papers of the cofounders of the Sisters of Charity of Nazareth—Catherine Spalding (Ky.; Mother Superior), 1828-58 (55 letters); and John Baptist Mary David (Md., Ky.; Catholic missionary priest and bishop), 1821-41 (46 letters).   There are also a substantial number of letters of Stephen T. Badin (Ky.; pioneer Catholic missionary priest); Benedict Joseph Flaget (Ind., D. C., Md., Ky.; Catholic missionary priest and bishop); and Martin John Spalding (Ky.; Catholic priest, Bishop of Louisville, historian); and records of Nazareth Academy, 1814-1956, including business records, registration books, and numerous letters of pupils from many parts of the South.

RICHMOND

Eastern Kentucky State Teachers College Library.

Holdings: 225 pieces, relating chiefly to Kentucky history and literature.
    See unpublished records of the Hist. Records Survey in the National Archives.

LOUISIANA

BATON ROUGE

Department of Archives, Louisiana
State University Library. V. L. Bed-
sole, Head.

Holdings: 2,100,000 vols. and other items, and 250 additional cu. ft.,
1700-1955, relating chiefly to Louisiana, southwestern Mississippi, and
the lower Mississippi Valley. The
main groups are (1) personal and family papers and business, plantation,
and professional records, 1700-1955
(1,015,000 vols. and other items); (2)
the University's archives and related
materials, principally of the office of
the president, 1854-1954 (770 vols.
and 33,044 other items); (3) State and
parish (civil) archives, 1786-1933
(1,055,000 items), held by the Department as the archival unit of the University for the custody of public records;
and (4) records of the Survey of Federal
Archives and the Historical Records
Survey projects in Louisiana, 1936-43
(250 cu. ft.).

Papers of men who held Federal
office include those of James B. Aswell
(La.; State supt. of public education,
pres. of Northwestern Louisiana State
College, U. S. Rep.) and his family,
1890-1932 (35 vols. and 1,332 items);
Phanor Breazeale (La.; lawyer, U. S.
Rep.) and his family, 1806-1904 (74
vols. and 4,912 items); James Brown
(La.; U. S. Sen., Minister to France),
1804-27 (98 items); Thomas Butler
(Pa., La.; State dist. court judge, U.S.
Rep. from La.), and related families,
1768-1950 (172 vols. and 10,685
items); René L. De Rouen (La.; U. S.
Rep.), 1927-41 (about 25,000 items);
Ezekiel John Ellis (La.; lawyer, U. S.
Rep.) and his family, 1870-1920 (72
vols. and 7,173 items); Benjamin F.

Flanders (La.; teacher, Unionist,
U. S. Rep., Military Gov. of La.,
Mayor of New Orleans), 1827-89
(863 items); Edward J. Gay (La.;
planter, manufacturer, U. S. Sen.),
his grandfather Edward J. Gay (Mo.,
La.; planter, manufacturer, U. S.
Rep. from La.), and related families,
1805-1925 (100,000 vols. and other
items); William Pitt Kellogg (La.;
Gov., U. S. Sen.), 1873-76 (1,327
items); Ladislas Lazaro (La.; U. S.
Rep.), 1894-1928 (218 vols. and
6,046 items); Samuel D. McEnery
(La.; Confed. Army officer, Gov.,
U. S. Sen.), 1882-87 (42 items);
Ayers P. Merrill (Miss.; U. S. Minister to Belgium) and his family,
1835-66 (40 items); John H. Overton
(La.; U. S. Sen.), 1933-48 (8,000
items); Joseph E. Ransdell (La.; lawyer, U. S. Rep. and Sen.), 1898-1948
(28 vols. and 676 items); Edwin M.
Stanton (Ohio, D. C.; Sec. War), 1864-
66 (2 vols.); Henry Vignaud (La.;
journalist, Confed. diplomat, Sec. of
U. S. Legation in Paris, historian),
1862-1909 (385 items), including 75
letters of Louis Placide Canonge (see
below); Robert C. Wickliffe (La.; U.S.
Rep.), 1897-1912 (2 vols. and 70
items); and John G. A. Williamson
(N. C.; U. S. consul and Chargé d'Affaires in Venezuela) and his family,
1812-66 (3 diaries and 473 items).

Papers of Governors of the province, Territory, and State of Louisiana, in addition to a few of those mentioned above, include papers of the
Baron de Carondelet (La.; Spanish
gov.), 1791-96 (28 items); William
C. C. Claiborne (La.; Terr. and
State Gov.), 1804-5, 1812-13 (1 letter book and 5 items); Bernardo de
Gálvez (La.; Spanish gov.), 1778-81
(70 items); Manuel Gayoso de Lemos

(La.; Spanish gov.), 1792-1805 (42 items); Luther E. Hall (La.; judge, Gov.), 1912-15 (55 items); Thomas O. Moore (La.; Gov., secession leader), 1856-71 (707 items); Francis T. Nicholls (La.; Gov.), 1877-91 (1 letter book, 2 notebooks, and 19 items); and Jared Y. Sanders (La., Gov.) and his family, 1816-1950 (36 vols. and 976 items).

Papers of Army officers include those of Pierre G. T. Beauregard (La.; U. S. and Confed. Army officer, railroad pres.) and his family, 1818-1912 (107 vols. and 806 items); Joseph L. Brent (La.; Confed. Army officer) and his family, 1862, 1902-40 (1 diary, 1 notebook, and 32 items); Robert Butler (La.; War of 1812 officer), 1833-53 (109 items); Lemuel P. Conner (Miss., La.; Confed. Army officer, secession leader) and his family, 1767-1924 (1 diary, 17 account books, and 1,474 items); Samuel Wragg Ferguson (S. C.; Confed. Army officer) and his family, 1837-1920 (7 vols. and 127 items); Josiah Gorgas (Ala.; U. S. and Confed. Army officer), 1847-77 (1 letter book and 3 items); Joseph Jones (Ga., La.; Confed. Army surgeon, sanitarian), 1850-1900 (89 vols. and 2,815 items); St. John R. Liddell (Miss., La.; Confed. Army officer) and his family, 1813-1919 (49 vols. and 6,261 items); John A. Quitman (Miss.; Mexican War officer, Gov., U. S. Rep.) and his family, 1824-81 (3 account books, 1 memorandum book, and 17 items); William Tecumseh Sherman (La.; supt. of predecessor of La. State Univ., U. S. Army officer), 1859-90 (230 items); and Henry Wilson (Pa.; U. S. Army officer), 1819-85 (303 items).

Papers of college and university professors and presidents include those of David F. Boyd (Va., La.; Confed. Army officer, La. State Univ. pres.) and his family, 1802-1940 (323 vols. and 16,357 items); James H. Dillard (Va., Mo., La.; dean at Tulane Univ., pres. of Jeanes Foundation and John F. Slater Fund), 1899-1940 (134 items); Richard T. Ely (Md., Wis., Ill.; economist, prof. at Johns Hopkins, Wis., and Northwestern Univs.), 1700-1895 (11 vols. and 321 items); John Rose Ficklen (La.; historian, Tulane Univ. prof.), 1832-1906 (6 vols. and 43 items); Walter Lynwood Fleming (La., Tenn.; historian), 1908-15 (161 items); Joseph Lakanal (France, Ala., La.; French Revolutionary educator, pres. of College of Orleans, New Orleans), 1793-1834 (22 items); and Edwin L. Stephens (La.; pres. of Southwestern La. Institute), 1883-1940 (6 vols. and 6,656 items).

Papers of other individuals include those of Thomas Affleck (Ind., Miss., Tex.; horticulturist), 1807-79 (62 vols. and 925 items); Louis Placide Canonge (La.; journalist, dramatist), 1886-93 (87 letters); Stephen Duncan (Pa., Miss.; physician, factor, planter, bank pres.) and his family, 1814-99 (2 diaries, 9 other vols., and 351 items); Charles E. A. Gayarré (La.; lawyer, historian), 1720-1895 (14 vols. and 967 items); Joseph C. Hartzell (Ill., La., Africa; Methodist clergyman, missionary bishop for Africa), 1862-72, 1900-6 (1 vol. and 488 items); Charles Colcock Jones, Jr. (Ga., N. Y.; historian), 1865-93 (1 vol. and 77 items); Duncan F. Kenner (La.; Confed. statesman and Minister to France) and his family, 1854-88 (2 account books and 334 items); the Marquis de Lafayette (France; American Rev. War officer) and his family, 1805-48 (124 items); Eleanor Percy Ware Lee (Miss.; poet, novelist), 1830-49 (6 notebooks, 1 other vol., and 19 items); Robert M. Lusher (La.; State supt. of education), 1795-1931 (24 diaries, 2 other vols., and 109 items); Andrew D. Lytle (Ohio, La.; Civil War photographer), 1862-1904 (385 photographs); John W. Monette (Miss.; physician, historian), 1824 (1 vol.); Leona Queyrouse (La.; poet,

essayist, lecturer), 1810-1940 (54
vols. and 2,614 items); Henri Rémy
(La.; teacher, essayist, editor, historian), 1704-1848 (2 vols. and 315
items); Lyle Saxon (La.; author), 1923-
47 (8 vols. and 144 items); Raphael
Semmes (U. S. and Confed. Naval officer, lawyer), 1866-1911 (21 items);
James G. Taliaferro (Ky., La.; Republican Party leader, State supreme
court justice) and his family, 1787-
1934 (4 vols. and 895 items); and Edward Clifton Wharton (Tex., La.;
journalist, dramatist, critic) and his
family, including John Robert Baylor
(Confed. Army officer and statesman),
1825-1936 (6 diaries, 3 other vols.,
and 959 items).

There are also personal and family
papers of less distinguished individuals
that include correspondence with prominent national figures; papers throwing
light on the French heritage and culture
in Louisiana, including papers on four
generations of one French family, 1743-
1929 (36 vols. and 624 items), which
are especially useful for studies of
early 19th-century European travel and
of civilian life during the Civil War period; and a collector's compilation of
manuscripts, photographs, books, and
related printed materials pertaining
principally to steamboat and other
shipping on the lower Mississippi and
the Red Rivers, 1827-1954 (112 vols.
and 854 items). Among business records are records of a Louisiana sugar
plantation and sugar house, 1846-1915
(34 vols. and 30,000 items), and of a
firm of New Orleans cotton factors and
commission merchants, 1866-76 (102
vols. and 15,645 items), and noncurrent
records of the Southern Pine Association, New Orleans, 1903-48 (300 linear
ft.).

Significant groups of State archives
are records of the Executive Department, 1832-1928 (16,670 items); the
Secretary of State, 1873-1930 (81,975
items); the State Auditor, 1823-1933
(44,350 items); the Department of Edu-

cation, 1825-1931 (228,500 items);
the Railroad Commission, 1898-1919
(30,135 items); the Board of Control
of the State Penitentiary, 1879-1930
(43,168 items); and the Board of Control of the Leper Home, 1892-1921
(30,320 items). Parish records,
1786-1933 (88,218 items), consist
chiefly of district, parish, and probate court case papers for 6 of the
64 Louisiana parishes. Records for
what are now East and West Feliciana
Parishes, 1804-1926 (57,383 items),
include more than 40 groups of business papers, 1806-79 (96 vols. and
1,684 items).

Records of the Survey of Federal
Archives and the Historical Records
Survey projects in Louisiana, 1936-
43 (250 cu. ft.), consist of unpublished inventories of public and church
archives, of newspaper files, and of
manuscript collections; transcriptions
of some Louisiana colonial and Territorial records and of minutes of parish governing bodies; and related research material.

See Hist. Records Survey, Guide
for La., pp. 23-27, its Calendars of
Manuscript Collections in Louisiana
. . . Taber Collection (1938. 12 p.),
and its Guide to the Manuscript Collections in Louisiana: the Department of Archives, Louisiana State
University, Vol. 1 (1940. 55 p. Processed); and Forest History Sources,
pp. 30-34. For some accessions
since 1942 see "Historical News and
Notices," in Journal of Southern History.

—oOo—

Louisiana State Library. State
Capitol Grounds. Essae M. Culver, State Librarian.

Holdings: 112 linear ft., 1935-42,
relating chiefly to Louisiana history
and consisting of unprocessed research and related materials of the

WPA Writers' Program, Louisiana.

—oOo—

Louisiana State University Library.
Sidney B. Smith, Director of Libraries.

Holdings: 147 vols., consisting of
typed transcripts of certain Federal
archives and other materials relating
to Louisiana, 1673-1924, prepared by
the Survey of Federal Archives in Louisiana project. (The Department of
Archives, described immediately
above, is housed in the Louisiana State
University Library and is administratively a part of the Library.)

NEW ORLEANS 12

AGO Military Archives, Louisiana
Military Department. Jackson Bar-
racks. Thomas J. Harrison, Military
Historian.

Holdings: Noncurrent records of
the Office of the Adjutant General of
Louisiana, and other papers relating
chiefly to Louisiana, consisting of 912
vols., 371,369 pieces and microcopies
of them, 669 ft. of other records, and
a manuscript collection of 7,000 pieces,
1698-1946. Included are transcripts of
documents containing Louisiana military data, 1698-1936 (420 vols.); materials relating to Confederate personnel
and military units from Louisiana (166
vols. and 470,984 cards); various records of the United Confederate Veterans Association (226 ft.); Louisiana National Guard unit and personnel records
(50 feet and 22,425 microfilmed cards);
records of the Washington Artillery of
New Orleans, 1853-1924 (37 vols. and
2,000 pieces); and individual service
records of Louisiana men in World War
I (87,065 microfilmed cards). There
are also the Adjutant General's reports,
1809-1941, and general and special or-

ders, 1870-1945. The manuscript
collection, chiefly relating to the Confederate Army, contains papers of Joseph L. Brent (La.; Confed. officer),
1862-65; Richard Taylor (La.; Confed.
officer), 1863-65; and other Confederate officers. There are also records
of the Confederate Adjutant and Inspector General's Office, 1862-64; of Louisiana districts of the Army, including
material on labor and conscripts; and
of various Louisiana commands in Confederate service; and records relating
to Louisiana Confederate veterans.

NEW ORLEANS 15

Bibliotheca Parsoniana. 5 Rosa
Park. Edward Alexander Parsons,
Director.

Holdings: 10,000 items, relating
chiefly to Louisiana in the French,
Spanish, and early American periods,
but including also a collection of Oriental, classical, and Renaissance
manuscripts. There are papers of
Andrew Jackson (Tenn.; U. S. Army
officer, U. S. Pres.), especially pertaining to the Battle of New Orleans;
and of Jean Laffite, or Lafitte (La.,
Tex.; pirate, smuggler) and his brother Pierre; and, as a part of a collection relating to the Louisiana Purchase, letters, 1801-3, of Robert R.
Livingston (N. Y.; Minister to France).
There are also autograph collections
of documents and letters of French and
Spanish governors of Louisiana, 1699-
1803; and of American Governors of
Louisiana, 1803 to the present.
See Hist. Records Survey, Guide
for La., p. 1.

NEW ORLEANS 13

Department of Archives, New Orleans
Public Library. 1031 St. Charles
Ave. Margaret Ruckert, Head.

Holdings: About 50 vols. and several thousand pieces, 1769-1870, relating chiefly to colonial Louisiana and to New Orleans. Included are petitions, decrees, letters, and other records of the Cabildo, 1769-1803; miscellaneous Spanish and French documents, 1789-1816; and private dispatches of Esteban Rodríguez Miró (Spain, La.; colonial gov.), 1784-94. Records relating to the transfer of Louisiana include documents and letters of Pierre Clement deLaussat (France; colonial prefect) and of William C. C. Claiborne (La.; Terr. and State Gov.), 1803-4. There are also letters to Claiborne, 1804-14; proceedings of the New Orleans city council, 1803-29 (5 vols.); correspondence of the mayors of the city, 1805-52 (18 vols.); and records of the batture case of Jean Gravier and Edward Livingston, 1806-8. Numerous other official records of the city include police dockets, assessment rolls, ordinances, and financial papers.

NEW ORLEANS

Federal Records Center, GSA. Bldg. 10, Naval Station. Chief.

Holdings: A large quantity of noncurrent or semicurrent records, chiefly of recent date, consisting of (1) records of U. S. Navy overseas bases in European and South American areas, from 1941, and Navy and Marine Corps flight training records, from 1924; and (2) records of nonmilitary agencies of the U. S. Government in Louisiana. Most of these records have been appraised for disposal after specified periods of time, but some will be preserved because of their enduring value. Included in the latter category are records of U. S. district courts, from 1803; and 19th-century records of the Bureau of Customs.

NEW ORLEANS 12

Hotel Dieu Library. 2004 Tulane Ave.

Holdings: 109 pieces, consisting of registers of patients, case files, and other manuscripts relating to this hospital.

See Hist. Records Survey, Guide for La., p. 2.

NEW ORLEANS 18

Howard-Tilton Memorial Library, Tulane University. Robert L. Talmadge, Director of Libraries; (Mrs.) Connie G. Griffith, Archivist.

Holdings: In the Archives Department, 570 vols. and 240,392 items, 1562-1950, relating chiefly to New Orleans and Louisiana. The Middle American Research Institute Library and the Rudolph Matas Medical Library are separately described.

The oldest items are medieval manuscripts (10 vols. and 26 pieces). For the French and Spanish periods of Louisiana history there are, in addition to a few items mentioned below, French land grants in Louisiana, 1753-69 (110 items); photostats of dispatches of the Spanish governors, 1766-91 (25 vols.), with English translations; papers of the Baron de Carondelet (La.; Spanish gov.), 1793-97 (27 items); and in the Kuntz Collection, papers dealing with the revolution of 1768, the Company of the Indies, the government of New Orleans and Louisiana, and the Bouligny, de Kernion, Dauterive, Maison Rouge, de Coulanges, de Villemont, Villars, d'Auberville, and de Grandpré families, 1655-1876 (430 items). Personal papers of the early period include those of Père Antoine, also known as Padre Antonio de Sedella (La.; priest), 1798-1807 (6 vols.).

Personal papers for the period between the cession of Louisiana to the United States and the Civil War include those of William C. C. Claiborne (La.; Terr. and State Gov.), 1800-18 (19 items); Myra Clark Gaines, wife of Edmund Pendleton Gaines (U. S. Army officer), 1834-61 (221 items); James Gallier, Jr. (La.; architect), 1839-60 (205 items); Andrew Hynes (Tenn.; officer at Battle of New Orleans), 1814-16 (51 items); Benjamin Henry Latrobe (Pa., D. C., Md.; architect, engineer), 1807-32 (46 items); John McDonogh (La.; merchant, philanthropist), 1802-50 (6,436 items); Robert Mills (S. C., Pa., D. C.; architect, engineer), 1802-53 (36 items including a 2-vol. diary); Julien Poydras (La.; planter, poet, Terr. Delegate to Cong., philanthropist), 1792-1822 (2 vols.); and François Dominique Rouquette (La.; poet), 1839-52 (7 vols., including a 2-vol. diary).

Papers of persons prominent during the Civil War include those of Pierre G. T. Beauregard (La.; U. S. and Confed. Army officer, railroad pres.), 1839-88 (291 items); Jefferson Davis (Miss.; Confed. Pres.), 1862-88 (107 items); Alexander Dimitry (La.; U. S. Minister to Costa Rica and Nicaragua, Confed. Assistant Postmaster Gen.), 1859-95 (2 vols. and 17 items); Albert Sidney Johnston (Tex.; U. S. and Confed. Army officer), see William Preston Johnston, below; Henry D. Ogden (La.; jurist, Confed. Army officer), 1862-65 (86 items); John Leonard Riddell (La.; physician, botanist, Confed. postmaster at New Orleans), 1831-65 (28 vols. and 15 items); George G. Shepley (Maine; Civil War officer, military gov. of La.), 1861-65 (49 items); John Slidell (La.; U. S. Rep. and Sen., Confed. diplomat), 1829-65 (1 letter book and 185 items); and Paul Tulane

(La., N. J.; merchant, philanthropist), 1823-86 (32 items). There are also several diaries covering the Civil War period and a collection of 145 items relating to the Confederate Army, 1861-65.

Papers of a later period include those of William Beer (La.; librarian), 1892-1924 (4,760 items); Roark Bradford (Ga., La.; journalist, author), 1930-49 (155 items); Mary E. Burt (Ill., N. Y.; educator, author), 1898-1919 (40 items); George Washington Cable (La., Mass.; short-story writer, novelist), 1855-1927 (20,000 items), which contain 41 letters to Cable from Andrew Carnegie (Pa., N. Y.; industrialist, philanthropist), 13 from Calvin Coolidge (Mass.; U.S. Pres.), and 238 from Richard Watson Gilder (N. Y.; editor, poet); Thomas C. Catchings (Miss.; lawyer, U. S. Rep.), 1839-1931 (3,140 items); Brandt Van V. Dixon (Mo., La.; pres. of H. Sophie Newcomb College), 1887-1901 (121 items); Minnie Maddern Fiske (La., N. Y.; actress), 1865-1935 (53 items); Charles E. A. Gayarré (La.; lawyer, historian), 1857-95 (45 items); Randall Lee Gibson (La.; planter, U. S. Rep. and Sen.), 1875-92 (130 items); Robert Glenk (La.; sugar chemist, State Museum director), 1897-1949 (2,802 items); Lafcadio Hearn (Ohio, La., Japan; author), 1886-91 (70 items); Ethel Hutson (La.; suffragist, artist), 1913-20 (1,077 items); William Preston Johnston (Va., La.; Confed. Army officer, pres. of La. State and Tulane Univs.), 1803-1900 (11,184 items), including papers of Albert Sidney Johnston and other family papers; Joseph Finley Joor (La.; botanist), 1871-92 (103 items); Grace Elizabeth King (La.; short-story writer, novelist), 1917-20 (58 items); Albert Caruthers Phelps (La.; journalist, author, artist), 1885-1906 (11 vols. and

17 items); Lyle Saxon (La.; author),
1929-45 (3,297 items); Ruth McEnery
Stuart (La.; short-story writer), 1879-
1912 (90 items); Ellsworth Woodward
(La.; artist), 1914-39 (528 items); and
William Woodward (La., Miss.; artist,
prof. of architecture at Tulane Univ.),
1893-1901 (280 items).

Other personal papers include
those of the Favrot family, chiefly
1750-1825 (2,000 items), and of several other distinguished Louisiana
families, 1710-1945. There are also
papers of several Louisiana plantation
owners, mostly for the pre-Civil War
period, and of a few New Orleans merchants. Small groups of papers include
those of a physician, a ship chandler,
an engineer, several lawyers, and numerous other persons.

Also included are a collection of
maps of New Orleans and other parts
of Louisiana, 1608-1938 (749 items);
official records of New Orleans, 1770-
1893 (85 vols. and 1,177 items); records of the Poydraw Home (for orphans), 1817-1943 (10,000 pieces); and
records of a few churches, 1805-1900
(3 vols.). Records relating to science
and art include those of the Louisiana
section of the American Chemical Society, 1906-50 (24 vols. and 580
items); L'Athenée Louisianais, 1876-
86 (215 items); the New Orleans Academy of Sciences, 1858-1949 (252
items); the New Orleans Botanical Society, 1932-41 (1,040 items); and the
Southern States Art League, 1921-47
(907 items). There are also records
of two New Orleans banks, 1827-1903
(166 vols. and 1,114 items); and of the
Street and Electric Railway Union,
1902-40 (39 vols. and 6,961 items).
World War II letters, 1941-45, number 253.

The Louisiana Historical Association Collection, which is on permanent
deposit in the Library's Archives Department, is separately described below under the name of the Association.
See Hist. Records Survey, Guide

for La., pp. 14-16; and De Ricci,
Census, p. 741.

NEW ORLEANS 12

Louisiana Historical Association.
Confederate Memorial Hall, 929
Camp St. Kenneth Trist Urquhart,
Executive Secretary.

Holdings: 150,000 items, 1753-
1920 but primarily 1861-65, relating
chiefly to the Confederate States of
America and the Confederate Army
in the Civil War. Among the records
dated before the Civil War are papers
on the New Orleans campaign, 1814-
15 (554 pieces), including many
morning reports of units of the U.S.
Army and the Tennessee militia; and
papers of Albert Sidney Johnston
(Tex.; U.S. and Confed. Army officer) as U.S. Army paymaster at Austin, Tex., 1848-56 (3,651 pieces). Papers of Jefferson Davis (Miss.; U.S.
Rep. and Sen., Sec. War, Confed.
Pres.), 1845-91 (4,270 pieces), constitute a major group and include
many official documents issued by
Davis as Confederate President.
There are also records of and relating to the executive departments of
the Confederate States, 1861-65 (1,152
pieces); the Confederate Adjutant and
Inspector General's Office (3,702
pieces); the Confederate Navy and Marine Corps (2,725 pieces); several military departments and districts of the
Confederacy (11,356 pieces); Confederate armies and troop units other
than Louisiana units (1,700 pieces);
and Louisiana units in Confederate
service (7,025 pieces). Included also
are manuscripts relating to Civil War
battles (2,000 pieces); maps, plans,
drawings, and plates of uniforms
(500 pieces); miscellaneous account
books, diaries, and reminiscences
from the Civil War period, and papers of Confederate veterans' orga-

nizations, including the associations of veterans of the Army of Northern Virginia and the Army of Tennessee. (All of the materials described in this entry, while still the property of the Association, are housed in the Archives Department, Howard-Tilton Memorial Library, Tulane University.)

See Hist. Records Survey, Guide for La., p. 4.

—oOo—

Louisiana Historical Society, 521 Carondelet Bldg.

Holdings: Included are transcripts of records in French archives relating to colonial Louisiana, 1678-1769, and to the transfer of Louisiana to the United States, 1803.

See Hist. Records Survey, Guide for La., p. 5; Roscoe R. Hill, American Missions in European Archives (1951), p. 110; and John S. Kendall, "Historical Collections in New Orleans," in N. C. Hist. Review, 7:463-476 (Oct. 1930).

NEW ORLEANS 16

Louisiana State Museum. 709 Chartres St.

Holdings: 400,000 pieces, relating chiefly to colonial Louisiana and to Confederate military history. Included are records of the Superior Council of Louisiana, 1717-69; judicial records of Spanish Louisiana, 1769-1803; some papers dealing with the Battle of New Orleans, 1815; and a large quantity of Confederate military records. Also included are papers of Daniel Clark (La.; Delegate to Cong. from the Terr. of Orleans, merchant); and 5 Civil War dispatch books of Richard Taylor (La.; Confed. Army officer).

See Hist. Records Survey, Guide for La., pp. 6-8; and John S. Kendall,

"Historical Collections in New Orleans," in N. C. Hist. Review, 7:463-476 (Oct. 1930).

NEW ORLEANS 18

Middle American Research Institute Library, Tulane University. Edith B. Ricketson, Institute Librarian.

Holdings: 108 linear ft. and 142 cu. ft., 1348-1960, relating chiefly to Mexico, Central America, and the West Indies. Included are the C. I. Fayssoux Collection of papers of William Walker (La., Calif.; leader of filibustering expeditions to Nicaragua), 1857-80 (551 pieces); a collection of Yucatecan letters, 1778-1863 (856 pieces); treatises on Middle American languages; and extensive government archives, especially for Guatemala.

See Hist. Records Survey, Guide for La., pp. 16-18, its Calendar of the Fayssoux Collection of William Walker Papers (1937. 28 p. Processed), and its Calendar of the Yucatecan Letters (1939. 240 p. Processed); and Marie Hunter Irvine, "Administrative Papers: Copies Relating to New Spain," in the Institute's Miscellaneous Series, No. 5 (1948. 28 p.).

NEW ORLEANS

Newmark Library. 836 Cambronne St.

Holdings: 737 pieces and 1 bundle, 1926-37, consisting of a collection pertaining to the American Old Catholic Church movement in the United States and Canada.

See Hist. Records Survey, Guide for La., p. 11.

NEW ORLEANS 12

Rudolph Matas Medical Library, Tu-
land University.   1430 Tulane Ave.
William D. Postell, Librarian.

Holdings: Several hundred vols.
and pieces, largely 19th century, relating chiefly to the history of medicine in Louisiana.   Included are
papers of Stanford Emerson Chaillé
(La.; Confed. Army surgeon, medical
dean, public health and yellow fever
specialist); Frederick Ludwig Hoffman (N. J., Pa.; statistician), a study
of public health in Louisiana, 1770-
1913 (3 vols.); Joseph Jones (Ga.,
La.; physician, sanitarian, Confed.
Army surgeon), including notes on investigations in Andersonville Prison;
Charles Edmund Kells (La.; pioneer
in dental x-ray), papers on dentistry;
and Rudolph Matas (La.; surgeon).
There are also medical diplomas, fee
bills, licenses, and correspondence;
records of early Louisiana medical
societies; records of early medical
schools, including the register of students, 1835-1900, of the Medical College of Louisiana (now Tulane) and
lecture notebooks of faculty and students; a card index of the writings of
Louisiana physicians to 1940, with
biographical references; a bibliography
on medicine in Louisiana; ledgers and
prescription books of Louisiana physicians; the official register of licen-
sure of physicians in Louisiana, 1816-
54; and 19th-century records of Charity
Hospital in New Orleans.

NEW ORLEANS 18

St. Mary's Dominican College Library.
7300 St. Charles Ave.   Sister Mary
Reginald, Librarian.

Holdings: 250 pieces, 1860-1955,
relating to the Order of Dominican
Sisters in Louisiana.   Included are
annals of the Order; and correspondence on religious and civil life in Louisiana.

NEW ORLEANS 12

School of Medicine Library, Louisiana State University.   1542 Tulane
Ave.   Librarian.

Holdings: 283 pieces, from 1814,
relating to medical subjects, particularly to yellow fever and the plague.
Included are some papers of Aristides Agramonte (Cuba; physician, bacteriologist); and a manuscript history
of hospitals in Louisiana and one of
medicine in East Baton Rouge Parish,
La.
   See Hist. Records Survey, Guide
for La., p. 8.

NEW ORLEANS 25

Xavier University Library.   3912
Pine St.   Sister M. Redempta, Librarian.

Holdings: 7,000 pieces, and 2 filing cabinets, 1733-1950, relating
chiefly to the American Negro and to
New Orleans and its vicinity.   Included are a diary of Albert G. Brice
(La.; lawyer), 1858 (1 vol.); some
correspondence of Charles E. A.
Gayarré (La.; lawyer, historian),
1888; photostats of registers of bap-
tism, marriage, and burial of free
persons of color, 1733-1808; and
copies of manifests for slaves on
ships arriving, for the most part, in
ports in Louisiana, Texas, Florida, and
Mississippi, 1832-57 (5,500 pieces).
   See Hist. Records Survey, Guide
for La., p. 20.

SHREVEPORT

Centenary College Library.   2911

Centenary Blvd. (Mrs.) Alice Alben, Acting Head Librarian.

Holdings: About 40 vols. and 5,000 other pieces, 1825-1950, consisting chiefly of materials relating to Centenary College and minutes of annual meetings of the Louisiana Conference of the Methodist Episcopal Church, South, 1847-1950.

See Hist. Records Survey, Guide for La., p. 21.

MAINE

ALFRED

Parsons Memorial Library. (Mrs.) Bertha F. Drew, Librarian.

Holdings: A small quantity of papers, relating chiefly to Alfred and its vicinity. Included are records of the "Female Religious Society" of the local Congregational church, 1816-19; records of local Baptist, Congregational, and Methodist churches; a copy of the diary of Gen. Samuel Leighton, 1818-48; many papers of John Holmes (Maine, Mass., R. I.; lawyer, U. S. Rep. and Sen.); and a few letters of Usher Parsons (Maine; physician, prof. of anatomy and surgery at Brown Univ.).
See Ring, Reference List for Maine, index.

AUBURN

Androscoggin Historical Society. County Bldg. John E. Libby, Director.

Holdings: Over 100 vols. and 10,000 pieces, dating from 1759 but chiefly of the 19th century, relating to Androscoggin County and its residents. Included are diaries and other papers of Amos Davis (Maine; surveyor and early Lewiston settler), 1764-1807; a diary of Capt. Andrew Giddinge, 1759, with notes on the Louisbourg expedition; and 50 vols. of the diary of his son, Andrew Robinson Giddinge, known as Squire Giddinge, 1784-1839. There are also official records of the towns of Danville, 1802-58, and Lewiston, including 3 vols. of assessor's books for Lewiston, 1801-50; records of

school districts in the county, 1825-68 (3 vols. and several pieces); extensive vital records of Androscoggin towns, especially Lewiston, from the time of settlement; records of a Baptist church in Lewiston, 1818-59 (1 vol. and 4 pieces); petitions for and records of a toll bridge at Lewiston, 1797-1807 and 1823-65; and records of a horse railroad company, 1881-98.

—oOo—

Auburn Public Library.

Holdings: Papers relating chiefly to Auburn. Included are records of a local library association, 1845-65; an art club, 1880-1920; and an art and literature club, 1890-1902. There are also copies of letters sent by the Confederate Treasury Department, 1862-64 (1 vol.).
See Ring, Reference List for Maine, index.

AUGUSTA

Department of State. Harold I. Goss, Secretary of State.

Holdings: The State of Maine has no State archives organization but legislative and other governmental papers are on file in the Department of State. For some other State records see the State Library, in Augusta, and the Maine Historical Society, in Portland.

—oOo—

Kennebec Historical Society. 10 High St. Ethel Colby Conant, Secretary.

Holdings: A small quantity of manuscripts, chiefly 19th century, relating mainly to Kennebec County. Included are sermons and other papers of Rev. Ezekiel Emerson (Maine; Congregational minister), 1795-1818; papers of Sylvester Judd, Jr. (Mass., Maine; Unitarian minister, author); account books of a grocery store, 1752-1813; logbooks and account books of several vessels, 1794-1810; records of a local academy, 1795-1862; and some Civil War papers.

See Ring, Reference List for Maine, index.

—oOo—

Maine State Library. (Mrs.) Marion B. Stubbs, Librarian.

Holdings: Uncataloged papers, 1636-1933, relating chiefly to Maine. Included are numerous family histories and other genealogical materials; a few diaries and journals; collections of miscellaneous documents pertaining to a number of Maine towns; transcripts and other papers concerning the northeastern boundary, 1700-1843 (29 vols.); census records, 1821-80 (158 vols.), including schedules for Maine of the U.S. censuses of agriculture and industry, 1850-80; returns of the election of 1819 on the Maine constitution (227 pieces); plans of the Maine State House by Charles Bulfinch (Mass.; architect); papers of Israel Washburn (Maine; U.S. Rep., Gov.), 1858-63 (204 letters); and various papers on Maine's participation in the Civil War.

See Ring, Reference List for Maine, index.

BANGOR

Bangor Public Library. 145 Harlow St. L. Felix Ranlett, Librarian.

Holdings: An undetermined quantity of manuscripts, 1636-1955, relating chiefly to Bangor and eastern Maine. Some were formerly the property of the Bangor Historical Society. Included are papers of Fannie Hardy Eckstorm (Maine; author), resulting from her research on American Indians (25,000 items); the diary of Thomas Fayerweather, recording his exploration of Maine, 1720; a field book, 1797, other papers, and a copy of a diary of Park Holland (Maine; surveyor); records of various Bangor churches (75 items); an extensive collection of genealogical manuscripts, by Charles Edward Banks, pertaining to York County, Maine; and papers on the gold rush to California, 1849-51 (22 items).

BLUE HILL

Ladies' Social Library. (Mrs.) Dorris Parker, Librarian.

Holdings: Uncataloged manuscripts, from the late 18th century to the present, relating chiefly to Blue Hill. Included are records of the Library since 1868; early journals of the local academy; information about vessels built in Blue Hill, 1792-1891; letters, 1843-53, dealing with the history of Blue Hill and Sedgwick; records of a granite company; and some town records, 1765-1930.

See Ring, Reference List for Maine, index.

BRUNSWICK

Bowdoin College Library. Kenneth J. Boyer, Librarian.

Holdings: 252 vols., 15 boxes, 1,500 pieces, and other materials that occupy 10 filing drawers and 14 bookshelves, largely of the 19th century and relating chiefly to Maine or to alumni, faculty members, and administrators of Bowdoin College. Included are papers of Edward Abbott (Maine, Mass.; Congregational and Episcopal minister, editor of the Literary World), 1877-1902 (200 pieces); Jacob Abbott (Mass., N.Y., Maine; Congregational minister, author of children's books) and his family, 1756-1873 (10 bookshelves); Jesse Appleton (N.H., Maine; Congregational minister, pres. of Bowdoin College), 1807-19 (3 vols. of letters and 15 boxes of sermons); Horatio Bridge (Maine; lawyer, U.S. naval officer), 1 folder; Parker Cleaveland (Mass., Maine; chemistry prof. at Bowdoin College), 1805-37 (1,110 pieces); Elisha Eaton (Maine; early settler), 1756-74 (1-vol. diary); William Pitt Fessenden (Maine; U.S. Rep. and Sen., Sec. Treas.), 1854-73 (1,500 items); Nathaniel Hawthorne (Mass.; novelist), 1838-63 (71 letters); Oliver Otis Howard (U.S. Army officer, Commissioner of Freedmen's Bureau, Howard Univ. pres.), 1843-1908 (207 vols.); William DeWitt Hyde (Mass., Maine; Congregational minister, pres. of Bowdoin College), 1885-1917 (2 drawers of letters and sermons); Franklin Pierce (N.H.; U.S. Rep. and Sen., U.S. Pres.), 1837-69 (11 letters); Theodore Roosevelt (N.Y.; Gov., U.S. Pres.), 1891-1902 (15 letters); Joseph Sherman (Maine, Tenn.; college prof., pres. of Jackson College, Tenn.), 1826-49 (5 vols.); Charles Asbury Stephens (Maine; author of boys' stories, scientist), 2 vertical files of literary manuscripts and related materials; and Kate Douglas Wiggin (Calif.; author of books for girls), 1867-1923 (36 vols.). There are also sketches of and notes on Maine flowers (16 vols.); papers on the early history of Brunswick; and some papers relating to Unitarian churches in Maine.

—oOo—

Pejepscot Historical Society.

Holdings: Papers, 1716-1900, relating chiefly to Brunswick and its vicinity. Included are ledgers and other papers of Isaac Lincoln (Maine; Brunswick physician), 1803-59 (600 pieces); and several sermons of Joseph McKeen (Mass., Maine; Congregational minister, pres. of Bowdoin College), 1783-1806. There are also some judicial records, records of a musical education society and of other organizations, church records, Civil War letters, papers relating to schools, and account books and other business records of merchants and tradesmen.

See Ring, Reference List for Maine, index.

CALAIS

Calais Free Library. Edith L. Beckett, Librarian.

Holdings: Papers of James Shepherd Pike (Maine; journalist, author, Minister to the Netherlands), chiefly 1823-70, including his diaries and letters from Charles Anderson Dana (N.Y.; newspaper editor, Asst. Sec. War), 1850-81 (101 items), Horace Greeley (N.Y.; editor of New York Tribune, U.S. Rep.), 1850-72 (50 items), and other journalistic and political leaders. The Library also has some papers relating to the lumber business, Civil War recruiting, and other aspects of the history of Calais and vicinity.

See Ring, Reference List for Maine, index.

DOVER-FOXCROFT

Thompson Free Library.

Holdings: Genealogies of local families and some records of the Piscataquis Historical Society.

See Ring, Reference List for

Maine, index.

ELLSWORTH

Black House. Ernest T. Paine, Chairman of the Black House Committee.

Holdings: 200 vols. and many other papers, 1797-1880, relating chiefly to lands on the Kennebec and the Penobscot, merchandising, lumbering, ships, canals and railroads, and other business interests of the Black family of Ellsworth. Included is some correspondence between John Black and Lord Ashburton, 1836-44, containing information about boundary difficulties between Maine and Canada.
See Ring, Reference List for Maine, entry 550.

HALLOWELL

Hubbard Free Library. (Mrs.) Helen C. Robinson, Librarian.

Holdings: 10 vols., 350 pieces, and 1 chest of papers, 1790-1897, relating chiefly to Hallowell. Included are the records of the following local organizations: a Congregational church, 1790-1897 (4 vols., 11 pieces, and 1 chest); a Unitarian church, 1823-68 (2 vols.); a Universalist meeting house, 1843-69 (bound manuscript record of deeds of pews); a debating society, 1822-29 (2 vols. and 323 pieces); and a carpet factory, 1851-59 (1 account book).

HOULTON

Cary Library. Helen K. Atchison, Librarian.

Holdings: 242 pieces, 1745-1844, relating chiefly to land, lumbering,

schools, churches, business, and other activities in Houlton. Included are 9 account books, 1771-1834.
See Ring, Reference List for Maine, index.

ISLEFORD

Isleford Museum, Little Cranberry Island. Superintendent, Acadia National Park, Bar Harbor.

Holdings: A small collection of manuscripts, 17th-19th centuries, relating to the history and settlement of the area of Mount Desert Island and the Cranberry Isles. Included are account books and other records of several general stores and a number of logs and other ships' papers. (The Museum is open periodically during the summer.)
See Ring, Reference List for Maine, index.

KENNEBUNK

Kennebunk Free Library.

Holdings: Papers relating chiefly to Kennebunk. Included is a record of the activities of a local society for Civil War soldiers' relief, 1861-65.
See Ring, Reference List for Maine, index.

KENNEBUNKPORT

Louis T. Graves Memorial Public Library. Lucy A. Maling, Librarian.

Holdings: A small quantity of material relating chiefly to Kennebunkport. Included are records of a church, 1771-1907 (1 vol.), a temperance society, 1831-40 (1 vol.), and a shipbuilding company, 1857-58.

See Ring, Reference List for
Maine, index.

LEWISTON

Bates College Library. Iva Foster,
Librarian.

Holdings: Included are drafts of
four plays by William Clyde Fitch
(N.Y.; playwright); a notebook (formerly in the Cobb Divinity School
Library) of the treasurer of the Society of Theological Research, New
Hampton, N.H., 1855-65; some notebooks, sermons, and other papers relating to Free Baptists; and much
material regarding Bates College.

LINCOLN

Lincoln Historical Society. (Mrs.)
Bessie T. Achorn, Secretary. 47
Fleming St.

Holdings: A small collection relating to Lincoln and Penobscot County. Included are some account books
and papers about local railroad construction and early steamboating on
the upper Penobscot, papers on the
settlement of Lincoln, some family
records, and sketches of citizens
and industries.
See Ring, Reference List for
Maine, Part III, p. xiii.

OGUNQUIT

Ogunquit Free Library.

Holdings: 1 portfolio of miscellaneous letters, 1778-1916, including
autographs of several national political leaders.
See Ring, Reference List for
Maine, entry 1636.

ORONO

Department of History and Government, University of Maine. Edward
F. Dow, Head.

Holdings: 50 letters resulting
from the activities of a Kansas aid
society with headquarters in Bangor,
1855-57.
See Ring, Reference List for
Maine, entry 1777.

—oOo—

University of Maine Library. Louis
T. Ibbotson, Librarian.

Holdings: A small quantity of papers, 1741-1915, relating chiefly to
the University and to several towns in
Maine. Included are papers of and
concerning Merritt Caldwell Fernald
(Maine; pres. of Maine State College,
predecessor of the Univ. of Maine),
1870-1913; and records of a Baptist
church in Palermo, Maine, 1809-45
(2 vols.).
See Ring, Reference List for
Maine, index.

PORTLAND

Maine Historical Society. Marion B.
Rowe, Librarian.

Holdings: Many thousands of papers, relating chiefly to 19th-centu-
ry Maine but including 9 medieval
manuscripts.
Papers of persons who held important office under the Government
of the United States include those of
Nathan Clifford (Maine; U.S. Rep.,
Attorney Gen., Minister to Mexico,
Supreme Court Justice), 1831-81 (2
boxes of legal opinions and 3 packages of letters); Henry Dearborn
(Maine, Mass.; Rev. War and War of
1812 officer, U.S. Rep., Sec. War),

1800-14 (88 pieces); John Holmes (Maine; lawyer, U.S. Rep. and Sen.), 1796-1833 (2 vols., 1 box, and 1 portfolio); Henry Knox (Mass., Maine; Rev. War officer, Sec. War), 1789-1806 (11 boxes), relating to business interests in Maine; Stephen Longfellow (Maine; lawyer, U.S. Rep.), 1800-55 (7 vols. and 17 notebooks and receipt books); Rufus McIntire (Maine; lawyer, commissioner to settle Maine boundary, U.S. Rep.), 1823-55 (25 pieces); Edward Preble (Maine; U.S. naval officer), 1799-1805 (1 vol. and 1 envelope file), relating chiefly to the war with Tripoli; George F. Shepley (Maine; Civil War officer, military Gov. of La., U.S. circuit court judge), 1820-69 (a large quantity); Francis Ormand Jonathan Smith (Maine; U.S. Rep.), 1818-88 (26 packages), including 3 packages of letters to him from Samuel F. B. Morse (Mass., N.Y.; artist, inventor), 1839-60; George Thacher (Mass., Maine; Member Continental Cong., U.S. Rep. from Mass., jurist), 1780-1800 (1 box); Thomas Gilbert Thornton (Maine; U.S. marshal for Maine), 1789-1824 (3 vols. and 4 boxes); and Peleg Wadsworth (Mass., Maine; Rev. War officer, U.S. Rep.), 1794-1837 (77 letters).

Papers of other persons include those of Thomas Barclay (N.Y.; British consul gen., commissioner to carry out provisions of the Treaty of Ghent), 1799-1827 (7 boxes), relating in large part to the northeastern boundary controversy; Samuel Deane (Maine; Congregational clergyman), 1789-1814 (75 sermons); Elijah Kellogg (Maine, Mass.; Congregational clergyman, author), 1836-1901 (1 large box); William King (Maine; merchant, shipowner, Gov.), 1760-1852 (22 boxes and 4 packages); Grenville Mellen (Maine, Mass., N.Y.; author), 1815-41 (3 vols. and 1 package), chiefly literary manuscripts; Sir William Pepperell (Mass., Maine; merchant, pres. of Mass. Council, colonial ar-

my officer), 1716-56 (1 vol. and 1 package); Alexander Ramsay (Scotland, Maine, N.Y.; anatomist), 1806-24 (12 packages), chiefly lectures; and Samuel Waldo (Mass., Maine; merchant, land speculator, King George's War officer), 1631-1828 (2 vols. and 1 map collection).

There are also records of the Pejepscot Proprietors, 1636-1865 (10 vols.); the Kennebec Purchase records, 1749-1822 (24 vols., miscellaneous packages, and maps), including a map of 1751; various records of or pertaining to many towns; early deeds; numerous account books, diaries, sermons, and groups of family papers; and scattered church records. The Robert Trelawny Collection includes documents relating to Maine, 1631-1809. Included also are ship registers issued at Wiscasset, 1832-64 (10 vols.), many ships' logs, and papers relating to shipbuilding and other aspects of maritime history. Other papers relate to medical instruction, antislavery activities, turnpikes and railroads, the lumber industry, Indians and Indian languages, and the Revolutionary and Civil Wars. There is a collection of transcripts of documents on the northeastern boundary problem, 1700-1822 (24 vols.); and an autograph collection (59 cases), including several thousand letters of signers of the Declaration of Independence, U.S. Presidents, and other celebrities, chiefly political and literary.

See Ring, Reference List for Maine, index; De Ricci, Census, p. 749; and Forest History Sources, pp. 35-37.

—oOo—

Portland Society of Natural History.

Holdings: Chiefly records of the Society and lectures, reports, and other papers relating to various aspects of natural science in Maine, 1845 to the present.

See Ring, Reference List for Maine, index.

SACO

York Institute.

Holdings: An unknown quantity of papers, 1748-1897, relating chiefly to Saco and its vicinity. Included are a few sermons, a copy of the second census of York County, merchants' account books, and papers pertaining to lumbering, shipping, and other business activities.

See Ring, Reference List for Maine, index.

SEARSPORT

Penobscot Marine Museum. Clifford N. Carver, President.

Holdings: In the Lincoln Colcord Memorial Library, some 15 cu. ft. of manuscripts relating chiefly to shipbuilding and shipping in the Penobscot Bay region during the 19th century. Included are logbooks, charts, account books, ledgers, and business letters.

SOUTH BERWICK

Fogg Memorial Library.

Holdings: Papers, 1790-1902, relating chiefly to political and business activities in South Berwick and its vicinity. Included are a few papers pertaining to the distribution of prize money to heirs of men who served under John Paul Jones (Rev. War naval officer).

See Ring, Reference List for Maine, index.

WATERVILLE

Colby College Library. John R. McKenna, Librarian.

Holdings: A small collection, including some papers of Edwin Arlington Robinson (Maine, N.Y.; poet) and of other American and English writers. There are also minutes of a religious association at Bowdoinham, 1793-1818, records of some country churches, and a few manuscript sermons.

See Ring, Reference List for Maine, index.

—oOo—

Waterville Historical Society. Silver St.

Holdings: An unknown quantity of papers, 1708-1918, relating chiefly to Waterville and vicinity. Included are a few diaries, papers pertaining to Colby College, some records of the towns of Waterville and Winslow, and an autograph collection of letters of political, military, and industrial leaders in the United States.

See Ring, Reference List for Maine, index.

WILTON

Goodspeed Memorial Library.

Holdings: 43 vols. and 300 other pieces, 1811-58, consisting chiefly of tax and other financial records of the town of Wilton.

See Ring, Reference List for Maine, index.

YORK

Old Gaol Museum. Etta Falkner, Director.

Holdings: 30 vols. and 150 pieces, 1702-1870, relating chiefly to the York area. Included are ships' logs and papers, deeds, account books and journals, manuscript arithmetics, and letters; items relating to the Old Gaol, 1793-1860; excerpts from town records of York, 1652-1868; and a few papers of David Sewall (Maine; U.S. dist. judge), 1735-1825.

MARYLAND

ANNAPOLIS

Hall of Records of Maryland. Morris L. Radoff, Archivist and Records Administrator.

Holdings: 15,000 vols., 5,000 rolls of microfilm, and 3,000,000 pieces, 1635-1955, consisting of (1) noncurrent official records held as the State's archival agency, and (2) other papers relating chiefly to Maryland. In the first category are colonial records from as early as 1635; records (or photographic copies of records) of all of the counties, many dating from the colonial period; and noncurrent executive, legislative, and judicial records of the State extending well into the 20th century. In the second category are church records, 1692-1951 (400 vols.); business records, including records of iron furnaces and mercantile firms of the colonial period, 1752-1912 (300 vols.); various family papers, 1641-1954 (12,000 pieces); maps, 1606-1953 (200 pieces); and photographs (3,000 pieces).

See various publications of the Hall of Records, especially Catalogue of Archival Material (1942. 161 p.), Calendar of Maryland State Papers (1943-58. 7 vols.), Annual Reports of the Archivist (1935 to date), Index Holdings, September 1959 (12 p.), and The County Courthouses and Records of Maryland (Vol. 1, 1960; Vol. 2, scheduled for 1961, will contain a catalog of county records). Louis Dow Scisco has described in detail records of 14 counties for the colonial period in Md. Hist. Magazine, vols. 21-26 (1926-31). See also Morris L. Radoff, "Early Annapolis Records," ibid., 35:74-78 (Mar. 1940).

United States Naval Academy Library. Vernon D. Tate, Librarian.

Holdings: 328 pieces, 1759 to the present, relating chiefly to the U.S. Navy. The greater part of the holdings consist of ships' logs, journals, order books, letter books, and watch, quarter, and station bills (131 vols.), and of the journal of the officer-of-the-day, U.S. Naval Academy, 1845-1955 (171 vols.). Papers of individuals include a volume on the transactions resulting from the voyage to Pacific islands made by William Compton Bolton (U.S. naval officer), up to 1831 known as William Bolton Finch, 1829; letters of Franklin Buchanan (U.S. naval officer, first Naval Academy Supt.), 1838-47 (7 vols.); letters of Richard Dale (Rev. War and U.S. naval officer, 1802 (1 vol.), and of Samuel Francis Du Pont (U.S. naval officer), 1843-44 (1 vol.); the war diary of August Francis Fechteler, known as Frank Fechteler (U.S. naval officer), on the U.S.S. Paducah, 1917-18 (1 vol.); letters of John Dandridge Henley (U.S. naval officer), 1808-12 (1 vol.); a letter book of Richard B. Jones (U.S. consul at Tripoli), 1814-19; a journal of Winfield Scott Schley (U.S. naval officer), 1877-78; an orderly book of William Smallwood (Md.; Rev. War officer, Gov.), 1778; and papers of Charles Stewart (U.S. naval officer), 1843-51 (1 vol.). There is also a volume by a British officer, dealing in large part with British operations in the United States during the War of 1812.

—oOo—

United States Naval Academy Museum.

Capt. Wade DeWeese, USN (Ret.), Director.

Holdings: A quantity of 18th- to 20th-century manuscripts relating chiefly to the history of the U. S. Navy. They consist of three collections: the Rosenbach Collection, 1776-1865 (81 pieces), of letters or other documents from the hands of naval heroes, inventors, and statesmen; the Zabriskie Collection (213 pieces), of similar composition; and a miscellaneous collection (several hundred pieces) acquired through the years from many individual donors.

In one or more of these collections there are over 100 letters to and from David Glasgow Farragut (U. S. naval officer) and other documents relating to him; a number of letters of Robert Fulton (N. Y.; inventor) and many documents tracing the development of steam navigation; hundred of letters and other documents by and relating to John Paul Jones (Rev. War naval officer), including his letter book, 1778-79; letter books of John Marston (U. S. naval officer), 1850, 1860-62; 2 letter books of Robert Morris (Pa.; financier, Member Continental Cong.), 1781-84; 48 letters of Horatio Lord Nelson (England; naval officer); a quantity of the correspondence of Joshua R. Sands (U. S. naval officer), 1830-79; and 15 papers of George Washington (Va.; U. S. Pres.), 1750-98, and an account book of his overseer of Mount Vernon, 1762-84. Included also are a number of ships' logs, among them the log of the U. S. S. Constitution, 1803-4; several manuscripts relating to the Monitor, among them a "personal log" kept by her paymaster, 1862-65, and a letter by her commanding officer giving an account of the battle with the Merrimac; individual pieces or small amounts of papers representing all the distinguished naval officers in U. S. history; and commissions or letters signed by U. S. Presidents, Secretaries of the Navy, and other noted Americans.

See the Museum's Catalogue of the Rosenbach Collection of Manuscripts (1956. 10 p.), its Catalogue of the Christian A. Zabriskie Manuscript Collection (1956. 6 p.), and its Catalogue of Manuscripts (1957. [99] p.).

BALTIMORE 1

Archives of the Archdiocese of Baltimore. 408 North Charles St. Rev. George L. Hopkins, Chancellor; Rev. John Joseph Gallagher, Archivist.

Holdings: 60,000 items, 1745-1947, formerly known as the Baltimore Cathedral Archives, and consisting chiefly of the archives of the Roman Catholic Archdiocese of Baltimore. Included are records of the administrations of all the Archbishops: John Carroll, 1789-1815 (1 vol. and 16 boxes); Leonard Neale, 1815-17 (1 vol. and 2 boxes); Ambrose Marechal, 1817-28 (2 vols. and 12 boxes); James Whitfield, 1824-34 (1 vol. and 2 boxes); Samuel Eccleston, 1834-51 (5 boxes); Francis Patrick Kenrick, 1851-63 (2 vols. and 7 boxes); Martin John Spalding, 1863-72 (4 vols. and 10 boxes); James Roosevelt Bayley, 1872-77 (4 vols. and 5 boxes); James Gibbons, 1877-1921 (12 vols. and 92 boxes); and Michael J. Curley, 1921-47 (2 vols., 79 boxes, and 8 file drawers). There are also Papal bulls and briefs relating to the Archdiocese of Baltimore, 1784-1871 (1 box); records of the Chancery Office, 1851-1947 (63 vols., 101 boxes, and 40 file drawers); and records of the Cathedral of the Assumption, 1782-1947 (104 vols. and 2 file drawers).

See John Tracy Ellis, "A Guide to the Baltimore Cathedral Archives," in Catholic Hist. Review, 32:341-360 (Oct. 1946).

BALTIMORE 10

Baltimore Yearly Meeting of Friends (Hicksite). Stony Run Meetinghouse, 5114 North Charles St. La Verne H. Forbush, Custodian of Records.

Holdings: Records of the Society of Friends (Hicksite) in Maryland, 550 vols., since 1672. Included are records of the Baltimore Yearly Meeting, 1672-1898; the Baltimore Quarterly Meeting, 1759-1895; the Baltimore Monthly Meeting, 1792-1906; the Fairfax Quarterly Meeting, 1787-1882; and the Center Quarterly Meeting, 1833-83; and records of other divisions of the Society of Friends (Hicksite).
See Allison, Inventory, pp. 15-19.

BALTIMORE

Baltimore Yearly Meeting of Friends (Orthodox). Homewood Friends' Meeting House, 3107 North Charles St. (Mrs.) Elizabeth Winslow Stewart, Recorder.

Holdings: 327 vols., 7 boxes, 52 folders, 18 binders, and 24 packages, dating from 1699 and relating to the Society of Friends, chiefly in Maryland and Virginia. Included are minutes and other records of the Baltimore Yearly Meeting of Friends (Orthodox), from 1829; the Dunnings Creek (Pennsylvania) Half Years Meeting, 1909-19, and constituent meetings; the Baltimore Quarterly Meeting, from 1807 to date, with gaps, and minutes and records of its constituent meetings; and the Baltimore Monthly Meeting, 1829-32 and 1863-1955. There are

also minutes and records of the Virginia Yearly Meeting, 1702-1844; the Virginia Half Years Meeting, 1844-1911; and the Virginia Quarterly Meeting, from 1844; minutes of the Upper (Virginia) Quarterly Meeting, 1745-1844; and minutes and other records of the Western (Virginia) Quarterly Meeting, 1797-1817, and of its constituent meetings, such as White-oak Swamp, Henrico County, Va., 1699-1824, and the Cedar Creek Monthly Meeting, 1739-1893.

BALTIMORE 1

Enoch Pratt Free Library. 400 Cathedral St. Robert S. Ake, Assistant Director.

Holdings: 1,188 pieces, 1629-1949, relating chiefly to Maryland. Included is a collection of letters and other documents, relating to the early history of Maryland, that were originally among the private papers of the Lords Baltimore. Among papers of literary men are a number of Edgar Allen Poe letters and family papers, 1800-80, and some literary manuscripts and letters of Henry Louis Mencken (Md.; author, editor, critic), 1889-1949 (150 vols. and numerous unbound files).
See the Library's Descriptive Catalog of the Exhibition of Documents Relating to the Early Days of the Colony of Maryland ([193-?; 16] p. Processed).

BALTIMORE 30

Fort McHenry National Monument and Historic Shrine. The Superintendent.

Holdings: 20,000 documents on microfilm dealing with Fort McHenry, 1776-1958. Many of these documents have been reproduced by the Xerox process, bound in chronological order, and cross-referenced. (Included is possibly the finest collection of the War of 1812 material dealing with the British Chesapeake Bay campaign.) There are also the Mrs. Reuben Ross Holloway papers, 1917-31 (50 pieces), relating chiefly to the movement for the adoption of "The Star-Spangled Banner" as the official national anthem; a collection of letters and other documents belonging to the Commandant of Fort McHenry during World War I; and 1,500 photographs of drawings, paintings, and live objects, 1776-1958, dealing with Fort McHenry and the Baltimore area.

BALTIMORE 18

Johns Hopkins University Libraries. John H. Berthel, Librarian.

Holdings: 40 vols. and 31,898 letters and other items. Included are 9 medieval manuscripts, some papyri, and a number of Icelandic manuscripts; but most of the holdings are 19th- and 20th-century items that relate in large part to Johns Hopkins University. (Not included in the present entry are the holdings of the William H. Welch Library of the Johns Hopkins Medical School, which are described separately below.)

Papers of individuals, which consist largely of letters to and from, include those of Herbert Baxter Adams (Md.; historian, Johns Hopkins Univ. prof.), 1876-1901 (5,956 items); Isaiah Bowman (Md.; geographer, Johns Hopkins Univ. pres.), not cataloged; Basil L. Gildersleeve (Md.; Greek prof. at Johns Hopkins Univ.), 1862-1922 (incompletely cataloged); Daniel Coit Gilman (Md.; author, Johns Hopkins Univ. pres.), 1842-1901 (11,320 items); Frank J. Goodnow (Md.; adviser to Chinese Govt., Johns Hopkins

Univ. pres.), 1891-1932 (14,600 items); Sidney Lanier (Ga., Md.; poet), 1857-81 (3,262 items); Francis Lieber (S. C., N. Y.; political scientist, prof. at Univ. of S. C. and Columbia Univ.), 1835-72 (124 letters by him); John Stuart Mill (England; reformer, economist), 1819-73 (111 items); Henry A. Rowland (Md.; physicist at Johns Hopkins Univ.), 1876-1901 (3,852 items); John Banister Tabb (Va., Md.; priest, poet, English prof.), 1895-1909 (42 letters by him); and Edward Lucas White (Md.; poet), not cataloged.

See De Ricci, Census, pp. 753-755.

BALTIMORE

Maryland Diocesan Library. 17 East Mt. Vernon Pl. Rev. L. O. Forgueran, Librarian.

Holdings: More than 300 vols. and numerous unbound papers, 1681-1953, consisting chiefly of official records of the Protestant Episcopal Diocese of Maryland. Included are journals of annual conventions, papers of committees, and bishops' correspondence. There are also sermons, diaries, and other papers of bishops and ministers, and correspondence of a merchant of Maryland's Eastern Shore, 1741-66 (4 vols.).

See Allison, Inventory, pp. 13-15; and Hist. Records Survey, Inventory of the Church Archives of Maryland; Protestant Episcopal, Diocese of Maryland, pp. 45-61 (1940. Processed).

BALTIMORE 1

Maryland Historical Society. 201 West Monument St. James W. Foster, Director; John D. Kilbourne, Librarian.

Holdings: About 1,500 linear ft.,

1582 to date, relating chiefly to Maryland history but including much of national interest.

The Calvert Papers, the private papers of the proprietors of Maryland, 1582-1770 (1,300 items), include government, land, and colonization records of the colony, records of the Maryland-Pennsylvania boundary dispute, and personal papers of the Calvert family. In addition to these quasi-official papers, the Society has colonial county rent rolls, Revolutionary War oaths of allegiance, militia lists and commissions, minutes of the Frederick County Committee of Observation, 1775-76, and War of 1812 muster rolls.

Papers of political leaders include those of John Adams (Mass.; Member Continental Cong., diplomat, U.S. Pres.), 1780-1817 (15 items); John Quincy Adams (Mass.; U.S. Rep. and Sen., diplomat, Sec. State, U.S. Pres.), 1811-43 (14 items); Joel Barlow (Conn.; poet, Minister to France), 1803-36 (46 items); Theodorick Bland, Jr. (Va.; Member Continental Cong., Rev. War officer, U.S. Sen.) and his family, 1757-1860 (11 boxes); Charles J. Bonaparte (Md.; municipal and civil service reformer, Sec. Navy, Attorney Gen.), 1905-26 (300 items); Charles Carroll of Carrollton (Md.; Member Continental Cong., U.S. Sen.) and his family, 1658-1883 (30 boxes); Alexander Hamilton (N.Y.; Rev. War officer, Member Continental Cong., Sec. Treas.), 1789-99 (29 items); Robert Goodloe Harper (S.C., Md.; lawyer, War of 1812 officer, U.S. Rep. from S.C. and Sen. from Md.) and his family, 1748-1880 (1,000 items); Benjamin C. Howard (Md.; War of 1812 officer, U.S. Rep., U.S. Supreme Court reporter), 1809-82 (20 boxes); John Eager Howard (Md.; Rev. War officer, Member Continental Cong., Gov., U.S. Sen.), 1752-1827 (2 vols. and 15 boxes), and the Howard family, 1662-1918 (3 boxes); Reverdy Johnson

Md.; U.S. Sen., Attorney Gen., Minister to Great Britain), 1821-74 (115 items); James McHenry (Md.; Rev. War officer, Member Continental Cong., Sec. War), 1774-1816 (231 items); James Madison (Va.; U.S. Rep., Sec. State, U.S. Pres.), 1803-36 (46 items); James A. Pearce (Md.; lawyer, U.S. Rep. and Sen.), 1829-62 (150 items); William Penn (England, Pa.; founder of Pa.), 1681-99 (16 items); William Pinkney (Md.; U.S. Attorney Gen., diplomat, U.S. Rep. and Sen.), 1804-19 (2 letter books and 41 items); Robert Smith (Md.; Sec. Navy, Sec. State), 1797-1842 (40 items); Samuel Smith (Md.; Rev. War and War of 1812 officer, U.S. Rep. and Sen.), 1777-1837 (51 items); Roger Brooke Taney (Md.; U.S. Attorney Gen., Sec. Treas., Chief Justice), 1811-62 (107 items); George Washington (Va.; Rev. War Commander in Chief, U.S. Pres.), 1775-98 (62 items); Woodrow Wilson (N.J.; pres. of Princeton Univ., Gov., U.S. Pres.), 1901-13 (12 items); and William Wirt (Va., Md.; U.S. Attorney Gen.), 1786-1860 (9,000 items).

Papers of military leaders, in addition to some of those named above, include those of Harry Gilmor (Md.; Confed. Cavalry officer, leader of the "Partisan Rangers"), 1862-65 (75 items); Mordecai Gist (Md.; Rev. War officer), 1775-83 (4 vols.); Nathanael Greene (R.I.; Rev. War officer), 1780-83 (57 items); Edward Simpson (U.S. naval officer), 1840-43 (1 vol.), journal kept while he was a midshipman; William Smallwood (Md.; Rev. War officer, Gov.), 1776-91 (71 items); Isaac R. Trimble (Md.; Confed. Army officer), 1861-63 (50 items); Otho Holland Williams (Md.; Rev. War officer, collector of customs at Baltimore), 1744-94 (1,200 pieces); and William Henry Winder (Md.; lawyer, War of 1812 officer), 500 letters dealing with his military career.

Papers of other persons include

those of Elizabeth Patterson Bonaparte (Md.; wife of Jerome, the brother of Emperor Napoleon), 1785-1879 (700 items), including letters of the Bonaparte family; Francis Scott Key (Md., D.C.; lawyer, poet), 1811-26 (4 boxes); Benjamin Henry Labrobe (Pa., D.C., Md.; architect, engineer) and his family, 1796-1853 (52 vols. and 11 boxes); William Patterson (Md.; shipping merchant, banker, railroad capitalist), 1786-1830 (4 vols.); Lewis H. Steiner (Md.; physician, chief of the U.S. Sanitary Commission), 1861-83 (2 vols. and 91 items); and David Bailie Warden (U.S. consul at Paris, author), 1797-1846 (4,100 items).

Extensive holdings of business papers include records of a Baltimore iron company, 1703-37 (3 vols.); a mining and manufacturing company in Allegany County, 1790-1943 (39 vols. and 5 boxes); a general merchandise store in Waynesboro, Pa., accounts with Baltimore firms, 1820-60 (5 boxes); a Baltimore shipbuilder, 1831-38 (3 vols.); an electric railway company near Baltimore, 1906-23 (6 boxes); a Baltimore mercantile company, 1785-1871 (97 vols.); and an iron furnace, 1851-90 (13 vols.). There are also records of ship arrivals and departures and ship news kept by the Baltimore Merchants Exchange reading room, 1832-99 (72 vols.); papers relating to trade with West Indian and Mediterranean ports in the 18th and 19th centuries; a collection of account books concerning iron manufacture and plantation affairs, 1732-1880 (80 vols. and 6 boxes); and documents relating to the Baltimore and Ohio Railroad, 1827-30 (21 items).

Other records include those of an Episcopal church in Baltimore, 1856-1930 (5,000 items); the Female Bible Society of Annapolis, 1829-47 (2 vols.); the Maryland State Colonization Society, 1827-1902 (84 vols. and 5 boxes); the Baltimore Library Co., 1796-1855 (32 vols. and 2 boxes); an opera house

in Baltimore, 1873-1917 (8 account books); the Confederate Soldiers' Home at Pikesville, 1891-1932 (12 vols.); and the Knights of Labor at Ellicott City and Baltimore, 1886-1902 (1 vol.).

See articles in Md. Hist. Magazine, especially William D. Hoyt, Jr., "The Papers of the Maryland State Colonization Society," 32:247-271 (Sept. 1937), and "The Warden Papers," 36:302-314 (Sept. 1941) and 38:69-85 (Mar. 1943), and Alfred R. James, "Sidelights on the Founding of the Baltimore and Ohio Railroad," 48:267-309 (Dec. 1953); Hist. Records Survey, Calendar of the General Otho Holland Williams Papers in the Maryland Historical Society (1940. 454 p. Processed); and David B. Tyler, "'Time and Waste Books' of James Williamson, Builder of the Ann McKim," in American Neptune, 3:26-34 (Jan. 1943).

BALTIMORE 18

Methodist Historical Society of the Baltimore Conference. Lovely Lane Museum and Library, 22d and St. Paul Sts. Kenneth Ray Rose, Curator; Rev. Edwin Schell, Librarian (acting).

Holdings: 6,000 pieces, 1773-1958, relating chiefly to Methodism. Included are minutes of the Baltimore Conference of the Methodist Church, 1800-1955; reports and other records of Baltimore Conference committees and organizations, 1816-1953; records of Methodist congregations in Baltimore and elsewhere in Maryland, 1792-1945; steward books of Baltimore, Frederick, Berkeley, and West Harford circuits, 1794-1866; a number of journals of ministers, late 18th century and later; 63 letters of Francis Asbury (Methodist bishop), 1790-1815, and smaller quantities of

letters of many other bishops; papers
of John Franklin Goucher (Md.; philanthropist, Methodist minister, pres.
of Woman's College of Baltimore, now
Goucher College), including letters
from missionary leaders the world
over, 1880-1922; Methodist Sesqui-
centennial papers, 1930-34; and documents relating to Methodist reunion,
1879-1930.

BALTIMORE 2

Peabody Institute of the City of Baltimore. 1 East Mt. Vernon Pl. Lloyd
A. Brown, Librarian.

Holdings: 130 vols., 1812-70, con-
sisting of the papers of John Pendleton
Kennedy (Md.; lawyer, novelist, U.S.
Rep., Sec. Navy).
    See Lloyd W. Griffin, "The John
Pendleton Kennedy Manuscripts," in
Md. Hist. Magazine, 48:327-336 (Dec.
1953).

BALTIMORE 1

Walters Art Gallery. Dorothy Miner,
Librarian and Keeper of Manuscripts.

Holdings: Over 1,000 pieces, from
the 3d century B.C. to the 20th century
A.D., selected primarily for their artistic interest. Included are 767 ancient, medieval, and Renaissance illuminated manuscripts from Europe
and the Near East. There are also
170 letters of Catherine the Great
(Russia; Empress); correspondence
between Thomas S. Cullen (Md.; surgeon) and Henry Walters (Md.; engineer, capitalist, art collector), concerning the founding of the School of
Art as Applied to Medicine at the
Johns Hopkins University (160 letters);
and miscellaneous letters of 19th-cen-
tury French artists.
    See De Ricci, Census, pp. 757-856.

BALTIMORE 5

William H. Welch Medical Library,
Johns Hopkins University. 1900
East Monument St. Sanford V. Lar-
key, Director and Librarian; Janet
B. Koudelka, Curator of Rare Books
and Archives.

Holdings: In the Library proper
there are a few Arabic and medieval
medical manuscripts, over 100 letters of Edward Jenner (England; physician, discoverer of vaccination);
some early American material on
vaccination; and 3 vols. of lecture
notes, believed to be on lectures by
Benjamin Rush (Pa.; physician, Member Continental Cong., prof. at Univ.
of Pa.) and Philip Syng Physick (Pa.;
surgeon, prof. at Univ. of Pa.). The
Archives Collection consists largely
of material relating to the Johns Hopkins medical institutions: School of
Medicine, School of Hygiene and Public Health, and the Johns Hopkins
Hospital, and to leading members of
their faculties. Included are papers
of John Jacob Abel (prof. of pharmacology), 100 boxes; Thomas S. Cullen
(surgeon, prof. of gynecology), 15
boxes on deposit from Enoch Pratt
Free Library, Baltimore; Walter
Dandy (prof. of neurosurgery), 12
boxes; William S. Halsted (prof. of
surgery), 40 boxes; Howard A. Kelly
(prof. of gynecology), 38 boxes;
Franklin P. Mall (prof. of anatomy),
collection being assembled; Lewis
Weed (prof. of anatomy, dean of
medical faculty), collection being assembled; and William Henry Welch
(director of School of Hygiene and
Public Health, prof. of the history of
medicine), 220 filing boxes.

BETHESDA

National Library of Medicine. Frank
B. Rogers, Director.

Holdings: 110 linear ft., since 1094, relating chiefly to medicine and allied subjects. Included are Arabic, Turkish, and Persian medical manuscripts, 11th-19th centuries (156 items); and early Western medical manuscripts, 13th-15th centuries (42 items). The noncurrent archives of the Library, 1840-1950 (99 ft.) include correspondence of John Shaw Billings (D. C., N. Y.; surgeon, U. S. Army officer, director of the Surgeon-General's Library and the New York Public Library).

See Dorothy M. Schullian and Francis E. Sommer, A Catalogue of Incunabula and Manuscripts in the Army Medical Library ([1948.] 361 p.).

EMMITSBURG

St. Joseph's Central House, Daughters of Charity of St. Vincent de Paul. Sister Josephine, Provincial Secretary and Archivist.

Holdings: 208 vols., 1786-1954, relating chiefly to the Catholic Church in the United States. An important collection consists of the papers of Elizabeth Ann Bayley Seton (N. Y., Md.; Catholic convert, founder and Mother Superior of the Sisters of Charity of St. Joseph), 1786-1820 (17 vols.), consisting of diaries, reflections, instructions, memoranda, and letters to Mother Seton from Simon W. G. Bruté de Rémur (Md., Ind.; first Bishop of Vincennes), 1811-38; John Carroll (Md.; Archbishop of Baltimore), 1805-11; John L. A. M. L. de Cheverus (Mass., France; first Bishop of Boston), 1805-20; John Dubois (Va., Md., N. Y.; Bishop of New York), 1807-42; Louis Guillaume Valentin Du Bourg (Md., La.; Bishop of New Orleans), 1808-28; and Robert Goodloe Harper (S. C., Md.; lawyer, U. S. Rep. from S. C., War of 1812 officer, U.S. Sen. from Md.), 1818-20.

Included also are 19 bound volumes of letters from William H. Elder (Miss., Ohio; Bishop of Natchez and of Cincinnati), 1864-91; John Joseph Hughes (Pa., N. Y.; Bishop of New York), 1828-47; John Baptist Purcell (Md., Ohio; Bishop of Cincinnati), 1835-43; Joseph Rosati (La., Mo.; Bishop of St. Louis), 1828-40; and John Timon (Md., N. Y.; Bishop of Buffalo), 1842-59; and a volume of letters and medical reports on cholera, 1832. Other materials consist of Civil War papers, 1861-65 (3 vols.); Spanish-American War papers, 1898 (7 vols.); a register of St. Joseph's Academy, 1813-60 (1 vol.); and, dating from 1809 to the present, annals and diaries (50 vols.), account books (10 vols.), and mission histories (100 vols.).

FREDERICK

C. Burr Artz Library (Public Library). Josephine P. Etchison, Librarian.

Holdings: Chiefly 28 letters, 1768-1824, relating mainly to Maryland. Included are letters from George Washington (Va.; U. S. Pres.) and other prominent men to Thomas Johnson (Md.; Member Continental Cong., Gov., U. S. Supreme Court Justice).

TAKOMA PARK (WASHINGTON 12, D. C.)

Seventh-day Adventist Theological Seminary Library. Mrs. Robert H. Mitchell, Librarian.

Holdings: A collection of advent sources, relating to the second advent movements and the history of the church. The seminary has access also to certain administrative documents still in the possession of the nearby General Conference of Seventh-day Adventists and, upon approval of the Board of Trustees of the Ellen G. White Publications, to certain papers of Ellen G. White, prophet of the church, which are also in the General Conference building.

See Jason Horn, "Seventh Day Adventist Activities," in Am. Archivist, 17:221-224 (July 1954).

WOODSTOCK

Woodstock College Archives.   Rev. Edward A. Ryan, Archivist.

Holdings: 210 cu. ft., 1640-1955, relating to activities of members of the Society of Jesus (Jesuits), in Maryland, eastern and central Pennsylvania, and, to some extent, the New England States and New York. Included are letters, sermons, record books, ledgers, diaries, and other documents, especially before 1870. For the period beginning in

1870, acquisitions have been largely restricted to archival material from Woodstock College. The Archives contain most of the material formerly in a collection, now dispersed, which was referred to as the "Maryland-New York Province S. J. Archives, New York." Papers of individuals include those of John Carroll (Md.; first Archbishop of Baltimore, founder of Georgetown College), 1770-1815 (230 letters and 50 sermons); John McElroy (D. C., Md., Mass.; priest, first commissioned Roman Catholic U. S. Army chaplain, founder of Boston College), 1805-68 (20 diaries and 100 letters); and Adam Marshall (Md.; schoolmaster, often called the first Roman Catholic U. S. Navy chaplain), 1824-25 (a diary and some letters). There is also a collection of letters of Agustín de Iturbide (Mexico; revolutionist, Emperor) and his chaplain José Antonio Lopez, 1816-24 (200 letters and several documents).

See Thomas Hughes, S. J., History of the Society of Jesus in North America, 1:25-27 (1908).

MASSACHUSETTS

AMESBURY

Amesbury Public Library. 149 Main St. Teresa B. Castle, Librarian.

Holdings: A small collection, largely 19th century, relating chiefly to Amesbury. Included are correspondence about the estate of John Greenleaf Whittier (Mass.; poet); business and other records of the Rocky Hill Meeting House (Congregational), which contain some petitions to the Massachusetts General Court; much material on carriage-making at Amesbury; and records of a company that engaged in the early manufacture of automobiles.

AMHERST

Amherst College Library. Newton F. McKeon, Director.

Holdings: 200 vols., 1 box, and 495 pieces, dating principally from the 18th century to the present, relating chiefly to New England and to English and American literature. Included are copies of the public letters of Jeffrey, Lord Amherst (British commander in chief in America), 1745-84, from the Public Record Office, London (photostats of 55 vols. and microfilm of 98 vols.); letters of Calvin Coolidge (Mass.; U.S. Pres.), 1915-23 (37 items), chiefly to Frank W. Stearns (Mass.; Boston merchant); literary manuscripts of Emily Dickinson (Mass.; poet), 1844-86 (850 poems and drafts), together with hundreds of her letters and with correspondence of her family and her first editor, Mabel Loomis Todd (Mass., 1887-98, and of the donor of the pa-

pers, Millicent Todd Bingham (D.C.; editor, author), 1929-55; papers of William Clyde Fitch (N.Y.; playwright), 1879-1902 (11 vols. and 36 pieces); literary manuscripts, including original worksheets and final typescripts, of Rolfe Humphries (N.Y.; poet), 1911-58 (3 vols. and 151 poems in several drafts); lecture notes and other papers of Sir Richard Claverhouse Jebb (England; classicist), 1859-1905 (26 vols. and 5 pieces); letters of Viola Roseboro' (N.Y.; editor and writer of fiction), 1936-44 (1 box); and papers of Richard P. Wilbur (Conn.; poet), 1947-58 (22 pieces), principally poems in several drafts including manuscripts of two published volumes. There are also an autograph collection of documents of signers of the Declaration of Independence (1 vol.); a collection of autograph letters of Presidents and other prominent persons, 1520-1903 (40 pieces); and a collection of miscellaneous letters and poems of English and American, chiefly New England, writers, 19th and 20th century (175 pieces).

See Hist. Records Survey, Guide for Mass., p. 3; and John C. Long, Lord Jeffrey Amherst, p. 327 (1933). Charles F. Jenkins, in Autographs of the Signers of the Declaration, p. 11 (1926), describes the collection, listed as the property of Herbert L. Pratt, now at Amherst College.

—oOo—

Jones Library. Amity St. William F. Merrill, Director.

Holdings: 2,500 pieces, 1786-1955, relating chiefly to Amherst. Included are some papers of Ray Stannard Baker, also known as David

Grayson (Mass.; journalist, biographer of Woodrow Wilson); Emily Dickinson (Mass.; poet), 1860-85; Helen Hunt Jackson (Mass., R. I., Colo.; poet, novelist), 1830-85; and Noah Webster (Mass., Conn., N. Y.; lexicographer, author), 1811-22. There are also papers dealing with Shays' Rebellion, 1786-87; and records of local churches, 1786-1908. There are also some manuscripts and memorabilia of Robert Frost (N. H., Mass.; poet, lecturer), some personal correspondence of John W. Burgess (N. Y., R. I.; political scientist), and a few letters of Eugene Field (Mo., Ill.; journalist, poet).

See Hist. Records Survey, Guide for Mass., p. 5.

—oOo—

Joseph B. Eastman Foundation. Amherst College. George Goodwin, Jr., Director.

Holdings: Chiefly letters, speeches, and other papers of Joseph B. Eastman (Mass., D. C.; Interstate Commerce Commissioner, Federal Coordinator of Transportation), for the most part 1918-36, but with some of earlier and later years.

—oOo—

University of Massachusetts Library. Benton L. Hatch, Associate Librarian.

Holdings: A small quantity, mainly papers of former faculty members.

ANDOVER

Memorial Hall Public Library. Miriam Putnam, Librarian.

Holdings: A small quantity of papers, 1773-1865, relating chiefly to Andover and its citizens during the

Civil War. Included are company and other military records, 1861-65 (11 notebooks, 4 metal files, and 16 muster rolls); and records of Civil War committees of citizens, 1861 (5 notebooks of records and accounts and 2 rolls listing disbursements to aid volunteers' families).

See Hist. Records Survey, Guide for Mass., p. 6.

ATTLEBORO

Attleboro Public Library. Joseph L. Sweet Memorial.

Holdings: 740 items, 1702-1912, relating chiefly to the locality. Included are military items, 1815-61; tax records, 1830 and 1850-58 (1 vol. and several pieces); and family papers, 1745-1912 (654 items).

See Hist. Records Survey, Guide for Mass., p. 7.

AUBURN

Auburn Free Public Library. Mona Adshead, Librarian.

Holdings: 3 vols. and 29 pieces, 1791-1935, relating chiefly to Auburn. Included are weather reports, 1821-24 and 1829-36; and the town treasurer's records, 1847-75.

See Hist. Records Survey, Guide for Mass., p. 8.

BARRE

Barre Town Library.

Holdings: 259 pieces, 1753-1914, relating chiefly to Barre. Included are some official town records, 1753-1863, and church records, 1767-1845.

See Hist. Records Survey, Guide

for Mass., p. 9.

BEVERLY

Beverly Historical Society. 117 Cabot
St. Ruth H. Hill, Historian-Librarian.

Holdings: 20,000 manuscripts relating chiefly to the town. Included
are ship logs and papers, 1712-1880;
wharf records, 1721-1821; various
town and school records; records of
the U. S. Naval office at Beverly,
1784-1800; records of a volunteer infantry company, 1861; and records of
a local Congregational church.
See Hist. Records Survey, Guide
for Mass., p. 12.

—oOo—

Beverly Public Library. 32 Essex St.

Holdings: 169 pieces, including
papers of Asa Gray (N. Y., Mass.;
botanist, prof. at Harvard Univ.), 60
letters; and some correspondence of
Lucy Larcom (Mass.; author, teacher).

BOSTON 46

American Academy of Arts and Sciences. 280 Newton St. Brookline
Station. Ralph W. Burhoe, Executive Officer.

Holdings: 2,500 pieces, 1747-
1955, relating to science and scientists. Included are papers of Benjamin Peirce (Mass.; mathematician,
astronomer, librarian), 1818-80
(960 pieces); papers of Benjamin
Thompson, Count Rumford (Mass.,
England, Bavaria; physicist, inventor, philanthropist) and his daughter,
1775-1854 (627 pieces); letters and
other manuscripts by or concerning
other noted scientists, 1780-1955;

and minutes of meetings of the Academy, 1780-1954. There are also
items of meteorological interest,
chiefly observations in Massachusetts,
1754-1865 (29 vols. and 29 pieces),
including observations and meteorological journals of Enoch Hale (Mass.;
physician), 1818-48 (5 vols. and 12
pieces); Edward Augustus Holyoke
(Mass.; physician), 1754-1829 (4
vols.); James Jackson (Mass.; physician, prof. at Harvard Medical
School), 1826-65 (11 vols.); and Edward Wigglesworth (Mass.; clergyman, Harvard prof. of divinity),
1780-93 (1 vol. and 1 piece).
See Hist. Records Survey, Guide
for Mass., p. 14; and the Academy's
Items of Meteorological Interest in
the Archives of the American Academy of Arts and Sciences (n. d. 5 p.
Processed).

BOSTON 8

American Board of Commissioners
for Foreign Missions. 14 Beacon
St. Mary Alden Walker, Librarian
and Research Secretary.

Holdings: 500,000 pieces (some
bound in 2,600 vols., some in boxes,
and some in filing cabinets), 1810 to
date, consisting of letters, diaries,
reports, and other papers relating to
foreign missionary activities of the
Congregational churches chiefly, but
also of the Old School Presbyterian
churches, 1812-37, the Central and
Southern Presbyterian churches,
1812-39, the New School Presbyterian churches, 1812-70, and the Dutch
Reformed Church, 1826-57. (The
bulk of the material is on deposit in
Houghton Library, Harvard University. Contemporary correspondence is
retained in the Board offices for 10
years, after which it is sent to Harvard. Permission to use the manuscripts must be obtained from the

Librarian of the American Board.)

Foreign areas and periods of work are Angola, 1880 to date; Borneo, 1836-49; Bulgaria, 1858-1933; Ceylon, 1816 to date; China, 1830-1951; Czechoslovakia, 1873-1932 (from 1873 to 1918 this was the Austrian mission); French Equatorial Africa, 1842-70; Greece, 1830-69, 1894 to date; Hawaii, 1820-63; India, 1813 to date; Japan, 1869 to date; Liberia, 1834-42; Mexico, 1872 to date; Persia, 1834-70; the Philippines, 1903 to date; Siam, 1831-48; South Africa, 1835 to date; Southern Rhodesia, 1893 to date; Spain, 1872-1933; and Turkey, Syria, Lebanon, 1820 to date.

For a period American Indian missions were considered foreign missions, and there are records, 1817-83, relating to work among the following tribes: Abnaki, Cayuse, Cherokee, Chickasaw, Choctaw, Creek, Dakota (Sioux), Mackinac, Maumee, Nez Percé, Ojibway, Osage, Pawnee, Seneca, Stockbridge, and Tuscarora.

See Mary Alden Walker, "The Archives of the American Board for Foreign Missions," in Harvard Library Bulletin, 4:52-68 (winter 1952), and "India and Ceylon in the Archives of the American Board of Foreign Missions," in Indian Archives (New Delhi), 7:95-99 (July-Dec. 1953); and Dorothy Oxman Helly, "The American Board for Foreign Missions in South Africa," in Quarterly Bulletin of the South African Library, 11:129-143 (June 1957).

BOSTON 63

Baker Library, Harvard University Graduate School of Business Administration. Donald T. Clark, Librarian; Robert W. Lovett, Chief, Manuscript Division.

Holdings: 41,000 vols., 4,000 boxes, and 200 crates, 1200-1955, but largely of the 18th and 19th centuries, relating chiefly to business history in the United States. In the following description, the holdings are arranged according to broad categories determined by the Library. A few of the older or more personal papers listed below are the property of the Houghton Library, Harvard University.

Records relating to the genetic industries include papers on farming, 1704-1925 (75 vols. and 1 box), chiefly ledgers, account books, and daybooks; lumbering, 1800-98 (7 vols. and 25 boxes); fishing, 1719-1865 (25 vols. and 5 boxes); and whaling, 1774-1922, but chiefly 19th century (41 vols. and many logbooks).

Records concerning mining and metallurgy include papers on iron mining (chiefly New England but some South and West), 1650-1918 (9 vols., 3 boxes, and 62 pieces); gold and silver mining (Calif., Nev., Mont., Mexico, and Colombia), 1866-1928 (46 vols. and 20 boxes); coal mining (chiefly Pa.), 1830-1901 (45 vols. and 13 boxes); petroleum (Tenn., Pa., Mass., and Canada), 1833-1942 (10 vols. and 5 boxes); and quarrying (Vt. and Mass.), 1851-1930 (38 vols. and 6 boxes).

Manufacturing records include those concerned with sugar refining, 1830-72 (6 vols. and 16 boxes); cotton textile manufacture, 1710-1938 (7,034 vols., 826 boxes, and many large crates), among them records of the Dwight Manufacturing Co., 1832-1933 (936 vols., 141 boxes, and 10 crates), the Pepperell Manufacturing Co., chiefly 1839-1928 (1,000 vols. and 95 boxes), and the Slater Companies (Mass., N. Y., R. I.), 1793-1926 (693 vols. and 107 boxes); woolen goods manufacture, 1815-1948 (1,245 vols., 430 boxes, and many crates); tailoring and hat making, 1736-1857 (12 vols. and 17 boxes); the making of wood products, 1759-1907 (95 vols., 5 boxes, and 2 crates);

iron manufacture, 1795-1910 (546 vols., 26 boxes, and 3 crates); the manufacture of textile machinery, 1834-1948 (1,186 vols., 44 boxes, and 1 crate); shipbuilding and repair, 1822-1933 (26 vols., 18 boxes, and 1 crate); wire manufacturing (in Mass. and other States), 1822-1935 (228 vols. and 21 boxes), chiefly records of the American Steel and Wire Companies; manufacture of jeweler's ware and watches, 1830-1931 (1,222 vols., 67 boxes, and 1 crate); pottery manufacture, 1747-1938 (2 vols. and 6 crates); manufacture of chemicals and chemical products (Fla., Pa., N.Y., Mass., and Canada), 1807-99 (75 vols. and 2 boxes); leather manufacture, chiefly boots and shoes, 1673-1924 (422 vols., 3 boxes, and 2 crates).

Records of the printing and publishing industries, 1798-1900 (901 vols., 85 boxes, 9 crates, and 1 chest), include a ledger, 1798-1826, with names of subscribers to the Boston Gazette; records of the Boston Transcript, chiefly 1867-1941 (300 vols., 52 boxes, and 9 crates); a diary and account books kept by John James Audubon (Pa., Ky., La., N.Y.; artist, ornithologist), 1839-55 (8 vols.), when he was soliciting for the sale of his books; and account books and letter books of Ticknor and Fields (Mass.; publishers), 1847-1900 (117 vols.).

The recreation industries are represented by records of theaters and museums, 1825-1905 (Boston, 50 vols.; N.Y., 14 vols.; and Philadelphia, 3 vols. relating to Barnum's Museum).

In the category of engineering construction are records concerning general construction, 1724-1880 (134 vols. and 116 boxes), including papers of Loammi Baldwin, Sr. and Jr. (Mass.; civil engineers); road building, 1825-72 (4 vols.); water supply, 1837-47 (16 vols.); and railroads, 1809-94 (15 vols. and 44 boxes).

Under land transportation services are grouped records of toll roads and bridges (New England and Md.), 1803-1916 (17 vols. and 1 box); steam railroads, 1829-1945 (936 vols., 262 boxes, and 11 crates), including records, 1831-87, deposited by the Boston and Albany Railroad (337 vols., 10 boxes, and 9 crates); electric railroads (chiefly Mass., Maine, and Ohio), 1898-1945 (11 vols., 57 boxes, and 28 crates).

Records concerning water transportation services include coastwise shipping (chiefly New England), 1732-1915 (105 vols. and 20 boxes); ocean shipping (see also marketing services, below), 1727-1911 (337 vols. and 139 boxes), also Hunnewell family papers, chiefly of James Hunnewell (Mass., Hawaii; sea captain, merchant), 1823-69 (83 bundles and 17 boxes); ships' logs, 1781-1896 (114 vols., including logs of whaling vessels); and records of wharves and docks, 1778-1943 (222 vols. and 6 boxes, of which 45 vols. and 3 boxes concern the Erie Basin Dock Co., N.Y.).

Records concerning marketing services include, besides those on ocean shipping, above, others on foreign marketing, 1739-1922 (1,826 vols., 751 boxes, and 57 crates). Among these are 16 vols. and 29 boxes of records concerning the Pacific Fur Co. and the American Fur Co. and their China trade; 3 letter books of John Jacob Astor (N.Y.; fur trader, financier); 4 vols. of records of a Hudson Bay Co. post in Canada; and a voluminous collection of Heard family papers, 1754-1898 (770 vols., 307 boxes, and 25 crates), which contain papers of Augustine Heard (Mass.; sea captain, China merchant), 1813-68 (121 vols.). Records concerning domestic wholesale services, 1712-1948 (3,588 vols., 402 boxes, and many crates), include the Hancock family papers, 1712-1854, which contain 14 boxes of papers of John Han-

cock (Mass.; merchant, Pres. of Continental Cong., Gov.), 1763-94, chiefly business records. Among the many
records on retail selling are those of
general stores, 1685-1927 (910 vols.
and 93 boxes); food stores, 1747-1878
(45 vols. and 6 boxes); shoe stores,
1830-1932 (2 vols. and 3 crates);
jewelry stores, 1830-1925 (150 vols.,
30 boxes, and many crates); hardware
stores, 1800-69 (6 vols., 4 boxes, and
5 crates); department stores, 1826-
1942 (101 vols. and 36 boxes); peddlers,
1849-77 (21 vols. and 1 box); advertising firms (Mass. and N. Y.), 1830-1919
(52 vols. and 18 boxes); and real estate
firms (New England, N. Y., and Wash.),
1643-1921 (107 vols. and 37 boxes).

Records of financial services concern banking, 1784-1945 (170 vols.,
67 boxes, and 4 rolls of microfilm),
including much material on Jay Cooke
and Co.; and investment banking and
stock exchange operations, 1790-1933
(60 vols., 12 boxes, and 1 crate). Insurance records, 1781-1916 (119 vols.,
11 boxes, and 6 crates), include correspondence of Elizur Wright (Ohio,
Mass.; actuary), 1845-85 (2 boxes).
Legal professional services, 1768-
1945, are represented by 78 vols. and
12 boxes.

Records relating to governmental
services include tax and customs records, 1658-1888 (10 vols. and 9 boxes); records of the Illinois Land Agency, 1846-98 (16 vols. and 5 boxes);
papers of Justin Smith Morrill (Vt.;
U. S. Rep. and Sen.), 1867-97 (3 boxes), chiefly concerning the tariff; and
letters from railroad men to William
Zabena Ripley (Mass.; economist,
special examiner on railway consoli-
dations for the U. S. Interstate Commerce Commission), 1921-23 (2
crates).

Foreign manuscripts comprise
some from England, Scotland, and
Wales, 1200-1907 (70 vols. and 2
boxes); and from Italy, including Me-
dici family account books, 1400-1600

(144 vols.) and Barberini family accounts, 1630-1818 (81 vols.); and a
small quantity of French, Spanish,
and German manuscripts.

See Robert W. Lovett, List of
Business Manuscripts in Baker Library (2d ed., 1951. 213 p. Processed); and Forest History Sources,
pp. 44-46.

BOSTON   8

Boston Athenaeum. 10½ Beacon
St. Walter Muir Whitehill, Director and Librarian.

Holdings: A considerable quantity of manuscripts, 1644-1949, relating chiefly to Massachusetts and
New England.

Included are papers of Edward
Bass (Mass.; Episcopal bishop), 1
vol. of sermons; Charles Knowles
Bolton (Mass.; librarian, antiquarian), 1916-49 (50 vols.); Phillips
Brooks (Mass.; Episcopal bishop),
1871-91 (19 letters); Joseph Stevens
Buckminster (Mass.; Unitarian clergyman, author), 1 box of sermons
and other papers; John Davis (Mass.;
U. S. dist. court judge), 1796-98,
1821, 1841 (letters, bankbooks, and
agricultural notebook); Francis Hin-
des Groome (England, Scotland; Ro-
many scholar and author), 35 vols.
of manuscripts on gypsies; Isaac
Hull (U. S. naval officer), 1810-42
(18 vols.); Alexander Parris (Maine,
Mass.; architect), 1804-10 (1 vol.,
plans of houses in Boston and Portland); Ezekial Price (Mass.; sec. to
the Admiralty Board), 1754-96 (38
vols. of accounts, insurance and notarial records); William Smith Shaw
(Mass.; librarian), 1798-1806 (10
large boxes of correspondence); Isaac Sprague (Mass.; artist and naturalist), 1843 (1 vol. diary of a
trip to the Missouri River with John
James Audubon); Richard Clipston

Sturgis (Mass.; architect), 1889-1932 (137 notebooks); John Wingate Thornton (Maine, Mass.; antiquarian), 1850-76 (3 vols., journal and letters); Samuel Topliff (Mass.; news dealer, author), 1828-29 (1 vol., letters); Benjamin Waterhouse (Mass.; physician), 1801 (1-vol. manuscript on vaccine); and John Greenleaf Whittier (Mass.; poet, abolitionist), 1837-89 (53 letters). There are also groups containing small numbers of personal letters from each of several persons, chiefly Americans but a few Englishmen, distinguished in art, the theater, literature, and other fields.

The holdings also include diaries and account books, 1644-1886 (94 vols.); customhouse records of Boston and Salem, 1744-74 (3 vols.); ships' logs, 1762-1830 (7 vols.); and a receipt book of a glass manufactory in Boston, 1787-94. Legal records include court records of Suffolk County, Mass., 1671-1795 (6 vols.); dockets of U. S. district and circuit courts in Massachusetts, 1804-31 (2 vols.); and papers of the U. S. district attorney for Massachusetts, 1861-64.

See Hist. Records Survey, Guide for Mass., pp. 16-19; and Library of Congress, Manuscripts in Public and Private Collections in the United States, pp. 29-31 (1924).

BOSTON 15

Boston Medical Library. 8 The Fenway.

Holdings: Papers relating chiefly to medicine. Included are 45 manuscripts written before 1500, some of which deal with alchemy, general science, and superstition; and later manuscripts (500 pieces), on medical subjects. There are also some papers of Benjamin Waterhouse (Mass.; physician).

See Hist. Records Survey, Guide

for Mass., p. 20; and James F. Ballard, A Catalogue of the Medieval and Renaissance Manuscripts and Incunabula in the Boston Medical Library (1944. 246 p.).

BOSTON 17

Boston Public Library. Milton E. Lord, Director and Librarian; Richard G. Hensley, Chief Librarian, Division of Reference and Research Services; Zoltan Haraszti, Keeper of Rare Books.

Holdings: 120,000 pieces, dating from the 12th century to 1954, relating chiefly to American history and literature.

The Chamberlain Collection, bequeathed to the Library by Mellen Chamberlain (Mass.; historian, librarian), 1592-1900 (350 vols.), includes manuscripts relating to Massachusetts history, primarily in the colonial and Revolutionary periods (12 vols.); to New Hampshire, 18th-19th century (3 vols.); to the Salem witchcraft episode, 1636-1781 (2 vols.); to Quaker persecutions in Boston, 1661 (1 vol.); to the campaign of John Burgoyne (England; army officer), 1777 (1 vol.); and to George Washington, 1750-1850 (5 vols.). There are also autograph letters of signers of the Declaration of Independence (3 vols.); of other famous men of the Revolutionary period (20 vols.); and of American artists, inventors, lawyers and judges, literary personages, and political leaders. The European section of the collection contains documents autographed by writers, musicians, artists, scientists, actors, and others. Some of the papers of individuals listed below are in this collection.

Papers of clergymen include those of John Cotton (Mass.), 1632-80 (141 pieces); Thomas Wentworth

Higginson (Mass.; abolitionist, Civil War officer, social reformer, author), 1854-1909 (250 pieces); Abiel Holmes (Mass.), sermons, 1786-1823 (48 vols.); Thomas Starr King (Mass., Calif.), sermons, 1834-77 (30 vols.); Richard, Increase, and Cotton Mather (Mass.), 1632-89 (7 vols.); Theodore Parker (Mass.; theologian, abolitionist, publicist), 1832-58 (8 vols.); and Thomas Prince (Mass.; theologian, scholar), 1717-58 (15 pieces).

An antislavery collection, 1798-1902 (13,000 pieces), includes the diary and letters of John Brown (Pa., N.Y., Kans.), 1838-59 (4 vols.); papers of David Lee Child and Lydia Maria Francis Child (Mass.), 1827-75 (5 vols.); correspondence of William Lloyd Garrison (Mass.), 1830-79 (49 vols.); and account books, 1839-66 (20 vols.), of Garrison's Liberator. See also Thomas Wentworth Higginson and Thomas Starr King, above.

Papers of men prominent in politics and diplomacy include those of John Adams (Mass.; Member Continental Cong., diplomat, U.S. Pres.), 1764-1814 (40 pieces) and books from his library, many of which contain copious marginal notes; George Bancroft (Mass., N.Y.; historian, Sec. Navy, Minister to Great Britain and Germany), 1850-74 (50 pieces); Thomas Pennant Barton (Pa., N.Y.; Sec. of U.S. Legation in Paris, bibliophile), 1842-64 (12 vols.); James Elliott (Vt.; lawyer, U.S. Rep., War of 1812 officer) and a Samuel Elliot of Vermont, 1794-1845 (110 pieces); Edward Everett (Mass.; clergyman, Gov., Minister to Great Britain, U.S. Rep. and Sen., Sec. State, Harvard Univ. pres.), 1812-60 (124 pieces); Dwight Foster (Mass.; U.S. Rep. and Sen.), 1780-1807 (1 vol. and 18 pieces); John Hancock (Mass.; merchant, Pres. of Continental Cong., Gov.), and Thomas Hancock (Mass.; merchant), 1726-1816 (2 vols.); Thomas Hinckley (Mass.; last Gov. of Plymouth Colony),

1676-99 (141 pieces); Henry Knox (Mass., Maine; Rev. War officer, Sec. War), 1777-96 (1 vol.); George Thacher (Mass., Maine; Member Continental Cong., U.S. Rep., jurist), 1770-99 (5 vols.); and William D. Williamson (Mass., Maine; historian, Gov. of Maine), 1820-44 (35 pieces).

Papers of literary figures include those of Thomas Bailey Aldrich (N.Y., Mass.; poet, story writer, editor), 1880-96 (43 pieces); James M. Barrie (Scotland; novelist, dramatist), 1902-36 (71 pieces); Edward Bulwer-Lytton (England; novelist), 1851-73 (140 pieces); Wilkie Collins (England; novelist), 2 vols.; George William Curtis (N.Y.; author, editor, orator), 1842-92 (125 pieces); Charles Dickens (England; novelist), 1839-67 (60 pieces); Emily Dickinson (Mass.; poet), 1862-86 (1 vol.); Norman Douglas (England; author), 1 vol.; Mary Katherine Keemle Field, known as Kate Field (Mass., R.I., N.Y.; journalist, author, lecturer, actress), 1860-90 (1,725 pieces), including many letters from Anthony Trollope (England; novelist); Margaret Fuller, Marchioness Ossoli (Mass.; critic, social reformer), 1836-50 (200 pieces); Rufus Wilmot Griswold (Vt., N.Y.; journalist, author, literary executor of Edgar Allan Poe), 1829-56 (1,202 pieces); Louise Imogen Guiney (Mass., England; poet, essayist), 1888-99 (55 pieces); Sophia Peabody Hawthorne, wife of Nathaniel Hawthorne (Mass.; novelist), 1851-71 (275 pieces), chiefly letters to James Thomas Fields (Mass.; author, publisher) and his wife, Annie Adams Fields (Mass.; author); Lucy Larcom (Mass.; author, teacher), 1879-93 (70 pieces); Thomas William Parsons (Mass.; poet, translator of Dante), 1847-92 (50 pieces); Epes Sargent (Mass.; journalist, poet), 1835-81 (100 pieces); Cecilia Laighton Thaxter (N.H., Mass., Maine; poet),

1873-93 (288 pieces), chiefly letters to Annie Adams Fields; Lilian Whiting (Mass.; literary editor, critic, author), 1883-1923 (3 vols.); and Walt Whitman (N. Y., D. C., N. J.; poet), 1874-91 (20 pieces plus 32 pieces of Whitmaniana).

Other personal papers include those of Nathaniel Bowditch (Mass.; astronomer, mathematician), 1786-1838 (32 vols.); Dorothea Lynde Dix (Mass.; humanitarian), 1836-39 (40 pieces); John Sullivan Dwight (Mass.; music critic, editor, leader at Brook Farm), 1832-92 (329 pieces); Charles Folsom (Mass.; teacher, editor, librarian), 1822-70 (1,946 pieces); Simon Greenleaf (Maine; lawyer, author), 1830-39 (40 pieces); John Hull (Mass.; silversmith, colonial mintmaster and treasurer, merchant), 1657-75 (3 commonplace books); Hugo Munsterberg (Germany, Mass.; philosopher, psychologist, professor, author), 1890-1916 (2,600 pieces); Theophilus Parsons (Mass.; chief justice of Mass. supreme court), 1707-1813 (3 vols.); Theophilus Parsons, Jr. (Mass.; lawyer, professor, writer), 1816-65 (5 vols.); Samuel Sewall (Mass.; merchant, jurist), 1681-1719 (9 commonplace books); and Thomas Augustus Watson (Mass.; telephone technologist, shipbuilder), 1873-1932 (11 boxes).

There are also medieval manuscripts, 12th-16th century (100 pieces); Revolutionary War orderly books (15 vols.); a collection of manuscripts relating to the West Indies, 1742-1851 (39 vols.); some business records, including cash books and ledgers of the East India Dock Co., 1827-80 (9 vols.), and papers relating to the Atlantic Telegraph Co., 1856-71 (1 vol.); and holograph scores of musical composers, chiefly modern.

See Hist. Records Survey, Guide for Mass., pp. 21-25, and A Calendar of the General Henry Knox Papers, Chamberlain Collection, Boston Pub-

lic Library (1939. 19 p. Processed); Ring, Reference List for Maine, items indexed under Boston Public Library, especially Historical Manuscripts in the Public Library of the City of Boston, Nos. 1 to 5, 1900-4, its Bulletin, More Books, and Boston Public Library Quarterly; and De Ricci, Census, pp. 917-929.

BOSTON 14

Boston Society of Natural History. Museum of Science, Science Park. (Mrs.) Olga Noxon, Librarian.

Holdings: 4,000 pieces, chiefly of the 19th century, relating to natural history and the Society. Included are papers of Jacob Whitman Bailey (U. S. Army officer, botanist, chemist, zoologist), 2 vols. of letters and maps; papers of Thaddeus William Harris (Mass.; entomologist, librarian), 1823-56, including many drawings illustrating his studies; letters, notes, drawings, and other papers of Samuel Hubbard Scudder (Mass.; entomologist), less than 100 pieces; and smaller quantities of the papers of other 19th-century naturalists. Many other manuscripts formerly held by the Society have been transferred to Harvard University and to the University of Southern California.

See Hist. Records Survey, Guide for Mass., pp. 26-28.

BOSTON 15

Boston University Libraries. 725 Commonwealth Ave. Robert E. Moody, Director.

Holdings: Papers, 1638-1953, consisting of (1) the archives of the University (200 linear ft.); and (2) manuscripts relating chiefly to Boston and New England (170 vols., 24 boxes, 9 cartons, and some 1,200 pieces).

In the University archives are papers of faculty members and administrators, including Melville M. Bigelow (Mass.; law prof., legal writer), 1878-1920 (7 boxes); Edgar Sheffield Brightman (Mass.; philosophy prof.), 1910-53 (35 boxes); Dallas Lore Sharp (Mass.; English prof., writer on nature), 1885-1929 (5 boxes and 450 letters); and William Fairfield Warren (Mass.; clergyman, pres. of Boston Univ.), 1860-1928 (correspondence and miscellaneous papers).

Papers of other individuals include those of F. Lauriston Bullard (Mass.; Presbyterian and Congregational minister, editor, authority on Abraham Lincoln), 1910-50 (20 boxes and 100 notebooks); the Earl of Dartmouth (British Sec. State), 1775 (1 letter book); Thomas Foxcroft (Mass.; minister in Boston), 1720-60 (150 pieces and a large number of sermons); Jonathan Mayhew (Mass.; Puritan clergyman, early Unitarian), 1648-1774 (139 pieces); Richard Saltonstall (Mass.; colonial official), 1638 (1 commonplace book); Benjamin Wadsworth (Mass.; Congregational minister, pres. of Harvard College), 1717-19 (25 sermons); and Charlotte Barrell Ware (Mass.; agriculturalist), 1900-45 (9 large cartons). The Lincolniana Collection contains about 60 autograph letters and memoranda by Abraham Lincoln (Ill.; U.S. Rep. and U.S. Pres.), and the papers of Truman H. Bartlett (Mass.; sculptor), 1890-1921 (2 boxes), many of which concern Lincoln photographs.

There are also business accounts, 1795-1878 (19 books); records of the Boston Mercantile Library Association, 1820-98 and later (18 vols. and 3 boxes); "The Imports and Exports Compared With the Excess of Each Country from Christmas to Christmas 1764," a volume from the papers

of Lord Melville; and autograph collections of signers of the Declaration of Independence, signers of the Constitution, U.S. Presidents, and scientists, chiefly chemists (400 pieces). There are also manuscript copies of Samaritan books (30 vols.) and of the Samaritan Pentateuch (a 110-ft. scroll); and correspondence of Jacob, High Priest of the Samaritans, with William E. Barton (Mass., Ill.; Congregational minister, member of the American Board of Commissioners for Foreign Missions, author), 1904-20 (1 box).

BOSTON 9

Bostonian Society. Old State House. Barrett Williams, Secretary.

Holdings: 3,000 items, 1629-1925, relating chiefly to Boston. Included is a collection, 1629-1881 (12 vols. containing about 1,000 items), of autographed letters and documents and engraved portraits, 5 vols. of which relate to the colonial and Revolutionary periods, 1 to the Constitution signers, and 6 to the Presidents and their Cabinets, 1789-1881. There are also old maps of Boston, proclamations, and manuscripts concerning volunteer fire companies, 1770-1875.

See Hist. Records Survey, Guide for Mass., p. 32.

BOSTON 8

Congregational Library. 14 Beacon St. Rev. John A. Harrer, Librarian.

Holdings: A quantity of 18th-19th century manuscripts, relating chiefly to the Congregational Church. Included are correspondence of Henry Martyn Dexter (Mass.; clergyman, editor of the Congregationalist) with

men of clerical and literary prominence in the United States and England;
journals and letters of Gideon Hawley
(Conn., Mass.; missionary to the Indians), 1753-1806 (4 vols.); a diary of
Cotton Mather (Mass.; clergyman, author), 1715-16; and correspondence of
Charles Turner Torrey (Mass., Md.;
clergyman, abolitionist) with prominent abolitionists and statesmen.
There are also many individual letters
and sermons of prominent ministers;
materials on Congregational history;
and records of a number of Congregational churches, chiefly in New England.

See Allison, Inventory, pp. 26-34.

BOSTON 10

Insurance Library. 89 Broad St.

Holdings: 20 vols. and 340 pieces,
1684-1906, relating to fire, marine,
and casualty insurance, and accident
and fire prevention. Included are policies, 1795-1873; and records of insurance companies that formed a committee to handle all San Francisco fire
claims, 1906 (1 vol.).

See Hist. Records Survey, Guide
for Mass., p. 35.

BOSTON 15

Isabella Stewart Gardner Museum.
163 Worthington St. William N.
Mason, Assistant Director.

Holdings: A collection of medieval
and Renaissance manuscripts (27 vols.
and 28 pieces), consisting chiefly of
religious items, with some legal documents and a few miscellaneous pieces.
There are also many personal letters
to the collector, Mrs. Isabella Stewart Gardner, from well known persons—John Singer Sargent (England;
painter); Francis Marion Crawford

(N.Y., Italy; novelist); Bernard Ber-
enson (Mass., Italy; art critic); and
others.

See Morris Carter, A Choice of
Manuscripts and Bindings in the Collection of Isabella Stewart Gardner;
and De Ricci, Census, pp. 930-936.

BOSTON 33

[Massachusetts] Archives Division.
State House. Joseph D. Ward, Secretary of the Commonwealth.

Holdings: 326 folio vols., 1620
to date, consisting chiefly of official
records of the Colony, Province,
State, and Commonwealth. Included
are military records concerning Indian wars, the Revolutionary War,
and Shays' Rebellion, 1637-1787;
maps and plans, 1630 to date; immigration records, 1848-91, and naturalization records, 1885-1931; election returns for the entire period of
Massachusetts history; General Court
records, 1629-1833; house journals,
1730 to date; senate journals, 1780
to date; and records of Massachusetts
constitutional conventions, 1820-1919.
Included also are correspondence of
Thomas Hutchinson (Mass.; colonial
Gov., merchant) and his family, 1741-
74 (1,543 pieces in 3 vols.), and papers relating to Massachusetts that
were assembled by him, 1625-1771
(264 pieces in 3 vols.).

BOSTON

Massachusetts Diocesan Library.
1 Joy St. Rev. John R. Dallinger,
Register of the Diocese.

Holdings: 20,000 items, 1688-
1937, relating chiefly to the Episcopal
Church in Massachusetts. Included
are papers, some of them sermons,
of the following Episcopal bishops of

Massachusetts: Edward Bass, 1754-1803 (2 vols. and 60 pieces); Phillips Brooks, 1858-93 (2 vols. and 1,000 pieces); Manton Eastburn, 1819-72 (4 vols. and 195 pieces); Alexander Viets Griswold, 1817-87 (5 vols. and 20 pieces); William Lawrence, 1873-1937 (71 pieces); Benjamin Henry Paddock, 1873-90 (1 vol. and 78 pieces); Samuel Parker, 1688-1844 (1 vol. and 150 pieces); and Charles Lewis Slattery, 1860-1930 (854 pieces). There are also papers of Abraham Jarvis (Conn.; Episcopal bishop), 1764-1812 (1 folder and 117 pieces).

The archives of the diocese, 1724-1930 (208 vols., 26 boxes, and 534 pieces), include acts of the bishops; records of the Board of Missions and of church committees and associations, including those of the New England Temperance Society, 1893-1921 (5 vols.); convention records; and sermons, 1724-1930 (1 vol. and 142 pieces). There are also records of Boston churches, 1747-1927 (44 vols. and 222 pieces); records of churches outside Boston, chiefly in Massachusetts, 1719-1926 (14 vols. and 66 pieces); and miscellaneous papers, chiefly of clergymen, 1733-1908 (17 vols. and 2,196 pieces).

See Hist. Records Survey, A Description of the Manuscript Collections in the Massachusetts Diocesan Library (1939. 81 p. Processed).

BOSTON 15

Massachusetts Historical Society. 1154 Boylston St. Stephen T. Riley, Director.

Holdings: A large quantity of papers, dating from 1200 but especially strong for the 17th, 18th, and early 19th centuries, relating chiefly to Massachusetts and to New England men important in American history. In the paragraphs that follow are dis-

cussed, first, some of the many groups of family papers in the Society (with family papers also among some of the groups identified later as those of individuals); second, papers of individuals of the colonial and early national period; third, papers of individuals, chiefly of the 19th century and a few of the 20th; and last, papers of organizations and institutions and other miscellaneous holdings.

Family Papers

One of the largest groups of papers is the Adams papers, 1639-1938 but chiefly 1755-1915 (over 300,000 pages), formerly owned and administered by the Adams Manuscript Trust. These consist of a huge chronological document file, containing letters received and other loose papers of the entire family, 1639-1889 (60,000 items); other papers, segregated, of John Adams (Mass.; Member Continental Cong., diplomat, U.S. Pres.), consisting of his diary, 1755-1804, and his autobiography (2,566 pages in all) and letter books, 1776-1826 (5,558 items); papers of John Quincy Adams (Mass.; U.S. Rep. and Sen., diplomat, Sec. State, U.S. Pres.), consisting of his diary, 1779-1848 (14,898 pages), and letter books, 1781-1848 (9,061 items); and papers of Charles Francis Adams (Mass.; U.S. Rep., Minister to Great Britain), consisting of his diary, 1820-80 (10,933 pages), and letter books, 1826-81 (6,300 items). There is also a miscellany, 1756-1889 (30,000 pages), arranged by generation and under generation by individual, consisting of papers of all members of the family (excluding the diaries and letter books of the three Adams statesmen) and including literary manuscripts, drafts of speeches, legal and business papers, and political material. Letters received and and sent by members of the fourth generation of the family (children of Charles Francis Adams) through the year 1889 are filed in the main chronological file; their other and later papers are in segregated files and include those of Charles Francis Adams II (Mass.; Civil War officer, railroad expert, historian), 1861-1915 (41 vols. and 26 boxes), including his diaries (35 vols.); and portions of the papers of Henry Adams (Mass.; Harvard prof., historian, author), 1890-1938 (14 boxes). Abigail (Mrs. John) Adams, Louisa Catherine (Mrs. John Quincy) Adams, and Marian (Mrs. Henry) Adams are among the women well represented in the Adams family papers. (The Adams Papers through the year 1889 have been published on microfilm by the Society. A multivolume but selective letterpress edition is also in progress, to be published by the Belknap Press of Harvard University Press.)

Among many other groups of family papers are those of the Abbott family, 1803-83 (1 box), including papers of Josiah Gardner Abbott (Mass.; judge); the Amory family, 1698-1890 (150 vols. and 16 boxes), including papers of Thomas Coffin Amory (Mass.; lawyer, biographer); the Appleton family, 1538-1941 (25 vols. and 20 boxes), including papers of Nathan Appleton (Mass.; merchant, U.S. Rep.) and Thomas Gold Appleton (Mass.; essayist, poet, artist); the Austin family, 1769-1883 (2 boxes), including papers of James Trecothick Austin (Mass.; lawyer, political leader); the Brooks family, 1743-1897 (1 box), including papers of Charles Brooks (Mass.; Unitarian clergyman, promoter of teacher training schools); the Bulfinch family, 1720-1914 (1 box), including papers of Charles Bulfinch (Mass.; architect); the Codman family, 1781-1944 (3 vols. and 2 boxes), including papers of Charles Russell Codman (Mass.; lawyer, State legislator); the Dana family,

1693-1920 (60 vols. and 66 boxes), including papers of Richard Dana (Mass.; colonial jurist), Francis Dana (Mass.; Member Continental Cong., State chief justice), Richard Henry Dana (Mass.; lawyer, poet, essayist), and Richard Henry Dana (Mass.; sailor, author, lawyer); the Dow family, 1643-1825 (8 boxes), papers collected by George Francis Dow (Mass.; author, antiquarian); the Gilman family, 1737-1908 (2 vols. and 3 boxes), including papers of Nicholas Gilman (N.H.; Member Continental Cong., U.S. Rep. and Sen.); the Higginson family, 1795-1908 (4 boxes), including papers of Stephen Higginson (Mass.; merchant, U.S. naval agent); the Hutchinson-Oliver family, 1637-1859 (4 vols. and 2 boxes); the Jeffries family, 1686-1835 (33 vols.), including papers of John Jeffries (Mass.; physician, scientist); the Lee family, 1661-1914 (86 vols. and 14 boxes), including papers of Henry Lee (Mass.; merchant, publicist) and Henry Lee (Mass.; merchant, banker, State legislator); the Minot family, 1684-1920 (400-500 boxes), including papers of William Minot (Mass.; lawyer); the Page family, 1835-1929 (4 boxes), including papers of Walter Gilman Page (Mass.; artist); the Prince family, 1686-1720 (1 vol.), including papers of Thomas Prince (Mass.; theologian, scholar, Congregational minister); the Quincy family, 1635-1886 (39 vols. and 27 boxes), including papers of Josiah Quincy (Mass.; colonial lawyer, patriot); Samuel Quincy (Mass.; colonial lawyer, loyalist), and Josiah Quincy (Mass.; State legislator, municipal reformer, Harvard College pres.); the Saltonstall family, 1524-1936 (70 boxes), including papers of Sir Richard Saltonstall (Mass.; founder of Watertown), Richard Saltonstall (Mass.; colonial official), Gurdon Saltonstall (Conn.; colonial Gov.), and Leverett Saltonstall (Mass.; mayor of

Salem, U.S. Rep.); the Seaver family, 1672-1813 (1 box), including papers of Ebenezer Seaver (Mass.; farmer, U.S. Rep.); the Sedgwick family, 1698-1946 (55 vols. and 108 boxes), including papers of Theodore Sedgwick (Mass.; Member Continental Cong., U.S. Rep. and Sen.) and Catherine Maria Sedgwick (Mass.; novelist); the Sullivan family, 1735-1857 (20 vols.), including papers of James Sullivan (Mass.; Member Continental Cong., Gov.); and the Warren family, 1738-1921 (131 vols. and 4 boxes), including papers of John Collins Warren (Mass.; surgeon, prof. at Harvard Medical School).

Personal Papers of the Colonial and Early National Period

Papers of men who held public office in the colonial or early national period include those of Theodore Atkinson (N.H.; colonial chief justice, French and Indian War officer), 1725-66 (1 box, photostats); Jonathan Belcher (Mass., N.J.; merchant, colonial Gov.), 1723-55 (10 vols.); Samuel Brown (Mass.; U.S. naval agent), 1799-1805 (3 boxes); Aaron Burr (N.Y.; Rev. War officer, U.S. Sen., Vice Pres.), 1777-1801 (32 letters); David Cobb (Mass.; Rev. War officer, U.S. Rep.), 1708-1833 (4 boxes); Thomas Cushing (Mass.; merchant, Member Continental Cong.), 1773-1857 (1 box); William Cushing (Mass.; provincial judge, U.S. Supreme Court Justice), 1664-1814 (3 vols.); Nathan Dane (Mass.; lawyer, Member Continental Cong.), 1663-1894 (15 boxes); John Davis (Mass.; Comptroller of U.S. Treasury, U.S. dist. court judge), 1627-1846 (4 vols.); Henry Dearborn (Mass.; Rev. War and War of 1812 officer, U.S. Rep., Sec. War), 1791-1838 (1 box); Thomas Dwight (Mass.; U.S. Rep.), in the Dwight-Howard papers, 1673-1902 (3 boxes); Elbridge Gerry (Mass.; Member Continental Cong., U.S. Rep., Gov., U.S. Vice Pres.), 1772-1882 (2 vols. and 1 box); John Hancock (Mass.; Pres. of Continental Cong., Gov.), 1728-1815 (1 vol. and 2 boxes); Thomas Jefferson (Va.; Member Continental Cong., Gov., Minister to France, Sec. State), U.S. Pres.), 1705-1826 (77 vols. and 3 boxes); Henry Knox (Mass.; Rev. War officer, U.S. Sec. War), 1770-1828 (65 vols. and 5 boxes); Benjamin Lincoln (Mass.; Rev. War officer), 1778-79 (1 vol.), letter book; Levi Lincoln (Mass.; U.S. Rep. and Attorney Gen.), 1796-1857 (1 vol.); William Livingston (N.Y., N.J.; Member Continental Cong., Rev. War officer, Gov. of N.J.), 1695-1839 (6 vols. and 13 boxes); and James Otis (Mass.; Member of Stamp Act Congress, political pamphleteer), 1642-1823 (3 vols. and 1 box).

Papers of other officials during the early period include those of Robert Treat Paine (Mass.; Member Continental Cong., jurist), 1687-1900 (76 vols. and 4 boxes); Richard Penn (Pa., England; Lt. Gov. of Pa., Member Parliament) and Thomas Penn (England, Pa.; proprietor of Pa.), 1750-58 (1 folder), consisting of letters to Richard Peters (Pa.; Member Continental Cong., U.S. dist. court judge); Timothy Pickering (Mass.; Rev. War officer, Postmaster Gen., Sec. War, Sec. State, U.S. Sen. and Rep.), 1759-1829 (66 vols. and 8 boxes); Matthew Ridley (Md.; merchant, Md. agent), 1754-1836 (6 vols. and 15 boxes); Theodore Sedgwick (Mass.; Member Continental Cong., U.S. Rep. and Sen.), 1768-99 (5 boxes); Samuel Sewall (Mass.; merchant, jurist), 1672-1729 (18 vols.); Joseph Story (Mass.; U.S. Rep., U.S. Supreme Court Justice), 1797-1845 (3 vols. and 2 boxes); James Sullivan (Mass.; Member Continental Cong., Gov.), 1770-1808 (2 boxes); Increase Sumner (Mass.; jurist, Gov.), 1782-94

(3 vols.), legal records; George Thacher (Mass., Maine; Member Continental Cong., U. S. Rep. from Mass., jurist), 1667-1867 (5 boxes); Meshech Weare (N. H.; chief justice and Pres. of N. H.), 1776-85 (2 vols.); Jacob Wendell (Mass.; merchant, Indian Commissioner), 1687-1846 (2 boxes); and John Winthrop (Mass.; colonial Gov.), his son John Winthrop (Mass., Conn.; colonial Gov. of Conn.), and Robert Charles Winthrop (Mass.; U.S. Rep. and Sen.), 1498-1894 (38 vols.). Other papers of importance for the early period are transcripts of instructions to Governors of Massachusetts, 1631-1775 (8 boxes); miscellaneous papers, 1200-1952 (20 boxes); miscellaneous bound papers, 1629-1908 (21 vols.); miscellaneous bound papers relating to Massachusetts, Massachusetts and Connecticut, Massachusetts and New York, and New England, 1644-1777 (8 vols.); records of the Corporation of New England, 1655-85 (1 vol.); and papers relating to Shays' Rebellion, 1786-87.

Among papers of many clergymen and other professional men of the early period are those of John Andrews (Md., Pa.; Episcopal clergyman, prof. and provost of Univ. of Pa.), 1772-76 (1 box), copies of letters; Jeremy Belknap (Mass.; Congregational clergyman, historian), 1637-1813 (37 vols. and 10 boxes); Benjamin Colman (Mass.; Presbyterian clergyman, author), 1697-1763 (2 vols.); Andrew Eliot (Mass.; Congregational clergyman), in the Andrews-Eliot papers, 1662-1811 (1 vol.); Benjamin Guild (Mass.; educator), 1774-79 (1 box), diary; Gideon Hawley (Conn., Mass.; missionary to Indians), 1754-1806 (1 box); John Lathrop (Mass.; clergyman), 1758-1816 (4 boxes); Cotton Mather (Mass.; Congregational clergyman, author), 1681-1734 (6 vols. and 2 boxes), including his Biblia Americana and parts of his diary; Increase Mather (Mass.; Congregational clergyman, author, colonial agent in London), 1669-1709 (4 vols.), including part of his diary; Samuel Mather (Mass.; Congregational clergyman, author), 1759-85 (1 vol.); Ebenezer Parkman (Mass.; Congregational clergyman), 1721-82 (11 boxes), consisting of his diary partly in photostat; William Pratt (Mass.; Congregational elder), 1695-1701 (1 vol.), journal; William Pynchon (Mass.; magistrate, trader), 1640 (2 vols.); William Pynchon (Mass.; lawyer), 1778-88 (1 box), a diary; Robert Sandeman (Scotland, Conn.; religious sectarian), 1764-1804 (1 vol.); Jonathan Sewall (Mass., England, Canada; lawyer, writer, loyalist), 1757-89 (1 vol.); Joseph Sewall (Mass.; Congregational clergyman) in the Robie-Sewall Papers, 1611-1905 (4 boxes); John Thomas (Mass.; physician, Rev. War officer), 1746-91 (11 vols.); and John Warren (Mass.; surgeon, prof. at Harvard Medical School), 1776-1815 (1 vol.).

Papers of many other persons of the early period include those of Samuel Carey (Nicaragua; plantation owner), 1757-1820 (23 vols. and 6 boxes); Nathaniel Cutting (Mass.; shipmaster), journals, 1786-93; Caleb Davis (Mass.; merchant), 1684-1828 (38 vols.); Thomas English (Mass.; shipowner), 1787-1808 (1 vol. and 1 box); Moses Greenleaf (Mass., Maine; mapmaker, author), 1776-80 (1 vol.); William Heath (Mass.; farmer, Rev. War officer), 1774-1814 (29 vols. and 1 box); Thomas Hollis (England; Whig, sympathizer with colonial cause), 1759-71 (1 vol.); Joshua Huntington (Conn.; Rev. War officer, shipbuilder) and his nephew Joshua Huntington (Conn., Mass.; Congregational clergyman), in the Huntington-Wolcott papers, 1698-1899 (6 boxes); Jean Paul Mascarene (Nova Scotia; soldier, Lt. Gov.), 1687-1839 (1 box); James Murray (Mass.; loyalist), 1766-81 (8 vols.); Joseph Palmer (Mass.; manufacturer, Rev. War officer), 1774-86 (1 vol.); Sir William Pepperell (Mass., Maine; merchant, pres. of Mass. council, colonial army officer), 1699-1779 (2 vols.); Paul Revere (Mass.; patriot, craftsman), 1746-1854 (39 vols. and 17 boxes); William Rotch (Mass.; whaling merchant), 1785-92 (1 box); Samuel Phillips Savage (Mass.; merchant), 1702-1829 (3 vols. and 5 boxes); Samuel Waldo (Mass., Maine; merchant, land speculator), 1743-44 (1 box); Artemas Ward (Mass.; French and Indian War and Rev. War officer), 1684-1775 (8 vols. and 1 box); James Warren (Mass.; Rev. War officer, political leader), in the Warren-Adams papers, 1750-1814 (4 vols.); Mercy Otis Warren (Mass.; historian, poet, dramatist), 1703-81 (1 vol. and 3 boxes); Israel Williams (Mass.; farmer, land speculator, French and Indian War officer, loyalist), 1730-80 (2 vols.); and John Winslow (Mass.; militia officer), 1634-1854 (6 vols. and 2 boxes).

Besides the papers mentioned above, there are many other diaries, journals, and letters of the colonial and early national period. Listed below are papers of many other individuals, chiefly of the 19th century, a few 20th-century papers, and some papers of organizations.

Papers Chiefly of the Nineteenth Century

Papers of men who held office under the Federal Government include those of John Forrester Andrew (Mass.; lawyer, U.S. Rep.), 1861-92 (1 vol. and 3 boxes); George Bancroft (Mass., D.C.; historian, Sec. Navy, Minister to Great Britain and to Germany), 1678-1890 (54 vols. and 47 boxes); George Sewall Boutwell (Mass.; Gov., Commissioner of Internal Revenue, U.S. Rep. and Sen., Sec. Treas.), 1853-1905 (1 box); Thomas Jefferson

Coolidge (Mass.; merchant, Minister to France), 1884-1904 (19 vols. and 1 box); William Crowninshield Endicott (Mass.; State supreme court justice, Sec. War), 1665-1950 (55 vols. and 17 boxes); William Eustis (Mass.; Rev. War surgeon, U.S. Rep., Sec. War, Minister to the Netherlands, Gov.), 1777-1829 (1 box); Alexander Hill Everett (Mass.; Minister to Spain, editor of the North American Review, Commissioner to China), 1818-57 (13 vols. and 3 boxes); Edward Everett (Mass.; clergyman, Gov., Minister to Great Britain, pres. of Harvard Univ., U.S. Rep. and Sen., Sec. State), 1823-65 (208 vols. and 62 boxes); William Everett (Mass.; lawyer, clergyman, college prof., U.S. Rep.), 1844-1910 (6 vols. and 8 boxes); Dwight Foster (Mass.; U.S. Rep. and Sen.), 1757-1884 (8 vols.), plus 2 boxes of family papers; William Cameron Forbes (Mass.; Gov. Gen. of Philippines, Ambassador to Japan), 1904-46 (10 vols.); John Milton Hay (Ill., D.C.; sec. to Pres. Lincoln, poet, diplomat, Sec. State), a photographic copy of his diary; William Jarvis (Mass., Vt.; merchant, U.S. consul at Lisbon), 1799-1843 (1 box); Amos Kendall (Ky., D.C.; journalist, Postmaster Gen.), 1829-61 (1 box); Henry Cabot Lodge (Mass.; U.S. Rep. and Sen.), 1745-1924 (120 boxes); and John Davis Long (Mass.; Gov., U.S. Rep., Sec. Navy), 1863-1922 (115 vols. and 68 boxes).

Papers of other Federal officeholders include those of Horace Mann (Mass., Ohio; lawyer, educator, U.S. Rep. from Mass., pres. of Antioch College), 1825-94 (10 vols. and 23 boxes); Jonathan Mason (Mass.; lawyer, U.S. Sen. and Rep.), 1803-75 (1 vol. and 1 box); George von Lengerke Meyer (Mass.; Minister to Italy and to Russia, Postmaster Gen., Sec. Navy), 1900-18 (55 vols. and 21 boxes); Marcus Morton (Mass.;

U. S. Rep., Gov.), 1818-64 (3 vols.); Richard Olney (Mass.; wool merchant, U. S. Rep., member of World War Foreign Debt Commission), 1847-1934 (4 vols. and 6 boxes); Harrison Gray Otis (Mass.; U. S. Rep. and Sen.), 1691-1870 (5 vols. and 9 boxes); Jonathan Russell (R. I., Mass.; merchant, diplomat, U. S. Rep.), 1804-21 (3 boxes); Winthrop Sargent (Mass., Ohio, Miss.; Rev. War officer, Sec. of Northwest Terr., Gov. of Miss. Terr.), 1771-1916 (2 vols. and 12 boxes); Charles Sumner (Mass.; U. S. Sen.), 1864-70 (1 vol. and 1 box, plus 500 letters scattered in various collections); Martin Van Buren (N. Y.; U. S. Sen., Gov., Sec. State, U. S. Pres.), 1807-82 (1 box); Amasa Walker (Mass.; U. S. Rep., author), 1823-92 (8 vols. and 1 box); Winslow Warren (Mass.; lawyer, collector of customs at Boston), 1893-97 (2 vols.); and Daniel Webster (N. H., Mass.; U. S. Rep. and Sen., Sec. State), 1805-87 (3 boxes).

Among papers of men who held State and local office, in addition to some named above, are those of John A. Andrew (Mass.; lawyer, abolitionist, Gov.), 1772-1896 (14 vols. and 24 boxes); Samuel Turell Armstrong (Mass.; publisher, banker, State legislator, mayor of Boston), 1812-50 (5 vols.); Peter Chardon Brooks (Mass.; merchant, State legislator), 1789-1848 (24 vols.), consisting of journals and farm books; Samuel Foster McCleary (Mass.; Boston city clerk), 1704-1899 (3 boxes); Thomas Handasyd Perkins (Mass.; merchant, State legislator, philanthropist), 1773-1853 (33 vols. and 4 boxes); John Phillips (Mass.; State legislator, mayor of Boston), 1656-1860 (2 boxes); Samuel Putnam (Mass.; judge of State supreme court), 1775-1857 (1 box); James Murray Robbins (Mass.; State legislator), 1639-1858 (8 vols. and 2 boxes); William Eustis Russell (Mass.; lawyer, Gov.), 1881-1913 (44 vols. and 20 box-

es); Lemuel Shaw (Mass.; State chief justice), 1648-1923 (22 boxes); William Sturgis (Mass.; merchant, State legislator), 1798-1816 (3 vols. and 1 box); and Gardiner Tufts (Mass.; State agent), 1867-91 (9 vols.).

Among papers of 19th-century merchants, other than those mentioned above, are those of Samuel Cabot (Mass.; merchant in the China trade), 1713-1859 (1 vol. and 3 boxes); Franklin Gordon Dexter (Mass.; Boston merchant), 1840-70 (4 boxes); Henry Grew (Mass.; Boston merchant), 1801-65 (7 boxes); James Hunnewell (Mass., Hawaii; sea captain, merchant), 1829-71 (2 boxes); Thomas Lamb (Mass.; Boston merchant), 1783-1865 (19 boxes); Amos Lawrence (Mass.; merchant, philanthropist), 1811-45 (16 vols. and 1 box); Amos Adams Lawrence (Mass.; merchant, treasurer of the New England Emigrant Aid Society, philanthropist), 1803-87 (102 vols. and 6 boxes); Ebenezer William Sage (Mass.; merchant in Bordeaux, France), 1805-33 (2 boxes); Charles Stoddard (Mass.; Boston merchant), 1684-1920 (2 boxes); Edward Silas Tobey (Mass.; merchant, capitalist, director of steamship companies and banks), 1798-1891 (7 vols. and 3 boxes); and Thomas Wren Ward (Mass.; merchant), 1717-1913 (8 vols. and 9 boxes).

Among papers of many religious leaders are those of Henry Whitney Bellows (N. Y.; Unitarian minister, editor of religious magazines, pres. of the U. S. Sanitary Commission), 1831-1907 (58 boxes); Christopher Pearse Cranch (Mass., N. Y.; painter, critic, poet, Unitarian minister), 1834-91 (2 boxes); George Edward Ellis (Mass.; Unitarian minister, editor, Harvard Divinity School prof., historian), 1812-95 (34 vols. and 25 boxes); Paul Revere Frothingham (Mass.; Unitarian minister), sermons (23 boxes); Ezra Stiles Gannett (Mass.; Unitarian minister), 1816-

1916 (3 boxes); Thaddeus Mason Harris (Mass.; Unitarian Minister), 1735-1842 (1 box); Joshua V. Himes (Mass., Mich., Ill., S. Dak.; reformer, leader in the Second Advent movement), 1839-67 (1 box); Abiel Holmes (Mass.; Congregational minister), 1788-1826 (1 vol. and 2 boxes); William Jenks (Mass.; Congregational minister), 1651-1903 (3 boxes); George Leonard (Mass.; Unitarian minister), 1821-81 (7 vols.), diary; Charles Lowell (Mass.; Unitarian minister), 1653-1867 (1 vol.); William Henry Lyon (Mass.; Unitarian minister, author), 1888-1914, sermons (2 boxes); Theodore Parker (Mass.; theologian, Unitarian minister, publicist), 1826-60 (13 vols.); Ephraim Peabody (Mass.; Unitarian minister), 1802-68 (3 boxes); John Pierce (Mass.; Congregational minister, antiquarian), 1798-1849 (21 vols.); Joseph Tuckerman (Mass.; Unitarian minister), 1803-63 (1 box); James M. Whiton (Mass., N. J., N. Y.; Congregational minister, author), 1821-57 (3 boxes); and Noah Worcester (N. H., Mass.; Congregational and Unitarian clergyman, editor), 1815-69 (3 boxes), relating chiefly to the Massachusetts Peace Society.

Among papers of historians and antiquarians are those of Charles Knowles Bolton (Mass.; librarian, antiquarian), 1875-1950 (14 vols.), diary; Mellen Chamberlain (Mass.; historian, librarian), 1639-1900 (10 vols.); Charles Deane (Mass.; merchant, historian), 1602-1889 (33 vols.); Henry Herbert Edes (Mass.; businessman, manager title insurance firm, antiquarian), 1648-1917 (7 vols. and 5 boxes); Allen French (Mass.; author, historian), 48 vols. containing notes on the American Revolution; Richard Frothingham (Mass.; historian, author), 1683-1895 (8 boxes); Frederick Lewis Gay (Mass.; antiquarian), 1374-1902 (3 boxes), also transcripts of papers, 1630-1776 (124 vols.); Samuel Abbott Green (Mass.; physi-

cian, Civil War surgeon, antiquarian, author), 1700-1915 (11 boxes); John Torrey Morse (Mass.; lawyer, historian), 1861-1935 (4 boxes); Francis Parkman (Mass.; historian), transcripts of papers, 1565-1768 (100 vols.), also correspondence (12 boxes) and diaries (25 vols.); William Hickling Prescott (Mass.; historian, author), 1775-1875 (19 boxes); James Ford Rhodes (Mass.; historian), 1889-1927 (17 vols. and 14 boxes); James Schouler (Mass., Md.; lawyer, historian, prof. at Johns Hopkins Univ., author), 1840-72 (1 vol. and 2 boxes); Horatio Gates Somerby (Mass.; genealogist), 1668-1867 (1 box); Thomas Wallcut (Mass.; book collector, antiquarian), 1671-1866 (2 vols.); Justin Winsor (Mass.; historian, librarian), 1879-97 (45 vols.); and Joseph Emerson Worcester (Mass.; lexicographer, geographer, historian), 1816-65 (7 vols.).

Papers of educators and writers not already mentioned include those of George Bemis (Mass.; lawyer, publicist), 1794-1901 (9 vols. and 6 boxes); Jacob Bigelow (Mass.; physician, botanist, prof. at Harvard Medical School, author), 1777-1879 (3 boxes); Henry Van Ness Boynton (Ohio, D. C.; Civil War and Spanish-American War officer, newspaper correspondent), 1835-1905 (2 boxes); Caroline Healey Dall (Mass., D. C.; reformer, author), 1811-1911 (122 vols. and 19 boxes); George Barrell Emerson (Mass.; educator), 1789-1894 (12+ boxes); Annie Adams Fields (Mass.; author) and James Thomas Fields (Mass.; publisher, author, editor of Atlantic Monthly), 1847-1911 (4 vols. and 2 boxes), diaries; Charles Folsom (Mass.; U. S. Navy chaplain, teacher, librarian, editor), 1732-1871 (5 vols.); William Bently Fowle (Mass.; textbook writer, publisher and editor of the Common School Journal), 1754-

1914 (2 boxes); William Watson Goodwin (Mass.; Hellenist, Harvard prof.), in the Watson-Goodwin papers, 1692-1911 (2 boxes); Henry Williamson Haynes (Maine, Vt., Mass.; Univ. of Vt. classics prof., archeologist, author), 1803-1911 (2 boxes); Mark Hopkins (Mass.; theologian, Williams College pres.), 1790-1887 (2 boxes); Samuel Gridley Howe (Mass.; educator of blind, reformer, abolitionist), 1838-74 (1 box); James Jackson (Mass.; physician, prof. at Harvard Medical School), 1831-52 (1 box); Edmund Quincy (Mass.; author, abolitionist), 1822-86 (2 boxes); George Ripley (Mass., N.Y.; reformer, editor, literary critic), 1839-81 (1 box); Mary Cochrane Rogers (Mass.; author), 1870-1929 (5 boxes); Horace Elisha Scudder (Mass.; author, editor), 1877-1905 (1 box); Catherine Maria Sedgwick (Mass.; novelist), 1798-1866 (4 boxes); Charles Card Smith (Mass.; writer, sec. of Boston Gas Light Co.), 1808-1915 (1 box); Thomas Russell Sullivan (Mass.; playwright, short-story writer), 1891-1903 (4 vols.), journal; and George Ticknor (Mass.; historian, author, Harvard prof.), 1809-71 (1 box).

Other groups of personal papers include those of Gardner Weld Allen (Mass.; physician), 1811-1935 (3 boxes); Edward Atkinson (Mass.; industrialist, economist, author), 1836-1905 (79 vols. and 24 boxes); Francis Channing Barlow (N.Y.; lawyer, Civil War officer), 1861-64 (1 box); Erastus Brigham Bigelow (Mass.; inventor of power looms, economist), 1832-79 (3 boxes); Nathaniel Ingersoll Bowditch (Mass.; lawyer, land conveyancer), 1805-61 (1 box), together with the Bowditch title books, 1630-1858 (60 vols.); Francis Brooks (Mass.; lawyer), 1858-91 (2 boxes), journals; Jacob J. Brown (U.S. Army and War of 1812 officer), 1812-49 (6 boxes); John Brown (Pa., N.Y., Kans.; abolitionist), 1859-85 (1 vol. and 1

box), consisting of papers relating to Brown; Peleg W. and Henry P. Chandler (Mass.; lawyers), 1718-1888 (4 boxes); John Brazer Davis (Mass.; lawyer), 1819-37 (2 vols.); Clarence R. Edwards (U.S. Army officer), 1886-1931 (27 boxes); Daniel Chester French (Mass.; sculptor), 1896-1927 (1 box); William Howard Gardiner (Mass.; lawyer), 1708-1893 (3 boxes); George Henry Gordon (Mass.; lawyer, U.S. Army and Civil War officer), 1842-85 (6 boxes); Henry Ware Hall (U.S. Army officer), 1851-64 (3 vols.); John Tyler Hassam (Mass.; lawyer), 1738-1889 (3 boxes); Francis John Higginson (Mass.; physician), 1783-1905 (6 boxes); Charles Thomas Jackson (Mass.; chemist, geologist), 1840-96 (1 vol. and 1 box); and Francis Jackson (Mass.; reformer, pres. of the Anti-Slavery Society), 1691-1844 (1 box).

Included also are papers of William T. G. Morton (Mass.; dentist, anesthetist), 1846-76 (1 vol.); George Read Nutter (Mass.; lawyer), 1905-36 (35 vols.), diary; John Eliot Parkman (U.S. naval officer), 1853-94 (2 vols.); John Percival (U.S. naval officer), 1826-40 (1 box); Willard Phillips (Mass.; lawyer, author), 1769-1875 (15 boxes); Fitz-John Porter (N.Y.; U.S. Army officer, police and fire commissioner of New York City), 1862-89 (2 boxes); George Henry Preble (U.S. naval officer, author), 1732-1887 (44 vols. and 6 boxes); Samuel Miller Quincy (Mass.; lawyer, Civil War officer), 1861-87 (1 box); John Osborne Sargent (Mass., N.Y.; lawyer, journalist, author), 1831-91 (3 vols.); James Savage (Mass.; lawyer, antiquarian), 1804-1906 (10 vols. and 2 boxes); Henry Dwight Sedgwick (N.Y., Mass.; lawyer), 1739-1955 (77 boxes), and other Sedgwick papers, 1698-1860 (20 boxes); Frederick Cheever Shattuck (Mass.; physician), 1802-1912 (47 vols.); Lemuel Shattuck (Mass.; statistician, geneal-

ogist, public health pioneer), 1805-67
(4 vols. and 2 boxes); William D. So-
hier (Mass.; lawyer), 1654-1901 (10
boxes); Frederic Jesup Stimson
(Mass.; lawyer, author), 1802-1949
(5 vols. and 8 boxes); Henry Walbridge
Taft (Mass.; lawyer), 1759-1904 (2
vols.); Samuel Waldron (N. J.; manufacturer), 1818-39 (2 boxes); Edmund
March Wheelwright (Mass.; architect),
1776-1950 (3 boxes); and Ralph Randolph Wormeley (Va., England; British naval officer), in the Wormeley-
Latimer papers, 1802-65 (1 box).

Included also in the Society's holdings are records of the Assistant Fire
Society, 1783-1819 (1 vol.); Brook
Farm, 1842-47 (3 vols. and 1 box);
Bunker Hill Monument Association,
1825-1919 (36 vols. and 4 boxes); Humane Society, 1787-1903 (5 boxes);
Independent Christian Society, 1791-
1840 (1 box); Kansas Aid Committee,
1856-57 (1 box); Massachusetts Anti-
Suffrage Association, 1895-1921 (9
vols. and 2 boxes); Massachusetts
Colonization Society, 1842-1911 (1
box); New England Freedman's Aid
Society, 1862-73 (10 vols.); and Society of the Cincinnati, 1765-1911 (22
boxes). There are also papers relating to the northeast boundary (4 vols.
and 5 boxes); notes on Martha's Vineyard, 1600-1899 (18 vols.); papers
relating to the towns of Charlestown,
1734-1840 (1 box), and Groton, 1696-
1883 (9 vols. and 1 box); and the
George Peabody Wetmore collection
of papers on Rhode Island commerce,
1706-1835 (21 vols.). Among the notable autograph collections are the
Charles E. French collection, 1337-
1899 (28 vols.); the Grenville H. Norcross collection, 1489-1937 (11 boxes); the Alexander C. Washburn collection, arranged by subject (26 vols.);
and the Robert C. Waterston collection, arranged alphabetically (4 vols.).
There are also many diaries, sermons,
and account books not noted above; and
many other papers relating to ships

and shipping, merchandising, other
business, and banking. There are
copies of epitaphs from cemeteries
in New England and New York, 1839-
1919 (19 vols.); and transcripts from
the Vatican archives (18 vols.).

See Handbook of the Massachusetts Historical Society, 1791-1948,
pp. 118-141 (1949), and detailed reports of acquisitions in the Proceedings of the Society.

BOSTON

Massachusetts New-Church Union.
134 Bowdoin St. Horace B. Black-
mer, Manager.

Holdings: 19 folio vols. of photo-
facsimiles of manuscripts, 1746-59,
of Emanuel Swedenborg (Sweden;
theologian).
See Hist. Records Survey, Guide
for Mass., p. 37.

BOSTON 15

Medical School Library, Harvard
University. Ralph T. Esterquest,
Librarian.

Holdings: A considerable number
of papers, 1782 to date, relating to
medicine. Included are lecture notes,
1805-8, on a course in surgery given
at the University of Pennsylvania by
Philip Syng Physick (Pa.; surgeon)
and Casper Wistar (Pa.; physician,
anatomist); manuscripts of professors who have taught at the Medical
School since 1782 and at the Harvard
School of Public Health since 1922;
and the archives of the Medical
School, representing chiefly the 20th-
century work in its various departments.

—oOo—

Museum of Fine Arts. 465 Huntington Ave.   Richard B. K. McLanathan, Associate Curator of Decorative Arts.

Holdings: 57 medieval and Renaissance manuscripts, 1200-1600, representing the fine arts of calligraphy and illumination.
   See De Ricci, Census, pp. 942-948, which describes 48 of the items.

—oOo—

New England Conservatory of Music Library.   290 Huntington Ave. Carol M. Walden, Librarian.

Holdings: A collection of musical manuscripts dating from 1500 and of other items by or relating to European and American composers.
   See Hist. Records Survey, Guide for Mass., p. 42.

BOSTON 8

New England Historic Genealogical Society. 9 Ashburton Pl. Dr. Arthur Adams, Librarian.

Holdings: 175,000 pieces, many of which are manuscripts, relating chiefly to genealogy and American and English local history.   The collection of English parish registers is especially large.

BOSTON 15

New England Methodist Historical Library.   745 Commonwealth Ave. J. Rex Shepler, Librarian.

Holdings: 7,477 pieces, 1784-1954, relating chiefly to the Methodist Church in New England.   Included are minutes of the quarterly conference of Providence and Mansfield circuit, 1815-45; records of the New England Conference

of Presiding Elders, 1869-76; records of various societies operating under the New England Conference, 1859-83; and records of the New England Methodist Historical Society, 1859-72. There are also records of conventions, societies, and churches (chiefly in Mass.), 1803-99; diaries, autobiographies, biographies, and many sermons, 1826-98; and a collection of letters of clergymen, 1787-1884 (350 pieces), that contains letters from many early Methodist leaders, among them John Wesley, Francis Asbury, Thomas Coke, and George Pickering.
   See Allison, Inventory, pp. 56-59.

BOSTON

Old South Meeting House.   Washington and Milk Sts.   Charles G. Loring, Consulting Architect.

Holdings: 2 vols. and 100 pieces, 1670-1879, constituting part of a historical exhibit.   Included are a number of sermons, 1703-76, some by prominent clergymen; a group of poems written by well known authors, 1879, when funds were raised to preserve the meeting house; and a few letters by George Washington (Va.; Rev. War Commander in Chief, U. S. Pres.).
   See Hist. Records Survey, Guide for Mass., p. 45; and Old South Meeting House, Inventory of Exhibits (1950. [13] p. Processed).

BOSTON 14

Society for the Preservation of New England Antiquities.   Harrison Gray Otis House, 141 Cambridge St. E. Florence Addison, Assistant to Director.

Holdings: 6,000 pieces, 1700-1902, relating chiefly to New Eng-

land. Included are commonplace books
of several individuals, 1788-1867 (6
vols.); various family papers; and
3,033 blueprints and plans of historic
houses and buildings.

See Hist. Records Survey, Guide
for Mass., p. 46.

BOSTON 33

State Library of Massachusetts. State
House. I. Albert Matkou, Acting
Librarian.

Holdings: 250 vols. and over 2,000
pieces, 1602-1929, relating chiefly to
Massachusetts. Included are the original manuscript of the "History of
Plimoth Plantation," by William Bradford (Gov. of Plymouth Colony); records of the General Court of Massachusetts, 1628-1778 (33 vols.); journals of the State's house of representatives and senate, 1780-1864 (160
vols.); school reports and returns of
Massachusetts towns, 1834-94 (138
vols.); and records of several towns,
including Brighton, 1816-55. Military
records, 1719-1899, include an orderly book of Washington's headquarters
at Cambridge, 1775; some records of
Massachusetts regiments, 1758-1818;
a journal kept aboard the frigate Constitution, 1825-26; and records of the
Massachusetts Volunteer Aid Association during the Spanish-American War,
1898-99. There are also some papers
of Calvin Coolidge (Mass.; Gov., U. S.
Pres.), 1895-1924; and correspondence of Nathaniel Greene (N. H., Mass.;
journalist, politician), 1829-30 (50
pieces).

See Hist. Records Survey, Guide
for Mass., p. 38; and the Library's
Catalogue of the State Library of Massachusetts (1880. 1,148 p.).

BOYLSTON

Boylston Public Library.   Mrs. Owen

Kennedy, Librarian.

Holdings: 5 vols. and 5 pieces,
1802-91, consisting chiefly of sermons, 1802-24.

See Hist. Records Survey, Guide
for Mass., p. 47.

BROOKLINE

Brookline Public Library.   Elizabeth
Butcher, Librarian.

Holdings: A small quantity of
manuscripts, 1773-1938, relating
chiefly to Brookline. Included are
account books of the Brookline postmaster, 1829-42; records of the Whig
town committee of Brookline, 1850-
53; records (compiled) of Brookline
men in the Civil War; and minutes of
the Thursday Club, 1872-1938 (8 vols.).
There are also sermons and other papers of John Pierce (Mass.; Congregational minister, antiquarian), 1773-
1849; and copies of papers of Edward
Augustus Wild (Mass.; physician, Cri-
mean War surgeon, Civil War officer),
1855-56.

CAMBRIDGE 38

Episcopal Theological School Library.
99 Brattle St. Elisabeth Hodges, Librarian.

Holdings: 59 vols., 3 cartons, 5
boxes, and 31 pieces, dated from the
late 18th century to the present, relating chiefly to the Episcopal Church
and the Theological School. Included
are sermons of Edward Bass (Mass.;
Episcopal bishop), 1 box; addresses,
sermons, journals, and other papers
of George Hodges (Pa., Mass.; Episcopal clergyman, dean of the Theological School), 1881-1907 (33 vols.
and 31 pieces); notes of Maximilian L.
Kellner (Mass.; theologian, Oriental-

ist, prof. at the Theological School), 1 box; and sermons of Samuel Parker (Mass.; Episcopal bishop), 1 box. There are also a collection of autograph letters of Episcopal bishops from Samuel Seabury to the present (5 vols.); material on the history of the prayer book (5 vols. and 3 cartons); and trustees' minutes and other records of the Theological School (12 vols. and 1 box).

—oOo—

Harvard University Libraries. Paul H. Buck, Director.

The holdings of the Harvard University Libraries include an immense and complex network of research materials in manuscript form. In the following section are treated first the University Archives, then the Houghton Library of the Harvard College Library, and thereafter the many specialized libraries, in scientific and other fields, that have manuscripts in their custody. Subsidiary libraries not in Cambridge are treated elsewhere under the appropriate locality: Baker Library and Medical School Library under Boston; Harvard Forest Library under Petersham, Mass.; and Dumbarton Oaks Library under the District of Columbia.

See Alfred C. Potter, The Library of Harvard University (4th ed., 1934. 186 p.), for general information. Notes and articles on manuscript collections are in the Harvard Library Bulletin, 1947 to date.

Harvard University Archives. Widener Library. Clifford K. Shipton, Custodian.

Holdings: 78,839 pieces (i.e., vols., boxes, bundles, etc.), consisting of records of the University, theses, and material relating to the University. Included are records of the Corporation since 1643, the Board of Overseers since 1650, the faculty since 1725, and the treasurer since 1669. There are also the personal papers of most of the men (presidents, professors, and others) known "chiefly for their Harvard connection." These papers include a large number of undergraduate diaries.

See Clifford K. Shipton, "The Harvard University Archives: Goal and Function," in Harvard Library Bulletin, 1:101-108 (winter 1947), and "Collections of the Harvard University Archives," ibid., 1:176-184 (spring 1947); and The Harvard University Archives (3d ed., 1947. 10 p.).

Houghton Library of the Harvard College Library. William A. Jackson, Librarian; W. H. Bond, Curator of Manuscripts.

Holdings: About 300 stack sections of manuscripts, of every period, relating to many aspects of world history but especially to English literature and American literature and history. Identifications of the more important collections are grouped below, for the most part geographically and then (for England and the United States) according to the occupations represented. Many persons listed are also represented by printed volumes from their libraries, containing more or less extensive marginalia. It should be emphasized that the absence of a person's name from the list does not necessarily indicate a lack of material for that person. In most instances quantities are approximate only. The standard storage box, frequently cited as a unit of measurement, contains an average of 150 pieces.

Early manuscripts include some 2,000 Indic manuscripts, mainly in Sanskrit, Prakrit, and Pali; 66 Hebrew manuscripts; 70 Greek papyri, 200 B. C. to A. D. 100; about 200 Arabic manuscripts and over 200 Syriac, Georgian, and other Near Eastern manuscripts (many from the archives of the American Board of Commissioners for Foreign Missions); and over 3,800 cuneiform clay tablets, 2100-500 B. C. There are also the John Pierpont Morgan collection of photographs of Greek, Georgian, and Armenian manuscripts, largely gathered from monastic libraries of the Near East and Europe (70,000 folios of negatives and photographic and photostatic prints), supplemented by a large collection of photographic and other facsimiles of material of paleographical interest in the library of the Classic Department; and European manuscripts of the medieval and Renaissance periods (700 vols., including over 400 Latin manuscripts). Many of these last belong to a collection selected for its bearing on the history and arts of the book. The Celtic collection includes nearly 400 rolls of microfilm copies of medieval Celtic manuscripts, with some 40 vols. of more modern Irish and Welsh manuscripts. There are also 50 Icelandic manuscripts, chiefly legal works of the 17th-19th centuries.

Papers from modern continental Europe include, for Portugal, about 60 manuscripts and over 500 letters, a large number those of João III; papers of the Academia Solitaria, 1754 (3 vols.); and miscellaneous documents and letters of historical interest, from the collection of Fernando Palha, 16th-19th centuries (about 50 vols.), including 3 vols. of printed and manuscript documents on the Armadas of 1588-1633. For Spain there are over 70 manuscripts and numerous letters and papers, including 34 boxes of the Escoto papers, which bear on the Spanish period of Cuban history. Manuscripts in Catalan (7 vols. and 1 box) include 2 vols. by or about Ramon Lull.

Among some 300 vols. and boxes of French papers are lectures on French history given by F. A. Aulard at the Sorbonne, 1886-1922 (35 vols.); reports of the Commission des Reguliers, 1766-68 (6 vols.); Hermetic and occult treatises, 15th-18th centuries (14 vols.); papers of the Anterroches family, 1788-1835 (3 boxes); papers of Aimé Louis Victor du Bosc, marquis de Radepont, mostly relating to French expeditions to Mexico, 1850-64 (10 boxes); a large collection of French royal letters and documents, 16th-19th centuries; collections of French songs and verse, 17th-18th centuries (23 vols.); documents concerning the Jewish community in the Comtat Venaissin, 15th-18th centuries (3 boxes); materials on the Dreyfus case (5 boxes), including about 50 letters of Dreyfus and official records of Devil's Island; 6 literary manuscripts of Emile Zola, including several on Dreyfus, and about 50 letters; scientific manuscripts prepared for but not published in the <u>Description des arts et métiers</u>, 18th century, mainly by René Antoine Ferchault de Réaumur, Henri Duhamel du Monceau, and Auguste Denis Fougeroux de Bondaroy (7 vols.), with notes on beetles by Réaumur (1 vol.); lexiques of the works of Michel de Montaigne and Raymond Sébon, compiled by Grace Norton (Mass.; author), 17 vols.; and manuscripts on Ottoman history and the Crusades, mainly but not all in French, collected by Count Paul Riant (130 vols. and printed catalogue), including a manuscript inventory of charters in the Sainte-Chapelle (9 vols.). Manuscripts of French literary men include those of Paul Verlaine (5 manuscripts and 1 letter); Anatole France (4 manuscripts and 3 letters); Voltaire (5 manuscripts and 12 letters); Alexandre Dumas père (4 manuscripts and 4 letters) and fils (1 manuscript and 3 letters); Jules Laforgue (3 manuscripts and 2 letters); Rémy and Edmond de Goncourt (5 vols., of which 4 contain portions of the Journal); Alphonse Daudet (4 manuscripts, including 3 notebooks and 2 letters); Fréderic Mistral (6 manuscripts and 4 letters); Victor Hugo (9 manuscripts and 6 letters, plus 1 vol. of correspondence with Juliette Drouet); and Romain Rolland (about 90 letters, mainly to Lucien Price); and microfilm of notebooks and manuscripts of Paul Valery, 28 rolls, heavily restricted until 1980.

For Germany and Austria, there are the Regensburg Reichstag Relations, printed and manuscript, 1746-1805 (110 vols.); letters and papers of Christoph Daniel Ebeling (geographer, author of works on music), 1794-1817 (30 vols.); papers of Georg Wilhelm Friedrich Hegel (philosopher), 1821-24 (1 box); literary manuscripts and letters of Heinrich Heine (poet), 1823-56 (2 vols. and 5 boxes); letters of Hermann von Helmholtz (physicist, anatomist, physiologist) and his wife, 1847-97 (109 pieces); papers of Hugo von Hofmannsthal (poet, critic, dramatist), 1888-1929 (29 boxes); literary manuscripts and letters of Rainer Maria Rilke (poet, novelist), 1895-1926 (6 boxes, including collateral material); letters of Stefan Zweig (author), 1909-41 (123 pieces); and letters of Wilhelm II of Germany, 1923-29 (83 pieces). Recent accessions include papers and memorabilia of the Prussian court collected by Mary (Lee), gräfin von Waldersee (17 vols. and 6 boxes); notes by J. J. Enker on lectures by Ferdinand Hitzig, Alexander Schweizer, and August Ebrard at Zurich, 1846-48 (7 vols.); letters of Josephine von Wertheimstein (2 vols.); letters of Theodor Gomperz (2 vols.); diaries of Carl Gustav Josephi and Wilhelm Josephi, partly of travels in the U. S. and Mexico, 1865-82 (18 vols.); papers of Thomas Mann (1 manuscript and 1 vol. of letters); accounts submitted by refugees on the

topic, "My Life in Germany Before and After January 3), 1933" (24 boxes); and papers of Richard Beer-Hofmann (30 boxes).

From Norway there are letters of Roald Amundsen to Fredrik Herman Gade (1 box). From Russia there are papers of Lev Trotskii (109 boxes, a typed guide, and a section closed to readers until 1981); literary manuscripts by various hands, including Dostoevskii, Pushkin, Gorkii, and Mayakovsky; a collection of early manuscript maps of Siberia; and letters of Rimskii-Korsakov (15) and other Russian composers.

Papers of British poets include those of Robert and Elizabeth Barrett Browning, 1837-87 (59 letters and 6 literary manuscripts); Samuel Taylor Coleridge, 1794-1833 (86 letters and literary manuscripts); Austin Dobson and Frederick Locker-Lampson, 1874-93 (180 pieces of their correspondence); Cecil Day-Lewis (1 vol.); John Donne, from 1620 (2 letters and 9 commonplace books containing poetry and sermons); William Hayley, 1780-1817 (1 box of letters received); William Ernest Henley, 1894-1902 (34 letters); A. E. Housman (about 40 letters and 5 manuscripts); John Keats, 1814-20 (82 letters, 27 literary manuscripts and much collateral material); Edward Lear, 1846-88 (32 vols., 50 letters, and 4,000 drawings); Charles Lloyd (6 vols. of notebooks); John Masefield, 1903-52 (2,400 letters, mostly restricted, and 25 literary manuscripts); Alexander Pope, 1711-44 (41 letters and 10 literary manuscripts); George William Russell (6 vols.); Percy Bysshe Shelley (6 letters, 7 literary manuscripts, 2 important notebooks, and 2 vols. of family papers); Robert Southey, 1792-1838 (38 letters and 26 literary manuscripts); Stephen Spender (1 vol.); Algernon Charles Swinburne, 1866-98 (15 letters and 21 literary manuscripts); Alfred, Lord Tennyson,

1823-92 (400 pieces, including 72 notebooks); Dylan Thomas, 1940-53 (75 pieces); William Wordsworth, 1801-49 (83 letters and 11 literary manuscripts); and William Butler Yeats, 1891-1935 (80 letters and literary manuscripts and 5 rolls of microfilm). There is a large collection of material dealing with ballads and popular verse, mainly assembled by the Harvard scholars Francis James Child, George Lyman Kittredge, and Hyder Edward Rollins, including the papers of Thomas Percy (bishop), 1750-1800 (4 boxes) and 4 shelves of manuscript transcripts of ballads in the British Museum and elsewhere. There is also a collection of some 50 commonplace books, mostly of English poetry, 16th-18th centuries.

Papers of British dramatists include literary manuscripts and letters of James Matthew Barrie, 1888-1934 (20 pieces); letter books of George Etherege, 1688-89 (2 vols.); and papers of George Bernard Shaw, 1897-1939 (125 pieces), including revised play scripts. See also the Theatre Collection, below.

Among papers of British novelists are those of Charlotte, Emily, and Patrick Branwell Brontë, 1829-53 (28 letters and 17 literary manuscripts); Wilkie Collins (44 letters and 5 literary manuscripts); Charles Dickens, 1839-70 (71 letters and 2 literary manuscripts); James Joyce (about 50 letters, manuscript of Stephen Hero, revised page proof of Ulysses); Rudyard Kipling, 1885-1935 (189 letters and 7 literary manuscripts); George MacDonald (8 vols., including 2 novels and a collection of early verse); Mary Russell Mitford, 1813-54 (310 pieces); Robert Louis Stevenson, 1883-94 (75 letters and 10 literary manuscripts); and William Makepeace Thackeray, 1832-63 (229 pieces). There are also manuscripts of novels, or substantial portions of novels, by Joseph Conrad, Benjamin Disraeli,

Thomas Hardy, D. H. Lawrence, Charles Lever, Leonard Merrick, George Moore, Frederick Rolfe (Baron Corvo), Edith Oenone Somerville, and Anthony Trollope.

Papers of other British prose writers include those of Sir Max Beerbohm, 1896-1952 (about 250 letters, 23 literary manuscripts, and 30 drawings); John Boyle, 5th Earl of Cork and Orrery, and his forebears, 1657-1755 (44 vols.); Thomas Carlyle, 1834-75 (4 literary manuscripts and 137 letters, including 106 to Ralph Waldo Emerson), also 500 printed volumes with copious annotations; Thomas De Quincey, 1818-59 (197 pieces); Charles Lutwidge Dodgson, known as Lewis Carroll, 1844-94 (42 pieces and 2 boxes of collateral material); Havelock Ellis (3 vols.); Sir Edmund William Gosse, 1880-1925 (356 pieces); and John Ruskin, 1854-88 (463 pieces), chiefly letters to Charles Eliot Norton (Mass.; editor, fine arts prof. at Harvard Univ.).

Other important British papers are those of Sir Francis Bernard (colonial Gov. of N.J. and Mass.), 1758-79 (13 vols.); Randolph Caldecott (artist, illustrator), 1866-86 (2 boxes of letters, 1 box of drawings, and 1 box of sketchbooks); George Canning (statesman), 1791-1822 (82 pieces); Walter Crane (painter, illustrator), 1861-1910 (1 box of letters, 75 sketchbooks, and numerous individual designs); George Bubb Dodington, Lord Melcombe (politician), 1749-61 (2 boxes, including his diary); Thomas Gage (commander in chief in America), 1759-73, correspondence with John Bradstreet (Canada; British and colonial officer), 187 pieces; Horatio Lord Nelson (naval officer), 1760-1869 (250 pieces), including correspondence with Lady Hamilton, the log of H. M. S. Victory, and collateral material; William Tryon (colonial Gov. of N.C.), 1764-71 (1 vol. letter book and council minutes); and Gilbert

White of Selborne (clergyman, naturalist), 1739-93 (11 boxes). There are
also 20 vols. of parliamentary records,
mostly of the House of Commons, 1625-
82.

Canadiana include the Chadenat Collection of early legal documents and papers, 1599-1822 (187 pieces); "Relations" of the 17th century; many letters,
journals, and maps of Canadian interest; a series of papers of James Wolfe
(England; general) and the siege of Quebec, including 6 letters of Wolfe, letters of Amherst, Townshend, Lans-
downe, and Dorchester, numerous maps
and prints, the articles de capitulation,
and the letter book of Adm. Sir Charles
Saunders, 1759. Among various literary manuscripts are papers of Bliss
Carman (poet), 1888-1927 (170 pieces),
and Thomas Chandler Haliburton (judge,
writer), 2 boxes.

Papers of U. S. Presidents include
some of John Adams (Mass.), 1815 (20
pieces), consisting of letters written to
James Lloyd (Mass.; U. S. Sen.), containing Adams' recollections of political events in the Revolutionary War;
Herbert Hoover (Calif.), 1913-47 (57
letters), including 37 letters to William
Cameron Forbes (see below); Abraham
Lincoln (Ill.), 1830-65 (38 pieces), including 17 letters; Theodore Roosevelt
(N. Y.), 1868-1919, a huge collection,
in part deposited by the Theodore Roosevelt Association of New York City, including diaries, 1868-86, literary manuscripts, and 235 letters to his son
Kermit, 1902-16, 211 to his son Theodore and Theodore's wife, 1889-1918,
and 130 to Joseph Bucklin Bishop
(Mass., N. Y.; secretary of the Isthmian Canal Commission, editor of the
Roosevelt letters); George Washington
(Va.), 1750-99 (88 pieces), including
55 letters to Benjamin Lincoln (Mass.;
Rev. War officer); and Woodrow Wilson (N. J.), a folder of letters, 1889-
1902, to Frederick Jackson Turner
(Wis., Mass., Calif.; historian), and
59 letters, 1913-18, to Walter Hines

Page (N. C., N. Y.; publisher, editor,
Ambassador to Great Britain).

Papers of other men holding high
office in the Federal Government include those of William Cameron
Forbes (Mass.; Gov. Gen. of Philippines, Ambassador to Japan), 1870-
1950 (200 vols. and 20 boxes); Joseph Clark Grew (Mass.; Under Sec.
State), 1909-45 (174 vols. and 30 folders); David Franklin Houston (S. C.,
Tex., Mo.; political scientist, college
pres., Sec. Agriculture, Sec. Treas.),
1891-1928 (3 boxes); Abbott Lawrence
(Mass.; manufacturer, Minister to
Great Britain), 9 vols.; Arthur Lee
(Va.; Member Continental Cong., diplomat), 1760-92 (8 vols.); Jay Pierrepont Moffat (D. C.; foreign service officer, consul-gen. at Sydney, Australia), 44 vols. and 5 boxes, restricted;
Walter Hines Page (N. C., N. Y.; journalist, Ambassador to Great Britain),
1870-1918 (33 vols., 105 boxes, and 2
portfolios); William Pinkney (Md.; U.S.
Attorney Gen., diplomat, U. S. Rep.
and Sen.), 1794-1816 (1 vol.); William
Woodville Rockhill (Pa.; diplomat, orientalist), 1874-1914 (3,000 pieces);
Charles Sumner (Mass.; U. S. Sen.),
1830-74 (200 boxes); Daniel Webster
(N. H., Mass.; U. S. Rep. and Sen.,
Sec. State), 1805-74 (500 pieces, including 300 letters to Franklin Haven);
and Paine Wingate (N. H.; Member
Continental Cong., U.S. Sen. and Rep.)
and his family, 1732-1850 (256 pieces).

Among papers of historians are
those of Brooks Adams (Mass., 1887-
1916 (310 pieces); Henry Adams
(Mass.), 1859-1918 (586 pieces);
John Lothrop Motley (Mass.), 1830-
76 (104 letters); Francis Parkman
(Mass.), 1853-86 (65 pieces); Jared
Sparks (Mass.), 1820-66 (40 boxes of
personal correspondence), also historical manuscripts and transcripts collected by him (266 vols. and 9 boxes);
William Roscoe Thayer (Mass.), 1883-
1922 (59 boxes and 94 pieces); and
Frederick J. Turner (Wis.), 1889-

1902 (1 box).

Papers of clergymen and philosophers include those of Henry Ward Beecher (Mass., Ind., N.Y.; Congregational clergyman), 1850-87 (61 pieces); Phillips Brooks (Mass.; Episcopal bishop), 1865-93 (110 pieces); James Freeman Clarke (Mass.; Unitarian minister) and his family, 1647-1937 (1,400 pieces), and additional Clarke papers (29 boxes) including papers of the Freeman, Huidekoper, and Hull families; William James (Mass.; philosopher), 1862-1910 (36 boxes and 367 pieces); George Herbert Palmer (Mass.; philosopher) and Alice Freeman Palmer, 1842-1933 (6 boxes of correspondence and family papers, restricted); Josiah Royce (Mass.; philosopher), 1880-1916 (100 vols.), including many notebooks and manuscripts; and George Santayana (Mass., Italy; poet, philosopher), 1886-1938 (87 manuscripts and letters).

Papers of poets include those of Conrad Aiken (Ga., Mass.), 1924-30 (14 vols.); Joel Barlow (Conn.; poet, diplomat), 7 boxes; Emily Dickinson (Mass.) and her family, 1810-1950 (25 boxes), including 1,000 poems, 200 letters, and much collateral material; Thomas Stearns Eliot (Mass., England), 1898-1955 (1 box and 43 pieces); Oliver Wendell Holmes (Mass.), 1828-94 (2,500 pieces); Henry Wadsworth Longfellow (Maine, Mass.), 1814-82 (250 literary manuscripts, 2,800 letters, and 15,000 letters received); Amy Lowell (Mass.), 1894-1925 (24 vols. and 39 boxes); James Russell Lowell (Mass.), 1839-91 (14 boxes); Archibald MacLeish (Mass., D.C.), 20th century (3 vols.); Josephine Preston Peabody (N.Y., Mass.), 1894-1922 (2,000 pieces); Edgar Allan Poe (Va., Mass., Md., Pa., N.Y.), 1839-47 (23 pieces); Frederic Prokosch (Wis., Italy), 1929-33 (4 vols.); Edwin Arlington Robinson (Maine, N.Y.), 1890-1933 (13 vols. and 347 pieces); Alan Seeger (N.Y.), 20th century (3 boxes and 2

vols.); and Celia Laighton Thaxter (N.H., Mass., Maine), 1864-94 (92 pieces), including 80 letters from John Greenleaf Whittier. The Pickard-Whittier papers include papers of the poet, 1866-89 (33 pieces), and of his biographer, Samuel Thomas Pickard, 1800-1900 (19 boxes).

Among papers of novelists are those of Louisa May Alcott (Mass.) and her father Amos Bronson Alcott (Mass.; social reformer), in the Alcott-Whitman papers, 1858-76 (8 boxes); Edward Bellamy (Mass.), 1860-98 (17 notebooks, 100 literary manuscripts, and 54 letters), also much collateral material; Samuel L. Clemens, better known as Mark Twain (Mo., Calif., N.Y., Conn.), 1870-1909 (200 pieces); Francis Marion Crawford (N.Y., Italy), 1875-1909 (216 pieces); Brian Oswald Donn-Byrne, known as Donn Byrne (N.Y., Ireland), manuscripts of 5 books; Robert Grant (Mass.), 1890-1940 (900 pieces); Nathaniel Hawthorne (Mass.), 1837-63 (35 pieces); William Dean Howells (Mass., N.Y.), 1850-1900 (over 2,000 pieces, including 5 novels); Henry James (Mass., England), 1850-1916 (26 boxes and 700 pieces), also much material of his father and family; F. Van Wyck Mason (Mass., Md.), typescripts of 10 novels; Herman Melville (N.Y., Mass.), 1839-91 (545 pieces); Mary Noailles Murfree, known as Charles Egbert Craddock (Tenn.), manuscripts of 2 novels; John (Henry) O'Hara (Pa., N.Y.), 20th century (2 vols. and 4 boxes); Upton Sinclair (N.J., Calif.), 1901-51 (79 pieces), including correspondence on the Sacco-Vanzetti case; William Ware (N.Y., Mass.), 19th century (3 novels); and Thomas Wolfe (N.C., N.Y.), 1908-38 (100 boxes), in the William B. Wisdom Collection.

Papers of other authors include those of Thomas Bailey Aldrich (N.Y.,

Mass.), 1846-1907 (5,000 pieces), including many connected with the <u>Atlantic Monthly</u>; Gamaliel Bradford (<u>Mass.</u>), 1878-1932 (121 vols.); George Washington Cable (La., Mass.), 1874-1913 (88 pieces); John Jay Chapman (N. Y.), 1905-31 (4,000 pieces); George William Curtis (N. Y.), 1842-92 (16 boxes and 372 pieces); Joseph Dennie (Mass., N. H., Pa.), 1753-1809 (3 folders and 55 pieces); Ralph Waldo Emerson (Mass.), 1825-82 (11,000 pieces), on deposit by the Ralph Waldo Emerson Memorial Association, including 10,000 letters to Emerson and his family, hundreds of his own letters, 140 vols. of journals, and many literary manuscripts; and James Thomas Fields (Mass.), 1831-81 (4 manuscripts, 93 letters, about 300 letters received, including 163 from Longfellow), together with the records of the publishing firm of Ticknor and Fields and its successors to 1900 (125 vols.). There are also papers of Lafcadio Hearn (Ohio, La., Japan), 1877-1904 (176 pieces); Mark Antony De Wolfe Howe (Mass.), 26 boxes of correspondence; Washington Irving (N. Y.), 1821-59 (57 letters); Henry James the elder (N. Y., Mass.), 9 boxes and 39 pieces; Thomas Allibone Janvier (Pa., N. Y.), 1874-1913 (55 pieces); Sarah Orne Jewett (Maine), 1876-1907 (31 boxes); John Phillips Marquand (Mass.), 20th century, correspondence; Jacob Bailey Moore (N. H., N. Y., Calif.), 1827-53 (4 boxes); Charles Eliot Norton (Mass.), 1847-1908 (11 boxes and 8,300 letters received); James Parton (Mass.), 1842-91 (1,200 pieces); Horace Elisha Scudder (Mass.), 1858-1902 (31 boxes); Bayard Taylor (Pa.), 1844-78 (5 vols., 3 portfolios, and 1,100 pieces); Benjamin Thompson, Count Rumford (Mass., England, Bavaria), 2 boxes; Henry David Thoreau (Mass.), 20 letters, 5 vols., and 1 box of manuscripts; and George Edward Woodberry (Mass., N. Y.), 1874-1929 (5 boxes).

The papers of Alexander Woollcott (5,500 pieces) contain letters to Woollcott from literary personages: Marie Adelaide Belloc, better known as Mrs. Belloc Lowndes (102 letters); Archibald MacLeish (64); Alice Duer Miller (59); Kathleen Norris (56); Laura E. Richards (114); Booth Tarkington (82); Rebecca West (53); and Thornton Wilder (196). Among Woollcott's theatrical correspondents were Minnie Maddern Fiske (46); Lynne Fontanne and Alfred Lunt (131); George Kaufman (48); and Harpo Marx (56).

Among papers of abolitionists and social reformers are those of Dorothea Lynde Dix (Mass.), 1826-86 (1 vol., 35 boxes, and 600 pieces); Margaret Fuller, Marchioness Ossoli (Mass.), and her family, 1662-1870 (23 vols., 4 boxes, and 100 letters), including 49 letters to Emerson; William Lloyd Garrison (Mass.), 1839-78 (3 boxes and 52 pieces); Thomas Wentworth Higginson (Mass.), 1842-1911 (162 letters and 1,600 letters received); Julia Ward Howe (Mass.), 1827-1910 (60 vols., 15 boxes, and 1,000 pieces); and Samuel Gridley Howe (Mass.), 1832-76 (700 pieces), including correspondence with Charles Sumner, 1840-74 (375 pieces).

Papers of Harvard professors, in addition to those mentioned elsewhere, include those of Francis James Child, 1842-96 (350 pieces); Charles Folsom, 1808-64 (1 box and 33 pieces); George Lyman Kittredge, 1881-1938 (2 vols., 2 boxes, and 20 pieces); John Livingston Lowes (Ind., Mo., Mass.), 1928-46 (300 pieces); Andrews Norton, 1795-1852 (16 boxes and 400 pieces); Benjamin Peirce, 1840-80 (11 boxes); Charles Sanders Peirce, 1880-1914 (35 boxes); Bliss Perry, 1884-1941 (550 pieces); Willard Phillips, 1806-40 (10 vols.); and Joseph Alois Schumpeter (Austria, Germany, Mass.), 1930-48 (16 boxes). Papers of many more Harvard teachers and graduates are in the Harvard University Archives.

Other papers include those of Louis Agassiz (Switzerland, Mass., S. C.; zoologist, prof. at Harvard and Medical College of S. C.), 1821-73 (200 pieces); John James Audubon (Pa., Ky., La., N. Y.; artist, ornithologist), 1813-48 (250 letters and drawings); Frederick Shepherd Converse (Mass.; composer), 1898-1936 (9 vols. of musical manuscripts); Nicholas Cooke (R. I.; Gov.), 1775-82 (73 pieces); George Gershwin (N. Y.; composer), 35 letters to Isaac Goldberg (Mass.; author); Edwin Lawrence Godkin (N. Y.; editor of the Nation), 1845-1917 (9 boxes and 140 pieces); Henry Lee Higginson (Mass.; banker), 1865-1919, a vast file of papers dealing with financial matters, Harvard University, and the Boston Symphony Orchestra; James Hunnewell (Mass., Hawaii; sea captain, merchant) and his family and firm, 1809-79 (15 vols. and 16 boxes); John Jeffries (Mass.; physician, scientist), 1768-1819 (100 pieces), including much material relating to his balloon crossing of the English Channel in 1785; Sylvester Judd, Jr. (Mass., Maine; Unitarian minister, author), 1835-53 (18 boxes); Thomas Bird Mosher (Maine; publisher and editor of belles-lettres), 1872-1923 (1,650 pieces); Charles Stewart (N. J.; Rev. War officer, Member Continental Cong.) and his descendants, 1774-1899 (600 pieces); Samuel Tucker (Mass., Maine; Rev. War naval officer) and his descendants, 1774-1884 (6 vols.); Henry Villard (Ill., Mass., Oreg., N. Y.; journalist, financier), 1855-1900 (16 shelves); and Oswald Garrison Villard (N. Y.; journalist, editor of the Nation), 1892-1949 (4,000 pieces).

The Theatre Collection, concerning both the American and the English stage, comprises about 10 stack sections of manuscripts, 1600-1955. It includes account books of various theaters; more than 1,000 annotated prompt books; and manuscripts of published and unpublished plays. Papers

of dramatists include those of Charles Dibdin (England), 1745-48 (1 box and 1 vol.); John Howard Payne (N. Y., 1804-9 (16 vols. and 30 pieces); Richard Brinsley Sheridan (England), 1780-1815 (several hundred pieces), including material about the Theatre Royal, Drury Lane. Papers of actors include those of Edwin Booth (Md., Calif., Mass., N. Y.), 1860-90 (1 vol. and 30 pieces); David Garrick (England); 1750-79 (3 vols. and 70 pieces); John Gilbert (Mass., N. Y.), 1850-85 (40 letters); and Edmund Kean (England), 1810-30 (3 vols. of correspondence). There are also papers of the drama critic, Roswell P. Dague (N. Y.), 1898-1932 (81 vols.), and a collection of several thousand autograph letters of theatrical interest.

The Houghton Library also maintains a general file of over 15,000 pieces of autograph and other manuscript material not associated with its larger collection of papers, and there are smaller collections of autographs brought together by various persons, including a set of the signers of the Declaration of Independence. The music collection, 1580-1950 (500 pieces), includes 224 manuscript vols. of librettos of 1,500 Italian operas, and the original manuscript scores of most of the compositions of John Knowles Paine (Mass.; Harvard prof., composer), 1875-1906 (44 vols.). The Abbott Lawrence Rotch Collection contains material dealing with the winds and early aeronautics, including 18th-century papers about ballooning. There are 75 vols. of logs of whaling and merchant ships, 1753-1879. There are also records of the Loyal Legion (69 boxes); and the Norton-Harjes Ambulance Corps, 1914-23 (9 vols. and 31 boxes), including letters of soldiers and prisoners.

The archives of the American Board of Commissioners for Foreign Missions, 1812-1945 (45 stack sections), are on deposit in the Library. For a description, see under name of the Board, in Boston.

See W. H. Bond, "Manuscript Collections in the Houghton Library," in Autograph Collectors' Journal, 4 (no. 3):32-39 (spring 1952); De Ricci, Census, pp. 964-1020; and Justin Winsor, Calendar of the Sparks Manuscripts in Harvard College Library, With an Appendix Showing Other Manuscripts (1889. 88 p.). Current acquisitions are recorded in the annual Houghton Library Report of Accessions (since 1941-42).

Andover-Harvard Theological Seminary Library. James Tanis, Librarian.

Holdings: Papers relating chiefly to the Congregational Church in Massachusetts. Included are letters and other writings of Jonathan Edwards (Mass.; clergyman, theologian), 1733-57; sermons of James Pierpont (Conn.; clergyman), 1685-1713, and of Solomon Stoddard (Mass.; clergyman), 1719-27; records of ministerial associations, 1719-1863 (5 vols.); papers of societies of missionary inquiry, 1808-99; and papers relating to the founding of the Seminary. There are also some Bible texts of European origin.

See Allison, Inventory, pp. 22-25; and De Ricci, Census, p. 1049.

Arnold Arboretum and Gray Herbarium. 22 Divinity Ave. (Mrs.) Lazella Schwarten, Librarian.

Holdings: Thousands of pieces, dated from 1790 onward, relating chiefly to botany. The major group consists of papers of Asa Gray (N.Y., Mass.; botanist); among them journals, literary manuscripts, 800 folders of his letters, and many letters to him, chiefly from distinguished European and American scientists.

Letters to Gray from abroad include those of James Backhouse (England; nurseryman), 1870-84 (40 pieces); John Ball (Ireland; Alpinist, botanist), 1880 (50 pieces); George Bentham (England; botanist), 1839-83 (250 pieces); Pierre-Edmond Boissier (Switzerland; botanist), 1841-85 (50 pieces); Francis Boott (England; physician, botanist), 1839-63 (200 pieces); Alphonse de Candolle (Switzerland; botanist), 1839-80 (100 pieces); Ernest Cosson (France; botanist), 1861-84 (50 pieces); Charles Robert Darwin (England; naturalist, author), 1855-81 (155 pieces); Joseph Decaisne (France; botanist), 1841-81 (30 pieces); William Turner Thistleton-Dyer (England; editor), 1881-87 (30 pieces); August Wilhelm Eichler (Germany; botanist), 1869-85 (50 pieces); August Fendler (Germany; botanist), 1848-82 (62 pieces); Elias Magnus Fries (Sweden; botanist), 1849-70 (40 pieces); Henry Fletcher Hance (England; botanist), 1858-82 (30 pieces), chiefly concerning his botanical studies in China; William Henry Harvey (Ireland; botanist), 1845-67 (150 pieces); Joseph Dalton Hooker (England; botanist, explorer, collaborator with Darwin), 1844-87 (200 pieces); William Jackson Hooker (England; botanist), 1834-65 (150 pieces); Johann Georg Christian Lehmann (Germany; botanist), 1874-87 (200 pieces); Karl Friedrich Philipp von Martius (Germany; surgeon, naturalist), 1839-67 (50 pieces); Ferdinand Jacob Heinrich von Mueller (Germany; botanist), 1854-88 (100 pieces); William Munro (England; army officer, botanist), 1858-72 (40 pieces); Daniel Oliver (England; botanist), 1862-87 (30 pieces); William Thompson (England; naturalist, ornithologist), 1860-86 (50 pieces); and Nathaniel B. Ward (England; botanist), 1840-65 (30 pieces).

Letters to Gray from Americans include those of Spencer F. Baird (Pa., D. C.; zoologist, Sec. of Smithsonian Institution, U. S. Commissioner of Fish and Fisheries), 1846-87 (100 pieces); Michael Schuck Bebb (Ill.; botanist), 1859-87 (40 pieces); Samuel B. Buckley (Tex.; naturalist, State geologist), 1843-62 (40 pieces); William Marriott Canby (Pa., Del.; botanist, banker), 1861-87 (150 pieces); Alvan Wentworth Chapman (Ga., Fla.; physician, botanist), 1842-87 (50 pieces); Moses Ashley Curtis (N. C., S. C.; Episcopal clergyman, botanist), 1836-72 (150 pieces); James Dwight Dana (D. C., Conn.; mineralogist, geologist, zoologist, Yale prof.), 1836-86 (50 pieces); William Darlington (Pa.; physician, botanist), 1836-62 (150 pieces); Élie Magliore Durand, known as Elias Durand (France, Md., Pa.; pharmacist, botanist), 1843-73 (100 pieces); Daniel Cady Eaton (Conn.; botanist, Yale prof.), 1835-87 (100 pieces); George Engelmann (Germany, Mo.; meteorologist, physician, botanist), 1840-84 (450 pieces); George Julius Engelmann (Mo.; gynecologist), 1884-87 (20 pieces); William Gilson Farlow (Mass.; botanist), 1872-87 (40 pieces); Edward Lee Greene (Colo., Calif., D. C.; botanist, prof. at Univ. of Calif. and Catholic Univ.), 1868-87 (150 pieces); Joseph Henry (N.Y., N.J., D. C.; physicist, prof. at College of N. J., Sec. of Smithsonian Institution), 1838-77 (110 pieces); Leo Lesquereux (Switzerland, Mass., Ohio; paleobotanist), 1850-83 (100 pieces); and Horace Mann (Mass., Ohio; educator, U. S. Rep. from Mass., pres. of Antioch College), 1864-69 (40 pieces).

Letters to Gray from other Americans include those of Stephen Thayer Olney (R. I.; merchant, botanist), 1848-72 (40 pieces); Charles Christopher Parry (Iowa; botanical explorer), 1861-87 (200 pieces); Thomas Minott Peters (Ala.; State chief justice, amateur botanist), 1851-86 (50 pieces); Cyrus G.

Pringle (Vt.; plant breeder, botanical explorer), 1884-87 (50 pieces); George Palmer Putnam (N. Y., England; book and magazine publisher), 1844-59 (50 pieces); John Howard Redfield (Conn., N. Y., Pa.; businessman, naturalist, conservator of Philadelphia Academy of Natural Sciences herbarium), 1878-86 (40 pieces); Charles Wilkins Short (Ky.; physician, botanist, prof. at Transylvania Univ. and Medical Institute of Louisville), 1836-62 (100 pieces); William S. Sullivant (Ohio; botanist, bryologist), 1840-72 (200 pieces); George Thurber (R. I., Mich., N. Y.; botanist, physician, editor of the American Agriculturist), 1852-88 (40 pieces); John Torrey (N. Y.; botanist, chemist, college prof.), 1830-73 (353 pieces); Edward Tuckerman (Mass.; lichenologist, Amherst prof. of botany), 1843-86 (200 pieces); Sereno Watson (Mass.; botanical explorer, curator of Gray Herbarium), 1869-86 (40 pieces); Charles Wilkes (U. S. naval officer, explorer), 1848-73 (50 pieces); and Charles Wright (Tex., Conn.; botanical explorer), 1845-85 (150 pieces).

There are also letters of William Baldwin (Pa., Del., Ga.; physician, botanist) to William Darlington (Pa.; physician, botanist), 1836-62; and papers of Stephen Elliott (S. C.; botanist, bank pres.), 1790-1829, among them 24 letters from James Macbride (S. C.; physician, botanist) and 30 letters, 1808-15, from Gotthilf Henry Muhlenberg (Pa.; Lutheran clergyman, botanist). Included also are papers of George Engelmann (Germany, Mo.; meteorologist, physician, botanist), 1833 (1 package), containing letters to Henry Shaw (Mo.; businessman, founder of the Mo. Botanical Garden), concerning the beginnings of the garden; and a collection of autograph manuscripts of distinguished botanists, 16th-19th centuries (2,000 pieces).

Farlow Reference Library of Crypto-gamic Botany. 20 Divinity Ave. Nancy Buck, Librarian.

Holdings: 20,000 pieces, 1855-1931, pertaining to the Library's special field. Included is a series of 161 vols. of correspondence, consisting chiefly of letters from American and European scientists to William Gilson Farlow (Mass.; botanist), 1877-93. This series contains also extensive correspondence of Thomas Potts James (Pa., Mass.; botanist), 8 vols., 625 letters, with Leo Lesquereux (Switzerland, Mass., Ohio; paleobotanist); and letters to Frank Shipley Collins (Mass.; botanist); Job Bicknell Ellis (N.Y., N.J.; botanist, mycologist); and William Starling Sullivant (Ohio; botanist, bryologist). The library has also 5,000 letters to Roland Thaxter (Mass.; botanist), 1890-1931, including over 50 letters apiece from Albert F. Blakeslee (Mass., Conn., N.Y.; botanist), Carroll W. Dodge (Mass., Mo.; mycologist), Joseph H. Faull (Canada, Mass.; botanist, forest pathologist), and William A. Setchell (Conn., Mass., Calif.; botanist).

Fogg Museum of Art.   E. Louise Lucas, Librarian.

Holdings: A small quantity of manuscripts, 13th-17th centuries, of value primarily as works of art. Included are European manuscripts, 13th-16th centuries (3 vols. and 3 pieces); and Persian manuscripts of the 16th and 17th centuries (5 vols. and 5 leaves).
See De Ricci, Census, p. 1050.

Graduate School of Design Library. Katherine McNamara, Librarian.

Holdings: Included are professional papers of Charles Eliot (Mass.;

landscape architect), 1880-97 (1,061 pieces), including photographs and some printed materials; Charles Mulford Robinson (N.Y.; city planner, author), 1890-1917; Warren Henry Manning (Mass.; landscape designer), 1880-1938 (100 pieces), including maps and plans; Robert Whitten (N.Y.; city planner), 1898-1936 (6 boxes); and Arthur C. Comey (Mass.; city planner), 1910-54 (plans and other materials, not yet cataloged). There are some manuscripts in the David Blucher Memorial Collection, 1920-56, comprising the professional library of Walter H. Blucher (Ill.; planning consultant). Among the holdings are also 7,740 maps and plans and 11,538 photographs.

Harvard-Yenching Institute.   A. Kaiming Chiu, Librarian.

Holdings: Included are Chinese manuscripts, 17th and 18th centuries (400 vols.), relating to local government and collected literary works of individual schools and the Chinese theater; 200 Japanese manuscripts, 1300-1900, chiefly relating to Buddhism and other oriental religions; a few Korean manuscripts, of which the earliest are 4 volumes of holographic books by Queen Sun-won, 1778-1854, about Korean history; and a few Manchu, Mongolian, and Tibetan manuscripts relating to Buddhism.
    See Serge Elisséeff, "The Chinese-Japanese Library of the Harvard-Yenching Institute," in Harvard Library Bulletin, 10:73-93 (winter 1956).

Industrial Relations Library. Littauer Center of Public Administration. (Mrs.) Claire Brown, in charge.

Holdings: 3 cartons and about 20,000 pieces, chiefly 20th century, relating to labor unions and labor-

management relations. Included are
records of the National Maritime Union, Boston Local (Deep Ships), consisting of correspondence, minutes of
meetings, ballots, and financial records, all prior to 1942 (3 cartons);
miscellaneous papers of the Glaziers
Union, Boston Local 1044, prior to
1942; labor-management arbitration
decisions by umpires and arbitrators
(12,000 pieces), chiefly typewritten
carbon copies; and labor-management
agreements (6,000 items, mimeographed or printed in a few copies),
especially strong in agreements between 1935 and 1947.

Isham Library of Early Instrumental
Music. Arthur Tillman Merritt,
Curator.

Holdings: Over 1,700 items, relating chiefly to early vocal and instrumental music. Included are the
Dresel Collection of 102 manuscript
arrangements of music of Bach, Han-
del, Mozart, and others; the Schmid
Collection of 310 items of 18th-cen-
tury manuscript music for stringed
instruments; the Tuttle Collection,
which contains an invaluable thematic
index compiled from the most important manuscript sources for the music
of the English virginalists; and 363
microfilms of manuscript music and
of early editions, from the 12th to the
19th centuries.
    See Archibald T. Davison, "The
Isham Memorial Library," in Harvard
Library Bulletin. 6:376-380 (autumn
1952); and Willi Apel, "The Collection
of Photographic Reproductions at the
Isham Memorial Library," in Journal
of Renaissance and Baroque Music,
1:68-73, 144-148, 235-238 (Mar.,
June, and Dec. 1946).

Law Library. Earl C. Borgeson,
Librarian.

Holdings: Miscellaneous manuscripts relating chiefly to English
and American law. Included are medieval and Renaissance manuscripts
on English and foreign law, produced
before 1601 (150 vols. and 1,081
pieces); manuscripts on American
law (200 pieces), including notebooks
and correspondence of lawyers, judges, and law teachers; and an extensive collection of letters, diaries,
and other papers of Oliver Wendell
Holmes (Mass.; U.S. Chief Justice),
1841-1935.
    See De Ricci, Census, pp. 1021-
1048.

Littauer Center of Public Administration Library. (Mrs.) Ruth H.
Grant, Assistant Librarian.

Holdings: 72 ft. of shelves, 32
filing drawers, and 12 cartons of papers, 1938-46, consisting of transcripts of proceedings of the National
War Labor Board, 1942-46 (51 ft.)
and documents relating to cases considered by the Board (20 filing drawers); records of the Boston regional
office of the Office of Defense Transportation, 1942-44 (21 ft.); working
papers of the Boston regional office
of the Office of Price Administration,
1941-46 (12 cartons); and correspondence of the American Committee for
Nonparticipation in Japanese Aggres-
sion, 1938-Jan. 1941 (12 filing drawers).

Museum of Comparative Zoology
Library. Jessie B. MacKenzie,
Librarian.

Holdings: 16 filing cabinets of
material of the 19th and 20th centuries, relating chiefly to zoology and
geology. Included are papers of
Louis Agassiz (Switzerland, Mass.,
S.C.; zoologist, prof. at Harvard

and Medical College of S. C.), 1836-73 (110 letters), and numerous manuscripts of other members of the Museum's staff; drawings, letters, journals, and account books of Alexander Wilson (Scotland, Pa.; ornithologist), and of John James Audubon (Pa., Ky., La., N. Y.; artist, ornithologist); and a large collection of autograph letters of zoologists and geologists.

Peabody Museum. 11 Divinity Ave. Margaret Currier, Librarian.

Holdings: A small collection of manuscripts, 16th-19th centuries, relating to archeology and anthropology. Included are photographic reproductions of manuscripts dealing with the languages and peoples of Central America and Mexico (300 vols.); and transcripts of 347 Spanish manuscripts, chiefly from Mexico and New Mexico, 1521-1845 (13 vols.).

Semitic Museum. Frank M. Cross, Jr., Curator.

Holdings: 2,552 pieces, manuscript or inscribed, 2500 B. C. to A. D. 1500, relating to the ancient Near East, Judaism, Islam, and Christianity. Included are 2,000 cuneiform tablets from Mesopotamia, 2500-300 B. C.; 2 ancient Egyptian coffin cases, 700-200 B. C.; 10 South Arabian inscriptions, 200 B. C. to A. D. 300; 59 sheets of Greek papyri, 100 B. C. to A. D. 500; and 481 vols. of manuscripts, chiefly in Syriac and Arabic, A. D. 500-1500 (now deposited in the Houghton Library).

CAMBRIDGE

Longfellow House.

Holdings: A few letters of Louis

Agassiz (Switzerland, Mass., S. C.; zoologist, prof. at Harvard and Medical College of S. C.), Asa Gray (N.Y., Mass.; botanist, Harvard prof.), and Henry Wadsworth Longfellow (Maine, Mass.; poet).

CAMBRIDGE 39

Massachusetts Institute of Technology Libraries. William N. Locke, Director.

Holdings: Some 19th-century papers relating chiefly to science, architecture, and city planning. Included are correspondence of William Barton Rogers (Md., Va., Mass.; geologist, pres. of Mass. Institute of Technology); and papers of Thomas Gaffield (scientist, glass manufacturer), including diaries, account books, records of experiments, and letters from American and foreign scientists concerning glass, photography, and light.

CAMBRIDGE 38

Radcliffe Women's Archives, Radcliffe College. Barbara M. (Mrs. Peter H.) Solomon, Director.

Holdings: A considerable quantity of papers, 19th and 20th centuries, relating chiefly to the activities of women in the United States.
Among papers of suffragists and reformers are those of Olympia Brown (Mass., Conn., Wis.; feminist, first American woman to become an ordained minister), 1849-1926; Elizabeth Glendower Evans (Mass.; reformer), 1882-1937 (5 vols. and 9 boxes); Matilda Joselyn Gage (N. Y., Ill.; suffragist, author), 19th century; Julia Ward Howe (Mass.; abolitionist, feminist, author), 1869-1910 (9 vols. and 1 box); Harriet

Burton Laidlaw (N. Y.; suffragist, philanthropist), 1886-1948 (15 boxes); Catharine Waugh McCulloch (Ill.; suffragist, lawyer), 1874-1943 (15 boxes); Leonora O'Reilly (N. Y.; labor organizer), 1886-1938 (27 vols. and 18 boxes); Maud Wood Park (Mass.; suffragist), from 1896 (32 boxes); Grace Thompson Seton (Conn.; author, suffragist), 1911-52 (2 boxes); Anna Howard Shaw (Mass., N. Y.; minister, physician, suffragist), 1898-1919 (12 vols. and 12 boxes); Jane Norman Smith (N. Y.; feminist), 20th century (several cartons); Nellie Nugent Somerville (Miss.; suffragist, State legislator), 1896-1951 (14 vols. and 3 boxes); Ella S. Stewart (Ill.; suffragist), 1899-1936 (1 box); Harriet Beecher Stowe (Ohio, Mass., Conn.; author, abolitionist), with papers of her father, Lyman Beecher (Conn., Mass., Ohio; Presbyterian clergyman) and other members of the Stowe and Beecher families; Elizabeth Hewes Tilton (Mass.; reformer), 1920-45 (11 vols. and 9 boxes); and Sue Shelton White (Tenn.; lawyer, suffragist).

Papers of public officials and social workers include those of Florence Ellinwood Allen (N. Y., Ohio; jurist), 1921-53 (1 box and 3 scrolls); Mary Anderson (D. C.; Chief of U. S. Women's Bureau), 1921-50 (4 boxes); Mary Williams Dewson (Mass., Maine; industrial economist, social worker, member of U. S. Social Security Board), 1896-1952 (1 box); Katherine G. Howard (Mass.; Assistant Federal Civil Defense Administrator), from 1950 (6 boxes); Frieda Segelke Miller (N. Y., D. C.; Director of U. S. Women's Bureau); Maud Nathan (N. Y.; social worker), 1890-1938 (12 scrapbooks); Frances Perkins (N. Y.; State industrial commissioner, U.S. Sec. Labor), 1926-45 (8 boxes); Edith Rockwood (D. C.; U. S. Children's Bureau official), 1932-52 (1 box); Anna Churchill Moulton Tillinghast (Mass.;

Universalist minister, suffragist, U. S. Commissioner of Immigration), 1911-45 (1 vol. and 1 box); Miriam Van Waters (Mass.; social worker, supt. Framingham, Mass., Reformatory for Women, author), 20th century (a substantial collection); Mary N. Winslow (D. C.; member of Inter-American Committee of Women and National Women's Trade Union League), 1923-51 (2 boxes); and Ellen Sullivan Woodward (D. C.; member of U. S. Social Security Board), 1939-46 (1 box).

Other papers include those of Elizabeth Cabot Cary Agassiz (Mass.; pres. of Radcliffe College), 1838-1907, 1918-20 (3 boxes); Fannie Fern Andrews (Mass.; author, scholar in field of diplomacy), 1902-45 (91 vols. and 222 boxes); Mary Ritter Beard (N. Y.; historian), 1935-45 (1 file drawer of papers relating to the World Center for Women's Archives); Sarah Knowles Bolton (Mass.; author), 1881-1915 (2 boxes), including 24 vols. of diaries; LeBaron Russell Briggs (Mass.; pres. of Radcliffe College), 1903-25 (6 vols. and 9 boxes); Lydia Maria Francis Child (Mass.; author, abolitionist), 1845-80 (57 items); Ada Louise Comstock (Mass.; pres. of Radcliffe College), 1923-43 (1 file drawer); Helen Temple Cooke (Mass.; educator), 1858-1951 (1 box), including 4 vols. of her grandmother's diaries; Helen Miller Davis (N. Y.; author, educator), 1902-54 (2 boxes); Vera Micheles Dean (N. Y.; author, research director of Foreign Policy Association), 1948-53 (2 boxes of literary manuscripts); Alice Hamilton (Ill., Mass.; physician), 1910-52 (3 boxes); Inez Haynes Irwin (Mass.; author), 1872-1954 (4 boxes), including 25 vols. of diaries; Mary Corinna Putnam Jacobi (N. Y.; physician), 1851-1906 (1 box); Kate Campbell Hurd Mead (Conn.; physician), 1939 (3 boxes of a manuscript, "Medical Women in the Eastern Hemisphere");

and Emma Guffey Miller (Pa., D.C.; Democratic National Committeewoman). Included also is a collection of 139 letters and 10 diaries representing Massachusetts domestic life, 1801-37.

There are also many records of or concerning women's organizations, including the following: American Association of University Women, 1886-1927 (11 vols. and 5 boxes); Associated Countrywomen of the World, 1936-55 (3 boxes); Bureau of Vocational Information, New York, 1915-32 (38 boxes); Central Committee on Friendship Dinners, 1927-50 (4 boxes); Connecticut Committee for Equal Rights, 1943-54 (6 boxes); Consumer's League of Massachusetts and of Connecticut, 1908-54 (30 boxes); International Assembly of Women, South Kortright, N.Y., 1946 (3 vols. and 1 box); Institute of Women's Professional Relations, 1928-41 (4 boxes); Women's Educational and Industrial Union, Boston, 1878-1933 (9 boxes); Women's Joint Legislative Committee for Equal Rights, 1943-48 (1 box); and Woman's National Farm and Garden Association, 1903-54 (12 boxes).

See Radcliffe Women's Archives (1953. 6 p. Processed), and subsequent yearly leaflets.

CAMBRIDGE

Shepard Historical Society of the First Church in Cambridge, Congregational. Mason and Garden Sts.

Holdings: 143 vols. and 2,000 pieces, from 1638, relating chiefly to the church. Included are 42 sermons by and other papers of or relating to Thomas Shepard (England, Mass.; Congregational clergyman), and correspondence and 462 sermons of Alexander McKenzie (Mass.; Congregational clergyman), 1856-1910. There are also sermons of the following Congregational ministers: Nehe-

miah Adams, 1833-38; John Davenport, 1649-52; Abiel Holmes, 1783-1836; and Jonathan Mitchell, 1667-88.

See Hist. Records Survey, Guide for Mass., p. 53.

CHESTNUT HILL 67

Boston College Library. Rev. Terence L. Connolly, Director.

Holdings: 5,000 pieces, from the 17th to the 20th centuries, relating chiefly to Catholic writers and to the island of Jamaica. Included are papers of the following English poets: Alice Meynell, 1875-1923 (37 letters and literary manuscripts); Coventry Patmore, 1853-96 (87 letters and literary manuscripts); and Francis Thompson, 1888-1907 (549 letters and literary manuscripts). The Special Irish Collection contains papers relating to the American branch of the Irish Land League, 1880-82 (110 pieces), chiefly letters and other papers from Charles Stewart Parnell (Ireland; nationalist leader) and Fanny Parnell. In the Williams Ethnological Collection are manuscripts, 1930-31, on the folklore of Jamaica (4,100 pieces); and land grants, plantation records, and other papers, chiefly of the 17th and 18th centuries (250 pieces). There are also medieval and Renaissance manuscripts (3 vols.).

See Terence L. Connolly, An Account of Books and Manuscripts of Francis Thompson ([1937.] 79 p.); the Library's Catalogue of Books, Manuscripts, etc. in the Caribbeana Section of the Nicholas M. Williams . . . Collection (1932. 133 p.); and De Ricci, Census, p. 1061.

CONCORD

Concord Free Public Library. Dorothy E. Nyren, Librarian.

Holdings: 965 pieces, 1664-1875 (but chiefly of the 19th century), relating to Concord. Included are papers of Ephraim Wales Bull (Mass.; horticulturist, developer of the Concord grape), 1828-67 (545 items); Ralph Waldo Emerson (Mass.; essayist, poet), 1835-73 (45 pieces); and Franklin Benjamin Sanborn (Mass.; abolitionist, journalist, biographer, philanthropist), 1858-1912 (285 pieces). There are some surveying maps of Henry David Thoreau (Mass.; essayist, poet), and small groups of letters and papers of many other prominent men. Much of the material concerns slavery, abolition, and the Civil War.

See Hist. Records Survey, Guide for Mass., p. 58.

DEDHAM

Dedham Historical Society. Mrs. Edward S. Baker, Librarian.

Holdings: Thousands of papers, 1638-1954, relating to Dedham and Norfolk County. Included are papers of Fisher Ames (Mass.; lawyer, U.S. Rep.), 1775-1808 (hundreds); and of Horace Mann (Mass.; educator, lawyer, U.S. Rep.), 1823-52 (24 folders), with his lecture notes taken as a law student in Litchfield, Conn. (4 vols.). There are also records of an agricultural society, 1849-82 (6 large vols.); a cotton manufactory, 1807-26 (2 vols.); two teachers' associations, 1830-32 and 1848-1907 (3 vols.); a turnpike corporation, 1802-56 (many vols. and folders); two fire companies, 1800-86 (9 vols.); a fruit growers' protective association, 1865-70 (2 vols.); and two library associations, 1854-89 (4 vols. and 1 package). Records relating to churches include a diary of Samuel Dexter (Mass.; Con-

gregational clergyman), 1722-52 (1 vol.); a collection of sermons, 1683-1832 (2 bundles and 58 pieces); and records of three local churches (Congregational and Episcopal), 1638-1890 (a large filing case, a chest, and a box).

DEERFIELD

Pocumtuck Valley Memorial Association. Memorial Hall. Mary W. Wells, Curator.

Holdings: 20,000 pieces, 1600-1841, relating chiefly to the Indians and the early settlers of the region. Included are local account books, 1700-1850; sermons, 1725-1841 (1,500 pieces); a Revolutionary War collection, 1770-83 (160 pieces); and letters of about 30 Deerfield families, of the 18th and 19th centuries.

See Hist. Records Survey, Guide for Mass., p. 61.

DORCHESTER

Dorchester Historical Society. 195 Boston St. Robert W. Lovett, Librarian.

Holdings: Several groups of family papers; records of local organizations such as the Dorchester Turnpike and Dorchester Athenaeum; papers relating to the distribution of books to soldiers in Washington during the Civil War; and several letters relating to Shays' Rebellion.

DORCHESTER 25

Federal Records Center, GSA. Box 96, Uphams Corner Station. Chief.

Holdings: A large quantity of noncurrent or semicurrent records, chiefly of recent date, of nonmilitary agencies of the U.S. Government in Massachusetts, Maine, New Hampshire, Vermont, Rhode Island, and Connecticut. Most of these records have been appraised for disposal after specified periods of time, but some will be preserved because of their enduring value. Records in the latter category include those of U.S. district courts and predecessor circuit courts, from 1789; U.S. Court of Appeals, from 1891; Bureau of Customs, from 1784; Coast Guard, from 1882; Fish and Wildlife Service, from 1891; Weather Bureau, from 1884; Immigration and Naturalization Service, from 1891; and Geological Survey, from 1886.

FRAMINGHAM CENTER

Edgell Memorial Library.

Holdings: 2 vols. and 407 pieces, 1669-1872, relating chiefly to Framingham and the vicinity. The two volumes are records of women's church and charitable associations, 1818-43.
See Hist. Records Survey, Guide for Mass., p. 62.

—oOo—

Framingham Natural History and Historical Society.

Holdings: 1,500 pieces, 1626-1931, relating to Framingham and the vicinity. Included are correspondence of local residents, 1705-1825; sermons; military papers, 1689-1812; town and county records, 1705-1875; records of a local academy, 1826-55; and Grand Army of the Republic records, 1894-1901.
See Hist. Records Survey, Guide for Mass., p. 63.

GROVELAND

Langley-Adams Library. Mrs. J. B. Wood, Librarian.

Holdings: 12 vols. and 39 pieces, 1847-1937, relating to the locality. Included are records of two civic associations, 1883-1916; a fire engine company, 1847-87; and a Grand Army of the Republic post.
See Hist. Records Survey, Guide for Mass., p. 65.

HAVERHILL

Haverhill Historical Society. Donald C. Freeman, President.

Holdings: 98 vols. and 4,065 pieces, 1642-1958, relating to the town and its citizens. Included are papers of and about Hannah Dustin, or Duston (Mass.; pioneer), and her family, 1657-1736 (8 vols. and 102 pieces); papers of and concerning William Henry Moody (Mass.; U.S. Rep., Sec. Navy, Attorney Gen., U.S. Supreme Court Justice), 1876-1928 (484 pieces); and papers of Benjamin Perley Poore (Mass., D.C.; journalist, editor, author) and his family, 1791-1886 (346 pieces).
See Hist. Records Survey, Guide for Mass., p. 66.

—oOo—

Haverhill Public Library. 35 Summer St. Mrs. Edgar S. Lindsley, in charge of special collections.

Holdings: 445 vols. and 597 pieces, 1658-1944, relating chiefly to Haverhill. Included are letters and literary manuscripts of John Greenleaf Whittier (Mass.; poet), 1835-92 (138 pieces); ledgers and account books of business firms, 1757-1918 (31 vols.); and some town records, 1708-1933 (49 vols. and 93 pieces). There are also diaries, 1784-1901 (90 vols.); sermons, 1768-1874 (42 pieces); church records, 1709-1944 (177 vols. and 106 pieces); and records of families and local societies, 1658-1937 (27 vols. and 161 pieces). There are also medieval and Renaissance manuscripts (3 vols.).

See Hist. Records Survey, Guide for Mass., p. 68; and De Ricci, Census, p. 1062.

HOLLISTON

Holliston Historical Society.

Holdings: 10 vols. and 150 pieces, 1700-1925, relating chiefly to Holliston and the vicinity. Included are records of the local Free Soil Party, 1848-49; school and academy records, 1797-1878; and church records, 1788-1879.

See Hist. Records Survey, Guide for Mass., p. 70.

HOPEDALE

Bancroft Memorial Library. (Mrs.) Constance L. Clark, Librarian.

Holdings: 108 items, 1849-1908, consisting of papers of and about Adin Ballou (Mass.; Universalist clergyman, founder of the Hopedale Community) and records of the community.

IPSWICH

Ipswich Historical Society Library. Thomas Franklin Waters Bldg. Mrs. Charles Galacar, Librarian and Curator. Waters Memorial, 40 South Main St.

Holdings: 25 vols., 1 chest, and 3 filing drawers of papers, 1635-1883, relating chiefly to Ipswich. Included

are ships' logs, 1830-70 (25 vols.); nautical charts (1 sea chest); and accounts, receipts, bills, and other ships' documents (1 filing drawer). There are also miscellaneous manuscripts, 1635-1883 (2 filing drawers), consisting of sermons, diaries, account books, records of local organizations (such as the record book, 1825, of an early female academy), letters, family papers from 1820, and military records of local interest.

See Hist. Records Survey, Guide for Mass., p. 73.

—oOo—

Ipswich Public Library. Hester L. Mitchell, Librarian.

Holdings: 5 vols. and 179 pieces, relating chiefly to Ipswich. Included are memoirs of Daniel Webster (N.H.; U.S. Rep. and Sen., Sec. State), by an unknown author; addresses by Webster and Manasseh Cutler (Mass.; Congregational clergyman, botanist, colonizer); and sermons by Ipswich clergymen, 1744-1897 (56 pieces).

See Hist. Records Survey, Guide for Mass., p. 72.

—oOo—

Ipswich Town Hall. Anthony A. Murawski, Town Clerk.

Holdings: 1,600 items, 1633-1898, consisting chiefly of administrative records of the town. Included are early deeds to property, Revolutionary War papers and Civil War papers, and early church records.

See Hist. Records Survey, Guide for Mass., p. 75.

LANCASTER

Public Library.

Holdings: 407 pieces, 1675-1913,

chiefly relating to Lancaster. Included are papers concerning Shays' Rebellion, 1786-87; miscellaneous military papers, 1756-1896; church records, 1779-1905; correspondence concerning the opening of a normal institute, 1852-53; and papers relating to slate quarries in Lancaster and in Vermont, 1786-1809.

See Hist. Records Survey, Guide for Mass., p. 76.

LEXINGTON

Lexington Historical Society. P.O. Box 114. Mr. and Mrs. Edwin B. Worthen, Jr., Curators.

Holdings: Various discourses, sermons, account books, and diaries relating chiefly to Lexington. Included are sermons of Jonas Clark (Mass.; Congregational minister), and papers of local families.

MARBLEHEAD

Marblehead Historical Society. 161 Washington St. Mrs. Ralph T. Lloyd, Executive Secretary.

Holdings: Chiefly ledgers and account books relating to Marblehead. Included are papers of John Glover (Mass.; shipowner, Rev. War officer), among them lists of crews of privateers during the Revolution.

MARLBOROUGH

Marlborough Public Library.

Holdings: 14 vols., 1,247 pieces, and 3 cu. ft., 1680-1903, relating chiefly to Marlborough. Included are papers of Horatio Alger (Mass., N.Y.; writer of books for boys), 1844-1903; miscellaneous Revolutionary War and

Civil War papers; school records, 1805-50; church records, 1700-1851; and diaries and notebooks, 1781-1877.

See Hist. Records Survey, Guide for Mass., p. 79.

MEDFORD

Medford Historical Society. 10 Governor's Ave.

Holdings: 2,000 pieces, 1675-1874, relating chiefly to Medford. Included are papers of several local families, 1681-1848; a few letters and business papers relating to the slave trade, 1759-69; the Hall papers, 1725-1843 (600 pieces), chiefly relating to business; records kept by a physician and apothecary, 1786-1816 (6 vols.); and records of a turnpike company, 1803, 1806.

See Hist. Records Survey, Guide for Mass., p. 80.

MEDFORD 55

Tufts University Libraries. Reference Librarian.

Holdings: The Ryder Collection of Confederate Archives, 1861-65 (788 pieces), consisting largely of morning reports and other records pertaining to military prisons in Richmond, Va.

See Historical Records Survey, A Calendar of the Ryder Collection of Confederate Archives at Tufts College (1940. 168 p. Processed).

—oOo—

Universalist Historical Library, Crane Theological School. Tufts University. Ernest Cassara, Librarian.

Holdings: A collection of archives

and manuscripts belonging to the Universalist Historical Society.

MENDON

Mendon Historical Society. Main St. Mrs. Raymond Thomas, Secretary.

Holdings: A small quantity of manuscripts, chiefly 19th century, relating to Mendon. Included are records of Mendon Proprietors (1 vol.); records of an anti-horse-thief society and of a local bank; family papers; and several church histories and papers on local history.

See Hist. Records Survey, Guide for Mass., p. 82.

NANTUCKET

Nantucket Historical Association. P. O. Box 1016. George W. Jones, President.

Holdings: (1) Fair Street Historical Museum contains genealogical data, vital statistics, ledgers, letters, and diaries, 1660-1900; and records of the local Society of Friends, 1792-1890. (2) In the Whaling Museum there are shipping papers, account books, assurance policies, and records of the whaling industry in Nantucket, 1810-60; and logs of whaling ships, 1790-1864 (115 vols.).

NATICK

Morse Institute Public Library. 14 East Central St. Elizabeth H. Partridge, Librarian.

Holdings: 7 vols. and several pieces, 1754-1920, relating chiefly to Natick. Included are papers of Henry Wilson (Mass.; U. S. Sen. and Vice Pres.), 1862-73 (1 vol. and a

few letters); and records of a woman-suffrage organization, 1882-1920 (3 vols.).

NEW BEDFORD

Friends' Meeting House. Spring and 6th Sts.

Holdings: Archives of the Sandwich Quarterly Meeting of Friends, 1672-1894. Included are originals or copies of records of the Dartmouth, Nantucket, New Bedford, Pembroke, Sandwich, and Westport monthly meetings.

See Allison, Inventory, p. 67.

—oOo—

Old Dartmouth Historical Society. 18 Johnny Cake Hill. Philip F. Purrington, Curator.

Holdings: A collection of some thousand vols. and miscellaneous pieces, 1785-1922, but chiefly 19th century, relating to whaling, seafaring, and the merchant trade out of New Bedford. Included are accounts and letter books of Jonathan Bourne (Mass.; whaling merchant), 1848-61; miscellaneous letters and accounts of William Rotch, Sr. and Jr. (Mass.; whaling merchants), 1785-1818; and many papers of other New Bedford merchants and firms, 1816-88. There are also diaries of Samuel Rodman, Jr. (Mass.; merchant and meteorologist), 1821-59; logbooks, chiefly of whaling vessels, 1812-94 (600 vols.); and crew lists of various ships, 1836-1922. There is also a collection of whaling prints and paintings of merchant and whaling vessels.

NEWTON CENTER

Andover Newton Theological School

Library. 169 Herrick Rd. Robert W. Sillen, Librarian.

Holdings: 6,000 pieces, of the late 18th and 19th centuries, relating chiefly to Baptists in New England. Included are extensive papers of Isaac Backus (Conn., Mass.; Baptist clergyman), 1746-1806; and smaller quantities of papers of Irah Chase (Vt., Mass.; Baptist clergyman, prof. at Newton Theological Institute), 1825-45, and of James Pierpont (Conn.; Congregational clergyman), 1685-1713; and other papers that were formerly in the New England Baptist Library, Boston. There is also a large chest of business papers of a Boston wholesale firm, 1748-1812, including correspondence with its European agents.
See Allison, Inventory, pp. 34-56.

NORTH BROOKFIELD

Quoboag Historical Society. Haston Library Bldg.

Holdings: 500 pieces, 1735-1936, relating to the Brookfields, Warren, and New Braintree. Included are Civil War papers (50 pieces), papers of several local families, and a few business records.
See Hist. Records Survey, Guide for Mass., p. 86.

NORTHAMPTON

Forbes Library. West St. Lawrence E. Wikander, Librarian.

Holdings: 900 vols. and 25,000 pieces, 1661-1955, relating chiefly to Northampton and western Massachusetts.
Included are papers of James Wells Champney (Mass., N.Y.; painter, illustrator), 1861-89 (7 vols. and 435 pieces); Calvin Coolidge (Mass.; Gov., U.S. Pres.), 1895-1929 (28 vols. and 51 boxes), including both personal and official papers; James Monroe Crafts (Mass.; farmer, merchant, local historian), 1850-79 (500 pieces); Charles Edward Forbes (Mass.; judge, founder of Forbes Library), 1839-80 (42 vols. and 2,500 pieces), including a diary covering 42 years; Clarence Hawkes (Mass.; author), 57 vols., chiefly literary manuscripts; Joseph Hawley (Mass.; lawyer, "Son of Liberty"), 1655-1788 (7 vols. and 90 pieces), including papers of Hawley's father and grandfather; and Sylvester Judd (Mass.; compiler of historical materials), 1806-60 (90 vols. and 20 pieces), including 64 vols. of notes concerning an earlier period, on history, topography, genealogy, and the social, economic, and religious life of Hampshire County, the Connecticut Valley, and Massachusetts in general.
There are also papers of Elbridge Kingsley (Mass., N.Y.; engraver, painter), "reminiscences," to 1900 (1 vol.); Gerald Stanley Lee (Mass.; author), 1890-1944 (20 cartons); Benjamin Smith Lyman (Mass., Pa.; geological notebooks, principally on Japan; Seth Pomeroy (Mass.; gunsmith, colonial and Rev. War officer), 1745-? (76 pieces and 2 vols. of transcripts), including his diary of the expeditions to Louisbourg, 1745, and Crown Point, 1755; and Caleb Strong (Mass.; lawyer, U.S. Sen., Gov.), 1775-1819 (132 pieces), including several papers on Shays' Rebellion.
Besides some archives of Hampshire County and others of its towns, the Library has extensive archives of the town of Northampton, to 1883 (50 vols. and 15,000 pieces). These include records of town meetings, officers, and committees, some of the period of the American Revolution; financial and tax records; school records; records of fire companies and

the fire department, and vital records.

There are also letters written to a Massachusetts judge by prominent persons, 1900-37 (3 vols.); account books (88 vols.), besides others in the personal papers listed above; records of Congregational Church associations (19 vols. and 460 pieces), including 1 vol., 1731-47, Jonathan Edwards, scribe; 500 sermons, 1670-1828; diaries, commonplace books, memoirs, travel journals, weather records, and notebooks (45 vols.), as well as some among the personal papers; records of local business institutions, 1855-76 (3 vols. and 283 pieces); many military records, beginning in 1713; papers of families, chiefly of the Northampton area; papers relating to land operations in West Virginia, 1790-1853 (1,018 pieces); and records of local societies (41 vols. and 300 pieces), including records of a woman-suffrage association.

Forbes Library is the official repository for the inspectors' reports on official records of towns, cities, and counties in Massachusetts, made by the Historical Records Survey of the Works Progress Administration between 1935 and 1943 (132 bundles and index).

See Hist. Records Survey, Guide for Mass., p. 88.

—oOo—

Northampton Historical Society. 58 Bridge St.

Holdings: Included are some manuscripts of Martha J. Lamb (Mass., Ill., N.Y.; author, editor).

—oOo—

Smith College Library. Dorothy King, Curator of Rare Books.

Holdings: Historical and literary manuscripts, 18th-20th centuries, including papers of the Barrows family (Mass., Conn.), 1798-1891 (125

pieces); Anna Hempstead Branch (Conn.; poet), 1780-1937 (10,000 pieces); Bliss Carman (Canada; poet), 1861-1929 (2,500 pieces); John Cropper (Va.; Rev. War officer), 1777-1838 (18 letters written mainly during the Rev. War); Ellen Anderson Gholson Glasgow (Va.; novelist), 1930-45 (50 letters); Frances Elizabeth Clarke McFall, known as Sarah Grand (England; novelist), 1893-1918 (48 letters to her publisher); Anne Morrow Lindbergh (Mass., Conn.; author), manuscript of North to the Orient, with all relevant papers; Hiram Putnam (Mass., N.Y.; sea captain), 1780-1888 (100 pieces), including correspondence having to do with the Continental Congress; and Edith Wharton (N.Y.; novelist), 1902-20 (13 letters). There are also single letters from a number of authors, artists, musicians, and other persons. (The Sophia Smith Collection, named in honor of the founder of Smith College, is separately described below.)

Sophia Smith Collection, Smith College Library. Margaret S. Grierson, Director.

Holdings: A large quantity of manuscripts, chiefly of the 19th and 20th centuries and relating for the most part to the intellectual and social history of women.

Included are papers of Susan B. Anthony (N.Y.; suffragist, reformer), 1856-1905 (59 letters); Clara Barton (Mass., D.C.; founder of the American Red Cross), 1874-1910 (45 pieces); Lillie Devereux Blake (Pa., N.Y.; suffragist, author), late 19th century (a large collection); Carrie Chapman Catt (Iowa, N.Y.; suffragist), 1906-47 (182 letters); Nancy (Mrs. Charles Thomas) Cushman, better known as Nancy Cox-McCormack (Tenn., N.Y.; sculptor, author), 20th century (500 letters), including 189 from Louise de Koven Bowen (Ill.; social worker); Ethel E. Dreier (N.Y.; suffragist, political leader), 20th century (a large collection); Sophie Drinker (Pa.; musicologist), 1933-48 (16 vols.); Elaine Goodale Eastman (Mass., N.H.; author, worker for Indians' rights), 20th century (50 pieces); Geraldine Farrar (N.Y., Conn.; singer), after 1925 (137 letters); William Lloyd Garrison (Mass.; abolitionist, reformer) and his family, 1829-1908 (5,000 letters) with as many more from fellow reformers; Henry George (Calif., N.Y.; economist), 1888-97 (59 letters); Julia Collier Harris (Ga., Tenn.; journalist, author), 19th century (a large selection), including 67 letters from Henry Louis Mencken (Md.; author, editor, critic); and Clara E. Laughlin (Ill.; author, travel service director), 20th century (a large collection).

Other papers include those of Dorothy Mabel (Reed) Mendenhall (N.Y., Wis.; physician), chiefly 20th century (a large collection); Elizabeth Cutter Morrow (N.J.; author, wife of Dwight Morrow) and her family, 1880-1954 (40,000 pieces); Lucretia Coffin Mott (Mass., Pa.; Quaker preacher, abolitionist, feminist), 1835-78 (138 letters); Sarah Payson Willis Partin, known as Fannie Fern (Mass.; author), 19th century (32 letters and a large collection of related manuscript material); the Peabody sisters—Elizabeth, Mary, and Sophia (Mass.; educators), 1820-34 (87 letters); Parker Pillsbury (Mass., N.H.; reformer), 1860-97 (50 letters); Florence Rena Sabin (Md., N.Y., Colo.; anatomist, prof. Johns Hopkins Univ., Member Rockefeller Institute for Medical Research), 20th century (a large collection); Margaret Sanger (N.Y.; leader of birth-control movement), 1928-55 (50,000 pieces); Josephine Schain (Minn., N.Y.; social worker), 1920's-53, personal correspondence and material relating to woman suffrage, including records of the Pan Pacific Women's Association; Ida

M. Tarbell (Pa., N.Y.; author), 1896-1942 (1,000 letters and several manuscripts); Florence Guertin Tuttle (N.Y.; author), 20th century (68 pieces); and Mary van Kleeck (N.Y.; social research worker, director of social studies of Russell Sage Foundation), 1922-57 (a large collection), including correspondence and material relating to her pioneer work in social research. There are also papers of other important persons in less quantity, and a collection of records from the files of the National Young Women's Christian Association relating to the problem of household employment, 1933-39.

See Friends of the Smith College Library, Annual Reports, 1943 to date, and the College's The Sophia Smith Collection (1959. 15 p.).

NORTHBOROUGH

Northborough Historical Society. Gale Memorial Library.

Holdings: 23 vols. and 940 pieces, 1610-1930, relating chiefly to Northborough. Included are town records, 1731-1845; church records, 1730-1909; school records, 1780-1912; military papers, 1720-1920; diaries and account books; and records of local societies, 1800-1930, including a peace society, a temperance club, and a library and lyceum society.

See Hist. Records Survey, Guide for Mass., p. 90.

PEABODY

Peabody Historical Society. 35 Washington St.

Holdings: 16 vols. and 715 pieces, 1635-1914, relating chiefly to Peabody and the vicinity. Included are records of Congregational, Unitarian, and Baptist churches, 1669-1886; town records, 1752-1896; school records, 1810-1905; business papers, 1700-1842; and military papers, 1775-1864.

See Hist. Records Survey, Guide for Mass., p. 93.

PETERSHAM

Harvard Forest Library. Hugh M. Raup, Director.

Holdings: A small quantity of papers, of the 19th and 20th centuries, relating to forestry and allied subjects. Included are papers of Austin Cary (Maine; forester on U. S. Forest Service staff), 1897-1935 (70 notebooks, a series of reports, and some correspondence). providing information chiefly about Maine Woodlands.

—oOo—

Petersham Historical Society. Mrs. Donald F. Haines, President.

Holdings: 1,500 pieces, 1737-1863, relating chiefly to Petersham. Included are papers of Solomon Willard (Mass.; sculptor, architect, builder of Bunker Hill Monument), 1824-27 (5 booklets); town records, 1754-1839 (530 pages); and records of a Church of Christ (Covenanter), 1738-1857 (141 pages). There are also reports of Revolutionary committees of the town, 1774-76; other papers relating to the Revolution and Shays' Rebellion; and 57 notebooks of a farmer, 1860-1917.

See Hist. Records Survey, Guide for Mass., p. 94.

PITTSFIELD

Berkshire Athenaeum. Robert G. Newman, Librarian.

Holdings: 20 vols. and 500 pieces, of the 18th and 19th centuries, relating chiefly to town and church history in Pittsfield and the vicinity. Included are Shaker books and papers, 18th and 19th centuries (250 pieces), among them 100 musical manuscripts; records of a Quaker church in Adams and other Quaker records, 18th and 19th centuries; statistics of other churches and religious bodies of the same period (20 vols.); and some 250 sermons. There are also more than 50 letters of Herman Melville (N. Y., Mass.; novelist) and his family.

QUINCY

Adams National Historic Site. Superintendent.

Holdings: 5 vols. and 17 pieces, 1770-1910, relating to members of the Adams family. Included are papers of John Adams (Mass.; Member Continental Cong., diplomat, U. S. Pres.), 1770-1821 (3 vols. and 4 pieces), the volumes being docket books and other legal memoranda, 1770-76. There are also engagement books of Abigail Brooks Adams, wife of Charles Francis Adams (Mass.; U. S. Minister to Great Britain), 1863-68 (2 vols.); and an inventory of the furnishings of the "Old House," 1910.

READING

Reading Antiquarian Society. Parker Tavern, 103 Washington St. Mrs. Robert M. Barclay, Secretary, 26 vine St.

Holdings: A small collection, 1720-1916, relating chiefly to Reading. Included are 2 diaries, 1778-1809; business papers of a clock maker, including letters from agents in the United States and India, 1832-60 (several hundred pieces); business papers and diaries of J. W. Manning (Mass.; Reading nurseryman), 1847-1916 (112 vols.); and 100 letters of a Civil War soldier.

See Hist. Records Survey, Guide for Mass., p. 95.

REVERE

Revere Public Library. Nina E. Cross, Librarian.

Holdings: 199 pieces, 1637-1890, relating chiefly to Revere and vicinity. Included are town records, 1702-1885; maps, 1802-71; and family account books, 1825-55.

See Hist. Records Survey, Guide for Mass., p. 97.

SALEM

Essex Institute. 132 Essex St. Dean A. Fales, Jr., Director.

Holdings: A large collection of records, occupying over 2,000 sq. ft. of floor space, relating chiefly to the maritime history of the United States, especially that of Massachusetts. Included are 1,850 logs and sea journals, 1753-1906; customs records of Salem, Marblehead, Beverly, Newburyport, Ipswich, and Gloucester, 1738-1925 (occupying about 1,000 sq. ft. of floor space); records of entrances and clearances of Boston and all Essex County, Mass., ports, 1686-1765 (7 vols.); and many records relating to the China trade.

Papers of individuals include those of the following Members of Congress: Henry Bowen Anthony (R. I.; journalist, Gov., U. S. Sen.), 1860-74 (1 folder); Nathaniel P. Banks (Mass.; Civil War officer, U. S. Rep., Gov.), 1840-91 (21

vols. and 105 boxes); Rufus Choate (Mass.; lawyer, U. S. Rep. and Sen.), 1828-59 (1 folder); William Cogswell (Mass.; lawyer, Civil War officer, U. S. Rep.), 1861-93 (1 vol.); Caleb Cushing (Mass.; U. S. Rep., U. S. Attorney Gen., diplomat), 1829-64 (1 envelope); Manasseh Cutler (Mass.; U. S. Rep., Congregational clergyman, botanist, an organizer of the Ohio Company), 1763-1837 (1 envelope); Tristram Dalton (Mass.; U. S. Sen.), 1781-1814 (1 envelope); Nathan Dane (Mass.; lawyer, Member Continental Cong.), 1783-1835 (1 envelope); James Henry Duncan (Mass.; lawyer, U. S. Rep.), 1824-50 (1 portfolio); Benjamin Goodhue (Mass.; merchant, U. S. Rep. and Sen.), 1771-1814 (5 vols.); Thomas Allen Jenckes (R. I.; lawyer, U. S. Rep.), 1864-70 (1 folder); George Bailey Loring (Mass.; surgeon, U. S. Rep.), 1843-50 (22 vols. concerning patients at the Marine Hospital, Chelsea, Mass.); Samuel Lyman (Conn., Mass.; lawyer, U. S. Rep.), 1795-1800 (1 envelope); Benjamin Pickman (Mass.; lawyer, businessman, U. S. Rep.), 1762-1842 (12 vols.); Robert Rantoul, Jr. (Mass.; lawyer, reformer, U. S. Sen. and Rep.), 1836-51 (2 boxes); Nathan Read (Mass., Maine; iron manufacturer, inventor, U. S. Rep.), 1771-1847 (5 vols. and 3 envelopes); Christopher Robinson (R. I.; lawyer, U. S. Rep.), 1859-61 (1 folder); Leverett Saltonstall (Mass.; mayor of Salem, U. S. Rep.), 1755-1840 (16 vols.); William Henry Seward (N. Y.; Gov., U. S. Sen., Sec. State), 1852-57 (1 folder); Nathaniel Silsbee (Mass.; ship captain, merchant, U. S. Rep. and Sen.), 1799-1844 (2 vols., 1 box, and 1 portfolio); Joseph Story (Mass.; U. S. Rep., U. S. Supreme Court Justice), 1823-32 (1 vol. of charges to juries); George Thacher (Mass., Maine; Member Continental Cong., U. S. Rep., jurist), 1783-1857 (1 envelope); and Henry Alexander Wise (Va.; U. S. Rep.,

Minister to Brazil, Gov.), 1836-59 (1 vol.). See also Stephen Clarendon Phillips, Timothy Pickering, and Daniel Appleton White, below.

Papers of sea captains, shipowners, and merchants include those of Charles Moses Endicott (Mass.; sea captain, antiquarian), 1794-1858 (3 vols.); John Glover (Mass.; Rev. War officer, shipowner), 1775-81 (7 vols. of orderly books); William Gray (Mass.; merchant, shipowner, Lt. Gov.) and his son of the same name, 1804-52 (1 envelope); Aaron Lopez (R. I., Mass.; merchant), 1764-69 (1 envelope); George Peabody (Mass., D. C., Md.; merchant, financier, philanthropist), chiefly 1830-57 (140 boxes and many letters and account books); Stephen Clarendon Phillips (Mass.; merchant, U. S. Rep.), 1828-33 (2 envelopes); and David Pingree (Mass.; merchant, shipowner), 1826-79 (110 vols. and 175 boxes). See also Benjamin Goodhue and Nathaniel Silsbee, above.

There are also papers of William Bentley (Mass.; Unitarian clergyman, author), 1783-1819 (1 box); Joseph Barlow Felt (Mass.; clergyman, antiquarian, librarian) and his family, 1709-1868 (3 vols.); John Higginson (Mass.; clergyman, author), 1698-1760 (1 envelope and 1 package); and Samuel Johnson (Mass.; independent liberal preacher, educator, author), 1832-80 (7 boxes and 6 envelopes).

Other papers are those of Charles Edgar Clark (U. S. naval officer), 1898-1904 (1 envelope); Mary Abigail Dodge (Mass.; author), 1856-96 (3 boxes); Nathaniel Hawthorne (Mass.; novelist), 1 vol., 2 boxes, and 1 envelope; Edward Augustus Holyoke (Mass.; physician) and his family, 1653-1828 (29 vols., 1 portfolio, and 2 envelopes); Lucy Larcom (Mass.; author, teacher), 1849-92 (4 boxes); Timothy Pickering (Mass., Pa.; Rev. War officer, Postmaster Gen., Sec. War, Sec. State, U. S. Sen. and Rep.), 1771-1827 (12 vols. and 17 envelopes),

including diaries, Adams correspondence, 1773-78, relating to the Wyoming Valley, Pa., and material on the Ohio Co.; Pickering's son, John Pickering (Mass.; lawyer, philologist), 1781-1848 (11 vols. and 7 envelopes); Edward Staniford Rogers (Mass.; horticulturist), 1813-1901 (1 envelope); William Wetmore Story (Mass.; sculptor, essayist, poet), 1862-93 (2 envelopes); Daniel Appleton White (Mass.; U. S. Rep., jurist), 1790-1861 (20 boxes); and John Greenleaf Whittier (Mass.; poet, abolitionist), 1824-91 (27 vols.).

Among the holdings are 2,200 account books; 1,800 cartoons collected by George Francis Dow (Mass.; author, antiquarian); and much genealogical material for New England families of both local and national importance. There are also records of Salem churches, 1629-1898 (5 shelves); scrapbooks of papers of the New England Society for Propagating the Gospel Among the Indians; diaries of clergymen, 1700-1926; and several thousand sermons.

See Allison, Inventory, p. 68; Howard Corning, "The Essex Institute of Salem," in Business Hist. Society, Bulletin, 7 (no. 5):1-5 (Oct. 1933); Muriel E. Hidy, "The George Peabody Papers," ibid., 12:1-6 (Feb. 1938); Hist. Records Survey, Guide for Mass., pp. 99-105; Forest History Sources, pp. 41-43; and Library of Congress, Manuscripts in Public and Private Collections in the United States, pp. 38-40 (1924).

—oOo—

Peabody Museum of Salem. M. V. Brewington, Curator of Maritime History.

Holdings: 2,300 vols. and 1,900 boxes of manuscripts, consisting of logbooks, journals, account books, and miscellaneous papers relating to maritime history, shipbuilding, and trade with the Far East, Africa, and the Pacific Islands. Included are papers of Benjamin Williams Crowninshield (Mass.; merchant, Sec. Navy) and Jacob Crowninshield (Mass.; sea captain, U. S. Rep.); papers relating to the building of the USS Essex, 1799 (5 boxes), including correspondence with Paul Revere (Mass.; patriot, craftsman); letter books, correspondence, and ship plans of Josiah Fox (Mass.; U. S. naval constructor), 1794 ff. (4 vols. and 960 letters); 11 boxes containing the journal and private papers of Richard Palmer Waters during his term as U. S. Consul in Zanzibar; and 1 journal and 3 boxes of letters of John B. Williams, U. S. Consul in New Zealand.

SHREWSBURY

Shrewsbury Historical Society. Howe Memorial Library.

Holdings: 900 pieces, dating from 1731 and relating chiefly to Shrewsbury. Included are military papers, records of churches and other organizations, store accounts, and some town records.
See Hist. Records Survey, Guide for Mass., p. 106.

SOUTH HADLEY

Mount Holyoke College Library. Flora B. Ludington, Librarian.

Holdings: 69 vols. and 9,500 pieces, 1811-1955, relating chiefly to the College but including some other papers. Papers relating to Mount Holyoke Seminary and College, chiefly from 1834, include letters and documents of earlier date relating to Mary Lyon (Mass.; pioneer in women's education, founder and pres. of Mt. Holyoke College) and letters addressed to the Seminary and College by many persons, concerning women's education, missionary work in the United States and elsewhere, and other subjects. There are also papers of Lyman Beecher (Conn., Mass., Ohio; Presbyterian clergyman) and his family, 1822-94 (41 pieces on indefinite deposit); Charles P. Chandler (Mass.; Civil War officer), 1861-62 (1 vol. and 60 pieces); and Nathaniel W. Leighton (N. Y.; Civil War surgeon), 1861-64 (1 vol. and 40 pieces).

SOUTH NATICK

South Natick Historical, Natural History and Library Society. Mabel A. Parmenter, Attendant, 4 Merrill Rd.

Holdings: A few pieces dated from 1652, relating chiefly to the village and its vicinity. Included are photostatic copies of letters of John Eliot (Mass.; Congregational clergyman, missionary to the Indians, translator, author), 1652-57; and scattered letters of several persons of national importance.
See Hist. Records Survey, Guide for Mass., p. 107.

SOUTH SUDBURY

Goodnow Public Library.

Holdings: 166 pieces, 1654-1841, relating chiefly to the locality. Included are some church papers, 1710-1835; town records, 1705-1820; and 2 account books, 1769-1839.
See Hist. Records Survey, Guide for Mass., p. 108.

SOUTHBOROUGH

Fay Library. (Mrs.) Sarah V. Stivers

Hutt, Librarian.

Holdings: 350 pieces, 1727-1925, relating chiefly to Southborough. Included are a collection of papers of and relating to Francis Ball Fay (Mass.; U. S. Rep.), 1771-1866; a few school records, 1828-30; and records of a local Grand Army of the Republic post, 1878-1925 (3 vols.).

See Hist. Records Survey, Guide for Mass., p. 109.

SPRINGFIELD 3

Connecticut Valley Historical Museum. William Pynchon Memorial Bldg. Juliette Tomlinson, Director.

Holdings: Included are account books of John Pynchon (Mass.; Springfield merchant, public servant), 1651-1713 (7 vols.); a court record book of Hampshire County, Mass., 1663-76 (1 vol.); a diary of Joseph Stock (Mass.; Springfield artist), 1833-45; and records of a few business concerns in the vicinity of Springfield, transferred from the former Smith College Council of Industrial Studies.

SPRINGFIELD 5

Springfield City Library. John A. Humphry, Director.

Holdings: A small collection of manuscripts, chiefly of the 19th century, relating to the history of Springfield. Included are papers of three prominent lawyers, 1788-1851 (19 vols.); correspondence of other persons of local distinction (4 boxes); a diary; hotel registers, 1838-1912 (217 vols.); and a number of day books and account books of miscellaneous local businesses of the 18th and 19th centuries. There are also European manuscripts of the 12th to the 15th

centuries.

See De Ricci, Census, p. 1066.

STOCKBRIDGE

Historical Room, Stockbridge Library. Grace B. (Mrs. Graham D.) Wilcox, Curator.

Holdings: 109 vols. and several thousand pieces, 1751-1955, relating chiefly to Stockbridge. Included are some papers of the Stockbridge Indians, 1762; account books, 1788-1905 (30 vols.); records of two Congregational churches, 1758-1896 (8 vols. and 3 boxes); town papers, 1770-1885 (2,219 pieces); tavern records, 1775-95 (10 vols.); and records of debating clubs, 1806-71 (3 vols.), a turnpike association, 1806-50 (1 vol.), and a village improvement society, 1853-1955 (10 vols.). There is also a collection of autograph letters, chiefly by New Englanders of the 18th and 19th centuries.

TAUNTON

Old Colony Historical Society. 66 Church Green. W. Wallace Austin, Secretary.

Holdings: 10,100 pieces, 1638-1927, relating chiefly to the "Old Colony" and local history. Included are the diary and other papers of Francis Baylies (Mass.; scholar, lawyer, U. S. Rep., Chargé d'Affaires in Argentina), 1790-1862 (300 pieces); account books, 1791-1836 (50 vols.), concerning an academy, farming, merchandising, shipping, and manufacturing; Congregational and Baptist church records and sermons, 1729-1927 (75 pieces); public records of Taunton and nearby towns, 1638-1911; and records of an

iron works, 1683-1880 (165 pieces).
See Hist. Records Survey, Guide
for Mass., p. 112.

TEMPLETON

Narragansett Historical Society of
Templeton, Massachusetts, Inc.
Henry R. Wheeler, President.

Holdings: 27 vols. and 756 pieces,
1597-1934, relating chiefly to Templeton. Included are military records,
1800-67 (477 items); town records,
1809-1901; church records and sermons, 1792-1860; and ledgers and day
books, 1824-55.
See Hist. Records Survey, Guide
for Mass., p. 113.

WALTHAM 54

Waltham Public Library. 735 Main
St.

Holdings: 39 vols. and 457 pieces,
1721-1921, relating chiefly to Waltham and vicinity. Included are sermons, 1721-50; records of the Young
Men's Christian Association, 1863-73
(92 pieces) and of the Young Men's
Christian Union, 1889-96 (2 vols.);
and records of a farmers' club, 1857-
92 (8 vols.). There are also records
of Rumford Institute, 1826-87 (6 vols.);
a ladies' hospital aid society, 1888-
1921 (5 vols.); two literary associations, 1857-1905; and a "social library," 1790-1852.

WATERTOWN

Historical Society of Watertown.
Watertown Public Library. Francis
Lightbody, President.

Holdings: Several hundred pieces,
1664-1897, relating chiefly to Water-

town and vicinity. Included are papers
of Henry Ware (Mass.; Unitarian clergyman, prof. at Harvard College),
1803-5. There are also diaries, account books, and sermons.
See Hist. Records Survey, Guide
for Mass., p. 119.

WAYLAND

Wayland Free Public Library. Concord St.

Holdings: 6 vols. and 39 pieces,
1695-1848, relating chiefly to Wayland and vicinity. Included are journals and accounts of two local physicians, 1722-58 (4 vols.), among them
a diary kept at Crown Point, 1758; a
few town records of East Sudbury and
Concord, 1742-1841; minutes of a
temperance society, 1833; and some
military papers, 1775-1816.
See Hist. Records Survey, Guide
for Mass., p. 120.

WELLESLEY

Wellesley College Library. Hannah
D. French, Research Librarian.

Holdings: 2,400 pieces, relating
chiefly to European and American literature. Included are 53 medieval
and Renaissance manuscripts; 47 letters to Alice Stone Blackwell (Mass.;
journalist, reformer), 1922-36,
chiefly concerning the freedom of India; 1,500 letters of Elizabeth Barrett
Browning and Robert Browning (England; poets); and a journal of Charles
Sumner (Mass.; U. S. Sen.), 1857 (1
vol.).
See De Ricci, Census, pp. 1067-
1078.

WEST BOYLSTON

Beaman Memorial Public Library.

(Mrs.) Marion Snow, Librarian.

Holdings: 8 vols. and 3 pieces, 1867-1919, consisting of records of a local Grand Army of the Republic post.

WESTBOROUGH

Westborough Historical Society. 7 Parkman St. (Mrs.) Rachel R. Dearing, President.

Holdings: 1,071 pieces, 1724-1932, relating chiefly to Westborough. Included are diaries, 1724-1865; town records, 1737-1836; sermons and church records, 1766-1836; military records, 1812-64; and school records, 1816-95.
See Hist. Records Survey, Guide for Mass., p. 122.

WESTFORD

J. V. Fletcher Library.   May E. Day, Librarian.

Holdings: 13 vols. and 9 pieces, 1727-1869, relating chiefly to Westford. Included are account books, 1785-1869 (3 vols.); church records, 1727-1864 (3 vols.); and records of a "society library," 1797-1859 (2 vols.).
See Hist. Records Survey, Guide for Mass., p. 123.

WEYMOUTH 88

Tufts Library.   Eleanor T. Cooney, Librarian.

Holdings: 5 vols. and 355 pieces, 1749-1925, relating chiefly to Weymouth. Included are papers of and relating to Cotton Tufts (Mass.; physician, member of U.S. Constitutional

Convention, pres. of Mass. Medical Society), 1755-1809 (54 pieces).
See Hist. Records Survey, Guide for Mass., p. 124.

WILLIAMSTOWN

Roper Public Opinion Research Center, Williams College.   P.O. Box 1270.   Philip K. Hastings, Director.

Holdings: A large quantity of punch card decks, questionnaires, code books, and other materials resulting from studies made since 1936 by 44 opinion research organizations, 18 of them American and 26 foreign.
See The Roper Public Opinion Research Center at Williams College (1958. 32 p.).

—oOo—

Williams College Library.   Wyllis E. Wright, Librarian.

Holdings: 100 vols., 35 boxes, and several hundred pieces, 1700-1951, relating chiefly to Williams College.   Included are papers of Samuel Chapman Armstrong (Mass., Va.; Civil War officer, founder of Hampton Institute), 1860-93 (4 vols. and 1 box); William Cullen Bryant (Mass., N.Y.; poet, newspaper editor), 1819-78 (20 pieces); Paul Ansel Chadbourne (Maine, Mass.; pres. of Williams College), 1850-83 (1 box); Chester Dewey (Mass.; Congregational clergyman, pioneer scientist, prof. at Univ. of Rochester), 1808-36 (1 box); Mark Hopkins (Mass.; pres. of Williams College, theologian), 1815-87 (7 vols. and 123 pieces); James Bissett Pratt (Mass.; educator, philosopher), 1898-1944 (30 vols. and 20 boxes); Edwin Arlington Robinson (Maine, N.Y.; poet), 1910-35 (50 pieces); Francis Lynde Stetson (N.Y.; lawyer), 1862-

1917 (9 boxes); and Ephraim Williams (Mass.; colonial soldier, founder of Williams College), 1747-55 (1 vol. and 15 pieces).

WINTHROP 52

Winthrop Public Library. Dorothy L. Kinney, Librarian.

Holdings: 1,750 pieces, early 17th to 20th centuries, relating chiefly to Winthrop. Included are Methodist Church records, 1817-1904 (137 pieces); accounts, 1600-1800 (563 pieces); and receipts, tax bills, deeds, letters, and papers of 2 farms.
See Hist. Records Survey, Guide for Mass., p. 125.

WOBURN

Woburn Public Library. Pleasant St.

Holdings: Several vols. and 9,000 pieces, 1592-1896, relating chiefly to Woburn. Included are some military papers; account books and other business papers; records of a local church, 1756-1874; three collections of surveyors' plans (1,371 pieces); a diary with an eyewitness account of the Battle of Lexington; and a collection of autographs, 1631-1884.
See Hist. Records Survey, Guide for Mass., p. 126.

WORCESTER

American Antiquarian Society. Salisbury St. and Park Ave. Clifford K. Shipton, Director.

Holdings: Over half a million documents, 1634 to recent date, but largely of the 18th and 19th centuries, on 1,320 running feet of shelving in the Society's manuscript room. They re-

late chiefly to the United States and particularly to Massachusetts. The leading collections are listed below in alphabetical order as requested by the Society.
Abbot, Ephraim (Mass.; Congregational clergyman), 1812-24 (2 vols. of diaries and many sermons), also 1 box of Abbot family papers, 1801-1904. Account books (about 500), including arms manufacturing; auctioneering; banking; blacksmithing; bookplates; book-selling; canals; carriage and coach making; Confederate Army ordnance stores and provisions; doctors and druggists; engraving; farm accounts, including spinning, knitting, and weaving; French and Indian War, Col. Bradstreet accounts; furs and work thereon; hardware; harness making and saddlery; horses, stud account of a horse dealer; hotels and taverns; household accounts; importers; insurance; jewelers; labor, general carpentry and shipbuilding; land speculation; legal records; lithographers; loans, records of United States Loan Office, Boston, 1785-91; lotteries; machinists and manufacturers; mills, grist and saw; music, publishing and teaching; peddlers; shingles, timber; shipping and shipbuilding; shoe-making; slaves, sale of; stage lines; storekeepers' records, general, grocery, meat, fish; tailors; tanners; tinsmiths; toll bridges; and type foundry, order and font books. Agard, Charles W. (New Bedford, Mass.), manuscripts and notes on ships, shipping, the slave trade, whaling, and the Civil War (6 boxes). Allen, Jolley (Mass.; Boston merchant), 1776-80 (1 vol.), minute book and journal. Allen, Thomas (Mass., Conn.; merchant and ship owner of Boston and New London), 1737-1835 (9 boxes). American Antiquarian Society, 1812-1956 (247 boxes), correspondence. American Art Association (New York City), 1887-1918 (175 boxes), journals, ledgers, ac-

counts of auction sales and sundry records; and the Thomas E. Kirby collection of notes, memos, and data pertaining to same (14 boxes). Atwater, Caleb (N.Y., Ohio; lawyer, archeologist), 1818-25, letters and drawings on Indian antiquities in Ohio.

Baldwin, Christopher C. (Mass.; lawyer, editor, librarian of American Antiquarian Society), 19th century (11 vols. and 4 boxes), including diaries and letters. Baldwin, Simeon Eben (Conn.; chief justice of State supreme court, Gov.) and his family (1 vol. and 12 boxes), including correspondence of his brother George W. Baldwin (Mass.; Boston lawyer), 1856-78 (4 boxes). Barnstable, Mass., records of the West Parish, 1668-1807. Barton, Ira Moore (Mass.; State legislator, probate judge), correspondence, including 15 letters, 1861-66, from his cousin Clara Barton (Mass., D.C.; philanthropist, founder of the American Red Cross), and legal papers (2 boxes). Bayley, Frank W. (Mass.; Boston art dealer), 1920's and 1930's (6 boxes), correspondence. Bentley, William (Mass.; Unitarian clergyman, author), 18th and early 19th centuries (44 vols.). Bicknell, Thomas W. (R.I., Mass.; R.I. commissioner of public schools, editor of educational journals), 1855-1924 (1 box). Bigelow, Andrew (Mass.; minister to the "Poor of All Boston"), 1806-99 (30 diary vols. and 6 boxes). Binney, Amos (Mass.; naval agent, commander of Charlestown Navy Yard), 1811-14 (1 letter book). Blackstone Canal Company, from Providence to Worcester, 1823-31 (3 vols. and 1 box). Bolton, Charles Knowles (Mass.; librarian of Boston Athenaeum, antiquarian), 1900-45 (38 vols.), including a few diaries of his wife Sarah K. Bolton (Mass.; author). Boston Town Records, 1631-60 (1 vol. and 2 boxes), miscellaneous papers. Bowen, Clarence Winthrop (N.Y., Conn.;

editor, publisher of the Independent, historian), 1869-1934 (13 vols.), plus a large collection of his scrapbooks, with correspondence and personal papers. Bradstreet, John (Canada; British and colonial officer), 18th century (5 vols.), including correspondence with William Shirley (England, Mass.; colonial Gov., French and Indian War officer), 1755-56, Jeffery Lord Amherst (British commander in chief in America), 1758-63, Thomas Gage (British commander in chief in America), 1764-67, and the supply service, 1754-73. Brigham, Elijah (Mass., letters, documents, legal papers of the interrelated Brigham, Phillips, and Waters families, 1754-1880 (2 boxes). Buckingham, Philo B. (Conn.; Civil War officer), 1862-65 (2 boxes), including over 100 letters to his wife. Bullard family of Sherburne, Holliston, Northbridge, and Sutton, Mass., 1724-1842 (2 boxes). Bullock, Alexander H. (Mass.; editor, judge, Gov.), chiefly 1860-80 (4 boxes). Burr, Aaron (N.Y.; Rev. War officer, U.S. Sen. and Vice Pres.), 1772-1818 (1 vol. of about 100 letters received).

Cabot, William B. (Mass.; engineer, explorer), 1923, manuscript on Indian place names of Massachusetts (94 pages typed and indexed). Carey, Mathew (Pa.; publisher, economist), 1788-1857 (41 vols. and 1 box), chiefly papers of his firm and its successors. Carter, Robert, known as King Carter (Va.; public official, landholder), 1772-93 (1 diary and 1 box of transcripts). Cathcart, James Leander (Pa.; U.S. consul and diplomatic agent), 1788 and 1795 (2 vols.), journals of negotiations between the United States and the Regency of Algiers. Chandler, John (Mass., England; loyalist), 18th century (1 vol.), papers relating to his claim for compensation for losses in American Revolution. Chapin, Seth (Congregational clergyman), 1825 (21 letters), constituting "A Journey through New England to New York." Chase, Lucy (Mass.; Quakeress, educator of Negroes), 1824-1902 (2 boxes), including slave dealers' papers, 1846-64, and letters and papers taken from Pres. Jefferson Davis' offices after the fall of Richmond. Cheever family, 1783-1885 (24 boxes), chiefly the papers of George Barrell Cheever (Mass., N.Y.; Congregational and Presbyterian clergyman, editor, author, abolitionist), his brother Henry T. Cheever (Mass.; traveler, author, Congregational minister), and his sister Elizabeth Bancroft Cheever Washburn (Mass.; philanthropist). Civil War, 1861-65 (1 vol. and 2 boxes), letters from soldiers and miscellaneous papers. Clouet, Alexandre de, 1855-59, notes (in French) at Louisiana College. Cobbett, William (England, Pa.; journalist, publicist), 1796-1800 (1 ledger kept as a bookseller in Philadelphia). Cole, George Watson (N.J., Calif.; librarian, bibliographer), 1851-1939 (5 vols. and 72 boxes), including materials on Bermuda and missions in California. Conant, Edwin (Mass.; lawyer), 1792-1886 (2 boxes), documents relating chiefly to Worcester and vicinity. Confederate Army, Southern States, 1861-63 (1 vol.), invoices of ordnance and ordnance stores. Copeland and Day, Boston publishers and importers of fine books, 1880-1900 (1 box of correspondence). Corwin, Jonathan (Mass.; keeper of general store in Salem), 1655-79 (2 small account books), one containing some family records. Craigie, Andrew (Mass., N.Y.; Rev. War officer, merchant, financier, land speculator), 1717-1815 (8 vols. and 11 boxes), including 550 letters on the Scioto Land Co., 1787-90. Curwin papers, 1640-1796 (575 items), containing correspondence of the Sewall, Curwin, Cotton Mather, Dummer, and Yale families (400 items), papers on the Louisburg

campaign, 1755, and early churches near Boston, and letters on horticulture from P. Collinson of London to Col. John Custis of Williamsburg, Va., 1734-45 (4 vols.). Cuyler, Cornelius (N.Y.; fur trader, mayor of Albany, supplier of troops in French and Indian War), 1724-36 and 1752-64 (2 letter books).

Davenport, John (England, Conn., Mass.; Congregational clergyman), 17th century (200 pages), sermons, essays, and other papers. Davis, Isaac (Mass.; lawyer, banker, State legislator, mayor of Worcester), 1816-52 (38 vols.). Davis, John (Mass.; U.S. Rep. and Sen., Gov.), 1824-54 (3 vols.), also letters to and from his wife Eliza, 1825-53 (1 vol.), commissions signed by various Governors, military drafts for training, 1770-76, and other official documents. DePuy, Henry F. (Pa., Md.; bibliographer, antiquarian, collector of Americana), notes on American historical subjects (3 boxes, 4 filing drawers, and 1 card file). Devens, Charles (Mass.; lawyer, Civil War officer, State supreme court justice, U.S. Attorney Gen.), correspondence, accounts, and other papers relative to raising funds to erect in Worcester, Mass., a bronze equestrian statue of him, by the sculptor Daniel Chester French, dedicated 1926 (2 boxes). DeVinne, Theodore L. (N.Y.; printer, typographical authority, writer on printing), 1883-1911 (90 pages of letters). Dighton Rock, Dighton, Mass., essay by Charles R. Hale in 1865 on its inscriptions, with a plate and drawings, and 2 sketches in oil on canvas of the inscriptions, in a folder. Drake, Samuel G. (Mass.; Boston bookseller, antiquarian, historian), 1860's and 1870's (2 folders). Drowne, Shem (Mass.; Boston tinsmith, wood carver, coppersmith), 1720-21, 1754-68 (1-vol. day book). Dudley, Mass., town papers, 1747-1859 (3 binders). Dumez, Jean Baptiste, photostats of his autobiography in French, written in early 1800's, part of the Edward L. Tinker Collection of Louisiana material (325 pages). Dunn, Robinson Potter (R. I.; Presbyterian clergyman, rhetoric and English prof. at Brown Univ.), 1890's (2 vols.), chiefly letters concerning his career and death. Earle, Pliny, Jr. (Mass.; physician, psychiatrist), 1837-91 (1 vol. and 9 boxes), including correspondence, medical and travel notes, lectures, case notes, articles on insanity, and diaries. Ebeling, Christoph Daniel (Germany, Austria; geographer, collector of maps and books relating to America), a small notebook and a book of sermons, both in German. Engleman, John B. (Va.; printer, publisher of music books, music teacher), synopses of letters written 1856-59 (1 vol.). Evans, Griffith (sec. of the commission under article 6 of Jay Treaty for the compensation of Royalists), 1797-99 (1 vol. and 1 folder).

Farnam, Mary Baker (R. I., Mass.; Quakeress), 1811-29 (1 vol.), a diary of her religious travels. Fessenden, Thomas (N. H.; clergyman at Walpole), 1773-1805 (32 sermons). Fisher, Jonathan (Maine; Congregational clergyman at Blue Hill, author, poet, artist), 1798-1834 (700 pages of diary transcripts). Fiske, Nathan (Mass.; Congregational clergyman at Brookfield), 1754-99 (7 vols.), including diaries. Fitch, Thomas (Mass.; Boston magistrate, merchant), 1702/3-11 (1 letter book), including many letters to English merchants. Forbes, Harriette M. (Mass.; bibliographer, historian), materials on early New England (8 vols. and 6 boxes). Foster, Dwight (Mass.; U. S. Rep. and Sen.), 1772-1819, journals covering 27 years and letters to his wife, 1772-99 (8 vols.), and also Foster family papers, 1750-1884 (27 boxes). Foster, Stephen Symonds (N. H., Mass.; abolitionist, temperance and woman suffrange advocate) and his wife, Abigail Kelley Foster (Mass.; abolitionist, feminist), 1836-1921 (400 letters). Franklin and Hall, work book, 1759-89 (1 vol. of photostats). French, Edwin Davis (N. Y.; engraver, bookplate designer), 1894-1906 (16 vols. and 1 box). French and Indian War (11 vols.), including letters on the Louisbourg Expedition and operations in New York of Sir William Johnson (N. Y.; French and Indian War officer, supt. of Indian affairs). Frost, Donald McKay, notes for and text of a monograph on "General William H. Ashley and the Northwest Fur Trade," 1822-30 (1 box). Gage family papers, including papers of Thomas Hovey Gage (Mass.; physician, treasurer of Clark Univ.), 1849-1909 (2 boxes); Homer Gage (Mass.; physician), 1877-1930 (1 box); and T. Hovey Gage (Mass.; lawyer), 2 boxes pertaining to Worcester County artists. Gale, Frederick W. (Mass., Mo.; lawyer), 1828-54 (2 vols. and 3 file boxes), including 450 letters and 4 European journals. Gay, Ebenezer (Mass.; Congregational clergyman at Hingham), 18th-century sermons. Goddard Family Papers, 1713-1867, letters, diaries, sermons, and other papers of several members of the family, stemming from Charlestown, Mass. (5 vols. and 1 box). Goodwin, Isaac (Mass.; lawyer, author), early 19th century (4 vols. and 9 boxes). Gookin's Christian Indians, "An Historical Account of the doings and sufferings of the Christian Indians in New England in the years 1675-1677," by D. Gookin, London, manuscript copy (200 pages). Goss, Elbridge H. (Mass.; Melrose banker, author), 1854-1908 (1 box), correspondence. Gough, John B. (Mass.; Worcester lecturer, author, temperance advocate), 19th century (29 vols., 1 folio, and 3 boxes).

Hale, Robert (Mass., 18th century (2 vols.), including treatises in various fields and a journal of an expedition to Nova Scotia in 1731. Hallam,

Robert A. (Conn.; Episcopal clergyman), 1857 (3 vols.), journal of a trip to Europe. Hamilton, Alexander (N.Y.; Rev. War officer, Member Continental Cong., Sec. Treas.), 1791-94 (1 vol.), chiefly Treasury Department circulars. Hancock family papers, including letters of Thomas Hancock (Mass.; merchant), 1735-50, a description and inventory of John Hancock house, and notes on genealogy (6 boxes). Hardinge, Benjamin (Mass.; scientist, inventor, physician, author, lecturer), 19th century (2 boxes). Harris, Joseph (N.Y.; missionary to the seamen of N.Y.), 1859-63 (1 journal). Harris, Thaddeus Mason (Mass.; Unitarian clergyman, librarian, naturalist), notes on American history and archeology (5 vols.). Harvard, Mass., Shaker church records, 1790-1875 (2 vols.). Haswell, Anthony (Mass., Vt.; printer, editor, ballad writer), chiefly 18th century (3 vols.), containing letters, ballads, and a journal of his journey from Bennington, Vt., to New York in 1796. Haven, Samuel Foster (Mass.; archeologist, editor, librarian of American Antiquarian Society), 1790-1881 (6 boxes). Heartman, Charles F. (antiquarian bookseller, publisher, editor, bibliographer), a bibliography on cards of German books relating to America (2 boxes). Heath, Daniel C. (Maine, N.Y., Mass.; educator, member of publishing firm of Ginn and Heath, founder of D.C. Heath and Co.), correspondence, 1873-1908 (1 box). Henshaw, William (Mass.; French and Indian and Rev. War officer), 1758-59 and 1775-77 (orderly books and 5 boxes of journals). Hewes, David (Mass., Calif.; pioneer, merchant, builder, orchardist), letters relating to his career at Yale and text for a genealogy of the Hewes family, 19th century (1 box). Hoar, George Frisbie (Mass.; U.S. Rep. and Sen.), 1877-1904 (6 boxes). Hodges, Samuel (Mass.; U S consul at the Cape Verde Islands, manufacturer), 1812-

27 (9 boxes). Howells, William Dean (Mass., N.Y.; novelist, literary critic, editor), 1903-14 (199 letters), chiefly correspondence with publishers. Hull, John (Mass.; silversmith, colonial mintmaster and treasurer, merchant), 1670-80 (1 vol.), diary, memoirs, and letter book. Hull, Joseph (Conn.; collector of customs at New London), 1733-61, accounts of fees collected. Huntington family papers (1 box), chiefly the Revolutionary records of Joshua Huntington (Conn.; Rev. War officer).

Jennison, Samuel (Mass.; Worcester banker, historian, biographer), 19th century (16 boxes of biographical notes). Kinnicutt, Thomas (Mass.; lawyer, State legislator, probate judge), 1828-57 (2 boxes), chiefly family papers and documents. Lancaster, Joseph (England; originator of the Lancasterian system of education), 19th century (17 boxes). Larned, Samuel (R.I.; sec. of U.S. Legation and Chargé d'Affaires in Chile, Chargé d'Affaires in Peru and Bolivia), 19th century, family papers and official documents bearing signatures of U.S. Presidents and other officials (12 boxes). Lee and Shepard (Mass.; Boston publishers), 1861-1942 (12 boxes of correspondence). Lincoln, Enoch (Mass., Maine; U.S. Rep., Gov. of Maine), 19th century (7 vols.). Lincoln, Levi, Jr. (Mass.; U.S. Rep., Gov., mayor of Worcester), 1793-1864 (6 vols. and 1 box). Lincoln, Levi, Sr. (Mass.; U.S. Rep. and Attorney Gen.), 1793-1909 (6 vols. and 1 box). Lincoln, Waldo (Mass.; genealogist, pres. of American Antiquarian Society), 1871-1933 (17 vols. and 1 box). Lincoln, William (Mass.; Worcester lawyer, legislator, antiquarian, historian), 19th century (30 vols. and 16 boxes), including family papers. Logbooks (26 vols.). Louisiana manuscripts, 1782-1935 (4 vols. and 3 boxes), constituting the Edward Larocque Tinker Collection.

Maine, State of, 1640-1840 (2 boxes), miscellaneous papers and documents. Marston, Philip B. (England; poet), 19th century (1 box), including literary manuscripts and a diary. Massachusetts, miscellaneous papers and documents, 1639-1877 (4 boxes), preserved by William Lincoln. Massachusetts Civil War, 1861-65, records of the 15th Regiment, Massachusetts Volunteers (3 boxes and 14 vols.); 18 music books of the band and drum corps of the 25th Regiment of Massachusetts Volunteers (1 box); and "Descriptive Book" of the 34th Regiment of Massachusetts Volunteer Infantry, 1862-65, containing a list of officers and men (1 vol.). Massachusetts colonial records, documents, and accounts, 1666-1787 (1 vol.); Provincial Congress records, 1735-36 (1 vol.), and Legislative Committee, 1779-82 (1 vol.). Massachusetts Militia, records, 1819-59 (4 vols.). Mather family papers (15 boxes), including papers of the Congregational clergymen Richard Mather (1 box), Increase Mather (3 boxes), Cotton Mather (7 boxes), and Samuel Mather (3 boxes). Melyen, Jacob (Mass.), 1691-96 (1 letter book). Mexican War, Justin H. Smith (Mass., N.H.; historian, Dartmouth College prof.), transcripts in Spanish, 1846-48 (3 boxes). Mexico, manuscripts of a legal nature (in Spanish), 1749-61 (1 vol.) and 1751-94 (1 vol.). Millbury, Mass., records of the First Congregational Church, 1830-55 (6 vols.).

Nason, Elias (Mass.; schoolmaster, Congregational clergyman), 1831-62 (7 vols.), correspondence. New England Company, 17th century (1 box), transcripts of early records. New England Council, records of the Council for New England, 1622-23. Nichols, Charles L. (Mass.; physician, bibliophile), bibliographical material on Worcester imprints, almanacs, correspondence (5 boxes). Norcross, Grenville H. (Mass.; Boston lawyer), 1861-75 and 1911-37 (42 vols.), including autographs and diaries. Oakes, William (Mass.; Ipswich botanist), 1823-48 (1 box), letters received. Orderly books, including French and Indian War (4 vols.), Revolutionary War (42 vols.), and War of 1812 (2 vols.). Otis, Bass (Mass., N.Y., Pa.; portrait painter, engraver, pioneer lithographer), 1815-53 (1 vol. of accounts), containing numerous sketches. Paine family of Worcester, Mass., 1768-1864 (28 vols. and 7 boxes), including papers of William Paine (Mass.; physician, loyalist, surgeon-gen. of British forces in the American Revolution). Park, Lawrence (Mass.; writer on colonial art), 2 boxes of correspondence. Parker family papers, Shirley, Mass., 18th and 19th centuries (19 vols.), including diaries and account books. Parkman, Ebenezer (Mass.; Congregational clergyman at Westborough), 1719-1812 (12 vols. of diaries and 2 boxes), including letters and some family papers. Peabody, Stephen (N.H.; minister at Atkinson), 1777-1814 (13 vols.), diaries and accounts. Penn, Thomas (England, Pa.; proprietor of Pa.), 1752-72 (1 vol.), copies of letters to Richard Peters (Pa.; provincial official, Episcopal clergyman). Pepperell, Sir William (Maine; merchant, pres. of Mass. Council, jurist, colonial Army officer), 1745 (1 vol.), a journal of the expedition against Louisbourg. Perkins, Jacob (Mass.; inventor), biographical material (1 box). Perkins, John (Mass.; physician), 18th century (2 vols.), including his memoirs, notes on medical cases, curiosa, and recipes. Phillips, Henry A. (Mass.; architect, genealogist), 12 boxes of genealogical notes. Porter, Jacob (Mass.; physician, botanist, writer), 19th century (3 boxes), papers on local history, nature, and biblical subjects. Preble, George Henry (U.S. naval officer, author), 1861-80 (7 vols.), chiefly correspondence about U. S. flag. Proclamations and orders in council, 1630-1815, copies from English archives in 1918 by C. S. Brigham (2 vols.).

Rockwell, John A. (Conn.; Norwich lawyer, jurist, author), 19th century (3 boxes), correspondence and other papers relating to early American canals and railroads. Rogers, John (N. Y., Conn.; sculptor), 19th century (1 box), including correspondence. Rogers, Robert (Mass., N. H., England; colonial ranger), 1766-67, original and photostat journals. Rumball-Petre, Edwin A. (clergyman, writer, bibliophile and dealer in rare Bibles), 20th century (1 box), correspondence, mostly on Bibles. Russell, Richard (Mass.; colonial treasurer), 1649 (1 vol.), notes on sermons by Zechariah Symmes and Thomas Allen. Salisbury family, 1674-1905 (63 vols. and 68 boxes), including papers of Stephen Salisbury I (Mass.; merchant, landowner), Stephen Salisbury II (Mass.; builder, banker, philanthropist), and Stephen Salisbury III (Mass.; bank pres., sponsor of explorations in Central America, patron of Worcester institutions, pres. of American Antiquarian Society). Sayward, Jonathan, 1760-97 (1 folio binder), diaries. Scandlin, William G. (Mass.; sailor, missionary, Unitarian minister, Civil War chaplain), 1849-70 (1 box), including a seaman's log and a Civil War diary. Scituate, Mass., 1707-91 (8 vols.), records of families, and extracts from town and church records. Scofield, James M. (Conn., Calif., Mass.; publisher of Hartford Post, insurance executive), correspondence and diaries, 1824-71 (5 boxes), and family papers, 1872-1930 (1 box). Sewall family, 1634-1905 (12 boxes), containing legal, personal, and military papers of several descendants of Henry Sewall (Mass.; early settler in Newbury). Sewall, William B. (Maine; lawyer, editor), 1813-45 (10 vols. of diaries). Shaw-Webb family, 1756-

1881 (6 boxes), letters and genealogical notes of the Shaw, Leonard, Stetson, and Webb families, first in southeastern Massachusetts, later in Maine. Shays' Rebellion, 1786 (1 box), containing petitions, orderly books, correspondence, and reports of trials. Shea, John Gilmary (N. Y., N. J.; historian, author, editor), 1 box, a catalog of his library. Shepard, Thomas (England, Mass.; Congregational clergyman), 17th-century sermons and notes, also papers of his son Thomas Shepard II (Mass.; clergyman), and his grandson Thomas Shepard III. Slavery, 1834-57 (1 box), papers relating chiefly to the antislavery movement in Massachusetts. Sleeper, John S. (Mass.; sailor, shipmaster, newspaper editor, mayor of Roxbury), 19th century (1 box), manuscripts of sea stories under his pen name "Hawser Martingale." Smith, Sidney L. (designer, etcher, engraver), 1 vol. and 10 boxes, including correspondence, drawings, and bookplate proofs. Sprague, John (Mass.; Dedham and Boston physician), 1713-1815 (1 box), including letters and legal documents. Stage routes of the Boston and New York mail stages by the way of Worcester, Springfield, Hartford, and New Haven, 1800-5 (1 vol.), and accounts of the northern lines, Boston, Fitchburg, Athol, Greenfield, 1845 (1 vol., 2 boxes, and 1 folio). Stearns, Samuel (Mass., Vt.; physician, astronomer), 18th and 19th centuries (2 vols. and 1 box), including his "North American Dispensatory," and other writings. Sullivan, Thomas Russell (Mass.; banker, playwright, short-story writer), correspondence (6 boxes). Sutton, Mass., 1743-1910 (6 boxes and 5 vols.), town records, church records, miscellaneous historical papers, and a history of Sutton by Christopher C. Baldwin (Mass.; lawyer, editor, librarian of American Antiquarian Society). Sweetser, Seth

(Mass.; pastor of Central Church, Worcester), 1838-78 (3 vols.), sermons, lectures, and weather records. Swett, Samuel (Mass.; Boston merchant), 1774-1853 (3 boxes), chiefly concerning the Swett and Sprague families.

Taggart, Samuel (Mass.; Presbyterian clergyman at Colrain, U. S. Rep.), 1803-15 (2 vols. of letters). Tenney, Jonathan (educator, editor), 19th century (6 vols.), letters on education and family genealogy.   Terry, James (Conn.; collector of bookplates and data on early Conn. libraries), chiefly 19th century (8 boxes), correspondence and notes.   Thomas, Isaiah (Mass.; printer, publisher, historian of the press, founder of the American Antiquarian Society), 1754-1831 (28 vols. and 7 boxes), including letters, diaries, accounts, and the manuscript of his "History of Printing." Ticknor, Caroline (Mass.; Boston author), letters and manuscripts (2 boxes). Trumbull, James Hammond (Conn.; historian, philologist, bibliographer), a dictionary of Eliot's Indian Bible (4 vols.). Tuckerman, Edward (Mass.; lichenologist, Amherst prof. of botany), 1841-78 (9 vols.), correspondence. Twichell, Ginery (Mass.; stagecoach operator, pres. of Boston and Albany R. R., U. S. Rep.), 19th century (1 vol. and 4 boxes), accounts, documents, and other papers.   United States Revolution, 1775-87 (6 vols.), letters, military records, and other papers. Waldo family, 1647-1900 (13 vols. and 2 boxes), including papers of Daniel Waldo (Mass.; merchant) and Albigence Waldo (Conn.; Rev. War surgeon). Wallcut, Thomas (Mass.; Boston book collector, antiquarian), 1762-1832 (3 boxes), letters and miscellaneous papers. War of 1812 (1 box), letters and documents. Ward family, Shrewsbury, Mass., 18th and 19th centuries (17 vols. and 38 boxes), including papers of Artemas Ward (Mass.; Rev. War officer) and his son Thomas W. Ward (Mass.; sheriff of

Worcester County), 1805-24. Washburn, Charles G. (Mass.; U. S. Rep., manufacturer, author), 19th and 20th centuries (19 vols. and 11 boxes), including family papers and papers relating to Theodore Roosevelt (N. Y.; Gov., U. S. Pres.), Henry Cabot Lodge (Mass.; U. S. Rep. and Sen.), and William H. Taft (Ohio; U.S. Pres., Chief Justice). Washington, George (Va.; Rev. War Commander in Chief, U. S. Pres.), 1775-81 (2 original letters and several copies, and photostats), also 2 military documents forged by Robert Spring (England; forger) and the original bill of sale for them. Waters, Jason (Mass.; Sutton storekeeper, scythe manufacturer, State legislator), 1812-29 (22 vols.), memoranda and account books. Waters family, gun makers and cotton goods manufacturers of Millbury, Mass., 1742-1885 (5 boxes), family papers, business letters, accounts and factory payrolls. West, Samuel (Mass.; Boston clergyman, Rev. War chaplain), 1 vol. of memoirs. West, Richardson and Lord, Boston booksellers, 1792-1886 (5 boxes), correspondence, orders, and receipts. Whig Party Convention in Worcester, Mass., 1840 (1 box), lists of delegates, speeches, and details of organization,   and data on Whig campaign of 1844 in Worcester County (1 box). Williams, Roger (Mass., R.I.; founder of R. I. Colony), 1637-77 (4 letters). Willoughby, William A. (Conn.; Civil War soldier), 1861-64 (1 box), letters to his wife. Winchester family and collateral lines of New Haven, Conn., 1843-72 (2 boxes), letters and genealogical notes. Winslow, John (N. Y.; Brooklyn lawyer, historian), 1844-98 (1 box). Wood, Sumner G. (Mass.), "Homes and Habits of ancient Blandford" (1 box). Woodward family of Worcester, Mass., 1832-1946 (11 boxes), including papers of Samuel B. Woodward (Conn., Mass.; physician, pioneer on mental diseases), and Samuel B. Woodward (Mass.; physician, surgeon, banker), letters, medical papers, and genealogical notes. Worcester County, Mass., 1718-1873 (9 boxes), miscellaneous letters, notes, and documents. Worcester, Mass., 1686-1949 (16 boxes), miscellaneous papers.

WORCESTER 3

Clark University Library. 1 Downing St. Tilton M. Barron, Librarian.

Holdings: A small and miscellaneous collection, including some medieval and Renaissance manuscripts (11 vols.); orderly books for certain Pennsylvania troops in the Continental Army, 1780-82 (8 vols.); correspondence between Jonas Gilman Clark (Mass.; founder of Clark Univ.) and Granville Stanley Hall (Md., Mass.; psychologist, pres. of Clark Univ.), 1888-95 (61 letters); papers of Carroll Davidson Wright (Mass., D.C.; Commissioner of U.S. Bureau of Labor, pres. of Clark College); and a group of account books, minutes, letters, and other papers, from 1889, relating to Clark University.
See De Ricci, Census, p. 1089.

—oOo—

College of the Holy Cross Library. Rev. William L. Lucey, Librarian.

Holdings: 55 vols., 3 boxes, 3 file drawers, and over 4,250 pieces, 1770-1953, relating chiefly to literature and to Catholic literary, political, and ecclesiastical persons. Included are papers of Louise Imogen Guiney (Mass., England; essayist, poet), 1861-1920 (3,100 pieces), which contain 141 letters written by her father during the Civil War; James Augustine Healy (Mass., Maine; Bishop of Portland), 1848-98 (13 diaries and 3 boxes of oth-

er papers); Michael Earls (Mass.; priest, author), 1902-36 (402 letters), among them letters from Andrew O'Connor (Mass., France; sculptor), 1922-35 (50 pieces), and other prominent figures; Joseph John Reilly (Mass., N.Y.; author, educator), 1914-50 (300 pieces and 2 file drawers), which include 62 letters of William Lyon Phelps (Conn.; educator, author), 1921-36. There are also important papers of David Ignatius Walsh (Mass.; Gov., U.S. Sen.), 1896-1947 (8 letter books and 1 file drawer of correspondence); personal and family papers of Dorothy Godfrey Wayman, known as Theodate Geoffrey (Mass.; journalist, author), 1862-1953 (2 vols. and 300 pieces); and a collection on Irish immigrants and their descendants in Worcester, 1840-1900 (19 vols.).

WORCESTER 8

Worcester Historical Society. 39 Salisbury St. (Mrs.) Elizabeth T. Cassidy, Director.

Holdings: 20,000 pieces, 1663-1934, relating chiefly to Worcester and Worcester County. The collections include the several large groups mentioned below.
Family and personal papers, 1723-1908 (12,469 items), include those of Pliny Earle (Mass.; inventor, cotton-machinery manufacturer) and his family, 1789-1888 (356 items); and papers of Abigail Kelley Foster, known as Abby Kelley (Mass.; abolitionist, feminist) and her husband, Stephen Symonds Foster (N.H., Mass.; abolitionist, temperance and woman-suffrage advocate), 1837-93 (118 items). Among the various family collections are sermons and papers relating to churches, papers relating to colonial wars and the Civil War, and papers of lawyers, manufacturers,

hardware merchants, and other businessmen.

The City of Worcester Manuscript Collection, 1707-1936 (3,000 items), contains many items relating to law, medicine, banking, trades, and businesses in Worcester; official municipal records and political papers; records of an agricultural society, 1819-91 (8 vols. and 5 pieces); and records of a military academy, 1862-1906 (6 vols.). There are sermons and records of Congregational, Baptist, and Universalist churches in Worcester and other religious papers. In the County of Worcester Manuscript Collection, 1667-1889 (1,200 items), 39 towns are represented, chiefly by private papers of their citizens. There are also records of antislavery societies, 1835-65 (3 vols. and 2 pieces).

Miscellaneous military papers, 1758-1902 (55 bundles), aside from military papers in groups of family papers and among the papers of towns, include records chiefly concerning the Revolution and the Civil War. There are also war diaries, 1759-78 (3 vols.), and 1861-65 (2 vols.). Other holdings include militia returns, reports, and orders; regimental and company orders; and similar military materials. Among the holdings also there are records of the Worcester Natural History Society and its predecessors, 1829-1909 (1,777 items); and papers relating to Massachusetts, outside Worcester County, and other New England States, 1663-1897 (850 items).

See Hist. Records Survey, Guide to Manuscript Collections in the Worcester Historical Society (1941. 54 p. Processed); and Forest History Sources, p. 46.

MICHIGAN

ADRIAN

Adrian College Library.

Holdings: 44 vols., 1859-1915, relating chiefly to the College. Included
are records of a quarterly conference
of the Methodist Church at Henry, Ill.,
1867-68.

—oOo—

Adrian Public Library. Emma Sihler,
Librarian.

Holdings: 26 vols. and several
other items, relating chiefly to Adrian
and vicinity.
See Hist. Records Survey, Guide
for Mich., p. 1.

—oOo—

Siena Heights College Library.

Holdings: 2 vols. and 8 pieces, of
miscellaneous character. Included is
a 15th-century illuminated manuscript.
See Hist. Records Survey, Guide
for Mich., p. 2.

ALLEGAN

Allegan Public Library. Claxton E.
Helms, Librarian.

Holdings: 35 items, 1833-1921,
consisting of some township records
and other papers of local interest.
There are 8 letters to Lucius Lyon
(Mich.; U.S. Rep. and Sen.), 1833-
44.
See Hist. Records Survey, Guide
for Mich., p. 5.

ANN ARBOR

Kelsey Museum of Archaeology, University of Michigan. 434 South State
St. Enoch E. Peterson, Director.

Holdings: 170 cuneiform Neo-
Babylonian and Assyrian clay tablets
and 267 Greek and Latin inscriptions.

—oOo—

Michigan Historical Collections, University of Michigan. Lewis G. Van
der Velde, Director; F. Clever Bald,
Assistant Director.

Holdings: 9,700 vols. and 1,250,000
pieces, 1765-1959, relating chiefly to
Michigan and the University of Michigan. A "box," as used below to indicate quantity of manuscripts, is a
container 12"x11"x3".
The papers of persons who served
as Members of the U.S. Congress include those of Kinsley S. Bingham
(Mich.; Gov., U.S. Rep. and Sen.),
1820-61 (1 box); Royal S. Copeland
(Mich., N.Y.; physician, prof. at
Univ. of Mich., U.S. Sen.), 1889-
1938 (37 vols. and 10 boxes); Louis
C. Cramton (Mich.; State rep., U.S.
Rep.), 1920-33 (5 ft.); William W.
Crapo (Mass.; lawyer, U.S. Rep.),
1853-1928 (2 boxes); Alpheus Felch
(Mich.; Gov., U.S. Sen.), 1794-1856
(7 boxes); Woodbridge N. Ferris (Ill.,
Mich.; school administrator, Gov. of
and U.S. Sen. from Mich.), 1904-28
(1 vol. and 250 pieces); Lucius Lyon
(Mich.; land surveyor, U.S. Sen. and
Rep.), 1826-51 (72 items); Blair
Moody (Mich.; news analyst and com-
mentator, U.S. Sen.), 1930-54 (38
vols. and 30 ft.); George Washington
Patterson (N.Y.; land agent, U.S.

Rep.), 1847-99 (11 boxes); John Patton, Jr. (Pa., Mich.; lawyer, U.S. Sen.), 1888-1905 (200 items); John T. Rich (Mich.; Gov., U.S. Rep.), 1869-1925 (9 vols. and 20 pieces); Oliver L. Spaulding (Mich.; Civil War officer, U.S. Rep., Asst. Sec. Treas.), 1862-1921 (9 vols. and 6 boxes); and William W. Wedemeyer (Mich.; lawyer, U.S. Rep.), 1890-1913 (1,200 pieces).

Among the papers of other persons holding high public office are those of John J. Bagley (Mich.; Gov.), 1871-76 (2 vols. and 566 pieces); Roy D. Chapin (Mich.; automobile manufacturer, Sec. Commerce), 1907-35 (162 boxes); William A. Comstock (Mich.; manufacturer, Gov.), 1901-34 (48 vols. and 14,000 pieces); Thomas M. Cooley (Mich.; State supreme court justice), 1850-98 (16 vols. and 6,500 pieces); Henry H. Crapo (Mass., Mich.; agriculturist, lumber executive, industrialist, Gov.), 1836-1907 (67 vols. and 12,000 pieces); Charles M. Croswell (Mich.; State legislator, Gov.), 1851-84 (5 vols.); William De Kleine (Mich., D.C.; public health officer, medical director of American Red Cross), 1900-55 (3 vols. and 6 ft.); Joseph Ralston Hayden (Ill., Mich.; political science prof. at Univ. of Mich., Vice-Gov. Gen. of the Philippine Islands), 1920-45 (60,000 pieces); Franklin William Knox (Mass., Mich., N.H., Ill.; newspaper editor and publisher, Sec. Navy), 1909-12 (19 boxes); Charles Moore (Mich., D.C.; Chairman of U.S. Fine Arts Commission, writer), 1901-40 (5 vols. and 441 pieces); Chase S. Osborn (Ind., Wis., Mich.; newspaper publisher, author, explorer, Gov.), 1895-1949 (186 vols. and 604 boxes); George Bryan Porter (Pa., Mich.; lawyer, Terr. Gov. of Mich.), 1765-1837 (50 items); Andrew D. White (N.Y., Mich.; pres. Cornell Univ., U.S. Minister to Germany), 1865-1903 (82 items); and Warner Wing (Mich.; chief justice of State supreme court), 1837-70 (85 pieces).

Included also are the papers of Elizabeth M. Chandler (Pa., Mich.; author, editor, abolitionist), 1830-52 (125 pieces); Lloyd C. Douglas (Ind., Mich., Ohio, Calif.; clergyman, writer), 1916-51 (4 ft.); Horatio S. Earle (Vt., Mich.; State sen. and highway commissioner), 1870-1934 (51 vols.); Bela Hubbard (N.Y., Mich.; geologist, surveyor), 1835-93 (69 vols. and 12 items); Henry B. Joy (Mich.; automobile manufacturer, World War I officer, pres. of Lincoln Highway Assn.), 1887-1937 (23 vols. and 10,000 pieces); Frank A. Manny (N.Y., Mass., Mich.; educator), 1890-1946 (9 ft.); Randolph Rogers (N.Y., Mich., Italy; sculptor), 1853-92 (1 box); Charles R. Sligh (Mich.; furniture manufacturer, State sen.), 1842-1932 (54 vols. and 12 ft.); George O. Squier (Mich.; U.S. Army officer, electrical engineer, inventor), 1883-1934 (22 vols. and 12 boxes); Nathan Thomas (Ohio, Mich.; physician, abolitionist), 1818-92 (4 vols. and 650 pieces); and Bryant Walker (Mich.; lawyer, conchologist), 1873-1931 (15 vols. and 11,000 pieces).

Numerous business records are present, among them records of several lumber companies, flour and woolen mills, general stores, a carriage-bicycle-automobile business, 1872-1915, automobile manufacturing concerns, the Erie and Kalamazoo Railroad, 1830-1952, and the Postum Company, 1896-1943 (230 vols.).

Organizational holdings include extensive records of the Synod of Michigan, the various presbyteries, and several individual congregations of the Presbyterian Church; records of Baptist, Congregational, Methodist, and other church organizations; American Home Missionary Society papers, 1825-47 (5 rolls of microfilm copies); and records of two Michigan communal societies, the

Alphadelphia Association, 1844-57 (6 vols. and 2 boxes), and the German Christian Agricultural and Benevolent Society of Ora Labora, 1850-93 (3 vols. and 1 box). There are also records of the Ann Arbor chapter of the Daughters of the American Revolution, 1896-1938 (5 vols. and 500 pieces); the Michigan Library Association, 1908-58 (17 boxes); the Michigan Commandery of the Military Order of the Loyal Legion of the United States (3 vols. and 100 pieces); the American Association of University Women, Michigan Division and Ann Arbor branch, 1902-58 (25 vols. and 2 boxes); and the Ann Arbor Visiting Nurses Association, 1935-48 (14 vols.).

There are many diaries, some county and township archives, and many school records. Included also are important groups of manuscripts relating to agriculture, banking, the Civil War, education, Indians, labor, legal practice, medicine, dentistry, political parties, railroads, real estate, and many other subjects.

Manuscripts relating especially to the University include official records of the University and its various administrative units, 1817-1959 (1,500 vols. and 300,000 pieces). There are collections of papers of several regents of the University including Lucius Lee Hubbard (Ohio, Mich.; geologist), 1871-1935 (38 vols. and 13 boxes); James O. Murfin (Ohio, Mich.; lawyer, judge), 1903-40 (22 boxes); Walter H. Sawyer (Ohio, Mich.; physician), 1904-31 (23 boxes); and Peter White (N.Y., Wis., Mich.; banker, State rep. and sen.), 1851-1903 (39 ft.).

Among the papers of faculty members are those of James B. Angell (R.I., Vt., Mich.; pres. of Univ. of Vt. and Univ. of Mich., Minister to China and Turkey), 1866-1916 (51 boxes); Arthur Lyon Cross (Vt., Mich.; historian), 1898-1940 (28 vols. and 38 boxes); Henry Simmons Frieze (Mass.,

R.I., Mich.; classicist, acting pres. Univ. of Mich.), 1854-89 (18 vols. and 550 items); Erastus O. Haven (Mass., N.Y., Mich., Ill.; clergyman, pres. Univ. of Mich., Northwestern Univ., and Syracuse Univ.), 1838-73 (1 vol. and 8 items); William Herbert Hobbs (Mich.; geologist, glaciologist), 1915-50 (11 vols. and 3 boxes); William J. Hussey (Calif., Mich.; astronomer), 1879-1926 (20 vols. and 13 boxes); Harry B. Hutchins (Mich.; pres. of Univ. of Mich.), 1909-29 (65 boxes); Francis W. Kelsey (Mich.; classicist, archeologist), 1900-27 (28 vols. and 1 box), containing correspondence about the University of Michigan Near East Research Expedition; Victor H. Lane (Ohio, Mich.; lawyer, judge, law prof.), 1897-1929 (1 vol. and 18 boxes); Howard B. Lewis (Conn., Ill., Mich.; biological chemist), 1930-54 (12 ft.); Alfred H. Lloyd (Mich.; philosopher), 1915-26 (14 vols. and 3 boxes); Andrew C. McLaughlin (Mich.; historian), 1885-1947 (8 vols. and 1 box); John Monteith (Mich.; Presbyterian minister, pres. of Univ. of Mich.), 1797-1871 (7 vols. and 5 boxes); Eliza M. Mosher (Mass., N.Y., Mich.; physician, dean of women), 1846-1928 (3 vols. and 11 boxes); William Harold Payne (Mich., Tenn.; pedagogy prof. at Univ. of Mich., chancellor of Univ. of Nashville, pres. of Peabody Normal School), 1865-1933 (12 vols. and 275 pieces); Jesse S. Reeves (Ind., Mich.; lawyer, political scientist), 1913-41 (5 vols. and 57 boxes); Fred N. Scott (Mich.; writer, English prof.), 1892-1932 (32 vols. and 2,250 pieces); Henry Philip Tappan (N.Y., Mich.; clergyman, pres. of Univ. of Mich.), 1840-83 (4 vols. and 1 ft.); James C. Watson (Mich., Wis.; astronomer, director of observatories at Univ. of Mich. and Univ. of Wis.), 1855-79 (9 vols. and 65 pieces); Robert M. Wenley (Scotland, Mich.; philosopher, au-

thor), 1879-1929 (33 vols. and 5,750
pieces); Horace L. Wilgus (Mich.; law
prof., author), 1879-1935 (7 vols. and
2,700 pieces); Alexander Winchell
(Ala., Mich., N.Y.; geologist), 1837-
91 (188 vols. and 3,900 pieces); and
Fielding H. Yost (W. Va., Tenn.,
Mich.; football coach), 1901-46
(15,000 pieces).

See Hist. Records Survey, Guide
to Manuscript Collections in Michigan:
Vol. I, Michigan Historical Collections,
University of Michigan (1941. 239 p.
Processed); University of Michigan,
The Michigan Historical Collections
of the University of Michigan (rev.
1955. 14 p.); University of Michigan,
Michigan Men in the Civil War (1959.
32 p.); and Forest History Sources,
pp. 51-55. Information about new accessions is in the annual Report of
the Michigan Historical Collections,
1941-42 to date.

—oOo—

University Library, University of
Michigan. Frederick H. Wagman,
Director; Harriet C. Jameson, Rare
Book Librarian.

Holdings: 360 vols., 24 packages,
and 40,000 pieces, relating importantly to the University and to Michigan
but also containing manuscripts of
wider interest. The Kelsey Museum
of Archaeology, the Michigan Historical Collections, the Law Library, and
the William L. Clements Library are
separately described.

Among the non-American holdings
are 237 ancient, medieval, and Renaissance manuscripts in Latin and Greek;
836 Islamic manuscripts; some Greek
ostraka; 10,000 papyri; and 100 miscellaneous manuscripts, 16th-19th
centuries, written in Latin, German,
French, Dutch, Italian, and English
and pertaining chiefly to European history and politics. There are also 200
music scores or partial scores written

before 1800. Other non-American
manuscripts include papers of William Harcourt, 3d Earl (England; Army officer), 1788-1825 (75 pieces);
copies of diplomatic and private correspondence of William Pitt (England; Prime Minister), 1758-61 (250
pages), chiefly letters to Pitt; papers
from the collection of Henry Dundas,
Viscount Melville, 1742-1811 (700
pages), chiefly concerning the Anglo-
French War, 1793-95; papers of Karl
Heinrich Rau (Germany; prof. of political economy at Heidelberg, Baden
Privy Counselor), 1774-1870 (4 vols.
and 100 pieces); and papers relating
to John Lewis Bruckhardt (Switzerland; traveler in Egypt, Arabia, and
the Levant), collected in the Near
East (92 pieces).

Personal and official papers of
University administrators and faculty
members include those of William
Warner Bishop (Mich.; Univ. librarian), to 1940 (1,200 pieces); Raymond
Cazallis Davis (Mich.; Univ. librarian), 1877-1908 (3 vols., 1 box, and
200 pieces), chiefly official correspondence; William Herbert Hobbs
(Mich.; geologist, glaciologist, historian), 1864-1953 (900 pieces), including several hundred letters from
outstanding polar explorers; Douglass
Houghton (Mich.; geologist), 1837-45
(2 vols.); and Calvin Thomas (Mich.,
N.Y.; German professor and Goethe
scholar at the Univ. of Mich. and Columbia Univ.), 1875-96 (1 packing
case).

Non-University collections include the Maurice Browne-Ellen Van
Volkenberg Collection on the American and English theater, comprising
many hundreds of pieces of correspondence and memorabilia of the
founders of the Chicago Little Theater, 1912-17, and of producers of
plays in New York and London, 1920-
42. There are also papers of Hugo
Erichsen (Ill., Mich.; physician, author, editor), 1880-89 (640 pieces),

chiefly letters from authors of several nationalities; Hermann Kiefer (Germany, Mich.; physician, surgeon with revolutionary troops in 1849, U.S. consul at Stettin, Univ. of Mich. regent), 1840-1900 (3 vols. and 75 pieces); and the Worcester Philippine Collection, consisting of papers of Dean C. Worcester (Mich.; member of U.S. Philippine Commission, sec. of interior of Philippine Insular Government, coconut and sugar processor), chiefly 1900-13 (1,200 pieces), assembled during his official service in the Philippine Islands but also including reports and other Philippine material acquired later. Another outstanding collection is the Hawaiian Islands History sources, consisting of photostats and transcripts. Included are copies of materials in the Archives of Hawaii —from the Captain Cook Collection, the Gregg Collection, 1853-66, and the records of the Hawaiian Islands Department of Foreign Affairs, 1889-93.

Another significant collection is the Joseph Labadie Collection, 1870-1941 (50 vols., 24 packages, and 2,000 pieces), which includes 11 filing drawers of correspondence and other papers of Charles Joseph Antoine Labadie (Mich.; labor leader, Greenbacker, editor of labor journals), 1870-1933, and of Agnes Inglis (Mich.; historian of protest movements in the U.S., former curator of the Labadie Collection). There are some records of early craft unions, 1859-1904, papers concerning the Knights of Labor and the American Federation of Labor, and a quantity of material on the Tom Mooney and Sacco-Vanzetti cases and on the Spanish Civil War. Also in the Library are several autograph collections, 1694-1940 (5 vols. and 546 pieces), one of which, assembled by Samuel P. Langley (Pa., D.C.; astronomer, Sec. of Smithsonian Institution, pioneer in aviation), includes some 160 letters written to Langley

or members of his family, 1856-1903.

The Transportation Library (Leo Natanson, Divisional Librarian), administratively a part of the University Library, contains 278 vols. and 19,400 pieces, 1792-1935, relating chiefly to the construction of railroads, bridges, tunnels, harbors, and waterways and to other aspects of transportation engineering. Included are papers of Charles Ellet (Va., Pa., D.C.; civil engineer), 1827-87 (18,000 pieces); Oliver Evans (Pa.; inventor), 1792-1808 (2 vols. and 4 pieces); and Francis Lee Stuart (N.J.; engineer with Nicaragua and Isthmian Canal Commissions and railroads and port authorities in U.S.), 1892-1935 (160 vols., 300 pieces, and 30 cu. ft.). There are also records of a Detroit railway, 1848-1934 (113 vols. and 700 pieces).

See Hist. Records Survey, Guide to Manuscript Collections in Michigan: Vol. II, University of Michigan Collections, pp. 1-43 and 63-78; and De Ricci, Census, pp. 1103-1126.

—oOo—

University of Michigan Law Library. Esther Betz, Assistant Director.

Holdings: 38 vols. and 4,200 case files, consisting chiefly of records of Territorial and State courts of Michigan, 1796-1857, deposited by the Michigan Historical Commission.

See Hist. Records Survey, Guide for Mich., p. 10.

—oOo—

William L. Clements Library, University of Michigan. Howard H. Peckham, Director.

Holdings: 200,000 pieces, 1542-1950, relating most especially to the period of the American Revolution but containing also large and valuable groups pertaining to other periods of United States history, to Great Britain, and to Latin America. The size of groups mentioned below is given chiefly in terms of linear feet.

Importantly related to United States history in the colonial period are papers of Sir Jeffrey Amherst (British commander in chief in America), 1758-64 (2 ft.); George Clinton (N. Y.; Gov.), 1697-1759 (6 ft.); Thomas Gage (British commander in chief in America and last royal governor of Mass.), 1754-83 (49 ft.); William Henry Lyttleton (British colonial governor of S. C.), 1751-60 (5 ft.); Sir William Mildmay (British diplomat), 1748-56 (1 ft.); and Lord Shelburne (British statesman and Sec. of State for the Southern Department), 1663-1797 (34 ft.).

Of major importance for the American Revolution are the papers of Gen. Gage and Lord Shelburne (see above); Sir Henry Clinton (British commander in chief in America), 1750-1812 (80 ft.); Lord George Germain (British Sec. of State for America), 1683-1785 (6 ft.); William Knox (British Undersecretary of State for America), 1757-1809 (3 ft.); Frederick Mackenzie (England; British Army officer in America), 1755-83 (3 ft.); Thomas Townshend, 1st Viscount Sydney (British statesman), 1685-1829 (4 ft.); Sir John Vaughan (British army commander in the West Indies), 1779-81 (1 ft.); and George Wray (British artillery officer), 1770-93 (2 ft.). There are confidential army reports from the library of Frederick Lord North (British Prime Minister), 1770-82 (3 ft.). Information about Hessian troops is in the Baron Friedrick von Jungkenn papers, 1775-84 (2 ft.). For the American side there are papers of Nathanael Greene (R. I., Ga.; Rev. War officer), 1775-86 (25 ft.); and John Holker (French consul in Philadelphia), 1770-1816 (1 ft.). Relating especially to negotiations for peace between Britain and the United States are photostats of papers of Charles James Fox (British statesman), 1781-83 (175 items); and papers of David Hartley (British diplomat), 1783-85 (1 ft.). The Library also has a set of the "Facsimiles of Manuscripts in European Archives Relating to America, 1773-1783," compiled by Benjamin F. Stevens.

For United States history between the Revolution and the Civil War there are papers of the Baldwin family, chiefly of Loammi Baldwin, Sr. and Jr. (Mass.; civil engineers), 1662-1864 (3 ft.); James G. Birney (Ky., Ala., N. Y., Mich.; antislavery leader), 1816-57 (7 ft.); Isaac Bonsall (Pa., N. Y., Ohio; Quaker missionary to the Indians), 1803-23 (4 journals); Henry C. Carey (Md., Pa.; economist, publisher), 1829-35 (130 items); Lewis Cass (Mich.; Terr. Gov. and Supt. Indian Affairs, Sec. War, Sec. State, U. S. Sen.), 1774-1921 (6 ft.); the Croghan family, chiefly of William Croghan (Va., Ky.; Rev. War officer) and his son George (U. S. Army officer), 1788-1848 (65 items); Peter Force (D. C.; historian, editor), 1820-68 (2 ft.); Henry Goulburn (British commissioner to negotiate the Treaty of Ghent), 1813-14 (200 items); Josiah Harmar (U. S. Army officer), chiefly 1785-92 (10 ft.); Christopher Hughes (Md.; diplomat), 1814-50 (5 ft.); Owen Lovejoy (Ill.; abolitionist), 1828-64 (200 items); Lucius Lyon (Mich.; U. S. Sen. and Rep., surveyor-gen. for Ohio, Ind., and Mich.), 1812-52 (8 ft.); James McHenry (Md.; Rev. War officer, Member Continental Cong., Sec. War), 1777-1820 (1 ft.); Anthony Wayne (Pa.; Rev. War officer), 1785-1830 (4 ft.); and William Wilson (N. Y.; judge, manager of the Livingston estate), 1790-1850 (12 ft.). The Weld-Grimké papers, 1822-98 (4 ft.), include papers of Theodore D. Weld (N. Y., Mass.; abolitionist) and of Sarah M. and Angelina Grimké (S. C., N. Y.; antislavery crusaders and advocates of woman's rights).

For the period of the Civil War and later in the United States there are papers of Russell A. Alger (Mich.; Civil War officer, Gov., U.S. Sec. War and Sen.), 1862-1907 (3 ft.); papers of Frank J. Hecker (U.S. Army officer), 1891-1904, relating to the Spanish-American War and the Isthmian Canal Commission (1 ft.); some correspondence of Theodore Roosevelt (N.Y.; Spanish-American War officer, Gov., U.S. Pres.), 1885-1919 (290 items); and papers of Claude H. Van Tyne (Mich.; historian), 1895-1930 (2 ft.).

Included also are papers of the following British leaders that relate to the present United States in relatively small degree or not at all: Baron Brougham and Vaux (lawyer and essayist), 1807-66 (2 ft.); George Canning (statesman), 1791-1827 (214 items); John Wilson Croker (statesman and essayist), 1803-57 (17 ft.); George III (King of Great Britain), 1784-1810 (5 ft. of typescripts of unpublished letters); the 1st and 2d Viscounts Melville (statesmen), 1600-1885 (10 ft.); Horatio Lord Nelson (naval officer), 1781-1805 (116 items); George Townshend (Lord Lieutenant of Ireland), 1767-72 (2 ft.); and Peter Warren (Admiral), 1744-51 (1 ft.).

Holdings in the field of Latin-American history include copies of letters by Bucareli y Ursua (Viceroy of New Spain), 1771-78 (2 ft.); papers of Porfirio Diaz (Mexico; gen. and Pres.), 1856-1903 (3 ft.); archives of the State of Zacatecas, Mexico, ca. 1561-1870 (43 ft.); Mexican viceregal cedulas and ordinances, 1773 (3 ft.); special collections on Yucatan, 1772-1898 (200 items), and Guatemala, 1760-1879 (200 items); a few miscellaneous manuscripts in Indian languages; and numerous scattered items dating from as early as 1542.

Materials that relate chiefly to the collecting of books and manuscripts include the papers of William L. Clem-

ents, 1914-34 (8 ft.); correspondence of George Brinley, 1846-75 (1 vol.); letter books of Henry Stevens, Jr. (Vt., England; bookdealer, bibliographer), 1852-66 (2 ft.); papers of Henry Vignaud (La.; journalist, Confed. diplomat, sec. of U.S. Legation in Paris, historian), 1840-1922 (2 ft.); a special collection of letters of various book collectors, 1810-1950 (1 ft.); and papers of the Bradford Club (a New York organization of bibliophiles), 1859-67 (1 ft.).

In addition to the papers of persons mentioned above, which for the most part constitute separate groups, papers of the following persons of prominence in the United States are scattered throughout several groups: 18 papers of John Adams, 19 papers of John Quincy Adams, 35 letters by Henry Clay, 128 papers of Benjamin Franklin, 15 papers of Alexander Hamilton, 97 letters to and from Thomas Hutchinson, 33 letters to and from Andrew Jackson, 91 letters to and from Thomas Jefferson, 38 papers of Henry Laurens, 57 papers of Chancellor Robert R. Livingston, 16 papers of James Madison, 26 papers of James Monroe, 18 papers of Timothy Pickering, 11 papers of James K. Polk, 47 letters of William H. Seward, 110 papers of William T. Sherman, and 147 papers of George Washington.

See Guide to the Manuscript Collections in the William L. Clements Library, compiled by William S. Ewing (1953), and the earlier and more detailed edition with the same title, compiled by Howard H. Peckham (1942).

—oOo—

Washtenaw Historical Society.
F. Clever Bald, Historial.

Holdings: 13 vols. and 7 boxes, 1822-1949, relating chiefly to Wash-

tenaw County. Included are diaries and
account books, manuscript papers on
county history; and extensive correspondence on the successful search for
the remains of William A. Fletcher
(Mich.; chief justice of State supreme
court), 1916-18. (The Society's manuscripts are on deposit in the Michigan Historical Collections, University
of Michigan.)

BAY CITY

Bay County Historical Museum.
County Building. Mrs. Allen T.
Greenman, Allen T. Greenman,
Curators.

Holdings: A few manuscripts,
1819-1934, relating to the county. Included are records relating to Indians
and to lumbering; and an inventory of
Bay County archives, listing records
for 1759 to 1934.

BENTON HARBOR

Benton Harbor Public Library.
(Mrs.) Eleanor G. Whitney, Librarian.

Holdings: 3 vols. and 41 pieces,
1817-1920, relating chiefly to St.
Joseph and Benton Harbor. Included
are a few papers dealing with the ship
canal, 1860-70.

BIG RAPIDS

Ferris Institute Library. 400 Oak
St. (Mrs.) Goldie T. Nott, Librarian.

Holdings: 32 vols., consisting of
copies of letters, 1892-99, of Woodbridge N. Ferris (Ill., Mich.; pres.
of Ferris Institute, Gov. of and U.S.
Sen. from Mich.).

DEARBORN

Dearborn Historical Mseum. Leonard G. Johnson, Chief Curator.

Holdings: 30 filing drawers and
100 vols., 1808-1954, relating chiefly to the immediate locality. Included are papers of Alexander G. Abell
(Mich., Calif.; diplomatic messenger
from U.S. to the Republic of Texas,
1843, and U.S. consul in Hawaii,
1845), 1 box of correspondence;
George W. Haigh (Mich.; Civil War
officer), $1\frac{1}{2}$ ft., relating to a volunteer regiment; some local township,
school, and church records; and several collections relating to local business and political activities.

—oOo—

Ford Motor Company Archives.
Henry E. Edmunds, Archivist.

Holdings: 6,154 linear ft. of papers, 1864 to date, consisting of (1)
noncurrent records of the Ford Motor
Co. and its subsidiaries (4,110 ft.);
(2) personal papers of Henry and Ed-
sel B. Ford (Mich.; automobile manufacturers) and their family (1,197
ft.); and (3) corporate and personal
records relating importantly to the
automotive industry, contributed by
donors outside the Ford Motor Co.
(847 ft.). In addition, there is a special library (1,263 ft.), containing the
personal books of Henry and Clara
Ford as well as other published materials relating especially to Henry Ford
and to the automotive industry.
    Company records are in the follow-
ing broad functional categories: corporate, 1903-21 (3 ft.), including articles of incorporation, by-laws, and
minutes; executive, 1899 to date
(2,070 ft.), including correspondence
of the office of the president of the
company; engineering, 1896-1953 (120
ft.), including drawings and specifica-

tions for cars; financial, 1901-53 (355 ft.); general counsel, 1903-50 (170 ft.), including legal case files; industrial relations, 1902 to date (246 ft.), including sociological department case studies and personal papers of Samuel S. Marquis (Mass., Mich.; Episcopal clergyman, head of the department); manufacturing, 1903-53 (407 ft.), including plant engineering reports, production reports and schedules, and war contracts and production data; public relations, 1903 to date (977 ft.); sales and advertising, 1903 to date (332 ft.); tax counsel, 1903-47 (19 ft.), including income and excise tax returns; and branch operations, 1905-54 (301 ft.).

There are also records of over 60 Ford subsidiaries and companies controlled by Henry Ford, 1881-1951 (875 ft.). These include coal mining companies, 1911-42 (285 ft.); lumbering companies, 1881-1946 (24 ft.); a Brazilian rubber plantation, 1925-46 (19 ft.); foreign Ford manufacturing or distributing companies, 1911-49 (55 ft.); tractor manufacturing and distributing companies, 1916-38 (29 ft.); marine and rail transportation companies, 1920-46 (55 ft.); hydroelectric power companies, 1919-52 (15 ft.); real estate and home construction companies, 1913-50 (60 ft.); three hotels, 1922-50 (61 ft.); and a radio broadcasting company, 1929-34 (2 ft.). There are records of other automobile companies in which Henry Ford played an active part, 1899-1907.

Personal papers and non-company records include the papers of 119 individuals. The most important group of these is the Fair Lane Papers, 1864-1950, accumulated by Henry Ford and his wife Clara and including correspondence, diaries, household records, and social records. Other collections of Henry Ford papers include records of his Georgia plantations and the records of the Neutral Conference for Continuous Mediation, 1915-17, which

Ford financed. Papers of other men include a few of Henry Ford II and Benson Ford (Mich.; automobile manufacturers); and two of the original stockholders of the Ford Motor Co.—John W. Anderson (Ind.; inventor, manufacturer), 1903-5, and Alexander Y. Malcomson (Mich.; fuel merchant, Ford Motor Co. vice pres. and treas.), 1903-23. There are also papers of Sir Percival Perry (founder of the Ford Motor Co. of England, Ltd.), 1917-48.

Supplementing the original papers are tape-recorded "oral history" reminiscences of more than 200 employees, friends, and other associates of Henry Ford. The photographic collection, 1897-1950 (569 ft.), includes 40,000 prints, snapshots, and photographs relating to Henry Ford and his family; 57,000 photographs and negatives made at the request of Ford or his office; 23,000 engineering photographs and negatives; and 37,000 negatives of the Autocar Co., oldest existing manufacturer of automobiles and trucks.

See Owen W. Bombard, "A New Measure of Things Past," in American Archivist, 18:123-132 (Apr. 1955); Henry E. Edmunds, "The Ford Motor Company Archives," ibid., 15: 99-104 (Apr. 1952); Wayne C. Grover, Fair Lane: A Business Archive (Ford Motor Company Archives, 1953. 5 p.); and the Ford Motor Company Archives, Bulletins.

DETROIT 26

Archdiocese of Detroit Chancery. 1234 Washington Blvd. Bernard Kearns, Chancellor.

Holdings: 400 pieces, dating from 1801 and relating to the Catholic Church in the Detroit area. Included are papers of Gabriel Richard (Mich.; Catholic missionary, educator, Terr.

Delegate to Cong.), 1801-42, among
them a diary; and correspondence concerning Indian missions.

See Hist. Records Survey, Guide
for Mich., p. 18.

DETROIT 2

Burton Historical Collection, Detroit
Public Library. 5201 Woodward Ave.
James E. Babcock, Chief.

Holdings: 3,000 linear ft. of papers, 1690-1955, relating to New
France, the Old Northwest, Michigan,
and Detroit.

Papers of individuals who held
Federal office include those of Austin
Blair (Mich.; Gov., U.S. Rep.), 1836-
73 (2 vols. and 17,500 pieces); Lewis
Cass (Mich.; Terr. Gov., Sec. War,
Minister to France, U.S. Sen., Sec.
State), 1780-1877 (3,000 pieces);
Grover Cleveland (N.Y.; U.S. Pres.),
1892-97 (1,250 pieces); Edwin Denby
(Mich.; U.S. Rep., Sec. Navy), 1918-
24 (900 pieces); Alpheus Felch (Mich.;
lawyer, Gov., U.S. Sen.), 1820-97
(1,250 pieces); Jacob M. Howard
(Mich.; lawyer, U.S. Sen.), 1796-
1872 (20 vols. and 2,700 pieces); Lucius Lyon (Mich.; U.S. Sen. and Rep.,
surveyor-gen. for Ohio, Ind., and
Mich.), 1839-52 (1 vol. and 37 pieces);
James McMillan (Mich.; railroad executive, U.S. Sen.), 1851-1930 (151
vols. and 49,750 pieces); John Thomson Mason (Va.; sec. of Mich. Terr.,
commissioner to the Cherokee Indians),
1792-1890 (4,000 pieces); William C.
Maybury (Mich.; lawyer, U.S. Rep.,
mayor of Detroit), 1868-1901 (300
pieces); Thomas W. Palmer (Mich.;
lumberman, U.S. Sen., Minister to
Spain), 1858-1913 (385 vols. and 34,000
pieces); Gabriel Richard (Mich.; Catholic missionary, educator, Terr. Delegate to Cong.), 1784-1832 (300 pieces);
Henry Rowe Schoolcraft (N.Y., Mich.;
explorer, ethnologist, supt. of Indian

affairs for Mich.), 1805-69 (2 vols.
and 2,000 pieces); Solomon Sibley
(Mich.; lawyer, Terr. Delegate to
Cong., mayor of Detroit), 1750-1918
(2 vols. and 19,200 pieces); Ross Wilkins (Mich.; U.S. dist. judge), 1827-
93 (1 vol. and 450 pieces); James
Witherell (Vt., Mich.; physician,
Mich. Terr. judge and sec., U.S.
Rep.), 1779-1830 (5 vols. and 300
pieces); William Woodbridge (Ohio,
Mich.; lawyer, Gov., U.S. Sen.),
1763-1860 (57 vols. and 35,250 pieces); and Augustus Brevoort Woodward
(N.Y.; U.S. judge for Mich. Terr. and
Fla. Terr.), 1782-1827 (1 vol. and
3,500 pieces).

Papers of clergymen include
those of Charles Brooks (Mass.; Unitarian clergyman, promoter of teacher training schools), 1793-1870 (19
vols. and 200 pieces); George Duffield (Pa., Mich.; Presbyterian minister), 1794-1868 (130 vols. and 300
pieces); John Gottlieb Ernestus Heckewelder (Pa., Ohio; Moravian missionary to the Indians, author), 1786-
1809 (15 pieces); Henry Warren Hicks
(Mich.; Methodist minister), 1842-
1912 (94 vols. and 4,500 pieces); and
Eleazer Williams (N.Y., Wis.; Episcopal missionary to the Indians),
1838-44 (27 pieces).

Papers of men in the armed forces
include those of William Alexander,
known as Lord Stirling (N.J., N.Y.;
Rev. War officer), 1771-87 (15 pieces); Richard Butler (Pa., U.S. Army
officer), 1776-91 (14 pieces); Green
Clay (Ky.; War of 1812 officer),
1813-18 (179 pieces); Jacob Kingsbury (U.S. Army officer), 1783-1835
(37 vols. and 1,500 pieces); Alpheus
Starkey Williams (Conn., Mich.; journalist, Mexican and Civil War officer,
U.S. Minister to El Salvador, U.S.
Rep.), 1832-1920 (6 vols. and 1,000
pieces); and Melancthon Taylor Woolsey (N.Y.; War of 1812 naval officer),
and his son, Melancthon Brooks Woolsey (N.Y.; Civil War naval officer),

1804-92 (26 vols. and 7,000 pieces).

Papers of others include those of Clarence Monroe Burton (Calif., Mich.; lawyer, collector of historical manuscripts), 1874-1931 (39 vols. and 25,000 pieces); John Farmer (Mich.; cartographer, surveyor), 1829-79 (3 vols. and 50 pieces); Theodore Henry Hinchman (Mich.; druggist, wholesale grocer, bank pres., State sen.), 1823-1929 (10 vols. and 6,500 pieces); Samuel Huntington (Ohio; State supreme court judge, Gov.), 1777-1814 (150 pieces); George Ironside (Ontario; fur trader, British Indian agent) and his son George, who succeeded his father as Indian agent at Amherstburg and later at Manitowaning, 1779-1848 (53 vols. and 4,500 pieces); George Johnston (Mich.; explorer, fur trader), 1813-62 (27 vols. and 1,500 pieces); James F. Joy (Mich.; lawyer, pres. of Mich. Central and other railroads), 1830-90 (64,750 pieces); Benson J. Lossing (N.Y.; wood engraver, author, editor), 1718-1884 (300 pieces); Stevens Thomson Mason (Mich.; Terr. sec., Gov.), 1831-42 (300 pieces); Paul McPharlin (Mich., N.Y.; puppeteer, designer), 1908-49 (46 vols. and 13,800 pieces); John Porteous (Scotland; fur trader from Albany, N.Y.), 1761-1800 (8 vols. and 150 pieces); and Nathaniel Parker Willis (Mass., N.Y.; author, editor), 1832-65 (119 pieces).

Family papers that throw much light on Michigan history are those of the John Askin family (N.Y., Mich., Ontario; fur traders and merchants), 1704-1891 (37 vols. and 5,000 pieces); the Boltwood and Shepard families (R.I., Conn., Mich.; lawyers, scientists, ministers, and educators), 1754-1895 (10,500 pieces); the Campau family (Mich.; French officials, merchants, fur traders, real estate dealers), 1715-1928 (50 vols. and 11,250 pieces); the family of Alexander Harrow (Scotland, Mich.; British naval officer on the Great Lakes, founder of Algonac,

Mich.), 1779-1810 (9 vols.); that of Angus and Alexander Mackintosh (Scotland, Mich., Ontario; fur traders, shipbuilders), 1728-1835 (6 vols., 50 pieces, and 3 reels of microfilm); that of Charles Christopher Trowbridge (Mich.; explorer, banker, philanthropist, mayor of Detroit, railroad executive), 1702-1925 (60 vols. and 9,000 pieces); and the Williams family, including John R., his father Thomas, and his son Gershom Mott (N.Y., Mich.; fur traders, merchants, lawyers, and public officials), 1726-1923 (48 vols. and 8,250 pieces).

There are extensive collections of business and legal records, including many relating to the building and operation of railroads in Michigan, the Great Lakes region, and the West. Some of these railroad companies are the Detroit, Lansing, and Lake Michigan; Grand Rapids and Indiana; Michigan Southern and Northern Indiana; Chicago and Aurora; Illinois Central Chicago, Burlington and Quincy; Atchison, Topeka and Santa Fe; and Union Pacific. There are papers pertaining to the sale and purchase of land, including records of the U.S. land office at Detroit, 1804 (454 pages); and of the Allegan Land Co., 1835-49 (2 vols.). Also in this group are records of Etienne Dutilh and Co. of Philadelphia and others of the Dutilh family in various parts of Europe, relating chiefly to export-import trade, 1755-1874 (15,000 pieces); accounts of financial agents of the British Government during the Revolutionary War, 1775-82 (9 vols.); papers relating to the American Fur Co.; records of Detroit merchants during the American Revolution; records of a number of plank road companies; and papers relating to Pacific trade and seal fishing, 1782-99. There are many records relating to shipping and shipbuilding on the Great Lakes, 1792-1930, including (besides the Harrow and Mackintosh papers mentioned above) records of the Detroit and Cleveland Navigation Co., 1891-1930 (45 vols. and 35,000 pieces). There are also logs of Great Lakes vessels; logs of several ocean vessels, 1818-44, from New England ports; journals and diaries of land and sea travel; and papers relating to the Detroit and Mackinac customs offices, 1789-1876 (7 vols. and 5,500 pieces), and to the work of the Great Lakes Coastal Survey, 1838-76 (1,500 pieces).

Other records include papers relating to the French and Indian War, the American Revolution, the War of 1812 (particularly the "Northwestern Army"), the Mexican War, the Civil War, and the Spanish-American War; and records of the United Spanish War Veterans, 1898-1942 (42 vols. and 2,500 pieces). There are also notarial records of the French consulate at Norfolk, Va., 1784-1866 (12 vols.); a record book of the superintendent of Indian affairs in Michigan, 1805-17 (1 vol.); and records of a Michigan immigration agent, 1848-80 (14 vols.), 5 Detroit hospitals, 1855-1945 (42 vols.), and a baseball association of Detroit, 1874-76 (1 vol.). Church records include those of Ste. Anne's Church, Detroit, 1704-1887 (14 vols. and 80 pieces); and of 50 other Catholic and Protestant churches in Michigan, 1817-1943 (145 vols. and 500 pieces). There are also transcripts of archives and other papers pertaining to Detroit and the Northwest, copied from originals in Canada, France, and England, and in other States of this country.

See "Descriptive List of the Papers of Governor Austin Blair," in Mich. History Magazine, 1 (no. 2): 133-148 (Oct. 1917); Floyd B. Streeter, Michigan Bibliography, 2:91-145 (1921); L. O. Woltz, "Source Material of the Detroit Public Library as Supplied by the Acquisition of the Burton Historical Collection," in Mich. History Magazine, 6:386-399 (1922);

Clarence M. Burton, "The Burton Historical Collection of the Public Library, Detroit," in Bibliographical Society of America, Papers, 16:10-16 (1922); Louise Rau, "Dutilh Papers," in Business Hist. Society, Bulletin, 13:73 (Nov. 1939); and Forest History Sources, pp. 47-49.

—oOo—

Detroit Institute of Arts. 5200 Woodward Ave. Edgar P. Richardson, Director.

Holdings: A large quantity of manuscripts and copies of manuscripts relating chiefly to art in the United States, in the custody of the two administrative units shown immediately below.

The Library. Carol Selby, Librarian.

Holdings: A few medieval and Renaissance manuscripts (7 vols. and 4 pieces); letters, poems, and sketch books of Thomas Cole (Ohio, Pa., N.Y.; landscape painter, poet), 1839-48 (18 vols. and 3 boxes); correspondence, designs, and photographs of Paul McPharlin (Mich., N.Y.; puppeteer, designer), 1927-48 (30 ft.); and 20,000 entry forms with biographical information, submitted with art objects for the annual exhibitions of Michigan artists, from 1945.

See De Ricci, Census, p. 1133.

Archives of American Art. (Mrs.) Miriam Lucker Lesley, Archivist.

Holdings: A rapidly growing collection of approximately 750,000 documents relating to American painters, sculptors, craftsmen, scholars, collectors, critics, and institutions. The major part of the holdings to date are microfilm copies (344 rolls) of art manuscripts and other material in depositories in the Philadelphia and New York areas. Among the institutions cooperating in the project were the Pennsylvania Academy of the Fine Arts, the American Philosophical Society, and the Art, Manuscript, and Prints Divisions of the New York Public Library. The filmed materials also include records of such private galleries as the Downtown, Albert Duveen, and Willard.

Outstanding original documents include the correspondence files of Art in America, 1937-56 (7 ft.); working papers and correspondence of Theodore Bolton (N. Y.; librarian, author), 20th century (6 ft.); letters of Frederick Edwin Church (N. Y.; landscape painter), 1866-98 (40 pieces); correspondence and working papers of Mary Bartlett Cowdrey (N. Y., Mass.; writer, museum official), 20th century (open file); correspondence and working papers of Marie De Mare (France, N. Y.; lecturer), before 1953 (5 boxes), for a biography of George P. A. Healy (Mass., Ill.; portrait painter); letters, account books, and memorabilia of Louis M. Eilshemius (N. J., N. Y.; artist), 19th and 20th centuries (3 ft.); letters and sketches of Lyonel C. A. Feininger (Germany, N. Y.; painter, art teacher), 1890-1920 (1 vol. and 50 items); working papers, correspondence and photographs collected by August Florian Jaccaci (France; artist), in preparing for the publication of Noteworthy Paintings in American Private Collections, 1907, of which he was a joint editor with John LaFarge (N. Y.; painter, worker in stained glass), 14 ft.; letters written to Miner K. Kellogg (Ohio; painter) by patrons of art and diplomats (1 vol. and 134 items); the collected papers of W. Langdon Kihn (N. Y., Conn.; artist, specializing in portraits of Indians), 20th century (18 ft.); correspondence of Sylvester Rosa Koehler

(Mass.; artist, museum curator) while editor of the American Art Review, 1879-81 (24 ft.); correspondence files, scrapbooks, and business papers of the Macbeth Gallery, New York, 1892-1953 (118 ft.); the diary of Rubens Peale (N. Y.; painter, museum manager), 1862-65 (4 vols.); working papers of Anna Wells Rutledge, chiefly relating to art in the South (2 ft.); biographical material collected from living American artists by George W. Stevens (Ohio; editor, director of Toledo Museum of Art), 1910 (167 items); letters and working papers of Nelson C. White (Conn.; art collector, writer), for monographs on the artists Abbott H. Thayer (N. Y., N.H.), J. Frank Currier (Mass.), and Dwight William Tryon (N. Y.), before 1951 (4 ft.); and the account book, autobiography, sketchbooks, and other papers of Worthington Whittredge (Ohio, N.Y., N.J.; landscape painter), 19th century (3 ft.).

A new program of tape recording the reminiscences of living artists and other figures in the art world was begun in 1958. By the end of 1959 these included Isabel Bishop, Charles Burchfield, Alson Skinner Clark, Philip Evergood, Edward Fowles, Marsden Hartley, Edward Hopper, Sheldon Keck, Elizabeth McCausland, Paul Manship, Charles Sheeler, Abraham Walkowitz, and William Zorach.

See reports on accessions in the Art Quarterly and in the Institute's Bulletin.

—oOo—

Detroit Public Library. 5201 Woodward Ave. Ralph A. Ulveling, Director.

Holdings: (1) Miscellaneous historical and literary manuscripts, 1789-1955; and (2) the Burton Historical Collection, which is separately treated above. Included in the first

category are autograph collections of
letters and documents of the signers
of the Declaration of Independence and
of U. S. Presidents; a diary of George
Washington (U. S. Pres.), Oct. 1, 1789-
March 10, 1790 (1 vol.); papers of
Laura Ingalls Wilder (Mo.; writer of
children's stories); and some literary
manuscripts.

DETROIT 21

Marygrove College Library.   8425
West McNichols Rd.   Sister M.
Claudia, Librarian.

Holdings: A small collection, consisting of 14th- and 15th-century manuscripts (2 vols.); and manuscripts of
English and American authors, chiefly 19th century (8 portfolios).
See Hist. Records Survey, Guide
for Mich., p. 22.

—oOo—

University of Detroit Library.
McNichols Rd. at Livernois Ave.
Rev. A. H. Mattlin, S. J., Director
of Libraries.

Holdings: 3 scrapbooks and 334
pieces, 1722-1940, of miscellaneous
character, including papers relating
to the early history of Detroit; a collection of autograph letters of American scientists, statesmen, and other
leaders; and a few vols. of medieval
liturgical manuscripts.
See Hist. Records Survey, Guide
for Mich., p. 23.

DETROIT 2

Wayne State University Archives.
144 General Library.   Philip P.
Mason, Archivist.

Holdings: 500 linear ft. of records

of all of the units of the University
including the College of Medicine,
which was organized in 1868; the
College of Education, organized in
1881; and the College of Liberal
Arts, organized in 1917. In addition
the Archives contains collections of
private papers of faculty members.

—oOo—

Wayne State University Libraries.
G. Flint Purdy, Director of Libraries.

Holdings: (1) A collection of archival and documentary materials on
Detroit labor history, 1933 to date
(several thousand pieces), concerned
especially with the early years of the
United Automobile Workers; (2) the
Hermann Hesse (Switzerland; author)
Collection, including 276 manuscripts,
61 of which are of poems; and (3) the
Richard and Robert Jacob Collection,
containing autograph letters and documents of signers of the U. S. Constitution, members of the U. S. Supreme
Court, and other American statesmen,
1760-1900 (275 items). Included also
are 50 letters and other papers of
Charles Lee (England, Va.; Army officer), and 100 letters of a Massachusetts soldier during the Civil War.

EAST LANSING

Michigan State University Library.
Richard E. Chapin, Director of Libraries.

Holdings: A substantial collection, relating chiefly to the University and other land-grant institutions.
Included are papers of Perry G. Holden (Ill., Iowa; agricultural educator),
20th century (20,000 items), relating
primarily to corn hybridization; papers of Douglas C. McMurtrie (Ill.;
typographer, author), 20th century

(100,000 pieces), containing material on the history of early printing in the United States; a collection on veterinary medicine; and a few literary manuscripts and drafts.

—oOo—

Michigan State University Museum. Frank N. Elliott, Curator of History.

Holdings: A recently established collection of manuscripts relating to agricultural, forest, and other aspects of the history of Michigan. Included are papers of Henry Chamberlain (Mich.; merchant, State legislator), 1813-1905 (12 vols. and 5 boxes), relating to politics and the State board of agriculture; Richard M. Hoar (Mich.; leader in Upper Peninsular political and economic activities), 1860-1912 (89 vols. and 7 boxes); John G. Parkhurst (Mich.; lawyer, Civil War officer, Minister to Belgium), 1846-1906 (diaries and 1 box of letters); and Henry Waldron (Mich.; railroad executive, U. S. Rep.), 1832-81 (1 box).

FLINT 3

Flint Public Library. 1026 East Kearsley St. Ransom L. Richardson, Director.

Holdings: 200 items, relating chiefly to Flint and Genesee County. Included is a small collection of diaries and other Civil War papers.
See Hist. Records Survey, Guide for Mich., p. 25.

FLUSHING

Flushing Township Public Library.

Holdings: 12 vols. and several pieces, 1836-1935, relating chiefly to Flushing and Clayton townships, Genesee County. Included are some local business and church records, 1842-64.
See Hist. Records Survey, Guide for Mich., p. 26.

GRAND RAPIDS 2

Grand Rapids Public Library. Donald W. Kohlstedt, Director; (Mrs.) Laura Weiss, Librarian, Michigan Room.

Holdings: 125,000 items, dated from 1829, relating chiefly to Kent County, Mich. Included are papers of John Strachan Lawrence (Mich.; lawyer, master in chancery), 1849-1924; Lucius Lyon (Mich.; U. S. Rep. and Sen.); and Carl E. Mapes (Mich.; lawyer, U. S. Rep.), 1925-38. There are also several diaries, including one, 1829-40, of an early missionary to the Indians; some church records; records relating to the excavation of Indian mounds in the Grand Rapids area; and records relating to men of Kent County in World Wars I and II.
See Hist. Records Survey, Guide for Mich., p. 27.

—oOo—

Grand Rapids Public Museum. 54 Jefferson Ave. SE. The Director.

Holdings: 3,000 items, consisting chiefly of papers on the Civil War, World War I, lumbering, and local business enterprises. There are also photographs of early Michigan lumbering operations and of Grand Rapids scenes.

GRAYLING

Hartwick Pines Memorial Hall. Leonard Jensen, Manager.

Holdings: 140 items, relating to Edward E. Hartwick (U.S. Army officer), especially during the Spanish-American War and World War I.

HARTLAND

Cromaine Library. (Mrs.) Florence B. Dearing, Librarian.

Holdings: 220 items, 1783-1936, including a collection of autograph letters of American statesmen, philanthropists, authors, lawyers, and scientists; papers relating to the World War I thrift drive in Cleveland, Ohio; and some account books, township records, and other papers of local interest.

HILLSDALE

Hillsdale College Library. Librarian.

Holdings: 3,500 pieces, 1859-1938, consisting chiefly of diaries, notes, letters, and other papers of Will Carleton (Mich., N.Y.; poet) and some papers relating to the College.
See Hist. Records Survey, Guide for Mich., p. 32.

HOLLAND

Museum of the Netherlands Pioneer and Historical Foundation.

Holdings: 3,966 items, relating chiefly to the colonization and development of western Michigan by Dutch immigrants and their descendants. Included are papers of Albertus C. Van Raalte (The Netherlands, Mich.; founder of the settlement at Holland).
See Hist. Records Survey, Guide for Mich., p. 34.

HOUGHTON

Keweenaw Historical Society.
Houghton Public Library.

Holdings: 100 vols. and 150 folders, consisting chiefly of journals, correspondence, and other records of 140 copper-mining companies of the Lake Superior region. Included are some letters of Douglass Houghton (Mich.; geologist, Univ. of Mich. prof.).
See Hist. Records Survey, Guide for Mich., p. 35.

HUDSON

Hudson Public Library.

Holdings: 21 vols. and a few pieces, 1832-97, chiefly of local interest. Included are a Civil War diary; some local township records, 1844-56; and records of local stores, 1832-72.
See Hist. Records Survey, Guide for Mich., p. 36.

ITHACA

Thompson Home Library.

Holdings: 6 vols., 1866-1928, chiefly of local interest. Included are records of a Congregational church, 1866-93; and two literary societies, 1874-1918.
See Hist. Records Survey, Guide for Mich., p. 36.

JACKSON

Jackson City Library. Michigan Ave. West. Ruth Foster, Director.

Holdings: 24 vols. and a number

of pieces, dated from 1830, relating chiefly to the locality. Included are cemetery and church records of Jackson County, 1830-70; programs of a local athenaeum, 1898-1918 (20 vols.); and historical essays on the county (4 vols.).

KALAMAZOO 45

Charles C. Adams Center for Ecological Studies, Western Michigan University. Thane S. Robinson, Director.

Holdings: 300,000 pieces, 1886-1960, relating chiefly to ecology in its broadest sense. There are original manuscripts and correspondence relating to ecology (23 filing cabinets), among which are 200 papers written by Charles Christopher Adams (Ill., Mich., N.Y.; ecologist, director of the New York State Museum), 1892-1955, with his accompanying notes. There are 40 filing drawers of manuscripts and correspondence of Frederic Edward Clements (Nebr., Minn., D.C.; ecologist, prof. at Univs. of Nebr. and Minn., research associate at Carnegie Institution); Henry Chandler Cowles (Ill.; botanist, Univ. of Chicago prof.); John Dewey (Mich., Ill., N.Y.; philosopher, educator, prof. at Mich., Chicago, and Columbia Univs.); David Starr Jordan (Ind., Calif.; naturalist, pres. of Ind. and Stanford Univs.); Aldo Leopold (Wis.; forester in U.S. Forest Service, Univ. of Wis. prof. of wild life management); Gifford Pinchot (D.C., Conn., Pa.; Chief of U.S. Forest Service, Yale forestry prof., Gov. of Pa.); Ernest Thompson Seton (Canada, N.Y.; naturalist, artist, author); Victor Ernest Shelford (Ill.; zoologist, prof. at Univ. of Ill.); and H. G. Wells (England; novelist). There are 3 filing drawers of correspondence

with Theodore Roosevelt (N.Y.; Gov., U.S. Pres.).

KALAMAZOO 49

Kalamazoo College Library.

Holdings: Chiefly (1) a collection relating to the College, 1832-1933 (40 vols., 500 pieces, and 2 filing cases); and (2) the Michigan Baptist State Convention Collection, 1825-1906, which contains letters and pastoral reports (800 pieces), journals and daybooks of missionaries and circuit riders in western Michigan (20 vols.), and record books of the convention (16 vols.).

See Hist. Records Survey, Guide for Mich., p. 38.

KALAMAZOO

Kalamazoo Public Library. Jeanetta Sagers, Reference Librarian.

Holdings: A small quantity, including some records of local churches, 1836-1907; and a collection, 1879-99, containing several letters on woman suffrage from Susan B. Anthony (N.Y.; suffragist, reformer) and letters dealing with the establishment of a woman's professorship at the University of Michigan (90 pieces).

See Hist. Records Survey, Guide for Mich., p. 39.

—oOo—

Kalamazoo Public Museum. 315 South Rose St. Alexis A. Praus, Director.

Holdings: A small quantity of papers deposited by the Kalamazoo County Historical Society, including diaries and photographs relating to

State and local history; a collection on the history of printing, 4000 B. C. to A. D. 1700 (42 pieces), including a few cuneiform inscriptions and oriental manuscripts and some European and American papers; and the Edward J. Stevens Collection of historical data, consisting of more than 15,000 cards containing information on Michigan pioneers from 1815 to 1850.

—oOo—

Ladies' Library Association. 333 South Park St.

Holdings: Included is a collection containing autograph letters of several national figures, 1852-80.
See Hist. Records Survey, Guide for Mich., p. 41.

KALAMAZOO 45

Western Michigan University Library. Katharine M. Stokes, Librarian; Alan S. Brown, Archivist.

Holdings: 14 file drawers, 300 bound vols., and 1 suitcase, 1896-1959, containing records of the institution, and pertaining to the history of rural life and education studies in the institutions of higher education in the United States. Included are papers of Ernest Burnham (Mich.; head of the University's department of rural life and education), 1896-1940 (1 suitcase and 2 file drawers); and Dwight B. Waldo (Mich.; pres. of the University), 1904-36 (2 file drawers).

LANSING

Michigan Historical Commission Archives. State Records Center, DeWitt Rd. Geneva Kebler, Archivist in Charge.

Holdings: 1,737 ft., 1798-1958, consisting of permanent records of all units of Michigan government. Included are records of 4 cities and towns, 4 townships, and 15 counties. Records of the Secretary of State (115 ft.) date from 1798, and the Governors' papers (565 ft.) from 1805.

LANSING 13

Michigan State Library.

Holdings: An unknown quantity of papers, 1812-1937, relating chiefly to Michigan as a Territory and State. Included are Civil War records, World War I records (374 vols.), and transcriptions of vital statistics and land records from the records of various counties.
See Hist. Records Survey, Guide for Mich., p. 43.

MACKINAC ISLAND

Astor House.

Holdings: 6 vols. and 8 pieces, including 1 letter book, 1820-24, and 5 ledgers, 1821-66, of the American Fur Co.
See Hist. Records Survey, Guide for Mich., p. 44.

MARQUETTE

Marquette County Historical Society. Care of Peter White Public Library. Phyllis S. Rankin, Librarian.

Holdings: 6,385 pieces, 1794-1955, relating chiefly to Marquette County and the Upper Peninsula of Michigan. Included are papers of William A. Burt (Mich.; inventor, surveyor), 1839-1925 (100 pieces), and of Alpheus Felch (Mich.; Gov., U.S. Sen.), 1794-1864 (500 pieces). There are also papers relating to iron mining, lumbering, and railroads, and 2,000 photographs relating to these topics.

See Hist. Records Survey, Guide for Mich., pp. 44-46.

MOUNT PLEASANT

Central Michigan College Library. Jesse B. Thorpe, Librarian; Arthur M. Fish, Clarke Historical Collection Librarian.

Holdings: 63 vols. and 7,800 pieces, 1775-1951, relating primarily to Michigan. Among papers of some 70 Michigan men and institutions are those of Lewis Cass (Mich.; Terr. Gov., Sec. War, U.S. Sen., Sec. State), 1802-30 (129 pieces); Robert Navarre (Mich.; Detroit settler and fur trader), 1775-1800 (280 pieces); John H. Pitezel (Mich.; author, Methodist minister and missionary to the Indians), 1828-54 (3 vols. and 85 pieces); Orlando Metcalfe Poe (U.S. Army officer, engineer), 1851-84 (487 pieces and 38 maps); and Joseph Rowe Smith (U.S. Army officer, engineer) and his son, an Army surgeon, 1823-1920 (1 vol. and 312 pieces). There are also records of the Port of Detroit, 1790-1833 (131 pieces); records of the American Fur Co. post on Mackinac Island, 1810-48 (2 vols. and 88 pieces); and papers of a Mackinac merchant, 1815-75 (1,900 pieces), a pioneer Washtenaw County doctor, 1826-92 (2 vols. and 390 pieces), and a superintendent of the Saginaw Valley and St. Louis Railroad, 1872-92 (1,687 pieces).

MUSKEGON

Hackley Public Library. Webster

Ave. and Third St. Clifford B. Wightman, Director.

Holdings: 400 items, relating chiefly to Muskegon and vicinity since about 1838. Included also is a small collection of autograph documents of persons of national prominence.

See Hist. Records Survey, Guide for Mich., pp. 47-49.

NAZARETH

Nazareth College Library. Sister Catherine Siena, Librarian.

Holdings: An autograph collection of 25 letters of miscellaneous character, 1707-1813.

See Hist. Records Survey, Guide for Mich., p. 49.

NILES

Fort St. Joseph Historical Museum.

Holdings: 11 vols. and 61 pieces, 1699-1898 but mainly 19th century, relating chiefly to Fort St. Joseph and the city of Niles and its vicinity. Included are daybooks and account books of local business enterprises, 1828-98 (8 vols.); company muster rolls of the French and Indian War, 1754; and a few Black Hawk War and Civil War letters.

See Hist. Records Survey, Guide for Mich., p. 49.

PONTIAC

Pontiac City Library. Adah Shelly, Librarian.

Holdings: 12 vols. and 16 file boxes of copies and compilations of

records, from 1820, relating to Oakland County. Included are copies of
cemetery records and of birth, death,
and marriage records; and histories
of early Oakland County families.

See Hist. Records Survey, Guide
for Mich., p. 52.

PORT HURON

Port Huron Public Library. 1115
Sixth St. Dorothy M. Mitts, Librarian of History Research.

Holdings: 81 vols. and 4,000 items,
1807-1950, relating chiefly to Port Huron and St. Clair County, Mich. Included are papers of Omar D. Conger
(Mich.; geologist, judge, U.S. Rep.
and Sen.), over 50 pieces; and Thomas
W. Palmer (Mich.; U.S. Sen., Minister to Spain), over 50 letters. There
are also papers of two judges and a
physician; account books, 1831-61;
records of sawmills, flour mills, and
stores; court reports and dockets;
census records; and church records.

See Hist. Records Survey, Guide
for Mich., p. 53.

SAGINAW

Hoyt Public Library. Janes and
Jefferson Aves. Gladys Blakely,
Librarian.

Holdings: 19 vols., 7 folders, and
2 packages, 1860-1936, consisting of
records of a cooperative farming
community and other papers relating
chiefly to Saginaw and vicinity.

See Hist. Records Survey, Guide
for Mich., p. 54.

SAULT STE. MARIE

Carnegie Public Library. Ellen
Green, Assistant Librarian.

Holdings: 800 letters, comprising (1) the American Fur Co. Collection, 1830-70, largely letters from
various posts to the company's factor at the "Sault"; and (2) the papers
of George Johnston (Mich.; explorer,
fur trader), 1828-69. There are 14
letters of Lewis Cass (Mich.; Terr.
Gov., Sec. War, U.S. Sen., Sec.
State).

See Hist. Records Survey, Guide
for Mich., p. 55.

SOUTHFIELD

Duns Scotus College Library. Nine
Mile and Evergreen Rds. Rev. Librarian.

Holdings: 2 Renaissance manuscripts and 16 other items of miscellaneous character.

See Hist. Records Survey, Guide
for Mich., p. 21.

THREE OAKS

Chamberlain Memorial Museum.
North Elm St.

Holdings: 8 vols. and 3 pieces,
1837 to the 20th century, relating to
Three Oaks and its vicinity. Included is a diary, 1837-50 (5 vols.), recording weather conditions and com-
modity prices in the area.

See Hist. Records Survey, Guide
for Mich., p. 57.

THREE RIVERS

Three Rivers Public Library. Mrs.
E. W. Richardson, Librarian.

Holdings: A small collection,
consisting chiefly of cemetery records for most of St. Joseph County,
World War I records for the county's

soldiers, and a few letters depicting pioneer life in Michigan.

See Hist. Records Survey, Guide for Mich., p. 58.

TRAVERSE CITY

Con Foster Museum.

Holdings: An unknown quantity of papers, from 1803 to date, relating chiefly to lumbering. Included are a ledger of the Astor Fur Co., 1803-8; and records of a local lumbering firm, 1851 to date.

See Hist. Records Survey, Guide for Mich., p. 59; and Forest History Sources, p. 49.

MINNESOTA

COLLEGEVILLE

St. John's University Library.

Holdings: 3 filing drawers, 1855-1940, relating chiefly to the work of the Benedictine Fathers in Minnesota. Included are letters and other documents concerning the White Earth Mission to the Chippewa Indians in Minnesota; diaries, letters, and photographs of members of the order; and documents relating to the founding of St. John's Abbey.

See Hist. Records Survey, Guide for Minn., p. 4.

DULUTH 12

St. Louis County Historical Society. 2228 East Superior St. Mrs. Josiah E. Greene, Executive Secretary.

Holdings: 74 file drawers, 16 transfer drawers, 2,600 folders, and 65 packages, 1833-1955, relating chiefly to St. Louis County and northeastern Minnesota. Included are diaries of Edmund Franklin Ely (Minn.; missionary to the Chippewa Indians), 1833-54 (20 vols.) and many of his letters and other papers; papers of John Stone Pardee (Minn.; newspaperman); papers of Leonidas Merritt (Minn.; pioneer miner, explorer); and records of the Great Lakes—St. Lawrence Tidewater Association, 1919-39 (24 file drawers). There are also reminiscences of pioneers; records of traders operating in several areas of Lake Superior; other records relating to explorations and the Indians; homestead records; and records relating to lumbering, iron mining and development, fishing, shipping, railroads,

and immigration. There are paintings and charcoal drawings of Chippewa Indians of this area, by Jonathan Eastman Johnson, known as Eastman Johnson (Mass., N.Y.; genre and portrait painter), 1856-57 (32 items); 750 photographs picturing the establishment and rise of Duluth and other cities of St. Louis County; and numerous maps of the area.

See Hist. Records Survey, Guide for Minn., p. 5; and Grace L. Nute, "The Edmund Franklin Ely Papers," in Minn. History, 6:343-354 (Dec. 1925).

FAIRMONT

Martin County Historical Society. Pioneer Museum, 304 East Blue Earth Ave. R. C. Hunt, President.

Holdings: A small collection, 1840-1960, relating chiefly to Martin County. Included are records of schools, churches, businesses, and other organizations; records of several townships in Martin County; diaries of early English settlers; records of Democratic county conventions, 1879-80; some papers pertaining to the post office at Iowa Lake, Iowa, 1890-91; and some business files of the early 1900's.

See Hist. Records Survey, Guide for Minn., p. 8.

FARIBAULT

Rice County Historical Society. Thomas Buckham Memorial Library. Brigid A. Coughlin, Curator pro tem.

Holdings: 850 pieces, 1851-1934, relating chiefly to Rice County. Included are records of various local businesses, among them the ledger of a lumber company at Northfield, 1884-91; records of fraternal, charitable, and other organizations; diaries; and 288 photographs and paintings. Also present are some papers of Henry B. Whipple (Minn.; Episcopal bishop, reformer of the U.S. Indian Service), 1851-72.

See Hist. Records Survey, Guide for Minn., p. 9.

GLENWOOD

Pope County Historical Society. Courthouse. Olive Barsness, Secretary.

Holdings: 14,000 folders, 37 vols., 100 other pieces, and 1,437 typed cards, 1866-1945, relating chiefly to Pope County. Included are records of the county commissioners of Pope County, 1866-76, and of the city commissioners and village council of Glenwood, 1881-1905; early records of churches, fire companies, schools, and fraternal and business organizations; and records of the Minnewaska National Farm Loan Association, 1918-35. There are also short individual autobiographies of 14,000 county residents, with some genealogical information; and cards giving the service histories of 1,437 persons in the armed forces in World War II.

See Hist. Records Survey, Guide for Minn., p. 11.

GRAND MARAIS

Cook County Historical Society. Olga Soderberg, President.

Holdings: 75 pieces, 1800-1956, relating to the North Shore; early ex-

plorations along the international boundary; fur-trading posts at Saganaga, Grand Marais, and Grand Portage; life stories of pioneers; and schools, churches, and other local organizations.

HUTCHINSON

McLeod County Historical Society. 115 South Jefferson St.

Holdings: An unknown quantity of papers, 1855-1922, chiefly of local interest. Included are a large collection of papers of Asa Hutchinson (Minn.; singer, a founder of Hutchinson) and his family, and many papers of Lewis Harrington (Minn.; road surveyor, railroad land agent, a founder of Hutchinson); business records, 1870-90; a diary of an overland trip to California in the early 1850's; and a meteorological record kept in McLeod County, 1822-1922.

See Hist. Records Survey, Guide for Minn., p. 13; and description in Minn. History, 20:347-349 (Sept. 1939).

LAKE CITY

Wabasha County Historical Society. Lake City Public Library. Mrs. John W. Murdoch, President.

Holdings: 7 vols. and 200 pieces, 1857-1906, relating chiefly to Lake City and Wabasha County. Included are records of a company of Minnesota volunteers, 1864-65 (111 pieces); and business records, including those of a lumber mill and lumber yards, 1857-93, a sorghum mill operated in the 1880's, and a pharmacy, 1863-97 (3 vols.). There are also genealogies of county families and a centennial history of the local Congregational church, written in 1957. (This

Society was formerly the Lake Pepin
Valley Historical Society.)

See Hist. Records Survey, Guide
for Minn., p. 14.

LITCHFIELD

Meeker County Historical Society.
Independent Printing Office.

Holdings: 1 vol. and 1 bundle,
1862-1932, relating chiefly to early
settlement in Meeker County and the
Sioux Indian uprising of 1862. Included are records of the Old Settlers Association, 1872-1932.

See Hist. Records Survey, Guide
for Minn., p. 15.

LITTLE FALLS

Morrison County Historical Society.
County Courthouse.

Holdings: 9 vols. and 1,281 pieces,
1805-1940, chiefly of local interest.
Included are a transcript of a diary of
Zebulon M. Pike (U.S. Army officer,
explorer), 1805-6; several hotel registers, 1881-1922; and 1,111 biographies, compiled in 1936-38, of persons who lived in the county.

See Hist. Records Survey, Guide
for Minn., p. 16.

MANKATO

Blue Earth County Historical Society.
606 South Broad St.   G. S. Petterson,
Curator.

Holdings: 150 vols. and 63 folders,
1853-1911, relating chiefly to Mankato
and Blue Earth County. Included are a
diary of John Marsh (Minn., Calif.;
pioneer, physician, etymologist); a diary of Jesse L. Reno (U.S. Army officer), 1853-54, giving details of building

the military road from Sioux City,
Iowa, to Mendota, Minn.; and correspondence of Morton S. Wilkinson
(Minn.; U.S. Sen. and Rep.), 1858-
69, with his law partner in Mankato,
chiefly concerning problems of the
Civil War. There are also letters of
an enlisted man for the whole Civil
War period; county archives; and records of law firms, businesses,
churches, schools, and social and
fraternal organizations.

See Hist. Records Survey, Guide
for Minn., p. 17, and description in
Minn. History, 21:104-106 (Mar.
1940).

MINNEAPOLIS

Archives of the English Evangelical
Lutheran Synod of the Northwest.
2310 Stevens Ave.

Holdings: 6 file drawers of papers, 1891-1954, consisting of the
archives of the synod. Included are
minutes of the conventions of the synod; and papers relating to pastors,
congregations, the Lutheran League,
the Women's Missionary Society, the
Brotherhood, conferences, Bible
camps, and home missions. Some
of these papers were formerly in the
library of the Northwestern Lutheran
Theological Seminary.

See Hist. Records Survey, Guide
for Minn., pp. 20, 24.

MINNEAPOLIS 4

Augsburg Archive Society. Augsburg
College and Theological Seminary.
Iver Olson, Archivist.

Holdings: A quantity of papers,
1851-1932, relating chiefly to Augsburg College and Seminary and to the
Lutheran Free Church in the Northwest. Included are letters, notes of

sermons, and other papers of Georg
Sverdrup (Minn.; theologian, pres. of
Augsburg Seminary), 1876-1907
(12,100 pieces), and of Sven Oftedal
(Minn.; Lutheran clergyman).

See Hist. Records Survey, Guide
for Minn., p. 18.

MINNEAPOLIS 3

Hennepin County Historical Society.
1516 Harmon Pl.   Joseph W. Zalusky,
Executive Secretary.

Holdings: A small quantity of manuscripts, in addition to numerous museum pieces, that are chiefly of local
interest.   Included are several diaries;
some miscellaneous records of churches, schools, and business organizations; and papers relating to Indian
missions.

See Hist. Records Survey, Guide
for Minn., p. 47.

MINNEAPOLIS 4

Historical Society of the Minnesota
Conference of the Methodist Church.
Minnesota Methodist Headquarters,
305 West Franklin Ave.   Earl F.
Baumhofer, Secretary-Historian.
5429 Logan Ave., South, Minneapolis
19.

Holdings: A collection dating from
1856 and as yet only partially organized,
relating to the Methodist Church in Minnesota.   Included are minutes and other
records of the Minnesota Conference,
from 1856 to the present, and of the
Northern Minnesota Conference during
the time of its existence; and records
or church histories of most of the
Methodist churches in Minnesota.
There are also some papers of Minnesota Methodist ministers and some
miscellaneous manuscript materials.

MINNEAPOLIS 3

Minneapolis Public Library.   Glenn
M. Lewis, Librarian.

Holdings: 43 vols. and portfolios
and 1,200 pieces, 18th-20th centuries,
relating chiefly to Minneapolis and its
cultural life.   The major group consists of records of the Minnesota
Academy of Science, 1873-1929 (38
vols. and portfolios), among which
are several hundred letters concerning the academy's expedition to the
Philippines, 1890-96.   There are also records of two old settlers' associations, 1867-76 and 1919-38 (2 vols.
minutes of the Minneapolis Press
Club, 1882-92 (1 vol.); minutes
of the Minneapolis Board of
Trade, 1895-99 (1 vol.); and an autograph collection, 18th-20th centuries
(1,000 pieces), representing all U. S.
Presidents and many signers of the
Declaration of Independence.   In the
Music Department, in addition to a
15th-century Gregorian chant, there
is a collection of musical manuscripts
by local composers (151 scores), including 80 scores by Willard Patton
(Maine, Minn.; composer and teacher),
and 21 scores by Emil Oberhoffer
(Minn.; symphony orchestra conductor).

MINNEAPOLIS 14

University of Minnesota Library.
E. B. Stanford, Director of Libraries.

Holdings: A quantity of manuscripts, mainly of the 19th and 20th
centuries, of miscellaneous character but relating chiefly to the University.

The Archives Division holds the
noncurrent files, records, and documents of University officers and departments; and papers of the following

men who have been prominently connected with the University: Lotus Del-
ta Coffman (Minn.; Univ. pres.), 1921-
39 (6 filing drawers); William Watts
Folwell (Minn.; political scientist,
historian, Univ. pres.) and his family,
1882-1948 (34 vols. and 91 folders);
Guy Stanton Ford (Ill., Minn., D.C.;
historian, Univ. pres.), 1891-1958 (5
vols., 13 boxes, and 175 folders); Cyrus Northrop (Minn.; Univ. pres.) and
his family, 1836-1923 (8 vols. and 124
folders); Fred Beal Snyder (Minn.;
lawyer, Univ. regent), 1912-50 (3 vols.
and 98 folders); and Frank K. Walter
(Pa., N.Y.. Minn.; Univ. librarian),
1882-1948 (34 vols. and 91 folders).

The James Ford Bell Collection
contains several manuscript maps,
charts, and roteiros; memoranda, letter books, and other papers of various
officials of European overseas trading
companies; accounts of eastern travels
from the 15th century; the papers of
the De Mey van Streefkerk family relating to plantations in Dutch Guiana (3
vols.); papers from the Maurepas family archive relating to French colonization of Louisiana and to De Lozier
Bouvet's proposed exploration of the
South Pacific (16 pieces); and a number of commentaries on various aspects of European commerce prior to
the 19th century.

The Special Collections Department contains some medieval and
Renaissance manuscripts (9 vols.),
and some manuscript musical scores.
Included also are a miscellaneous collection of 200 letters of political and
literary persons, 18 account books of
several early 19th-century American
merchants, some 500 letters of authors and illustrators of children's
books, over 100 manuscripts and
typescripts of various children's authors, and manuscripts of published
books and the personal papers of
Frederick Feikema Manfred (Minn.;
author).

See De Ricci, Census, pp. 1137-

1139; Frank K. Walter and Virginia
Doneghy, Jesuit Relations and Other
Americana in the Library of James F.
Bell, pp. 197-201, 318, 362, 377
(1950); and John Parker, The James
Ford Bell Collection; a List of Addi-
tions, 1951-54, pp. 3, 19, 35 (1955).

MONTEVIDEO

Chippewa County Historical Society.
Windom Bldg., North First St.

Holdings: 40 vols. and 232 pieces, 1852-1940, relating chiefly to
Chippewa County. Included are papers of Stephen R. Riggs (Minn.; missionary to the Sioux Indians), 1859-62
(71 pieces); and copies of county archives and school reports, historical
sketches of churches, and biographies of pioneers, compiled in 1936-
37 (22 vols.).
See Hist. Records Survey, Guide
for Minn., p. 29.

MOORHEAD

Clay County Historical Society.
(Mrs.) Ida M. Larson, Curator.

Holdings: 1,200 items, relating
chiefly to Clay County. Included are
papers on churches, townships and
municipalities, schools, pioneer pastors, Red River trails and transportation, the Civil War, and Indian disturbances.
See Hist. Records Survey, Guide
for Minn., p. 31.

NEW ULM

Brown County Historical Society.
(Mrs.) Leota M. Kellet, Curator.

Holdings: 30,000 pieces, 1854-
1960, relating chiefly to Brown

County and the Minnesota Valley region. They comprise the following groups: (1) Pioneers and their families, 1855-1960 (9,000 pieces), including letters, personal photographs, diaries, narratives, and family histories; (2) Sioux Indians, 1855-66 (1,200 pieces), including papers on reservations, Fort Ridgely, missions, and the Sioux uprising of 1862; (3) Brown County, 1857-1960 (2,400 pieces), including some public records, census schedules of 1857, 1860, 1865, 1880, and 1885, and papers on settlement and history, the development of steamboat and railroad transportation, business, and industry; (4) New Ulm, 1855-1960 (3,000 pieces), including papers relating to the Turnverein, local German culture, early settlers, the Sioux attack, churches, schools, business, and industry; (5) land companies, 1854-59 (260 pieces), including records of the Chicago Land Co. and the Turners' Settlement Society of Cincinnati; (6) military history, 1861-1945 (1,300 pieces), including rosters, soldiers' diaries, and other papers relating to the Sioux uprising, the Civil War, the Spanish-American War, and World Wars I and II; and (7) an autograph collection of letters and signed photographs, 1890-1925 (3,271 pieces), of world-famous persons in many fields of human endeavor.

NORTHFIELD

Carleton College Library. James H. Richards, Jr., Librarian.

Holdings: A small collection dealing almost exclusively with the history of the College and with certain individuals who have figured in its development.
See Hist. Records Survey, Guide for Minn., p. 33.

—oOo—

Northfield Public Library.

Holdings: 30 vols., 3 boxes, 1 package, and 68 pieces, 1832-1933, relating chiefly to Northfield. Included are papers of John L. Scofield (Minn.; Civil War surgeon), 1832-88 (60 items), some of which relate to a Negro hospital in Memphis, Tenn.; and records of a post of the Grand Army of the Republic, 1884-1933 (25 vols. and 1 piece).
See Hist. Records Survey, Guide for Minn., p. 35.

—oOo—

Norwegian-American Historical Association. St. Olaf College. Lloyd Hustvedt, Secretary.

Holdings: 8 filing cases and 120 pieces, 1856-1925, relating chiefly to Norwegian pioneers in Minnesota and other States, Norwegian Lutheran Church history, and St. Olaf College.
See Hist. Records Survey, Guide for Minn., p. 36.

PIPESTONE

Pipestone Historical Society. Courthouse.

Holdings: 2 vols. and 50 other pieces, 1857-1927, chiefly of local interest. Included are miscellaneous materials on exhibit at the Pipestone National Monument and memoirs of Warrington G. Brown (Minn.; State legislator).
See Hist. Records Survey, Guide for Minn., p. 38.

ROCHESTER

Historical Committee, Mayo Clinic. Isabel Farr, Secretary.

Holdings: Extensive files of correspondence and other material of William J. and Charles H. Mayo (Minn.; surgeons, founders of the Mayo Clinic and the Mayo Foundation for Medical Education and Research).

—oOo—

Olmsted County Historical Society. 213 3d Ave. SW.   P. O. Box 976. Clark J. Pahlas, Director.

Holdings: 270 vols. and 600 pieces, 1826-1953, chiefly of local interest. Included are diaries, one a Civil War diary of 1863; a scrapbook of Civil War letters; records of school districts in the county, 1866-1935 (171 vols.); business records, 1826-1925 (40 vols.); and records of local organizations, including a fire department, a woman's temperance group, a Grand Army of the Republic post, and 3 churches.
See Hist. Records Survey, Guide for Minn., p. 41.

ROSEAU

Roseau County Historical Society. Municipal Bldg.   I. A. Sunset, Curator.

Holdings: 91 vols. and 2 other pieces, 1890-1932, consisting chiefly of local township and school records.
See Hist. Records Survey, Guide for Minn., p. 43.

ST.   CLOUD

St. Cloud State Teachers College Library.

Holdings: Several hundred items, consisting chiefly of the papers of Alvah Eastman (Minn.; St. Cloud newspaper editor).
See Hist. Records Survey, Guide for Minn., p. 44.

Stearns County Historical Society. St. Cloud Public Library. Merle Lennartson, Secretary.

Holdings: 12 vols. and 2,741 other pieces, 1835-1939, relating chiefly to Stearns County. Included are some county and township archives, and 1,500 biographies of pioneers.
See Hist. Records Survey, Guide for Minn., p. 45.

ST.   JOSEPH

College of St. Benedict Library. Sister Conchessa Keegan, Librarian.

Holdings: A few hundred pieces relating to various activities of members of the Catholic clergy and laity in the Middle West, particularly in Minnesota and Wisconsin. Included are records of the College, a school for girls and young women.
See Hist. Records Survey, Guide for Minn., p. 46.

ST.   PAUL 1

Catholic Historical Society of St. Paul.   St. Paul Seminary, 2200 Grand Ave.   Rev. Thomas J. Shanahan, Archivist.

Holdings: 110 vols., 30 boxes, and 1,600 photographs, 1785-1948, relating chiefly to activities of Catholic clergy and laymen of Minnesota. Included are papers of Thomas Langdon Grace (Minn.; Bishop of St. Paul), 2 boxes; Jean Mathias Pierre Loras (Ala., Wis. Terr., Iowa; Bishop of Dubuque), 32 items; Anatole Oster (Catholic missionary), 3 boxes; and Augustin Ravoux (Minn.; missionary to the Sioux, priest), 1815-1906 (1 box). There are also records of the Ninth National Eucharistic Congress,

St. Paul, 1941 (4 boxes, 400 photographs, and motion pictures); and 70
account books from various sources.

See Hist. Records Survey, Guide
for Minn., pp. 49-50; and the Society's Acta et Dicta, 7 vols. (1907-36)
and index (1955), for description of
acquisitions during that period.

—oOo—

College of St. Catherine. 2004 Randolph Ave.   Sister Marie Inez, Librarian.

Holdings: 8 notebooks, 1 vol., and
30 pieces, 1850-1931, relating chiefly
to the Catholic Church and Sisters of
St. Joseph. Included is a small autograph collection of letters by noted
individuals of Europe and America.

See Hist. Records Survey, Guide
for Minn., p. 51.

ST. PAUL 8

Evangelical Lutheran Church Archives.
Luther Theological Seminary, Como
Ave. and Luther Pl.   Valborg E. Bes-
tul, Librarian.

Holdings: A collection, 1837 to
recent date, relating to the Norwegian Lutheran Church of America and
its predecessors and the successor
Evangelical Lutheran Church. Included are minutes of the general and
district conventions of the church,
from 1917; and minutes and other
documents, from 1843, of three former church bodies that united in
1917: the Synod of Norwegian Evangelical Lutheran Church in America,
the United Norwegian Lutheran
Church in America, and Hauges Norwegian Evangelical Lutheran Synod.
There are also extensive microfilm
copies of records of congregations
in the Evangelical Lutheran
Church.

ST. PAUL 1 6

Forest History Society, Inc. 2706
West Seventh Blvd.   Elwood R.
Maunder, Director.

Holdings: 60 transcripts of tape-
recorded oral history interviews with
persons important in fields of forest
products industry history, forestry
history, and the history of conservation in the United States; a catalog of
unpublished source materials in widely scattered libraries and other repositories throughout the United States
and Canada dealing with the field of
forest history; and manuscripts covering a variety of subjects in this field,
especially those related to the history
of the U.S. Forest Service, forestry
related associations, and individual
companies involved in lumbering and
pulp and paper business. There is
also a fine collection of old pictures
related to this special subject field.

ST. PAUL 1

Historical Committee of the Baptist
General Conference. Bethel Theological Seminary, 1480 North Snelling Ave.   Virgil A. Olson, Secretary; David Guston, Archivist.

Holdings: A substantial collection, 1850-1960, consisting chiefly
of the archives of the Baptist General Conference of America (formerly
the Swedish Baptist General Conference) and of Bethel College and
Seminary. Included are minutes of
the annual general conferences of the
church, beginning in 1856; nearly
complete files of the periodicals that
have served as organs of the denomination since 1871; records of individual churches throughout the United
States; and many church histories.
There are also papers of a number
of Swedish Baptist clergymen, from

1850, including those of John A. Edgren
(Minn.; Civil War naval officer, dean
of the Swedish Baptist Theological Seminary), 1871-87, autobiography and letters; G. Arvid Hagstrom (Minn.; pres.
of Bethel Institute), 1914-41 (30 filing
drawers), correspondence and diaries;
Karl J. Karlson (Minn.; dean of Bethel
Theological Seminary), 1922-48 (37
vols.), mostly theological; C. G. Lager-
gren (Minn.; dean of the Swedish Baptist Theological Seminary), manuscripts, largely theological (4 filing
drawers); F. O. Nillson (Sweden, Minn.;
Baptist clergyman), 1850-81, a diary
and several other documents and letters; and H. C. Wingblade (Minn.; pres.
of Bethel College and Seminary), 1941-
54 (4 filing drawers), correspondence.
There are also many diaries, autobiographies, and letters of other pioneer
clergy and settlers.

See Adolf Olson, "The Archives of
the Historical Society, Baptist General
Conference of America," in Swedish
Pioneer Historical Quarterly, 5:79-87
(July 1954).

ST. PAUL 2

James Jerome Hill Reference Library.
80 West Fourth St. Russell F. Barnes,
Librarian.

Holdings: A small collection, 1842-
1930, of miscellaneous character. Included are papers relating to a proposed merger of the Great Northern
Railroad and the Northern Pacific Railroad (327 items).

See Hist. Records Survey, Guide
for Minn., p. 56.

ST. PAUL 1

Minnesota Historical Society.
Russell W. Fridley, Director;
Lucile M. Kane, Curator of Man-
uscripts.

Holdings: A large quantity of
manuscripts, 1769-1953, relating
chiefly to Minnesota and the Upper
Mississippi Valley.

Papers of U.S. Presidents and
Cabinet members include those of
Frank B. Kellogg (Minn.; lawyer, U.S.
Sen., Ambassador to Great Britain,
Sec. State), 1907-37 (21 vols. and 33
boxes); Abraham Lincoln (Ill.; U.S.
Pres.), 1854-65 (11 items); William
DeWitt Mitchell (Minn., D.C., N.Y.;
U.S. Attorney Gen.), 1871-1956 (1
vol. and 6 boxes); Alexander Ramsey
(Minn.; Gov., U.S. Sen., Sec. War),
1827-1933 (5 vols. and 15 boxes);
George Washington (Va.; U.S. Pres.),
1754-96 (31 items); and William
Windham (Minn.; lawyer, U.S. Rep.
and Sen., Sec. Treas.), 1861-1943 (2
vols. and 2 boxes).

Papers of Members of Congress
include those of Moses K. Armstrong
(Minn.; U.S. Rep.), 1856-72 (1 box);
Moses Edwin Clapp (Minn.; lawyer,
U.S. Sen.), 1873-1929 (1 reel of microfilm of correspondence); Solomon
G. Comstock (Minn.; lawyer, U.S.
Rep.), 1872-1923 (47 vols. and 58
boxes); Cushman K. Davis (Minn.;
lawyer, Gov., U.S. Sen.), 1888-98
(2 vols. and 15 boxes); Ignatius Donnelly (Minn.; U.S. Rep., People's
Party leader), 1850-1909 (38 vols.
and 95 boxes); William S. King
(Minn.; U.S. Rep.), 1849-1906 (81
items); John Lind (Minn.; lawyer,
Gov., U.S. Rep., special agent to
Mexico), 1870-1933 (13 vols. and 13
boxes); James Manahan (Minn.; lawyer, U.S. Rep.), 1883-1932 (8 vols.
and 9 boxes); Knute Nelson (Minn.;
Gov., U.S. Sen.), 1861-1934 (270
boxes); Henry M. Rice (Minn.; U.S.
Sen., Indian Commissioner) and family, 1824-1942 (2 boxes); Thomas D.
Schall (Minn.; lawyer, U.S. Rep. and
Sen.), 1884-1932 (3 boxes); Henrik
Shipstead (Minn.; U.S. Sen.), 1913-53
(1 vol. and 33 boxes); James A. Taw-
ney (Minn.; U.S. Rep.), 1876-1919 (4

vols. and 15 boxes); Henry George Teigan (N. Dak., Minn.; leader in Farmer-Labor movement, newspaper editor, U.S. Rep.), 1916-41 (51 boxes); and Andrew J. Volstead (Minn.; lawyer, U.S. Rep.), 1910-24 (2 vols. and 5 boxes).

Papers of other officials of the Federal and State governments include those of Elmer Ellsworth Adams (Minn.; State legislator) and his family, 1860-1951 (5 vols. and 61 boxes); Christopher C. Andrews (Minn.; Civil War officer, Minister to Norway and Sweden, State forestry commissioner), 1843-1930 (21 vols. and 13 boxes); Theodore C. Christianson (Minn.; lawyer, Gov.), 1925-30 (6 boxes); Charles Burke Elliott (Minn.; justice of Minn. and Philippine Islands supreme courts), 1886-1934 (9 vols. and 1 box); Willis A. Gorman (Minn.; lawyer, Gov.), 1852-57 (71 items); William G. LeDuc (Minn.; Civil War officer, railroad promoter, U.S. Commissioner of Agriculture) and family, 1791-1918 (22 vols. and 6 boxes); Andrew R. McGill (Minn.; Gov.) and family, 1794-1931 (2 vols. and 13 boxes); William R. Marshall (Minn.; journalist, Civil War officer, Gov.), 1858-94 (2 boxes); Floyd B. Olson (Minn.; Gov.), 1923-36 (4 boxes); Leonard A. Rosing (Minn.; State political leader), 1893-1909 (2 vols. and 1 box); and Henry H. Sibley (Minn.; fur trader, Gov.), 1815-91 (90 vols. and 18 boxes).

Papers of explorers or fur traders include those of Norman W. Kittson (Minn.; fur trader), 1851-75 (7 vols.); Nathaniel P. Langford (Mont.; pioneer explorer) and family, 1819-1942 (27 vols. and 3 boxes); Auguste L. Larpenteur (fur trader) and family, 1792-1913 (9 vols. and 1 box); Stephen H. Long (U.S. Army officer, explorer), 1817-23 (6 items, including a 3-vol. journal); and Martin McLeod (Minn.; fur trader), 1830-83 (9 vols. and 2 boxes).

Papers of journalists and literary figures include those of Paul Southworth Bliss (N. Dak.; journalist, poet), 1934-36 (2 boxes); James Gray (Minn.; newspaper editor), 1867-1916 (17 vols. and 5 boxes); Lynn Haines (Minn.; editor of Searchlight on Congress), 1909-31 (61 boxes); Hans Mattson (Minn.; newspaper editor), 1861-65 (1 box); Edgar Wilson Nye, known as Bill Nye (Wyo., N.Y.; journalist, humorist, lecturer) and family, 1881-1936 (1 vol. and 1 box); Ole E. Rolvaag (Minn.; novelist, prof. at St. Olaf College), 1896-1934 (13 reels of microfilm of correspondence); John H. Stevens (Minn.; newspaper editor), 1838-89 (3 boxes); James W. Taylor (Ohio, Minn.; author, journalist), 1852-94 (4 vols. and 13 boxes); and Joseph Albert Wheelock (Minn.; newspaper editor) and family, 1803-1906 (5 boxes).

Papers of University of Minnesota faculty members include those of Clarence W. Alvord (Ill., Minn.; historian), 1847-1928 (2 vols. and 8 boxes); Gisle Bothne (Minn.; prof. of Scandinavian languages), 1905-34 (3 boxes); Solon J. Buck (Minn., Pa., D.C.; historian, archivist), 1906-35 (18 boxes); Oscar W. Firkins (Minn.; dramatic critic, prof. of literature) and family, 1876-1934 (11 vols. and 19 boxes); William Watts Folwell (Minn.; political scientist, historian, pres. of the Univ.), 1769-1933 (26 vols. and 129 boxes); and Alfred Owre (Minn., N.Y.; dental surgeon at Univ. of Minn. and Columbia Univ.), 1884-1936 (13 boxes).

Other personal papers include those of George Antoine Belcourt (Canada, Minn.; Catholic missionary to Chippewa Indians), 1832-57 (1 box of copies of letters and 2 reels of microfilm of dictionary of Chippewa language); Edwin H. Brown (Minn.; architect), 1919-34 (9 boxes); William Fuson Davidson (Minn.; steamboat owner on the Upper Mississippi) and his family, 1817-1919 (340 vols. and

156 boxes); Robbins Gilman (Minn.; leader in social welfare activities and motion picture improvement) and his family, 1699-1952 (7 vols. and 93 boxes); Sherman Hall (Minn.; Congregational clergyman, missionary to Chippewa Indians), 1831-75 (1 box); Charles M. Loring (Minn.; national leader in civic betterment work), 1875-1922 (5 vols.); Edward Duffield Neill (Minn.; Presbyterian clergyman, historian, pres. of Macalester College), 1827-1930 (13 vols. and 8 boxes); Gideon H. and Samuel W. Pond (Conn., Minn.; Congregational missionaries to Indians), 1833-91 (2 vols. and 3 boxes); Stephen R. Riggs (missionary to Indians), 1851-62 (9 vols. and 117 pieces); Alpheus Beede Stickney (Minn.; lawyer, railroad pres.), 1895-1916 (1 box); Henry B. Whipple (Minn.; Episcopal bishop, reformer of U.S. Indian Service), 1862-88 (42 boxes); and Howard Y. Williams (Minn.; official in liberal parties and League for Independent Political Action), 1924-52 (5 vols. and 40 boxes).

Papers important for religious history include an extensive collection of records of and papers relating to the Protestant Episcopal Church, Diocese of Minnesota, 1845-1939 (113 vols. and 22 boxes); papers collected by the Historical Society of the Methodist Episcopal Church, Minnesota Annual Conference, 1840-1909 (7 vols. and 2 boxes); and records of individual Congregational, Lutheran, Presbyterian, and other churches.

Records of or relating to various organizations include those of the American Association of University Women, Minnesota Branch, 1889-1942 (10 vols. and 1 box); American Fur Co., 1803-66 (16 boxes and 5 reels of photostatic, typewritten, and microfilm copies); American Home Missionary Society, Minnesota Branch, 1859-79 (3 vols.); American Immigration Co. (to sell cutover lands in Wisconsin and Minnesota), 1906-51 (36 vols.

and 50 boxes); Architects' Small Home Service Bureau, of Minneapolis, 1920-41 (67 vols. and 193 boxes); Better Business Bureau, of Minneapolis, 1912-25 (11 vols. and 60 boxes); Cigar Makers' International Union of America, St. Paul local, 1879-1933 (74 vols.); the Democratic-Farmer-Labor State Central Committee, 1944-54 (35 boxes); Farmer-Labor Association, Minnesota, 1924-48 (4 vols. and 7 boxes); Grand Army of the Republic, Department of Minnesota, 1866-1925 (213 vols. and 44 boxes); Irish-American Colonization Co., of Dublin, Ireland, 1872-1909 (5 vols. and 3 boxes); various units of Minnesota Infantry, chiefly for the Civil War period (13 vols. and 10 boxes); Minnesota Academy of Medicine, 1887-1931 (8 vols.); Minnesota Equal Franchise League, St. Paul, 1911-17 (1 box); Minnesota Federation of Women's Clubs, 1896-1945 (8 vols. and 3 boxes); Minneapolis Humane Society, 1884-1941 (2 boxes); Minnesota State Dental Association, 1882-1932 (7 vols. and 2 boxes); Minnesota Woman Suffrage Association, 1894-1921 (24 vols. and 12 boxes); National Nonpartisan League, 1915-27 (1 vol., 12 boxes, and 1,200 cards); and the Prohibition Party, Minnesota State Executive Committee, 1888-1919 (2 vols. and 1 box).

There are account books for a company dealing in furs, a hardware store, a general merchandise store, and a nursery; records of a real estate company, a grain elevator, Missouri River steamboats, a log-rafting firm, and several lumber companies; diaries of farmers and farmers' wives, a Union soldier in Libby prison and one in Andersonville prison, a Methodist circuit rider in Indiana, a midshipman at the U.S. Naval Academy, and pioneers on trips to California and elsewhere; and papers of a turnverein, a musical society, and several local granges.

See Grace L. Nute and Gertrude W. Ackermann, Guide to the Personal Papers in the Manuscript Collections of the Minnesota Historical Society (1935. 146 p.); Lucile M. Kane and Kathryn A. Johnson, Manuscript Collections of the Minnesota Historical Society (1955. 212 p.); annual reports of the director of the Society and articles describing particular groups of manuscripts in Minn. History (1915 to date), passim; and Forest History Sources, pp. 56-70.

—oOo—

State Archives and Records Service, Minnesota State Archives Commission. 117 University Ave. Robert M. Brown, State Archivist.

Holdings: Official records of the Territory and State of Minnesota. Included are files of the Governor, the secretary of state, the State auditor, the attorney general, the State treasurer, the surveyor general of logs and lumber, the Department of Education and the State College Board, the Railroad and Warehouse Commission, the Department of Conservation, the Department of Agriculture, State institutions, the Grand Army of the Republic, and the State census schedules through 1905. There are also certain county and municipal records.
See Forest History Sources, pp. 71-73.

—oOo—

Weyerhaeuser Library, Macalester College. James F. Holly, Librarian.

Holdings: A substantial quantity of materials relating chiefly to Macalaster College. Included are historical records of the College; records of the Presbyterian Synod of Minnesota, 1858 to date; some manuscripts and a few other papers of Edward Duffield Neill (Minn.; historian, Presbyterian clergyman and founder of Macalester College); an extensive collection of correspondence, notes, and other papers of James Wallace (Minn.; faculty member and pres. of Macalester College); and a small number of scattered letters of a few persons of national importance.

ST. PETER

Gustavus Adolphus College Library. Odrun E. Peterson, Librarian.

Holdings: 1,000 vols., letter files, and folders, dating from 1850 and consisting of official records of the college and the Minnesota Conference of the Augustana Evangelical Lutheran Church. The conference records include records of Minnesota College (formerly of Minneapolis), other conference institutions, and many churches. There are also correspondence and writings of Eric Norelius (Minn.; Evangelical Lutheran clergyman, author, founder of the predecessor of Gustavus Adolphus College), 1851-1916.

—oOo—

Nicollet County Historical Museum. Mrs. M. E. Stone, Curator.

Holdings: 248 pieces, 1851-1910, chiefly of local interest. Included are records of an early store, 1860-61, and of an early temperance organization; histories of churches and cemeteries, from 1853 (49 pieces); military records and records of civilian war work during World War I (57 pieces); and local family papers and letters.

JACKSON

Mississippi Conference Methodist
Historical Society. Millsaps College
Library. Rev. J. B. Cain, Presi-
dent.

Holdings: Chiefly records of the
Mississippi Annual Conference of the
Methodist Church; and letters, a diary, and other papers of William Wi-
nans (Miss.; Methodist clergyman).

—oOo—

Mississippi Department of Archives
and History. Charlotte Capers, Director.

Holdings: 5,000 vols. and 2,750,000
other pieces, consisting of (1) official
records, held by the Department as archival agency of the State, and (2) other
papers relating chiefly to Mississippi.

The former category includes records of land titles and other records
of French, British, and Spanish administration of the region that is now
Mississippi, 1699-1798 (102 vols.);
records of the Mississippi Territory,
1798-1817 (112 vols.); and executive,
legislative, and judicial records of the
State, 1817-1940 (4,000 vols. and
2,500,000 other pieces). Included are
records of the Bank of the State of
Mississippi, 1810-44 (250 vols. and
38,257 other pieces); and numerous
muster rolls, order books, and other
military records, especially for the
period of the Civil War.

Papers of persons who held im-
portant administrative office under the
U. S. Government include those of
Charles W. Buck (Miss., Ky.; lawyer,
Minister to Peru), 1852-1922 (11 vols.
and 607 other pieces); William C. C.

Claiborne (Tenn.; Miss., La.; Gov.
of Miss. and La. Terrs., Gov. of
La., U. S. Rep. from Tenn., Sen.
from La.), 1801-16 (12 vols.); Jef-
ferson Davis (Miss.; U. S. Rep. and
Sen., Sec. War, Confed. Pres.),
1840-1905 (7 vols. and 557 other
pieces); Lucius Q. C. Lamar (Miss.;
Confed. Army officer, U. S. Rep. and
Sen., Sec. Interior, U. S. Supreme
Court Justice), 1854-1918 (5 vols.
and 240 other pieces); and Robert J.
Walker (Pa., Miss.; U. S. Sen. from
Miss., Sec. Treas., Gov. of Kansas
Terr.), 1821-69 (71 pieces).

Papers of persons who served in
the U. S. Congress, in addition to
some of the above, include those of
James L. Alcorn (Miss.; lawyer, Gov.,
U. S. Sen.), 1839-1906 (3 vols. and 52
other pieces); John F. H. Claiborne
(Miss., La.; lawyer, journalist, historian, U. S. Rep. from Miss.), 1804-
81 (7 vols. and 16 other pieces);
James Z. George (Miss.; Confed. Army officer, U. S. Sen.), 1845-88 (334
pieces); Patrick Henry (Miss.; lawyer, Confed. Army officer, U. S.
Rep.), 1855-1935 (5 vols. and 39 other pieces); John A. Quitman (Miss.;
planter, Mexican War officer, Gov.,
U. S. Rep.), 1812-60 (3 vols. and
2,529 other pieces); and John Sharp
Williams (Miss.; planter, U. S. Rep.
and Sen.), 1898-1923 (2 vols.).

Other personal papers include
those of John C. Burrus (Miss.;
planter), 1831-1918 (2,152 pieces);
Emery C. Chandler (Miss.; planter,
businessman), 1886-1917 (1,945
pieces); Charles Clark (Miss.; lawyer, planter, Confed. Army officer,
Gov.), 1810-92 (24 vols. and 305
other pieces); John J. Coman (Miss.;
businessman, sec. penitentiary),
1889-1936 (4,041 pieces); Harris

Dickson (Miss.; lawyer, novelist), 1888-1946 (25 vols. and 2,013 other pieces); William Dunbar (Miss.; planter, scientist, explorer), 1776-1810 (7 vols. and 34 other pieces); Samuel G. French (Miss.; Confed. Army officer), 1844-1904 (1 vol. and 675 other pieces); Thomas E. Helm (Miss.; planter, businessman), 1848-1934 (43 vols. and 1,387 other pieces); Henry Hughes (Miss.; writer, apologist for slavery), 1837-59 (16 vols. and 10 other pieces); Thomas J. McKean (Pa.; Civil War officer), 1862 (91 pieces); relating to the Battle of Corinth; John W. Monette (Miss.; physician, historian), 1825-51 (2 vols. and 145 other pieces); William Priestley (Miss.; businessman), 1833-1932 (3 vols. and 1,915 other pieces); Dunbar Rowland (Miss.; lawyer, historian, archivist), 1885-1937 (6,653 pieces); Daniel Ruggles (Va.; Confed. Army officer), 1862-65 (310 pieces), relating to operations in Mississippi; Clarence L Sivley (Miss.; lawyer, planter), 1892-1943 (3 vols. and 1,892 other pieces); John M. Stone (Miss.; Gov.), 1861-1926 (1 vol. and 156 other pieces); Oscar J. E. Stuart (Miss.; lawyer, Confed. Army officer), 1840-1948 (40 vols. and 2,019 other pieces); Benjamin L. C. Wailes (Miss.; planter, agriculturist, geologist, prof. at Univ. of Miss.), 1772-1859 (16 vols. and 174 other pieces); William T. Walthall (Ala., Miss.; journalist, Confed. Army officer, U. S. Consul in British Guiana), 1855-1932 (3,721 items); and William N. Whitehurse (Miss.; land office official), 1845-89 (1,770 pieces).

Records of organizations include those of the Daughters of Confederate Veterans and United Daughters of the Confederacy, 1894-1952 (16 vols. and 1,706 other pieces); the Independent Order of Odd Fellows, 1848-1941 (25 vols. and 4,310 other pieces); Jefferson College, 1803-1936 (35 vols. and 8,867 other pieces); the Lions International, District 30, 1938-48 (1,720 pieces); the Mississippi Historical So-

ciety, 1910-37 (2,080 pieces); the Mississippi Library Association, 1936-44 (842 pieces); the Synod of Mississippi, Southern Presbyterian Church, 1828-1901 (24 vols.), including records of several presbyteries and individual churches; and the United Spanish War Veterans, 1926-47 (5 vols. and 4,582 other pieces). Business records include plantation journals and other papers, records of commission merchants at Natchez from as early as 1799, records of railroads from 1852, and account books and other papers of numerous business firms. There are also extensive transcripts of official records in France, Great Britain, and Spain that pertain to the region that is now the State of Mississippi, 1678-1820.

See "An Official Guide to the Historical Materials in the Mississippi Department of Archives and History," an appendix of the 12th Annual Report of the Director of the Department, Nov. 1912—Oct. 1913; and lists of accessions in the Department's Biennial Reports for 1937-39 to 1951-53.

STATE COLLEGE

Mitchell Memorial Library, Mississippi State University. Forrest C. Palmer, Director of Libraries.

Holdings: 7 vols. and 19 pieces, 1817-1900, relating chiefly to Mississippi. Included are diaries of Mississippi River planters, 1850-53, 1870-83 (2 vols.); and journals and notes of William Starling (Miss.; planter, chief engineer of Mississippi Levee Board), 1882-83, 1897-99 (3 vols.).

UNIVERSITY

Mississippi Collection, University of

Mississippi Library. Dorothy Zolli-
coffer Oldham, Curator.

Holdings: 1,200 vols. and 87,500
items, consisting of ledgers, letter
books, letters, diaries, literary manuscripts, land grants, deeds, wills,
maps, minute books, and charters.
The largest individual collection comprises the papers of Byron Patton Harrison, known as Pat Harrison (Miss.;
U. S. Rep. and Sen.), 1920-41 (1,095
vols. and 42,500 items). There are
also papers relating to the Women's
suffrage movement in Mississippi,
from 1897 (3 vols. and 101 items);
records of a chapter of the Daughters
of the American Revolution (16 linear
ft.); and some historical, literary, and
miscellaneous manuscripts (12,000
pages).

—oOo—

University of Mississippi Lumber
Archives.   John H. Moore,

Director.

Holdings: A collection of records,
chiefly 20th century, of the lumber industry of the Mid-South. Most of the
documents concern operations in the
Southern pine area of southern Mississippi. Older records are those of a
Natchez firm. R. F. Learned and Son,
Inc., 1829-1945 (100 cu. ft.).

VICKSBURG

Vicksburg and Warren County Historical Society. Old Court House Museum.
(Mrs.) Eva W. Davis, Director.

Holdings: 200 vols., 1803-1900, and
150 other manuscripts, 1823-66, consisting of miscellaneous papers relating
to Vicksburg, to Mississippi, and to the
South before and during the Civil War.
Included are receipts for slaves, letters written during the Siege of Vicksburg, scrapbooks, and diaries.

MISSOURI

ARROW ROCK

Arrow Rock Tavern.

Holdings: 6 vols. of account books and ledgers, 1834-56. Included are account books of John Sappington (Mo.; physician), 1837-38 (2 vols.).
See Hist. Records Survey, Guide for Mo., p. 1.

CANTON

Culver Stockton College Library.

Holdings: 200 pieces, consisting of correspondence, sermons biographies, church records, and other manuscripts relating to the Disciples of Christ.
See Hist. Records Survey, Guide for Mo., p. 1.

COLUMBIA

Christian College Library. Peggy McCully, Librarian.

Holdings: 32 vols. and 65 pieces, 1851-1959, relating chiefly to the College.
See Hist. Records Survey, Guide for Mo., p. 1.

—oOo—

State Historical Society of Missouri. Richard S. Brownlee, Director.

Holdings: (1) Noncurrent official records of the State, 120,771 pieces, 1821-1903, and (2) a large collection of other manuscripts relating chiefly to Missouri and the Middle West. In the latter group are papers of George C. Bingham (Mo.; portrait and genre painter) and his family, 1814-1930 (166 pieces); Daniel R. Fitzpatrick (Mo.; political cartoonist), 1917-52 (1,476 pieces), consisting of manuscript cartoons; Garland C. Broadhead (Mo.; geologist, engineer, prof. at Univ. of Mo.), 1853-1908 (295 pieces); Odon Guitar (Mo.; Civil War officer), 1862-64 (253 pieces); Abiel Leonard (Mo.; State supreme court judge, political leader), 1786-1896 (3,114 pieces); Meredith M. Marmaduke (Mo.; Gov.), 1823-86 (347 pieces); James S. Rollins (Mo.; U.S. Rep.), 1830-88 (2,300 pieces); John Sappington (Mo.; physician), 1800-87 (1,684 pieces); and Thomas A. Smith (U. S. Army officer), 1809-43 (1,817 pieces). Also included are a collection of Ozark folksongs (3,305 pieces); letters from service men and women in World War II (1,680 pieces); records of various churches in Missouri; some county records; papers of pioneer clergymen; and numerous journals and ledgers providing information for business and social history.
See "Manuscript Collection of Gen. Thos. A. Smith, Belonging to the Society," in Mo. Hist. Review, 6:209 (July 1912); Hist. Records Survey, Guide for Mo., p. 2; and notes in the Mo. Hist. Review, 1940-51.

—oOo—

Western Historical Manuscripts Collection, University of Missouri. Lewis E. Atherton, Director.

Holdings: 1,500 items, 1800-1959, relating to the Mississippi Valley, the West, and especially Missouri.

Some of the holdings are more specifically identified below.

Papers of Members of Congress, all Missourians except as otherwise indicated, include papers of Senators David Rice Atchison, 1837-86 (5 vols. and 19 folders); Forrest C. Connell (Gov., U.S. Sen.), 1941-51; James P. Kem, 1946-52 (44 boxes); Peter Norbeck (S. Dak.), 1921-36 (10 folders); Roscoe Conkling Patterson, 1930-44 (10 folders); and of Representatives Samuel Washington ("Wat") Arnold, 1947-48 (20 folders); C. Jaspar Bell, 1935-49 (60 file boxes); Marion T. Bennett, 1943-48 (4 file cases); Perl D. Decker, 1879-1939 (53 folders); William H. Hatch, 1870-87 (17 folders); Ralph F. Lozier, 1909-40 (39 drawers); and Clyde Williams, 1922-41 (11 folders).

Papers of other political leaders, all Missourians, include those of Jesse W. Barrett (State attorney gen., Republican leader), 1908-53 (1,850 folders); Dwight H. Brown (State sec. of state), 1937-40 (23 folders); Benjamin B. Cahoon (lawyer), 1842-89 (67 folders); Daniel Dunklin (Gov.), 1815-56 (34 folders); North T. Gentry (State attorney gen., historian), 1879-1947 (16 vols. and 233 folders); Herbert S. Hadley (Gov., prof. of law at Univ. of Colo., chancellor of Washington Univ.), 1876-1943 (50 vols. and 1,051 folders); Charles M. Hay (lawyer, prohibition leader), 1919-33 (442 folders); Arthur M. Hyde (Gov.), 1919-24 (1,288 folders); Laurance M. Hyde (judge, State supreme court), 1943-49 (305 folders); Abiel Leonard (judge, State supreme court), 1769-1863 (882 folders); Guy B. Park (Gov.), 1933-37 (20 file drawers); Forrest Smith (Gov.), 1948-52 (32 boxes); Lloyd C. Stark (Gov.), 1937-41 (22 file drawers); and Francis M. Wilson (U.S. Dist. Attorney), 1928-32 (10 boxes).

There are papers of persons, chiefly Missourians, of prominence in other fields: Albert Brisbane (N.Y.;

Fourierist), 19th century (2 rolls of microfilm, letters of Brisbane and other Utopians); Xenophon Caverno (farm leader), 1917-41 (120 folders); Green Clay (diplomat, Sec. of U.S. Legation in Italy), 1866-69 (60 letters, chiefly dealing with Garibaldi); Carl Crow (journalist, observer in the Far East), 1903-45 (3 vols. and 332 folders); Enoch H. Crowder (U.S. Judge Advocate Gen.), 1881-1936 (12 file boxes); Chester C. Davis (agricultural economist), 1924-28 (1,042 folders); Robert N. Denham (National Labor Relations Board gen. counsel), 1919-54 (1,753 folders); Flora Hartley Greene (civic leader), 1905-31 (216 folders); William Hirth (farm leader), 1926-34 (344 folders); Walter E. Meyer (lawyer), 1930's (35 boxes), relating to St. Louis Southwestern Railroad; John G. Neihardt Nebr., Mo.; author), 1896-1950 (358 folders); George N. Peek (Ill.; manufacturer, Agricultural Adjustment Administrator), 1917-45 (890 folders); Homer P. Rainey (Tex., Mo.; pres. of Univ. of Tex. and Stephens College), 1919-52 (1,962 folders); Edward M. Shepard (geologist at Drury College), 1844-1939 (50 folders); H. E. Slusher (farm leader), 1940-59 (10 file boxes); and Kimbrough Stone (U.S. Circuit Court of Appeals Judge), 1897-1958 (956 folders).

Manuscripts relating particularly to the University of Missouri include papers of Thomas A. Brady (vice pres. of the Univ.), 1944-49; John W. Connaway (prof. of veterinary science), 1885-1944 (171 folders); Ella V. Dobbs (prof. of applied arts), 1923-35 (11 folders); Charles W. Greene (prof. at Univ. Medical School), 1898-1938 (58 folders); A. Ross Hill (pres. of the Univ.), 1914-30 (24 folders); Frederick H. Middlebush (pres. of the Univ.), 1895-1952 (56 letter files and 2 boxes); Frederic B. Mumford (dean, College of Agriculture), 1868-1947 (321 folders);

Herman Schlundt (prof. of chemistry), 1914-38 (1,465 folders); and Jonas Viles (prof. of history), 1914-40 (200 folders). There are also records of the University's athletic committee, 1934-47 (97 folders); of its board of curators, 1839-1910 (46 rolls of microfilm); of its chapter of Sigma Xi, 1920-45 (265 folders); of its College of Agriculture, 1897-1944 (5 file drawers and microfilm); of its School of Business and Public Administration, 1940-59 (20 boxes); of its history department, 1909-37 (174 folders); and of the Army Air Forces training program at the University, 1943-44 (272 folders).

Business records include account books and other papers of banks and trust companies, general stores, flour mills, a tobacco company, an insurance company, a ferry company, lead and other mines, and a land agency and loan company. There are records of farming and animal breeding, extensive materials collected for a history of the livestock industry, papers relating to the purchase of slaves, the papers of a claim agent of the Chicago, Burlington, and Quincy Railroad, and minutes of a local union of brewers and maltsters. Included also are records of the Maramec Iron Works, 1817-91 (331 vols. and 515 folders); of the Missouri Land and Lumber Co., 1880-1945 (610 vols. and 52 drawers); and of the Ozark Land and Lumber Co., 1887-1923 (99 vols. and 688 folders).

Miscellaneous papers include debates and proceedings of the Missouri Constitutional Convention of 1845-46; several diaries of journeys to California about 1850; letters of a Montana cattle rancher, 1881-1914 (255 pieces); account books of several physicians and records relating to medical societies; some church records; letters relative to the Civil War and the westward movement, 1840-1900 (25 folders); several World War I letters and 6,000 World War II letters; records of the Missouri Council of Defense, 1940-45 (20 file drawers); records of Christian College, 1847-1953 (17 vols. and 461 folders); and papers of or pertaining to the Missouri Constitutional Convention of 1943-44 (more than 2,200 folders).

See University of Missouri, Guide to the Western Historical Manuscripts Collection (1952. 125 p.) and the Supplement (1956. 53 p.); and Forest History Sources, p. 75.

CONCEPTION

Conception Abbey. Rev. Norbert Schappler, Librarian.

Holdings: 15,000 pieces, mainly 1873-1923, relating to the Abbey, theology, and missions of the Catholic Church in Missouri and the Dakotas. Included are 37 manuscript leaves from liturgical books, 10th-15th centuries; and the personal diary and correspondence of Frowin Conrad (first superior of the Abbey), 1873-1923 (2 filing drawers).

INDEPENDENCE

Harry S. Truman Library. Philip C. Brooks, Director.

Holdings: 2,200 cu. ft. of papers, 1934-53, relating chiefly to the public career of Harry S. Truman (Mo.; U.S. Sen. and Pres.). They include the papers of Mr. Truman as Senator and Vice President, 1934-45 (72 cu. ft.), and as President, 1945-53 (1,890 cu. ft.). Also in the collection are papers of some of the members of Mr. Truman's White House staff, 1945-53 (107 cu. ft.); papers of Bess Wallace Truman and Margaret Truman, 1945-53 (60 cu. ft.); records of the White House Social Office, 1945-53 (25 cu. ft.); records of the Democratic National Committee, 1945-52 (7 cu. ft.); and records of certain Presidential commissions and committees (39 cu. ft.). There are also the papers of Oscar L. Chapman (Colo.; Sec. Interior), 1933-53 (27 cu. ft.); and Charles G. Ross (Mo.; press sec. to the President), 1945-50 (7 cu. ft.).

KANSAS CITY 10

Federal Records Center, GSA. 2306 East Bannister Rd. Chief.

Holdings: A large quantity of noncurrent and semicurrent records, chiefly of recent date, of nonmilitary agencies of the U.S. Government in Iowa, Kansas, Minnesota, Missouri, Nebraska, North Dakota, and South Dakota. Most of the records have been appraised for disposal after specified periods of time, but some will be preserved because of their enduring value. Records in the latter category include those of U.S. district courts and predecessor circuit courts, from 1824; Missouri Basin Survey Commission, 1952-53; Bureau of Indian Affairs, from 1869; Weather Bureau, from 1880; Bureau of Customs, from 1844; and Immigration and Naturalization Service, from 1906. There are also several file drawers of material on Mount Rushmore National Monument and the project of sculpturing colossal figures of Presidents Washington, Jefferson, Lincoln, and Theodore Roosevelt on Mount Rushmore, S. Dak., including letters received by Gutzon Borglum (N.Y.; sculptor of the memorial).

LEXINGTON

Lexington Historical Society.

Holdings: An unknown quantity of papers, 1825-1918, relating chiefly to Missouri and the Southwest. Included are records of a banking house and mercantile company, 1825-47 (17 vols.), pertaining to trade on the Santa Fe Trail, Mexico, steamboats, and the outfitting of pioneer traders and shippers; minutes of the city council and other records of Lexington, 1867-1918; and some financial records of Central College.

See Hist. Records Survey, Guide for Mo., p. 6.

LIBERTY

William Jewell College Library. Opal R. Carlin, Librarian.

Holdings: (1) Some miscellaneous manuscripts in the main library, including a collection of photographic reproductions of the writings of Balthasar Hubmaier (Austria; heretic), 16th century (6 vols.); and manuscripts of American poets in the Ted Malone (Mo., N.Y.; poet, radio director) Collection; and (2) the Missouri Baptist Historical Society's collections, 1846-1960 (140 vols. and 1,364 pieces), relating chiefly to the Baptist Church in Missouri, and including sermons, minutes of the Missouri Baptist General Association, minutes and reports of various churches and district associations in Missouri, and letters from prominent Baptists.

See Hist. Records Survey, Guide for Mo., pp. 7-8, and the Survey's Information Concerning the Manuscript Depository Collection of the Missouri Baptist Historical Society (1941. 4 p. Processed).

ST. CHARLES

Lindenwood College Archives. Mildred Kohlstedt, Librarian.

Holdings: Several hundred papers,

1800-60, relating to the early development of Missouri. Included are an uncataloged collection of diaries, journals, and letters of Maj. George C. Sibley (Indian agent, explorer, educator), pertaining to Fort Osage, 1808-24; and papers relating to the establishment of Lindenwood School for Young Ladies at St. Charles, 1827.

ST. LOUIS 5

Concordia Historical Institute. 801 DeMun. Rev. Aug. R. Suelflow, Director.

Holdings: 200,000 pieces, 1700 to date, relating chiefly to the Lutheran Church in the United States, Canada, and foreign mission fields. The Institute is the official depository for the archives of the Lutheran Church—Missouri Synod. The largest single collection pertains to the immigration from Saxony to America, 1838-39; there are sermons and letters of its leader, C. F. W. Walther (Lutheran clergyman, founder of Concordia Theological Seminary and organizer of the Synod), and diaries, letters, and documents of other Lutheran leaders.

ST. LOUIS 3

Federal Records Center, GSA. Chief.

Holdings: (1) Official personnel folders for former civilian employees of the U. S. Government in Washington, D. C., and elsewhere (transferred to the Center 30 days after the individual has left employment in Department of Defense agencies and 1 year after his departure from other agencies); (2) a locator file on civilians currently employed by the U. S. Government; and (3) noncurrent individual pay records, payrolls, and supporting payroll documents for most Federal agencies.

Most of these records have been or will be appraised for disposal after specified periods of time. Some records, however, particularly those for individuals who have gained prominence in public or private life, will be preserved.

ST. LOUIS 10

Missouri Botanical Garden Library. 2315 Tower Grove Ave. George B. Van Schaack, Librarian.

Holdings: 81 vols. and 16 linear ft., 1819-89, consisting chiefly of papers of George Engelmann (Germany, Mo.; meteorologist, physician, botanist) and business papers of Henry Shaw (Mo.; businessman, founder of the Mo. Botanical Garden). Engelmann's papers include notes and sketches, 1835-84 (58 vols.), on various genera or families of plants; several hundred letters to him from Asa Gray (N. Y., Mass.; botanist, prof. at Harvard Univ.), 1841-83; and several thousand letters from other world-famous botanists, 1841-84. The letters, documents, bills, and other business records of Henry Shaw, 1819-89 (16 linear ft.), are also available on microfilm at the Baker Library of Harvard University.

See Mo. Botanical Garden, Annual Report for 1889, and Bulletins for material on Henry Shaw.

ST. LOUIS 12

Missouri Historical Society. Jefferson Memorial. (Mrs.) Frances H. Stadler, Manuscripts Librarian.

Holdings: 1,190 vols. and 1,251,500 pieces, from 1664, relating to Missouri and the entire West as well as to Eastern and European backgrounds of persons and events in Missouri history.

Papers of political leaders who held high Federal office include those of William H. Ashley (Mo.; fur trader, explorer, U.S. Rep.), 1811-40 (1 vol. and 100 pieces); Richard Bartholdt (Mo.; U.S. Rep.), 1855-1932 (500 pieces); Edward Bates (Mo.; U.S. Rep., Sec. War, Attorney Gen.), 1807-66 (1 vol. and 15 pieces); Thomas Hart Benton (Mo.; U.S. Rep. and Sen.), 1790-1858 (185 pieces); William H. Bissell (Ill.; Gov., U.S. Rep.), 1825-61 (212 pieces); James O. Broadhead (Mo.; U.S. Rep., Minister to Switzerland) and his family, 1802-1903 (15 vols. and 500 pieces); David R. Francis (Mo.; Gov., Sec. Interior, Ambassador to Russia), 1889-1926 (50,000 pieces); George Harrington (D.C., N.Y.; Asst. Sec. Treas., Minister to Switzerland), 1840-90 (500 pieces); William T. Harris (Mo.; philosopher, author, U.S. Commissioner of Education), 1857-1909 (8 vols. and 2,000 pieces); Andrew Jackson (Tenn.; U.S. Pres.), 1813-39 (40 pieces); Thomas Jefferson (Va.; U.S. Pres.), 1763-1826 (876 pieces); Abraham Lincoln (Ill.; U.S. Pres.), 1854-66 (41 pieces); John B. C. Lucas (Pa.; U.S. Rep., U.S. dist. court judge, Acting Gov. of Mo. Terr.) and his son James H. Lucas (Mo.; banker, capitalist, philanthropist), 1754-1859 (5,000 pieces); and Samuel Treat (Mo.; U.S. dist. court judge, admiralty law prof. at Washington Univ.), 1815-91 (189 pieces).

Papers of other political leaders include those of Frederick Bates (Mo.; Gov.), 1800-64 (835 pieces and letter books, 1807-12); Charles D. Delassus (Lt. Gov. of Upper La.) and his family, 1758-1909 (551 pieces); William C. Lane (Mo.; physician, first mayor of St. Louis, Gov. of N. Mex. Terr.), 1823-37 (75 pieces); Alexander McNair (Mo.; Gov.), 1808-31 (35 pieces); and Amos Stoddard (lawyer, U.S. Army officer, Acting Gov. of La. Terr.), 1798-1804 (50 pieces).

Papers of military leaders, in addition to some of the above and some mentioned below, include those of Henry Atkinson (U.S. Army officer, commander of the "Yellowstone Expedition," 1813-35 (1 vol. and 23 pieces); Pierre G. T. Beauregard (La.; Confed. Army officer) and his family, 1779-1893 (2 vols. and 25 pieces); George Rogers Clark (Va., Ky., Mo.; Rev. War officer, explorer), 1755-1815 (550 pieces); Alexander W. Doniphan (Mo.; Mexican War officer, lawyer, political leader), 1846-87 (59 pieces); Ethan Allen Hitchcock (U.S. Army officer, author), and his nephew Henry Hitchcock (Mo.; lawyer, Civil War officer, dean of Washington Univ. school of law), 1786-1902 (2,000 pieces); Theodore Hunt (U.S. naval officer) and William P. Hunt (Mo.; commander of the Astoria overland expedition, postmaster), 1779-1840 (125 pieces); Stephen W. Kearny (U.S. Army officer), 1810-47 (several vols. and 43 pieces); Jacob Kingsbury (U.S. Army officer) and his son, James W. Kingsbury, 1791-1911 (80 pieces), containing much information on the War of 1812; Robert E. Lee (Va.; U.S. Army and Confed. Army officer), 1837-51 (76 pieces); Charles Parsons (Mo.; Civil War officer), 1862-64 (17 vols. and 7,000 pieces); S. Ledyard Phelps (U.S. naval officer), 1861-64 (360 pieces); George C. Sibley (Mo.; U.S. Army officer, Indian agent, educator), 1804-50 (5 vols. and 189 pieces); Samuel H. Starr (U.S. Army officer), 1846-67 (4 vols. and 206 pieces); and François and Jean B. Vallé (Mo.; commandants at Ste. Genevieve) and their family, 1664-1917 (1,135 pieces).

Papers of fur traders and explorers include those of David Adams (Mo.; fur trader, frontier guide), 1830-50 (diary and letters), relating chiefly to the Rocky Mountain area and the Bonneville Expedition; René

Auguste Chouteau and Pierre Chouteau, Sr. and Jr. (Mo.; merchants, fur traders, financiers), 1752-1872 (50,000 pieces); William Clark (Mo.; Terr. Gov., explorer, Indian agent), 1766-1839 (2,000 pieces, including journals, 1805-6); Thomas Forsyth (Ill., Mo.; Indian agent, explorer) and his family, 1793-1874 (200 pieces); Charles Gratiot (pioneer trader) and his family, 1769-1859 (5 vols. and 50 pieces); Meriwether Lewis (U.S. Army officer, explorer, Gov. of La. Terr.), 1804-35 (2 vols. and 33 pieces), including journal of expedition); Manuel Lisa (Mo.; fur trader), 1774-1836 (129 pieces); Pierre Menard (Ind., Ill.; fur trader, merchant, political leader) and his family, 1800-44 (457 pieces); William L. Sublette (Mo.; fur trader, merchant) and others of the family including his brother Milton, 1819-60 (500 pieces).

Papers relating to medicine include those of John Sappington (Mo.; pioneer in the use of quinine medication), 1803-86 (6 vols. and 2,727 pieces); Antoine F. Saugrain (Mo.; naturalist, physician, philosopher) and his family, 1788-1875 (100 pieces); John F. Snyder (Mo., Ill.; physician, Confed. Army officer, archeologist), 1839-1917 (657 pieces); and Robert J. Terry (Mo.; anatomist), 1912-38 (1,220 pieces).

Papers relating to journalism, literature, art, and the theater include those of William V. Byars (Mo.; editor, writer), 1876-1900 (1,000 pieces); Kate O'Flaherty Chopin (Mo.; novelist, poet), chiefly 19th century (700 items), including notebooks and correspondence; Fannie Cook (Mo.; author, civic worker), 1940-49 (20,000 pieces); Eugene Field (Mo.; poet, editor), 1872-95 (115 pieces); Noah M. Ludlow (Mo.; theatrical impresario), with papers of an actor and an etcher, 1778-1934 (1,500 pieces, including Ludlow's diaries, 1840-70); Frederic Remington (N.Y.; painter, author), 1877-95 (80 pieces); Solomon F. Smith, known as

Sol Smith (Mo.; comedian, theater manager), 1832-68 (1,058 pieces); Thomas L. Snead (Mo.; editor, States rights defender), 1866-87 (200 pieces); and Sara Teasdale (Mo., N.Y.; poet), 1904-32 (34 letters and manuscript poems), in 5 of the poet's published volumes, together with photographs and clippings.

Papers of other persons include those of Lillie Devereux Blake (Pa., N.Y.; reformer, author), 1847-1910 (2,000 pieces); James B. Eads (Mo.; engineer, designer of bridge across Miss. River at St. Louis), 1776-1924 (146 pieces); Rufus Easton (Conn., Mo.; judge, postmaster), 1796-1826 (50 pieces); Francis W. Gilmer (Va.; lawyer), 1814-26 (50 letters to Thomas Jefferson); Richard Graham (Mo.; Indian agent), 1795-1896 (7 vols. and 3,479 pieces); George E. Kessler (Mo.; city planner, landscape architect), 1904-23 (2,500 pieces); Albert B. Lambert (Mo.; industrialist, World War I aviation officer), 1936-46 (500 pieces relating to aeronautics); Justus Post (N.J., Mo., Ill.; U.S. Army officer), 1807-21 (1 vol. and 59 pieces), including his diary as agent of fortifications for New York Harbor, 1814; and Eleazer Williams (N.Y., Wis.; Episcopal missionary to Indians), 1786-1854 (3 vols. and 15 pieces), including his grammar of the Mohawk dialect.

In addition to the papers of individuals mentioned above there are collections relating to fortifications (Ft. Chartres, Kaskaskia, and Arkansas River posts), 1739-57 (100 pieces); lands, 1766-1885 (1,000 pieces), including Spanish land grants and Territorial and State land records; the Louisiana Transfer, 1803-4 (50 pieces), including the document of transfer of Upper Louisiana from Spain to France; and medicine, from 1776 (1,000 pieces). There are also military papers, 1776-1946 (11,385 pieces), covering the Missouri militia, the peacetime army, and wars from the Revolution through the Civil War, but very largely Civil War; papers relating to music, from 1795 (1,000 pieces); an autograph collection of Presidents' papers, from 1787 (200 pieces); papers relating to the Santa Fe trade and trail, 1823-48 (150 pieces); papers relating to slavery, 1770-1867 (250 pieces); steamboat papers, from 1802 (1,000 pieces); theatrical papers, 1823-80 (200 pieces); and microfilm of documents from the St. Louis Post Office relating to early airmail operations from St. Louis, 1918-30 (750 pieces), including a record book of flights to Chicago, many made by Charles Lindbergh (Mo., N.Y.; aviator).

Business records include those of the American Fur Co., 1802-58 (56 account books); Bemis Bros. Bag Co., from 1833 (100 pieces); a stove manufactory, 1839-74 (1,000 pieces); the predecessor of the St. Louis Chamber of Commerce, 1881-1926 (9 vols. and 5,000 pieces); and the Merchants' Exchange, St. Louis, 1871-1912 (91 vols. and 27,510 pieces).

Also included are a "Missouri governors" collection, including papers of commandants and Spanish Territorial governors, from 1725 (5,000 pieces); and archives of New Madrid, 1793-1804 (1,432 pieces), Ste. Genevieve, 1769-1850 (2,500 pieces), and St. Louis, 1763-1818 (2,952 pieces). There are also Missouri tax records, 1805-49 (2,000 pieces), and court records, 1804-50 (3,000 pieces), for the Federal and civil courts of the Territory of Louisiana (to 1812), the Territory of Missouri (to 1821), and the State of Missouri.

See Hist. Records Survey, Guide for Mo., p. 9.

ST. LOUIS 1

St. Louis Mercantile Library.   510

Locust.   Mary Dorward, Librarian.

Holdings: 8 vols. and 42 pieces, 1787-1850, relating chiefly to the early history of St. Louis and Louisiana Territory. Included are papers of Daniel Bissell (U.S. Army officer), 1800-20 (1 vol.); and René Auguste Chouteau (La., Mo.; trader, assistant in the founding of St. Louis), 1787-1819 (42 pieces). There are also a journal of the legislature of Louisiana Territory, 1806-9 (127 pages); and records of the St. Louis Lyceum, 1838-49 (169 pages).

See St. Louis Mercantile Library, Reference Lists, No. 1, Part 2, "Manuscripts Relating to Louisiana Territory and Missouri," pp. 17-22 (1898).

ST. LOUIS 19

St. Louis Roman Catholic Theological Seminary Library. 7800 Kenrick Rd. Patrick J. Mullins, C.M., Librarian.

Holdings: A large quantity of manuscripts, chiefly ot the 19th century, consisting of (1) archives of the seminary and (2) other papers relating to the Catholic Church in the Mississippi Valley and to the Archdiocese of St. Louis. Included are papers of Simon W. G. Bruté de Rémur (Md., Ind.; first Bishop of Vincennes), 1816-39 (138 letters); Louis Guillaume Valentin Du Bourg (Md., La.; pres. of Georgetown College, Bishop of New Orleans), 1815-53 (146 letters); Joseph Rosati (La., Mo.; Bishop of St. Louis), 1815-40 (17 vols.); and Peter J. Verhaegen (Mo., Md., Ky.; Jesuit teacher, provincial of the Md. Province of the Society of Jesus, pres. of St. Joseph's College at Bardstown, Ky.), 1830-41 (80 items). Also included are transcripts of documents from the Archives of the Congregatio de Propaganda Fide in Rome and from various other depositories.

See "The Historical Archives of the Archdiocese of St. Louis" and "Archives of Propaganda," in St. Louis Catholic Hist. Review, 1:24-39 (Oct. 1918) and 1:276-285 (July 1919).

ST. LOUIS 3

St. Louis University Library. 221 North Grand Ave. Joseph P. Donnelly, Librarian.

Holdings: 133 vols., 3,500 other items, 11,000 ft. of microfilm of manuscripts and 42,000 other manuscripts on microfilm, from the 1st century, B. C., to about 1850, relating chiefly to the religious and educational work of the Jesuit Order in the Middle West and Latin America. Included are baptismal and marriage records of early Kaskaskia, from 1695 (4 vols.); indexes and/or transcriptions of the records of early Catholic settlements in and around St. Louis; 33 vols. of papers of Pierre-Jean DeSmet (Jesuit missionary); papers of other priests and missionaries; and manuscripts relating to western exploration and the fur trade (1,400 pieces). There are also, on microfilm, the archives of the Curia of the Society of Jesus, pertaining to Jesuit activities in the Western Hemisphere (8,000 ft.); and microfilm (3,000 ft.) of selected Spanish archives (the Pastell collection), pertaining to Jesuit activities in Latin America. The Knights of Columbus Foundation is currently microfilming Vatican Library manuscripts (11,000,000 pages) and depositing the films in the St. Louis University Library. The Missouri Province Archives, which contain important material on Jesuit activities in the West, are at the University. Although they are not a part of the Library, the best approach to them is through the Librarian.

See Hist. Records Survey, Guide

for Mo., p. 10; The Knights of Columbus Foundation for the Preservation of Historic Documents at the Vatican Library (n.d. 11 p.); and Gilbert J. Garraghan, The Jesuits of the Middle United States, 3:598-599 (1938).

ST. LOUIS 30

Washington University Libraries. Andrew J. Eaton, Director of Libraries.

Holdings: 1,900 pieces, 1660 to date, and 102 microfilm reels for the Tudor period. The general library has papers of William K. Bixby (Mo.; manufacturer, book collector), 1857-1931 (500 pieces); William Greenleaf Eliot (Mo.; Unitarian minister, reformer, founder of Washington Univ.), 1854-87 (400 pieces); Eugene Field (Mo., Ill.; poet, journalist), 1873-94 (70 pieces); and scattered papers of other writers. There is a collection of Tudor poetry and drama in manuscript on microfilm. The School of Medicine Library has notebooks and other papers of William Beaumont (Mo.; surgeon, physiologist), 1812-53 (518 pieces).

WEBSTER GROVES 19

The Gallery of Living Catholic Authors, Inc. Webster College. 470 East Lockwood. Sister Mary Joseph, S. L., Archivist.

Holdings: A collection of more than 130,000 pages of manuscripts, in the form of separate pages and 150 complete volumes, written by living Catholic authors, 1932-60. They were written in 15 languages by more than 880 authors in the United States and 60 other countries. Included are 2,000 personal letters from Gallery members and many from non-mem-

bers; more than 1,000 signed photographs and photo-negatives; and 1,000
pages of bio-bibliographical data received from the authors in response
to a questionnaire.

See Hist. Records Survey, Guide
for Mo., p. 13; and Mary Joseph,
"The Gallery of Living Catholic Authors," in Catholic Library World,
11:111-115 (Jan. 1940).

MONTANA

BROWNING

Museum of the Plains Indian. Claude E. Schaeffer, Curator.

Holdings: 147 vols. and 139 bundles, 1873-1921, relating chiefly to the Blackfeet Indian Agency. Included are agents' miscellaneous letters, 1875-1915 (56 vols. and 25 bundles), and letters to Commissioners, 1884-1915 (29 vols.); and other Blackfeet Agency records, 1873-1921 (62 vols and 114 bundles), relating to marriages, births, deaths, schools, population censuses, land allotments, and other matters.

CROW AGENCY

Custer Battlefield National Monument. Box 116. The Superintendent.

Holdings: 18 vols., 53 boxes, and 87 pieces, 1857-1933, relating chiefly to the Civil War, the Seventh U.S. Cavalry, and the Battle of the Little Bighorn River and its participants. Included are the personal and military papers of George A. Custer (U.S. Army officer) and those of his widow relating to her husband's career, 1857-1933 (1 vol. and 12 boxes); and incomplete Seventh Cavalry records, 1866-1926 (17 vols. and 40 boxes). Throughout the collections are many letters written by prominent officers of the Civil War and Indian wars.

GLACIER NATIONAL PARK

The Superintendent.

Holdings: 4 vols. and a number of pieces, 1885-1912, relating to the park. Among letters from the personal file of a former superintendent of the park, 1908-12, are some by important officials of the U.S. Government.

HELENA

Historical Society of Montana. Veterans and Pioneers Memorial Bldg. Virginia Walton, Chief Librarian.

Holdings: 25,000 items, dating from 1851, relating chiefly to Montana. Included are Territorial and State archives; papers of James S. Brisbin (Pa.; Civil War and U.S. Army officer), Samuel T. Hauser (Mont.; pioneer entrepreneur, Terr. Gov.), and Martin Maginnis (Mont.; Terr. Delegate to Cong.); journals and diaries of early immigrants and explorers; and collections of business papers such as the records of a post trader at Fort Shaw, Mont., 1871-97, a stage-line company, 1878-79, a mercantile and cattle company, 1905-18, and banking companies, 1865-1900.

See Charles W. Smith, A Union List of Manuscripts in Libraries of the Pacific Northwest, passim (1931. 57 p.).

MISSOULA

Montana State University Library. Kathleen Campbell, Librarian.

Holdings: Papers of and per-

taining to Joseph M. Dixon (Mont.;
Gov., U. S. Rep. and Sen., Asst. Sec.
Interior), 1891-1933 (60,000 items);

and a small collection of letters and
literary manuscripts, chiefly of 19th-
century English authors (23 items).

NEBRASKA

CENTRAL CITY

Merrick County Historical Society.
Public Library.

Holdings: 1 vol. and 22 pieces,
including a diary, 1875-92, and information about 373 early settlers in
Nebraska.
See Hist. Records Survey, Guide
for Nebr., p. 5.

FORT CALHOUN

Washington County Historical Museum.
Edith L. Neale, Director.

Holdings: Several volumes and
other items, 1857-99, pertaining to
Fort Calhoun and Washington County.
Included are minutes of the town's
council, 1867-99; minutes of town
meetings of De Soto (now a "ghost
town"), 1857-73; a few hotel registers, 1874-96; several land grants;
and a few letters of pioneers. There
are also copies of many military records of troops at Fort Atkinson (site
of the present town of Fort Calhoun),
1819-27.

GRAND ISLAND

Hall County Historical Society. 300
West 2d St.

Holdings: 5 vols. and 200 pieces,
1858-1918, relating chiefly to Hall
County and the Platte Valley. Included is a daybook of an Army post at
Fort Kearney, Nebr., 1858-62.
See Hist. Records Survey, Guide
for Nebr., pp. 8-10.

HASTINGS

Hastings Museum. 1330 North
Burlington Ave. W. E. Eigsti,
Director.

Holdings: 400 items, 1860-1900,
relating chiefly to Adams County and
central Nebraska. Included are diaries of early settlers, 1860-75 (50
items), and collections on the Pawnee
Indians and the Oregon Trail.
See Hist. Records Survey, Guide
for Nebr., p. 10.

HOOPER

Dodge County Historical Society.
R. V. Graff, President, Fremont,
Nebr.

Holdings: 64 vols., 1819-1938,
relating chiefly to Dodge County and
the Platte Valley. Included are copies of some Mormon diaries, 1847-
52, and of a diary of Stephen H. Long
(U. S. Army officer, explorer), 1819-
20. (This Society was formerly the
"Old Settlers and Historical Association of Dodge County" and was located
in Fremont.)
See Hist. Records Survey, Guide
for Nebr., p. 5.

LINCOLN 4

Methodist Historical Society, Nebras-
ka Conference. Nebraska Wesleyan
University Library. (Mrs.) Frances
S. Paustian, Librarian and Custodian.

Holdings: A small collection, relating to the Methodist Church in Ne-

braska. Included are manuscript minutes of the Nebraska annual conferences, 1861-89; a collection of diaries;
some church histories; and many photographs of ministers, prominent laymen, conferences, churches, and
parsonages.

LINCOLN 8

Nebraska State Historical Society.
1500 R St. William D. Aeschbacher,
Director.

Holdings: 5,500 vols. (letter books,
record books, scrapbooks, etc.), 3,400
manuscript and letter boxes, 534 filing
cases and cartons, and 400 packages,
representing some 500 major collections, plus another 1,500 small collections (one envelope each), chiefly
1819-1953, consisting of (1) some archival materials of the State and local
governments, held by the Society as
Nebraska's archival agency; and (2)
personal papers and other records relating chiefly to Nebraska.
Personal papers include those of
Ned Culbertson Abbott (Nebr., Calif.;
educator of blind, historian), 1863-
1951 (77 vols. and 37 boxes); Bess
Streeter Aldrich (Iowa, Nebr.; novelist, short-story writer), 17 vols. and
18 boxes); Samuel Clay Bassett (Nebr.;
agriculturist, State legislator), 1910-
26 (3,130 items); George W. Berge
(Nebr.; editor, Populist), 1900-20 (8
vols. and 1 box); Wendell Berge (D.C.;
U.S. Asst. Attorney Gen.), 1938-53
(2 vols. and 6 boxes); John Gregory
Bourke (U.S. Army officer, ethnologist), 1870-93 (11 vols. and 6 boxes);
Charles Wayland Bryan (Nebr.; Gov.),
1923-35 (1 vol., 1 box, and 3 cartons); William Jennings Bryan (Nebr.;
U.S. Rep., Sec. State), 1890-1926 (6
boxes, mostly clippings, and 12 scrapbooks); Hugh Alfred Butler (Nebr.; U.S.
Sen.), 1945-54 (390 boxes), restricted;
Samuel M. Chapman (Nebr.; judge,

politician), 1871-1904 (13 boxes);
Robert LeRoy Cochran (Nebr.; State
engineer, Gov.), 1916-41 (12 boxes
and 43 cases), restricted; Oren Stur-
man Copeland (Nebr.; Mayor of Lincoln, U.S. Rep.), 1935-42 (6 vols.
and 2 boxes); Robert W. Furnas
(Nebr.; Civil War officer, Gov., editor, agriculturist), 1856-1905 (8,202
items); George Harrison Gilmore
(Nebr.; physician, historian), 57 linear ft., largely on Cass County; Nathan Kirk Griggs (Nebr.; lawyer, diplomat, composer), 1888-99 (49 letter
boxes and 78 letter books chiefly of
Griggs, Rinaker and Bibb law firm);
Dwight Palmer Griswold (Nebr.;
journalist, Gov., U.S. Sen.), 1940-
54 (11 boxes, 16 cases, and 6 scrapbooks), restricted; George Ward Hol-
dredge (Nebr., Wyo., Colo.; railroad
man), 1888-1923 (2,075 items in 7
boxes); Thomas P. Kennard (Nebr.;
State sec. state), 1867-71 (615 items
in 2 boxes); and James E. Lawrence
(Nebr.; editor), 1928-57 (48 boxes
and 4 cartons).
Other personal papers include
those of Samuel R. McKelvie (Nebr.;
Gov., member Federal Farm Board),
1919-34 (6 boxes and 9 scrapbooks);
Adam McMullen (Nebr.; Gov.), 1920-
59 (4 vols., 4 boxes, and 1 carton);
Thomas Jefferson Majors (Nebr.; U.S.
Rep., Lt. Gov.), 1863-91 (302 items);
Oliver Perry Mason (Nebr.; State
chief justice), 4 boxes, material on
State constitutional convention of 1871;
Samuel Maxwell (Nebr.; State chief
justice, U.S. Rep.), 1853-1901 (4,700
items); J. Sterling Morton (Nebr.;
Terr. sec., editor, U.S. Sec. Agri-
culture), 1853-1902 (111 letter books
and 32 filing drawers); Robert Valen-
tine Muir (Nebr.; prohibitionist, re-
former), 1871-1913 (894 items); John
G. Neihardt (Nebr., Mo.; author),
1920-49 (1 folder and 1 scrapbook);
George William Norris (Nebr.; U.S.
Rep. and Sen.), 1894-1944 (2 boxes);
Frank J. North (Nebr.; scout), 1864-

77 (1 box); Luther Hedden North (Nebr.; scout), 1874-1935 (267 items in 2 boxes); Hiram Winnett Orr (Nebr.; orthopedic surgeon), 1892-1956 (8 vols. and 3 boxes); Arthur L. and Harry O. Palmer (Nebr., Calif.; lawyers), 1910-59 (7 vols., 8 boxes, and 1 carton); John Joseph Pershing (U. S. Army officer, World War I Commander in Chief), 6 vols. and 1 box, memorabilia; Val Peterson (Nebr.; journalist, Gov.), 1947-53 (27 cases), restricted; Charles W. Pool (Nebr.; State sec. state), 1898-1928 (1,579 items in 3 boxes); Louise Pound (Nebr.; prof. at Univ. of Nebr., literary scholar, folklorist), 30 boxes including pamphlet collection; Roscoe Pound (Nebr., Mass.; legal scholar, Dean of Harvard Law School), 1 box and collection of writings, 101 items; Eli S. Ricker (Nebr.; judge, student of Indian history), 1,500 items, including records of interviews with Indians; William Ritchie (Nebr.; lawyer, politician), 1948-52 (10 boxes), restricted; Ernest J. Sias (Nebr.; preacher, lecturer, founder of Lincoln Aeronautical Institute), 1907-52 (3 vols. and 1 box); Christian A. Sorensen (Nebr.; State attorney gen., public power advocate), 1917-56 (48 cartons and 32 scrapbooks); Karl Stefan (Nebr.; U. S. Rep.), 1928-41 (12 cases), restricted; William Stolley (Nebr.; pioneer), 1874-94 (6 boxes); Thomas H. Tibbles (Nebr.; preacher, journalist, Populist), 1 box; William Henry Werkmeister (Nebr., Calif.; philosopher), 3 boxes on Germans in Nebraska; and William Henry Woods (Nebr.; pioneer, historian), 1857-1927 (44 vols. and 1 box). There are also many letters and diaries of pioneers and some Civil War materials.

Other collections include records of the American Association of University Women (Nebr.), 1890-1931 (4 boxes); the Central Nebraska Public Power and Irrigation District, 1929-44 (12 cases and 25 reels of microfilm); the Chicago, Burlington and Quincy Railroad agricultural office, Omaha, 1902-53 (180 vols. and 424 boxes); the Farmers Alliance (Nebr.), 1885-1901 (19 vols. and 6 boxes); the Grand Army of the Republic (Nebr.), 84 vols. and 57 boxes; the Lincoln Police Department, 1871-1930 (331 vols.); the Milldale Ranch Co. (Nebr.), 1893-1946 (51 boxes); the Nebraska Woman's Suffrage Association (9 vols. and 4 boxes); the North Central Association of Colleges and Secondary Schools, 1889-1943 (38 boxes), reports and applications; the Patrons of Husbandry (Nebr.), 1887-1921 (8 vols.); the Sons of the American Revolution (Nebr.), 1890-1931 (6 vols. and 16 boxes); and the U. S. land offices in Nebraska, 1854-1933 (518 vols.). There are also farm sale bills (especially for 1930's); sample ballots; and 65,000 photographs, including 3,000 sod house pictures.

See Hist. Records Survey, Guide for Nebr., pp. 11-13; and lists of accessions in the annual reports of the Society, published in the December issues of Nebr. History, 1951-55, and in the Society's Historical News Letter, published monthly since 1946.

LINCOLN

University of Nebraska Libraries. Frank A. Lundy, Director.

Holdings: A small quantity of manuscripts relating chiefly to Nebraska. Included are papers of J. Sterling Morton (Nebr.; Terr. Sec., U. S. Sec. Agriculture, editor, founder of Arbor Day), 1850-1902 (60,000 pieces), and Kenneth S. Wherry (Nebr.; businessman, World War I naval flier, lawyer, U. S. Sen.), 1892-1951 (50,000 pieces). A few manuscripts of and collected by the Lancaster County Medical Association (Lincoln) have been given to the University of Nebraska Libraries.

OMAHA 2

Joslyn Art Museum. 2218 Dodge St.
Mildred Goosman, Registrar.

Holdings: A small collection, including a 15th-century missal from
Italy; 55 leaves of medieval and Renaissance manuscripts; 2 vols. from
India, in Sanskrit and Hindi; a papyrus
fragment from Egypt; and a few papers
of Thomas B. Cuming (Iowa, Nebr.;
journalist, Acting Gov. of Nebr.
Terr.).

—oOo—

Omaha Public Library.   Frank E.
Gibson, Director.

Holdings: 60 vols. and 2,000
pieces, 1403-1917, consisting chiefly
of miscellaneous materials on Omaha
and Nebraska, 1843-1917; an extensive autograph collection containing
letters and other documents signed by
persons of prominence in Europe and
the United States, including signers of
the Declaration of Independence and
U.S. Presidents; some Revolutionary
War muster rolls; and drafts on the
U.S. Army for supplies used in Indian
battles.
    See Hist. Records Survey, Guide
for Nebr., pp. 27-29.

OMAHA

Presbyterian Theological Seminary.
718 Omaha National Bank Bldg.

Holdings: 9 vols. and 1,322 pieces,
1826-1937, relating chiefly to the Seminary and to the Presbyterian Church.
Included are part of a diary of a theological student at Princeton, 1826; and
papers relating to the trial for heresy
of Charles A. Briggs (N.Y.; Presbyterian minister, theology prof.), 1890-91
(300 pieces).
    See Hist. Records Survey, Guide
for Nebr., pp. 29-31.

—oOo—

Union Pacific Museum.   15th and
Dodge Sts.

Holdings: 4,000 pieces and 3 cartons, 1800-1930, relating chiefly to
railroad transportation and especially to the Union Pacific Railroad. Included are the Mortimer L. Schiff
Collection of letters, drawings, tracings, and other documents on railroads in England and the United States,
1800-1905 (490 items); a small collection of papers by and relating to Abraham Lincoln (Ill.; U.S. Pres.), 1860-
79; and a miscellaneous collection of
Union Pacific Railroad records, 1865-
1930, including 14 photograph albums.
    See Hist. Records Survey, Guide
for Nebr., pp. 32-34.

NEVADA

RENO

Nevada State Historical Society.
P. O. Box 1129.   (Mrs.) Clara S.
Beatty, Director.

Holdings: A large quantity of papers, 1843-1945, relating chiefly to
settlement, mining and other businesses, political activities, and the
woman-suffrage movement in Nevada.
Personal papers include those of Emmett D. Boyle (Nev.; mining engineer, Gov.), a large quantity; Samuel
B. Doten (Nev.; entomologist, Univ.
of Nev. prof.) and his mother (2
trunks); Anne Martin (Nev.; feminist,
political leader); Francis G. Newlands (Nev.; U.S. Rep. and Sen.), containing material on irrigation and the
improvement of the Mississippi and
other river systems; James Warren
Nye (N.Y., Nev.; Terr. Gov., U.S.
Sen.), a diary; Tasker Lowndes Oddie (Nev.; miner, Gov., U.S. Sen.),
4 tons; Key Pittman (Nev.; U.S. Sen.),
1904-33 (a large quantity), containing
material on the Senate Foreign Relations Committee; Reinhold Sadler (Nev.;
Gov.), a large quantity; James G.
Scrugham (Nev.; Gov., U.S. Rep. and
Sen.), 1914-45 (1 filing cabinet), including papers and photographs concerning the excavations at Lost City,
Nev.; and William M. Stewart (Nev.;
U.S. Sen.), 1887-1904 (letter books
and 79 boxes).   There are also business papers of a creamery, a bank,
and a salt works; the records of the
discontinued Nevada-Central Railroad; account books of mercantile and
mining companies; maps of the work-
ings of the Tonopah and Goldfield
mines; a book showing the first assay
of the Virginia lode; and a book with a
list of the early shareholders in the
Sutro Tunnel.   Also included are records of several World War II organizations, among them the State Council
of Civilian Defense; and some State
and county archives.

AMHERST

Amherst Public Library.

Holdings: Included are proprietors' records of Amherst, 1728-71 (1 vol.); and a few letters by persons of national influence, 1812-65.

See Hist. Records Survey, Guide for N.H., p. 2.

CANDIA

Smyth Public Library.

Holdings: 17 vols. and 10 pieces, 1814-1908, relating chiefly to Candia. Included are papers concerning a sawmill and a hat factory.

See Hist. Records Survey, Guide for N.H., p. 4.

CLAREMONT

Fiske Free Library.

Holdings: 25 vols. and 1,071 pieces, 1771-1926, relating chiefly to Claremont. Included are church records (7 vols. and 52 packages); diaries and account books, 1796-1871; letters; and a sailor's log of 1797.

See Hist. Records Survey, Guide for N.H., p. 5.

CONCORD

New Hampshire Historical Society. 30 Park St. Mrs. Russell B. Tobey, Librarian.

Holdings: 600 linear ft. of volumes and boxes, 1623 to date, relating chief-ly to New Hampshire. In quantity, the holdings are almost equally divided between manuscripts owned by the Society and manuscripts at present deposited by the Secretary of State of New Hampshire and by individual churches throughout the State. Boxes used as containers average 12" x 11" x 3", each holding 150 to 200 pieces; volumes vary in size.

Among the Society's most important holdings is the main body of extant papers, chiefly personal, of Franklin Pierce (N.H.; U.S. Rep. and Sen., Mexican War officer, U.S. Pres.), 1820-69 (1,500 pieces in 1 vol. and 10 boxes). Closely related are papers of the President's father, Benjamin Pierce (Mass., N.H.; Rev. War officer, Gov. of N.H.), 1807-44 (1 box); his brother-in-law, John McNeil (N.H., Mass.; U.S. Army officer, collector of customs at Boston), 1815-50 (5 boxes); and his campaign manager, John H. George (N.H.; lawyer), 1840-70 (12 boxes).

Papers of other political leaders and men who held important public office include those of Charles Gordon Atherton (N.H.; lawyer, U.S. Rep. and Sen.), 1831-52 (1 box); Jonathan Belcher (Mass., N.J.; merchant, colonial Gov.), 1730-53 (3 vols.); Charles Henry Bell (N.H.; lawyer, U.S. Sen., Gov.), 1860-90 (1 box); Samuel Dana Bell (N.H.; State chief justice), 1850-68 (1 box); William Burleigh (Maine; lawyer, U.S. Rep.), 1823-27 (1 box); William E. Chandler (N.H.; lawyer, Sec. Navy, U.S. Sen.), 1853-1917 (5 vols., 40 diaries, and 109 boxes); Salmon Portland Chase (Ohio; Gov., U.S. Sen., Sec. Treas.), 1846-61 (1 envelope); Rufus Choate (Mass.; lawyer, U.S. Rep. and Sen.), 1824-32 (1 envelope); Bradbury Cilley (N.H.;

farmer, U.S. Rep.), 1810-30, Joseph Cilley (N.H.; Rev. War officer, political leader), 1781-98, and Joseph Cilley (N.H.; farmer, U.S. Sen.), 1826-64 (1 box); Charles Doe (N.H.; State chief justice), 1856-95 (1 box); Timothy Farrar, Jr. (N.H., Mass.; lawyer, N.H. State judge, author), 1771-1821 (1 box); George G. Fogg (N.H.; lawyer, newspaper publisher, Minister to Switzerland, U.S. Sen.), 1831-81 (2 boxes); Jonathan Freeman (N.H.; farmer, U.S. Rep.), 1787-1806 (1 box); Jacob H. Gallinger (N.H.; physician, U.S. Rep. and Sen.), 1865-1918 (10 boxes); James A. Garfield (Ohio; U.S. Pres.), 1880 (a few letters in Chandler papers); John Taylor Gilman (N.H.; shipbuilder, Member Continental Cong., Gov.), 1796-1823 (1 envelope); Joseph A. Gilmore (N.H.; railroad executive, Gov.), 1842-66 (7 boxes); Horace Greeley (N.Y.; editor of New York Tribune, U.S. Rep.), 1850-72 (1 envelope); John P. Hale (N.H.; lawyer, U.S. Rep. and Sen., Minister to Spain), 1822-74 (2 vols. and 23 boxes); Isaac Hill (N.H.; newspaper editor, U.S. Sen., Gov.), 1814-50 (1 box); John Langdon (N.H.; Rev. War officer, Gov., U.S. Sen.), 1770-1819 (2 boxes and 1 envelope); Arthur Livermore (N.H.; State chief justice, U.S. Rep.), 1818-49 (1 envelope); and Samuel Livermore (N.H.; State chief justice), 1780-86 (1 vol. and 1 envelope).

Papers of other individuals in the category named above include those of Jeremiah Mason (N.H., Mass.; lawyer, U.S. Sen. from N.H.), 1801-45 (1 box); David L. Morril (N.H.; physician, Presbyterian clergyman, U.S. Sen., Gov.), 1799-1810 (1 box); Robert Morris (Pa.; financier, Member Continental Cong., U.S. Sen.), 1780-1800 (a number of items with the Stark papers); George H. Moses (N.H.; newspaper editor, U.S. Rep.), 1893-1924 (3 boxes); John Fabyan Parrott (N.H.; U.S. Rep. and Sen.), 1792-1836 (9 boxes); Nathaniel Peabody (N.H.; Rev. War of-

ficer, Member Continental Cong., physician), 1767-1815 (1 box); Charles H. Peaslee (N.H.; lawyer, U.S. Rep.), 1831-61 (1 box); Austin F. Pike (N.H.; lawyer, U.S. Rep. and Sen.), 1849-86 (6 boxes); William Plumer (N.H.; U.S. Sen., Gov.), 1780-1850 (5 vols.); William Plumer, Jr. (N.H.; U.S. Rep.), 1815-54 (1 box); Tristram Shaw (N.H.; U.S. Rep.), 1834-43 (5 boxes); John Sullivan (N.H.; Rev. War officer, Member Continental Cong., Pres. of N.H., U.S. dist. court judge), 1770-95 (9 vol.); Mason W. Tappan (N.H.; lawyer, U.S. Rep., Civil War officer), 1855-69 (4 boxes); Amos Tuck (N.H.; lawyer, U.S. Rep.), 1842-79 (1 box); Richard Waldron III (N.H.; provincial sec., councilor), 1713-53 (2 vols.); Daniel Webster (N.H., Mass.; lawyer, U.S. Rep. and Sen., Sec. State), 1800-52 (20 vols. and 3 boxes); John Wingate Weeks (Mass.; U.S. Rep. and Sen., Sec. War), 1812-49 (2 boxes); John Wentworth (N.H., Nova Scotia; last royal Gov. of N.H.), 1765-98 (1 box); Paine Wingate (N.H.; Member Continental Cong., U.S. Sen. and Rep.), 1800-26 (1 box), consisting of letters from his brother, Joseph; and Levi Woodbury (N.H.; Gov., U.S. Sen., Sec. Navy, Sec. Treas., U.S. Supreme Court Justice), 1813-51 (1 box).

Papers of other individuals include those of Jeremy Belknap (N.H., Mass.; Congregational clergyman, historian), 1760-90 (1 box); Nathaniel Bouton (N.H.; Congregational clergyman, historian), 1840-78 (1 box); John Farmer (N.H.; antiquarian, genealogist), 1806-39 (10 boxes); John G. Foster (N.H.; U.S. Army officer), 1850-70 (1 box); Nathaniel Hawthorne (Mass., N.H.; novelist), 1852-63 (a number of items in the Pierce papers); Samuel Langdon (Mass., N.H.; Congregational clergyman, pres. of Harvard College), 1779-87 (2 manuscripts); Dudley Leavitt (N.H.; mathematician, au-

thor of textbooks), 1815-49 (1 envelope); Abiel A. Livermore (N.H., Ohio,
N.Y., Pa.; Unitarian clergyman), 1836-
48 (6 vols. and 1 box); Charles S. Mellen (N.H., Mass.; railroad pres.),
1888-1922 (7 vols. and 11 boxes); Edna Dean Proctor (N.H., N.Y.; poet),
1840-1920 (1 box), containing letters
from John Greenleaf Whittier; Edmund
Roberts (N.H.; merchant, diplomatic
agent in the Far East), 1815-36 (1
box); Lyman Spalding (N.H., N.Y.;
physician, surgeon), 1800-21 (1 box);
John Stark (N.H.; Rev. War officer),
1743-1814 (6 vols.); Celia L. Thaxter (N.H., Mass., Maine; poet), 1870-
91 (1 envelope); John Greenleaf Whittier (Mass.; poet, abolitionist), 1860-
91 (1 box); and Noah Worcester (N.H.,
Mass.; Congregational and Unitarian
clergyman, peace society organizer),
1790-1837 (1 box).

The Society's manuscripts also
include 18th- and 19th-century account
books; diaries; logbooks and other
shipping records; maps; military records; school records; minutes of associations, corporations, and other
organizations; and genealogical miscellany.

Among manuscripts deposited by
the Secretary of State of New Hampshire, there are records of the Province to 1786, with additional related
papers to 1800 (in volumes and boxes); deeds to 1772; town records to
1825; court records to 1770, with an
additional file of 30,000 court documents; 3,800 wills; executive and legislative records to 1840 (a number of
boxes of loose papers); papers of
Meshech Weare (N.Y.; colonial leader, chief justice and Pres. of N.H.),
1647-1837 (14 vols.), consisting
chiefly of collected manuscripts concerning New Hampshire, and some papers of John Wentworth, 2 vols.

See Allison, Inventory, p. 69; and
Hist. Records Survey, Guide for N.H.,
p. 6.

New Hampshire State Library.
(Mrs.) Mildred P. McKay, State
Librarian.

Holdings: 1,000 vols., 15,000
sheets, and extensive quantities of
uncounted materials, 1690-1890, relating chiefly to New Hampshire.
There are executive, legislative, and
judicial records of the Colony and
State (10,000 sheets) that are uncataloged. Personal papers include those
of Josiah Bartlett (N.H.; physician,
Member Continental Cong., State chief
justice and Gov.) and family, 1704-
1864 (22 vols. and 3 boxes); Charles
Henry Bell (N.H.; lawyer, U.S. Sen.,
Gov.), 1823-93; John Harris (N.H.;
State supreme court justice), 1769-
1845; and Matthew Patten (N.H.; colonial judge, surveyor, town official),
1719-95 (10 boxes); and the Plumer
Collection, 1782-1854 (121 vols. and
81 bundles), containing papers of William Plumer (N.H.; U.S. Sen., Gov.)
and William Plumer, Jr. (N.H.; U.S.
Rep.). There are also various military papers, 1775-1849; extensive
personnel records of the Amoskeag
Manufacturing Co.; records of the
League of New Hampshire Arts and
Crafts and of other agencies; and miscellaneous diaries, town records, family papers, and church records. In
various groups are scattered papers
of a number of prominent persons associated with New Hampshire.

See Hist. Records Survey, Guide
for N.H., p. 8.

DOVER

Dover Public Library. Mildred E.
Morrison, Acting Librarian.

Holdings: Several hundred pieces,
1662-1901, relating chiefly to Dover
and vicinity. Included are a few letters; a Civil War diary and other mi-

litary records, 1861-65; and minutes
of a local Baptist church, 1843-1901,
and of various other local organizations.

See Hist. Records Survey, Guide
for N.H., p. 9.

DURHAM

University of New Hampshire Library.
Thelma Brackett, Librarian.

Holdings: A small collection of
manuscripts, from 1736, consisting
chiefly of scattered records of the
town of Durham, records of the Durham Community Church (8 vols.), some
papers of local families, and miscellaneous documents of or relating to the
University. (The records of the Amoskeag Manufacturing Co., formerly in
this Library, are now in the Baker Library, Harvard Business School,
Boston, Mass.)

See Hist. Records Survey, Guide
for N.H., p. 11.

EXETER

Exeter Public Library. Harriette M.
Pirnie, Librarian.

Holdings: 44 pieces, 1733-1848,
consisting of miscellaneous papers relating to New Hampshire. Included is
an unpublished biography of Peter Coffin (N.H.; judge of the superior court
of the province).

See Hist. Records Survey, Guide
for N.H., p. 16.

—oOo—

Phillips Exeter Academy Library.
Rodney Armstrong, Librarian.

Holdings: 500 pieces, 1770 to date,
relating chiefly to the town of Exeter

and its Academy. Included are speeches, sermons, letters, and literary manuscripts by former students. Among
the alumni or other persons connected
with the Academy represented in this
special collection by 25 pieces or more
are Benjamin Abbot (N.H.; principal of
the Academy), 1813-49; George Bancroft (Mass., N.Y.; historian, Sec. Navy, Minister to Great Britain and Germany), 1838-74; Edward Everett
(Mass.; clergyman, Gov., Minister to
Great Britain, pres. of Harvard Univ.,
U.S. Rep. and Sen., Sec. State), 1807-
64; John Taylor Gilman (N.H.; shipbuilder, Member Continental Cong.,
Gov.), 1774-1828; and Daniel Webster
(N.H., Mass.; U.S. Rep. and Sen.,
Sec. State), 1838-52. There is also
a special collection on the Phillips
family, notably John Phillips (N.H.;
philanthropist, founder of Phillips Exeter Academy) and Samuel Phillips
(Mass.; State legislator, founder of
Phillips Academy, Andover). The
papers of George E. Woodbury (Mass.,
N.Y.; poet, critic) contain much autograph material addressed to him by
scholars and authors. The Alumni
Authors Collection contains literary
manuscripts by many distinguished
persons. There is a special collection dealing with the mutiny on the
Bounty, containing letters and other
materials by James Norman Hall
(Iowa, Tahiti; author). There is also a special collection of materials
by and about Kenneth Roberts (Maine;
novelist, journalist), dealing particularly with his Northwest Passage.

FARMINGTON

Goodwin Library.

Holdings: 3 vols. and 50 pieces,
1813-70, relating chiefly to Farmington. Included are records of a
temperance society, 1843-48; and a

musical association, 1866-70.

See Hist. Records Survey, <u>Guide</u> for N. H., p. 17.

HANOVER

Dartmouth College Library. Richard W. Morin, Librarian; Ethel Martin, Archivist.

<u>Holdings</u>: 30,000 pieces, 1730 to date, relating chiefly to Dartmouth College and its faculty and alumni, to New Hampshire and colonial Connecticut, to the early religious history of New England, to Indian missions, and to arctic exploration.

Papers of political leaders include those of Josiah Bartlett (N. H.; physician, Member Continental Cong., State chief justice, Gov.), 1774-94 (200 pieces); Rufus Choate (Mass.; U. S. Rep. and Sen.), 1815-58 (50 pieces); Nathaniel Peabody (N. H.; Rev. War officer, Member Continental Cong., physician), 1815-54 (25 folders); George Perkins Marsh (Vt.; U. S. Rep., Minister to Turkey and Italy), 1835-68 (30 pieces); Daniel Webster (N. H., Mass.; U. S. Rep. and Sen., Sec. State), 1,500 pieces; and Levi Woodbury (N. H.; Gov., U. S. Sen., Sec. Navy, Sec. Treas., U.S. Supreme Court Justice), 1811-51 (100 pieces).

Papers of religious leaders include those of Asa Burton (Vt.; Congregational clergyman), 1776-1828 (500 sermons); Samson Occom (Conn., N.Y.; Indian clergyman, missionary), 1743-89 (300 pieces); John Sergeant (Wis.; missionary to the Stockbridge Indians), 1804-24 (15 vols. of a journal); Eleazar Wheelock (Conn., N. H.; Congregational clergyman, pres. of Dartmouth), 1728-79 (4,000 pieces); and Nathaniel Whitaker (Conn., Mass.; Presbyterian clergyman), 1762-72 (150 pieces).

Papers of authors include those of Winston Churchill (N. Y., N. H.; nov-

elist), a large quantity; Joseph Conrad (England; novelist), 1894-1924 (80 letters); Robert Bontine Cunninghame Graham (Scotland; author), 1903-36 (332 pieces); Robert Frost (N. H., Mass.; poet), 1912-52 (126 pieces); Richard Hovey (Mass., N. Y.; poet), 1864-1900 (several hundred pieces); Henry James (Mass., England; novelist), 1892-1911 (98 pieces); and Eugene O'Neill (N. Y.; dramatist), 1914-35 (58 pieces).

There are also records of the College, 1769 to date (several thousand pieces); papers of various doctors, lawyers, and merchants, 1770-1891 (95 vols.); minutes of ecclesiastical councils of Congregational churches, chiefly in Vermont, 1803-16; and a large collection of movie scripts, 1935-49, and radio scripts, 1940-50, consisting of actors' mimeographed copies.

The Stefansson Collection, consisting of material relating chiefly to the polar regions, is a separately administered unit of the Library. In its manuscript section there are numerous travel journals of explorers, scientists, and whalers, among them 25 journals of English whaling captains of the Baffin Bay—Davis Strait "whale fisher," 1870-1924; and the results of extensive research on permafrost and geography. By far the largest group of papers consists of journals, diaries, correspondence, and reports of Vilhjalmur Stefansson (N. Y.; arctic explorer, geographer, anthropologist, writer), covering a 50-year period from his earliest arctic expeditions. Other important groups of papers are those of William Gilder (N.Y., N.J.; journalist, explorer); Ernest deKoven Leffingwell (explorer, geologist, commander of Stefansson's first arctic expedition); and Edwin Tappan Adney (N. Y., Canada; artist, anthropologist, writer). On indefinite loan are sketch books, literary manuscripts, and other papers of Belmore Browne (Calif.; artist, mountain climber, writer). Other names represented in the manuscript section are C. Raymond Beazley (England; historian, geographer); William Herbert Hobbs (Mich.; geologist, glaciologist, Univ. of Mich. prof.); Umberto Nobile (Italy, Ill.; aeronautical engineer, arctic explorer); Russell W. Porter (Calif.; astronomer, topographer, arctic explorer); and Sir George Hubert Wilkins (Australia; polar explorer).

See Allison, <u>Inventory</u>, pp. 70-82.

HOPKINTON

New Hampshire Antiquarian Society. Rachael Johnson, Curator.

<u>Holdings</u>: Several hundred pieces, from as early as 1700, relating chiefly to New Hampshire. Included are account books of stores, inns, blacksmiths, and doctors, 1778-1889; school records, 1807-35; surveys of early roads and land grants; sermons, 1740-1882 (1,100 items), and some church records; manuscript music books of a regimental band; many letters of early New Hampshire Governors and other officials and of other persons; and papers of or about the Long family, which included local printers and Stephen H. Long (U.S. Army officer, explorer).

MANCHESTER

Manchester Historic Association. 129 Amherst St. Harlan A. Marshall, Curator.

<u>Holdings</u>: A quantity of manuscripts, dated largely in the 19th century and relating chiefly to Manchester. Personal papers include those of Samuel Blodget (Mass., N.H.; mer-

chant, manufacturer, canal builder); Joseph Kidder (N.H.; early settler in the Manchester community); Frederick Smyth (N.H.; banker, railroad executive, Gov.), a large collection; John Stark (N.H.; Rev. War officer); and Ezekiel A. Straw (N.H.; textile manufacturer, Gov.), 1857 (a diary). There are also 556 pattern and office books of two Manchester textile firms, the Amoskeag Manufacturing Co. and the Manchester Print Works, 1855-86.

NEW IPSWICH

New Ipswich Historical Society.

<u>Holdings</u>: 6 vols. and 200 pieces, 18th-19th centuries, relating chiefly to New Ipswich. Included are letters, diaries, sermons, and town records.

See Hist. Records Survey, <u>Guide</u> for N.H., p. 27.

PETERBOROUGH

Peterborough Historical Society.

<u>Holdings</u>: 62 vols. and 16 bundles, 1738-1924, relating chiefly to Peterborough and Sharon. Included are records of a Methodist church, 1825-1924 (15 vols.); diary (copy) and sermons of Elijah Dunbar (N.H.; Congregational minister), 1799-1824; and several other diaries.

See Hist. Records Survey, <u>Guide</u> for N.H., p. 28.

ROCHESTER

Rochester Public Library. (Miss) M. Felice Baril, Librarian.

<u>Holdings</u>: 1,042 sermons by Joseph Haven (N.H.; Congregational clergyman), 1775-1825, and a few other items of local interest.

BLAIRSTOWN

Blair Academy Museum.

Holdings: 230 pieces, 1800-1932, relating chiefly to Blairstown. Included are some Presbyterian and Methodist church records, Civil War papers, and records of Blair Academy.
See Hist. Records Survey, Guide for N.J., p. 2.

BURLINGTON

Burlington County Historical Society. James Fenimore Cooper House. Mrs. H. Pugh, President.

Holdings: 2 ledgers of an iron works, early 19th century, and a few miscellaneous papers relating to the county.

CAMDEN

Walt Whitman House. 300 Mickle St. (Mrs.) Eleanor Ray, Custodian.

Holdings: 200 pieces, 1884-92, consisting of correspondence and other papers of Walt Whitman (N.Y., D.C., N.J.; poet).

CAPE MAY

Cape May County Historical Museum. Cape May Court House. Karl A. Dickinson, Curator.

Holdings: Miscellaneous papers, 1681-1940, relating chiefly to Cape May County and southern New Jersey. Included are some Quaker records,

1681-1841.
See Hist. Records Survey, Guide for N.J., p. 5.

EAST ORANGE

Upsala College Library.

Holdings: Several letters of Abraham Lincoln (Ill.; U.S. Pres.).
See Library Quarterly, 11:271 (July 1941).

EDGEWATER

Edgewater Free Public Library.

Holdings: 70 pieces, 1787-1879, relating chiefly to Edgewater. Included are the minutes of two temperance societies.
See Hist. Records Survey, Guide for N.J., p. 6.

FORT MONMOUTH

U.S. Army Signal Corps Museum. Helen C. Phillips, Historian-Director.

Holdings: 30 vols., 20 boxes, and 8,000 pieces, 1854-1950, relating to the U.S. Army Signal Corps. The largest group consists of papers of Albert James Myer (U.S. Army officer), 1854-80 (14 vols., 10 boxes, and 3,500 pieces), concerning chiefly the organizing of the Signal Corps, 1863, and the establishment of the Corps' weather-reporting service, 1870. There are also records of the Signal Corps Veteran Association of the Spanish-American War, 1900-50 (12 vols., 6 boxes, and 400 pieces). In these 2 groups and in other smaller ones there are letters and documents from U.S. Presidents and military leaders. There are 133 original first copies of documents (total 237 pages) from General Douglas MacArthur to the Japanese Imperial Government laying down the terms of surrender of the Japanese in August 1945 and replies from the Japanese Government to General MacArthur.

FREEHOLD

Monmouth County Historical Association. 70 Court St. Librarian.

Holdings: 10,000 pieces, 1667-1919, relating to Monmouth County. Included are some papers of and concerning Philip Freneau (N.Y., Pa., N.J.; poet, journalist); town books of Middletown, 1667-1848 (2 vols.); Freehold township records, 1730-1873 (4,000 pieces); records of various churches, 1790-1919; a number of sermons, 1741-1882; maps of the Battle of Monmouth; about 1,000 Civil War papers; and records of Monmouth County men in World War II.
See Hist. Records Survey, Guide for N.J., pp. 9-11.

HADDONFIELD

Haddonfield Historical Society. Public Library.

Holdings: 50 vols. and 1,000 pieces, the earliest dated 1643, consisting of letters, diaries, deeds, minutes of local organizations, business and court ledgers, and other papers relating chiefly to Haddonfield and its vicinity. There are a few papers of persons of national prominence.

See Hist. Records Survey, Guide for N.J., p. 12.

HOBOKEN

Stevens Institute of Technology Library. Frances I. Duck, Librarian.

Holdings: Papers of John Stevens and Edwin A. Stevens (N.J.; engineers, inventors, and promoters of mechanical transportation) and other members of the Stevens family, 1664-1870 (6,500 pieces); and papers of Frederick W. Taylor (Pa.; efficiency engineer, inventor), 1869-1915 (thousands of items). The latter group includes European diaries, 1869-70; manuscripts of many of his articles and correspondence concerning them; correspondence, 1887-1915, with many distinguished men; and photographs and lantern slides.
See Hist. Records Survey, Guide for N.J., p. 12, and its Calendar of the Stevens Family Papers (1940-41. 2 vols. Processed); and Elizabeth G. Hayward, A Classified Guide to the Frederick Winslow Taylor Collection (1951. 45 p.).

JERSEY CITY

Board of Education. 2 Harrison Ave.

Holdings: 16 large steel boxes containing a collection made by William H. Richardson, of papers relating chiefly to colonial New Jersey. Included are some papers on the controversy between John Fitch (N.J., Pa.; inventor) and Robert Fulton (N.Y.; civil engineer, inventor) about the invention of the steamboat.
See Hist. Records Survey, Guide for N.J., p. 13.

JERSEY CITY 2

Hudson County Historical Soci-

ety. Free Public Library, 472 Jersey
Ave. Edmund W. Miller, Historian.

Holdings: 1,000 pieces, 1663-1882,
relating chiefly to Jersey City and Hudson County. Included are some miscellaneous business records of canal,
bridge, and railroad companies.
See Hist. Records Survey, Guide
for N.J., p. 14.

—oOo—

Jersey City Public Library Museum.
472 Jersey Ave.

Holdings: 500 papers, 1656-1907,
consisting chiefly of miscellaneous records of Bergen Township and of Jersey City, some Revolutionary War letters, and other papers relating to Jersey City and its vicinity.
See Hist. Records Survey, Guide
for N.J., p. 15.

LAKEWOOD

Georgian Court College Library.
Sister Mary Patrice, Librarian.

Holdings: 26 pieces, consisting
chiefly of papers of an Italian family
in Venice, 1693; and a Bible, 1647,
Douay version.

MADISON

Drew University Library. Arthur E.
Jones, Jr., Librarian; Lawrence O.
Kline, Methodist Librarian.

Holdings: 13,200 items, 1710-
1940, consisting chiefly of correspondence and other papers of Methodists and about Methodism. Included
are papers of Francis Asbury (Methodist bishop), 1760-1816 (125 letters);
journals and correspondence of Free-
born Garrettson (itinerant Methodist

minister), 1767-1857; and papers
formerly held by the Methodist Historical Society of New York. There
are also some correspondence and
other papers of Thomas Gibbons
(Ga., N.J.; U.S. dist. court judge,
steamboat operator, plaintiff in
Gibbons vs. Ogden), 1803-33; 2
notebooks of Sir Leslie Stephen (England; philosopher, biographer); and a
collection of autograph letters of
Presidential cabinet members (Washington through Wilson).
See Allison, Inventory, pp. 82-84
and 136.

—oOo—

Madison Historical Society. Madison Public Library. Mrs. W. H.
Burnet, Custodian, 83 Prospect St.

Holdings: 250 items, 1804-1911,
chiefly of local and genealogical interest. Included are several land
deeds and a hotel register, 1887-
1911.
See Hist. Records Survey, Guide
for N.J., p. 18.

MENDHAM

Free Public Library.

Holdings: 5 vols., 1799-1871,
consisting of record books of the local library company and account
books, 1808-10 and 1835-43, of two
local general stores.
See Hist. Records Survey, Guide
for N.J., p. 19.

MORRISTOWN

Morris County Historical Society.
May B. Leonard, Corresponding
Secretary.

Holdings: 200 pieces, 1809-45,

relating chiefly to Powerville and Boonton, N.J., but containing material on Fredericktown, Ohio. Included are records relating to the iron business in northern New Jersey, 1816-45 (107 pieces); military papers, 1812-19 (13 pieces); and church and missionary society records, 1822-35 (13 pieces).

—oOo—

Morristown Library. May B. Leonard, Librarian.

Holdings: 847 items, 1748-1954, relating to Morris County and its vicinity. Included are an autobiography of Jacob Green (N.J.; Presbyterian minister, pres. of College of N.J.); and a typed transcript of the diary of a local carpenter and sawmill owner, 1793-1867 (5 vols.). There are also minutes or other records of a local academy, 1792-1830; a female charitable society, 1813-1913; and the county medical association, 1816-1904.

See Hist. Records Survey, Guide for N.J., p. 20.

—oOo—

Morristown National Historical Park. Superintendent.

Holdings: 1,300 items, 1666-1861, relating chiefly to the Revolutionary War period and especially to the Continental Army encampments at Morristown in the winters of 1777, 1779-80, and 1781-82. Included are papers of Jacob Ford (N.J.; Rev. War officer, owner of powder and iron works) and his family, 1736-1902 (9 boxes); Joseph Morris Lindsley (N.J.; architect and builder), 1809-21 (1-vol. journal), including an account of a trip to Ohio in 1814; and George Washington (Va.; Rev. War Commander in Chief, U.S. Pres.), 1773-98 (95 pieces); and scattered letters and papers of American soldiers, statesmen, and political

figures, 1771-1848. There are also Continental Army orderly and Quartermaster's receipt books, 1778-80 (6 vols.); and letter books of managers of an iron furnace, 1775-78 (1 vol.), and a plantation owner and merchant, 1779-86 (1 vol.). Reproductions of papers include transcripts of documents in German archives relating to German troops in the Revolutionary War, 1776-83, mainly in French and German, with some translations (41 boxes); photostats of letters of Joseph Lewis (N.J.; Rev. War quartermaster), 1779-80 (104 pieces); and transcripts of papers of Anthony Wayne (Pa.; Rev. War officer), 1765-81 (10 vols.). Recently acquired and not included in the description above are extensive Washington and Revolutionary War manuscripts collected by Lloyd Wadell Smith (N.J.; broker, collector).

MOUNT HOLLY

Free Library. Rhoda H. Barnitz, Library Director.

Holdings: 2 pieces, one of which is a drawing of the Mt. Holly jail by Robert Mills (S.C., Pa., D.C.; architect, engineer), 1808.

NEW BRUNSWICK

New Brunswick Theological Seminary Library. Peter N. VandenBerge, Librarian.

Holdings: 335 vols. and 120 packages, 1720-1950, consisting chiefly of the archives of the Reformed Church in America. Included are some records relating to the Seminary; General Synod minutes from 1771; minutes of 6 particular synods in New York, New Jersey, Michigan, Illinois, and Iowa, from 1771 (the earliest dates for the different minutes depending on the dates of organization of the synods); minutes of 26 classes, 1771-1950, with varying dates of organization (140 vols. and 100 packages); all denominational reports of the church; and local church records, 1720-1940.

See Hist. Records Survey, Guide for N.J., p. 28; and Allison, Inventory, pp. 84-88.

—oOo—

Rutgers University Library. Donald F. Cameron, Librarian; Donald A. Sinclair, Curator of Special Collections.

Holdings: 500,000 items, relating chiefly to the United States, with about 75 per cent relating to New Jersey. They consist of papers and records of individuals and families, societies and other organized groups, businesses (from single merchants and craftsmen to sizable corporations), and scattered governmental agencies; surveyors' and other land records; and some monographs.

Papers of individuals include those of Nicholas Bayard (N.Y.; colonial leader, sec. province of N.Y., mayor of New York City), 1648-1834 (13 vols. and 7 boxes); John Romeyn Brodhead (N.Y.; diplomat, historian), journals, 1839-49, and correspondence, drafts, notes, and transcripts (with a few originals) of Dutch and other documents relating to New York and America generally, 1670-1870 (10 boxes); George Hammell Cook (N.J.; prof. at Rutgers College, State geologist), 1836-80 (27 boxes); Benjamin B. Cooper (N.J.; land speculator), 1800-1920 (16 boxes), more than half relating to the Holland Land Co. and some to south Jersey lands; John Croes (N.J.; teacher, Episcopal bishop), 1786-1832 (1,068 items); Mahlon Dickerson (N.J.; Gov., U.S. Sen., Sec. Navy), 1783-1857 (66 items), including his diary,

1809-19; Joseph S. Frelinghuysen (N.J.; insurance executive, Spanish-Am. War officer, U.S. Sen.), 1898-1948 (125 boxes), including his correspondence with Warren G. Harding (Ohio; U.S. Pres.) and other political leaders and including also some family papers from 1730; Robert Stockton Green (N.J.; judge, U.S. Rep., Gov.), 1887-90 (517 items); William Elliot Griffis (Pa., N.Y., N.J.; educator in Japan, Congregational minister, author), 1870-1920 (120 boxes), including 30 boxes of material on Japan; Samuel Blanchard How (N.J., Ga., Pa.; Presbyterian and Reformed Church clergyman, Dickinson College pres.), 1799-1888 (7 boxes); William Paterson (N.J.; U.S. Sen., Gov., U.S. Supreme Court Justice), 1766-1806 (600 items); Washington A. Roebling (N.J., N.Y.; bridge builder, Civil War officer), 1821-1927 (4 boxes), chiefly relating to Civil War activities; Ferdinand S. Schenck (N.J.; physician, U.S. Rep., judge of State court of errors and appeals), 1731-1879 (4,391 items); Israel Shreve (N.J.; Rev. War officer), 1771-1813 (361 items); George Sykes (N.J.; surveyor, conveyancer, U.S. Rep.), 1700-1880 (20 boxes), including 4 boxes of political letters received; Peter D. Vroom (N.J.; Gov., U.S. Rep., Minister to Prussia), 1799-1873 (2,000 items); Garret Dorset Wall (N.J.; U.S. Sen., judge of State court of errors and appeals), 1785-1861 (632 items); Marcus L. Ward (N.J.; candle manufacturer, Gov., U.S. Rep.), 1840-80 (5 boxes); Anthony Walton White (N.J., Pa.; Rev. War officer), 1775-1803 (750 items); John R. Williams (N.Y., Mich.; fur trader, merchant, lawyer), 1795-1854 (4 boxes), including 154 items of Thomas Williams (N.Y., Mich.; fur trader, merchant, lawyer), 1767-1804; and Yznaga del Valle (N.Y.; sugar broker, owner of plantations in La. and Cuba, builder of Tunis and Sanctu Espiritu R.R., Zaza, Cuba),

1854-78 (30 vols.).

Family papers important for New Jersey and U.S. history are those of the Morris family, 1670-1875 (14 boxes), including papers of Lewis Morris (N.Y., N.J.; chief justice of N.Y., colonial Gov. of N.J.), Robert Hunter Morris (N.J., Pa.; chief justice of N.J., colonial Gov. of Pa.), and Robert Morris (N.J.; State chief justice, U.S. dist. court judge); the Neilson family, 1690-1937 (160 boxes), including papers of John Neilson (N.J.; merchant, Rev. War officer, Member Continental Cong.), James Neilson (N.J.; merchant, canal and railway promoter), and James Neilson, Jr. (N.J.; civic leader, philanthropist, Rutgers College trustee, promoter of scientific farming); and the Parker family, 1764-1866 (600 items), including papers of James Parker (N.Y., N.J.; member of N.J. Provincial Council and Board of Proprietors, loyalist) and James Parker, Jr. (N.J.; landowner, philanthropist, U.S. Rep.).

Materials of literary interest include several collections. The J. Alexander Symington Collection, 1800-1930 (65 boxes), consists of letters and literary manuscripts, both originals and transcripts, of or concerning English writers active in the last half of the 19th and the early 20th century. Included are papers of George Borrow (England; novelist), 123 items; John Drinkwater (England; poet, playwright), 1914-22 (1 vol. of letters); André Gide (France; author), letters (150 pages); Sir Edmund William Gosse (England; critic, poet), several hundred letters received, including letters of Viscount Haldane (England; Member of Parliament, Sec. of State for War, Lord Chancellor), 1904-28 (3 vols.); Letitia Elizabeth Landon (England; poet, novelist), 1827-38 (100 letters); Algernon Charles Swinburne (England; poet), letters to William Michael Rossetti (England; art critic), 1862-1908 (3 vols.), and other Swinburne letters and manu-

scripts (3 boxes); Walter Theodore Watts-Dunton (England; critic, poet), 1889-1907 (7 letter books); William Wilberforce (England; philanthropist, Member of Parliament, abolitionist), letters (1 vol.); John Wilson, known as Christopher North (Scotland; poet, essayist, critic), letters, 1812-44; Thomas James Wise (England; bibliographer, book collector), letters received (3,000 pieces); and several Brontë family manuscripts. Also in the Library are collections of papers of and concerning William Dean Howells (Mass., N.Y.; novelist, literary critic, editor of <u>Atlantic Monthly</u>), 1859-1917 (115 items); Joyce Kilmer (N.J., N.Y.; poet), 1899-1934 (600 items in 4 scrapbooks); and Walt Whitman (N.Y., D.C., N.J.; poet), 1863-87 (23 pieces), together with photographs, magazine excerpts, and annotated proof, 1839-88 (30 pieces), and writings, 1885-1921, about Whitman by William Sloane Kennedy (Conn., Pa., Mass.; anthologist, literary biographer) and others. The Kriendler Collection of modern American authors, 1930-55 (20 boxes), includes literary manuscripts of John O'Hara (N.Y.; novelist, short-story writer).

Included also in the Library are records of businesses, from single merchants and craftsmen to sizable corporations, and records of many societies and other organized groups. Microfilm copies of manuscripts total about 250 reels. Among them are records of the Society for the Propagation of the Gospel in Foreign Parts, London, 1783-1901 (64 reels), including letters and reports of the missionaries in Australia, 1789-1900; the complete records of the West New Jersey Society, London, 1692-1920 (14 reels); and minutes and surveys of the Council of Proprietors of the Western Division of New Jersey, 1688-1951 (14 reels). Microfilms of records of several New Jersey

churches have been made by the Library.

In the Rutgersensia Collection of
material of all types relating to Rutgers University are some 650 boxes
of manuscript and similar items. The
University archives, 1771-1959, consist of incomplete official papers of
the Board of Trustees, 1771-1955;
correspondence and other papers of
several recent presidents, registrars,
and secretaries, 1905-59, and of certain offices and departments; prize essays and theses; entrance records; and
records of fraternities and other affiliated organizations. In the collection
also are biographical files concerning
deceased faculty and alumni, and miscellaneous manuscripts not archival in
character but otherwise identified
closely with Rutgers in some way.

NEWARK 4

New Jersey Historical Society. 230
Broadway. William H. Gaines, Jr.,
Librarian.

Holdings: 100,000 items, relating
chiefly to New Jersey. Papers of individuals include those of John Insley
Blair (N. J.; capitalist, philanthropist,
instrumental in organization of various
railroads), 1830-99 (1,500 items), in-
cluding diaries, account books, and
business and family correspondence;
Joseph P. Bradley (N. J.; U. S. Supreme
Court Justice), 1836-92 (5,000 items);
Mahlon Dickerson (N. J.; Gov., U. S.
Sen., Sec. Navy), 1782-1852 (1,000
items); Philemon Dickerson (N.J.; Gov.,
U. S. Rep., U. S. dist. court judge),
1820-60 (350 items); Ebenezer Elmer
(N. J.; physician, Rev. War surgeon,
U. S. Rep.), 1776-85 (14 vols. of Rev.
War journal and other documents);
Lindley Miller Garrison (N.J., N.Y.;
lawyer, Sec. War), 1913-16 (225
items), including notes on cabinet
meetings; Sanford B. Hunt (N.Y., N.J.;

physician, newspaper editor), 1837-
92 (600 items), among them Civil War
hospital reports; Lawrence Kearny
(N. J.; U. S. naval officer), 1814-44
(5 vols. of logbooks and letter books);
Philip Kearny (N. J.; U. S. Army officer), 1861-63 (80 items); Lewis Morris (N.Y., N.J.; chief justice of N.Y.,
colonial Gov. of N. J.), 1730-46 (100
items); Robert Hunter Morris (N. J.,
Pa.; chief justice of N. J., colonial
Gov. of Pa.), 1734-58 (170 items);
Charles Wolcott Parker (N. J.; State
supreme court justice), 20th century;
Peter D. Vroom (N. J.; Gov., U. S.
Rep., Minister to Prussia) and his
son Garret D. W. Vroom (N. J.; may-
or of Trenton, judge of State court of
errors and appeals), 1783-1893
(10,000 items); and Marcus L. Ward
(N. J.; candle manufacturer, Gov.,
U. S. Rep.), 1851-83 (1,000 items).
Several autograph collections contain
letters and other documents of signers of the Declaration of Independence and prominent New Jersey persons, and a number of Revolutionary
War letters. There are also numerous account books and other business
records, sermons, genealogical papers, military records relating to
the American Revolution and other
wars, records of private organizations and associations, and extensive
groups of miscellaneous manuscripts
reflecting many aspects of New Jersey history.

See Fred Shelley, A Guide to the
Manuscripts Collection of the New Jersey Historical Society (1957. [81]
p.).

NEWARK 1

Newark Museum. 43-49 Washington
St. Katherine Coffey, Director.

Holdings: 84 items, 1619-1875,
of miscellaneous character, including letters and other papers of a

number of prominent Americans.

See Hist. Records Survey, Guide
for N. J., p. 23.

—oOo—

Public Library. 5 Washington St.
James E. Bryan, Director.

Holdings: In the Art Department,
a collection of 500 autograph letters
and documents, chiefly of literary and
musical figures with New Jersey con-
nections. Included are letters of Timothy Cole (Ill., N. Y.; wood engraver),
1880's–1922 (70 pieces), describing
his making of engravings of master-
pieces in European galleries. The Library has also clippings, bibliographical notes, letters, and other papers
which formed the basis of published
works on American music by John
Tasker Howard (N. Y.; musician, composer, author), 20th century (3½ file
drawers).

NEWTON

Dennis Memorial Library.

Holdings: 5 vols. containing information copied from headstones in
old cemeteries in Sussex County, 1700-
1900, with histories of each cemetery.
See Hist. Records Survey, Guide
for N. J., p. 29.

—oOo—

Sussex County Historical Society.
Main and Church Sts.

Holdings: 2,500 pieces, relating
chiefly to Sussex County. Included
are some records of old churches,
school records, business records, a
collection of Revolutionary and Civil
War papers, and papers of the families
of John W. Griggs (N. J.; lawyer, Gov.)
and William Newell (N. J.; Gov.).

See Hist. Records Survey, Guide
for N. J., pp. 29-31.

PATERSON

Passaic County Historical Society.
Lambert Castle, Valley Rd.
D. Stanton Hammond, President
and Librarian.

Holdings: 3,000 items, 18th-20th
centuries, relating chiefly to Passaic
County and its vicinity. Included are
papers of Albert H. Heusser (N. J.;
author, founder of the Historical Society); Abram S. Hewitt (N.Y., N.J.;
iron manufacturer, U. S. Rep. from
N. Y., mayor of New York City,
philanthropist); and Garret A. Hobart
(N. J.; lawyer, Republican leader,
U. S. Vice Pres.). There are also
books and papers of the Society for
Establishing Useful Manufactures,
1791-1840 (300 items); Revolutionary
War, Civil War, and Spanish-American War papers; many political, business, and church records; and copies
of family, church, and public records
(4 large letter files), made by a New
Jersey genealogist. On deposit are
voluminous papers belonging to the
Genealogical Society of New Jersey
(402,000 pieces), consisting of copies
of cemetery inscriptions and family
Bible records relating to New Jersey
families, and many compilations of
family histories.
See Hist. Records Survey, Guide
for N. J., pp. 32-34.

PATERSON 1

Paterson Museum. 268 Summer St.
Director.

Holdings: 200 pieces, consisting
of letters, sketches, blueprints, and
historical notes of John P. Holland
(N. J.; inventor), concerning his sub-

marine experiments and invention, 1875-1900.

PLAINFIELD

Seventh Day Baptist Historical Society. Seventh Day Baptist Bldg., 510 Watchung Ave. Evalois St. John, Librarian.

Holdings: Archives of the Seventh Day Baptist Church in the United States, including many church records, diaries, genealogies, and other papers, 17th-20th centuries, but chiefly 19th century. (Some of these materials formerly constituted the Seventh Day Baptist Denomination Collection in the Alfred University Library, Alfred, N.Y.) Included are manuscript records of the Seventh Day Baptist General Conference and its predecessors, 1743-1936 (5 vols., 2 packages, and 3 pieces), among many volumes that are printed; and of the German Seventh Day Baptist Conference, 1823-70 (1 vol.). There are also records of regional associations of the denomination, including papers or copies of papers, dating from 1697, of churches in 17 States, scattered from Rhode Island and Connecticut to Virginia and westward through the middle States to Oklahoma, Colorado, and Idaho; records of or relating to several church schools; and records of the Seventh Day Baptist Memorial Board, 1906 to date (5 vols. and several containers). There is also a collection made by Julius Friedrich Sachse (Pa.; antiquarian, author), containing chiefly rare books printed at the Ephrata Community but with some manuscripts, 1739-1850 (16 vols.). This collection contains a letter book, a diary, scattered Ephrata letters bound with other materials, recipes, and musical manuscripts (8 vols.), including some manuscript music of Johann Conrad Beissel (Pa.; founder of the Ephrata Community).

See Hist. Records Survey, Inventory of the Church Archives of New Jersey: Baptist Bodies—Seventh Day Baptist Supplement, pp. 45-161 passim, but especially pp. 92-150 (1939. Processed); and, for the Alfred University collection, the Survey's Guide for N.Y. State, p. 44.

PRINCETON

Princeton University Library. William S. Dix, Librarian; Howard C. Rice, Jr., Chief, Department of Rare Books and Special Collections.

Holdings: 270 filing drawers and 4,200 ft. of shelved manuscripts, some bound (about 18,600 pieces) and others in boxes and cartons, including representative manuscripts and other records of the ancient world, Islamic manuscripts from the 9th to the 20th century, medieval and Renaissance manuscripts, and manuscripts of modern times, mainly English and American. In this description the manuscript groups are discussed in the following order: ancient, oriental, and medieval and Renaissance manuscripts; manuscripts of British origin; papers representing modern continental Europe; and American manuscripts. By far the largest group, the American manuscripts, is divided into those of the post-Columbian period, 18th-century materials, manuscripts in the Andre deCoppet Collection, nonliterary materials of the 19th and 20th centuries, literary materials of those centuries, and papers of interest for New Jersey and for Princeton University. Many of the holdings are in large collections assembled and donated by alumni and friends of the University; not all of these collections are mentioned by name in the following discussion. Nor does this entry note all the names of individuals, including some very important ones, for whom significant manuscripts are to be found, either as single examples in numerous collections of American and foreign autographs or as parts of collections of correspondence and other papers that are noted. In the quantities given below, a box indicates about 500 pieces and a carton about 1,500. Various restrictions govern the use of certain manuscripts, especially those in collections of 20th-century papers.

There are in the Library some 1,000 cuneiform tablets, of Sumerian, Babylonian, and Assyrian origin; approximately 240 Babylonian cylinder and stamp seals; and some 5,000 ancient Greek, Roman, and Near Eastern coins. An epigraphical collection of approximately 120 original pieces and castings includes inscriptions, in various languages and scripts, illustrating the development of writing in the Near East and Europe. There are also some 400 papyri, most of which are fragments from Roman Egypt, about 300 B.C. to A.D. 500, but a few of which are from ancient Egypt, of a far earlier date. Greek, Coptic, Christian, and Arabic papyri are represented.

With relatively few exceptions the Princeton collection of Arabic, Turkish, and Indic manuscripts constitutes one of the main divisions of the comprehensive Garrett Collection. There are more than 10,000 volumes, dating from earliest Islamic times to the 19th century and representing almost all Moslem lands and scripts and disciplines. The Library has also representative manuscripts from Oceania and Southeast Asia, including such areas as the Philippines, Burma, Cambodia, Ceylon, Laos, and Thailand. Most of these manuscripts too are in the Garrett Collection. In the Gest Oriental Library are some 3,000 manuscripts, the earliest of which is believed to date from the 6th century A.D. More than 2,000 of the Gest

manuscripts, most of which are Chinese, were written before 1602.

The Library's collection of medieval and Renaissance manuscripts, noteworthy for examples of both artistic and textual importance, includes books of hours, psalters, and other kinds of religious books, as well as many secular manuscripts. There are numerous texts of classical authors. Important among the Garrett manuscripts, for the study of Byzantine art, are 12 Greek Christian manuscripts dating from the 9th to the 13th century. Also included in this collection are representative manuscripts in Armenian, Coptic, Ethiopian, Old Slavonic, Samaritan, and Syriac. Complementing the books of the medieval and Renaissance periods are three collections of legal documents. The Scheide Collection contains some 8,000 documents, 11th-19th centuries, in Latin, Italian, French, and English. Approximately 500 European letters and documents, 15th-17th centuries, form the Richardson Collection, and some 150 legal documents from the Logrono, Sona, Burgos, and Segovia provinces in Spain, 15th-17th centuries, constitute the Marden Collection. Among its papers of English origin the Library has contemporary or near-contemporary manuscripts of various of the works (before 1501) of the Venerable Bede, Boethius, Saint Bridget, John of Glastonbury, John Gower, Ralph Higden, Thomas Hoccleve, John Methan, and Richard Rolle, and a manuscript of the Chronicle of Brut. These manuscripts are in the Robert Garrett and the Grenville Kane collections.

Later papers of British origin include those in the John Wild Autograph Collection, which comprises letters and other documents of persons from Tudor times to the middle of the 19th century and includes some 2,000 autographs of royalty, statesmen, military and naval men, scientists and mathematicians, representatives of literature and the arts, and distinguished members of the peerage, the clergy, and the bar. Other significant papers of the 18th and 19th centuries, apart from those primarily of literary interest, include correspondence (200 pieces) between Paul Rycaut (diplomat and author) and William Blathwayt (Sec. at War), 1683-1704, containing political and diplomatic information from Hamburg and the Hanse towns. The group contains original letters of Rycaut with many copies of Blathwayt's replies. Papers of Richard Baggalay (Attorney Gen.), ca. 1874, relate to the suppression of the slave trade. There are also 50 letters of John Bright (Member of Parliament, reformer, free trader) to various correspondents.

The Morris L. Parrish Collection of papers of Victorian novelists includes papers of C. L. Dodgson, known as Lewis Carroll, among them more than 50 letters written by him, 1,800 mathematical papers, and other manuscripts; and letters by Sir James M. Barrie (over 150), Wilkie Collins (over 200), Charles Kingsley (over 200), Charles Reade (over 75), and Anthony Trollope (over 300), as well as other manuscript material relating to these novelists. The collection has also significant groups of letters and manuscripts of the following English novelists: William H. Ainsworth, William Black, Charlotte Brontë, Edward Bulwer-Lytton, Dinah Maria Craik, Charles Dickens, George Eliot, Elizabeth Gaskell, Thomas Hardy, Thomas Hughes, Charles James Lever, George Meredith, Robert Louis Stevenson, William Makepeace Thackeray, and Charlotte M. Yonge. Aside from this collection, the Library has papers of Aubrey Beardsley (artist, illustrator), from 1878 (90 letters and 60 drawings); papers concerning Marguerite, Countess of Blessington (Ireland; novelist), 1837-55 (70 pieces); and papers relating to T. Crofton Croker (Ireland; author, antiquarian), 1827-55 (83 pieces). There are also papers of or relating to George Cruikshank (artist, book illustrator, caricaturist), 500 pieces; correspondence of friends of Leigh Hunt (essayist, poet), 1826-71 (300 pieces); papers of John Davidson (poet, novelist, playwright), 1890-1909 (3 boxes), including letters and literary manuscripts; and Albany Fonblanque (editor of the Examiner), 1830-47. There are also papers of Charles Lamb (essayist) and his sister Mary, 1811-36 (12 letters and 2 literary manuscripts); William Charles Macready (actor, tragedian), 50 pieces; Charles Mathews (actor) and his son Charles James Mathews (actor, playwright), 5 boxes; Coventry Patmore (poet), 1850-96 (500 pieces), including manuscripts of poems and 250 pieces of correspondence with literary contemporaries; Hester Lynch Piozzi (author, friend of Samuel Johnson), 300 letters; John Ruskin (essayist, critic, reformer), 50 letters and 15 literary manuscripts; and Arthur Symons (poet, critic, translator), including manuscripts, typescripts, and printer's proofs (30 boxes). There are also some 1,200 letters and approximately 100 other manuscripts and documents relating to the studies of William Wordsworth (poet) and other figures of the Romantic movement made by George Maclean Harper (N. J.; prof. of English literature, Wordsworth scholar); papers of John Butler Yeats (Ireland; poet, artist), including some manuscripts of his poems, 200 letters, and drawings; and a smaller number of papers of William Butler Yeats (Ireland; poet) and other Irish authors of the early 20th century.

The Princeton Library has but few significant groups of papers representing modern continental Europe.

The Oranien-Nassau documents consist of some 5,000 original pieces and transcripts, 1707-63, relating to the House of Orange-Nassau from the 16th to the 18th century; emphasis is on the lawsuits following the death of William III of England. The most extensive papers of European origin are the archives of Eugene Beauharnais (Napoleon's stepson and viceroy in Italy, Duke of Leuchtenberg, Bavaria), 1805-24 (30,000 pieces), largely papers of his administration of Italy and minutes of the Commission de Liquidation, 1816-19, concerning claims arising from the Napoleonic wars. Other manuscripts of French interest are a series of historical autographs, approximately 400 documents and letters bearing signatures of the French kings from Louis XII through Louis XVI and signatures of notable political, and some literary, figures of each reign; another series of 150 French autographs, mainly those of political figures of the 16th through the early 19th century, and 100 letters and documents of the same period of leading figures of other continental countries, including Germany, Italy, Poland, and Spain. There are also 50 manuscripts of Johann Wolfgang von Goethe (Germany; poet, novelist, dramatist); representative autographs of a few other German literary figures of the 19th century; and musical autographs representing well known European composers from the 18th to the 20th century. Of a more modern period are significant holdings of manuscripts and correspondence of two American-born symbolist poets, Francis Vielé-Griffin and Stuart Merrill (300 pieces).

American papers from the Revolutionary War to the present time form the larger part of the Princeton manuscript holdings, although there are a few manuscripts of an earlier period. In the Garrett Collection are some 200 post-Columbian documents in Spanish and several Mayan languages, from the 15th to the early 19th century. In the Andre deCoppet Collection are several letters and other documents from the archives of Raymond de Fourquevaux (France; Ambassador to Spain), concerning the struggle between France and Spain over Florida in the mid-16th century. These papers include autograph material of Catherine de Medicis, wife of Henry II, King of France; and Charles IX, King of France. Because of its significance, mention is made of an individual manuscript, William Strachey's History of Travaile into Virginia Britannia (1612?), one of the three known copies of the work and believed to be partly in the author's handwriting.

Collections of American origin that consist primarily of 18th-century materials include a manuscript journal of Louis Alexandre Berthier (France; staff officer to Rochambeau in his American campaign), and his military maps depicting the route of Rochambeau's army from Newport to Yorktown, 1781. Of related interest is the "Journal particulier d'une campagne aux Indes Occidentales," 1781-82, by Joachim de Perron, Comte de Revel, who was attached to the French fleet under De Grasse, in 1780. There are also journals, correspondence, and other papers of Elias Boudinot (N.J.; Rev. War officer, Pres. of Continental Cong., U.S. Rep.), his brother Elisha, and other members of their family. The Hubbell papers, 1788-1848 (10,000 pieces), dealing with land transactions in New York, Georgia, Ohio, Mississippi, and Virginia, relate chiefly to the Genesee lands in western New York. Included are papers of Nathaniel Gorham (Mass.; businessman, Pres. of Continental Cong., land promoter), and Oliver Phelps (Mass., N.Y.; merchant, Rev. War officer, land promoter, U.S. Rep.), 1788-90, and his son and grandson; and, the largest part of the collection, papers of Walter Hubbell (N. Y.; lawyer), extending to 1848. The Stockton papers, 1702-1866, include papers of Richard Stockton (N. J.; Member Continental Cong., chief justice of N. J.) and Robert Field Stockton (U. S. naval officer). The papers of the Boudinot and Stockton families, with those of the allied Bradford and Field families, all of New Jersey, are contained in more than 15 boxes. The Library has relatively small but significant groups of manuscripts of the 18th-century presidents, trustees, faculty, and students, and early benefactors of the College of New Jersey, which was to become Princeton University. Papers of the college presidents include those of Aaron Burr, Sr. (N. J.; Presbyterian minister), Samuel Davies (Va., N. J.; Presbyterian minister), Jonathan Dickinson (N. J.; Presbyterian minister), Jonathan Edwards (Mass., N. J.; Congregational minister), Samuel Finley (N. J., Pa.; Presbyterian minister), and John Witherspoon (Scotland, N. J.; Presbyterian minister, Member Continental Cong.). A small but significant fragment of the correspondence of Thomas Foxcroft (Mass.; minister in Boston) contains letters received from Jonathan Dickinson and Aaron Burr, Sr. (N. J.; Presbyterian ministers), and from Experience Mayhew (Mass.; minister and missionary in Martha's Vineyard). There are also papers of Jonathan Belcher (Mass., N. J.; merchant, colonial Gov.) and Philip Vickers Fithian (N. J.; Presbyterian clergyman, Rev. War soldier).

More than 3,700 letters and documents of American figures of national importance from colonial times to the mid-20th century are to be found in the Andre deCoppet Collection. Those men whose manuscripts form some of the larger or more important groups, mostly numbering from 20 to 175 pieces, are, for the 18th and early 19th centuries: John Adams (Mass.; Member Continental Cong., diplomat, U. S. Pres.); James Buchanan (Pa.; U. S. Rep. and Sen., diplomat, Sec. State, U. S. Pres.); Benjamin Franklin (Pa.; printer, scientist, diplomat); Nathanael Green (R. I., Ga.; Rev. War officer); Alexander Hamilton (N. Y.; Rev. War officer, Member Continental Cong., Sec. Treas.); Andrew Jackson (Tenn.; U.S. Army officer and Pres.); Thomas Jefferson (Va.; Member Continental Cong., Gov., Minister to France, Sec. State, U. S. Pres.); James Madison (Va.; Member Continental Cong., U.S. Rep., Sec. State, U. S. Pres.); James Monroe (Va.; Member Continental Cong., U.S. Sen., diplomat, Gov., Sec. State, U. S. Pres.); Robert Morris (Pa.; financier, Member Continental Cong., U. S. Sen.); Zachary Taylor (Ky.; U. S. Army officer and Pres.); and George Washington (Va.; Rev. War Commander in Chief, U.S. Pres.). For the period of the Civil War the larger groups include papers of Ulysses S. Grant (U. S. Army officer, U. S. Pres.); Robert E. Lee (Va.; U. S. and Confed. Army officer, pres. of Washington College); and Abraham Lincoln (Ill.; lawyer, U. S. Rep. and Pres.). For the period 1865-1925 there are substantial amounts of papers for Presidents Grover Cleveland, Warren G. Harding, Theodore Roosevelt, William Howard Taft, and Woodrow Wilson. Also in this collection are papers in small quantity of many other persons distinguished in the 18th or 19th centuries, including nine 19th-century U. S. Presidents.

Other papers of American origin in the 19th century, other than those of literary interest, include papers of William Goldsmith Belknap (U. S. Army officer), 500 letters written during the Mexican War, and substantial papers of his son, William Worth Belknap (Iowa, D. C.; lawyer, Civil War officer, Sec. War). The Blair-Lee papers, 1733-1916, on deposit

(50 boxes), include chiefly correspondence, 1818-72, of Francis Preston Blair (Ky., D. C.; pres. of Bank of Ky., editor of Washington Globe) and of Samuel Phillips Lee (U. S. naval officer) with leading political, military, and naval men. Other papers include those of William Lewis Dayton (N. J.; State supreme court justice, U. S. Sen., Minister to France), 5 boxes); Joseph Henry (N.Y., N.J., D.C.; physicist, prof. at College of N.J., Sec. of Smithsonian Institution, pres. of National Academy of Science), 200 letters; and Charles Hodge (N. J.; Presbyterian theologian, prof. at Princeton Theological Seminary), 1820-70 (6,000 letters plus other manuscripts). A selected correspondence, 1870-1920, of Alpheus Hyatt (Mass.; zoologist, paleontologist, prof. at Mass. Institute of Technology and Boston Univ.), Alfred Goldsborough Mayer (Mass., N. Y., Fla.; museum curator, head of Carnegie Institution's Tortugas Laboratory), and Alfred Marshall Mayer (N. J.; physicist, prof. at Stevens Institute, authority on acoustics) contains letters of some 350 correspondents, chiefly scientists. There are also papers of Henry Flavel Lee (Pa.; clergyman), 4 boxes; John Maclean (N. J.; pres. of College of N. J.), 30,000 pieces, chiefly correspondence but including documents collected by Maclean for use in his history of the college; James McCadden, partner of James A. Bailey (Mich., Tenn., N. Y.; circus proprietor), including materials on the Barnum and Bailey and other circuses (12 boxes); and Samuel Miller (N.Y., N.J.; Presbyterian theologian, historian, prof. at Princeton Theological Seminary), 1790-1850 (1,500 pieces) and his son John Miller (Md., Va., N. J.; Confed. Army officer, Presbyterian clergyman). Included also are papers of the Civil Service Reform Association, 1881-85 (5 boxes).

Twentieth-century papers, other than literary collections, include those of Elmer Adler (N.Y., N.J.; printer, consultant to Princeton Univ. Press), together with archives of the Pynson Printers and the Colophon, 1920-51 (100 cartons); James Montgomery Beck (Pa.; U. S. Solicitor Gen., U.S. Rep.), 4 cartons; Harold G. Bowen (U.S. naval officer), on naval research (12 cartons); Arthur von Briesen (N. Y.; lawyer, pres. of Legal Aid Society), 1902-30 (25 boxes); Arthur Bullard (D. C.; foreign correspondent, U. S. State Dept. Russian expert, editor of Our World), 1,100 pieces; William Burgess (N.Y., N.J., Pa.; china and pottery manufacturer), 1908-25 (14 boxes); John Foster Dulles (N.Y., D.C.; lawyer, U. S. Sen., Sec. State), the main body of papers; Edward Mead Earle (N.Y., N.J.; history prof. at Columbia and Princton Univs.), research notes on aviation and military science (5 cartons); George Simpson Eddy (N.Y.; historian), research notes and correspondence with other 20th-century specialists on Benjamin Franklin (6 cartons); James V. Forrestal (N. Y.; pres. of Dillon, Read and Co., Sec. Navy, Sec. Defense), chiefly 1944-49 (20 filing drawers); Lindley Miller Garrison (N.J., N.Y.; lawyer, Sec. War), 1913-16 (25 boxes), chiefly of his writings; and Herbert Adams Gibbons (N. J.; journalist, author, lecturer), relating to his travels, principally in the Near East (15 boxes).

Among other nonliterary papers of the 20th century are those of Otto H. Kahn (N. Y.; banker, philanthropist), 1910-34 (99 filing drawers); Fred I. Kent (N. Y.; banker), including important correspondence with Presidents Hoover, Franklin D. Roosevelt, and Truman (16 cartons); Alfred James Lotka (N. J.; mathematician, statistician), including his writings on mathematics and social science; George McAneny (N. Y.; journalist, N.Y. City official, chairman of the N. Y. Transit Commission), 1885-

1953 (100 boxes); Hugh Lenox Scott
(U.S. Army officer and Chief of Staff),
drafts and typescripts of his writings
as a member of an American military
mission to Russia, 1917 (100 pieces);
and Woodrow Wilson (N.J.; pres. of
Princeton Univ., Gov., U.S. Pres.),
chiefly Wilson's outgoing letters (12
boxes), plus an undetermined number
of Wilson letters in other groups of
personal papers. Supplementing the
Wilson collection at Princeton are papers of his biographer, Ray Stannard
Baker, also known as David Grayson
(Mass.; journalist, author), mainly papers collected by him, 1918-19, as
chief of the American Press Bureau at
the Paris Peace Conference. Other
20th-century papers are the American
Civil Liberties Union archives, 1912-
49 (1,900 vols.); business records of
the Derrydale Press (34 cartons); the
Henry Holt archives, from 1858; and
the archives of Fight for Freedom,
Inc., and of Freedom House, 1940 (100
cartons).

In the field of American letters the
larger and more comprehensive collections are the papers of John Peale Bishop (Mass.; author, poet), 20 boxes, on
deposit; James Gould Cozzens (N.J.,
N.Y.; author), 20th century; F. Scott
Fitzgerald (N.Y.; novelist, short-
story writer), literary manuscripts
and correspondence (30 boxes); Alfred
Hodder (N.Y.; writer on literary, met-
aphysical, and political subjects), 40
boxes; Laurence Hutton (N.Y.; bibliophile, literary editor of Harper's
Magazine), 1850-1904 (20 boxes), including literary manuscripts and more
than 3,000 letters received from persons prominent in art and science;
William Vaughn Moody (Ill., N.Y.; poet, playwright, English prof. at Univ.
of Chicago), letters and manuscripts
(6 boxes); David Graham Phillips (N.Y.;
novelist), chiefly 1902-17 (10 boxes);
and Samuel Putnam (N.Y.; author, critic, editor of the New Review), 1927-33
(1,500 pieces), including letters of Jean

Cocteau (France; novelist, dramatist),
James T. Farrell (Ill., N.Y.; journalist, novelist), Ford Madox Ford (England; poet, critic, novelist), and Ezra
Pound (N.Y., Europe; poet). There
are also drama scripts, extensive
correspondence, photographs, programs, and other theatrical memorabilia collected by William Seymour
(N.Y., Mass.; actor-manager), 50
boxes; and papers of Booth Tarkington (Ind.; novelist, playwright), including literary manuscripts, correspondence, and photographs (200 boxes);
Ridgely Torrence (Ohio, N.Y.; poet,
dramatist, librarian) and his wife,
Olivia Dunbar Torrence, 1860-1950,
including literary manuscripts and a
voluminous correspondence; George
Crouse Tyler (N.Y.; theater manager
and producer), 1900-30 (50 boxes);
Carl Van Doren (N.Y.; biographer,
literary critic), including literary
manuscripts and correspondence (18
cartons); and Henry Van Dyke (N.Y.,
N.J.; Presbyterian minister, English
prof. at Princeton, poet, diplomat,
U.S. Navy chaplain), including literary manuscripts and correspondence
(60 boxes).

Smaller groups of papers relating
to American literature, journalism,
and literary scholarship include those
of Thomas Bailey Aldrich (N.Y.,
Mass.; poet, short-story writer, editor of Atlantic Monthly), 50 pieces;
George Henry Boker (Pa.; poet, dramatist), literary manuscripts (5
boxes); Robert Bridges (Pa., N.Y.;
author, editor of Scribner's Magazine), 12 boxes; William Eleroy Curtis (Ill.; journalist, author, first director of the Bureau of American
Republics), clippings of his writings
(200 vols.) and some correspondence;
Richard Watson Gilder (N.J., N.Y.;
editor, poet), 1880-1920, chiefly his
letters to Maria Lansdale (Pa.; traveler, author), with some manuscripts
of his poems; Joseph Howard (N.Y.;
journalist, columnist), scrapbooks of

clippings (102 vols.) and some correspondence; William Dean Howells (Mass., N.Y.; novelist, literary critic, editor of Atlantic Monthly), 1837-1920; Maria Lansdale (see above), 1884-1931 (5 boxes); Charles Godfrey Leland (Pa., England, Italy; humorist, poet, essayist); Mary A. Livermore (Mass., Ill.; reformer, suffragist), 1846-1905 (200 literary manuscripts); James Meeker Ludlow (N.Y., N.J.; Presbyterian minister, dramatist, author); Arthur B. Maurice (Conn.; author, editor of Bookman), 1899-1916 (200 letters), including some from important political and literary personages; A. Edward Newton (Pa.; bibliophile, essayist), some 500 letters from other book collectors; Eugene O'Neill (N.Y.; dramatist), manuscripts of 12 plays, with drawings and stage directions; Channing Pollock (N.Y.; dramatist, lecturer, publicist), literary manuscripts and correspondence (10 boxes); Don Carlos Seitz (N.Y.; newspaper manager, author), literary manuscripts (10 boxes); Charles Willis Thompson (N.Y., D.C., Pa.; political writer, journalist), chiefly clippings of his writings (44 vols. and 5 boxes); and James P. Walker (Mass.; publisher), 1840-68, including manuscripts of his religious articles and some of his correspondence as a member of the Boston publishing firm of Walker, Wise and Co. There are also the correspondence and business files of the Council on Books in Wartime, 1942-45 (12 filing drawers).

Many papers of New Jersey interest have already been noted in the personal papers of men identified with the State. The Library has other manuscripts, however, that are of interest mainly as papers documenting aspects of New Jersey history, or that of a particular locality within the State, or of a New Jersey family or business. In this category are papers of the Abbott family, 1707-1916 (10 boxes), including the correspondence of Charles Conrad Abbott (N.J.; naturalist, archeologist, author), 1843-1919; Samuel J. Bayard (N.J.; Democratic political writer), including much family correspondence during the Civil War (1,000 pieces); the Black family of Burlington County, including a diary, 1837-44, and farm journals, 1847-61 (4 vols.); Eli Field Cooley (N.J.; clergyman); the Gulick family, including a few legal papers, 1710-73, and 100 items on stage lines in New Jersey, 1797-1842; Thomas Potts Johnson (N.J.; lawyer), late 18th and early 19th centuries (3,000 pieces); John Joline and his son John Van Dyke Joline (N.J.; hotel proprietors), 1808-50 (8 vols.), hotel registers and accounts; Duane C. Minard (N.J.; State assistant attorney gen.), papers pertaining to the New Jersey—Delaware boundary disputes, beginning with the year 1664 (1,400 documents, charts, and maps in photocopy); William Paterson (N.J.; U.S. Sen., Gov., U.S. Supreme Court Justice) and his descendants, 1767-1867 (1,000 pieces), many relating to the College of New Jersey; Jonathan P. Scott (4 boxes), comprising documents relating to New Jersey history, including writings of Austin Scott (Mich., Md., N.J.; historian, pres. of Rutgers College); and Garret Dorset Wall (N.J.; U.S. Sen.) and his successors in legal practice to 1880 (3,000 pieces). There are also numerous smaller groups and single examples of account books, ledgers, commonplace books, letters, and other records of business enterprises, churches, societies, and individuals of New Jersey, many from the Princeton area.

Manuscripts relating to Princeton University (founded in 1746 as the College of New Jersey) consist generally of papers of the early benefactors, trustees, presidents, faculty, and administrative officers; college diaries, letters, and other records of undergraduates and distinguished alumni; and papers of

Princeton scientific expeditions, campus clubs and associations, and other organizations within or sponsored by the University. The Library is the custodian of certain papers, archival in nature, for the Secretary and other officers of the University. There are numerous groups of papers, large and small, of persons who have taught at Princeton or who have been otherwise connected with it. Most of these papers consist of manuscripts of professional writings, with research notes and, in some instances, substantial correspondence. Some of the more comprehensive of these manuscript groups have been noted above in this listing.

For the earlier manuscripts in the Library, see Philip K. Hitti and others, Descriptive Catalog of the Garrett Collection of Arabic Manuscripts in the Princeton University Library (1938. [724]p.); and Mohamad Etemad Moghadam and Yahya Armajani, Descriptive Catalog of the Garrett Collection of Persian, Turkish, and Indic Manuscripts, Including Some Miniatures, in the Princeton University Library (1939. 94 p.). De Ricci, Census, pp. 1176-1184, lists the medieval and Renaissance manuscripts of the Princeton Library at the time of that survey; see also pp. 493-495, 865-899, 1889-1900, and 2120-2131, for the more recently acquired collections of David A. Reed, Robert Garrett, Grenville Kane, and John H. Scheide, respectively.

For a general survey, see Alexander P. Clark, The Manuscript Collections of the Princeton University Library (1958. 32 p.). The Princeton University Library Chronicle, 1939 to date, contains notes and articles on the Library's manuscripts; special articles contain information about the papers of Ray Stannard Baker, Aubrey Beardsley, Eugene Beauharnais, Alexandre Berthier, John Davidson, Jonathan Edwards, F. Scott Fitzgerald, George McLean Harper, Charles Godfrey Leland, John Maclean, Samuel Miller, Eugene O'Neill, John Ruskin, Samuel Stanhope Smith, Booth Tarkington, and Woodrow Wilson. See also Allison, Inventory, pp. 91-93.

—oOo—

Theological Seminary Library. Kenneth S. Gapp, Librarian.

Holdings: 400 pieces, relating chiefly to the Theological Seminary of the Presbyterian Church in the United States of America. Papers of clergymen who were professors at the Seminary include those of Archibald Alexander (30 pieces); Charles Hodge (75 pieces); and Samuel Miller (31 pieces). There are also records of local churches within the bounds of the Synod of New Jersey (70 pieces).

See Allison, Inventory, pp. 88-91; and Hist. Records Survey, Guide for N.J., p. 37.

SALEM

Salem County Historical Society. (Mrs.) Irene Y. Green, President.

Holdings: 100 items, dated from 1675, relating chiefly to Salem and Gloucester Counties. Included are some deeds and business papers of the Fenwick colony, together with account books and journals of some of its prominent members; and minutes of a Friends meetinghouse.

SOMERS POINT

Atlantic County Historical Society. Somers Mansion. (Mrs.) Olive C. Rundstrom, President, 210 Showellton Ave., Absecon, N.J.

Holdings: About 100 vols. and

over 4,000 pieces, 1693-1944, relating chiefly to Gloucester (now Atlantic) County.   Included are papers of a county judge and a militia commander and sheriff, early 19th century (157 pieces).   There are also church materials, among them vital records of a Quaker meeting, 1693-1841, minutes of the monthly meeting, 1788-1803, and histories of 28 churches in the county, together with copied tombstone inscriptions and vital records; deeds, family papers, and many genealogical papers; records of 11 early public schools; material relating to 48 ships out of Great Egg Harbor; census records of Atlantic County, 1850-75; and many account and record books, 1785-1875, of iron works and glass works.

SOMERVILLE

Somerset County Historical Society. County Courthouse.

Holdings: 60 items, 1770-1900, relating chiefly to Somerset County. Included are some records relating to local churches and Bible, temperance, and reform societies; and the docket book of a justice of the peace, 1770-73.
See Hist. Records Survey, Guide for N. J., p. 41.

TRENTON 25

Division of the State Library, Archives and History, State Department of Education.   State House Annex.   Thomas Amelia, Head, Bureau of Archives and History.

Holdings: In the Bureau of Archives and History, a quantity of materials, 1674-1956, consisting of (1) some colonial, State, and local archives, chiefly before 1860, and

(2) other papers relating to New Jersey and the early history of the United States.   (The Bureau was formerly known as the New Jersey Public Record Office.)   In the first category are acts of the Assembly, 1681-1802 (25 vols.); correspondence of most of the Governors, from 1802 (several thousand pieces); Revolutionary War records, 1776-1801 (521 pieces), including papers of the New Jersey Council of Safety and papers on estates forfeited by Loyalists; records of insolvent debtors, 1747-1818 (3 vols.); inquests, 1688-1798 (4 vols.); naturalization records, 1749-1810 (1 vol.); minute books of defunct municipalities, 1697-1935 (145 vols.); loan office books for 2 counties, 1724-86 (4 vols.); and records concerning bridges, roads, canals, and turnpikes, 1744-1834 (1,573 pieces). The second category includes records of the East Jersey and the West Jersey Proprietors, 1674-1807 (1 vol. and 23 pieces); papers relating to the Continental Congress, 1777-88 (1 vol. and 30 pieces); and papers relating to the manor and forges of Ringwood, N. J., 1765-1900 (5 vols.) transferred from the New Jersey Department of Conservation and Development.   There are also papers of Robert Erskine (England, N. J.; geographer, engineer, Rev. War officer), some originals and 5 vols. of photostats, formerly in the Manor House, Ringwood, N. J.; William Livingston (N.Y., N.J.; Member Continental Cong., Rev. War officer, Gov. of N. J.), 1777-83 (60 pieces); and George Washington (Va.; U. S. Pres.), 1777-89 (34 pieces).
See Hist. Records Survey, Guide for N. J., pp. 38 and 43-45; and its Calendar of the New Jersey State Library Manuscript Collection (1939. 168 p.   Processed).

TRENTON 8

Free Public Library.   Edwin G.

Jackson, Library Director.

Holdings: 350 items, 1731-1932, relating chiefly to Trenton and its vicinity. Included are minutes of the city, 1792-1806; records of several volunteer fire companies, 1747-1932; records of the proprietors of the Trenton Academy, 1781-1859; minutes and reports of a Bible society, 1847-1917; the membership register and rolls of the local Young Men's Christian Association, 1869-78; and minutes of a local assembly of the Knights of Labor, 1888-92, and of locals of a potters' union and a pressers' union, 1893-99.

See Hist. Records Survey, Guide for N.J., p. 46.

TRENTON 7

New Jersey Department of Conservation and Economic Development. 520 East State St. (Mrs.) Olga G. Atkins, Supervisor of Historic Sites.

Holdings: A few papers in 3 historic house museums in the State, which are administered by the Department: (1) Boxwood Hall, in Elizabeth, containing 5 papers of Elias Boudinot (N.J.; Pres. of Continental Cong., U.S. Rep.); (2) Rockingham, in Rocky Hill, containing 5 papers of George Washington (U.S. Pres.); and (3) Wallace House, in Somerville, containing 8 miscellaneous papers.

See Hist. Records Survey, Guide for N.J., pp. 40 and 42.

TRENTON 25

New Jersey State Museum, State Department of Education. (Mrs.) Kathryn B. Greywacz, Director.

Holdings: A small collection of manuscripts of the 19th and 20th centuries, relating to New Jersey arche-
ology. Included are diaries, plans, and catalogs of archeological excavations and site surveys that have been under the Museum's sponsorship; and, on permanent deposit, the minutes and other records of the Archeological Society of New Jersey, 1931-59, and of the Eastern States Archeological Federation, 1933-59.

VINELAND

Vineland Historical and Antiquarian Society.

Holdings: 60 ft. of shelves, 1 trunk, and 2 large cabinets containing papers relating chiefly to Cumberland County and particularly to Vineland. In the 2 large cabinets are autograph letters of U.S. Presidents, signers of the Declaration of Independence, Supreme Court Justices, and Civil War soldiers.

See Hist. Records Survey, Guide for N.J., p. 48.

WEST ORANGE

Edison Laboratory National Monument. Main St. at Lakeside Ave. (Post Office address: P.O. Box 126, Orange, New Jersey.) Melvin J. Weig, Superintendent.

Holdings: 2,500 cu. ft., 1868-1931, consisting of the records left by Thomas A. Edison (N.J.; inventor) at his death, together with related materials assembled since that time from members of his family, friends, and associates; Thomas A. Edison, Inc. (now part of McGraw-Edison Co.); and other sources. Included are Edison's personal and business correspondence, 1868-1931; 3,400 laboratory notebooks; various record books, scrapbooks, and some thousands of loose sheets containing notes and sketches; Edison patents (1,093 American and many foreign) and patent applications; both bookkeeping and legal records and documents; 12,000 photographic negatives, with a selected print file; 5,000 cylinder and 15,000 disc phonograph records; and a small number of early motion picture films. Much documentary and other material on the genesis and early years of the telephone, phonograph, electric light and power, and motion picture industries is contained in these collections. There is also Edison's library of 10,200 books at the Laboratory and about 2,000 books at Glenmont, his home in nearby Llewellyn Park, some with marginal notes in the inventor's hand.

ALBUQUERQUE

University of New Mexico Library.
David Otis Kelley, University Librarian.

Holdings: An extensive group, dating from the Mexican period but mainly of the late 19th and early 20th centuries, and relating chiefly to New Mexico and the University. Included are papers of Holm Olaf Bursum (N. Mex.; stock raiser, U.S. Sen.), 500 letters; Thomas B. Catron (N. Mex.; lawyer, U.S. Sen.), 1878-1915 (a large quantity); Charles Francis Clarke (U.S. Army officer), 1847-82 (117 letters); Marion Dargan (N. Mex.; history prof. at the Univ. of N. Mex.), 800 pieces pertaining chiefly to New Mexican statehood; Albert Bacon Fall (N. Mex.; U.S. Sen., Sec. Interior), 1916-27 (6 vols. and 10 file boxes); Harvey B. Fergusson (N. Mex.; U.S. Rep.), 1910-11 (55 letters), relating chiefly to the New Mexico Constitutional Convention; Charles E. Hodgin (N. Mex.; Univ. of N. Mex. pres.), 1887-1925 (7 file boxes), relating chiefly to the University; Miguel Antonio Otero (N. Mex.; Terr. Gov.), 1890-1935 (43 vols., 14 letter boxes, and 2 file boxes); and Michael Steck (N. Mex.; Apache Indian agent), 1853-80 (9 file boxes).

Included also are papers and photographs relating to Indians, especially the Navajos, 1883-87, and an Apache dictionary; a picture collection on early New Mexico and Albuquerque (2,300 items); and a few diaries. Business records include records of a lumber company (1 vol. and 41 packets); business letters of a livestock agent for the Atchison, Topeka and Santa Fe Railroad, 1884-93 (26 vols.); records of a large ranch, 1893-1940 (76 vols. and 111 letter boxes); records of a firm dealing in wool, sheep, cattle, and general merchandise, 1902-37 (a large quantity); and ledgers, cash books, journals, correspondence, and other records of the First National Bank of Santa Fe, 1870-1926 (471 vols., 858 transfer files, and 71 boxes).

There are papers relating to old Mexico, including some public archives that were collected by a Belgian consul at Oaxaca; extensive collections of photographic copies of manuscripts relating to New Mexico and the Southwest in Spanish and Mexican archives, in the Museum of New Mexico in Santa Fe, and in other depositories in the United States, 1600-1875; a microfilm of the New Mexico private land claims records that are in the custody of the U.S. Bureau of Land Management in Santa Fe, 1685-1914 (72 cu. ft.); New Mexico Territorial archives, 1848-1912 (35 vols. and 209 file boxes); New Mexico county archives, 1860-1930 (260 file boxes, 163 letter boxes, 793 vols., and 500 linear ft.); and New Mexico State archives, 1912-35 (18 vols. and 63 file boxes). There are also field books of the U.S. Geographical Surveys West of the 100th Meridian, 1873-79 (53 vols.); and a collection of manuscript and printed scores, lyrics, and dramatic prose of Zarzuelas (Spanish light operas) given in Arizona and New Mexico early in the 20th century.

See Albert James Diaz, Manuscripts and Records in the University of New Mexico Library (1957. [57] p.); and Ralph E. Twichell, The Spanish Archives of New Mexico, vol. 1 (1914. 525 p.).

LAS VEGAS

New Mexico Highlands University
Library.   William S. Wallace,
Librarian and Archivist.

Holdings: 55 cu. ft. and 1,000
pieces, dated from 1820, relating
chiefly to the military history of the
Southwest, the Las Vegas region, and
the University.   Included is a collection of early regional photographs and
negatives.

ROSWELL

Roswell Museum and Art Center.
David Gebhard, Director.

Holdings: 900 items, 1867-1955,
relating chiefly to the political history of old Lincoln County, Chaves
County, and the city of Roswell.   Included are papers of John Simpson
Chisum (Tex., N. Mex.; cattleman) and
James John Hagerman (Colo., N. Mex.;
promoter of irrigation, railroad builder, land and cattle dealer); cattle and
sheep records; early reports on irrigation farming; and 127 photographs of
architecture and life in southeastern
New Mexico, 1874-1901.

SANTA FE

Historical Society of New Mexico.
State Museum of New Mexico.   Myra
Ellen Jenkins, Archivist.

Holdings: A considerable quantity
of archives and other manuscripts,
17th-20th centuries, relating chiefly
to New Mexico.   Included are a transcript of Father Bernardino de Saha-
gún's General History of the Affairs
of New Spain; records of the Spanish
and Mexican administrations in New
Mexico, 1621-1846 (13,087 folios),
at one time on deposit in the Library

of Congress; some Territorial and
State archives, including records
relating to the constitutional convention and military records, financial ledgers, and correspondence of
the Adjutant General's Office, 1854-
1916; and records of New Mexicans
in the U. S. Armed Forces in World
Wars I and II.   There are also the
Benjamin Read Collection, including
orders and decrees, 1715-1816 (2
vols.), and letters and other papers (315 pieces); a collection of
Spanish, Mexican, and American
manuscripts and autographs, 1512,
1680-1870 (299 folders), assembled
by Ralph E. Twitchell (N. Mex.;
railroad attorney, historian); and
the Historical Society of New Mexico Collection, 1587, 1656-1894
(252 folders), consisting of manuscripts, maps, and autographs.   Papers of individuals include those of
Manuel Alvarez   (N. Mex.; merchant,
U. S. consul and commercial agent
at Santa Fe), 1830-54 (6 vols. and
600 pieces); journals of Adolph F.
A. Bandelier (Ill., N. Y.; archeologist, anthropologist, explorer),
1880-1914 (6 vols.), and some of
his correspondence; papers of Le-
Baron Bradford Prince (N. Mex.;
chief justice and Terr. Gov., author), 1889-1921 (60 document
cases); public papers of Edmund G.
Ross (Kans., N. Mex.; journalist,
U. S. Sen. from Kans., Terr. Gov.
of N. Mex.), 1866-89 (20 document
cases); and the Vigil Papers, consisting of military papers, historical notes, and some correspondence, 1802-48 (140 pieces), of a
New Mexico official during the Mexican period and the American occupation.
     See Ralph E. Twitchell, The
Spanish Archives of New Mexico,
vol. 2 (1914. 683 p.); George P.
Hammond, "Manuscript Collections
in the Spanish Archives in New
Mexico," in Archives and Libraries;

Papers Presented at the 1939 Conference of the American Library Association, pp. 80-87 (1939. Processed);
and information about acquisitions in
the Annual Reports of the School of
American Research of the Archaeological Institute of America, 1939-51.

Museum of Navajo Ceremonial Art.
Kenneth E. Foster, Director.

Holdings: an undetermined quantity of manuscripts relating chiefly to
Navajo art and religion.

NEW YORK

ALBANY

Albany Institute of History and Art. 125 Washington Ave. Janet R. Mac-Farlane, Director.

Holdings: A considerable collection of manuscripts of the 17th, 18th, and early 19th centuries. Many of the papers relate to Albany County and the land transactions and estates of early Dutch families. Included are papers of Erastus Corning (N. Y.; merchant, railroad developer), 1810-70 (40,000 items); John Van Alen (N. Y.; U. S. Rep.), 1777-1825 (102 items); and John A. Ward (N. Y.; sculptor), 1874-1945 (700 items), chiefly correspondence about his work. There are also proceedings of Indian Commissioners, 1746, 1775, and 1784-90 (3 vols.); business account books, 1773-1872 (9 vols.); papers relating to Ulster County, 1768-1838 (113 items); records of the Albany Institute, 1770-1940 (400 items), the Albany Agricultural Society, the New York State Agricultural Society, 1792-1840 (58 items), and the Albany Society for the Promotion of Useful Arts, 1802-27 (34 items); a U. S. census of Albany County, 1800 (1 vol.); logs of New Bedford, Mass., whaling vessels, 1851-58 (5 vols.); and an autograph collection containing letters of U. S. Presidents and other important persons, 1766-1924 (110 items). Among family papers are the Cranch-Greenleaf-Whitney papers, 1749-1917 (217 items), containing a few letters of John Quincy Adams and his family; and papers of the family of John Van Schaick Lansing Pruyn (N. Y.; lawyer, U. S. Rep.), 1786-1908 (58 items).
See Hist. Records Survey, Guide for N. Y. State, pp. 1-8; and the Insti-

tute's "Checklist of Manuscript Holdings" (n.d. 3 p. Processed).

ALBANY 10

Harmanus Bleecker Library. 19 Dove St. Dorothy A. Vibbard, Head Librarian, Albany Public Library.

Holdings: 48 vols. and 30 pieces, consisting of records of the Young Men's Association for Mutual Improvement, 1833-1923 (36 vols. and 12 pieces); copies of correspondence of Harmanus Bleecker (N. Y.; U. S. Rep., Chargé d'Affaires in The Netherlands), 1839; and a few other papers relating to Albany.
See Hist. Records Survey, Guide for N. Y. State, p. 8.

ALBANY 1

New York State Library. Charles F. Gosnell, State Librarian.

Holdings: (1) Official records held by the Library as the State's archival agency (many series); and (2) other papers relating chiefly to the Colony and State of New York but including some materials on other States, particularly Vermont (5,000 vols. and 1,000,000 individual items). Most of these are in the Manuscripts and History Section of the Library; a few are in the Law Library and the Medical Library.
Records relating chiefly to the colonial period include the following archival material: New York Colonial Manuscripts—Dutch, 1630-64 (23 vols.), and English, 1664-1800 (82

vols.); Council Minutes, 1668-1783 (28 vols.); Land Papers, 1642-1803 (63 vols.); Original Books of Letters Patent, 1664-1712, 1731-86 (12 vols.); Books of Entry of the Port of New York, 1728-66 (10 vols.); and Proceedings Relating to the Boundary Line Between Massachusetts and Rhode Island, 1741-42 (1 vol.). Another important series is the papers of Sir William Johnson (N.Y.; French and Indian War officer, supt. of Indian affairs), 1733-1808 (22 vols. and 1,665 pages of transcripts from the British Public Record Office).

For the Revolutionary period there are a complete set of autographs of the signers of the Declaration of Independence (102 items); and papers of Andrew Elliott (England, N.Y.; Lt. Gov., customs collector of the Port of New York), 1775-83 (11 vols. and 300 items), including his correspondence, letter books, orders, and regulations as administrator of civilian affairs in the New York City area during the British occupation; Nicholas Herkimer (N.Y.; Rev. War officer), 1742-1842 (1 vol.); and John Williams (N.Y.; physician, Rev. War officer, U.S. Rep.), 1767-1841 (6 vols.). There are also proceedings of the Albany Committee of Correspondence, 1775-78 (2 vols.); "Manuscripts of the Colony and State of New York in the Revolutionary War," 1775-1800 (20 vols.), with gaps due to loss in the Capitol fire of 1911; certificates issued by the State treasurer for military service in the Revolution (10 vols.); audited accounts, 1782-94 (2 vols.); and Assembly papers, 1771-1831 (36 vols.), dealing with Revolutionary War soldiers' claims, Indian affairs, estates, schools, colleges, and other subjects.

Of interest for the late 18th and early 19th centuries are the papers of Harmanus Bleecker (N.Y.; lawyer, U.S. Rep., Chargé d'Affaires in The Netherlands), 1715-1872 (2,500 items); John Boyd (N.Y.; lawyer, U.S. Rep.),

1835-63 (100 items); George Clinton (N.Y.; Member Continental Cong., Rev. War officer, Gov., U.S. Vice Pres.), 1763-1844 (10 vols. and 115 items); John Pollard Gaines (Ky.; lawyer, soldier, U.S. Rep.), 1832-64 (6 boxes), including papers relating to his service in the Mexican War and as Governor of Oregon Territory; John Jay (N.Y.; Pres. of Continental Cong., diplomat, U.S. Chief Justice, Gov.), 1776-1816 (6 vols. and 40 items); Morgan Lewis (N.Y.; Rev. War and War of 1812 officer, jurist, Gov.), 1779-1835 (50 items); Zephaniah Platt (N.Y.; lawyer, Member Continental Cong.), 1774-1807 (200 items); Melancthon Smith (N.Y.; Member Continental Cong., Rev. War officer, merchant, lawyer), 1787-92 (35 items), mostly on ratification of the U.S. Constitution; John Tayler (N.Y.; Gov.), 1776-1855 (4 vols. and 125 items), chiefly concerning land; Daniel D. Tompkins (N.Y.; Gov., U.S. Vice Pres.), 1795-1844 (10 boxes and 20 items); and James Wilkinson (U.S. Army officer, Gov. of La. Terr.), 1777-1821 (19 items). "War of 1812 records," 1783-1826 (25 vols.), include accounts of the Governor, paymasters, and commissaries during the war and records concerning fortifications, arsenals, and military stores, 1795-1821, and concerning Indian affairs, 1783-1816.

The Van Vechten Collection, 1712-1828 (5,600 items), consists largely of land papers, court briefs, and other legal papers of Abraham Van Vechten (N.Y.; lawyer). Papers of Oliver Phelps (Mass., N.Y.; merchant, Rev. War officer, U.S. Rep.) and Nathaniel Gorham (Mass.; businessman, Pres. of Continental Cong., land promoter), 1788-1875 (235 vols. and 110 boxes), are chiefly records of land transactions in Maine, Vermont, Georgia, Michigan, and Ohio as well as in New York. The papers include, however, personal correspondence of members of the Phelps family (52 boxes), especially of Oliver Phelps, with prominent New Yorkers and New Englanders. Another large group is of land and business papers, 1795-1887 (10,000 items). Papers of Elkanah Watson (N. Y.; merchant, canal promoter, agriculturist, land speculator), 1778-1842 (50 vols. and 6,000 items), include correspondence, journals, account books, maps, and surveys.

Other manuscripts of the 19th century up to the Civil War include papers of Daniel Dewey Barnard (N. Y.; lawyer, U. S. Rep., Minister to Prussia), 1840-61 (12 vols.), including diaries; Benjamin Franklin Butler (N. Y.; lawyer, U. S. Attorney Gen., Sec. War), 1780-1858 (6 boxes, chiefly correspondence; Thomas Cole (Ohio, Pa., N. Y.; landscape painter, poet), 1821-47 (1,632 items), including sketch books; Amos Eaton (N. Y.; scientist, educator), 1789-1846 (3 boxes), including material on Rensselaer Polytechnic Institute; George Folsom (N.Y.; lawyer, U. S. Chargé d'Affaires in The Netherlands), 1812-1937 (5 vols.); Charles Kitchel Gardner (N. Y.; War of 1812 officer), 1803-65 (5 boxes); Washington Hunt (N. Y.; lawyer, U. S. Rep., Gov.), 1848-62 (42 items); William Learned Marcy (N. Y.; lawyer, U. S. Sen., Gov., Sec. War, Sec. State), 1837-60 (4,000 items), concerned largely with banks and canals; William Henry Seward (N. Y.; Gov., U. S. Sen., Sec. State), 1829-68 (237 items); Alfred Billings Street (N. Y.; poet, N. Y. State librarian), 1830-80 (16 vols. and 7 boxes), chiefly literary manuscripts; Aaron Vail (N. Y.; diplomat, Sec. of U. S. Legation in London, Chargé d'Affaires at London and Madrid), 1812-88 (23 vols. and 66 boxes), including diaries; John Ellis Wool (U. S. Army officer), 1812-69 (19 boxes and 21 items), relating chiefly to the War of 1812, the Mexican War, the Pacific Army Command, Indian wars, and the Civil War; and Silas Wright, Jr. (N. Y.; U. S. Sen.,

Gov.), 1833-47 (53 items).

Records covering the mid-19th century include many Civil War soldiers' letters and diaries; and papers of William Woods Averell (U.S. Army officer), 1836-1908 (11 boxes); John Adams Dix (N. Y.; U. S. Sen., Minister to France, Gov.), 1831-75 (90 items); Reuben Eaton Fenton (N. Y.; U. S. Rep., Gov., U.S. Sen.), 1855-79 (1 box); Edward Everett Hale (Mass.; Unitarian clergyman, humanitarian, author), 1833-1917 (172 vols. and 23 boxes), including diaries and journals; James Hall (N. Y.; geologist, paleontologist, Director of State Museum), 1830-1904 (15,000 pieces); David Bennett Hill (N. Y.; Gov., U. S. Sen.), 1872-1910 (16 vols. and 9 boxes); Franklin B. Hough (N. Y.; physician, natural scientist, Civil War surgeon, first forestry agent of U. S. Dept. of Agriculture, author), 1840-85 (75 vols. and 41 boxes); Edwin Denison Morgan (N. Y.; Gov., U. S. Sen.), 1833-82 (105 vols. and 15,000 items), including about 600 letters to John Frederick Kensett (Conn., N. Y.; artist), 1807-69; John Van Schaick Lansing Pruyn (N. Y.; lawyer, U. S. Rep.), 1832-1928 (11 vols.), chiefly journals, including material on the New York Central Railroad; Horatio Seymour (N. Y.; Gov.), 1830-86 (20 vols., 18 boxes, and 75 miscellaneous letters); Enos Thompson Throop (N. Y.; lawyer, Gov., U. S. Chargé d'Affaires in the Two Sicilies), 1824-72 (46 items); and Gouverneur Kemble Warren (U.S. Army officer), 1849-73 (11 vols., 3 boxes, and 4 chests), including records relating to exploring and mapping expeditions in the South, West, and Far West, and maps and reports of Civil War campaigns.

For the last half of the 19th century and the first half of the 20th century there are papers of George Sherman Batcheller (N. Y.; lawyer, Civil War officer), 1807-1943 (10 boxes and 3 packages), relating chiefly to his work as U.S. judge in the International Tribunal for Legal Administration of Egypt, 1876-85 and 1898, and as presiding officer at the Universal Postal Congress, 1897; William Croswell Doane (Mass., N.Y.; Episcopal bishop, poet), 1769-1932 (13 boxes), including correspondence and poems by him and his father, George Washington Doane (N.J.; Episcopal bishop, educator, hymn writer); Jacob Sloat Fassett (N.Y.; lawyer, financier, U.S. Rep.), 1913-23 (3 vols. of diaries); James Terry Gardiner (N.Y.; engineer, 1869-1912 (2 boxes), chiefly correspondence and reports on the Survey of the Fortieth Parallel and on the New York State Survey; Edward Lamson Henry (N.Y.; painter), 1858-1919 (800 pieces); Herbert H. Lehman (N.Y.; Gov., U.S. Sen.), 1933-44 (4 filing cases and 54 cartons); Charles Dwight Sigsbee (U.S. naval officer), 1860-1923 (7,000 pieces); and Alfred E. Smith (N.Y.; Gov.), 1919-29 (49 file drawers of official papers and 12 filing drawers and 1 box of personal papers).

Records relating to Vermont include papers on the New York—Vermont controversy, 1777-99 (1 vol.); and papers collected by Henry Stevens (Vt.; bibliophile), 1774-1850 (100 boxes), salvaged from the 1911 fire. The Stevens collection includes some papers of Ethan Allen (Vt.; Rev. War officer, commissioner from Vt. to the Continental Cong.); Heman Allen (Vt.; U.S. Rep., Minister to Chile); Ira Allen (Vt.; political leader); Silas Hemenway Jenison (Vt.; Gov.); and Isaac Tichenor (Vt.; Rev. War officer, jurist, U.S. Sen., Gov.); records concerning Vermont in the War of 1812; and records of the Burlington customhouse, 1825-36. Another large group of manuscripts (4,000 pieces) is made up of letters dealing chiefly with legal and business affairs in Vermont in the first half of the 19th century. Papers of Malcolm and Thomas Canfield (Vt.;

rail and lake transportation promoters), 1815-95 (28 folders and 2 packages), pertain chiefly to Vermont and Lake Champlain transportation companies and freight operations, and to logging in the Middle West.

In addition to the papers noted above, which for the most part constitute separate groups, papers of or concerning DeWitt Clinton (N.Y.; U.S. Sen., mayor of New York City, Gov.), 1788-1833 (25 items), and Philip John Schuyler (N.Y.; French and Indian War officer, Member Continental Cong., Rev. War officer, U.S. Sen.), 1757-1812 (250 items), some of which were formerly in the Schuyler Mansion, are scattered through several groups and in "miscellaneous papers." The Library also has many public records of the State not here noted and records of many counties, towns, and villages. Its holdings include also a large collection of early New York State church, Bible, and cemetery records, and materials concerning transportation, medicine, education, and the land and estates of prominent New York families, such as Banyar, Livingston, and Van Rensselaer.

See Hist. Records Survey, Guide for N.Y. State, pp. 9-39; Allison, Inventory, p. 93; Edna L. Jacobsen, "Manuscript Treasures in the New York State Library," in N.Y. History, 20:265-276 (July 1939), and, with Charles F. Gosnell, "History in the State Library," a series of articles in N.Y. History, vols. 27-29 (Oct. 1946—Jan. 1948). The Annual Report for 1911 of the N.Y. State Library lists its principal holdings previous to the Capitol fire, with information as to what was salvaged. The Annual Reports beginning with 1928 contain, in the section "Manuscripts and History," descriptions of principal accessions.

ANGELICA

Angelica Free Library.

Holdings: 108 items, 1794-1866, including 19 vols. of business records, 1802-66, and records of some land grants in Georgia, 1794-95 (68 certificates and related maps).

See Hist. Records Survey, Guide for N.Y. State, p. 49.

ANNANDALE-ON-HUDSON

Bard College Library. Marion E. Vosburgh, Librarian.

Holdings: 3 boxes (more than 525 pieces), 1707-1938, consisting of letters, business papers, and documents of the Bard family and of St. Stephen's College. Included is correspondence of Peter Bard (N.J.; judge), 1679-1734; John Bard (N.Y.; physician), 1716-99; Samuel Bard (N.Y.; physician), 1742-1821; William Bard (N.Y.; pioneer in life insurance), 1778-1853; and John Bard (N.Y.; founder of Bard College), 1819-99. The business records, besides family accounts, chiefly concern land in Dutchess County. The St. Stephen's College papers, 1860-1938, include letters and documents relating to the history of the college.

AUBURN

Cayuga County Historical Society. Cayuga Museum of History and Art. Walter K. Long, Director.

Holdings: A small collection of 18th and 19th century manuscripts, relating chiefly to western New York. Included are records concerning the Susquehanna Indians and some Iroquois tribes, commissioners' reports on Indian affairs, and studies of Indian linguistics; some journals and other records relating to the expedition led by John Sullivan (N.H.; Rev. War officer) against the Iroquois, 1779, in which New York militia under George Clinton (N.Y.; Rev. War officer, Gov.) participated; church histories for Auburn and Cayuga County and session records of Congregational churches, 1803-36; and an important collection of medical records beginning in 1806.

See Hist. Records Survey, Guide for N.Y. State, p. 50.

BABYLON

Babylon Library Association.

Holdings: Attorneys' account books relating to legal business in New York City and Long Island towns, 1869-83 (2 vols.).

See Hist. Records Survey, Guide for N.Y. State, p. 51.

BATAVIA

Holland Land Office Museum. West Main St.

Holdings: 40 vols. and 103 pieces, 1784-1889, relating chiefly to western New York. Included are Holland Land Co. records, 1801-69 (39 vols.), including records of the trust company that took over its affairs in 1837.

See Hist. Records Survey, Guide for N.Y. State, pp. 54-56.

BOONVILLE

Erwin Library. Mrs. George Traffarn, Librarian.

Holdings: 20,000 items, 1820-1923, chiefly official records of Boonville, and records of the Erwin Library and Institute, 1866-1906.

See Hist. Records Survey, Guide for N.Y. State, p. 57.

BROCKPORT

State Teachers College. (Mrs.) Mary
Lee McCrory, Librarian.

Holdings: 202 pieces, 1861-1903,
relating chiefly to a New York cavalry
company in the Civil War.
See Hist. Records Survey, Guide
for N. Y. State, p. 59.

BROOKLYN 25

Brooklyn Botanic Garden Library.
1000 Washington Ave. Marie G.
Giasi, Librarian.

Holdings: 700 letters, 1600-1940,
written by distinguished botanists and
other scientists.
See Hist. Records Survey, Guide
for New York City, p. 17.

BROOKLYN 38

Brooklyn Museum Library. Eastern
Parkway. William B. Walker, Librarian.

Holdings: A large quantity of Egyptian papyri, including 17 Aramaic documents of the 5th century B. C.; 10
Persian manuscripts; some medieval
and Renaissance manuscripts, 11th-
16th centuries (14 vols. and 7 maps);
and a number of East Indian, Japanese,
Mexican, and other manuscripts. There
are also papers of Gustavus Seyffarth
(Germany, N. Y.; archeologist, Egyptologist), 1826-29 (15 vols. of recorded Egyptian inscriptions); and many papers of Charles Edwin Wilbour (N. Y.;
Egyptologist), 1880-96.
See Hist. Records Survey, Guide
for New York City, pp. 18-20; and De
Ricci, Census, pp. 1193-1196.

BROOKLYN 17

Brooklyn Public Library. Francis R.

St. John, Chief Librarian.

Holdings: A small collection,
1752 to date. Included are local
church and business records, law papers, documents relating to transportation, and a hotel register; papers of
Benjamin De Casseres (N. Y.; author,
critic), among them 138 letters from
Henry Louis Mencken (Md.; author,
editor, critic), 1933-42; and letters
and miscellaneous papers of late
19th-century and 20th-century British and American authors (383
pieces).

BROOKLYN 16

Library of the Medical Society of
the County of Kings. 1313 Bedford
Ave. Wesley Draper, Librarian.

Holdings: 127 vols., chiefly 19th
and 20th centuries, relating to medicine. Included are a collection of
Willard Parker (N. Y.; surgeon), consisting of case records and notes on
medical topics, 1836-69 (25 vols.);
manuscripts on various medical
subjects by members of the Society
and others, dating from the Civil
War (60 vols.); and minute books of
the Society, since 1882.
See Hist. Records Survey, Guide
for New York City, p. 54.

BROOKLYN 1

Long Island Historical Society. 128
Pierrepont St. Helen P. Bolman,
Librarian.

Holdings: A collection relating
chiefly to Long Island and the early
history of the United States. Included are 123 letters of George Washington (Va.; Rev. War Commander in
Chief, U. S. Pres.); small quantities
of papers of some other distinguished

men of the Revolutionary and early national periods; genealogical materials, relating chiefly to Long Island families; and papers relating to American Indians, 1659-1885 (52 pieces).

See Hist. Records Survey, Guide for New York City, p. 50.

BUFFALO 16

Buffalo Historical Society. Delaware Park. Lester W. Smith, Chief of Research.

Holdings: 250 vols. and 250,000 pieces, since 1767, relating chiefly to Buffalo and the Niagara frontier. Included are papers of William Insco Buchanan (Ohio, Iowa, N.Y.; businessman, diplomat), 1899-1901 (18 vols.), consisting of his correspondence as Director-General of the Pan American Exposition; the Cary family, 1804-1923 ($2\frac{2}{3}$ linear ft.), consisting of papers of Trumbull Cary (N.Y.; Batavia banker, businessman) and his descendents; Grover Cleveland (N.Y.; Gov., U.S. Pres.), 75 pieces; Millard Fillmore (N.Y.; U.S. Rep., U.S. Pres.), 1849-53 (44 vols.), consisting of letters received as Vice President and President, and 200 pieces of earlier and later materials relating to him; Norman E. Mack (N.Y.; Buffalo newspaper publisher, member of Democratic National Committee), 1908-32 ($1\frac{2}{3}$ linear ft.), including correspondence with William Jennings Bryan, Alfred E. Smith, Franklin D. Roosevelt, Cordell Hull, and others; Peter Buell Porter (N.Y.; U.S. Rep., War of 1812 officer, Sec. War), 1809-44 (1,358 pieces), including 200 letters from and to Henry Clay (Ky., U.S. Rep. and Sen., Sec. State); the Sawyer family, 1840-1919 ($1\frac{2}{3}$ linear ft.), consisting of papers of James D. Sawyer (N.Y.; Buffalo businessman) and his descendants; Henry Randolph Storrs (N.Y.; U.S. Rep.), 1825-30 (6 vols.); and

Francis Adrian Van der Kemp (N.Y.; author), 1788-1829 (10 vols.). There are also Holland Land Co. papers, 1792-1829 (40 vols. and 200 pieces), including correspondence of Joseph Ellicott (Md., N.Y.; engineer, land agent, founder of Buffalo); records concerning Great Lakes shipping, 1776-1892 (1,100 pieces in the Van Cleve and Dobbins papers); several collections relating to Indians, 1797-1862 (400 pieces), including a manuscript Iroquois grammar compiled by Eleazer Williams (N.Y., Wis.; Episcopal missionary); Presbyterian and Baptist church records, 1812-81 (20 vols.); public records of Buffalo and Erie County, 1812-92 (3,500 pieces); records of the United States-Canada boundary survey, 1816-27 (217 pieces); records concerning the War of 1812, the Civil War (500 pieces), and the Fenian raid on Canada; and records of the Historical Records Survey, 1936-41 (13 linear ft.), consisting of uncompleted product materials of the Survey in western New York.

See Hist. Records Survey, Guide for N.Y. State, pp. 60-65; Allison, Inventory, p. 94; and Augustus H. Shearer, "Resources in Buffalo for the Study of American History," in Bibliographical Society of America, Papers, 16:6-9 (1922). Volume 14 of the Society's Publications contains a detailed catalog of its manuscripts, compiled to 1911.

BUFFALO 1

D'Youville College Library. 320 Porter Ave. Sister St. Ruth, Librarian.

Holdings: 2 vols. and 38 letters, 1842-1936, consisting of correspondence and other papers of John Timon (N.Y.; Bishop of Buffalo), 1847-65 (1 vol.); a work in Latin by William Turner (N.Y.; Bishop of Buffalo), 1891-92 (1 vol.); and letters to Edgar Wadhams (N.Y.; Bishop of Ogdensburg), 1842-65 (38 items).

See Hist. Records Survey, Guide for N.Y. State, p. 67.

BUFFALO 2

Grosvenor Reference Division, Buffalo and Erie County Public Library. 383 Franklin St.   (Mrs.) Margaret M. Mott, Deputy Director.

Holdings: 315 vols. and 33,500 other items, 371 B.C.–A.D. 1940, consisting chiefly of materials relating to local and western New York history from 1812. These are manuscripts formerly in the Buffalo Public Library and the Grosvenor Library, which in 1954 combined with the Erie County Library to form the present institution. Included are letters to William Farquhar Barry (U.S. Army officer), 1839-86 (50 items); records kept by a physician, 1818-52 (15 vols.); several diaries; autograph collections of letters of persons prominent in Europe and the United States, including some U.S. Presidents; and literary manuscripts of several English and American authors. Records relating chiefly to western New York churches and genealogy include original and copied records of many churches; copies of tombstone inscriptions; genealogical data for families prominent in the region; and copies of vital records of some towns in Vermont, New Hampshire, Connecticut, and Kentucky. There are also medieval and Renaissance manuscripts (5 vols. and 28 pieces), and some Near Eastern, Far Eastern, and French manuscripts, 371 B.C.–A.D. 1770.

See Hist. Records Survey, Guide for N.Y. State, pp. 65-74; and De Ricci, Census, pp. 1208-1212.

BUFFALO 14

University of Buffalo Library. 3435 Main St. Charles D. Abbott, Director of Libraries.

Holdings: A modern poetry collection, chiefly of printed items, but including sets of worksheet manuscripts showing poems in their various stages toward completion from first draft to final version, and some letters of contemporary English and American poets. The collection contains the "Paris Library" of James Joyce (Ireland; author); the Sylvia Beach Collection of James Joyce; the notebooks of Dylan Thomas (Great Britain; poet); and a large Robert Graves (Great Britain; author) manuscript collection, as well as considerable holdings of other celebrated authors.

See introduction by Charles D. Abbott to Poets at Work, pp. 1-36 (1948).

CALEDONIA

Big Springs Historical Society.

Holdings: 119 vols. and 700 pieces, 1812-1911, relating chiefly to the town and vicinity. Included are records of a general store, 1819-78 (100 vols. and 275 pieces); railroad and express company papers, 1836-75 (250 items); papers relating to the Erie and Genesee Valley canals, 1840-78 (125 items); and records kept by a local physician, 1872-1911 (19 vols.).

See Hist. Records Survey, Guide for N.Y. State, p. 74.

—oOo—

Caledonia Library Association. Mary Elliott Boyd, Librarian.

Holdings: A small quantity of papers, 1805-1909, chiefly pertaining to the town and vicinity. Included are records of general stores and a sawmill, 1805-59 (16 vols.); records of several local organizations; some marriage records, 1833-43; and assessment rolls, 1807-48, for Caledonia, LeRoy, and Geneseo.

See Hist. Records Survey, Guide for N. Y. State, p. 76.

CANANDAIGUA

Ontario County Historical Society.
Mrs. Ralph O. Stratton, Curator.

Holdings: 1,000 vols. and 4,000 pieces, 1764-1874, relating chiefly to Ontario County and western New York. Included are important papers of the land promoters, Oliver Phelps (Mass., N. Y.; merchant, Rev. War officer, U. S. Rep.) and Nathaniel Gorham (Mass.; businessman, Pres. of Continental Cong.), 1784-1818 (200 pieces); papers pertaining to the land purchases of Sir William Pulteney, 1791-1854 (350 items); and daybooks of Charles Williamson (England, N. Y.; land promoter, British agent in America), 1801-3 (3 vols.). There are also materials relating to the Iroquois, 1764-1847 (6 vols. and 28 pieces). Other records include those of several towns in Ontario County, 1796-1865, and records of an academy, churches, and other organizations in the county, 1795-1874. In the land papers mentioned above and in a collection of miscellaneous materials are a number of letters of Robert Morris (Pa.; financier, Member Continental Cong., U. S. Sen.) and documents relating to him, 1790-98.

See Hist. Records Survey, Guide for N. Y. State, pp. 77-81.

CANTON

St. Lawrence University Museum.

Holdings: 41 vols. and 13,500 pieces, relating chiefly to the University and St. Lawrence County. Included are University archives (18 vols. and 5,000 pieces); and papers of Silas Wright (N. Y.; lawyer, U. S. Rep. and Sen., Gov.), 1 vol. and 50 pieces, largely personal correspondence.

See Hist. Records Survey, Guide for N. Y. State, Supplement, pp. 1-3.

CENTER MORICHES

Museum, Manor of St. George.
Box 517. Chester G. Osborne, Curator of Manuscripts.

Holdings: 5,000 items, 1658-1954, relating chiefly to New York State and numerous members of the Tangier Smith family of the Manor of St. George, among them William Smith, known as Tangier Smith (N. Y.; colonial chief justice), 60 items, William Smith (N. Y.; Rev. War statesman), 100 items, and John Smith (N. Y.; U. S. Rep. and Sen.), 50 items.

CHATHAM

Chatham Public Library. (Mrs.) Margaret T. Hartigan, Librarian.

Holdings: 5 vols. and 16 pieces, 1860-1940, consisting chiefly of records of local temperance, literary, Sunday school, and civic societies.

See Hist. Records Survey, Guide for N. Y. State, p. 83.

CLINTON

Hamilton College Library. Walter Pilkington, Librarian.

Holdings: 175 vols. and 35,000

pieces, chiefly 1763 to date. Included
are papers of Henry Davis (Conn., Vt.,
N.Y.; clergyman, pres. of Middlebury
and Hamilton Colleges), 1800-35 (100
pieces); Samuel Kirkland (Conn., N.Y.;
missionary to Oneida Indians, founder
of Hamilton College), 1763-1807 (25
vols. and 646 pieces), including 25 diaries and 633 letters, many of them to
and from prominent men of his time;
Edward North (Conn., N.Y.; educator,
classicist), 1814-1902 (3,500 pieces),
comprising correspondence with Hamilton College alumni; Ezra Pound (N.Y.,
Europe; poet), since 1885; Clinton
Scollard (N.Y.; poet, educator), 1881-
1932 (25 vols. and 1,049 pieces), including some manuscript poems; and
Alexander Woollcott (N.Y.; critic,
journalist), 1887-1943 (200 pieces).
There are also the Hamilton College
collection, 1812 to date (100 vols.),
and several thousand journals, letters,
and account books relating chiefly to
central New York. Included too are
Renaissance manuscripts (2 vols. and
1 piece).

See Hist. Records Survey, Guide
for N.Y. State, p. 85; and De Ricci,
Census, p. 1221.

COBLESKILL

Cobleskill Public Library.

Holdings: 8 vols. and 8 pieces,
1933-39, chiefly copies of church records, 1774-1928, and town records,
1797-1812; and compilations of cemetery inscriptions and vital records
from family Bibles of Schoharie
County.

See Hist. Records Survey, Guide
for N.Y. State, p. 86.

CONSTABLEVILLE

Constable Hall. Mrs. H. D. Cornwall, President.

Holdings: Correspondence and numerous other papers of the Constable
family, late 18th and early 19th centuries, relating chiefly to New York
City business and social life. These
are mainly papers of William Constable (Pa., N.Y.; Rev. War officer,
merchant, land promoter). Included
are business letters from his partner,
Gouverneur Morris (N.Y.; Member
Continental Cong., diplomat), written
from France during the French Revolution; letters concerning business and
land transactions in northern New
York; and commercial letters and records from Europe and the West Indies addressed to New York merchants, 1790-1805 (104 pieces). There
are also lists of prices prevailing in
Marseilles, Bordeaux, Nantes, and
Liverpool, 1790-1805, and descriptions of market conditions at those
cities.

COOPERSTOWN

National Baseball Hall of Fame and
Museum. Sid C. Keener, Director.

Holdings: 8 vols., 6 boxes, and
other items, from 1861, relating
chiefly to baseball. Included are papers of Abner Doubleday (U.S. Army
officer, creator of the modern game
of baseball) and his wife, 1861-93 (1
box); correspondence of Abraham G.
Mills (N.Y.; pres. of National League
of Professional Baseball Clubs),
1883-84 (8 vols.); numerous score
books kept and donated by sports
writers and fans; early contracts
signed by some of the game's great
players; and many photographs.

—oOo—

New York State Historical Association and Farmers' Museum. Fenimore House. Dorothy C. Barck,
Librarian.

Holdings: 1,600 vols. and 107,000 pieces, principally 1750-1850, relating chiefly to agriculture, land holdings, small businesses and handicraft, schools, churches, and turnpikes of upstate New York and Otsego County.

Included are papers of Robert W. Chambers (N.Y.; novelist), 1901-30 (3 boxes); Lewis S. Chase (N.Y.; express and forwarding business), 1856-87 (3 boxes); George Clarke (N.Y.; colonial official, landowner) and his family, 1704-1887 (3 chests); William Cooper (N.J., N.Y.; landowner, judge, U.S. Rep.) and his family, 1790-1851 (70 pieces), including some literary manuscripts of his son James Fenimore Cooper (N.Y.; novelist), Zenas and Clifford France (N.Y.; Schoharie County hop dealers), 1870-1900 (25 vols. and 20 boxes); Hard and Peck, later George I. Peck and G. Clayton Peck (N.Y.; general storekeepers in New Lisbon), 1825-74 (32 account books, 20 inventories, and 11 boxes of invoices); John Holmes Prentiss (N.Y.; publisher, U.S. Rep.), 1837-60 (61 letters) plus family deeds and documents; Alvan Stewart (N.Y.; lawyer, antislavery reformer), 1 box of letters and biographical materials collected by his son-in-law Luther R. Marsh; Charles Stewart (N.J.; Rev. War officer, Member Continental Cong.), 1752-1800 (14 boxes); Charles Samuel Stewart (U.S. Navy Chaplain), 1822-41 (3 boxes), diaries and letters; Joel Turrill (N.Y.; judge) and his family, 1791-1874 (1 box); William Peter Van Ness (N.Y.; U.S. dist. court judge), relating to the Burr-Hamilton duel (35 items); and Reuben Hyde Walworth (N.Y.; U.S. Rep., State chancellor), 1827-66 (17 vols.), chiefly legal papers.

There are papers of families of New York State, among them Barber, of Washington County, 1762-1896 (2 boxes), Collins and Merriam, 1786-1922 (30 vols. and 11 boxes), Frey of Montgomery County, 1716-1914 (7 boxes), Hale of Elizabethtown, 1837-77 (3 boxes), Oatwell of New York City, 1815-99 (2 boxes), Otis of Onondaga County (1 box), and Putnam of Saratoga County, 1793-1869 (2 boxes). Present also are account books of farmers, general storekeepers, blacksmiths, weavers, and others, 1750-1885 (450 vols.); records of some schools and churches in Otsego County; and records of the Otsego County Bank, Cooperstown, 1830-65 (128 vols.).

See Hist. Records Survey, Guide for N.Y. State, pp. 88-92, and its Supplement, pp. 3-5; listings and notices in N.Y. History, 1951-55; annual reports of the Association in N.Y. History, 1951 to date; and Forest History Sources, p. 86.

CORNING

Corning Museum of Glass Library, Corning Glass Center. Paul N. Perrot, Assistant Director.

Holdings: 11 vols. and 34 documents, from the 12th to the 19th centuries, relating chiefly to glass but including some miscellaneous Renaissance manuscripts. There are ordinances and other documents of the Guild of Glaziers and Plumbers, York, England, 1598-1742 (2 vols.); formulas for glass used at the Glass House at Clyde, N.Y., and elsewhere, 1815-47 (1 vol.); and miscellaneous documents relating to the history of glassmaking.

CORTLAND

Cortland County Historical Society. County Court House. Mrs. Donald N. Elder, Executive Secretary.

Holdings: 450 vols. and 1,000 pieces, 1623-1950, relating chiefly

to Cortland and Cortland County. Included is a large collection concerning
Francis Bicknell Carpenter (N. Y.; portrait painter); account books of local
businesses, 1809-99 (150 vols.); town
and country records, 1794-1943 (125
original records, and 64 vols. and 330
folders of copies); vital records for all
towns in the county (copied), 1798-1950
(20 vols.); church records, 1799-1927
(20 vols. and other copied); school records, 1815-1943 (20 vols. and others
copied); genealogical materials compiled from records dating from 1623
(10 vols. and 310 folders); compiled records of Revolutionary War soldiers
from Cortland County; and records of
men and women in service in World
War II and the Korean conflict and of
civilian defense activities in Cortland
(64 folders).
   See Hist. Records Survey, Guide
for N. Y. State, p. 92.

COXSACKIE

Greene County Historical Society, Inc.
Bronck House. Mrs. Lester R. Smith,
Historian, 77 Summit Ave., Catskill.

   Holdings: 121 vols. and 20 bundles
of papers, 1636-1901, chiefly relating
to Greene County and New York State.
Manuscripts formerly in the Catskill
Public Library have been transferred
to the Society. Included are transcripts
of church records, 1652-1891, of genealogical interest for Greene and neighboring counties; papers relating to litigation, mortgages, and leases, 1703-
1901 (19 bundles); a few official records of Coxsackie and Greene County,
1775-1842 (2 vols. and 1 piece); and account books, 1800-75 (11 vols.), 4 of
which are of a general store in Catskill.
   See Hist. Records Survey, Guide
for N. Y. State, pp. 82 and 94-98.

EAST HAMPTON

East Hampton Free Library. 159

Main St. (Mrs.) Amy O. Brassford,
Librarian.

   Holdings: A small quantity of
court records, dating from 1661, including records of the Sessions Court
at Southampton, N. Y., 1661-78 (1
vol.), and books of justices of the
peace; and other papers in the Long
Island Collection.
   See Richard B. Morris, Early
American Court Records, p. 18
(1941).

—oOo—

Home Sweet Home Museum. 14
James Lane. Edward M. B. Strong,
Curator.

   Holdings: 40 pieces, 1813-51,
consisting chiefly of letters by John
Howard Payne (N. Y.; playwright,
actor, U S. consul at Tunis).

EAST MEADOW

Nassau County Historical Museum
and Library. Nassau County Park.
Edward J. Smits, Assistant Curator.

   Holdings: 10,000 pieces, 1660-
1960, relating chiefly to the Nassau
County area of Long Island. Included
are 5,000 photostats and other pieces
collected by a former county historian; records of local organizations,
18th and 19th centuries; family papers and genealogical materials; and
account books.

EDEN

Eden Free Library.

   Holdings: 2 vols., comprising
records of a temperance society,
1842-46, and a Shakespeare club,

1899-1904.

See Hist. Records Survey, Guide for N.Y. State, p. 102.

ELLENVILLE

Ellenville Public Library. 126 Canal St. (Mrs.) Dorothy H. Sanderson, Library Director.

Holdings: 1 vol. and 8 pieces, 1836-59, relating to a local glass company; copies of papers relating to the Delaware and Hudson Canal Co., and a collection of pictures of the canal; some Civil War material; and a few miscellaneous letters.

See Hist. Records Survey, Guide for N.Y. State, p. 103.

ELMIRA

Chemung County Historical Society, Inc. 425 East Market St. Clark Wilcox, Chemung County Historian.

Holdings: 94 vols. and 4,702 items, 1592-1935, relating chiefly to Elmira and Chemung County. Included are a logbook kept on the Peary Arctic Expedition, 1906 (1 vol.); mercantile and other business records, 1783-1874 (8 vols. and 125 pieces); miscellaneous military papers, 1779-1918, including records relating to the expedition led by John Sullivan (N.H.; Rev. War officer) against the Indians in 1779 (5 vols. and many loose papers); other material on the Indians of the area; Civil War letters and diaries; and records of various lodges and other organizations, 1793-1925, including complete records of clubs that were the origin of the 4-H clubs. There are also materials concerning Samuel L. Clemens, better known as Mark Twain (Mo., Calif., N.Y., Conn.; novelist, humorist), and some 3,000 biographies of citizens of the county.

See Hist. Records Survey, Guide for N.Y. State, pp. 103-106.

—oOo—

Elmira College Library. College and West Washington Aves. Anne J. Morse, Librarian.

Holdings: 12 vols. and 53 pieces, chiefly relating to the College. Included are archives of the College, 1855-77 (10 vols. and 17 pieces); and some musical scores and other papers of Charles Tomlinson Griffes (N.Y.; composer, pianist, teacher), 2 vols. and 36 pieces.

See Hist. Records Survey, Guide for N.Y. State, p. 106.

FONDA

Department of History and Archives. Old Courthouse, Railroad St.

Holdings: 170 vols. and 475 linear ft., 1560-1940, relating chiefly to Montgomery and Tryon Counties. Included are some official county records, 1742-1847 (5 vols. and 12,606 pieces); church records, 1734-1940 (64 vols.), including records of many Dutch Reformed churches; copies of cemetery records for several counties (9 vols.); genealogical records (compiled) for early county families, 16th century and later (3 file drawers); copies of town and village records, 1783-1934 (66 vols.); and copies of various manuscripts, 1665-1936 (24 vols. and several pieces), among them a 2-vol. "life" of Eleazer Williams (N.Y., Wis.; Episcopal missionary to the Indians), and the "private canal journal" of DeWitt Clinton (N.Y.; member N.Y. canal commission, Gov.), July-Aug. 1810 (1 vol.).

See Hist. Records Survey, Guide for N.Y. State, pp. 109-114.

FORT JOHNSON

Sir William Johnson Mansion.

Holdings: 4 vols. and 250 pieces, 1763-1889, relating chiefly to the surrounding territory. Included are military records, 1763-1889 (67 items), chiefly concerning the Revolution and the Civil War; and other records, 1717-1859 (1 vol. and 112 pieces), of or pertaining to persons prominent in New York State.
See Hist. Records Survey, Guide for N. Y. State, pp. 114-116.

FORT TICONDEROGA

Fort Ticonderoga Museum. Eleanor Murray, Curator and General Manager.

Holdings: 30 vols. and 300 pieces, 1736-1837, relating chiefly to military affairs in the area. Included are orderly books, 1175-78 (25 vols.), relating to Fort Ticonderoga and other forts and encampments; and other records, 1736-1837 (3 vols. and 250 pieces), some of which concern persons prominent in the French and Indian War and in the Revolution. There are also personal and business papers, including 3 vols., 1765-87, containing 500 pieces of correspondence and other papers of Philip Skene (N. Y.; merchant, founder of Skenesborough, now Whitehall).
See Hist. Records Survey, Guide for N. Y. State, p. 116.

FREDONIA

Darwin R. Barker Library. (Mrs.) Edna G. Dawley, Librarian.

Holdings: 23 vols. and 2,120 pieces, chiefly relating to Fredonia. Included are records of a local normal school, 1820-69 (3 vols. and 2 pieces); records of library, temperance, and other associations of the town, 1832-1906; church histories; and cemetery reports.
See Hist. Records Survey, Guide for N. Y. State, pp. 117-120.

GENESEO

Livingston County Historical Society.

Holdings: 500 items, 1764-1884, relating chiefly to the history of the county. Included are some early county, town, and school records, 1790-1871 (3 vols. and 60 items). There are also some maps, chiefly of railroad, stagecoach, and canal routes.
See Hist. Records Survey, Guide for N. Y. State, p. 122.

GENEVA

Hobart and William Smith Colleges Library. Elizabeth Thalman, Librarian.

Holdings: Several hundred items, 1798-1937, consisting chiefly of archives of the Colleges and their predecessors, Geneva Academy and Geneva College. These include charters, minutes, letters from alumni, and records of student societies. There are also a few papers of James Rood Doolittle (N. Y., Wis.; lawyer, U. S. Sen. from Wis.); papers of Benjamin Hale (Mass., N. Y.; scientist, Hobart College pres.), 1836-60 (12 vols. and 400 pieces); an unpublished history of Geneva, 1879 (4 vols.); and ornithological notes of the Long Island area (1 vol.).
See Hist. Records Survey, Guide for N. Y. State, pp. 123-125.

GLENS FALLS

Crandall Library. City Park. Leonard J. Freiser, Librarian.

Holdings: 70 vols. and 1,500 pieces, 1746 to date, relating chiefly to the town and nearby area. Included are some military papers of the Civil War period.
See Hist. Records Survey, Guide for N. Y. State, p. 126.

GLOVERSVILLE

Gloversville Free Public Library. 58 East Fulton St.

Holdings: 125 vols. and 150 items, 1796-1931, relating chiefly to Fulton County. Included are diaries, sermons, letters, and other papers of Elisha Yale (N. Y.; Congregational minister), 1803-54 (110 vols. and 100 other pieces).
See Hist. Records Survey, Guide for N. Y. State, pp. 127-129.

GOSHEN

Goshen Library and Historical Society. 203 Main St. Harry Hawkins Smith, Curator.

Holdings: A substantial collection, dating from about 1700, and chiefly relating to Goshen and Orange County. Included are papers of many families, among them the Seward family, including William Henry Seward (N. Y.; Gov., U. S. Sen., Sec. State); the Wickham family, including George D. Wickham (N. Y.; banker); and the Wilkin family, including James W. Wilkin (N. Y.; U. S. Rep.). There are also an account book of Henry Wisner (N. Y.; Member Continental Cong., powder manufacturer), 1777; other material relating to the Revolutionary War; some letters

of Alfred Neafie (N. Y.; Civil War officer), 1864; and miscellaneous letters, deeds, commissions, and other papers.
See Hist. Records Survey, Guide for N. Y. State, pp. 129-131.

GRANVILLE

Pember Library and Museum. Nellie B. Sheeler, Librarian.

Holdings: 7 vols. and 18 pieces, 1832-1935, relating chiefly to Granville and Washington County. Included are records of a Presbyterian church, 1782-1846 (6 vols. and 4 pieces); and an autograph collection, 1832-96 (1 vol.), of letters and documents signed by well known men.
See Hist. Records Survey, Guide for N. Y. State, p. 131.

HAMILTON

Colgate University Archives. Howard D. Williams, Archivist.

Holdings: 200 vols. and 175 boxes, 1756 to date, chiefly relating to the University and its administrators, faculty, students, and alumni. Included are records of the Baptist Education Society of the State of New York, 1822-1925 (12 vols. and 50 boxes); and letters exchanged between Charles Evans Hughes (N. Y.; Gov., U. S. Chief Justice) and his parents while he was a student at Colgate (then Madison) University, 1876-78 (77 pieces).
See Hist. Records Survey, Guide for N. Y. State, p. 133.

HEMPSTEAD

Hempstead Public Library. (Mrs.) Olga S. Bida, Acting Library

Director.

Holdings: 35 items, 1710-1889,
relating chiefly to Hempstead. Included are church and cemetery records
(some copied), 1805-89; and account
books of a physician, 1831-53.
See Hist. Records Survey, Guide
for N.Y. State, p. 138.

HERKIMER

Herkimer County Historical Society.
(Mrs.) Hazel C. Patrick, Secretary.

Holdings: A small collection, 18th
and 19th centuries, relating chiefly to
the county. Included are records (19
vols. and several pieces) of Fairfield
Academy and the successor College of
Physicians and Surgeons of the Western
District of New York, containing some
information about Asa Gray (N.Y.,
Mass.; botanist, Harvard Univ. prof.).
The Society is reported to have some
of the material once belonging to the
Ilion Free Public Library but not, ap-
parently, the records of the firm founded by Eliphalet Remington.
See Hist. Records Survey, Guide
for N.Y. State, pp. 138-140, and 150.

HOLLAND PATENT

Holland Patent Free Library.

Holdings: 5 vols. and 24 pieces,
1805-1934, relating chiefly to the locality. Included are a few school records, 1816-1934; and daybooks of a
blacksmith, 1805-10, and a physician,
1879-85 (2 vols.).
See Hist. Records Survey, Guide
for N.Y. State, p. 140.

HORNELL

Hornell Public Library. 64 Genesee

St. Mary P. Lester, Librarian.

Holdings: 2 vols. and 125 pieces,
1833-72, chiefly of local interest.
Included are weather reports, 1833-
68 (2 vols.); and letters concerning
lecture courses, 1859-72 (125 pieces), some bearing signatures of well
known persons.
See Hist. Records Survey, Guide
for N.Y. State, p. 142.

HUDSON

Hendrick Hudson Chapter Museum.
113 Warren St. Maude M. Benson,
Custodian.

Holdings: 17 vols. and 66 pieces,
1778-1902, relating chiefly to the history of the town and its vicinity. Included are the directory and bylaws
of the Proprietors of Hudson, 1784 (1
vol.); ships' cargo manifests, 1739-
44 (3 vols.); a logbook of a voyage
from London to Cape Horn, 1802-7;
the letter book of a merchant, 1782-
83; minutes of the Infants School Society, 1829-32 (1 vol.); and some
census records.
See Hist. Records Survey, Guide
for N.Y. State, pp. 142-144.

HUNTINGTON

Huntington Historical Society. High
St. and New York Ave. (Mrs.)
Elaine W. Walker, Librarian.

Holdings: 600 items, 1668-1932,
relating chiefly to Huntington and Suffolk County. Included are records of
a Presbyterian church, from 1723,
and an Episcopal church, from 1748;
a few records and several histories
of other local churches; a mercantile
collection, 19th century, including
account books of general stores (4
vols.), a sawmill, and a tombstone

maker (3 vols.); records concerning coastal shipping between New York and Sag Harbor, 1801-6; minutes of a local lyceum, 1867-68 (1 vol.); minutes of the Citizen's League, 1897-1904 (several vols.); Suffolk County census records, 1850-70; genealogical records (copied), including church, cemetery, and family Bible records (6 vols.); two collections of family records, including wills, deeds, and other papers, and a group of meteorological records, 1807-53; and several manuscript maps. There are also scattered military papers of the Revolutionary War, the War of 1812, and the Civil War; and complete service records of Huntington citizens in World Wars I and II.

See Hist. Records Survey, Guide for N. Y. State, p. 144.

—oOo—

Huntington Public Library. Stanley A. Ransom, Director.

Holdings: 7 vols. and a few pieces, relating chiefly to Huntington and Long Island. Included are a few pieces concerning Walt Whitman (N. Y., D. C., N. J.; poet); and records of a subscription library in Huntington in 1759.

See Hist. Records Survey, Guide for N. Y. State, pp. 145-147.

HYDE PARK

Franklin D. Roosevelt Library. Herman Kahn, Director.

Holdings: 7,600 cu. ft. of papers, 1535-1958, organized into 51 distinct groups. Two-thirds of the total are papers of Franklin D. Roosevelt (N.Y.; Gov., U.S. Pres.) and Mrs. Franklin D. Roosevelt. The remaining 2,500 cu. ft. are the papers, complete or fragmentary, of 62 nationally significant persons and organizations asso-

ciated with Franklin D. Roosevelt in the period 1920-45. Additional papers are constantly being received.

One manuscript group consists of papers of various antecedent members and branches of the Roosevelt family, 1535-1941 (32 cu. ft.), including a large quantity of papers of the Delano family. Papers of Franklin D. Roosevelt himself constitute the following 9 manuscript groups: papers relating to family, business, and other personal affairs, 1882-1945 (30 cu. ft.); general political correspondence, 1920-28 (3 cu. ft.); papers as N. Y. State senator, 1910-13 (12 cu. ft.), and as Assistant Secretary of the Navy, 1913-20 (45 cu. ft.); papers as Vice-Presidential candidate, 1920 (5 cu. ft.); papers pertaining to the campaign of 1924 (8 cu. ft.), and to that of 1928 (6 cu. ft.); and papers as Governor of New York, 1929-32 (50 cu. ft.), and as President, 1933-45 (3,500 cu. ft.). Roosevelt's collections of historical manuscripts, 1630-1942 (60 cu. ft.), are chiefly in the fields of New York in the 18th century, including an important group of Livingston family papers, U. S. naval history, and miscellaneous historical autographs.

Papers of personal and political associates of President Roosevelt include those of John M. Carmody (Pa., D. C.; industrial executive, Administrator of Rural Electrification Administration and of Federal Works Agency), 1900-58 (72 cu. ft.); Morris L. Cooke (Pa.; power and water resources authority, U. S. Rural Electrification Administrator, chairman of Pres. Truman's Water Resources Policy Commission), 1910-54 (107 cu. ft.); Wayne Coy (Ind., D. C.; journalist, administrative assistant to Roosevelt, Federal Communications Commission member), 1934-57 (11 cu. ft.); Mary Williams Dewson (Mass., Maine; industrial economist, social worker, director of Women's

Division of Democratic National Committee, U.S. Social Security Board member), 1925-51 (7 cu. ft.); William D. Hassett (Vt., D.C.; newspaper reporter, White House Sec.), 1935-55 (13 cu. ft.); Harry L. Hopkins (Iowa, N.Y.; U.S. Works Progress Administrator, Sec. Commerce, Presidential counselor), 1928-46 (125 cu. ft.); Louis McHenry Howe (Mass.; Presidential assistant and personal sec.), 1913-36 (30 cu. ft.); Emil Hurja (Alaska, Tex., N.Y.; journalist, businessman, Executive Director of Democratic National Committee), 1912-52 (65 cu. ft.); Harley M. Kilgore (W. Va.; U.S. Sen.), 1941-56 (59 cu. ft.); R. Walton Moore (Va.; U.S. Rep., Asst. Sec. State), 1922-41 (12 cu. ft.); Henry Morgenthau, Jr. (N.Y.; U.S. Sec. Treas.), 1866-1948 (300 cu. ft.); Herbert C. Pell (N.Y.; U.S. Rep., Ambassador to Portugal and Hungary, member of United Nations Commission for Investigation of War Crimes), 1912-49 (15 cu. ft.); Anna Eleanor Roosevelt (N.Y.; chairman of the United Nations Commission on Human Rights, U.S. Representative to the United Nations General Assembly), 1933-57 (1,000 cu. ft.), chiefly her correspondence, 1933-45; James Roosevelt (Mass., Calif.; Administrative Assistant to Pres. Roosevelt, U.S. Rep.), 1937-44 (13 cu. ft.); Samuel I. Rosenman (N.Y.; counselor to Roosevelt, State supreme court judge), 1928-46 (21 cu. ft.); Charles W. Taussig (N.Y.; manufacturer, Caribbean expert), 1928-48 (45 cu. ft.); Myron C. Taylor (N.Y.; personal representative of Pres. Roosevelt to the Vatican), 1938-47 (5 cu. ft.), including material on Taylor's international work with the problem of political refugees; Elbert D. Thomas (Utah; political science prof. at Univ. of Utah, U.S. Sen.), 1907-50 (100 cu. ft.); Henry A. Wallace (Iowa, N.Y.; Sec. Agriculture, Vice Pres.), 1941-45 (37 cu. ft.); and John G. Winant (N.H.; Gov., director of International Labor Office, U.S. Social Security Board Chairman, Ambassador to Great Britain), 1916-47 (100 cu. ft.).

The State of New York has placed in the Library the official records of two State offices for the period of Roosevelt's governorship, 1929-32: the Office of the Governor (80 cu. ft.), comprising Roosevelt's official correspondence; and the Office of the Lieutenant Governor (25 cu. ft.), comprising the official correspondence of Lt. Gov. Herbert Lehman. Records of other organizations include those of the Democratic National Committee, 1928-48 (200 cu. ft.), and of its Women's Division, 1933-44 (60 cu. ft.); the Republican National Committee, 1929-48 (17 cu. ft.), consisting of the "information file" on Roosevelt; the Office of the Chief of White House Social Entertainments, 1933-45 (60 cu. ft.); the President's Committee on Administrative Management, 1936-37 (8 cu. ft.); the Good Neighbor League, 1936-39 (8 cu. ft.); the National Committee of Independent Voters for Roosevelt and Wallace, 1940 (8 cu. ft.); and Mrs. Roosevelt's Press Conference Association, 1942-45 (1 cu. ft.). The Library has small quantities of papers of many other organizations and persons associated with Roosevelt, 1913-45, and statements and reminiscences by some 100 persons concerning their knowledge of and relationship with him, 1889-1952 (6 cu. ft.).

See Annual Reports of the Archivist of the United States on the Franklin D. Roosevelt Library, 1939-49; Annual Reports on the National Archives and Records Service (from Administrator of General Services, Annual Reports), 1950 to date; and Herman Kahn, "World War II and Its Background: Research Materials at the Franklin D. Roosevelt Library and Policies Concerning Their Use," in Am. Archivist, 17:149-162 (Apr. 1954).

ITHACA

Collection of Regional History and Cornell University Archives, Cornell University Library. (Mrs.) Edith M. Fox, Curator and University Archivist.

Holdings: Millions of pieces, largely of the 19th and 20th centuries, relating chiefly to the University and western New York. The Cornell University Archives and the Collection of Regional History are housed and administered together, and the two are integrated in the description below.

Papers of administrators and the founder of the University include those of Liberty Hyde Bailey (Mich., N.Y.; botanist, dean of College of Agriculture), 1888-1953 (5 ft.); George Lincoln Burr (N.Y.; Cornell librarian, historian), 1862-1938 (33 boxes and 3 storage cases); Ezra Cornell (N.Y.; capitalist, Cornell founder), 1828-1936 (13 ft.), also letters to Cornell in other groups of papers; Thomas Frederick Crane (N.Y.; dean of the Arts College and the Univ. faculty), 1890-1918 (3½ ft.); Edmund Ezra Day (Mich., N.Y.; Cornell pres.), 1923-50 (64 ft.); Livingston Farrand (N.Y.; Cornell pres.), 1921-39 (7 boxes and 25 storage cases); Bernhard Eduard Fernow (Pa., D.C., N.Y., Canada; forester, Chief of Division of Forestry of the U.S. Dept. of Agriculture, organizer of Cornell School of Forestry and of Univ. of Toronto forestry dept.), 1885-1922 (2 ft.); Francis Miles Finch (N.Y.; jurist, poet, Cornell trustee), 1851-80 (5 vols. and 12 boxes); Ernest G. Merritt (N.Y.; physicist, dean of Graduate School), 1890-1940 (2½ ft.), including correspondence relating to U.S. antisubmarine devices and submarine detection; Veranus A. Moore (D.C., N.Y.; bacteriologist, pathologist, prof. at George Washington and Cornell Univs., dean of Cornell Veterinary College), 1870-1931 (61 ft.); Henry W. Sage (N.Y.; merchant, lumber magnate, Cornell trustee), 1837-1930 (75 ft.); Jacob Gould Schurman (N.Y.; Cornell pres., U.S. Minister to China and Ambassador to Germany), 1878-1942 (45 boxes), including correspondence with Charles Evans Hughes, Theodore Roosevelt, and other prominent men; Robert H. Thurston (R.I., N.Y.; director of College of Engineering), 1859-1902 (417 pieces); Andrew D. White (N.Y.; Cornell pres., U.S. Minister to Germany), 1845-1912 (102 ft.); J. Du Pratt White (N.Y.; lawyer, Cornell trustee), 1915-39 (20 ft.); and Josiah B. Williams (N.Y.; banker, businessman, Cornell trustee), 1809-83 (47 ft.), also papers of his wife, 1824-1911 (5 ft.).

Papers of Cornell professors include those of George F. Atkinson (N.Y.; botanist), 1880-1918 (6 ft.); Carl L. Becker (Kans., Minn., N.Y.; historian), 1898-1945 (6 ft. and 1 ft. of photostats); James Ernest Boyle (N.Y.; agricultural economist), 1894-1938 (16 ft.); Julian P. Bretz (N.Y.; historian), 1905-51 (9 ft.), including political correspondence; John H. Comstock (N.Y.; entomologist), 1885-94 (12 boxes of letters received); Hiram Corson (N.Y.; author, literature prof.), 1852-1946 (7 ft.); Robert E. Cushman (N.Y.; political scientist), 1940-45, a collection of materials relating to civil liberties in the United States (15 ft.); Alexander Drummond (N.Y.; speech and drama prof.), 1917-56 (23 ft.); Charles Love Durham (N.Y.; classicist), 1897-1949 (17 boxes); Albert Bernhardt Faust (Md., Conn., N.Y.; German prof.), 1919-45 (9½ ft.); Willard Fiske (N.Y.; journalist, librarian, educator, bibliophile), 1847-1903 (7 ft.); Bryant Fleming (N.Y.; landscape architect), sketches and blueprints (27 ft.); Simon Henry Gage (N.Y.; biologist), 1892-1940 (3 ft.); James Morgan Hart (Ohio, N.Y.;

philologist), 1856-1916 (5 ft.); Charles Henry Hull (N. Y.; historian), professional notes (1 box); James George Needham (N. Y.; biologist, entomology prof.), 1892-1956 (2 ft.); Hugh Daniel Reed (N. Y.; zoologist), 1900-6 (4 vols.), relating to bird watching; James Edward Rice (N. Y.; poultry husbandry prof.), 1885-1950 (55 ft.); Willard W. Rowlee (N. Y.; botanist), 1905-23 (238 pieces); Dwight Sanderson (N. Y.; entomologist with various States, rural sociology prof.), 1894-1943 (6 ft.); Goldwin Smith (England, N. Y., Canada; historian), 1820-1910 (30$^1/_2$ ft.), including much correspondence on political questions and international relations, with important Englishmen and Americans; Ralph Stockman Tarr (Mass., N. Y.; geologist, geographer), 1883-1912 (2$^1/_2$ ft.), including material on irrigation surveys in New Mexico, Arizona, and Montana, 1883-89; George F. Warren (N. Y.; agricultural economist, adviser to Pres. Franklin D. Roosevelt), 1900-39 (11 ft.); Herbert H. Whetzel (N. Y.; plant pathologist), 1902-44 (9$^1/_2$ ft.), including materials on mycological explorations in Bermuda and Puerto Rico; Burton Green Wilder (Mass., N.Y.; neurologist, zoologist), 1857-1924 (6$^1/_2$ ft.); and Henry Shaler Williams (Conn., N. Y.; paleontologist, geologist), 1879-1912 (15 ft.).

Papers of men holding State and Federal office, besides Schurman and White, mentioned earlier, include those of George Bancroft (Mass., N.Y.; historian, Sec. Navy, Minister to Great Britain and to Germany), 1811-1901 (5$^1/_2$ ft.), chiefly family and personal correspondence; Alonzo B. Cornell (N. Y.; Gov.), 1866-1902 (286 pieces); Ira Davenport (N. Y.; capitalist, U. S. Rep.) and his family, 1800-1931 (20 ft.), including much material on land and railroad investment; Simon Newton Dexter (N. Y.; capitalist, canal commissioner), 1793-1896 (29 boxes and 2 microfilm reels of letters), in-

cluding much material on the Erie Canal and cotton and woolen manufacturing; Alexander S. Diven (N. Y.; lawyer, U. S. Rep., Civil War officer, railroad promoter) and his son, 1849-1940 (1 vol. and 13 boxes), relating to railroads and lands; John Morgan Francis (N. Y.; editor, U. S. Minister to Portugal and Austria) and his son and grandson, 1874-1906 (12 vols. and 43 pieces); Irving M. Ives (N. Y.; State legislator, U.S. Sen.), 20th century (350 ft.); Francis Kernan (N. Y.; U. S. Rep. and Sen.) and his family, 1776-1922 (230 ft.); Daniel S. Lamont (N. Y.; financier, private sec. to Pres. Cleveland, Sec. War), 1860-87 (990 pieces); Bert Lord (N. Y.; State legislator, U. S. Rep.), 1913-14 (1$^1/_2$ ft.), relating to State and local politics; Joseph A. McGinnies (N. Y.; speaker of State assembly), 1925-41 (1 reel of microfilm); John Magee (N. Y.; U. S. Rep.), 1820-50 (76 pieces); Edwin B. Morgan (N. Y.; U. S. Rep.), 1849-54 (302 pieces); Justin S. Morrill (Vt.; U. S. Rep. and Sen.), 1828-1912 (6 ft.); S. Fred Nixon (N. Y.; speaker of State assembly), 1899-1958 (10 reels of microfilm); Daniel A. Reed (N. Y.; lawyer, U. S. Rep.), 1920-59 (100 ft.); Horatio Seymour (N. Y.; Gov.) and his family, 1741-1886 (12 vols. and 7 boxes); Julius A. Skilton (N. Y.; physician, journalist, businessman, U. S. consul gen. in Mexico), 1830-1910 (30 ft.); Francis E. Spinner (N. Y.; merchant, banker, U. S. Rep. and Treas.), 1823-73 (3 vols. and 724 pieces); Willard Straight (N. Y.; diplomat, Far Eastern specialist, financier, World War I Army officer), 1857-1922 (90 ft.); William Sulzer (N. Y.; U. S. Rep., Gov.), 1890-1940 (32 ft.); Hugh White (N. Y.; railroad builder, cement manufacturer, U. S. Rep.) and his family, 1750-1933 (19 ft.); and Diedrich Willers (N. Y.; sec. to Gov. Horatio Seymour, State legislator), 1826-1927 (2 vols. and

20 boxes).

Papers of other individuals include those of Howard Edward Babcock (N.Y.; agricultural organizer, executive, prof. of marketing at Cornell Univ.), 1905-50 (60 ft.), pertaining chiefly to the Farm Bureau Federation and the Grange League Federation; Thomas K. Beecher (Pa., Conn., N.Y.; Congregational minister, editor), 1850-1901 (8 ft.); William Cockburn (N.Y.; surveyor), 1703-1827 (1 ft.), concerned with land surveys and investment in the colony and State of New York; Sarah Brown Ingersoll Cooper (N.Y., Ga., Calif.; social reformer, founder of kindergartens), 1842-1910 (13 ft.); John S. Crocker (N.Y.; Civil War officer), 1861-64 (120 letters); Frank Norton Decker (N.Y.; lawyer, dairyman), 1832-1946 (98 ft.), relating chiefly to New York State dairy problems and related farm issues; Henry Pelouze de Forest (N.Y.; Spanish-American War surgeon, public health officer, fingerprint expert), 1884-1942 (9 boxes); Richard Henry Edwards (N.Y.; Congregational clergyman, religious educator, social worker), 1897-1953 (30 ft.); Edward Eggleston (Ind., Minn., Ill., N.Y.; novelist, historian), chiefly 1852-1902 (16 ft.), including literary manuscripts; Asa Fitch (N.Y.; entomologist), 1831-65 (71 pieces); Henry Phelps Gage (N.Y.; physicist, inventor), 1886-1955 (26 ft.); Frank E. Gannet (N.Y.; newspaper editor and publisher) and his wife (a large collection); William R. George (N.Y.; founder of the George Junior Republic), 1859-1952 (33 ft.), both personal papers and papers of the Republic; John Greig (N.Y.; land agent), 1794-1870 (18 reels of microfilm); and Hiram G. Hotchkiss (N.Y.; producer of essential oils), 1828-1931 (50 ft.), relating to the essential oils industry and other business ventures.

Papers of still other individuals include those of Fred Lucius Kilborne (N.Y.; veterinarian, parasitologist), 1884-1936 (4 in.); Jay P. Kinney (N.Y., D.C.; forester), 1910-57 (4 ft.); Jonathan Ledyard (N.Y.; land investor) and his family, 1793-1884 (5 reels of microfilm); Howard McCormick (N.J.; painter, wood engraver), 1900-41 (10 ft.); Guy Humphreys McMaster (N.Y.; jurist, poet) and his son-in-law and partner, John F. Parkhurst, 1860-97 (19 boxes), chiefly legal papers; William G. Markham and Charles Puffer (N.Y., S.C.; sheep breeders, businessmen), 1853-1907 (10 ft. and 1 reel of microfilm); Asa M. Mattice (N.Y.; mechanical engineer, naval officer, 1862-99 (5 boxes); John D. Miller (N.Y., Pa.; agriculturist, lawyer), 1915-46 (37 ft.), relating to his activities as vice president and general counsel of the Dairymen's League; Chester C. Platt (N.Y.; newspaper editor, sec. to Gov. William Sulzer), 1873-1934 (7$\frac{1}{2}$ ft.); Henry S. Randall (N.Y.; agriculturist, author), 1845-71 (8 in.), relating to sheep raising and breeding; Arthur Bernard Recknagel (N.Y.; forester), 1951-54 (1 vol.), relating to his work as technical director of forestry of the St. Regis Paper Co.; Augustus Loring Richards (N.Y.; lawyer, dairy farmer), 1872-1951 (9 ft.); Matthew T. Scott (Ill., Iowa, Ky.; landowner), 1831-1900 (13 ft.), relating to investments in Iowa and Illinois lands; Montgomery Sicard (U.S. naval officer), 1855-73 (2 ft.); John C. Trautwine (Pa.; engineer) and his family, 1834-1947 (17 boxes); Canvass White (N.Y.; canal engineer, cement manufacturer), 1814-35 (2 ft.); William Pierrepont White (N.Y.; lawyer) and his family, 1728-1939 (60 ft.), relating chiefly to lands, railroads, canals, and highways; Jemima Wilkinson (R.I., N.Y.; "the Public Universal Friend"), 1772-1849 (3 reels of microfilm); Charles Williamson (England, N.Y.; land promoter, British agent in America), 1792-1803 (2 vols. and 38 pieces), concerning his land operations; and Benjamin

Wright (N.Y.; surveyor, engineer), 1790-1805 (49 field books and 30 survey maps).

Among the many records of organizations are papers of banks; churches and church organizations of many Protestant denominations; civil service reform organizations (chiefly the New York State Civil Service Reform Association), 1880-1941 (100 ft.); the Chatauqua organization, 1915-23 (200 items); the Dairymen's League, New York, New Jersey, and Pennsylvania, 1916-55 (187 ft.), including papers of predecessor companies; the Empire State Forest Products Association, 1912-58 (5 ft.); the Farmer's Union of the New York Milk Shed, 1939-57 (8 ft.), chiefly correspondence and other papers of Alfred C. Kuchler, secretary-treasurer, and Archie Wright, president; two fruit growers' associations, and a fruit packing cooperative, 1920-35 (2 ft.); the Holland Land Co., 1803-63 (51 vols. and 1 box); the Mosely and Motley Milling Co., 1879-1929 (90 ft.); the National Forestry Program Committee, New York and numerous other States, 1920-28, 1945-47 (16 in.); the West Virginia Pulp and Paper Co., 1910-52 (39 ft.); many and diverse manufacturing companies; plank road and turnpike companies; many railroad companies; schools; and several temperance societies.

There are also many account books of individuals and of general stores and other small businesses; a large number of diaries, chiefly 19th century, including Civil War diaries; over 100 vols. of hotel registers; and papers and accounts of physicians, small farmers, and inventors. Besides the records on lands and railroads mentioned above among some of the personal papers, there are voluminous land papers both for western New York and Pennsylvania and for those Middle Western States in which New York State investors, including Cornell University, had an interest; canal papers, including mate-

rial on the Erie Canal; and much material relating to railroads, both regional and national. Unusual collections include a group of immigrant letters (many in photostatic copies), 1724-1899 (192 pieces); and papers relating to spiritualism, phrenology, electromagnetism, and galvanism, 1838-1901 (1 vol. and 1,118 pieces).

See the 6 Reports of the Cornell University Collection of Regional History and the University Archives, covering acquisitions, 1942-58; and Forest History Sources, pp. 80-84.

—oOo—

Cornell Library Association. Tioga and Seneca Sts. Howard R. Brentlinger, Director.

Holdings: 133 items, 1814-90, including a journal kept on board a Salem, Mass., brig, "From River Plate to Pacific Ocean," 1822-24 (1 vol.); a few papers of Ezra Cornell (N.Y.; capitalist, founder of Cornell Univ.), 1863 (17 items), relating chiefly to his gift of the public library; and 20 items relating to the Ithaca-Owego railroad. Some of the Library's former holdings have been transferred to the DeWitt Historical Society of Tompkins County, in Ithaca.

See Hist. Records Survey, Guide for N.Y. State, pp. 150-152.

—oOo—

Cornell University Library. Stephen A. McCarthy, Director.

Holdings: 500 vols. and 28,000 pieces, dating from 300 B.C. to 1956, and covering a wide range of subjects. The holdings of the Collection of Regional History and Cornell University Archives, separately described above, are administratively under the jurisdiction of this Library.

Included are medieval and Renaissance manuscripts (105 vols. and 19 pieces); a Chinese Collection, 15th-19th centuries (57 vols. and 50 pieces), which includes 5 vols. of the early 15th-century Chinese encyclopedia, Yung-lo ta tien, and 31 vols. relating to the ambassadorship to China of Sir George Macartney (England; diplomat), 1792-94; the Wordsworth Collection, 1796-1850 (1,000 pieces), including correspondence, manuscripts, and documents by and about William Wordsworth (England; poet), his family, and his friends; and the Joyce Collection, 1895-1941 (1,000 pieces), including correspondence, manuscripts, and documents by and about James Joyce (Ireland; author), his family, and his friends. An important group of Americana is the Samuel J. May Anti-slavery Collection, 1757-1895 (2,500 pieces), consisting largely of the papers of James Miller McKim (Pa., N.Y., N.J.; abolitionist, Sec. of the American Freedman's Aid Commission) and Lydia Maria Francis Child (Mass.; author, abolitionist), and records of the Freedman's Aid Commission.

Papers of individuals include those of Daniel Willard Fiske (N.Y.; librarian, bibliophile), 1871-1904 (7,000 pieces); Benjamin Franklin (Pa.; printer, scientist, diplomat), 1751-88 (16 pieces); John Seely Hart (Mass.; educator, author), 1848-77 (850 letters received); Rudyard Kipling (England, India; author), 1895-1936 (250 pieces), letters and literary manuscripts; Wyndham Lewis (England; writer, painter), 20th century (120 manuscripts, 1,100 letters from him, and 4,000 letters received by him); George Jean Nathan (N.Y.; editor, author, dramatic critic), 20th century (100 manuscripts, 5 letters by him, and 1,500 letters received by him); Theodore Roosevelt (N.Y.; U.S. Pres.), 1883-1916 (115 pieces); George Bernard Shaw (England; playwright, novelist, critic), 1871-1904 (50 pieces), including literary manuscripts and corrected proofs; Booth Tarkington (Ind.; novelist, playwright), 1910-46 (50 pieces), including literary manuscripts and proofs; Bayard Taylor (Pa.; author, traveler), 1847-78 (4,000 pieces), mainly letters received and several notebooks and diaries; Moses Coit Tyler (Mich.; historian, biographer), 1854-1900 (2,000 pieces); and George Washington (Va.; Rev. War Commander in Chief, U.S. Pres.), 1746-89 (80 pieces), including military maps and plans drawn during the Revolution.

See Hist. Records Survey, Guide for N.Y. State, pp. 152-159; De Ricci, Census, pp. 1223-1254; and George H. Healey, The Cornell Wordsworth Collection: A Catalogue (1957).

—oOo—

DeWitt Historical Society of Tompkins County. Old Court House. William Heidt, Jr., Curator.

Holdings: 550 vols. and 5,000 pieces, 1775-1932, relating chiefly to Ithaca and Tompkins County. Included are papers of Ezra Cornell (N.Y.; capitalist, founder of Cornell Univ.), 1829-75 (1,000 items); notes on Indians in the region, by William Martin Beauchamp (N.Y.; archeologist, historian); correspondence of Simeon DeWitt (N.Y.; surveyor-gen.); and some legal papers of Josiah B. Williams (N.Y.; Ithaca banker, businessman). There are also many letters, diaries, and other papers of less prominent persons, including a group of letters, 1794-1827; official records, chiefly of Ithaca, 1818-93; records of Methodist, Presbyterian, and other churches, 1817-1928, and diaries of a Baptist minister, 1850-87 (37 vols.); school records, 1814-

1912; and records of mercantile and other business transactions, 1784-1932 (154 vols. and 800 pieces), including accounts of Nicoll Halsey (N.Y.; U.S. Rep.), 1817-48 (1 vol.).

See Hist. Records Survey, Guide for N.Y. State, pp. 159-166.

JAMESTOWN

Fluvanna Free Library.

Holdings: 4 vols. and 4 pieces, 1910-41, relating chiefly to the woman-suffrage movement in the Jamestown area.

See Hist. Records Survey, Guide for N.Y. State, p. 166.

JOHNSTOWN

Johnstown Historical Society.

Holdings: About 1940 there were 70 vols. and 250 pieces, 1738-1919, relating chiefly to central New York. Included were a few papers of Sir William Johnson (N.Y.; French and Indian War officer, supt. of Indian affairs), 1762-70; some miscellaneous military records, 1758-1919; and a number of account books and other business records, 1769-1874 (42 vols.). (In 1960 the manuscripts were in storage and inaccessible.)

See Hist. Records Survey, Guide for N.Y. State, pp. 167-171.

KEENE VALLEY

Keene Valley Library Association. (Mrs.) Blanche Isham, Librarian.

Holdings: 48 vols., relating chiefly to the Adirondacks and Keene Valley, and including manuscripts of the former Keene Valley Historical Society. There are 2 vols. of corres-

pondence and other manuscripts of William Henry Harrison Murray (Conn.; clergyman, author).

See Hist. Records Survey, Guide for N.Y. State, p. 173.

KINDERHOOK

Columbia County Historical Society. Louise Hardenbrook, Librarian (Valatie, N.Y.).

Holdings: 58 vols. and 1,300 pieces, 1686-1933, relating chiefly to Columbia County. Included are a journal of Peter Van Schaack (N.Y.; lawyer), 1769-95 (1 vol.), a register of his Supreme Court cases, 1790-1819 (1 vol.), and his account books, 1785-1835 (2 vols.). There is also a Van Buren family collection, 1787-1874 (87 items), containing at least 16 papers of Martin Van Buren (N.Y.; Gov., U.S. Pres.). There are also papers of an aqueduct company, 1784-1857 (56 items), and a turnpike company, 1799-1898 (1 vol. and 500 pieces); official records of the towns of Kinderhook and Austerlitz, 1809-66 (18 vols.); church and cemetery records, 1716-1933 (21 vols. and 41 pieces); school records, 1822-76; and account books, 1768-1883 (7 vols.), together with an undetermined quantity of business records among groups of family and personal papers.

See Hist. Records Survey, Guide for N.Y. State, pp. 175-181.

KINGSTON

Senate House Museum. (Mrs.) Mary Black Terwilliger, Historic Site Superintendent.

Holdings: 25,000 items, 1633-1954, relating chiefly to Kingston and Ulster County. Included are papers of Jacobus Severyn Bruyn (N.Y.;

Rev. War officer) and his descendants, among them Abraham Bruyn Hasbrouck (N.Y.; U.S. Rep., Rutgers College pres.); John Vanderlyn (N.Y.; historical and portrait painter), early 19th century (1,200 pieces); and Peter Van Gaasbeek (N.Y.; merchant, Rev. War officer, U.S. Rep.), 1773-97 (9 vols. and over 600 letters). There are also diaries, legal documents, account books, and business papers, 1652-1875; sermons and church records, chiefly of a Dutch Reformed church, 1660-1882 (92 vols. and 6,834 pieces); assessment rolls, 1730-1848; and much genealogical material. A collection of autograph items, assembled chiefly by Alton B. Parker (N.Y.; jurist), 1633-1954, contains documents bearing the signatures of colonial and State Governors of New York.

See Hist. Records Survey, Guide for N.Y. State, pp. 183-186.

LACKAWANNA 18

Lackawanna Public Library Museum. 560 Ridge Rd. Stella Bajorek, Librarian.

Holdings: 6 vols. and 22 pieces, 1861-1925, including a Civil War diary and a few letters by World War I participants.

See Hist. Records Survey, Guide for N.Y. State, p. 186.

LE ROY

Daughters of the American Revolution.

Holdings: 63 vols. and 262 pieces, 1800-1940, chiefly relating to Le Roy and vicinity. Included are ledgers and account books, 1811-76 (22 vols.); school and college records, 1852-97 (11 vols. and 1 piece); military records, 1800-1940; church and cemetery records, 1843-71; and a diary, 1847-53, 1864-68 (10 vols.).

See Hist. Records Survey, Guide for N.Y. State, pp. 188-190.

—oOo—

Le Roy Historical Society.

Holdings: 34 vols. and 1,500 pieces, 1800-1940, relating chiefly to the village. Included are genealogical records compiled for the years 1800-1940 (7 vols. and 1,000 pieces); and records of a local Baptist church and its church societies, 1816-1927 (26 vols.).

See Hist. Records Survey, Guide for N.Y. State, pp. 190-192.

LITTLE VALLEY

Cattaraugus County Memorial and Historical Building. Julia G. Pierce, County Historian (Allegany, N.Y.).

Holdings: 150 vols. and 2,035 pieces, relating chiefly to the county. Included are census returns, 1825-1915 (26 vols.); and extensive records of the county branch of the American Legion, since 1923.

See Hist. Records Survey, Guide for N.Y. State, p. 193.

LYONS

Wayne County Division of Archives and History. (Mrs.) Dorothy S. Facer, County Historian.

Holdings: A small and miscellaneous collection, relating chiefly to the county and collected by the Wayne County Historical Society. Included are a number of diaries and school, church, and business records; other manuscripts relating to county history (4 vols.); records (copied) of burials in Wayne County and some Ontario County cemeteries (11 vols.); genealogical records (a few vols. and many pieces); lists of soldiers from the county in the Revolutionary War, the War of 1812, and the Civil War (2 vols.); and "personal military records" of Wayne County men and women in World War II (20 vols.).

MOHAWK

Weller Library. Hilda Pearce, Librarian.

Holdings: 34 pieces, 1842-67, consisting of an autograph collection of letters by prominent Americans and some papers on the history of Mohawk.
See Hist. Records Survey, Guide for N.Y. State, p. 197.

MONTOUR FALLS

Montour Falls Memorial Library. Mrs. George M. Layton, Librarian.

Holdings: 50 vols. and 3,000 pieces, 1779-1895, chiefly official records of the town of Catharine and papers relating to miscellaneous business transactions.
See Hist. Records Survey, Guide for N.Y. State, pp. 198-200.

NEW PALTZ

Jean Hasbrouck Memorial House. Kenneth E. Hasbrouck, Secretary, Huguenot Historical Society.

Holdings: Over 500 items, 1675-1865, relating chiefly to the Huguenot settlement and later history of New Paltz and to Ulster County, N.Y. Included are over 50 papers of Josiah

Hasbrouck (N.Y.; U.S. Rep.); documents of the Duzine, the governing body of New Paltz, 1677-1800 (over 150 items); records of 12 Dutch Reformed churches and compiled records of Methodist churches in Ulster County; papers of local families; and papers of and concerning the Union Army near Richmond, Va., during the Civil War. (There are a few early papers in the Josiah Hasbrouck Mansion, 4 miles south of New Paltz.)

NEW ROCHELLE

Thomas Paine Memorial House.

Holdings: 600 items, 1702-1872, relating chiefly to Thomas Paine and to New Rochelle. Included are papers of Thomas Paine (Pa., N.Y.; Rev. political pamphleteer, author), 1775-1824 (43 items); official records of New Rochelle, 1777-1874 (300 pieces); military records, 1797-1863 (75 pieces); account books, 1804-54 (4 vols.); and some correspondence of several famous men. Some of the papers are source material for the Huguenot emigrés to New Rochelle.
See Hist. Records Survey, Guide for N.Y. State, pp. 206-208.

NEW YORK 32

American Academy of Arts and Letters. 633 West 155th St. Mrs. Matthew Josephson, Librarian.

Holdings: A large group, 1651-1930, including autographs and manuscripts by leading men and women of many nations, is now on deposit at the Library of Congress. The Academy has at its own premises a large collection of letters and manuscripts by members, living and deceased, of the National Institute of

Arts and Letters, the parent body of the Academy; these are in the fields of art, literature, and music, and are dated chiefly in the 20th century.

See Hist. Records Survey, Guide for New York City, p. 1.

NEW YORK 27

American Baptist Foreign Mission Society. 475 Riverside Dr.

Holdings: Early in 1960 many of the valuable archives of this Society (formerly in Boston, Mass.), dating from early in the 19th century, were said to be in a storage warehouse and not readily available for research; and it was suggested that communications regarding records of the Society be directed to the American Baptist Historical Society, 1100 South Goodman St., Rochester 20, New York.

See Allison, Inventory, p. 25.

NEW YORK 22

American Bible Society. 450 Park Ave. Margaret T Hills, Librarian.

Holdings: The correspondence and records of the Society from its founding in 1816. Included are correspondence and other records covering the work of the Society during this period in the United States and abroad, dealing with the publication, distribution, and translation of the Scriptures. There are papers relating to the American Committee that worked on the English Revised Version of 1881-85. Some of the presidents and vice presidents of the Society, including Elias Boudinot and John Quincy Adams, have been prominent in various phases of American history. Some of the records are being microfilmed, but all material dealing with policy or of a historical nature is being preserved in original

form.

See Allison, Inventory, p. 96.

NEW YORK 11

American Foundation for the Blind, Inc. 15 West 16th St. Helga Lende, Librarian.

Holdings: 2,500 pieces, since 1887, by or relating to Helen Keller (Conn.; deaf and blind author, lecturer).

NEW YORK 32

American Geographical Society Library. Broadway at 156th St. Nordis Felland, Librarian.

Holdings: 150 vols. and a quantity of miscellaneous documents relating chiefly to the history of the Society and to the progress of exploration and the development of geography in the United States since 1852. Included are the rough log of the U. S. brig Rescue, which took part in the search for the Arctic explorer, Sir John Franklin, 1850-51 (2 vols.); notes on the Peary Arctic Club's North Polar Expedition, 1908-9 (4 vols.); diary of Hudson Stuck (Alaska; Episcopal clergyman, archdeacon of the Yukon), 1912-13 (1 vol.), kept on his Mt. McKinley Expedition; and archives of the Society.

NEW YORK 28

American Irish Historical Society. 991 Fifth Ave.

Holdings: 1,248 items, consisting chiefly of a collection of letters and other papers, 1884-1901, relating to the Irish home-rule movement; and 109 parchment pages of Gaelic fragments, 1771.

See Hist. Records Survey, Guide for New York City, pp. 3-5.

NEW YORK 27

American Jewish Historical Society. 3080 Broadway. Isidore S. Meyer, Librarian.

Holdings: 150 boxes, 1590 to date, relating chiefly to the history of the Jews in America. Papers of individuals, which cover activities of the mature years of their lives, include those of Cyrus Adler (D.C., Pa., N.Y.; Semitic scholar, pres. of Dropsie College and Jewish Theological Seminary of America), 6 boxes; Bernhard Felsenthal (Ill.; rabbi, leading advocate of Zionism), 870 pieces; Bernard and Michael Gratz (Pa.; merchants), 18th century (1 box of letters); Rebecca Gratz (Pa.; philanthropist, founder of Hebrew Sunday School Society), 643 letters; Leon Huhner (N.Y.; lawyer, writer on American Jewish history), 20th century (2 boxes); Max J. Kohler (N.Y.; lawyer, author), 6 boxes, including collected papers relating to Baron Maurice de Hirsch (Germany; railway businessman, philanthropist); George Alexander Kohut (Tex., N.Y.; rabbi, Hebrew scholar, author), 8 boxes, among them collected documents relating to well known persons and families in American Jewry; Aaron Lopez (R.I., Mass.; merchant), 7 boxes; Isaac Moses (N.Y.; merchant) and his family, 2 boxes; Samuel Oppenheim (N.Y.; lawyer, author), 32 boxes, including a collection of originals and copies of documents relating to Jews in 17th-century Brazil and early New York and to Haym Salomon (N.Y.; merchant, banker, Rev. War financier); and Mordecai Sheftall (Ga.; Rev. War officer) and his family, 1776-90 (3,172 pieces), containing information about Continental troops in Georgia

and South Carolina. A collection given by Abraham S. W. Rosenbach (Pa.; bibliographer, author, dealer in rare books and manuscripts), 11 boxes, contains miscellaneous records of the colonial and Revolutionary periods as well as the Gratz, Lopez, and Sheftall papers noted above. The Society also has records of the Inquisition in Mexico, late 16th and early 17th centuries (1 box); and records of various Jewish organizations, among them the Jewish Agricultural Society and the Jewish Child Care Association of New York.

See Hist. Records Survey, Guide for New York City, pp. 5-9; Greene and Morris, Guide, p. xii and passim; and Isidore S. Meyer, "The American Jewish Historical Society," in Journal of Jewish Bibliography, vol. 4, nos. 1-2 (Jan.-Apr. 1943).

NEW YORK 24

American Museum of Natural History. Central Park West at 79th St. Hazel Gay, Librarian.

Holdings: 4,000 pieces, 1833-91, relating to natural history. Included are notebooks of early explorations in the West by Clarence King (D.C.; geologist), 1866-72; 4 unpublished vols. on butterflies by Titian Ramsay Peale (Pa.; naturalist, artist); 2,820 letters received by William Henry Edwards (W. Va.; entomologist), 1862-91; 741 letters received by George N. Lawrence (N.Y.; ornithologist), 1865-89, of which 201 were from Spencer F. Baird (Pa., D.C.; zoologist), 99 from Robert Ridgway (D.C.; ornithologist), and 55 from Joel A. Allen (Mass., N.Y.; zoologist); and manuscripts of John James Audubon (Pa., Ky., La., N.Y.; ornithologist, artist) that accompanied 46 plates in his Birds of America.

See Hist. Records Survey, Guide for New York City, pp. 9-11.

NEW YORK 32

American Numismatic Society. 156th St. and Broadway. Sawyer McA. Mosser, Executive Director.

Holdings: Interspersed among published material, there is an undetermined quantity of correspondence and other manuscripts relating chiefly to ancient Greek hoards and Roman coins and to coins, tokens, and medals in the United States.
See Hist. Records Survey, Guide for New York City. p. 11.

NEW YORK 21

American Society for Psychical Research Library. 880 Fifth Ave. Adele Wellman, Executive Secretary.

Holdings: 25 boxes, 1904-20, consisting of reports, correspondence, and other manuscripts relating to psychical research. Included are 7 vols. of Shaker music and inspirational writings; papers of James H. Hyslop (Ohio, N.Y.; psychologist and philosopher), on parapsychology and related subjects; and original automatic writings of Mrs. Leonore Piper (Mass.; medium), 1904-10 (20 boxes).
See Hist. Records Survey, Guide for New York City, pp. 14-16.

NEW YORK 12

Archives of the Franciscan Province of the Immaculate Conception (New York). 147 Thompson St. Rev. John-Marie Cassese, Archivist.

Holdings: Records and papers of many Franciscan friars, 1855 to date, relating to their work in the eastern section of the United States. Included are papers, 1855-1901, held jointly with the Province of the Most Holy Name of Jesus, bearing on the early history of both units; these papers have been microfilmed (23 rolls).

NEW YORK 17

Archives Section, United Nations Library. Marjan Stopar-Babsek, Chief.

Holdings: Noncurrent records of the United Nations, since 1946, and of its immediate predecessors, including some of the records of the League of Nations, 1919-46, and records of the United Nations Information Organization, 1941-46, the United Nations War Crimes Commission, 1943-48, the United Nations Relief and Rehabilitation Administration, 1943-49, the United Nations Conference on International Organization, San Francisco, 1945, and the United Nations Preparatory Commission, 1945-46.
See Robert Claus, "The United Nations Archives," in Am. Archivist, 10:129-132 (Apr. 1947); and Robert Claus and Irving P. Schiller, "The League of Nations and the United Nations," in Daniel H. Thomas and Lynn M. Case, eds., Guide to the Diplomatic Archives of Western Europe, pp. 321-347 (1959).

NEW YORK 36

Association of the Bar of the City of New York. 42 West 44th St. Sidney B. Hill, Librarian.

Holdings: Papers relating chiefly to the legal profession in New York. Included are a law register of

Alexander Hamilton (N. Y.; Member Continental Cong., Sec. Treas.), 1795-1804 (1 vol.), and a notebook by him, 1785; and transcripts of minutes of the New York Circuit Court of Oyer and Terminer, 1721-49 (2 vols.).

See Hist. Records Survey, Guide for New York City, p. 16; and Greene and Morris, Guide, p. xxi and passim.

NEW YORK 21

Atran Center for Jewish Culture. 25 East 78th St. Emanuel Nowogrudsky, Secretary.

Holdings: The Bund Archives of the Jewish Labor Movement, 1850 to date, which contains extensive manuscripts, as well as rare printed materials, pertaining to the Russian, other European, and American labor movements, with special emphasis on the Jewish labor and emancipation movement. (The collection was started more than 50 years ago in Geneva, Switzerland, by the Jewish Labor Bund.)

NEW YORK 15

Bank of New York Archives. 48 Wall St. James M. Shea, Public Relations.

Holdings: Archives of the bank, from 1784, consisting of old ledgers, minute books, and other papers, relating chiefly to its founding and operation and including letters of a considerable number of men important in the history of the United States, notably some by one of the bank's founders, Alexander Hamilton (N.Y.; Rev. War officer, Member Continental Cong., Sec. Treas.), 1784-1804 (24 letters).

NEW YORK 31

City College Library. West 139th St.

and Convent Ave. Jerome K. Wilcox, Librarian.

Holdings: A considerable quantity of papers of and relating to Townsend Harris (N.Y.; merchant, a founder of the City College of New York, Minister to Japan), including his journal, 1855-58 (5 vols.), his letter books, 1856-62 (5 vols.), and letters and documents to Harris (533 items).

NEW YORK 27

Columbia University Libraries. Morningside Heights and 116th St. Richard H. Logsdon, Director of Libraries.

Holdings: A large quantity of manuscripts, consisting of some 265 collections, 3000 B.C. to A.D. 1954, relating chiefly to New York and Columbia University but also pertaining to many other subjects. Most of the manuscripts are in the Department of Special Collections, which includes the Columbiana Division, and others are in the Avery Memorial Architectural Library, the East Asian Library, the Medical Library of the College of Physicians and Surgeons, the School of Law Library, and the Teachers College Library, as shown immediately below. The Lavanburg Library, with its extensive holdings of reports and other materials on housing and housing management, from 1928, formerly owned by the Fred L. Lavanburg Foundation, was turned over to Columbia University in 1957.

See the Libraries' Manuscript Collections in the Columbia University Libraries; a Descriptive List (1959. 104 p.).

Department of Special Collections. Roland Baughman, Head.

Holdings: Papers of political

leaders and public officials include those of John Adams (Mass.; U. S. Pres.), 1818 (16 pieces); Benjamin N. Cardozo (N. Y.; U. S. Supreme Court Justice, author), 1932-39 (35 pieces); DeWitt Clinton (N. Y.; U. S. Sen., Gov., philanthropist), 1785-1828 (24 vols.); John A. Dix (N. Y.; U. S. Army officer and Sen., Sec. Treas., Gov.), 1813-79 (1,226 pieces); Hamilton Fish (N. Y.; Gov., U. S. Sen., Sec. State), 1827-93 (1,000 pieces); Alexander Hamilton (N. Y.; Rev. War officer, Member Continental Cong., Sec. Treas.), 1791-1804 (57 pieces); John Jay (N. Y.; Pres. of Continental Cong., diplomat, U. S. Chief Justice, Gov.), 1764-1829 (2,000 items), constituting the main body of his papers; Thomas Jefferson (Va.; U. S. Pres.), 1786-1816 (21 items); Cyrus King (Mass.; U. S. Rep.), 1791-1817 (2 vols. and 3 correspondence files); Rufus King (Mass., N. Y.; Member Continental Cong., U. S. Sen. from N. Y., Minister to Great Britain) and his family, 1784-1854 (69 letters); Gouverneur Morris (N. Y.; Member Continental Cong., diplomat, U. S. Sen.), 1768-1816 (1,371 pieces); Herbert Parsons (N. Y.; lawyer, U. S. Rep.), 1898-1925 (14,700 Frances Perkins (N. Y.; State industrial commissioner, U. S. Sec. Labor), 1933-45 (87 boxes and 4 scrapbooks), office files while Secretary of Labor; William Sprague (R. I.; locomotive manufacturer, Gov., U. S. Sen.), 1861-71 (66 pieces); Samuel J. Tilden (N.Y.; Gov., lawyer), 1876-80 (2 boxes); Peter D. Vroom (N. Y.; Gov., U. S. Rep., Minister to Prussia), 1829-73 (4 vols.); Henry A. Wallace (Iowa, N. Y.; plant breeder, Sec. Agric., U.S. Vice Pres., Sec. Commerce), 12 boxes, correspondence and other papers; George Washington (Va.; Rev. War Commander in Chief, U. S. Pres.), 1778-98 (56 items and 2 diaries, 1795 and 1798); Daniel Webster (N. H., Mass.; U. S. Rep. and Sen., Sec. State), 1828-36 (25 pieces); and Woodrow Wilson (N. J.; pres. of Princeton Univ.), Gov., U. S. Pres.), 1910-12 (1,150 pieces).

Papers of members of the faculty of Columbia University include those of James Truslow Adams (N. Y.; historian), 1918-49 (6 vols. and 18 boxes); Charles Anthon (N. Y.; classical scholar), 1827-31 (2 vols.); Frederick Augustus Porter Barnard (Ala., Miss., N. Y.; prof. of mathematics and natural history, pres. of the Univ. of Miss. and Columbia Univ.), 1853-80 (8 vols. and 1 box); Franz Boas (N. Y.; anthropologist, philologist), 1898-1945 (35 vols. and 3 boxes), relating chiefly to the Chinooks; John Bartlet Brebner (N. Y.; historian), 1930-57 (15 boxes); John W. Burgess (N. Y., R. I.; political scientist), 1873-1930 (26 boxes); Nicholas Murray Butler (N. Y.; pres. of Columbia Univ.), 1900-47 (140 vols. and 274 boxes), and a special collection of his correspondence with U. S. Presidents, 1891-1946 (1,479 letters); Charles Frederick Chandler (Mass., N. Y.; industrial chemist, dean of Columbia School of Mines, pres. of New York City's Board of Health), 1852-1925 (uncounted); John Bates Clark (N. Y.; political economist), 1897-1938 (11 boxes); Henry Edward Crampton (N. Y.; zoologist), 1900-50 (6 boxes); Melvil Dewey (N. Y.; chief librarian and prof. at Columbia Univ., director of N. Y. State Library), 1870-1931 (6 vols. and 94 boxes); William A. Dunning (N. Y.; historian) and his family, 1781-1922 (16 boxes); Mortimer Lamson Earle (N. Y.; classical philologist), 1884-1905 (14 file boxes); Irwin Edman (N. Y.; philosopher), 20th century (12 boxes); John Erskine (N. Y.; English literature prof.), 40 boxes; Thomas Scott Fiske (N. Y.; mathematician), 1891-1926 (19 boxes); Franklin Henry Giddings (N. Y.; sociologist), 1890-1902 (18 letters); and Robert M. Haig (N. Y.; political economist), 1927-49 (45 cartons and 25 correspondence files).

Papers of other members of the Columbia University faculty include those of Samuel Johnson (Conn., N.Y.; Anglican clergyman, pres. of King's College), 1710-71 (85 vols.); William Samuel Johnson (Conn., N.Y.; Member Continental Cong., U.S. Sen. from Conn., pres. of Columbia College), 1753-1813 (100 pieces); Seth Low (N.Y.; merchant, pres. of Columbia College), 1863-1916 (4 vols. and 200 correspondence files); Edward Alexander MacDowell (N.Y.; pianist, Columbia Univ. prof.), 1894-1903 (32 letters); Daniel G. Mason (N.Y.; musician, composer, critic), 1894-1948 (15 cartons); James Brander Matthews (N.Y.; playwright, prof. of dramatic literature), 1871-1924 (58 vols. and 2,500 pieces); Wesley Clair Mitchell (Ill., Calif., N.Y.; economist), 1898-1948 (42 boxes); Clement C. Moore (N.Y.; Hebrew scholar, poet), 1856-63 (1 vol.); William Underhill Moore (N.Y., Conn.; prof. of law at Columbia and Yale Univs.), 1908-20 (18 boxes); Allan Nevins (N.Y.; historian), 1914-45 (75 boxes); Curtis Hidden Page (N.Y., N.H.; prof. of Romance languages and literature), 1895-1948 (2 boxes); Walter Rautenstrauch (N.Y.; industrial engineer), 1906-46 (35 boxes); Edwin Robert Anderson Seligman (N.Y.; economist), 1750-1939 (53 vols., 31 boxes, and 153 correspondence files), including, in addition to his personal and professional papers, historical letters of economists (2 boxes), papers of Ernest C. Jones (England; Chartist reformer, poet, novelist), 1819-69 (7 boxes), and papers relating to the cotton and textile industry, 1782-1815 (2 boxes); James T. Shotwell (N.Y.; prof. of history and international relations), 1914-45 (92 correspondence files and 18 boxes); David Eugene Smith (Mich., N.Y.; mathematician), 1100-1939 (305 vols. and 73 boxes), consisting of personal and professional correspond-

ence, 1900-39 (25 boxes), a collection of autograph letters of mathematicians, 1700-1900 (305 vols.), and deeds, charters, and miscellaneous papers, 1100-1800 (48 boxes); Mark Van Doren (N.Y.; poet), from 1916 (17 boxes); and George Edward Woodberry (Mass., N.Y.; poet, critic), 1890-1930 (14 boxes).

Papers of authors, in addition to some named elsewhere, include those of Park Benjamin (Mass., N.Y.; editor, poet), 1830-64 (11 boxes); Randolph Silliam Bourne (N.J.; essayist), 1910-18 (8 boxes); Millen Brand (N.J.; novelist, poet, short-story writer), 1930-57 (39 boxes); Henry Cuyler Bunner (N.Y.; editorial writer for Puck), 1877-96 (2 vols.); George Washington Cable (La., Mass.; short-story writer, novelist), 1887-1908 (412 items); Jules Champfleury (France; novelist), 1853-88 (7 vols. of notes and 27 letters); Samuel L. Clemens, better known as Mark Twain (Mo., Calif., Conn., N.Y.; novelist, humorist), 1900-9 (36 items); Moncure D. Conway (D.C., Ohio, Mass., England; Unitarian and Congregational clergyman, author), 1847-1907 (3,500 pieces); Hart Crane (Ohio; poet), 1909-32 (12 boxes); Stephen Crane (N.Y.; novelist), 1895-1908 (1,200 pieces); Ralph Waldo Emerson (Mass.; essayist, poet), 1814-82 (73 letters and 25 boxes of photostatic copies of letters located elsewhere); Mary Wilkins Freeman (Mass., N.J.; author), 1893-1901 (54 pieces); Henry Rider Haggard (England, South Africa; novelist), 1866-1925 (245 pieces); Sarah Orne Jewett (Maine; author), 1870-79 (72 letters); Thomas S. Jones (N.Y.; poet, editor), 1900-32 (42 boxes); Frances Anne Kemble, known as Fanny Kemble (England, Pa., Ga., Mass.; actress, author), 1848-60 (29 letters); Edna Kenton (N.Y.; short-story writer), 1903-36 (146 letters); Emma Lazarus (N.Y.; poet, essayist), 1868-87

(84 pieces); William Wilberforce Lord (Miss., N.Y.; clergyman, poet), 1844-99 (60 items); Donald Robert Perry Marquis, known as Don Marquis (N.Y.; playwright), 1910-37 (210 items); John Milton (England; poet), 1649-59 (1 vol.), copies of 156 letters written as secretary to Oliver Cromwell; John Ruskin (England; critic, author, reformer), 1859-89 (335 pieces); Lydia Howard Huntley Sigourney (Conn.; poet), 1830-62 (67 letters); Edmund Clarence Stedman (N.Y.; poet, anthologist, stockbroker), 1840-1930 (67 vols. and 114 boxes); Leo Tolstoy (Russia; novelist), 1897-1937 (124 pieces); Ella Wheeler Wilcox (Wis., N.Y., Conn.; poet), 1888-1919 (32 letters); and Herman Wouk (N.Y.; novelist, radio scriptwriter), since 1946 (24 boxes).

Papers of journalists, editors, and publishers include those of William Elroy Curtis (Ill.; journalist, traveler, first director of the Bureau of American Republics), 1888-92 (180 pieces); Azariah C. Flagg (N.Y.; newspaper editor, political leader), 1824-66 (100 pieces); Sydney Howard Gay (Mass., Ill., N.Y.; abolitionist, journalist, author, editor of New York Tribune), 1830-1900 (85 boxes); James Wellman Ripley Hitchcock, known as Ripley Hitchcock (N.J., N.Y.; art critic, journalist, author), 1885-1935 (18 boxes); George Arthur Plimpton (N.Y.; publisher), 17th century-1936 (5 boxes), including some personal papers, an autograph collection of papers of U.S. Presidents and other prominent persons, and a collection on slavery; Joseph Pulitzer (Mo., N.Y.; newspaper editor and publisher, U.S. Rep. from N.Y.), 1885-1911 (82 boxes); George Haven Putnam (N.Y.; publisher, author), 1904-21 (1 scrapbook and 800 items), some relating to national preparedness during World War I; Lincoln Steffens (Calif.; author, lecturer, editor of McClure's Magazine), 1890-1936 (5 vols. and 56 boxes); Oswald Garrison Villard (N.Y.; journalist, editor), 1850-1910 (20 boxes), relating to John Brown; William Allen White (Kans.; newspaper editor, author), 1909-43 (68 pieces); and Nathaniel Parker Willis (Mass., N.Y.; author, editor), 1827-29 (24 pieces).

Papers of other persons include those of Alexander Anderson (N.Y.; engraver), 1793-99 (3 vols.); Frederic Bancroft (N.Y., D.C.; historian, lecturer), 1890-1930 (70 boxes); the Bard family, 16th century-1882 (220 items), including a few letters from Samuel Bard (N.Y.; physician); Pierre Bayle (France, Holland; philosopher, critic), 1670-1706 (158 pieces); Pierre G. T. Beauregard (La.; U.S. and Confed. Army officer, railroad pres.), 1860-65 (500 items); Louis Hector Berlioz (France; composer), 1825-1953 (12 boxes); Elizabeth Blackwell (N.Y., England; first woman doctor of medicine in modern times), 1850-84 (152 pieces); Louis B. Boudin (N.Y.; lawyer), 1900-50 (500 pieces); Lewis Corey (Ill.; prof. of political economy at Antioch and Roosevelt Colleges), 1910-53 (28 boxes); Frederick Coykendall (N.Y.; business executive, managing director of Columbia Univ. Press), 1778-1940 (300 items), chiefly a collection of letters by literary figures; Charles Stewart Daveis (Maine; lawyer), 1815-60 (1,700 pieces), relating to the Maine-Canada boundary controversy and legal and political activity in Maine; Genevieve Earle (N.Y.; member of New York City Council), 1935-50 (13 boxes); Abraham Epstein (Pa., N.Y.; executive sec. of the American Association for Social Security, author), 1918-45 (5,000 pieces); William Hawkins Ferris (N.Y.; U.S. Treas. official), 1850-75 (314 items), including some correspondence of William Gilmore Simms (S.C.; author) and other literary figures; Robert Fulton (N.Y.; artist, civil engineer, inventor),

1809-30 (20 pieces); John Glover
(Mass.; Rev. War officer), 1775-81 (1
vol., copies); Josephine Sophie White
Griffing (Ohio, D. C.; social reformer,
suffragist), 1862-72 (53 letters);
George Leslie Harrison (N. Y.; lawyer, pres. of Federal Reserve Bank of
N. Y.), 1920-40 (12 correspondence
file drawers), relating chiefly to the
Federal Reserve System; Alonzo Barton Hepburn (N. Y.; State legislator,
banker, philanthropist), 1886-1918 (6
boxes); George Frederick William
Holls (N. Y.; publicist, specialist in
international law), 1890-1903 (28 vols.);
Lydiard Heneage Horton (Mass.; psychologist), 1900-45 (8 boxes); Alfred
Jeanroy (France; Romance language
scholar), 1727-1953 (50 boxes); Bru-
no Lasker (Germany, England, N. Y.;
social research worker), 1923-51 (15
boxes); and James Duane Livingston
(N. Y.; banker, investment securities
broker), 1787-1893 (2 boxes).

Papers of still other persons include those of George McAneny (N. Y.;
journalist, New York City official,
chairman of New York City Transit
Commission), 1902-40 (3 boxes); Sidney E. Mezes (Tex., N. Y.; pres. of
the Univ. of Tex. and the College of
the City of New York), 1918 (2 boxes),
relating to The Inquiry; William Barclay Parsons (N. Y.; civil engineer),
1899-1915 (1 box); Otto Rank (Austria;
psychotherapist, associate of Sigmund
Freud), 1903-30 (25 boxes); Charles
Stanley Reinhart (N. Y., France; genre
painter and illustrator), 1870-1956
(260 items); George Santayana (Mass.,
Italy; poet, philosopher), 1880-1940
(8 boxes); Anton Seidl (Germany, N. Y.;
musician, conductor), 1874-78 (4 boxes); William Shaw (England; merchant),
1860-1904 (497 items), correspondence
with Sir Basil Zaharoff (Turkey, Spain;
international armament contractor) and
others, relating to international munitions operations; Charles Stelze (N.Y.;
Presbyterian minister, sociologist),
1938-41 (14 boxes); James Stillman

(N. Y.; financier), 1851-1918 (480
items), among them 12 letters from
Grover Cleveland (N. Y.; U. S. Pres.);
Charlemagne Tower (Pa.; mining
capitalist, financier), 1830-89 (86
boxes); Frank A. Vanderlip (Ill., N.Y.;
financial editor, banker), 1884-1937
(25 cartons, 100 correspondence
files, and 15 scrapbooks); Peter Van
Schaack (N. Y.; lawyer), 1759-1843 (6
boxes); William John Wilgus (N. Y.;
civil engineer), 1935-37 (1,336 pieces), relating to U. S. and Canadian
railway relations; and Edith Elmer
Wood (N. Y.; author, advocate of woman's rights), 1890-1945 (119 letter
books and vertical files).

Records of various organizations
include those of King's College and
Columbia College, 1754-1890 (42 boxes); Daly's Theatre, New York, 1872-
99 (10 vols.); the Citizens Union of
New York City (concerning city politics), 1897-1938 (190 boxes); the New
York and Paris offices of the Carnegie Endowment for International
Peace, 1911-48 (500 vols., 124 cartons, and 900 correspondence files);
the Federated Press, which furnished
specialized news releases for labor
newspapers, 1918-41 (100 file drawers); the National Museum of Engineering and Industry, 1920-35 (15
boxes); and the Spanish Refugee Relief Association and related organizations, 1935-40 (100 boxes).

Included also are a collection relating to Venice and Venetian families,
15th-18th centuries (180 items); a
collection relating to Joan of Arc,
15th-20th centuries (52 pieces); papers relating to the history of Mexico, 1649-1858 (163 items); records
of cases argued before the Mayor's
Court of New York City, 1681-1819
(2,000 items); a collection of letters
by actors, actresses, and theatrical
managers, 1732-1902 (166 letters),
and one of letters by musical composers and performers, 18th-20th centuries (68 items); papers of the Otis

family of Massachusetts, 1687-1868 (349 items), and of the Philipse-Gouverneur family of Westchester and Dutchess Counties, N.Y., 1653-1874 (174 pieces); Typographic Library manuscripts relating to printers and printing, 1750-1938 (7 vols. and 34 boxes); papers of New York doctors and faculty members of the Medical School, 1773-1900 (6 boxes); a collection of letters of scientists, 1646-1904 (30 items); a collection of autographed letters of Presidents of the United States, 1789-1932 (2 vols.); Historical Records Survey compilations of messages and papers of the Presidents of the United States, 1862-1938 (8,030 pieces), and Congressional vote analyses, 1789-1942 (1,029 bundles); papers relating to Tammany Hall, 1776-1952 (36 vols. and 17 boxes); a collection of correspondence of privates and noncommissioned officers with their families and friends during the Civil War (1,336 pieces); the journal of the Joint Committee on Reconstruction of the U.S. Congress, 1865-67; and a collection on boxing and the prize ring (10 boxes). The Archive of Russian and East European History and Culture contains important unpublished materials for the areas indicated, 19th and 20th centuries.

Business records, many of them formerly in the library of the Columbia University Graduate School of Business, include records of a Boston merchant who traded with Newfoundland and Antigua, 1755-64, and other records of trade with the West Indies; farm accounts, 1783-1812 (23 vols.); customs declarations of merchants of New York City, 1789-1821 (100 pieces); records of a textile mill in the early 19th century; records of a firm of New York City merchants, 1790-1878 (7 boxes); records of a New York City shipping business, 1850-71 (47 vols.); War Labor Board materials relating to price and wage controls during World War II; a collection re-lating to motorbus and taxicab service in the United States, 1904-33 (10 correspondence file drawers); and the Robert H. Montgomery collection of account books and other business records, 15th-19th centuries (750 vols. and 10 boxes).

As a part of the University's oral history program, the Department has transcripts of tape-recorded interviews with men prominent in the Nation's affairs. These include William H. Allen (N.Y.; civic worker, author), William H. Anderson (N.Y.; prohibitionist, sec. American Christian Alliance), Martin C. Ansorge (N.Y.; lawyer, U.S. Rep.), Boris A. Bakhmeteff (Russia, N.Y.; Ambassador to U.S., civil engineer), William S. Bennet (N.Y.; lawyer, U.S. Rep.), George F. Chandler (N.Y.; surgeon, supt. N.Y. State Police), William W. Cumberland (N.Y.; economist, author), Malcolm W. Davis (N.Y.; international relations specialist), Albert D. Lasker (N.Y.; advertising expert), Edward A. O'Neal (Ala.; farm organization executive, pres. of American Farm Bureau Federation), Norman Thomas (N.Y.; Socialist candidate for U.S. Pres., author), and Henry A. Wallace (Iowa, N.Y.; plant breeder, Sec. Agriculture, U.S. Vice Pres., Sec. Commerce).

The Library also has a collection of Babylonian cuneiform tablets, 3000-300 B.C. (500 pieces); papyri, 6th-3d centuries B.C. (700 pieces); Islamic manuscripts, 800-1600 (350 vols.); medieval and Renaissance manuscripts (49 vols. and 155 pieces); Hebrew manuscripts, 10th-19th centuries (852 pieces); and Chinese manuscripts dealing with government, law, and history, 17th-20th centuries (69 pieces).

See Herbert W. Schneider, "A Note on the Samuel Johnson Papers," in Am. Hist. Review, 31:724-726 (July 1926); Nicholas N. Martinovitch, "Arabic, Persian and Turkish

Manuscripts in the Columbia University Library," in Am. Oriental Society, Journal, 49:219-233 (Sept. 1929); De Ricci, Census, pp. 1258-1272; Hist. Records Survey, Guide for New York City, pp. 20-26; Greene and Morris, Guide, pp. xxii-xxiv and passim; and the Oral History Research Office's The Oral History Collection of Columbia University (1960. 111 p.).

Avery Memorial Architectural Library. James Grote Van Derpool, Librarian.

Holdings: 10,000 original architectural drawings, mainly American, from 1798 to the present, but including some collections of 16th-, 17th-, and 18th-century European origin, chiefly Italian, English, and French. There are also some letters and other papers pertaining to architecture. The works of American architects include those of Alexander Jackson Davis (N.Y.), 1830-70 (1,600 items); Detlef Lienau (N.Y.), 1850-1900 (558 drawings), the only surviving collection of his drawings, which are chiefly of office buildings and domestic architecture in New York and vicinity; Harold Van Buren Magonigle (N.Y.), 1896-1935 (2,071 drawings); Frank Dempster Sherman (N.Y.), 1880-1915 (50 items); John Calvin Stevens (Mass., Maine), 60 items; Louis Henri Sullivan (Ill.), 1901-21 (8 vols. and 17 drawings); Richard Upjohn (Mass., N.Y.) and Richard M. Upjohn (N.Y.), 500 items; and William Robert Ware (Mass., N.Y.), 1894-1900 (1 box and 1 envelope). Non-American architects are represented by works of Jacques Lemercier (France), 1639 (1 vol.); and drawings and manuscripts of Sebastiano Serlio (Italy, France), 1550 (1 vol.). Numerous works of architectural partnerships include those of Carrère and Hastings, 1912-29 (500 items); and Delano and Aldrich, 1907-31 (100 items). A Washington, D.C., collec-

tion, 1796-1876 (40 items), includes a few letters by Pierre Charles L'Enfant (France, N.Y., D.C.; Rev. War officer, engineer, architect). Also included is correspondence of Edith Elmer Wood (N.Y.; author, advocate of low-cost housing and other reforms), 1890-1945 (115 files).

East Asian Library. Howard P. Linton, Librarian.

Holdings: A collection dealing with the decipherment and interpretation of early Chinese writing; rubbings from inscribed stone stelae of the thirteen classics of the orthodox Confucian Canon, 9th century; a collection on the genealogy of 32 Chinese families, 1765-1928; a "Chinese Treasure Collection," 1700-1927 (42 vols. and 29 Chinese cases), including 24 Chinese books in manuscript; and Indusco, Inc., files, 1938-48 (11 shelves), concerning the Chinese Industrial Cooperatives.

Medical Library, College of Physicians and Surgeons. Thomas P. Fleming, Librarian.

Holdings: Included are letters of John Green Curtis (N.Y.; physiologist), 500 items relating to the history of medicine, psychology, and vivisection; correspondence of Frederick Schiller Lee (N.Y.; physiologist), 1885-1930 (6 boxes); and archives of the College of Physicians and Surgeons, 1773-1900 (6 boxes).

School of Law Library. Miles O. Price, Law Librarian.

Holdings: A small quantity of manuscripts relating chiefly to American law. Included are some colonial laws, a few early reports and registers of cases, and a collection concerning American and foreign copyright law.

See Greene and Morris, Guide, pp. xxiv, 222, and 353.

Teachers College Library. 525 West 120th St. Eleanor M. Witmer, Librarian.

Holdings: 300 pieces of miscellaneous character, 17th-20th centuries, relating chiefly to education, nursing, and cookery. Included are a few Renaissance manuscripts, and 19 letters, 1854-1900, of Florence Nightingale (England; nurse, hospital reformer).

See De Ricci, Census, p. 1273; and Hist. Records Survey, Guide for New York City, p. 26.

NEW YORK 3

Cooper Union Library. Cooper Square. Charlotte Fishgold, Preparations Librarian.

Holdings: 10,500 pieces, 1783-1933, consisting of papers of Peter Cooper (N.Y.; manufacturer, inventor, philanthropist, founder of Cooper Union), 1783-1887 (4,500 pieces); and Abram S. Hewitt (N.J., N.Y.; iron manufacturer, U.S. Rep. from N.Y., mayor of New York, philanthropist), 1803-1933 (6,000 pieces).

NEW YORK 18

Engineering Societies Library. 29 West 39th St. Ralph H. Phelps, Director.

Holdings: A small quantity of correspondence, patent papers, legal documents, and other materials relating chiefly to engineering in the United States. Of special importance

are electrical and telegraphic materials. Included are some letters of Robert Fulton (N.Y.; civil engineer, inventor) and several papers relating to Samuel F. B. Morse (Mass., N.Y.; artist, inventor) and the telegraph. There are also unpublished technical papers of the American Society of Civil Engineers, the American Institute of Mining, Metallurgical and Petroleum Engineers, the American Society of Mechanical Engineers, the American Institute of Electrical Engineers, and the Society of Automotive Engineers; memoirs of deceased members of the American Society of Civil Engineers; and unpublished records of the American Engineering Council, Washington, D.C., 1920-40.

See Hist. Records Survey, Guide for New York City, p. 28.

NEW YORK 14

Federal Records Center, GSA. 641 Washington St. Chief.

Holdings: A large quantity of noncurrent and semicurrent records, chiefly of recent date, consisting of (1) records of nonmilitary agencies of the U.S. Government in New York, New Jersey, and Delaware, and (2) the nationwide records of field offices of the terminated Home Owners' Loan Corporation and the Displaced Persons Commission of World War II. Most of the records have been appraised for disposal after specified periods of time, but some will be preserved because of their enduring value. Records in the latter category include those of U.S. district courts and predecessor circuit courts, from 1789; U.S. Circuit Court of Appeals, from 1881; Bureau of Customs, from 1789; Internal Revenue Service, from 1862; Immigration and Naturalization Service, from 1792; Panama Canal Company, from 1849; Public Health

Service, from 1832; and Weather Bureau, from 1864.

NEW YORK 58

Fordham University Library. Fordham Rd. and Third Ave. Joseph T. Hart, Librarian.

Holdings: 13 vols. and 82 pieces, 1684-1877, relating chiefly to America in the second half of the 18th century, especially the Revolutionary War, and constituting part of the Charles Allen Munn Collection. Included are an orderly book of Nathanael Greene (R.I., Ga.; Rev. War officer), Nov. 1781–Jan. 1782; papers of Charles Willson Peale (Md., Pa.; portrait painter, naturalist), 1786-1814 (1 vol. and 3 pieces), including his diary for 1788-89; an orderly book of John Ross (N.J.; Rev. War officer), May–Aug. 1779; a journal of Isaac Senter (R.I.; Rev. War surgeon), 1775, kept on Arnold's expedition to Quebec; papers of John Trumbull (Conn., N.Y.; Rev. War officer, historical painter), 1777-1827 (2 letter books, 1 account book, 29 sketches and studies, and 11 other pieces); papers of Jonathan Trumbull, Jr. (Conn.; Rev. War officer, military secretary to General Washington), 1776-81 (2 letters and a 1-vol. journal, Aug.–Nov. 1781); papers of George Washington (Va.; Rev. War Commander in Chief, U.S. Pres.), 1750-87 (3 vols. and 10 pieces), including 3 orderly books, 1775-79, and 2 maps made by him, 1750 and 1787; and the manuscript autobiography of Benjamin West (Pa., England; historical painter). There is also a volume of minutes of meetings of the freeholders of Westmoreland County, Va., Nov. 1775–Aug. 1776.

See the Library's 2 mimeographed lists, one of items in the Munn Collection (6 p.), and the other of original studies and sketches by John Trumbull (2 p.).

NEW YORK 21

Frick Art Reference Library. 10 East 71st St. Hannah Johnson Howell, Librarian.

Holdings: 65,000 photographs of medieval and Renaissance illuminated manuscripts.

See Hannah Johnson Howell, "The Frick Art Reference Library," College Art Journal, 11:123-126 (winter 1951-52).

NEW YORK 11

General Theological Seminary of the Protestant Episcopal Church in the United States of America. 175 Ninth Ave. (Chelsea Square.) Niels H. Sonne, Librarian.

Holdings: A number of volumes and 62 letter-sized boxes of unbound manuscripts, relating chiefly to the Episcopal Church. Included are some Oriental manuscripts, papyri fragments, a Hebrew folio codex Bible on vellum dated 1264 A.D., and Latin manuscripts; a collection of medieval and Renaissance Bibles (15 vols.); autograph collections containing letters of American bishops of the Episcopal Church (48 letter-sized boxes); a number of sermons and diaries, including diaries of Thomas B. Chandler (N.J., England; Anglican clergyman, loyalist), 1775-85, and of Charles Inglis (N.Y., Nova Scotia; Anglican bishop), 1785-1816, and a typescript of the private diary of Eugene Augustus Hoffman (N.J., N.Y., Pa.; Protestant Episcopal clergyman, dean of General Theological Seminary). There are also 1,041 papers of Samuel Roosevelt Johnson, including many references to the Roosevelt and

Delano families of Hyde Park, N. Y.,
1818-1916; papers of Samuel Seabury
(N. Y., Conn.; first American Episcopal bishop), 1740-96 (250 documents,
including several bound vols.), and 3
boxes of papers of his descendants;
and numerous other letters and papers
pertaining to the Seminary and the
church.

See Hist. Records Survey, Guide
for New York City, pp. 35-37; and De
Ricci, Census, pp. 1284-1287.

NEW YORK 22

Grolier Club Library.   47 East 60th
St.   George L. McKay, Librarian.

Holdings: A small collection relating chiefly to the art of bookmaking.
Included are European and Oriental
manuscripts, 11th-17th centuries (22
vols.); miscellaneous autographed documents of authors, printers, and booksellers, 1703-1889 (135 pieces); and
autographs or presentation inscriptions
written or laid in books, 1502-1920
(170 pieces).   There is also a collection of authors' manuscripts, from
1681, chiefly catalogs of their own collections of books and prints and works
relating to bookmaking.

See Hist. Records Survey, Guide
for New York City, pp. 39-42; and De
Ricci, Census, pp. 1289-1291.

NEW YORK 32

The Hispanic Society of America Library.   Broadway between 155th and
156th Sts.   Jean R. Longland, Curator
of the Library; Clara L. Penney,
Bibliographer and Curator of Manuscripts.

Holdings: Manuscripts, mostly
Spanish and dating from the 12th to the
20th centuries, include royal, ecclesiastical, and papal documents with cal-
ligraphic decorations and seals; illuminated church service books,
15th-18th centuries; charters of Ferdinand and Isabel, Charles I, and the
four Philips; 15th-century indentures
and deeds of sale; 18th-century documents relating to a pottery factory
at Alcora; and navigators' charts
(portolanos) of Mediterranean and Atlantic sea routes.   Papers of individuals include a diary of Washington
Irving (N. Y.; author, U. S. Minister
to Spain), 1828-29, written while in
Spain; and some letters of William
Hickling Prescott (Mass.; historian,
author), and George Ticknor (Mass.;
historian, author).

See De Ricci, Census, pp. 1292-
1300; and the following publications
of The Hispanic Society of America;
E. L. Stevenson, Portolan Charts
(1911. 76 p.); Frances Spalding,
"Spanish Illumination, a Fragment
From a Choir Book and Three Related Antiphonaries," in Notes Hispanic,
pp. 59-95 (1943); Jean R. Longland,
"Granados and the Opera Goyesca,"
in Notes Hispanic, pp. 95-112 (1945);
Frances Spalding, Mudejar Ornament
in Manuscripts (1953. 58 p.); an account of "Library Collections" in A
History of The Hispanic Society of
America, Museum and Library,
1904-1954: With a Survey of the Collections (1954. 569 p.); The Hispanic
Society of America Handbook: Museum and Library Collections (1938.
442 p.), containing detailed information about "Manuscript maps" by Anna Pursche, and about "Manuscripts
and books" by Clara L. Penney; and
other items cited in Catalogue of Publications (1943. 151 p.).

NEW YORK 5

Holland Society of New York
Library.   15 William St.
Wilson V. Ledley, Executive
Secretary.

Holdings: An unknown quantity of
material, 17th-19th centuries, relating chiefly to the Dutch Reformed
Church in New York and to Dutch settlements in North America before 1675.
In addition to original records and
transcripts of records of numerous
Dutch Reformed churches, there are
some records of Lutheran, French Reformed, and German Reformed churches. Also included are some military
papers of the period of the American
Revolution; and many unpublished genealogies of early American families of
Dutch and French Huguenot ancestry
carried down to the early 1800's.

See the Society's Year Books, especially the one for 1912, pp. 1-52,
containing "Inventory and Digest of
Early Church Records in the Library
of the Holland Society of New York";
Hist. Records Survey, Guide for New
York City, p. 43; and Greene and
Morris, Guide, pp. xxv, 284-292,
and passim.

NEW YORK 27

Jewish Theological Seminary of
America Library. 3080 Broadway.
Nahum M. Sarna, Librarian.

Holdings: A large body of manuscripts, 9th-20th centuries, relating
to Jewish history and literature. Included in the manuscript collections
of Elkan Nathan Adler, Morris Stein-
schneider, and Mayer Sulzberger and
the Hyman G. Enelow Memorial Collection (9,000 pieces in all) are 15,000
leaves from the Cairo Genizah, containing letters, documents, responsa,
and fragments of many lost or uniden-
tified works; Biblical scrolls and codices, vocalized and unvocalized, representing the various traditions of
Biblical calligraphy, orthography,
and vocalization; early Hebrew and
Judeo-Arabic Bible commentaries
and early Jewish translations of the

Bible into Arabic; manuscripts relating to Rabbinic law, Jewish philosophy, theology, and mysticism;
early Hebrew poetry and liturgy; and
medieval scientific texts in Hebrew,
Arabic, and Judeo-Persian. The Library also has a considerable collection of archives and record books of
various European Jewish communities and institutions, predominantly
from Italy, Germany, and Central
and Eastern Europe; Karaitic Bible
commentaries and legal codes; Samaritan manuscripts and commentaries; a collection of modern letters, chiefly written by the key figures in German-Jewish Wissenschaft
of the 19th century; and representative Jewish marriage contracts, most
of them illuminated, mainly from Italy and the Orient, dating from the
11th century to the present. There
are also many maps, prints, photographs, and etchings relative to Jewish subjects; and microfilms and photostats of outstanding medieval Hebrew
manuscripts chiefly from the Vatican
Library, the Genizah Collection at
Cambridge University, the Bibliotheca Escorial in Madrid, the Bod-
leian Library, the British Museum,
and the Bibliothèque Nationale.

NEW YORK 4

Library of the Sons of the Revolution
in the State of New York. Fraunces
Tavern, Broad and Pearl Sts. Mildred Willcox Treen, Executive
Secretary.

Holdings: 157 pieces, 1740-1914,
pertaining to American history, chiefly during the Revolutionary period.
Included are autograph letters and
papers of the signers of the Declaration of Independence, 1752-1810 (48
pieces), and of the Constitution of the
United States, 1753-1823 (36 pieces).
See Hist. Records Survey, Guide

for New York City, p. 113; and Greene and Morris, Guide, p. xxxiv and passim.

NEW YORK 71

Manhattan College Library. Manhattan College Parkway. Brother C. Leo, Librarian.

Holdings: 124 pieces in 1 vol., May 5–Sept. 8, 1667, relating to the English-Dutch treaties of 1662 and 1667 and to the acquisition of New Amsterdam by England.
See Hist. Records Survey, Guide for New York City, p. 51.

NEW YORK 28

Metropolitan Museum of Art. Fifth Ave. and 82d St. James Humphry III, Librarian.

Holdings: In various organizational units there are a large collection of Persian, Arabic, and Indian manuscripts; a small collection of medieval and later European manuscripts, illustrative of the arts of illuminating and drawing; some letters and other documents by George Washington (Va.; U.S. Pres.), 25 items on deposit in New York Public Library; sketchbooks, notebooks, professional diary, and miscellaneous correspondence of Alexander Jackson Davis (N.Y.; architect); a miscellaneous collection of letters of American artists, chiefly of the late 19th century (200 items); and official papers of the Trustees of the Museum, 1870 to date.
See De Ricci, Census, pp. 1306-1309; H. I. Poleman, A Census of Indic Manuscripts in the United States and Canada, passim (1938. 542 p.); and Hist. Records Survey, Guide for New York City, pp. 59-61.

NEW YORK 27

Missionary Research Library. 3041 Broadway. Frank Wilson Price, Director.

Holdings: Manuscripts relating to Christian missions to foreign countries and other matters of interest to the Library's sponsors, the Division of Foreign Missions of the NCCC [National Council of Churches of Christ]–USA (formerly the Foreign Missions Conference of North America) and the Union Theological Seminary of New York. Included are archives of various missionary conferences and movements, among them the Edinburgh Conference, 1910; the International Missionary Council, especially for the early years, 1910-20; and the Movement for World Christianity, 1936-37. There are also papers of various eminent missionaries and administrators, including Henry G. Appenzeller (Methodist missionary to Korea); James W. Bashford (Methodist bishop and missionary to China), 1904-18 (54 vols. of diaries); John Franklin Goucher (Md.; Methodist minister, pres. of Woman's College of Baltimore, now Goucher College); Edward H. Hume (China, N.Y.; physician); George H. Jones (Methodist missionary to Korea); John R. Mott (N.Y.; Y.M.C.A. and ecumenical leader); and Robert E. Speer (N.Y., Conn.; Presbyterian missionary statesman). Also included are papers relating to early mission work among North American Indians.
See Hist. Records Survey, Guide for New York City, p. 62.

NEW YORK 38

Municipal Archives and Records Center. 238 William St. James Katsaros, Administrator.

Holdings: 30,826 vols., 1,710 maps, 1,580 file drawers, and 1,542 document drawers, 1675-1956, consisting chiefly of official records of New York City but containing also some other manuscripts relating to its history. Included are records of the city clerk, 1675 to date (1,503 document drawers and numerous vols.), among them papers of Newbold Morris (pres. of the city council, 1936-45), and Genevieve W. Earle (minority leader of the city council, 1912-49); minutes of the common council and Board of Aldermen, 1784-1938; rosters and ledgers of the police and fire departments, 1787-1865; tax-assessment records, 1808-1953 (20,000 vols.); an extensive series of mayoralty papers, 1837 to date, a valuable adjunct being a large quantity of the personal papers of Mayor Fiorello H. La Guardia; records of the city's civilian defense agency during World War II (42 file drawers), and of the city's temporary housing rent commission, 1945-48 (36 file drawers); and papers of the Historical Records Survey for New York City, 1938-41 (196 file drawers). Many official records of the city, formerly in the New York Public Library, are now in the possession of this Center.

See, for some of the records now in this depository, I. N. Phelps Stokes, The Iconography of Manhattan Island, 6:185-223 (1928); and Greene and Morris, Guide, pp. 208-211, 331-333.

NEW YORK 29

Museum of the City of New York. Fifth Ave. and East 104th St. Philip A. Rees, Librarian.

Holdings: 25,000 pieces, 1651-1954, relating chiefly to New York City and prominent families of the 18th and 19th centuries. Included are papers of John Quincy Adams (Mass.;

diplomat, U.S. Pres.), 1783-84 (26 pieces), consisting of letters to Peter Jay Munro; John Jay (N.Y.; Pres. of Continental Cong., diplomat, U.S. Chief Justice, Gov.), 1783-1818 (178 pieces); Samuel Jones (N.Y.; lawyer), 1759-1801 (100 pieces), including 50 opinions in estate and admiralty cases; Thomas Jones (N.Y.; jurist, loyalist), 1769-92 (3 vols. and 30 pieces); Philip Livingston (N.Y.; merchant, Member Continental Cong.), 1744-51 (64 pieces); and John Loudon McAdam (England; engineer) and his wife, 1823-52 (56 pieces). There are papers of the De Lancey family, 1686-1865 (3 vols. and 320 pieces), relating primarily to James De Lancey (N.Y.; Lt. Gov. of New York Province), James De Lancey (N.Y.; nephew of Lt. Gov. De Lancey, loyalist, leader of partisan troops), and William Heathcote De Lancey (N.Y.; Episcopal bishop). There are also extensive real estate papers, diaries of early New Yorkers, and papers of several New York business houses and churches of the 18th and 19th centuries.

See Hist. Records Survey, Guide for New York City, p. 63, and Guide for N.Y. State, Supplement, pp. 5-11; and Greene and Morris, Guide, p. xxvi and passim.

NEW YORK 28

National Audubon Society Library. 1130 Fifth Ave. R. Michel, Librarian.

Holdings: 50 papers relating chiefly to ornithology. Included are some letters and manuscripts of John James Audubon (Pa., Ky., La., N.Y.; artist, ornithologist), mostly 1843.

NEW YORK 29

New York Academy of Medicine.

2 East 103d St.   Gertrude L. Annan, Librarian.

Holdings: 4,987 items, 9th-20th centuries, relating chiefly to medicine in Europe and the United States.   Included are 16 medieval and Renaissance medical manuscripts; several diaries, among them one by Willard Parker (Vt., N.Y.; surgeon), 1837 (1 vol.), on a trip to France, and others by Peter Solomon Townsend, 1821-38 (21 vols.), on travels throughout England, France, and Cuba; and 33 letters of John and Samuel Bard (N.Y.; physicians), and correspondence of other 18th-century physicians.   There are also letters of David Hosack (N.Y.; physician, prof. at Columbia College and the College of Physicians and Surgeons), 85 pieces; papers of William Henry Welch (Md.; physician, prof. at Johns Hopkins Univ. and director of its School of Hygiene and Public Health), 61 pieces; lecture notes and letters by Valentine Mott (N.Y.; physician, authority on surgical anesthesia), 1815-68 (29 pieces); and numerous case books, lecture notes, collections of recipes, diplomas, and records of medical societies, especially of the New York area.   A large number of volumes of medical records of medical societies are not included in the total number of holdings of the Academy since they are the property of the societies, deposited for safekeeping.
See De Ricci, Census, pp. 1310-1313; Hist. Records Survey, Guide for New York City, pp. 64-66; and Greene and Morris, Guide, p. xxvi and passim.

NEW YORK 55

New York Botanical Garden Library.   Bronx Park. Elizabeth C. Hall, Librarian.

Holdings: A large collection of papers of John Torrey (N.Y.; botanist, chemist, college prof.), containing letters from most outstanding 19th-century botanists, including letters of Charles Robert Darwin (England; naturalist, author), George Engelmann (Germany, Mo.; meteorologist, physician, botanist), Asa Gray (N.Y., Mass.; botanist, Harvard Univ. prof.), and Constantine S. Rafinesque (Ky., Pa.; botanist, ichthyologist, prof. at Transylvania Univ.).

NEW YORK 22

New York Genealogical and Biographical Society.   122 East 58th St. Arthur Adams, Librarian.

Holdings: 40,000 vols. on genealogy, biography, and history, from colonial times to the present, consisting of copies of church records, cemetery inscriptions, and other sources of genealogical information.
See lists of accessions in the Society's quarterly N.Y. Genealogical and Biographical Record (1870 to date), especially 49:11-16 (Jan. 1918) and 52:152-157 (Apr. 1921), for a report on early New York church records transcribed; and Greene and Morris, Guide, p. xxvii and passim.

NEW YORK 24

New-York Historical Society.   170 Central Park West.   R. W. G. Vail, Director; James J. Heslin, Assistant Director and Librarian.

Holdings: A large number of collections, 17th-20th centuries, relating to many important aspects of American history at the national level and especially to the history of New York City.

Papers of Presidents and Vice Presidents of the United States include those of John Adams (Mass.; U. S. Vice Pres. and Pres.), 1775-1819 (70 pieces); John Quincy Adams (Mass.; U. S. Pres.), 1796-1845 (1 vol. and 67 pieces); Chester A. Arthur (N. Y.; U.S. Vice Pres. and Pres.), 1868-81 (8 letter books and 1 box); James Buchanan (Pa.; U. S. Pres.), 1829-65 (35 letters); Aaron Burr (N. Y.; U. S. Vice Pres.), 1779-1833 (70 letters from him and other papers); Grover Cleveland (N. Y.; U. Y. Pres.), 1884-1900 (30 pieces); George Clinton (N. Y.; Gov., U. S. Vice Pres.), 1769-1812 (160 letters from him and letters to and documents signed by him as Governor); Ulysses S. Grant (U. S. Army officer, U. S. Pres.), 1862-77 (35 pieces); William Henry Harrison (Ohio; U. S. Pres.), 1810-49 (13 pieces); Andrew Jackson (Tenn.; U. S. Pres.), 1797-1840 (21 letters from him and others to him); Thomas Jefferson (Va.; U. S. Vice Pres. and Pres.), 1781-1826 (130 letters from him and other papers and letters to him); Abraham Lincoln (Ill.; U. S. Pres.), 1858-65 (2 vols. and 2 boxes); James Madison (Va.; U. S. Pres.), 1784-1835 (134 pieces); James Monroe (Va.; U. S. Pres.), 1794-1824 (50 pieces); and George Washington (Va.; U. S. Pres.), 1765-98 (215 letters). The Society also has original bulletins about the condition of James A. Garfield (Ohio; U. S. Pres.), July–Sept. 1881 (1 vol.); and a collection of autographs and portraits of Presidents, 1789-1939 (1 vol.).

Papers of members of Presidents' cabinets include those of Salmon Portland Chase (Ohio; Gov., U. S. Sen., Sec. Treas., Chief Justice of U. S.), 1841-68 (30 letters); Henry Clay (Ky.; U. S. Rep. and Sen., Sec. State), 1817-45 (116 pieces); Jefferson Davis (Miss.; U. S. Rep. and Sen., Sec. War, Confed. Pres.), 1841-89 (54 letters); Edward Everett (Mass.; Gov., Minis-

ter to Great Britain, U. S. Rep. and Sen., Sec. State), 1818-63 (35 letters); Charles S. Fairchild (N. Y.; Sec. Treas.), 1873-1924 (7 boxes); Albert Gallatin (Pa., N. Y.; U. S. Rep., Sec. Treas., Minister to France and to Great Britain) and his family, 1258-1947 (20 vols., 82 boxes, and 1 safe); Alexander Hamilton (N. Y.; Rev. War officer, Member Continental Cong., Sec. Treas.), 1777-1804 (156 letters from him and others to him); Horatio King (Maine, D. C.; editor, lawyer, Postmaster Gen.), 1862-80 (2 vols.); Henry Knox (Mass.; Rev. War officer, Sec. War), 1777-1801 (260 pieces); Samuel Osgood (Mass., N. Y.; Rev. War officer, Commissioner of U. S. Treas., Postmaster Gen.), 1775-1812 (1 vol.); Timothy Pickering (Mass.; Rev. War officer, Postmaster Gen., Sec. War, Sec. State, U. S. Sen. and Rep.), 1777-1824 (300 letters); Richard Rush (Pa.; Attorney Gen., Sec. State, Minister to Great Britain and to France), 1813-59 (76 pieces); Robert James Walker (Pa., Miss.; U. S. Sen. from Miss., Sec. Treas., Gov. of Kansas Terr.), 1836-69 (100 letters); and Oliver Wolcott, Jr. (Conn., N. Y.; banker, Sec. Treas.), 1804-15 (2 account books), including information concerning trade with China.

Papers of public officials, not mentioned elsewhere, include those of James Alexander (N.Y., N.J.; surveyor-gen. of N. Y. and N. J., attorney gen. of N. J.) and William Alexander, known as Lord Stirling (N. J., N. Y.; surveyor-gen. of N.J., Rev. War officer), 1717-83 (6 vols. and 69 boxes); John Bailey (Mass.; U. S. Rep.), 1817-30 (77 pieces); Nicholas Bayard (N. Y.; colonial leader, sec. of the province of N. Y., mayor of New York) and his family, 1710-1848 (600 pieces); Gerardus Beekman (N. Y.; physician, colonial Gov.) and his family, 1709-1877 (15,000 pieces); Elias Boudinot (N. J.; Rev. War officer, Pres. of Continental Cong., U. S. Rep., Director of the Mint), 1771-1817 (50 pieces); DeWitt Clinton (N.Y.; U.S. Sen., mayor of New York, Gov.), 1788-1828 (10 vols. of diaries and 50 letters); George Clinton (N. Y.; colonial Gov.), 1744-53 (55 pieces); Cadwallader Colden (Pa., N. Y.; physician, scientist, author, colonial Lt. Gov. of N. Y.), 1711-55 (12 boxes); William Darlington (Pa.; physician, botanist, U. S. Rep.), 1800-62 (19 vols. and 1 folder); George Davis (U. S. Chargé d'Affaires in Tunis), 1804-8 (2 letter books); Chevalier Charles Frederick de Loosey (Austrian consul gen. at New York), 1843-68 (20 vols.), including letters from Emperor Maximilian of Mexico; James Duane (N. Y.; Member Continental Cong., mayor of New York, U. S. dist. court judge), 1765-95 (5 vols. and 10 boxes); William Duer (England, N. Y.; merchant, financier, Member Continental Cong.), 1752-99 (4 vols. and 11 boxes); Edward Henry Durell (La., N. Y.; U. S. dist. court judge in La., author), 1802-87 (20 vols. and 14 packages); Edmond Charles Genêt (France, N. Y.; French Minister to U. S.), 1792-1824 (200 pieces); Horace Greeley (N. Y.; editor of New York Tribune, U. S. Rep.), 1846-70 (61 letters); Jabez D. Hammond (N. Y.; U. S. Rep., county judge), 1826-52 (46 pieces); Benjamin Harrison (Va.; Member Continental Cong., Gov.), 1787-89 (1 vol.); and Daniel Horsmanden (N. Y.; chief justice of the Province), 1714-47 (2 vols.), relating to colonial history of New York, the John Peter Zenger case, and Indian affairs.

Other papers of public officials, not mentioned elsewhere, include those of John Jay (N. Y.; Pres. of Continental Cong., diplomat, U. S. Chief Justice), 1779-94 (1 vol. and 8 boxes); John Jay 2d (N. Y.; lawyer, Minister to Austria), 1846-83 (303 pieces); Sir William Johnson (N. Y.; French and Indian War officer, supt. of Indian affairs), 1747-75 (102 pieces); John Tabor Kempe (N. Y.; State attorney gen.), 1760-80 (15 boxes); John Alsop King (N. Y.; lawyer, U. S. Rep., Gov.), 1834-57 (1 box and 5 pieces); Rufus King (Mass., N. Y.; Member Continental Cong., U. S. Sen. from N. Y., Minister to Great Britain), 1787-1826 (55 vols. and 36 boxes); Robert R. Livingston (N.Y.; Member Continental Cong., Sec. of Foreign Affairs, Chancellor of N. Y., Minister to France) and his family, 1707-1880 (25,000 pieces); James Lovell (Mass.; Member Continental Cong.), 1777-82 (41 pieces); George B. McClellan, Jr. (N. Y., N. J.; U. S. Rep. from N. Y., mayor of New York), 1904-9 (4 letter books and 8 vols. of autographs); Edwin D. Morgan (N. Y.; Gov., Civil War officer, U. S. Sen.), 1859-63 (16 vols. and 1 box); William Plumer, Jr. (N. H.; U. S. Rep.) and his family, 1810-78 (1 folder); Le Baron Bradford Prince (N.Y., N. Mex.; chief justice and Gov. of N. Mex. Terr.), 1863-93 (1 box); Robert Barnwell Roosevelt (N. Y.; lawyer, newspaper editor, U. S. Rep., Minister to The Netherlands), 1892-96 (23 vols. and 1 box); George Frederick Seward (N. Y.; Minister to China, insurance co. pres.), 1890-1910 (4 boxes); Horatio Seymour (N. Y.; lawyer, Gov.), 1844-86 (4 boxes and 130 pieces); Daniel E. Sickles (N.Y.; Civil War officer, Minister to Spain, U. S. Rep.), 1851-1911 (1 box); William S. Smith (N. Y.; Rev. War officer, U. S. Rep.), 1781-1826 (33 letters); Ephraim George Squier (N.Y.; journalist, archeologist, U. S. Chargé d'Affaires in Central America), 1849-50, 1856-57 (7 vols. and 500 pieces), relating to Central America and the Clayton-Bulwer Treaty; William Sulzer (N. Y.; U. S. Rep., Gov.), 1914-41 (903 pieces); John W. Taylor (N. Y.; lawyer, U. S. Rep., antislavery leader), 1813-33 (7 boxes); Killian K. Van Rensselaer (N. Y.; lawyer, U.S.

Rep.) and his family, 1713-1858 (2 boxes); Gulian C. Verplanck (N. Y.; author, U.S. Rep.), 1830-70 (12 boxes); and Jonathan Mayhew Wainwright (N. Y.; Spanish-American War and World War I officer, U.S. Rep.), 1888-1943 (6 boxes).

Papers providing information for the military history of the American Revolution include papers of Benedict Arnold (Conn.; Rev. War officer, traitor), 1772-82 (140 pieces); Horatio Gates (Va., N. Y.; Rev. War officer, planter), 1750-99 (30 boxes); Aquila Giles (Md.; Rev. War officer) and his family, 1750-1838 (2 boxes); Udny Hay (Pa.; Rev. War officer), 1776-92 (168 pieces); Hugh Hughes (N. Y.; Rev. War officer), 1776-82 (19 vols.); Nathanael Greene (R. I., Ga.; Rev. War officer), 1777-84 (110 letters); William Heath (Mass.; Rev. War officer), 1775-83 (1 vol. and 125 pieces); the Marquis de Lafayette (France; American Rev. War officer), 1778-1831 (95 pieces); John Lamb (N. Y.; a leader of the Sons of Liberty, Rev. War officer, collector of customs at New York), 1765-95 (29 orderly books and 6 boxes); Benjamin Lincoln (Mass.; Rev. War officer), 1775-1807 (85 pieces); Alexander McDougall (N. Y.; merchant, Rev. War officer, Member Continental Cong.), 1756-95 (15 orderly books, 7 boxes, and 4,000 pieces); Allan McLane (Del.; Rev. War officer, U.S. marshal, collector of customs at Wilmington), 1775-1821 (3 vols.); William Malcolm (N. Y.; Rev. War officer), 1777-83 (6 vols. and 50 pieces); Joseph Reed (N. J., Pa.; lawyer, Rev. War officer, Member Continental Cong.), 1757, 1763-95 (12 vols. of correspondence); Baron Friedrich Wilhelm von Steuben (Prussia, France, N. Y.; Rev. War officer), 1778-82 (6 vols. and 6 boxes); Ebenezer Stevens (R. I., N. Y.; Rev. War officer, merchant), 1775-1814 (3 vols. and 3 boxes); Richard Varick (N. Y.; Rev. War officer, George Washington's record-

ing sec., mayor of New York), 1774-1828 (600 pieces); Jeremiah Wadsworth (Conn.; Rev. War officer, Member Continental Cong., U.S. Rep.), 1776-1800 (1 box); and Marinus Willett (N. Y.; Rev. War officer, mayor of New York), 1775-1808 (30 pieces). There are also letter books and account books of John de Neufville and Son, U.S. agents at Amsterdam during the American Revolution, 1780-85 (7 vols.); a large number of orderly books; and miscellaneous diaries, journals, letters, and other papers.

Papers of Army officers in other wars include those of Alexander R. Chisholm (S. C., N. Y.; Confed. Army officer, stockbroker), 1861-1901 (3 boxes); Henry Dearborn (Mass.; War of 1812 officer), 1812-13 (2 vols.), letters and orders; James Guthrie Harbord (N. Y.; U.S. Army officer in Spanish-American War and World War I, pres. of Radio Corp. of America), 1914-46 (16 vols. and 12 boxes); Francis Jay Herron (Iowa; Civil War officer), 1861-66 (1 letter book and 2 boxes); James P. MacIvor (N. Y.; Civil War officer), 1863-65 (30 pieces); Franz Sigel (Mo., N. Y.; Civil War officer, newspaper editor), 1861-89 (10 vols. and 7 boxes); Daniel Ullman (Del., N. Y.; Civil War officer), 1830-85 (2 boxes), formerly in the Historical Society of Delaware; and an assistant quartermaster and chief paymaster of the Confederate Army, 1861-64 (2 letter books). There are also numerous documents of miscellaneous types that relate to the French and Indian War, the War of 1812, and the Civil War.

Papers formerly belonging to the Naval History Society were given to the New-York Historical Society in 1925 and are now maintained in the Naval History Section. These, together with papers from other sources that relate to naval and other aspects of maritime history, include papers of John Barry (U.S. naval officer), 1781-1801 (signal book, letter book, and public and private correspondence); French Ensor Chadwick (U. S. naval officer), 1886-88 (12 letter books); Isaac Chauncey (U. S. naval officer), 1805-21 (6 letter books and 1 vol. of accounts); Gustavus Conyngham (Pa.; U. S. naval officer), 1777-79 (3 vols. and 1 portfolio); James Fenimore Cooper (N. Y.; novelist), 11 vols. and 1 box, consisting chiefly of manuscripts of his biographical sketches of John Paul Jones and Commodores Bainbridge, Barry, and O. H. Perry, and prints and manuscripts illustrating his history of the U. S. Navy; John Ericson (N. Y.; engineer, inventor, designer of the Monitor and other naval vessels), 1831-88 (1 vol. and 49 boxes); Gustavus Vasa Fox (Mass.; U. S. naval officer, Asst. Sec. Navy), 1841-83 (11 vols. of diary and 19 boxes); Samuel Dana Greene (U. S. naval officer), 1869-83 (10 vols.); Isaac Hull (U. S. naval officer, commandant of Boston and Washington Navy Yards), 1809-41 (15 vols. of letter books and order books); Edward Yorke McCauley (U. S. naval officer), 1845-76 (1 vol. and 2 packages), including his journal on Perry's expedition to Japan; Richard Worsam Meade 2d (U. S. naval officer), 1839-67 (4 vols. and 1 box); Richard Worsam Meade 3d (U. S. naval officer), 1853-95 (14 vols. and 2 boxes); David Dixon Porter (U. S. naval officer), 1841-70 (3 logbooks and 55 letters); and Henry Augustus Wise (U. S. naval officer, author), 1861-68 (15 vols. and manuscripts of 2 novels). There are also a number of logs of U. S. naval vessels; journals of cruises; the letter book of an agent seeking information for a railroad across the Isthmus of Panama, 1835-36; records of the United States Mail Steamship Co., 1848-59 (4 letter books and 12 logbooks of vessels plying between New York and Panama); a collection of miscellaneous manuscripts relating to U. S. naval officers and ships (8 boxes); and various papers from customhouses at Baltimore, 1763-1809 (4 vols. and 1 box), Bristol and Warren, R. I., 1801-55 (6 vols.), and New York, 1790-1835 (6 boxes).

Papers relating to architecture, the fine arts, music, and literature include papers of Ezra Ames (N. Y.; artist), 1790-1826 (40 pieces); Joel Barlow (Conn.; poet, diplomat), 1783-1811 (1 vol.); Marion Corbett England; author), 1839-40 (14 vols.), comprising journals of a trip to America; Ruth Draper (N. Y.; actress), 20th century (several cartons); Albert Eugene Gallatin (N. Y.; painter, author), 1916-50 (6 boxes); George F. Kunz (N. Y.; gem expert, vice pres. of Tiffany and Co.), 1882-1932 (2,129 pieces), chiefly letters to him from prominent people; Benson J. Lossing (N. Y.; author of popular historical works), 1850-90 (38 pieces); John McComb, Jr. (N. Y.; architect), 1803-25 (6 vols. and 1 box); Frank Moore (N. Y.; author), 1861-75 (1 letter book and 200 letters to him); William Sidney Mount (N. Y.; portrait and genre painter), 1841-68 (65 pieces); George B. Post (N. Y.; architect), drawings, ledgers, and letter books; John Ramage (N. Y., Canada; painter of miniatures), 1783-1802 (1 box); John Rogers (N. Y., Conn.; sculptor), 1837-1933 (635 pieces); I. N. Phelps Stokes (N. Y.; architect, iconographer), 1898-1937 (28 vols. and 36 boxes); Emma Thursby (N. Y.; singer), 1860-1921 (57 vols. and 7 boxes); John Trumbull (Conn., N. Y.; historical painter), 1787-1839 (8 vols., 1 box, and 2 packages); John Vanderlyn (N. Y.; historical and portrait painter), 1796-1852 (225 letters); and John Quincy Adams Ward (N. Y.; sculptor), 1857-1915 (800 pieces). There are also records of the American Academy of Fine Arts (New York City), 1803-40 (13 vols.); the Italian Opera Association (New York City), 1832-40 (1 vol.

and 1 package); and the American
Art Union (New York City), 1840-51
(109 vols. and 1 box); and correspondence, specifications, drawings, and
other records of McKim, Mead and
White (architects), from 1879 (350
file drawers, 300 bundles, and 500
tubes).

Papers relating especially to religious history include, in addition to
records of a number of New York
churches, papers of Titus Coan (N.Y.,
Hawaii; Presbyterian clergyman, missionary) and his wife, 1830-72 (2 boxes of letters); Francis L. Hawkes
(N.Y., La.; Episcopal clergyman,
historian), 1830-60 (6 boxes), and his
transcripts of documents in British depositories relating to the Anglican
Church in America, chiefly 18th century (17 vols.); John Henry Hobart
(N.Y.; Episcopal bishop, prof. at the
General Theological Seminary), 1757-
1830 (40 vols.); Samuel Johnson
(Conn., N.Y.; Anglican clergyman,
pres. of King's College), 1724-71 (1
vol. and 1 folder); Philip Milledoler
(N.Y., Pa., N.J.; German Reformed,
Presbyterian, and Dutch Reformed
clergyman, pres. of Rutgers College),
1785-1852 (2,000 items); John Murray
(Mass.; founder of Universalism in
America), 1799-1811 (1 vol. and 20
pieces); Benjamin T. Onderdonk (N.Y.;
Episcopal bishop), 1812-32 (3 vols.
and 5 boxes); Samuel Andrew Peters
(Conn., England, N.Y.; Anglican clergyman, Loyalist), 1773-1822 (8 vols.);
John S. Ravenscroft (Va., N.C.; Episcopal bishop), 1818-30 (3 vols.); Robert Seton (N.J., Italy; Catholic archbishop, author), early 20th century (2
boxes of diaries and notebooks); William Smith (Pa., Md.; Episcopal clergyman, educator), 1717-99 (3 vols.
and 1 folder); John Stanford (N.Y.;
Baptist clergyman, chaplain of the
New York State Prison), 1795-1832
(20 vols. and 2 packages); William
White (Pa.; Episcopal bishop), 1762-
1836 (3 vols. and 1 folder); and Wil-

liam R. Williams (N.Y.; Baptist
clergyman, pastor of Amity Street
Church in New York City) and his
family, 1834-35 (2 vols.).

Papers of various persons, not
identified elsewhere in this entry,
include those of Alexander Anderson
(N.Y.; engraver), 1793-1869 (1 box);
Thomas Barclay (British consul gen.
and commissioner for English prisoners in New York), 1812-14 (6
vols. and 11 boxes); Edwin Davis
French (N.Y.; engraver, bookplate
designer), 1896-1906 (165 pieces);
Robert Fulton (N.Y.; civil engineer,
inventor), 1809-16 (4 vols. and 2
boxes); Richard Harison (N.Y.; lawyer) and his family, 1732-1860 (10
boxes); Stephen Jumel (N.Y., France;
wine merchant) and his wife, who later married Aaron Burr, 1763-1852
(1,000 pieces); Joseph Keppler (Mo.,
N.Y.; caricaturist, founder of Puck),
1880-1903; John McKesson (N.Y.;
lawyer), 1761-1825 (11 vols. and 10
boxes); Jedidiah Morse (Mass.; Congregational clergyman, geographer),
1788-1822 (164 pieces); Eben E. Olcott (N.Y.; mining engineer, director
of Hudson River Day Line, banker),
1882-1905 (9 vols. and 15 boxes);
Henry O'Reilly (N.Y.; newspaper,
editor, pamphleteer, pioneer in the
erection of telegraph lines), 1825-80
(31 boxes, 55 scrapbooks and bundles); Alfred Paul (French representative at Richmond, Va., during the
Civil War), 1860-63 (7 vols.); John
Pintard (N.J., N.Y.; merchant, philanthropist), 1793-99 (3 vols. and 6
boxes); William Prince and his son
William Robert Prince (N.Y.; nur-
serymen, writers on horticultural
subjects) and family, 1817-1900 (2
boxes); Henry S. Randall (N.Y.; agriculturist, author), 1828-70 (114
pieces); Louisa Lee Schuyler (N.Y.;
leader in welfare work), 1863-65 (124
pieces); Granville Sharp (England; antislavery leader), 1768-73 (3 vols.);
Buckingham Smith (Fla.; lawyer,

antiquarian), 23 vols. and 3 boxes), including his collection of originals and transcripts of 16th-18th century materials relating to the Spaniards in North America, especially Florida; Gerrit Smith (N.Y.; philanthropist, abolitionist, U.S. Rep.), 1834-74 (45 letters); William Smith, known as Tangier Smith (N.Y.; colonial supreme court chief justice), and his family, 1666-1879 (3 boxes); Lysander Spooner (Mass.; lawyer, writer on political subjects, antislavery leader), 1845-62 (2 boxes); John Austin Stevens (N.Y.; financier, historian), second half of 19th century (22 vols. and 1 box); Thurlow Weed (N.Y.; newspaper editor, political leader), 1818-82 (152 pieces); and David Zeisberger (Pa., Ohio; Moravian missionary to the Indians), a dictionary of the language of the Delaware Indians. There are also papers of the Van Cortlandt family of New York, 1695-1820 (41 vols. and 100 pieces).

There are extensive holdings of business records. These include records of the Scioto Land Co., 1785-93 (2 boxes); papers of George Newbold (N.Y.; merchant, ironmonger, pres. of Bank of America), 1800-49 (4 vols. and 9 boxes), and of many other businessmen and business firms in New York City; records of the American Fur Co., 1831-47 (18,181 items); records of the Hudson River Day Line and other papers relating to steamboats on the Hudson River, 19th-20th centuries (hundreds of volumes and boxes); papers relating to the reorganization of the Erie Railway Co., 1874-78 (125 items); and records of meetings of the New York Board of Trade, 1878-1914 (13 boxes). There is a substantial collection of account books of persons and firms, chiefly in New York City and nearby areas. The papers of many persons named elsewhere in this entry contain business papers.

Papers relating especially to the Province and State of New York and to New York City are present in large quantities. Many of these are mentioned elsewhere in this entry. Others include journals of the General Assembly of the Province, 1698-1705 (1 vol.), and of the State, 1777-92 (15 vols.); various scattered court records, from 1680; and miscellaneous military papers. There are miscellaneous papers relating to Albany, N.Y., 1667-1865 (4 vols. and 10 boxes); to Schenectady, N.Y., 18th and early 19th centuries (3 boxes); and to other places within the State. For New York City in particular there are scattered official records of the city, dating from as early as 1706; an extensive collection of miscellaneous papers relating to many aspects of the city's history, from 1641 (23 boxes); and papers of 3 mayors of the city, chiefly for the periods of their official service: Stephen Allen, 1821-25, 1847-49 (20 vols.), James Harper, 1844-45 (1 box), and Abram S. Hewitt, 1887-88 (3 vols.). There are scattered records of the Tammany Society of New York City, 1789-1812 (5 vols.); and records of numerous associations, clubs, and societies of varied character.

Miscellaneous papers include a collection relating to Canada, 1694-1814 (2 boxes); a collection of correspondence and other papers on the slave trade and writings and reports of individuals about slavery, 18th-19th centuries (7 boxes); an autograph collection of letters of American statesmen, merchants, and journalists, 1762-1950 (613 pieces); official correspondence of the French administration at Port au Prince, Haiti, 1774-80 (3 letter books); a meteorological journal kept at Detroit, Mich., 1781-86; notes about the Jews of Charleston, S.C., 1783-1897 (2 vols. and 2 boxes); records of the Society for Promoting the Manumission of Slaves, New York City, 1786-1849 (11 vols.); minutes and other records of the United States

Military Philosophical Society, 1789-1813 (4 vols.); scattered records of the United States District Court for the Southern District of New York, 1805-13 (1 vol. and 1 box); papers of the French vice-consulate at Norfolk, Va., 1811-15 (1 vol.); journals and reports of the commissioners to carry into effect the 5th, 6th, and 7th articles of the Treaty of Ghent (11 vols.); minutes of the Society for the Prevention of the Absconding and Abduction of Slaves, Richmond, Va., 1833 (1 vol.); a letter book about the United States Sanitary Commission and miscellaneous papers of the Commission, 1861-64 (1 vol. and 1 package); minutes and letter books of the Committee for the Relief of East Tennessee, 1864-65 (3 vols.); and numerous diaries and travel journals.

See the Society's Survey of Manuscript Collections (1941. 96 p.); its Quarterly, for notes of accessions and special articles on collections (1917 to date); and its Annual Reports. See also Dorothy C. Barck, "New York Historical Society," in Business Hist. Society, Bulletin, 8:1-5 (Jan. 1934); Hist. Records Survey, Guide for New York City, pp. 69-73; Grace L. Nute, Calendar of the American Fur Company's Papers, in Am. Hist. Assn., Annual Report for 1944, vols. 2 and 3; Greene and Morris, Guide, pp. xxvii-xxix and passim; and Forest History Sources, p. 84.

NEW YORK 5

New York Law Institute Library. 120 Broadway. Lionel J. Coen, Librarian.

Holdings: Among the manuscripts in the special historical collection of this oldest law library in the city are a law register of Alexander Hamilton; a volume of law precedents of DeWitt Clinton, 1786-94; and some cases and opinions of Charles O'Conor (N. Y.; lawyer).

See Hist. Records Survey, Guide for New York City, p. 73.

NEW YORK 18

New York Public Library. Fifth Ave. and 42d St. Edward G. Freehafer, Director; Robert W. Hill, Chief, Manuscript Division.

Holdings: 9,000,000 pieces in the Manuscript Division proper, occupying 15,000 linear feet of shelving, and comprising adequate to superb examples of the recorded word, in most of its media, periods, and tongues—from Sumerian clay tablets to modern authors' scripts and the "make-up" of magazines. Additional manuscripts are in the following separately administered units of the Library: (1) William A. Spencer Collection of books finely bound and finely illustrated; (2) George Arents Collection on Tobacco, supplementing its printed rarities with manuscripts signed by 16th- and 17th-century public figures of Europe connected with the production or use of tobacco and by many significant American figures; (3) Henry W. and Albert A. Berg Collection, noteworthy for its emphasis on English and American literature and containing, in addition to its first editions, extensive holdings of literary manuscripts and correspondence of the 19th and 20th centuries; (4) Arthur Schomburg Collection on Negro history and culture, which is housed in the Library's 135th Street branch but is represented by a duplicate of its card catalog adjacent to the public card catalog in the Central Building; and (5) Music Division, which has 900 musical manuscripts, mostly of the 19th or 20th centuries, and numerous autographed letters. Most of the manuscripts described below are in the Manuscript Division, unless otherwise expressly stated; and the box cited as a unit of measurement is a container used in many archival and manuscript depositories that holds 200 to 250 items of ordinary correspondence.

The oldest materials in the Manuscript Division are 15,000 clay and stone tablets and stelae, almost entirely the result of collecting by Wilberforce Eames (N. Y.; bibliographer). Next in antiquity are its two specimen groups of Egyptian papyri or its six Hebrew amulets on beaten gold or silver. Medieval and Renaissance manuscripts of European origin, 270 items, are held by both the Manuscript Division and the Spencer Collection; and these two units also hold 8 Slavonic and 10 Hebrew codices, and several hundred other items of Near East or Far East origin or language, the Spencer Collection having had very extensive growth in such resources in recent years. Another collection of unique nature, related to documentation and certain specialized aspects of manuscript problems, is the Mortimer and Anna Neinken Collection of antique seals. This comprises 14,000 wax impressions of heraldic and guild arms, the earliest examples going back to about 1650.

Papers relating especially to Latin America include the Rich Collection (142 vols.), and papers in other collections providing information about Brazil, Mexico, Paraguay, Peru, Venezuela, and other countries. There are several small groups filed according to the country or area of the Western Hemisphere, outside the United States of America, to which they pertain. Also included is a set of photocopies of the series, "Papeles de Cuba," 1766-91 (30 vols. plus index), in the Archivo Generale de Indias, in Seville, Spain. Most of the Library's other holdings, described below, relate chiefly to the United States.

Papers of U.S. Presidents and Vice Presidents include those of John Adams (Mass.; Member Continental Cong., diplomat, U. S. Vice Pres. and Pres.), 1776-97 (24 pieces); John Quincy Adams (Mass.; U. S. Sen. and Rep., diplomat, Sec. State, U. S. Pres.), 1794-1840 (50 pieces); George Clinton (N. Y.; Member Continental Cong., Rev. War officer, Gov., U. S. Vice Pres.), 1777-81 (190 pieces); Warren G. Harding (Ohio; U. S. Sen. and Pres.), 1916-20 (121 pieces); Andrew Jackson (Tenn.; U. S. Rep. and Sen., U. S. Army officer, U. S. Pres.), 1806-64 (254 pieces); Thomas Jefferson (Va.; Member Continental Cong., Gov., Minister to France, Sec. State, U. S. Vice Pres. and Pres.), 1766-1826 (1-vol. expense book, 2 boxes, and 30 pieces scattered in various collections); Abraham Lincoln (Ill.; U. S. Rep. and Pres.), 1847-65 (4 boxes); James Madison (Va.; Member Continental Cong., U. S. Rep., Sec. State, U. S. Pres.), 1781-1835 (390 pieces); James Monroe (Va.; Member Continental Cong., U. S. Sen., Gov., diplomat, Sec. State, U. S. Pres.), 1778-1831 (1,297 pieces); Levi P. Morton (N. Y.; Gov., U. S. Rep., Minister to France, U. S. Vice Pres.), 1842-1920 (2 vols. of letter books, 22 vols. of scrapbooks, 1 vol. of autographs, and 15 boxes); James Schoolcraft Sherman (N. Y.; U. S. Rep. and Vice Pres.), 1883-1912 (7 vols. and 102 boxes); and George Washington (Va.; Rev. War Commander in Chief, U. S. Pres.) and his family (1 vol., 7 boxes, and 75 pieces in various autograph collections). Papers of Presidents insufficient to fill a box for the individual alone are filed in a series called "Presidential Papers" comprising 9 boxes; every President is represented.

Papers of other holders of public office in civilian capacities include those of Samuel Adams (Mass.; Member Continental Cong., Gov.), 1766-1803 (13 vols. and 1,695 pieces);

Newton D. Baker (Ohio; mayor of Cleveland, Sec. War), 1914-37 (75 pieces); James A. Bayard (Del.; U.S. Rep. and Sen.), 1800-14 (1 vol. and 40 pieces); Sol Bloom (N.Y.; U.S. Rep.), 1935-39 (30 cartons); James Leander Cathcart (Pa.; U.S. consul and diplomatic agent), 1785-1806 (400 pieces); DeWitt Clinton (N.Y.; U.S. Sen., mayor of New York, Gov.), 1790-1826 (52 pieces); George Clymer (Pa.; merchant, Member Continental Cong., U.S. Rep.), 1786-1834 (1 box); William Bourke Cockran (N.Y.; U.S. Rep.), 62 portfolios and 4 bundles); James Rood Doolittle (N.Y., Wis., Ill.; lawyer, U.S. Sen. from Wis.), 1848-90 (79 letters received); Charles P. Daly (N.Y.; chief justice of New York City court of common pleas), 1827-97 (5,000 pieces); James Duane (N.Y.; Member Continental Cong., mayor of New York, U.S. dist. court judge), 1750-1867 (4 vols. and 75 pieces); Azariah Cutting Flagg (N.Y.; newspaper editor, comptroller of N.Y. State and New York City), 1821-47 (8 vols.); Charles J. Folger (N.Y.; State chief justice, Sec. Treas.), 1881-84 (3 vols. and 6 boxes); Benjamin Franklin (Pa.; printer, scientist, diplomat), 1713-89 (3 vols. and 2 boxes); Edmond Charles Genêt (France, N.Y.; French Minister to U.S.) and his family, 1719-1851 (1 box and 18 pieces); Anthony J. Griffin (N.J.; lawyer, newspaper editor, U.S. Rep.), 1885-1935 (2 vols. and 50 boxes); and Thomas P. Grosvenor (N.Y.; U.S. Rep.), 1779-92 (2 vols.).

Papers of still other holders of public office include those of Alexander B. Hagner (Md.; D.C. supreme court justice), 1857-77 (185 pieces); Edward Hand (Pa.; physician, Rev. War officer, Member Continental Cong.), 1775-85 (215 pieces); Sam Houston (Tenn., Tex.; Gov., U.S. Sen.), 1828-60 (26 pieces); William Henry Jackson (Colo., Mich., N.Y.; artist, explorer, official photographer of U.S.

Geological Survey), 1862-1942 (47 vols. and 60 pieces); Henry Laurens (S.C.; merchant, planter, Pres. of Continental Cong.), 1780-81 (1 vol.), journal of his confinement in the Tower of London; Herbert H. Lehman (N.Y.; Gov., U.S. Sen.), 1926-56 (180 drawers, restricted); Robert R. Livingston (N.Y.; Member Continental Cong., Sec. of Foreign Affairs, Chancellor of N.Y., Minister to France), 1755-94 (100 pieces); William Livingston (N.Y., N.J.; Member Continental Cong., Gov. of N.J.), 1749-72 (2 vols.); Samuel Meredith (Pa.; Rev. War officer, Member Continental Cong., U.S. Treasurer), 1772-1811 (65 pieces); Nelson O'-Shaughnessy (N.Y.; U.S. foreign service official), 1904-24 (1 vol. and 3 boxes); Timothy Pickering (Mass.; Postmaster Gen., Sec. War, Sec. State, U.S. Sen. and Rep.), 1784-99 (1 vol. and 47 pieces); Lemuel E. Quigg (N.Y.; newspaper editor, U.S. Rep.), 1894-95 (3 boxes); John Quinn (N.Y.; electric light and power executive, U.S. Rep.), 1902-24 (13 vols.), restricted; E. Mont. Reily (Gov. of Puerto Rico), 1919-23 (115 pieces), including 40 letters from Warren G. Harding (U.S. Pres.); Thomas Rodney (Del., Miss. Terr.; Member Continental Cong., U.S. judge for Miss. Terr.), 1803-11 (1 vol.); and Charles H. Ruggles (N.Y.; U.S. Rep.), 1821-55 (1 box).

Papers of additional holders of public office include those of Sir Luke Schaub (England; Ambassador to France), 1714-36 (3 vols. and 2,150 pieces); Philip John Schuyler (N.Y.; French and Indian War officer, Member Continental Cong., Rev. War officer, U.S. Sen.), 1756-1805 (18 vols. and 49 boxes); Francis Ormand Jonathan Smith (Maine; U.S. Rep.), 1828-70 (140 pieces); William Smith (N.Y., England, Canada; Loyalist, chief justice of N.Y. and of Canada), 1763-83 (9 vols. and 6 boxes); John

Canfield Spencer (N.Y.; War of 1812 officer, U.S. Rep., Sec. War, Sec. Treas.), 1811-54 (58 pieces); William Stanhope, 1st Earl of Harrington (England; Ambassador to Spain), 1720-24 (100 pieces); Edward T. Tayloe (Va.; sec. to U.S. Ministers to Mexico and Colombia), 1819-58 (2 vols.); Almon Harris Thompson (Ill., D.C.; geographer for U.S. Geological Survey), 1871-75 (5 vols. and 1 folder); Samuel J. Tilden (N.Y.; Gov., lawyer), 1827-1930 (105 linear ft.); Robert Troup (N.Y.; landowner, U.S. dist. court judge) and his family, 1784-1870 (64 vols. and 24 boxes); Pierre Van Cortlandt (N.Y.; Lt. Gov.) and his son, Philip (N.Y.; Rev. War officer, U.S. Rep.), 1667-1890 (200 pieces); William Peter Van Ness (N.Y.; U.S. dist. court judge), 1795-1828 (100 pieces); Frank P. Walsh (Mo., N.Y.; lawyer, member of Industrial Relations Commission), 1909-39 (400 boxes); Gideon Welles (Conn.; newspaper editor, Sec. Navy), 1825-85 (1,400 pieces); Thomas W. Williams (Conn.; shipping merchant, U.S. Rep., railroad pres.), 1800-35 (22 boxes); William Williams (N.Y.; Commissioner of Immigration at Ellis Island), 1905-13 (3 vols. and 5 boxes); John Winthrop 2d (Mass., Conn.; colonial Gov. of Conn.), 1638-39 (59 pieces); Oliver Wolcott (Conn.; Rev. War officer, Member Continental Cong., Gov.), 1803-8 (5 vols.), partly restricted; Fernando Wood (N.Y.; shipping merchant, U.S. Rep., mayor of New York), 1859-71 (64 pieces); and Abraham Yates, Jr. (N.Y.; Member Continental Cong., Antifederalist, pamphleteer), 1686-1825 (7 boxes).

Papers of Army and Navy officers include those of William Alexander, known as Lord Stirling (N.Y., N.J.; surveyor-gen. of N.J., Rev. War officer), 1760-90 (200 pieces); Homer Crane Blake (U.S. naval officer), 1840-69 (2 vols.); Ezra Ayers Carman (N.J., D.C.; Civil War officer,

member Antietam Battlefield Board), 1855-1909 (2,000 pieces), relating particularly to his preparation of a map of Antietam battlefield; David Conner (U.S. naval officer), 1842-47 (2,600 pieces); George Croghan (U.S. Army officer), 1812-48 (110 pieces); John Adolphus Bernard Dahlgren (U.S. naval officer, commandant of Washington Navy Yard, chief of the Bureau of Ordnance), 1829-67 (2 vols.); Henry Dearborn (Mass.; Rev. War officer, Sec. War), 1777-81 (3 vols.); Percival Drayton (Pa.; U.S. naval officer, Chief of Bureau of Navigation), 1860-65 (78 pieces); Peter Gansevoort, Jr. (N.Y.; U.S. Army officer), 1787-1818 (34 vols. and 29 boxes); Horatio Gates (Va., N.Y.; Rev. War officer), 1760-1804 (8 vols. and 3 boxes); Francis V. Greene (N.Y.; U.S. Army officer, military historian, New York City police commissioner), 1862-1921 (8 vols., 2 packages, and 150 pieces); Mordecai Gist (Md.; Rev. War officer), 1777-79 (150 pieces); Henry Glen (N.Y.; Rev. War officer, U.S. Rep.), 1779-83 (85 pieces); Aaron Konkel Hayes (U.S. naval officer, commandant of navy yard at Norfolk), 1838-84 (6 vols.); John Lamb (N.Y.; Rev. War officer, collector of customs at New York) and his family, 1787-1855 (3 boxes); Robert E. Lee (Va.; U.S. and Confed. Army officer), 1846-65 (1 folder); and Benjamin Lincoln (Mass.; Rev. War officer), 1776-1806 (1 folder and 20 additional pieces in Emmet Collection).

Papers of other Army and Navy officers include those of Daniel Morgan (Va.; Rev. War officer, U.S. Rep.), 1777-1808 (250 pieces); John Wolcott Phelps (Vt.; Civil War officer), 1838-81 (85 vols. and 466 pieces); Friedrich Adolph von Riedesel (Germany; army officer serving in British Army during Am. Revolution), 1776-83 (158 pieces); Robert Rogers (N.H.; French and Indian War officer),

1760-61 (2 vols.); Winfield Scott (Va.;
U. S. Army officer), 1808-66 (11 pieces and 400 pages of typed copies); Robert Swartwout (N. Y.; merchant, War
of 1812 officer) and his family, 1806-
65 (1 vol. and 3 boxes); Albert Tracy
(N. Y., Maine; Mexican War and Civil
War officer, adjutant gen. of Maine),
1843-88 (2-vol. diary and 175 pieces);
Augustus Trowbridge (N. J.; physicist,
prof. at Princeton Univ., World War I
officer), 1917-19 (1 box); John Henry
Hobart Ward (N. Y.; Civil War officer),
1854-91 (55 pieces); Aaron Ward
Weaver (U. S. naval officer), 1851-87
(77 pieces); and Leonard Wood (physician, U. S. Army officer, military gov.
of Cuba, Gov. Gen. of the Philippines),
1899-1924 (a number of scattered pieces). Bound volumes of papers relating
to Army and Navy matters fill 15 ft. of
shelving, and there are 10 boxes of
loose items.

Papers of educational and religious leaders include those of Horace
N. Allen (Ohio; Presbyterian missionary to China and Korea, Minister to
Korea), 1884-1905 (44 vols. and 300
pieces); Joseph Anderson (Conn.; Congregational clergyman), 1856-1915
(70 pieces); Alfred Williams Anthony
(Maine; Free Baptist clergyman, prof.
at Bates College), 19th and 20th centuries (12 file drawers), consisting of
his correspondence and a large autograph collection; Henry Ward Beecher
(Ind., N. Y.; Congregational clergyman,
editor), 1860-84 (126 pieces); John
Bowne (N. Y.; Quaker leader), 1649-
1703 (1 vol.); John Betts Calvert (N.Y.;
Baptist clergyman, editor), 1876-79
(14 vols.); John Davenport (Conn.;
Congregational clergyman), 1638-93
(63 pieces); John H. Finley (N. Y.;
pres. of Knox College, College of the
City of N. Y., and Univ. of the State of
N. Y., editor of New York Times),
1900-40 (79 letter file boxes and 39
drawers); Walter Lynwood Fleming
(W. Va., La., Tenn.; historian, dean
at La. State Univ.), 1906-9 (19 box-

es); Albert Bushnell Hart (Mass.;
historian, prof. at Harvard Univ.),
1886-1926 (109 pieces); Henry Marcus Leipziger (N. Y.; educator, supt.
Hebrew Technical Institute), 1884-
1934 (6 vols. and 19 boxes); Jedidiah
Morse (Conn., Mass.; Congregational clergyman, geographer), 1793-
1815 (766 pieces); Richard Heber
Newton (Pa., Calif., N. Y.; Episcopal
clergyman, author), 1867-1910 (10
vols. and 1 box); Caroline Augusta
(Mrs. Henry) Soule (N. Y., Scotland,
England, N. J.; Universalist clergy-
woman), 1875-1916 (1 box); Henry
Dana Ward (Mass., N. Y., Pa.; Episcopal clergyman, Adventist), 1850-57
(1 vol.); and Edward Pearson Warner
(Mass.; prof. of aeronautics at Mass.
Institute of Technology), 1923-27 (4
boxes). Other papers relating to religious activities include records of
general and local church organizations
of the Methodist Church in New York
City and vicinity, 1780-1930 (450 vols.
and 3,000 pieces) deposited by the
Methodist Historical Society; papers
relating to the Seventh Day Adventist
Church (6 boxes); and a collection of
letters of leading American clergymen, 1711-1860 (172 pieces); and a
collection of Shaker records, 1830-
1910, a large portion of that time being represented by journals (49 items).

Papers of physicians, scientists,
and engineers include those of Bion J.
Arnold (Ill.; civil engineer, street
railway executive), 1906-41 (29 vols.
and 14 boxes); Theodric Romeyn Beck
(N. Y.; physician) and his family, 1750-
1850 (1,250 pieces); John W. Francis
(N. Y.; physician, prof. at Columbia
College), 1808-61 (9 boxes); Robert
Fulton (England, France, N. Y.; civil
engineer, inventor, artist), 1790-
1815 (3 vols. and 1 box); Louis P.
Gratacap (N. Y.; geologist, mineralogist), 1863-1909 (5-vol. diary); John
Griscom (N. Y., N. J.; chemist, prof.
at Columbia College), 1804-51 (1
box); Ferdinand Hassler (Switzerland,

N.Y., D.C.; geodesist, mathematician, supt. of U.S. Coast Survey), 1801-47 (3 boxes); Silas Weir Mitchell (Pa.; physician, neurologist, poet, novelist), 1900-13 (66 pieces); William B. Parsons (N.Y.; civil engineer, expert in field of transportation design and construction), 1881-1900 (12 bundles); Sidney A. Reeve (N.Y.; mechanical engineer), 1910-41 (18 ft.); Frank J. Sprague (N.Y.; electrical engineer, inventor, pioneer in railway electrification), 1876-1935 (75 ft.); Robert B. Stanton (N.Y.; civil and mining engineer), 1889-1922 (9 vols., 9 boxes, and 5 bundles); Joseph Gardner Swift (N.Y.; U.S. Army officer, civil engineer), 1825-58 (155 pieces); William John Wilgus (N.Y.; civil engineer, director of military railways for A.E.F.), 1904-45 (81 ft.); and Henry Wurtz (N.J., N Y.; chemist), 1850-80 (1 vol. and 300 pieces).

Papers of authors include those of Harold R. Atteridge (N.Y.; playwright), 1900-39 (1 box); Joseph Henry Benrimo (Calif., England; dramatist), 1906-41 (4 folders); Fred Gilbert Blakeslee (Calif.; writer on uniforms and costumes of the world), 1931-38 (11 vols.); William Cullen Bryant (Mass., N.Y.; poet, newspaper editor), 1804-1913 (20 boxes); Ellis Parker Butler (N.Y.; author), 1900-37 (2 boxes); Hayden Carruth (Minn., S. Dak., N.Y.; author of juvenile fiction, journalist), 1862-1932 (12 cartons); William Wallace Cook (Mich.; journalist, author), 1889-1919 (1,200 pieces); Frederick Samuel Dellenbaugh (N.Y.; artist, author), 1871-1934 (4 vols. and 2 boxes); Evert Augustus Duyckinck (N.Y.; literary editor, biographer), 1793-1889 (83 boxes); Emma C. Embury (N.Y.; short-story writer, poet, essayist), 1836-93 (6 boxes); Paul Leicester Ford (N.Y.; historian, novelist) and Worthington C. Ford (N.Y., Mass., D.C.; editor, historian) and their family, 1840-1950; Hamlin Garland (Mass., Ill., Calif.; novelist), 1889-

1910 (63 pieces); Isaac Goldberg (Mass.; author, critic), 1919-38 (28 boxes); Nathaniel Hawthorne (Mass.; novelist) and his wife, Sophia Peabody Hawthorne, 1841-61 (32 pieces); Lafcadio Hearn (Ohio, La., Japan; author), 1891-1902 (40 pieces); George S. Hellman (N.Y.; art critic and teacher, author, editor), 20th century (57 boxes); Josiah Gilbert Holland (Mass., N.Y.; author, editor), 1865-81 (175 pieces); Peter Irving (N.Y.; author), 1806-8 (1 vol.); Washington Irving (N.Y.; author, U.S. Minister to Spain), 1798-1859 (20 ft.), an integrated collection of letters, journals, manuscripts, and rare editions; Merle Johnson (N.Y.; illustrator, bibliographer, 11 boxes; Robert Underwood Johnson (Ind., N.Y.; editor, author, Ambassador to Italy), 1875-1937 (12 boxes), with emphasis on copyright movements; Adrian H. Joline (N.Y.; lawyer, author, book collector), 1894-1912 (71 pieces) and a 21-vol. manuscript "Dictionary of American Political Biography" compiled by him; and Elizabeth Jordan (N.Y., Mass.; editor, author), 1891-1946 (1 vol. and 2 boxes).

Papers of other authors include those of George Kennan (N.Y., D.C.; explorer, journalist, author, Russian scholar), 1856-1912 (5 boxes), containing letters from Russian political exiles; Paul Kester (N.Y., Va.; dramatist, poet), 1880-1933 (17,000 pieces); Herman Melville (N.Y., Mass.; novelist), 1837-89 (128 pieces); Henry Louis Mencken (Md.; author, editor, critic), 1896-1955 (125,000 pieces), restricted; James Oppenheim (N.Y.; poet, novelist), 1898-1932 (19 boxes); Edith Coues O'Shaughnessy (N.Y.; author), 1907-37 (1 vol. and 19 boxes); Edgar Allan Poe (Va., Md., Pa., N.Y.; poet, critic, short-story writer), 1841-49 (2 boxes); Edwin Arlington Robinson Maine, N.Y.; author, poet), 1897-1935 (15 ft.), consisting of letters, manuscripts, and rare editions; Don Carlos Seitz (N.Y.; newspaper manager, author), 1882-1934 (4 boxes); Seba Smith, known as Maj. Jack Downing (Maine, N.Y.; political satirist, newspaper editor), 1813-67 (1 box); Elizabeth Oakes Prince Smith (Maine, N.Y.; author, suffragist), 1852-91 (2 vols. and 3 boxes); Albert Ellsworth Thomas (N.Y.; journalist, dramatist), 1901-43 (1 box); Charles Hanson Towne (N.Y.; dramatist, poet), 1922-46 (14 vols. and 13 boxes); Carl Van Vechten (N.Y.; novelist, music critic), from about 1900 (60 ft.), an integrated collection of manuscripts, correspondence, and rare editions; Samuel Ward (N.Y.; lobbyist, financier, author), 1850-80 (3 vols. and 300 pieces); John Van Alstyne Weaver (N.Y., Conn.; novelist, poet, dramatist), 1912-32 (4 boxes); Noah Webster (Conn., N.Y., Mass.; lexicographer, author), 1764-1843 (14 boxes); Walt Whitman (N.Y., D.C., N.J.; poet), 60 manuscripts, memoranda, journals, and letters; William Winter (N.Y.; dramatic critic, historian, poet, essayist), 1864-1917 (1 vol. and 1 box); and Theodore Winthrop (N.Y.; novelist), 1847-57 (9 vols. and 2 boxes).

Papers of editors and publishers of newspapers and periodicals and of other persons in the communications field, in addition to several listed above as authors, include papers of James Gordon Bennett (N.Y.; editor and publisher of New York Herald), 1840-51 (2 boxes); John Bigelow (N.Y.; co-owner and editor of New York Evening Post, Minister to France, author), 1843-1911 (39-vol. diary, 24 other vols., and 38 boxes); Alexander Black (N.Y.; editor of Brooklyn Times), 1881-1926 (250 pieces); Robert Bonner (N.Y.; publisher of New York Ledger), 1860-92 (3,500 pieces); Richard Rogers Bowker (N.Y.; editor and publisher of book-trade periodicals), 1870-1935 (21 vols., 170 boxes, and 3 cartons); Udo Brachvogel (Mo., N.Y.;

editor of the N.Y. Belletristisches Journal, poet, translator), 1866-1925, including 55 letters from Carl Schurz, 1878-1906; Henry Burgess (England; inventor, economist, editor of Bankers Circular) and his family, 1799-1883 (3 vols. and 12 boxes); William Conant Church (N.Y.; journalist, editor of Galaxy Magazine, publisher of Army and Navy Journal), 1866-78 (6 boxes); Elmer Davis (D.C.; journalist, radio news analyst), 1940 (150 pieces); Robert Hobart Davis (N.Y.; editor of various periodicals, author), 1902-42 (32 boxes); Henry Barton Dawson (N.Y.; historian, editor of Historical Magazine), 1859-89 (1 box); Theodore Dwight (Conn., N.Y.; newspaper editor and publisher, U.S. Rep.), 1789-1843 (3 folders); Richard Watson Gilder (N.Y.; editor, poet), 1880-1909 (21 vols.); Parke Godwin (N.Y.; editor of New York Evening Post, author), 1804-1913 (17 boxes); Horace Greeley (N.Y.; editor of New York Tribune, political leader), 1836-72 (5 boxes); Mark Hawley (N.Y.; radio news analyst), 1935-40 (3 boxes), "fan" mail; George E. Jones (N.Y.; publisher of New York Times), 1845-94 (250 pieces); Hans V. Kaltenborn (N.Y.; radio news analyst), 1940 (50 pieces); St. Clair McKelway (N.Y.; editor of Brooklyn Daily Eagle), 1885-1915 (4 file drawers); George Palmer Putnam (N.Y., England; book and magazine publisher), 1843-71 (2 vols. and 835 pieces); Henry J. Raymond (N.Y.; founder and editor of New York Times, U.S. Rep.), 125 pieces; Albert Shaw (N.Y.; political scientist, editor of the American Review of Reviews), 1870-1940 (75 ft. and 32 file drawers); and Wilhelm Weitling (N.Y.; socialist, founder and editor of Die Republik der Arbeiter), 1850-71 (1 vol. and 3 boxes).

Closely related to the types of papers mentioned in the preceding paragraph are extensive records of printing and publishing firms, among them the Century Co., 1880-1914 (207 boxes); the Crowell-Collier Publishing Co. (publishers of Collier's, Woman's Home Companion, American Magazine, and other periodicals), since 1935 (750 ft.); Alfred A. Knopf, 1930-50 (3 boxes and 10 cartons); Life Magazine, Inc., 1925-30 (4 cartons); Pynson Press (publishers of Colophon), 1928-33 (14 packages); and the Chiswick Press (England), 1831-1933 (3 boxes). Included also are an account book of the Philadelphia printing house of Benjamin Franklin and David Hall, 1759-66; and records of the American Publishers' Copyright League and the Bureau of National Association of Book Publishers, 1887-1930 (9 vols. and 17 boxes).

Papers of actors and other leaders in the theatrical world, in addition to some dramatists mentioned above as authors, include papers of Phineas T. Barnum (Conn.; circus showman), 1846-76 (1 box); Robert H. Burnside (N.Y.; theatrical manager, producer of variety shows), 1894-1931 (4 vols. and 89 boxes); Charles B. Dillingham (N.Y.; owner and manager of the Globe Theatre), 1905-27 (23 cartons); Edward Harrigan (N.Y.; playwright, actor, producer), 13 vols.; Clare Tree Major (N.Y.; actress, theatrical director), 1917-54 (20 vols. and 3 boxes); Annie Russell and Dorothy Lockhart (N.Y., Fla.; teachers of dramatics), 1874-1936 (7 boxes); Edward Hugh Sothern and Julia Marlowe Sothern (England, N.Y.; actors), 1859-1950 (8 vols., 48 boxes, and 250 pieces); Frank J. Wilstach (N.Y.; theatrical manager), 1873-1933 (4 vols. and 7 boxes); and Walker Whiteside (N.Y.; actor), 1897-1936 (1 box). Other papers relating to theatrical activities include records of the American Dramatic Fund Association of New York, 1819-1903 (1 vol. and 1 box); the

Olympic Theatre (New York City), 1864-69 (2 vols.); the New York Theatre Co., 1885-94 (2 vols.); the Drama League of America (15 boxes); and the American Educational Theatre Association. Also included are the Malone Theatre Collection of letters of theatrical people, 1872-1910 (3 boxes); correspondence of German theatrical people, 1853-1917 (1 box); an autograph file (10 file drawers); and miscellaneous small groups and short writings on drama and theatres (26 vols. and 9 boxes); The Theatre Collection has a quantity of prompt-copies and scripts of plays. Philip Moeller (N.Y.; playwright) added to the Library's holdings the stage manager's scripts of four of Eugene O'Neill's works produced under Moeller's direction: they include correspondence relative to revisions and manner of staging.

Papers of architects, artists, engravers, and musicians include those of Samuel Putnam Avery (N.Y.; engraver, art connoisseur), 1897-1904 (74 pieces); David Blakely (N.Y., Ill.; manager of bands and orchestras, music publisher), 1862-97 (30 vols. and 18 boxes); Walter Damrosch (N.Y.; conductor, composer), 4 drawers, restricted; Alexander Jackson Davis (N.Y.; architect, artist), 1825-78 (8 vols. and 5 boxes); Ferdinand L. Dunkley (N.Y., La.; organist, music teacher), 1869-1956 (1 box); Asher B. Durand (N.Y., N.J.; engraver, painter), 1812-83 (6 boxes), and his son, John Durand (N.Y.; art editor and critic), 3 boxes; Edwin Davis French (N.Y.; engraver, book-plate designer), 1893-1906 (64 pieces); Eugenie M. Heller (N.Y.; painter), 1890-1936 (75 pieces); Charles F. McKim (N.Y.; architect), 1863-1909 (3 boxes); Harold Van Buren Magonigle (N.Y.; architect), 1910-35 (13 boxes); Archibald Robertson (N.Y.; miniaturist), 1762-80 (6 vols. and 58 pieces); Thomas Sully (Va., Pa.;

painter), 1792-1871 (3 vols.); John Trumbull (Conn., N.Y.; historical painter), 1780-1840 (2 boxes); Richard Upjohn and Richard M Upjohn (N.Y.; architects), 1839-78 (11 boxes); Calvert Vaux (N.Y.; landscape architect), 1865-1921 (1 box), including some papers of Frederick Law Olmsted (N.Y.; landscape architect); and James McNeill Whistler (Mass., France, England; painter, etcher), 1843-1918 (4 vols. and 1 box). (Extensive microfilming of materials about art and artists has been done from the above resources and from other collections of more general autographic nature for the Archives of American Art centered in the Detroit Institute of Arts.) The Manuscript Division also has two file drawers of other musical material, including scores and letters by the great European composers.

Papers of leaders of various "reform" movements include those of Susan B. Anthony (N.Y.; suffragist, reformer), 1868-1908 (90 pieces); Carrie Chapman Catt (Iowa, N.Y.; suffragist), 1910-47 (4 vols. and 6 boxes); Lydia Maria Francis Child (Mass.; author, abolitionist), 1838-43 (62 pieces); Dorothea Lynde Dix (Mass.; advocate of improved care for insane), 1848-68 (39 pieces); Henry George (Calif., N.Y.; economist, author, single-tax advocate), 1854-97 (19 boxes and 3 slip cases); Mary Hannah Hanchett Hunt (Mass.; educator, temperance advocate), 1890-1906 (8 boxes); Lola Maverick Lloyd and Rosika Schwimmer (Ill., Hungary, N.Y.; collaborators in movements for world peace, woman's rights, and social, health, and other reforms), 1870-1948 (1,750 linear ft., restricted); James Miller McKim (Pa., N.Y., N.J.; abolitionist), 1866-67 (1 vol.); Gerrit Smith (N.Y.; philanthropist, abolitionist, U.S. Rep.), 1819-74; Friedrich A. Sorge (Europe, N.Y., N.J.; socialist and labor leader), 239

pieces, including letters from Karl Marx (Germany, England; socialist); and Lillian D. Wald (N.Y.; leader in visiting nursing, settlement work and similar social services), 1893-1939 (10 file drawers).

Papers of business leaders include those of John Jacob Astor (N.Y.; fur trader, financier), 1792-1843 (1 box); Andrew Carnegie (Pa., N.Y.; industrialist, philanthropist) and his wife, 1890-1946 (750 pieces); William Constable (Pa., N.Y.; Rev. War officer, merchant, land promoter) and his family, 1774-1850 (25 vols. and 31 boxes); Robert H. Ingersoll (N.Y.; merchant, watch manufacturer), 1878-1920 (150 pieces); John Appleton Stewart (N.Y.; manufacturer), 1902-32 (1,850 pieces); William Rhinelander Stewart (N.Y.; real estate official, banker, philanthropist), 1882-1929 (12 ft., including 6 vols. of diaries); Moses Taylor (N.Y.; capitalist, pres. City Bank of New York City), 1832-88 (1,100 vols. and 53 cases), including records of the mercantile firm of Moses Taylor and Co.; and Timothy S. Williams (N.Y.; private sec. to two N.Y. Govs., pres. of Brooklyn Rapid Transit System), 1883-1932 (9 vols. and 12 boxes). These papers of individual business figures are richly supplemented by materials in the Library's classification of "mercantile papers," consisting of account books and boxed loose items reflecting trade and commerce, late 17th-20th centuries (24 linear ft.). Additional business data are found in extensive series of account books of Brown Brothers and Co., and Brown, Shipley and Co. (bankers), New York and London, 1825-89 (176 vols.); and Brewster and Co. (manufacturers of carriages and automobile bodies), New Haven, Conn., and New York, N.Y., 1837-1934 (155 vols.). Other business records include those of Fogg Brothers of Boston, 1847-1926 (300 pieces), relating to China trade, particularly in cotton cloth; Kleine Optical Co., 1906-23 (119 vols.); Stephens Coal Yards in New York City, 1850-93 (6 vols.); and I. and J. Townsend (iron merchants of Albany, N.Y.), 1801-1902 (22 vols. and 172 boxes).

Papers of other persons include those of Mathew B. Brady (N.Y., D.C.; photographer), 1863-65 (2 vols. of accounts); Ralph M. Easley (N.Y.; political economist, executive director of National Civic Federation), 1890-1940 (400 ft.); Henry A. Forster (N.Y.; lawyer, N.Y. State Bar Association official), 1917-32 (1 vol. and 13 boxes); Emma Goldman (N.Y.; anarchist leader), 1924-40 (2 boxes and 119 pieces); Samuel Gompers (N.Y., D.C.; labor leader), 48 vols. of transcripts from American Federation of Labor files, shelved in the Economics Division; Bolton Hall (N.Y.; lawyer, American Longshoremen's Union official), 1895-1938 (1 vol. and 34 boxes); Edward Kimball Hall (Mass., N.Y.; public utilities executive, National Collegiate Athletic Association official), 3 boxes; Joseph Hawley (Mass.; lawyer, "Son of Liberty") and his family, 1653-1789 (2 vols. and 251 pieces); James Lenox (N.Y.; book collector, philanthropist), 1825-79 (239 pieces); John Read (Pa., N.J.; lawyer, director of the Philadelphia Bank), 1816-73 (19 boxes); Samuel Bulkeley Ruggles (N.Y.; lawyer, civic leader), 1814-79 (1 box); Peter Smith (N.Y.; merchant, landowner), 1792-1843 (145 pieces); Delancey Stow and his father, William Sears Stow (N.Y.; lawyers), 1818-1918 (16 vols. and 94 boxes), cases in local and State courts; Norman Thomas (N.Y.; Socialist candidate for U.S. Pres., author), 1907-52 (95 boxes); and Nicholas Marie Alexandre Vattemore (France, N.Y.; founder of a system of international exchanges of books, ventriloquist, impersonator), 1849-64 (8 boxes).

The Library has a number of "collections," each of which contains papers brought together by previous owners or by the Library itself from many different sources. The George Bancroft Collection, 1585-1883 (416 vols.), consists of original papers and transcripts gathered by Bancroft (Mass., N.Y.; historian, Sec. Navy, diplomat) for his historical writings. The Emmet Collection (10,800 pieces), assembled by Thomas Addis Emmet (N.Y.; physician, antiquarian), relates to United States history, particularly the Revolutionary War period, and contains papers bearing the autographs of signers of the Declaration of Independence (3 complete sets) and many other distinguished Americans. The De Coursey Fales Collection, 18th-20th centuries (9 vols. and 9 boxes), contains literary and historical documents, principally English and American in origin. The Lee Kohns Memorial Collection (partly given, partly deposited) fills 16 portfolios and adds numerous European figures, not heretofore represented in the Division's holdings; there are noteworthy American historical figures also present. The Alfred J. Liebmann Collection on the History of Distilled Spirits contains 130 items. The Emma Mills Memorial Collection consists of selected letters from her correspondence with authors and actors who appeared in the programmes presented at her series of literary luncheons (by subscription) conducted in New York City for over 30 years beginning in the early 1920's; some of the authors have presented original manuscripts of their works in tribute to Miss Mills. The Theodorus Bailey Myers Collection (14 vols.) includes autograph letters and other documents of distinguished personages, among them signers of the Declaration of Independence; generals of the American Revolution, including British and Hessian generals (2 vols.); and noted

Frenchmen and Napoleonic marshals
(1 vol.); included also are papers of
Daniel Morgan (Va.; Rev. War officer,
U. S. Rep.), 2 vols.   The William Barclay Parsons Collection relates especially to engineering and transportation.
The David McNeely Stauffer Collection
(11 boxes) contains papers of American
engravers and literary and political
figures, especially of the Revolutionary and early national periods, and
papers pertaining to early Pennsylvania.   The Bradshaw H. Swales Collection on Baseball, 1876-1928 (8 vols.
and numerous boxes), comprises correspondence with players, rosters,
and other papers and is supplemented
by records of the Knickerbocker Baseball Club of New York, 1840's—1870's
(12 vols.).   The Whitney Collection
contains manuscripts on cookery and
medical recipes, 17th-19th centuries
(17 vols.).   Among many other collections are sets containing letters and
other papers signed by members of
of the Continental Congress, by members of the Federal Convention of 1787,
by Presidents and Vice Presidents of
the United States, and by French scientists.   There is also an Irish Historical Collection, gathered by William
J. A. Maloney (N. Y.; neurologist),
containing many O'Donovan Rossa papers, a body of material on Sir Roger
Casement, and materials of other
leaders in Irish political movements
directed toward the establishment of
the modern Irish Republic.

The Library has brought together
a collection of diaries kept by 241 persons, 17th-20th centuries; a smaller
collection of ships' logs; an alphabetical series of modern authors' typescripts of books (750 examples); a
group of uncataloged items about New
York Colony, State, and City (42 boxes) and similar materials for the other
States (30 boxes); and an alphabetical
series of "Miscellaneous Papers" (155
boxes).

Official records of various local,
State, and national governmental
units include those of the town of
Harlem (New York City), 1662-1760
(11 vols.); New York Supreme Court,
1735-72 (2 vols.); Vice-Admiralty
Court of New York, 1753-70 (1 vol.);
Commission of Inquiry into the Losses and Services of American Loyalists, 1783-90 (59 vols.), transcribed
from Public Record Office, London;
U. S. District Court for the District
of New York, 1796-98 (1 vol.); Confederate States of America, 1861-65
(6 vols. and 3 boxes), principally records of the War Department and the
Attorney General's office; and the official diary of the Federal Prohibition Administrator for New York,
1927-30 (2 vols.), restricted.   There
is a special collection of original records of Bergen County, N. J., and
adjacent counties in New York State,
18th-20th centuries (12 ft.) collected
by George H. Budke.   In addition to
governmental materials among the
papers of persons mentioned above
as holding official positions, there
are loose or stray items and small
groups of records of various Federal
agencies (8 boxes) filed by agency rather than by name of administrative
head.

Among the records of numerous
other organizations are those of
American Friends of Spanish Democracy, New York City, 1936-39 (10
bundles); Bibliographical Society of
America, 1925-37 (15 letter files
and 2 packages); Boston Committee
of Correspondence, 1772-75 (16 vols.
and 690 pieces); International Committee for Political Prisoners, 1933-
42 (20 vols.); National Civic Federation, an organization which pioneered
in labor-management relations and
later in anti-subversion work, 1899-
1937; National Self Government Committee, Inc., 1909-43 (45 cases and 4
boxes); National Shorthand Association's Standardization Committee,
1909-34 (34 vols.); New York World's

Fair 1939, 1936-41 (1,000 ft.); Palestine Economic Corporation, 1926-38 (22 cartons); Tammany Society or Columbian Order of New York City, 1791-1916 (7 vols. and 28 pieces); U. S. Sanitary Commission, 1861-69 (1,600 vols. and boxes); and Women's Peace Union, 1920-41 (9 boxes).

Miscellaneous papers include some on Gen. George Armstrong Custer and the Battle of the Little Big Horn (2 vols. and 4 letter files); materials on the Aleut language (2 boxes and 5 packages); a number of reports of mining engineers on gold, silver, copper, coal, iron, and other types of mines throughout the United States, 1863-70 (100 pieces); papers of the president of the Anti-Vivisection League of New York, 1917-18 (2 boxes); and registers of the Waldorf-Astoria Hotel, 1925-29 (51 vols.).

See New York Public Library, Bulletin, since 1897, especially "Manuscript Collections in the New York Public Library," 5:306-336 (July 1901), "Supplement to the List of 'Manuscript Collections' of 1901 . . . Embracing Principal Additions and Accessions to the End of 1914," 19:149-165 (Feb. 1915), and annual lists of "Manuscript Division Accessions," 1935-48, vol. 39-52; Hist. Records Survey, Guide for New York City, pp. 74-92; and Greene and Morris, Guide, pp. xxx-xxxiii and passim. There are special articles in the Bulletin on the papers of John Adams, John Quincy Adams, James A. Bayard, Udo Brachvogel, George Clinton, Charles Dickens, Percival Drayton, Emma C. Embury, Ralph Waldo Emerson, Benjamin Franklin, Robert Fulton, Henry George, Samuel Gompers, Lafcadio Hearn, Washington Irving, Andrew Jackson, George Kennan, Emma Lazarus, Abraham Lincoln, Karl Marx, Herman Melville, James Monroe, Timothy Pickering, Edgar Allan Poe, Edwin Arlington Robinson, Robert Rogers, James S. Sherman,

Robert B. Stanton, Moses Taylor, Robert Troup, Augustus Trowbridge, George Washington, James A. McNeill Whistler, Walt Whitman, John Winthrop, William Wordsworth, and William Butler Yeats. There are also special articles on the papers of the Colony and Manor of Rensselaerswyck, the William Barclay Parsons Collection, the Seventh Day Adventist papers, the collection on baseball, the Emmet Collection, American Loyalist papers, records of the Century Co., records of Brown Brothers and Co., papers relating to the Aleut language, and the Whitney Cookery Collection.

NEW YORK 21

New York Society Library. 53 East 79th St. Sylvia C. Hilton, Librarian.

Holdings: Relate chiefly to the United States during the American Revolution and the early Federal period. Included are papers of Benjamin Goodhue (Mass.; merchant, U. S. Rep. and Sen.) and his family, 1629-1845 (2,000 items); and a collection of autograph letters of the first seven Presidents and other prominent persons of the period.

See Hist. Records Survey, Guide for New York City, pp. 94-97.

NEW YORK 36

New York Times Museum. 229 West 43d St. Samuel A. Tower, Curator.

Holdings: 100 manuscripts dating from 3000 B. C. to the present and constituting part of an exhibit, with newspapers and printing equipment, on "The Story of the Recorded Word." Included are cones and tab-

lets with cuneiform inscriptions, papyri, parchment rolls, and modern
paper documents.

See Hist. Records Survey, Guide
for New York City, p. 97.

NEW YORK 3

New York University Libraries.
Washington Square. Paul von
Kruhm, Assistant to the Director.

Holdings: The Fales Collection
comprises more than 3,000 letters,
literary manuscripts, and other papers of English and American authors, especially of the 19th and 20th
centuries, among them 157 letters by
John Masefield (England; poet laureate). Other holdings are the papers
of Henry Barnard (Conn.; promoter
of common school education), 1830-
50, consisting of his journals and many letters to him; original unpublished
reports of the Labor Bureau, Inc., a
private research organization; and a
card index to early American periodicals, New York area, 1728-1870.
There are also several volumes of
medieval and Renaissance manuscripts, a modest collection of papyri,
and, in the Law Library, a collection
of English deeds, indentures, and
wills, dating from 1227 (113 pieces).
See Hist. Records Survey, Guide
for New York City, pp. 98-100;
Greene and Morris, Guide, p. xxxiii
and passim; and De Ricci, Census,
pp. 1346-1358.

NEW YORK 16

Pierpont Morgan Library. 29-33
East 36th St.   Frederick B. Adams,
Jr., Director.

Holdings: Tens of thousands of
individual pieces, relating to early
American history and English and

American literature, and containing
much of wider interest. Included
are an outstanding collection of Assyrian and Babylonial cylinder seals,
3500-500 B. C.; Egyptian papyri,
1200 B. C. —4th century A. D.; Near
Eastern manuscripts (the collection
of Coptic manuscripts is one of the
largest in existence); and medieval
and Renaissance illuminated and textual manuscripts, 6th-16th centuries
(900 pieces).

Papers of Presidents and Vice
Presidents of the United States include
those of John Adams (Mass.; U. S.
Vice Pres. and Pres.), 1767-1822 (17
pieces); John Quincy Adams (Mass.;
U. S. Pres.), 1796-1842 (27 pieces);
James Buchanan (Pa.; U. S. Pres.),
1816-68 (22 pieces); Aaron Burr (N.Y.;
U. S. Vice Pres.), 1770-1834 (18 piec-
es); John C. Calhoun (S. C.; U. S. Vice
Pres.), 1816-46 (22 pieces); Grover
Cleveland (N. Y.; U. S. Pres.), 1884-
1905 (14 pieces); George Clinton
(N. Y.; U. S. Vice Pres.), 1779-1801
(11 pieces); Calvin Coolidge (Mass.;
U. S. Pres.), 1924-32 (8 pieces), in-
cluding the manuscript of his Autobi-
ography; Elbridge Gerry (Mass.; U.S.
Vice Pres.), 1774-1814 (110 pieces);
Ulysses S. Grant (U. S. Army officer, U. S. Pres.), 1864-76 (11 piec-
es); Andrew Jackson (Tenn.; U. S.
Pres.), 1813-45 (72 pieces); Thomas
Jefferson (Va.; U. S. Vice Pres. and
Pres.), 1781-1824 (245 pieces);
Richard Mentor Johnson (Ky.; U. S.
Vice Pres.), 1812-48 (13 pieces);
Abraham Lincoln (Ill.; U. S. Pres.),
1839-65 (36 pieces); James Madi-
son (Va.; U. S. Pres.), 1782-1835 (23
pieces); James Monroe (Va.; U. S.
Pres.), 1793-1831 (29 pieces); The-
odore Roosevelt (N. Y.; U. S. Pres.),
1896-1918 (12 pieces), including the
manuscript of his Autobiography; John
Tyler (Va.; U. S. Vice Pres. and
Pres.), 1819-58 (10 pieces); Martin
Van Buren (N. Y.; U. S. Vice Pres.
and Pres.), 1826-56 (12 pieces); and

George Washington (Va.; U.S. Pres.), 1752-99 (114 pieces). There are less than 10 pieces each for 15 other Presidents and 7 other Vice Presidents.

Papers of American literary figures include those of William Cullen Bryant (Mass., N.Y.; poet, newspaper editor), 1820-77 (26 pieces); Ralph Waldo Emerson (Mass.; essayist, poet), 1838-67 (23 pieces); Nathaniel Hawthorne (Mass.; novelist), 1848-62 (49 pieces); Henry Wadsworth Longfellow (Maine, Mass.; poet), 1842-82 (88 pieces); James Russell Lowell (Mass.; poet, essayist, Harvard College prof., Minister to Spain and Great Britain), 1841-86 (59 pieces); Edgar Allan Poe (Va., Md., Pa., N.Y.; poet, critic, short-story writer), 1827-49 (35 pieces); Henry David Thoreau (Mass.; essayist, poet), 1835-61 (52 pieces); and Walt Whitman (N.Y., D.C., N.J.; poet), 1860-90 (68 pieces). There are also literary manuscripts and letters of English authors, including Jane Austen, Robert Browning, Charles Dickens (600 letters to Baroness Burdette Coutts, 1839-66), John Keats, Rudyard Kipling, John Milton, Percy Bysshe Shelley, and William Makepeace Thackeray.

Papers of other individuals include those of Edward Bass (Mass.; Episcopal bishop), 1775-98 (20 pieces); Benjamin Franklin (Pa.; printer, scientist, diplomat), 1746-85 (57 pieces); the Marquis de Lafayette (France; American Rev. War officer), 1777-1834 (2 vols.); Sir James Murray-Pulteney (England; English Rev. War officer), 33 vols.; Noah Webster (Conn., N.Y., Mass.; lexicographer, author), 1786-1843 (75 pieces); and Henry Wheaton (R.I., N.Y.; jurist, diplomat, historian of international law), 1824-48 (589 pieces).

There are collections of autograph letters and documents of popes, 12th to 20th centuries (150 pieces); royal and illustrious personages of the British Isles from Henry I and Henry V to George VI (2,000 pieces); rulers of France, Spain, Germany, Russia, and Italy, 13th to 20th centuries (1,500 pieces); Revolutionary War officers, 1774-1815 (147 pieces); signers of the Declaration of Independence, 1755-1812 (250 pieces); members of the first Continental Congress, 1757-99 (56 pieces); signers of the Articles of Confederation, 1769-97 (57 pieces); and signers of the Constitution, 1752-1823 (80 pieces). Also included are papers relating to the trial of Warren Hastings (English statesman), 1788 (2 vols.); papers relating to the siege of Yorktown by the American forces and the surrender of Cornwallis in 1781 (250 pieces); and papers of Episcopal bishops, 1775-1901 (2,000 pieces).

See Hist. Records Survey, Guide for New York City, pp. 100-105; the Library's The First Quarter Century of the Pierpont Morgan Library (1949. 67 p.); George K. Boyce, "The Pierpont Morgan Library," in Library Quarterly, 22:21-35 (Jan. 1952), and "Modern Literary Manuscripts in the Morgan Library," in Modern Language Assn. of American, Publications, 67 (no. 1):3-36 (Feb. 1952); and Greene and Morris, Guide, p. xxvi and passim.

NEW YORK 32

Queens Borough Public Library. 89-14 Parsons Blvd., Jamaica. Harold W. Tucker, Chief Librarian.

Holdings: 30,000 pieces, 1640-1902, relating chiefly to the four counties of Long Island. Included are numerous genealogical records, several groups of family papers, account books and transportation and other business records, and some records of towns and churches. Some of the material was collected by the Flushing Historical Society.

See Hist. Records Survey, Guide for New York City, p. 108.

NEW YORK 3

Society of Friends Records Committee. 221 East 15th St.   Keeper of Records.

Holdings: About 1,900 items, 1663 to date, consisting of records and papers of the New York Yearly Meeting of the Religious Society of Friends, the former Genesee Yearly Meeting, and their constituent meetings in New York, northern New Jersey, western Massachusetts, Connecticut and Vermont, Michigan, and a few in Canada. The record volumes are principally minutes of the various meetings, registers of births, deaths, and marriages, accounts of sufferings, and registers covering transfers of membership.   Unbound manuscripts include certificates of removal, land papers, and letters of members of the society.   Portraits of Friends and drawings and photographs of meeting-houses and schools supplement the manuscript collection.

See John Cox, Jr., "Quaker Records in New York," in N. Y. Genealogical and Biographical Record, 45: 263-269, 366-373 (1914); and Greene and Morris, Guide, pp. xxiv and 293-295.

—oOo—

Tamiment Institute Library.   7 East 15th St.   Louise Heinze, Librarian.

Holdings: 290 vols. and 62,550 pieces, relating chiefly to the history of labor and the radical movement in the United States.   Personal papers include those of August Claessens (N. Y.; author, lecturer, teacher, Socialist assemblyman), 1919-55 (720 pieces); Eugene V. Debs (Ind.;

labor leader, Socialist), 1898-1920 (20 vols. and 2,500 pieces); Morris Hillquit (N. Y.; Socialist leader), 1907-56 (500 pieces); Algernon Lee (N. Y.; Socialist, Director of the Rand School of Social Science), 1896-1952 (15 vols. and 4,500 pieces); Meyer London (N. Y.; lawyer, Socialist, U.S. Rep.), 1910-56 (5 vols. and 3,600 pieces); and various Socialist, Communist, and labor leaders in the United States, 1872-1959 (30,480 pieces).   Also included are minute and letter books of American Socialist and labor organizations, 1872-1926 (105 vols.); and records of the former Rand School of Social Science and its Meyer London Memorial Library, 1906-56 (82 vols. and 20,250 pieces).

See Hist. Records Survey, Guide for New York City, p. 109; Greene and Morris, Guide, p. xxxiv and passim; and Tamiment Institute Library Bulletin, 1957 to date.

NEW YORK 27

Union Theological Seminary Library. Broadway at 120th St.   Robert F. Beach, Librarian.

Holdings: Several thousand pieces, 13th century to date, relating chiefly to religious history.   Included are 6,000 leaves of medieval and Renaissance manuscripts; various European manuscripts, 17th-19th centuries; records of defunct Presbyterian parishes in Manhattan, 1830-1904; and sermons, lectures, correspondence, and other records of or relating to the Seminary, 1836 to date.   The Library also has custody of some manuscripts that were formerly in the library of the Auburn Theological Seminary, among them a number of early 19th-century sermons and the minutes of a few presbyteries in central New York.

See Allison, Inventory, p. 94; De Ricci, Census, pp. 1190 and 1637-1649; Hist. Records Survey, Guide for New York City, p. 116; and Greene and Morris, Guide, p. xxxiv and passim.

—oOo—

United Presbyterian Mission Library. 475 Riverside Drive. Room 1056. Madeline Brown, Librarian.

Holdings: Chiefly the correspondence, minutes, and other records of the Board of Foreign Missions of the United Presbyterian Church of North America and the Board of Foreign Missions of the Presbyterian Church in the U.S.A., and related organizations, concerning missionary work among Indians in the United States as well as the work of foreign missions.

NEW YORK 3

Walter Hampden Memorial Library. The Players, 16 Gramercy Park. Patrick F. Carroll, Librarian.

Holdings: Materials relating to the theater and notable stage figures. Included are 1,300 letters, among them 340 by Edwin Booth (Md., Calif., Mass., N.Y.; actor), 1833-93; 15,000 programmes and playbills, 1730-1959; and 15,000 photographs of the early American and English stage.

NEW YORK 21

Woodrow Wilson Foundation. 45 East 65th St. Julie C. Herzog, Executive Director.

Holdings: Archives of the Foundation, 1921 to date; and 39 letters, 1897-1921, from Woodrow Wilson (N.Y.; pres. of Princeton Univ., Gov., U.S. Pres.) to Helen Giddings Reid.

NEW YORK 28

Yivo Institute for Jewish Research. 1048 Fifth Ave. Mendel Elkin, Librarian; Rebecca Tcherikower, Archivist.

Holdings: 5,000 boxes, 15th-20th centuries, of manuscripts relating to Jewish life in the United States and other countries throughout the world. (The depository was formerly the Yiddish Scientific Institute—YIVO.)

Papers of individuals include those of Louis D. Brandeis (Mass., D.C.; U.S. Supreme Court Justice), 1924-35; John Dewey (Mich., Ill., N.Y.; philosopher, educator, prof. at Columbia Univ.), 1927-41; William Edlin (Calif., N.Y.; editor, journalist), 1896-1947 (23 folders); Horace N. Kallen (Mass., Wis., N.Y.; philosopher, dean of New School for Social Research), 1906-54 (76 boxes); Halpern Leivick (Russia, N.Y.; poet, dramatist), from 1919 (51 boxes and 52 folders); Kurt Lewin (Iowa; psychologist, prof. at Univ. of Iowa), 1934-41; Abraham Liessin (Russia, N.Y.; poet, editor, journalist), 1904-37 (40 boxes); A. Litwin (Russia, N.J., N.Y.; folklorist, journalist), 1900-35 (15 boxes); Kalman Marmor (Russia, Switzerland, Germany, England, Calif., N.Y.; historian, editor, journalist), 1880-1952 (106 boxes); Henry Louis Mencken (Md.; author, editor, critic), 1924-48; Samuel Niger-Charney (Russia, Poland, Germany, N.Y.; author, editor, critic), 1909-56 (62 boxes); David Pinski (N.Y.; dramatist, novelist), 1897-1949 (14 boxes); Morris Rosenfeld (N.Y.; poet, essayist), 1892-1923 (10 boxes); George Santayana (Mass., Italy; poet, philosopher), 1927-44; Charney B. Vladeck (Russia, Poland, N.Y.; assemblyman, New York City councilman, manager of the Jewish Daily Forward), 1914-37 (2 boxes); Stephen

S. Wise (N.Y.; rabbi, author), 1924-
40; and Chaim Zhitlovsky (Russia,
Switzerland, Germany, N.Y.; philosopher, lecturer), 1885-1947 (70 boxes).

There are papers relating to Jewish congregations, welfare and social
organizations, labor unions, political
parties, fraternal orders, schools,
and cultural organizations in the United States. Included are records of
the American Jewish Congress, 1915
to date (13 folders); Jewish religious
and secular schools and the Jewish
Education Committee, 1939 to date
(200 folders); the Agro-Joint in Soviet
Russia, 1920-37 (39 boxes); the Educational Alliance of New York City,
1910-53 (123 boxes); the Hebrew Immigrant Aid Society, 1903 to date
(4,000 folders); the National Desertion
Bureau, 1910-38 (17,000 cases); the
United Service for New Americans,
1934-52 (11 boxes); and the Workmen's Circle, 1892 to date (100 folders). Included also are 300 autobiographies of immigrants, chiefly
from Eastern Europe, who came to
the United States in the 1880's and
1890's; and letters from relatives in
Europe to immigrants in the United
States (10,000 pieces).

There are also papers relating to
Jewish communities in Germany,
France, and Poland (19th and 20th
centuries); Lithuania (20th century);
Rumania (19th and 20th centuries);
Austria (19th and 20th centuries);
Russia (19th century) and the Soviet
Union (20th century); Canada (20th
century); Latin American countries,
chiefly Argentina, Brazil, Chile, Cuba, Mexico, and Uruguay (20th century); and Palestine and Israel (19th
and 20th centuries). Included are papers of the Jewish Colonization Association, 1889-1913, pertaining to the
colonization of Jews in Argentina; and
papers relating to Jewish communal
life in Harbin, Shanghai, and Tientsin,
1919-40. There are 300,000 pages of

manuscripts, 15th-20th centuries, on
microfilm, including Jewish communal registers, 17th-19th centuries
(160,000 pages), from Italy, Germany, The Netherlands, Lithuania, and
Poland; and Hebrew and Yiddish manuscripts, mostly from Austrian and
German archives.

Official records of the Nazi re-
gime in Germany include archives of
the Ministry for Propaganda (70 folders), the Ministry of the Interior's
Expert for Racial Research (1,740
genealogical reports), and the Institute for the Study of the Jewish Question (150 folders and 8,000 registration cards of German Jews); and
"Hauptamt Wissenschaft" (14 folders), relating to German universities, scientific institutions, scientists, and scholars. Also included
are records of the Union Generale
des Israelites Françaises (40,000
registration cards of Jews in France
and other papers); papers pertaining
to many ghettos and concentration
camps in Europe; and papers relating to displaced persons camps in
Germany, Austria, and Italy (300
folders).

There are also manuscripts of
plays by Jewish dramatists (500
pieces); letters and manuscripts of
poets, writers, artists, and civic
leaders (20,000 pieces); and 30,000
photographs pertaining to Jewish life
the world over.

See Gerhard L. Weinberg, Guide
to Captured German Documents, p.
65 (1952).

NEW YORK 21

Zionist Archives and Library. 515
Park Ave. (Mrs.) Sylvia Landress,
Director and Librarian.

Holdings: An unknown quantity
of letters and other manuscripts relating chiefly to Zionism, Palestine,

and Israel. Included are some papers
of Louis D. Brandeis (Mass., D. C.;
U. S. Supreme Court Justice); Harry
Friedenwald (Md.; ophthalmologist,
surgeon); and Richard J. H. Gottheil
(N. Y.; prof. of Semitic languages at
Columbia Univ., author).

NEWBURGH

Historical Society of Newburgh Bay
and The Highlands. Crawford House,
189 Montgomery St. Sarah Corwin,
Director.

Holdings: 71 vols., 23 boxes, and
305 pieces, relating chiefly to Newburgh and the vicinity. Included are
military records, 1776-1865 (23
vols.); records of churches and charitable and temperance societies, 1764-
1869 (8 vols.); Orange County sheriff's
and court records, 1785-1891 (1 vol.
and 49 pieces); records of a volunteer
fire department, 1797-1900 (2 vols.
and 1 box); business accounts, 1831-
1916 (4 vols.); school records, 1814-
1900 (2 vols.); and assessors' and tax
records, 1854-71 (21 vols.). There
is also a historical collection by Oscar T. Barck (N. Y.; American historian, prof. at Syracuse Univ.).

—oOo—

Washington's Headquarters Museum.
Historic Site Superintendent.

Holdings: 24 vols. and 1,750 piec-
es, 1648-1900, relating chiefly to
Orange County, N. Y., land transac-
tions and militia service and to the
American Revolution in the Hudson
Valley. Included are papers of the
Clinton family, 1745-1821 (105 piec-
es), with some papers of George
Clinton (N. Y.; Member Continental
Cong., Rev. War officer, Gov., U. S.
Vice Pres.) and James Clinton (N. Y.;
Rev. War officer); DeWitt Clinton

(N. Y.; U. S. Sen., mayor of New York
City, Gov.), 1783-1828 (166 pieces);
Timothy Pickering (Mass.; Rev. War
Quartermaster Gen.) and his assist-
ants, 1780-90 (212 pieces); and
George Washington (Va.; Rev. War
Commander in Chief, U. S. Pres.),
13 letters. There are also papers of
the secret committee for obstructing
the Hudson River, 1776 (105 pieces);
papers relating to privateering during the Revolution (66 pieces); Burgoyne's general orders, June–Oct.
1777; and orderly books of a New
York Continental regiment, 1780, a
Massachusetts Continental regiment,
1781, and the First American Regiment, under Josiah Harmar (U. S.
Army officer), 1784-85; and garrison orders, Fort Harmar, 1787. The
War of 1812 is represented by the
logbook of a privateer, 1813-14; and
the Civil War by records of a New
York volunteer regiment, 1862-65 (2
vols.), and a record book of ammu-
nition issued by the Confederate
States Naval Laboratory, Richmond,
1861-65.

See E. M. Ruttenber, Catalogue
of Manuscripts and Relics in Washington's Head-Quarters (1890. 77
p.); and Hist. Records Survey, Guide
for N. Y. State, pp. 202-204.

NIAGARA UNIVERSITY

Niagara University Library. Bernard H. Dollen, Librarian.

Holdings: A small but growing
collection, mainly 19th century, relating chiefly to the University and
the Vincentian Order of the Catholic
Church. Included are some papers
of John Timon (N. Y.; Bishop of Buffalo) and a microfilm of his diary;
and a few letters by American authors.

NORTH COLLINS

North Collins Memorial Library.

Holdings: 10 vols. and 41 pieces, 1836-1923, consisting chiefly of 29 letters by a Civil War soldier and records of a Grand Army of the Republic post and its women's auxiliary.

See Hist. Records Survey, Guide for N. Y. State, p. 210.

OLD CHATHAM

Shaker Museum Foundation, Inc. Robert F. W. Meader, Director.

Holdings: Collections representing all the original Shaker colonies in America. Included are 160 vols. of diaries, letters, accounts, and other records; 35 vols. of manuscript music; 840 deeds, indentures, and miscellaneous manuscripts; and 525 photos.

ONEIDA

Madison County Historical Society. John I. Terrell, President.

Holdings: 20 vols., 2,100 pieces, and 19 folders, 1764 to date, relating chiefly to Madison County. Included are papers of Peter Smith (N. Y.; merchant, landowner) and his son Gerrit Smith (N. Y.; philanthropist, abolitionist, U. S. Rep.), 1764-1874 (100 items); and business records, 1791-1862 (9 vols. and 3 pieces), including account books and records of an iron company and a stagecoach line.

See Hist. Records Survey, Guide for N. Y. State, pp. 212-214.

OSWEGO

Oswego County Historical Society.

135 East 3d St.   Anthony Slosek, Curator.

Holdings: Letters to John Laurance (N. Y.; Rev. War officer, U. S. Rep. and Sen.), latter half of the 18th century; and some materials relating to the county, including minutes of a Presbyterian church, 1837-57 (1 vol.).

See Hist. Records Survey, Guide for N. Y. State, p. 217.

OXFORD

Oxford Memorial Library.   Lillian June Emerson, Librarian.

Holdings: 15 vols. and 100 pieces, 1617-1912, relating chiefly to Oxford. Included are school records, 1826-1912; town archives, 1794-1864; weather records, 1826-40 (1 vol.); records relating to stagecoach lines and a packet boat company, 1850-60; records of burials taken from cemeteries in Chenango County and a volume listing soldiers of the Revolutionary War buried in Oxford; genealogical materials; and a collection of photographs of the village (3 vols.).

See Hist. Records Survey, Guide for N. Y. State, pp. 217-219.

PALMYRA

King's Daughters Free Public Library and Historical Branch.   Mrs. Charles J. Ziegler, Custodian.

Holdings: 51 vols., 104 pieces, and 16 cu. ft. of manuscripts, 1717-1931, relating chiefly to Palmyra. Included are mercantile, milling, and other business records, 1717-1884 (20 vols. and 38 pieces); school records, 1833-93 (12 vols.); and military records (4 cu. ft.) pertaining to soldiers and veterans of wars from

the Revolution to World War I.
There are also materials relating
to Mormonism, to spiritualism, and
to the Erie and New York State
Barge Canals.

See Hist. Records Survey, Guide
for N. Y. State, pp. 220-222.

PENN YAN

Penn Yan Public Library.   Mrs.
George Jones, Librarian.

Holdings: 32 vols., 1831-1911,
consisting of diaries and letters of a
dentist and an attorney.

See Hist. Records Survey, Guide
for N. Y. State, p. 222.

PLATTSBURGH

Kent-Delord House Museum.   17
Cumberland Ave.   L. Newton Hayes,
Curator.

Holdings: 14 vols. and 3,513
pieces, 1768-1903, relating chiefly
to Plattsburgh. Included are the papers of a clergyman, 1857-1903 (3
vols. and 3,506 items); and a ledger
and daybook, 1768-84 (2 vols.), of a
Connecticut storekeeper.

See Hist. Records Survey, Guide
for N. Y. State, p. 224.

—oOo—

Plattsburgh Public Library.   Emma
F. Walter, Director.

Holdings: A small collection relating chiefly to Plattsburgh and its
vicinity.   Included are a number of
old maps and documents, and a few
letters from persons of more than
local importance.

See Hist. Records Survey, Guide

for N. Y. State, p. 225.

PORTVILLE

Portville Free Public Library.

Holdings: 48 vols. and 2 pieces,
1843-1916, relating chiefly to Portville. Included are account books
and correspondence of a general
store, 1849-85 (38 vols.); minutes of
a local Presbyterian church and affiliated societies, 1849-59 (5 vols.);
and minutes of the local library association.

See Hist. Records Survey, Guide
for N. Y. State, p. 227.

POUGHKEEPSIE

Adriance Memorial Library.

Holdings: 18 vols., 1718-1805,
of tax lists and court records of
Dutchess County.

See Hist. Records Survey, Guide
for N. Y. State, p. 229.

—oOo—

Vassar College Library.   Jean H.
McFarland, Librarian.

Holdings: 5,000 items, chiefly
1630 to date, relating for the most
part to anthropology, history, and
literature. Included are papers of
Ruth Fulton Benedict (N. Y.; anthropologist), 1887-1948 (8 vertical file
drawers, restricted use); Benson
John Lossing (N. Y.; wood engraver,
author, editor), 1856-91 (223 items);
Maria Mitchell (Mass.; astronomer,
teacher), 1862-90 (78 items); Elizabeth Cady Stanton (N. Y.; reformer, suffragist), 1792-1901 (115
items), among them a number of

letters from Susan B. Anthony (N.Y.; suffragist, reformer); Matthew Vassar (N.Y.; brewer, merchant, founder of Vassar College), 1826-68 (150 items); and Marian P. Whitney (N.Y., Conn.; educator), 1861-1946, relating to international women's organizations (2 vertical file drawers). There are also Egyptian papyri and medieval and modern European manuscripts (400 items); papers relating to the Indians of New York State, 1790-1831 (54 items); personal account books, 1630-1893 (16 vols.); letters and journals of several individuals, 1810-1905 (182 items), that give information on 19th-century shoemaking, legal work, shipping, business, army life, medicine, and life in the South and West; and Vassar College archives, 1861 to date (1,000 items).

See De Ricci, Census, p. 1856; and Hist. Records Survey, Guide for N.Y. State, pp. 229-233.

PURCHASE

Manhattanville College of the Sacred Heart Library. Mother Gertrude Buck, Librarian.

Holdings: A small collection of manuscripts of miscellaneous character. Included are correspondence of Alexander Hamilton Stephens (Ga.; U.S. Rep., Confed. Vice Pres., Gov.) with his brother Linton, 1834-72 (3,015 letters); a 15th-century breviary; bills of lading and letters, 1804-9, about shipping; letters, 1848, on political appointments and elections in Massachusetts; and diaries of World War I soldiers.

RIVERHEAD

Suffolk County Historical Society. Ernest M. Robinson, Custodian.

Holdings: 81 vols. and 2,000 pieces, 1666-1950, relating chiefly to Suffolk County. Included are fragmentary official records of several towns, 1679-1874 (3 vols. and 100 pieces); records of churches, clergymen, and a Bible society, 1731-1930; records of temperance societies, 1830-91 (50 pieces); mercantile and other ledgers and account books, 1693-1950 (40 vols.); and logs of sloops, 1830-39 (5 vols.). There are also many genealogical records.

See Hist. Records Survey, Guide for N.Y. State, pp. 235-239.

ROCHESTER   20

American Baptist Historical Society. 1100 South Goodman St. Rev. Edward C. Starr, Curator.

Holdings: An extensive collection, 1764-1936, consisting of (1) records held by the Society (formerly at Crozer Theological Seminary, Chester, Pa.) as the official depository of the American Baptist Convention and (2) the Samuel Colgate Baptist Historical Collection (formerly at Colgate University, Hamilton, N.Y.). Included are records of Baptist churches; church histories; reports of the American Bible Union and its correspondence, 1849-73 (143 vols.); records of the American and Foreign Bible Society; and correspondence and papers of the American Baptist Educational Society (30 boxes). There are also sermons and diaries of individuals, including the journal of Mary Lucinda Bonney Rambaut (N.Y., Pa.; educator, reformer), 1878-87.

See Hist. Records Survey, Guide for Pa., p. 11, and Guide for N.Y. State, pp. 135-138.

—oOo—

Colgate Rochester Divinity School

Library. 1100 South Goodman St.
Rev. Theodore Louis Trost, Librarian.

Holdings: 21 vols., 1806-1932, relating chiefly to the Baptist Church. Included are miscellaneous records of Baptist churches in western New York, 1806-1907 (11 vols.); and minutes of Dutch Reformed and German Evangelical church organizations, 1851-1932 (10 vols.).

See Hist. Records Survey, Guide for N. Y. State, p. 239.

ROCHESTER 7

Rochester Museum of Arts and Sciences Library. 657 East Ave. Helen R. Gordon, Librarian.

Holdings: 16,000 items, mainly 19th century, relating chiefly to science and local history. Included are some letters and other papers of Susan B. Anthony (N. Y.; suffragist, reformer); papers of Edward Bausch (N. Y.; inventor, author, chairman of optical co.) and William Bausch (N.Y.; vice pres. of optical co.); and legal papers relating to the Virginia lands of the estate of Sir William Pulteney (England; land speculator). There are also canal papers, including records of an Erie Canal superintendent, 1828, a packet boat company, 1846-47, and a resident engineer of the Genesee Valley Canal; records of an academy in Orleans County, N. Y., 1827-43; model account books devised by George Washington Eastman (N. Y.; founder of an early mercantile college); and a collection of account books, 1786-1890, including drugstore prescription books and accounts of a veterinarian. There are also writings on spiritualism, of the 1850's and 1860's; Civil War letters and other papers, 1861-65 (1 vol. and many pieces); and two small autograph collections.

See Hist. Records Survey, Guide for N. Y. State, p. 244.

ROCHESTER 4

Rochester Public Library. 115 South Ave. Harold S. Hacker, Director.

Holdings: In its Local History Division, 600 items, 1806-78, relating chiefly to Rochester and western New York. One collection contains correspondence relating to travel in the South, 1831-44 (100 pieces). The Division also has physical custody of the more extensive manuscripts, 1778-1898, belonging to the Rochester Historical Society. These include papers of or relating to Nathaniel Rochester (N. C., Md., N. Y.; Rev. War officer, merchant, founder of Rochester), 1788-1829, largely concerned with his land and banking activities; a large group of land papers, 1782-1888, among them correspondence and other papers of Charles Williamson (England, N. Y.; land promoter, British agent in America), and of Robert Troup (N. Y.; landowner, U. S. dist. court judge, agent for the Pulteney estate); and papers of or concerning Henry O'Reilly (N. Y.; editor, author, promoter of telegraph lines), 1826-78 (2,000 items).

See Hist. Records Survey, Guide for N. Y. State, pp. 242-247. Holdings are occasionally noted in the Library's quarterly Rochester History.

ROCHESTER

Rochester Theological Seminary Library. 246 Alexander St.

Holdings: 67 vols. and 700 pieces, dated from 1835, relating chiefly to German Baptist clergymen and the seminary. Included are papers of

Walter Rauschenbusch (N. Y.; clergyman, author), 1879-1918, among them
his diary, 1880-1918 (7 vols.), and
over 300 letters. There is also a diary, 1844-64 (25 vols.), of the first
German Baptist clergyman in the United States.

See Hist. Records Survey, Guide
for N. Y. State, p. 247.

ROCHESTER 12

St. Bernard's Seminary Library.
2260 Lake Ave. Rev. Robert F.
McNamara, Acting Archivist.

Holdings: 12 vols. and 18 cu. ft.,
1868-1909, relating to the Catholic
Church. The chief collection consists
of the papers of Bernard John McQuaid
(N. Y.; Bishop of Rochester), 1868-
1909 (12 vols. and 17 cu. ft.), including
autograph documents with signatures of
prominent churchmen and laymen.
There are also 200 papers of Louis
Aloisius Lambert (N. Y.; priest, journalist).

See Hist. Records Survey, Guide
for N. Y. State, p. 249.

ROCHESTER 4

Sibley Library, Eastman School of
Music. 44 Swan St. Ruth Watanabe,
Librarian.

Holdings: 1,200 items, 11th-20th
centuries, relating to music. Included are medieval and Renaissance treatises on music and fragments of liturgical manuscripts with musican notations, 11th-16th centuries (10 vols.
and 16 pieces); a number of European
and American musical compositions;
and some correspondence of musicians. The musical compositions are
originals and copies, written in Latin,
French, German, Italian, and English,
and include songs, chamber music,

orchestral works, operas, oratorios,
and cantatas by many famous composers. There are also a collection
of English manuscript music, 17th
century, containing fantasies and
dance tunes; and a volume of music
manuscripts written from memory
by Robert Louis Stevenson (England;
author) when he was in the South
Seas. Manuscripts of contemporary
composers include a large group of
holograph scores by Howard Hanson
(N. Y.; composer, conductor, director of the Eastman School) and representative works of other modern
American composers. There are also autograph manuscripts of musical
compositions by students of the
School.

See Hist. Records Survey, Guide
for N. Y. State, p. 240; and De Ricci,
Census, pp. 1871-1876.

ROCHESTER 8

Susan B. Anthony Memorial, Inc.
17 Madison St. (Mrs.) Martha L.
Howard, President.

Holdings: 200 pieces, chiefly
19th century, relating to the woman
suffrage movement and Susan B. Anthony (N. Y.; suffragist, reformer),
whose former home is the depository. Included are 50 letters from
prominent suffrage workers and a
few letters of Miss Anthony to her
relatives. There are also 125 photographs of women connected with
early suffrage work in a collection
assembled by Carrie Chapman Catt
(Iowa, N. Y.; pres. of American Woman Suffrage Association).

ROCHESTER 20

University of Rochester Library.
River Campus Station. John R.
Russell, Director; Margaret

Butterfield, Assistant Librarian in Charge of Special Collections.

Holdings: 2,000,000 pieces, consisting of (1) a small quantity of European manuscripts, chiefly legal, 12th-16th centuries (1 vol. and 8 pieces), and (2) a large quantity of other papers, 1750 to date, relating chiefly to the University of Rochester, New York State, and New Yorkers.

Papers of political leaders include those of Schuyler Colfax (Ind.; U.S. Rep., Vice Pres.), 1841-85 (65 pieces); Thomas E. Dewey (N.Y.; Gov.), 1934-54 (1,000,000 pieces); George Washington Patterson (N.Y.; manufacturer, land agent, U.S. Rep.), 1838-79 (5,000 pieces); William Henry Seward (N.Y.; Gov., U.S. Sen., Sec. State) and his family, 1776-1900 but chiefly 1840-72 (100,000 unbound letters, 4 boxes of the Grier-Seward family papers, and a large number of legal papers, diaries, account books, and petitions); and Thurlow Weed (N.Y.; newspaper editor, political leader), 1816-82 (14,000 pieces).

Papers of persons prominent in science and medicine include those of Carl Ethan Akeley (N.Y.; taxidermist, inventor, naturalist, explorer), 1901-28 (8 boxes); Chester Dewey (Mass., N.Y.; Congregational clergyman, pioneer scientist, prof. at Univ. of Rochester), 1819-67 (2 boxes), including daily meteorological observations for Rochester for 30 years; Herman LeRoy Fairchild (Pa., N.Y.; geologist, Univ. of Rochester prof.), 1875-1940 (28 boxes), also 1,000 photographs of geological formations; Edward Mott Moore (N.Y.; surgeon, prof. at Vt. Medical College and Univ. of Buffalo, pres. of N.Y. State Board of Health), 1765-1869 (302 pieces); Lewis Henry Morgan (N.Y.; ethnologist), 1840-81 (19,000 pages), including letters from distinguished scientists and historians; Arthur C. Parker (N.Y.; Rochester ethnologist and museum direc-

tor), 1860-1952 (13 boxes); Henry Augustus Ward (N.Y.; naturalist), 1850-1906 (8 filing drawers); Henry L. Ward (Wis.; Green Bay museum director), 1881-1943 (6 boxes); and Ira Solomon Wile (N.Y.; physician, psychiatrist), 1915-43 (19 boxes).

Other fields are covered by papers of Susan B. Anthony (N.Y.; suffragist, reformer), 1855-1938 (1 vol., 2 boxes, 1 portfolio, and 45 pieces); Claude Bragdon (N.Y.; architect), 1819-1947 (3,000 pieces); William Channing Gannet (N.Y.; Unitarian minister), 1850-1944 (48 boxes); Adam Gerard Mappa (The Netherlands, N.Y.; typefounder, land agent), 1778-1833 (40 pieces); Edward G. Miner (N.Y.; industrialist), 1835-1955 (52 transfer cases and 1,500 pieces); John Meredith Read, Jr. (Pa., N.Y.; lawyer, diplomat), 1850-80 (69 vols.); Nathaniel Rochester (N.C., Md., N.Y.; Rev. War officer, merchant, founder of Rochester) and his family, 1777-1888 (2 boxes and 32 pieces); William E. Werner (N.Y.; State court of appeals judge), 1898-1916 (400 pieces); and Louis Wiley (N.Y.; newspaperman), 1873-1936 (2,000 pieces).

Papers of prominent families in the region include those of the Breese-Stevens family, 1705-1923 (30 boxes), with material on Aaron Burr (N.Y.; Rev. War officer, U.S. Sen., Vice Pres.) and Samuel F.B. Morse (Mass., N.Y.; artist, inventor); the Huntington-Hooker family, 1833-1926 (1,500 pieces); the King family, 1811-74 (500 pieces); the Lyons family, 1876-1947 (2,000 pieces); the Schermerhorn family (letters from "The Hedges," N.Y.), 1831-1908 (1,393 items); the family of Erastus Darwin Smith (N.Y.; State supreme court justice), 1830-86 (1 box); and the Wadsworth family, including papers of James S. Wadsworth (N.Y.; Civil War officer), a microfilm of 5,000 items in private possession.

Papers of interest chiefly for

their subject matter include a collection of family papers of Samuel D. Porter, 1785-1912 (12 boxes), which contain material on the underground railroad and the Civil War; a collection of original drawings of cartoons by Thomas Nast, Clare Briggs, John Clubb, Gluyas Williams, and Elmer Messner (100 pieces); and theater manuscripts, 19th and 20th centuries (2 filing drawers). Business records, 1800-1955 (150 vols. and 178 transfer cases), include records of a printing house, 1905-55; and records of a local engineer, James Wood Colt, 1908-23 (1 box), which relate to the expansion of American interests in the Near East. Records of organizations include those of the Agricultural Improvement Association of New York State, 1911-17 (10 boxes); a Farmers' Library, 1808-75 (1 box); and the National Committee of Democrats-for-Willkie, 1940 (3$\frac{1}{2}$ filing cases). Included also is an autograph collection (2,500 pieces), containing manuscripts signed by U.S. Presidents and American and European leaders in literature, science, politics, law, and other fields of activity.

The University archives, 1845 to date (100,000 pieces), contain, in addition to official records of the University, papers relating to it. Included are papers of the following presidents of the University: Martin Brewer Anderson (Maine, N.Y.), 1835-89 (2,500 pieces); David Jayne Hill (Pa., N.Y.), 1850-1932 (25,000 pieces); Rush Rhees (N.Y.), 1900-35 (40,000 pieces); and Alan Valentine (N.Y.), 1935-50 (25,000 pieces). Papers of faculty members include those of Henry Fairchild Burton (Latinist), 2 vols. of literary and historical essays; Joseph Henry Gilmore (Baptist minister, hymn writer, Hebrew and English prof.), 1868-1908 (100 pieces); Asahel Clark Kendrick (classicist), 1832-1944 (500 pieces); Samuel A. Lattimore (chemist), 1849-1913 (25 pieces); William

Carey Morey (political scientist), 1873-1917 (31 pieces); and John Rothwell Slater (Ill., N.Y.; clergyman, editor, English prof.), 1905-54 (50 pieces). There are also diaries, correspondence, and personal papers of many alumni; among these are Truman Jay Backus (N.Y.; Vassar College prof., pres. of Packer Institute); Myron Tuthill Bly (N.Y.; lawyer, author, manufacturer); Charles Amos Hamilton (N.Y.; Supt. of State school for blind); and William Harkness (U.S. naval officer).

See De Ricci, Census, p. 1868; Hist. Records Survey, Guide for N.Y. State, pp. 250-253; R. F. Metzdorf, Catalogue of the Autograph Collection of the University of Rochester (1940. 176 p.); and Univ. of Rochester Library Bulletin, especially vol. 4, no. 3 (spring 1949).

ROME

Jervis Library Association. Washington and Elm Sts. William A. Dillon, Director.

Holdings: 16 vols. and 4,047 pieces, 1786-1878, relating chiefly to canals and railroads, many of the latter outside of New York State. These are chiefly papers of John Bloomfield Jervis (N.Y.; engineer), 1827-78 (13 vols. and 4,000 pieces).

See Hist. Records Survey, Guide for N.Y. State, p. 254.

SACKETS HARBOR

Pickering-Beach Historical Museum. Jennie Carpenter, Village Clerk.

Holdings: A small collection, 1807-58, relating chiefly to Sackets Harbor and the War of 1812 period. Included are a few letters of Horace Sawyer (U.S. naval officer); commissions, rosters, and similar military papers; and some photographs.

See Hist. Records Survey, Guide for N. Y. State, p. 256.

SAG HARBOR

Whaling Museum and Historical Society.

Holdings: 4 vols. and 7 pieces, 1791-1861, relating to whaling. Included are logbooks of 3 whaling vessels.

See Hist. Records Survey, Guide for N. Y. State, p. 258.

ST. BONAVENTURE

St. Bonaventure University Library. Rev. Irenaeus Herscher, Librarian.

Holdings: 125 vols. and many unbound manuscripts, 1842-1922, relating largely to the history of the Franciscan Order in New York and New England. Included are archives of the University and various church and seminary papers. There are also 15th-century European manuscripts (4 vols. and 1 piece). (This material is now on microfilm and is available only in that form.)

See Hist. Records Survey, Guide for N. Y. State, p. 46; and De Ricci, Census, p. 1877.

SARANAC LAKE

Saranac Lake Free Public Library.

Holdings: Chiefly materials assembled for a history of the Adirondacks, 1899-1920 (905 items).

See Hist. Records Survey, Guide for N. Y. State, p. 260.

SARATOGA SPRINGS

Saratoga County Historian's Office. County Bldg. Clifford E. Rugg, Historian.

Holdings: A small collection of manuscripts, largely 19th century, relating chiefly to Saratoga County. Included are proceedings of the county board of supervisors; church records; school reports from towns in the county, 1877-1902; account books; records concerning soldiers from the county in the Revolutionary and Spanish-American Wars and in World Wars I and II; copies of inscriptions in many Saratoga County cemeteries; vital records of Saratoga and nearby towns, 1883-1902; some genealogical materials; several biographies of county citizens; and 300 photographs.

See Hist. Records Survey, Guide for N. Y. State, pp. 52-54.

SCHENECTADY

Schenectady City History Center. City Hall. William B. Efner, City Historian.

Holdings: An extensive collection of materials relating to the history of Schenectady and the surrounding area. Included are many personal and business letters and other manuscripts, and a comprehensive collection of photographs dating from the early days.

SCHENECTADY 5

Schenectady County Historical Society. 32 Washington St. Curator.

Holdings: 222 vols., 9,000 pieces, and 25 linear ft. of other manuscripts, 1661-1940, relating chiefly

to the county and city of Schenectady.
Included are papers of Henry Glen
(N. Y.; Rev. War officer, U. S. Rep.),
1767-1813 (375 pieces); and copies of
letters to James Duane (N. Y.; Member Continental Cong., mayor of New
York, U. S. dist. court judge), 1776-87
(1 vol.), and of papers concerning his
land operations in eastern New York
and Vermont, 1775-98 (1 vol.). There
are also Presbyterian and Dutch Reformed church records, 1662-1938
(33 vols.); official records of Schenectady, 1707-1870 (32 vols.); military
records, 1778-1865 (7 vols.); business records, 1687-1871 (34 vols. and
many loose papers), including records
relating to turnpikes, stagecoach lines,
river and ocean shipping, and insurance; school records, 1816-1940 (1
vol. and 5,050 pieces); records of local temperance, medical, missionary,
and charitable societies, 1797-1868 (6
vols.); and a large collection of compiled materials on local history and
genealogy. Some of the above were
formerly owned by the Schenectady
Genealogical Society.
   See Hist. Records Survey, Guide
for N. Y. State, pp. 263-274.

—oOo—

Schenectady County Public Library.
Union St.   E. Leonore White, Library Director.

   Holdings: 8 vols. and 20 pieces,
1850-1938, chiefly records compiled
from cemeteries in Schenectady and
the vicinity, unpublished historical
sketches, and 3 vols., 1934-38, relating to the town of Scotia.
   See Hist. Records Survey, Guide
for N. Y. State, pp. 274 and 287.

SCHENECTADY 8

Union College Library.

   Holdings: 913 vols. and 69 ft.
dated from 1729, relating chiefly to
the College. The greater part consists of the archives of the College
and its predecessor, since 1785
(890 vols. and many pieces), including correspondence of presidents of
the College with important figures of
their day. There are also personal
papers of Tayler Lewis (N. Y.; orientalist, prof. at Union College), 1836-
66 (2 vols. and 1 box); miscellaneous
papers of John Howard Payne (N. Y.;
actor, playwright); a group of sermons, 1801-44 (335 items); and plans
and drawings of Union College buildings and grounds by Joseph Jacques
Ramee (France, N. Y.; architect and
landscape architect).
   See Hist. Records Survey, Guide
for N. Y. State, pp. 275-281.

SCHOHARIE

Schoharie County Historical Society.
Old Stone Fort.

   Holdings: 100 vols. and 5,000
pieces, 1711-1939, relating chiefly
to the county. Included are papers
of John Gebhard (N. Y.; lawyer, U. S.
Rep.), 1823-66 (750 items); official
records of some towns in the county,
1735-1900 (43 vols. and several
pieces); Dutch Reformed, Lutheran,
Methodist, and Presbyterian church
and cemetery records, 1784-1939;
military records, 1777-1863; and
business records, 1766-1855 (16
vols. and many miscellaneous pieces).
   See Hist. Records Survey, Guide
for N. Y. State, pp. 281-287.

SENECA FALLS

Seneca Falls Historical Society.
37 Fall St. (Mrs.) Virginia Martin,
Director.

Holdings: 64 vols., 1,133 pieces, and 3 cu. ft., 1769-1923, relating chiefly to Seneca Falls. Included are some papers of Amelia Jenks Bloomer (N. Y.; reformer), Elizabeth Cady Stanton (N. Y.; reformer, suffrage leader), and Susan B. Anthony (N. Y.; suffragist, reformer), 1839-92 (200 items); account books, 1798-1851 (8 vols.); Civil War diaries and letters (over 100 items); and records of a musical-literary society, 1897-1916 (8 vols.).
See Hist. Records Survey, Guide for N. Y. State, pp. 288-290.

SHERMAN

Minerva Free Library.

Holdings: 30 vols. and 3 pieces, relating chiefly to the locality. Included are local census records, 1825-45 (4 vols.); and Civil War records, 1860-65 (6 vols. and 2 pieces).
See Hist. Records Survey, Guide for N. Y. State, p. 290.

SMITHTOWN

Smithtown Library. Dorothea F. Hyle, Director.

Holdings: 1,000 items, 1703-1905, relating chiefly to Suffolk County. Included are papers of William Sidney Mount (N. Y.; painter), 19th century (2 notebooks and 3 letters); fragmentary official records of Suffolk County, 1703-1858 (412 pieces); and business records, 1703-1858 (7 vols. and 382 pieces).
See Hist. Records Survey, Guide for N. Y. State, Supplement, pp. 14-16.

SPRINGVILLE

Warner Museum and Concord His-

torical Society. Franklin and Main Sts. Lucy A. Bensley, Historian.

Holdings: A small collection, mainly 19th century, relating chiefly to the locality. Included are business records, 1851-97 (5 vols. and 20 pieces); school records, 1831-98 (2 vols. and 83 pieces); and histories of pioneer families.

STATEN ISLAND 6

Staten Island Historical Society. Richmondtown. (Mrs.) Hildegard J. Safford, Librarian.

Holdings: 7,000 pieces, 1680-1950, relating chiefly to Staten Island. Included are deeds, mortgages, and wills, 1680-1875; town and county documents, 1775-1898, many transferred from the county court; papers of prominent Staten Island families; and miscellaneous papers relating to trades, industries, and organizations. There are also some military papers, 1800-17, and microfilm copies of 20 journals and diaries of Hessian soldiers in America during the Revolutionary War. Among many trade and professional account books are ledgers of a physician, 1846-92 (21 vols.). Records on permanent loan include complete minutes of the Richmond County Medical Society, 1806-1939; and records of a Dutch Reformed church, to 1950, and of a Methodist church, 1802-67.

STATEN ISLAND 1

Staten Island Institute of Arts and Sciences Library. 75 Stuyvesant Pl. Mildred S. Powell, Librarian.

Holdings: Several thousand items relating chiefly to Staten Island but also containing papers of broader in-

terest. Included are some English
parchment deeds; a few French Renaissance manuscripts; notes gathered
from recollections of Staten Island residents by Charles Edward Anthon (N.Y.;
prof. of history and belles-lettres at
the College of the City of N. Y.) and his
father, John Anthon (N. Y.; lawyer), 8
vols.; correspondence, notes, and other papers of George William Curtis
(N. Y.; author, editor, orator), 583
items and 27 bundles; some literary
manuscripts of Florence Kingsley
(N. Y.; author of religious stories); a
large number of local ledgers; typed
copies of records of Staten Island
churches; and some genealogical materials.
     See De Ricci, Census, pp. 1881-
1883; and Greene and Morris, Guide,
p. xxxiv and passim.

—oOo—

Wagner College Library. Grymes
Hill. Donald T. Smith, Librarian;
Sophie K. Shields, Curator, Edwin
Markham Memorial Library.

     Holdings: In the main Library
there are 9 manuscripts on the history of the College and 4 diaries, on
microfilm, of Hessians stationed in
America during the Revolutionary War.
In the Edwin Markham Memorial Library, there are poems, letters, and
other papers of Edwin Markham (Calif., N. Y.; poet, lecturer), 1863-1938
(156 vols., 7 boxes, and 4,000 pieces);
papers of Thomas Lake Harris (N. Y.,
Calif.; Christian mystic, poet), 4 boxes, with editorial notes by Markham;
and a few other papers of miscellaneous character.

STILLWATER

Saratoga National Historical Park.
Superintendent.

Holdings: 268 pieces, 1769-85,
chiefly leases, deeds, receipts, tax
receipts, surveys, and commissions
of a local resident.

STONY BROOK

Suffolk Museum. Jane Des Grange,
Director.

     Holdings: A small collection,
mainly Revolutionary War and 19th
century, relating for the most part
to the Long Island families and areas
near Stony Brook. Included are papers of William Floyd (N. Y.; State
militia officer, Member Continental
Cong., U. S. Rep.) and two of his descendants, containing material on
shipping and whaling; letters and
memorabilia of William Sidney
Mount (N. Y.; painter) and his brothers Henry S. Mount and Shepard A.
Mount, less distinguished artists;
and a small but important group of
papers of and concerning Francis B.
Spinola (N. Y.; U. S. Rep., Civil War
officer).

SYRACUSE

Court of Appeals Library. Jefferson and Montgomery Sts.

     Holdings: 18 vols., 1877-1901,
consisting chiefly of stenographic
minutes of seven trials held in Onondaga and neighboring counties.
     See Hist. Records Survey, Guide
for N. Y. State, p. 296.

SYRACUSE 2

Onondaga Historical Association.
311 Montgomery St. Richard N.
Wright, President.

     Holdings: 200 vols. and 35,000

pieces, 1770 to date, consisting of (1) town, church, school, cemetery, business, and other records relating chiefly to Onondaga County, among which are small quantities of papers of New Yorkers prominent in the 19th century; and (2) the "Albany Papers," recovered from a Quebec paper mill in 1954, consisting of 25,000 pieces relating to roads, turnpikes, bridges, railroads, militia, construction of State buildings, and miscellaneous State expenditures in New York State, 1790-1860.

—oOo—

Syracuse Public Library. 335 Montgomery St. Gerald J. Parsons, Head, Genealogy and Local History Department.

Holdings: 400 vols., 3 cartons, and many other papers, largely 19th century, relating chiefly to Syracuse and Onondaga County. Included are copied church, cemetery, census, Bible, family, and local history records (400 vols.); genealogical notes on local families (3 cartons); a card index of Onondaga County citizens, chiefly before 1850 (30,000 cards); and an index of Syracuse newspapers to 1900. There are also 5 vols. of medieval and Renaissance manuscripts.
See De Ricci, Census, p. 1884.

SYRACUSE 10

Syracuse University Library. Lester G. Wells, Rare Book Librarian; James K. Owens, Archivist.

Holdings: 2,420 vols., 110,000 other pieces, and 1,600 boxes, 1775-1958. Included are 260 letters written from China and Europe by the sons of Anson Burlingame (Mass.; U.S. Rep., Minister to China), 1851-1922; papers of Levi Snell Chapman (N.Y.; lawyer,

State legislator) and his family for 3 generations (3,200 pieces) including antislavery and Civil War letters; papers of George Fisk Comfort (N.Y.; writer, painter, Fine Arts College dean at Syracuse Univ.), 1869-1909 (1,900 pieces), including papers of his wife, Anna Manning Comfort (N.Y.; physician, suffragist), and antislavery letters of his father, Silas Comfort (N.Y., Mo.; Methodist minister); letters and other papers of Stephen Crane (N.Y.; writer), 1871-1900 (30 pieces); papers of Moses DeWitt (N.Y.; early settler, surveyor), 1766-94 (1,250 pieces); a collection of Frederic W. Goudy (Ill., N.Y.; printer, type designer), consisting of manuscripts and type faces used in publications of his Village Press; the Gerrit Smith Miller collection, 1780-1880 (1,000 vols. and 61,500 pieces), containing papers of Peter Smith (N.Y.; merchant, landowner) and Gerrit Smith (N.Y.; philanthropist, abolitionist, U.S. Rep.); 400 manuscripts of Leopold von Ranke (Germany; historian); and 500 items relating to the life of Mary Edwards Walker (N.Y., D.C.; physician, Civil War assistant surgeon, feminist). There are also a collection of letters by and other papers relating to early American natural scientists, 1775-1850 (300 vols.); papers relating to Syracuse University and its alumni, 1870-1954 (40,000 pieces); minutes, reports, and other records of circuits, conferences, local churches, and other units of the Methodist Church in central and western New York, 1813-1900 (70 vols. and 3,000 pieces); and a local history collection, 1800-50 (1,000 vols. and other pieces), relating to temperance, abolition, the Millerite movement, and other aspects of the religious social, and economic history of the region within about 50 miles of Syracuse. Elsewhere in the Library is a volume of the Gospels in Greek, 14th century.

In the custody of the Archivist of
Syracuse University, and not open to
the general public until 1965, are papers of Averell Harriman (N. Y.; Gov.),
consisting of materials covering the
gubernatorial campaign, 1954, and
the records of the Executive Chamber, which included the Governor and
his personal staff, 1955-58 (50 vols.
and 1,600 boxes).

See the Library's Special Collections in the Syracuse University Library (1952. 9 p. Processed), and
its Leopold von Ranke Manuscripts
([1951.] 150 p.); Hist. Records Survey, Guide for N. Y. State, pp. 304-
307, and Calendar of the Gerrit Smith
Papers (1941-42. 2 vols. Processed);
Allison, Inventory, pp. 140-142; and
De Ricci, Census, p. 1885.

TICONDEROGA

Hancock House, Fort Ticonderoga
Association. Jane M. Lape, Librarian.

Holdings: 400 vols., 238 boxes
and portfolios, and 10,300 pieces,
1734-1925, relating chiefly to northern New York but including some
materials for Vermont. Included are
papers of or relating to James Austin
Holden (N. Y.; State historian), 1911-
16, speeches; John Elmer Milholland
(N. Y.; editor, reformer, inventor),
1887-1924 (32 vols. and 200 pieces);
Henry Howard Ross (N. Y.; War of
1812 officer, U. S. Rep.); Philip Skene
(England; British Army officer, founder of Skenesborough, now Whitehall,
N. Y.), 1759-75, letters; and Joseph
Weed (N. Y.; State legislator), 1812-
60, concerning the lumber industry
in New York State. There are also
letters of Duncan MacMartin (N. Y.;
State senator) and others, 1822-55,
relating to the development of iron
deposits in the Adirondacks; records
of a local railroad; and papers of two

captains on the Champlain Canal,
1820-1900. Scattered among many
collections are other business records, 1771-1904 (140 vols., 1 box,
and 102 pieces), relating to lumbering, iron mining, the hardware business, and general merchandising. Included also are town records of Elizabethtown, 1798-1828; and court
registers and dockets, 1811-61 (5
vols.). Church records include 66
Quaker letters, 1734-1887; records
of several parishes in Ticonderoga
and other Essex County towns; records of the Presbytery of Champlain;
and the collections of the historical
societies of the Troy Conference and
the Vermont Conference of the Methodist Episcopal Church.

See Hist. Records Survey, Guide
for N. Y. State, pp. 307-313.

—oOo—

Troy Conference Historical Society.
Pastor, First Methodist Church.

Holdings: 194 vols. and 3,198
pieces, 1790-1937, consisting of records of and papers relating to the
Troy Conference of the Methodist
Church, to individual churches within the conference, and to their ministers. Included are papers of
Matthias Swain (N. Y.; Methodist
minister), from 1790 (24 vols. and
64 pieces).

See Hist. Records Survey, Guide
for N. Y. State, pp. 317-319.

TROY

Emma Willard School. Pawling
Ave. Manette Swetland, Archivist.

Holdings: 75 items, 1814-1939,
consisting of letters, diaries, and
other papers of or relating to Emma
Hart Willard (Conn., Vt., N. Y.; educator, founder of the School, formerly

named Troy Female Seminary).

See Hist. Records Survey, Guide for N. Y. State, p. 314.

—oOo—

Russell Sage College Library. Margaret R. Meyer, Librarian.

Holdings: A small quantity, chiefly of local interest. Included are papers of Emma Hart Willard (Vt., N.Y.; educator, founder of Troy Female Seminary), 1 manuscript vol. of poems and 30 other pieces, among them letters and a diary for 1845.

UTICA 3

Oneida Historical Society. 600 Park Ave. Francis W. Cunningham, Curator of Historical Collections.

Holdings: 162 vols. and 14,285 pieces, 1588-1936, relating chiefly to Oneida County. Included are papers of and concerning Nicholas Herkimer (N.Y.; Rev. War officer) and his family, 1755-1800, 1879-96 (53 pieces); Baron Friedrich Wilhelm von Steuben (Prussia, N.Y.; Rev. War officer), 1787-1948 (1 vol. and 65 pieces); Francis Adrian Van der Kemp (N.Y.; author), 1609-1886 (3 vols. and 82 pieces); Benjamin Walker (N.Y.; land agent, U.S. Rep.), 1786-1850 (1 vol. and 107 pieces), including correspondence with Charles Williamson (England, N.Y.; land promoter, British agent in America); James Watson (Conn., N.Y.; Rev. War officer, merchant, U.S. Sen.), 1750-1886 (2 vols. and 1,475 pieces); and Nathan Williams (N.Y.; lawyer, U.S. Rep., War of 1812 officer), 1797-1834 (167 pieces). There are also an Erie Canal collection, 1816-45 (11 vols. and 93 pieces), including construction and survey field books and minutes and waybills and accounts of packet boat companies;

records of a plank-road company, 1762-1858 (1 vol. and 20 pieces); records of a textile mill company, 1809-1919 (85 vols.); letters of New York State newspaper publishers, 1846-47 (1 vol.), relating to the formation of the Associated Press for Telegraphic Dispatches and to the free delivery of newspapers; Uticana collections, 1807-1942 (20 vols. and 2,701 pieces); and an autograph collection (1 vol. and 5 envelopes). Account books and other business records are included in many groups of personal papers.

See A Catalogue of the Manuscript Holdings at the Oneida Historical Society (1952. 63 p. Processed).

—oOo—

Utica Public Library. 303 Genesee St. Alice C. Dodge, Librarian.

Holdings: A small collection, 1792-1949, relating chiefly to Utica and its vicinity. Included are records of two religious societies of Paris, N.Y., 1792-1821 and 1817-1920, and of the United Presbyterian Congregational Church in Paris, 1823-55 (6 vols.); meteorological observations for Utica, 1850-54 and 1887-1923; books of entries submitted by a mechanics association in annual fairs, 1860-62; minutes of an Americanization council, 1922-49; records of a musical club, 1906-35 (3 vols.); minutes of the Welsh Benevolent Society of Utica and Vicinity, 1894-1947 (2 vols.); and New York State census schedules for Oneida County: 1814, 1830, 1835, 1850, 1855, 1860, 1865, and 1875.

WARSAW

Warsaw Historical Society. Perry Ave. Lewis H. Bishop, Member.

Holdings: 5 vols. and 145 pieces,

1813-1910, relating chiefly to Warsaw. Included are the daybook of a physician, 1823 (1 vol.); business papers, 1837-51 (140 items); and records of a Sunday school, 1859-60 (1 vol.).

See Hist. Records Survey, Guide for N. Y. State, p. 325.

WATERLOO

Waterloo Library and Historical Society.

Holdings: 15 vols. and 31 pieces, 1779-1882, including business records, 1796-1866 (9 vols.); church and missionary society records, 1821-82 (4 vols.); and records of a temperance society, 1841 (1 vol.).

See Hist. Records Survey, Guide for N. Y. State, p. 328.

WATERTOWN

Jefferson County Historical Society. 225 Washington St.

Holdings: 104 vols. and 3,000 pieces, 1768-1929, relating chiefly to the county. Included are a diary of Samuel Holten (Mass.; Member Continental Cong., U. S. Rep., jurist), 1806 (1 vol.); and papers of Benjamin Wright (N. Y.; surveyor, engineer), 1802-26 (8 vols.), chiefly relating to land operations. There are also diaries and weather records kept by a resident of the county, 1831-92 (46 vols.); business records, 1768-1858 (36 vols. and 2,777 pieces), including account books of schooners on the Great Lakes, 1846-58 (17 vols.); and an autograph collection, 1846-76 (1 vol.).

See Hist. Records Survey, Guide for N. Y. State, Supplement, pp. 17-21.

WEST POINT

United States Military Academy

Archives. Sidney Forman, Archivist.

Holdings: 1,800 ft., 1802-1958, consisting of the permanently valuable records created by the Academy and documenting its activities as a national educational institution. Included are post order books; the academic, post, range, and fire regulations; the letter books emanating from the offices of the Superintendent of the Academy, the Commandant of Cadets and the Adjutant General, USMA; the loose letters received by the Office of The Adjutant General, USMA; cash books, ledgers, and statements from the Treasurer, USMA; cadet records; and the administrative records of the various academic departments. The USMA Archives also has custody of a vast photographic collection, which includes negatives and pictures of the West Point site, classroom scenes, individual cadets, and athletic events, 1900-57. There is a small collection of recordings of speeches and lectures given to the cadets, 1956-58. The records before 1817 are very scanty.

—oOo—

United States Military Academy Library. Col. William J. Morton, Jr., Librarian.

Holdings: 30,000 items, 1750 to date, relating chiefly to the Academy and to Army officers in command there. Included are papers of John Gregory Bourke (U. S. Army officer, ethnologist), 1872-96 (126 vols.); Alden Partridge (N. Y., Vt.; U. S. Army officer, military educator), 1812-18 (85 pieces); Joseph Gardner Swift (N. Y.; U. S. Army officer, military educator, civil engineer), 1804-62 (400 pieces); and Sylvanus Thayer (U. S. Army officer, engineer, military educator), 1808-69 (170 pieces). There is also a collection of order books, 1759-1806 (17 vols.), including one of James Wolfe (England; army officer), 1759; one of Israel Putnam (Conn.; Rev. War officer); one kept by Presley Neville (Pa.; Rev. War officer), 1778, as aide de camp to Lafayette (France; American Rev. War officer); and one of the company of Henry Vanderburgh (N.Y., Ind.; Rev. War officer), 1780, at West Point. Included too are letters and documents relating to the garrison at West Point, 1777-1841 (2 vols. and 47 pieces); papers relating to the Civil War, 1861-74; and many photographs.

See Hist. Records Survey, Guide for N.Y. State, pp. 333-338.

WESTFIELD

Patterson Public Library.

Holdings: 132 vols. and 73 pieces, 1806-1927, consisting chiefly of records of the Chautauqua County land office of the Holland Land Co., 1806-93 (132 vols.). Included is a letter book of George Washington Patterson (N.Y.; land agent, U.S. Rep.), 1844-64 (1 vol.).

See Hist. Records Survey, Guide for N.Y. State, pp. 331-333.

WHITE PLAINS

Westchester County Historical Society.   County Office Bldg. Mrs. Amos Struble, Secretary.

Holdings: A small collection, 1640-1939, relating chiefly to Westchester County. Included are official records of several towns in the county (some transcribed), 1640-1857; records of Baptist, Congregational, Methodist, and Presbyterian churches, 1702-1886; copies of cemetery inscriptions; and some account books and business and farming records, 1754-1859.

See Hist. Records Survey, Guide for N.Y. State, pp. 340-345.

YONKERS

Archbishop Corrigan Memorial Library, St. Joseph's Seminary. Dunwoodie.   Very Rev. Monsignor John H. Harrington, Librarian.

Holdings: An autograph collection of papers bearing the signatures of Presidents of the United States and Signers of the Declaration of Independence.

YONKERS

Hudson River Museum at Yonkers. Trevor Park, Warburton Ave.

Holdings: 350 items, 1760-1910, relating chiefly to Yonkers. Included are papers of and relating to Lyman Cobb (N.Y.; educator, author); minutes of a baseball club, 1873-80; and records of Yonkers businesses.

See Hist. Records Survey, Guide for N.Y. State, pp. 347-349.

ASHEVILLE

National Weather Records Center. Arcade Bldg. Roy L. Fox, Director.

Holdings: 141,000 cu. ft. of meteorological records, 1735-1959, recorded by the U. S. Weather Bureau, Air Force, Navy, and other U. S. meteorological services and in journals and diaries of private citizens, documenting the climate of the United States, its possessions, the oceans, and other world areas. Original records, 1735-1959 (76,000 cu. ft.), include surface observations, autographic records, and upper air observations. There are also manuscript weather maps and charts; and records of microfilm (57,500 reels), including copies of weather records before 1890, and copies of diaries, journals, and other records of various expeditions and special projects. This Center is the Weather Bureau's official depository for both current and noncurrent meteorological records. Some of the data in these records have been coded and recoded on 400 million punched cards of which 26 million have been placed on an additional 2,200 reels of microfilm.

—oOo—

Pack Memorial Public Library. Margaret Ligon, Head Librarian.

Holdings: In the Sondley Reference Library, 20 vols. and 3,038 other pieces, 1765-1945, relating chiefly to North Carolina. Included are papers of Horace Kephart (Mo., N.C.; librarian, author) and his mother (511 pieces); Forster A. Sondley (N. C.; at-torney, author), 57 literary manuscripts and 1,321 other pieces; and Charles Edward Waddell (N. C.; consulting engineer), 1908-45 (83 pieces), consisting of reports and industrial surveys relating to North Carolina and other southern States. There are also letters of Confederate soldiers (219 pieces and 18 fragments); a number of miscellaneous documents, 1765-1857, relating to North Carolina; 98 items relating to the Biltmore Forestry School; and several manuscripts of books.

CHAPEL HILL

North Carolina Collection, University of North Carolina Library. William S. Powell, Librarian.

Holdings: 5,012 manuscripts, 1570-1960, relating to North Carolina and North Carolinians. Included are 1,400 pieces relating to Thomas Wolfe (N. Y., N. Y.; author) and his family, 1890-1954; 11 concerning Sir Walter Raleigh (England; explorer, author); and 216 manuscripts of books by North Carolina authors. There are many single items relating to North Carolinians; manuscript maps; and microfilm and photostats of manuscripts relating to North Carolina in other depositories.

—oOo—

Southern Historical Collection, Manuscripts Department, University of North Carolina Library. James W. Patton, Director.

Holdings: 3,200,200 pieces, 1588-1955, relating chiefly to North Carolina and the other Southern States, particularly valuable for ante bellum political history, the plantation system and slavery, and military and civilian aspects of the Confederacy. The nucleus consists of manuscripts originally collected by the North Carolina Historical Society.

Papers of North Carolinians who held public office include papers of Eben Alexander (N. C.; Univ. of N. C. prof., Minister to Greece, Rumania, and Serbia), 1894-1937 (1 vol. and 35 pieces); Archibald Hunter Arrington (N. C.; planter, U. S. and Confed. Rep.) and his family, 1758-1939 (1,300 pieces); George Edmund Badger (N. Y.; Sec. Navy, U. S. Sen.) and his family, 1829-67 (17 pieces, 6 photostats, and 1 microfilm reel); Daniel Moreau Barringer (N.C.; U. S. Rep., Minister to Spain), 1807-85 (300 pieces); William Horn Battle (N. C.; State supreme court justice) and his family, 1765-1919 (3,000 pieces); Thomas Bragg (N. C.; U. S. Sen., Confed. Attorney Gen.), 1861-62 (1 vol.), diary; John Branch (N. C.; Gov., U. S. Rep. and Sen., Sec. Navy) and his family, 1784-1919 (28 vols. and 4,000 pieces); Bedford Brown (N. C.; planter, U. S. Sen.), 1835-75 (250 pieces); John Heritage Bryan (N. C.; U. S. Rep.) and his family, 1798-1870 (6,500 pieces); Thomas Burke (N. C.; Member Continental Cong., Gov.), 1744-89 (315 pieces); Hutchins Gordon Burton (N. C.; U. S. Rep., Gov.), 1809-39 (75 pieces); Marion Butler (N. C.; newspaper publisher, U. S. Sen., executive of farmers' organizations), 1854-1937 (8 vols. and 32,000 pieces); William Preston Bynum (N. C.; Confed. Army officer, State supreme court justice), 1826-1908 (9 vols. and 540 pieces); Tod Robinson Caldwell (N. C.; Gov.), 1833-76 (550 pieces); James Osborn Carr (N. C.; U. S. dist. attorney, Democratic Party leader) and his family, 1743-1938 (22 vols. and 1,250 pieces); Heriot Clarkson (N. C.; State

supreme court justice), 1862-1945 (2,000 pieces); Henry Groves Connor (N. C.; State supreme court justice, U. S. dist. court judge), 1830-1934 (15 vols. and 30,000 pieces); Robert Digges Wimberly Connor (N. C.; sec. of N. C. Historical Commission, Univ. of N. C. prof., Archivist of the U. S.), 1742-1950 (6 vols. and 14,000 pieces); William Richardson Davie (N. C.; Rev. War officer, Gov.), 1758-1819 (1 vol. and 124 pieces); Arthur Dobbs (Ireland, N. C.; colonial Gov. of N.C.) and his family, 1569-1845 (2 vols. of photostats and 3 microfilm reels); Robert Lee Doughton (N. C.; farmer, banker, U. S. Rep.), 1913-52 (60,000 pieces); John Willis Ellis (N. C.; lawyer, Gov.), 1844-61 (6 vols. and 1,000 pieces); and Charles Fisher (N. C.; lawyer, planter, U. S. Rep.), 1758-1896 (34 vols. and 3,500 pieces).

Papers of other North Carolinians who held public office include papers of William Gaston (N. C.; U.S. Rep., State supreme court justice), 1744-1914 (1,407 pieces); James Gillespie (N. C.; U. S. Rep.) and his family, 1720-1877 (701 pieces); William Alexander Graham (N. C.; U. S. Sen., Gov., Sec. Navy, Confed. Sen.), 1750-1927 (15 vols. and 14,600 pieces); John Bryan Grimes (N. C.; planter, State sec. state) and his family, 1712-1924 (6 vols. and 15,200 pieces); Edward Joseph Hale (N. C.; newspaper editor, Confed. Army officer, diplomat), 1857-1917 (11 vols. and 400 pieces); John Haywood (N. C.; State treasurer) and his family, 1752-1946 (114 vols. and 10,000 pieces); John Steele Henderson (N. C.; U. S. Rep.) and his family, 1759-1935 (4 vols. and 21,000 pieces); William Alexander Hoke (N. C.; State chief justice), 1750-1925 (21 vols. and 3,200 pieces); James Iredell (N. C.; U. S. Supreme Court Justice), 1759-89 (23 vols.); James Iredell, Jr. (N. C.; War of 1812 officer, Gov., U. S. Sen.), 1807-29,

1841 (2 vols.); Samuel Johnston (N.C.; Member Continental Cong., Gov., U.S. Sen.) and his family, 1676-1865 (26 microfilm reels); Thomas Dillard Johnston (N. C.; U. S. Rep.), 1845-96 (750 pieces); Hamilton Chamberlain Jones (N. C.; U.S. Rep.), 1947-53 (3,000 pieces, unarranged); John Hosea Kerr (N. C.; U.S. Rep.), 1923-52 (20,000 pieces); Claude Kitchen (N.C.; U.S. Rep.), 1887-1923 (30,000 pieces); Nathaniel Macon (N. C.; U. S. Rep. and Sen.), 1794-1837 (50 pieces); Matthias Evans Manly (N.C.; State supreme court justice) and his family, 1717-1928 (230 pieces); David Outlaw (N. C.; U.S. Rep.), 1847-55 (300 pieces); Lee Slater Overman (N. C.; lawyer, U.S. Sen.), 1920-30 (20,000 pieces); Robert Treat Paine (N. C.; U. S. Army officer, member of Mexican Claims Commission, U.S. Rep.) and his family, 1830-76 (275 pieces); Richmond Mumford Pearson (N. C.; State chief justice), 1816-78 (350 pieces); Ebenezer Pettigrew (N. C.; planter, U.S. Rep.) and his family, 1685-1926 (56 vols. and 14,000 pieces); and Richard Clauselle Puryear (N. C.; planter, U. S. and Confed. Rep.) and his family, 1810-1908 (226 pieces).

Papers of still other North Carolinians who held public office include papers of James Graham Ramsay (N. C.; physician, Confed. Rep., Republican Party leader) and his family, 1790-1930 (31 vols. and 2,200 pieces); Matt Whitaker Ransom (N. C.; Confed. Army officer, U.S. Sen., Minister to Mexico), 1845-1914 (30,000 pieces); Kenneth Rayner (N. C.; U.S. Rep., Solicitor of Treas.) and his family, 1675-1905 (500 pieces); Abraham Rencher (N. C.; U. S. Rep., Minister to Portugal, Gov. of N. Mex. Terr.), 1784-1883 (150 pieces); Thomas Ruffin (N. C.; State chief justice), 1753-1896 (50 vols. and 18,140 pieces); Daniel Lindsay Russell (N. C.; Confed. Army officer, U.S. Rep., Gov.), 1839-1910 (1,984 pieces); Thomas Settle, Jr. (N.C.;

State supreme court justice, U.S. dist. court judge) and his son, Thomas Settle III (N. C.; U. S. Rep.), 1784-1924 (5,230 pieces); John Humphrey Small (N.C.; lawyer, U.S. Rep.), 1874-1947 (35,000 pieces); Richard Stanford (N. C.; U. S. Rep.) and his family, 1767-1842 (76 pieces); Charles Manly Stedman (N.C.; U.S. Rep.), 1917 (300 pieces); John Steele (N. C.; U. S. Rep., Comptroller of Treas.) and his family, 1716-1861 (11 vols. and 2,700 pieces); David Lowry Swain (N. C.; lawyer, Gov., pres. of Univ. of N. C.), 1740-1896 (6 vols. and 1,100 pieces); Charles Randolph Thomas (N. C.; lawyer, U. S. Rep.), 1849-1931 (1 scrapbook and 100 pieces); Cyrus Thompson (N. C.; physician, State legislator and sec. state, People's Party leader), 1830-1931 (500 pieces); Zebulon Baird Vance (N. C.; U.S. Rep., Confed. Army officer, Gov., U. S. Sen.), 1854-94 (50 pieces); Alfred Moore Waddell (N. C.; Confed. Army officer, journalist, U.S. Rep.), 1859-1935 (7 vols. and 440 pieces); Lindsay Carter Warren (N. C.; U. S. Rep., Comptroller Gen.), 1924-54 (35,000 pieces); John Hill Wheeler (N. C.; historian, Minister to Nicaragua) and his family, 1837-64 (1 vol. and 45 pieces); Francis Donnell Winston (N. C.; U. S. dist. attorney, State superior court judge) and his family, 1828-1943 (1,300 pieces); Robert Watson Winston (N. C.; State superior court judge, author), 1839-1944 (8 vols. and 2,900 pieces); and Bartlett Yancey (N. C.; U. S. Rep.), 1800-28 (100 pieces).

Papers of Virginians who held public office include papers of William Byrd II (Va.; planter, colonial official, author), 1716-41 (2 vols.); George Coke Dromgoole (Va.; lawyer, U. S. Rep.), 1823-48 (700 pieces); Edmund Wilcox Hubard (Va.; planter, U. S. Rep.) and his family, 1741-1907 (53 vols. and 27,500 pieces); James McDowell, Jr. (Va.; Gov., U.S. Rep.),

1820-60 (238 pieces); Edmund Pendleton (Va.; Member Continental Cong., pres. Va. Committee of Safety and State supreme court of appeals), 1776-79 (48 pieces); John Randolph of Roanoke (Va.; U. S. Rep. and Sen.), 1800-63 (microfilm of 80 pieces); Nicholas Philip Trist (Va.; U. S. consul at Havana, special agent in Mexico) and his family, 1667-1903 (5,000 pieces); Henry St. George Tucker (Va.; U. S. Rep., dean of law at Washington and Lee and at Columbian Univs.) and John Randolph Tucker (Va.; U. S. Rep., dean of law at Washington and Lee Univ.) and their family, 1790-1932 (18 vols. and 20,000 pieces); James Alexander Walker (Va.; lawyer, Confed. Army officer, U. S. Rep.), 1855-1928 (450 pieces); Beverley Randolph Wellford (Va.; Asst. to Confed. Sec. War, U. S. circuit court judge) and his family, 1743-1927 (microfilm of 14 vols. and 285 pieces); and Henry Alexander Wise (Va.; lawyer, U. S. Rep., Minister to Brazil, Gov., Confed. Army officer), 1833-84 (100 pieces on microfilm).

Papers of South Carolinians who held public office or were important political leaders include papers of John Ewing Colhoun (S. C.; lawyer, planter, State legislator, U. S. Sen.), 1774-1810 (250 pieces); Franklin Harper Elmore (S. C.; bank pres., U. S. Rep. and Sen.), 1843-62 (52 pieces); James Hamilton (S. C.; U. S. Rep., Gov.), 1810-62 (50 pieces and microfilm of 40 pieces); James Henry Hammond (S. C.; U. S. Rep. and Sen., Gov.), 1831-57 (61 pieces); Wade Hampton 3d (S. C.; planter, Confed. Army officer, Gov., U. S. Sen.) and his family, 1791-1908 (475 pieces); William Lowndes (S. C.; planter, U. S. Rep.) and his family, 1754-1941 (8 vols. and 345 pieces); Andrew Gordon Magrath (S.C.; lawyer, Gov.), 1861-67 (75 pieces); Richard Irvine Manning (S. C.; planter, Gov., U. S. Rep.), John Laurence Manning (S. C.; planter, Gov.), Stephen Decatur Miller (S. C.; planter, U. S. Rep.

and Sen., Gov.), and James Chesnut (S. C.; lawyer, U. S. Sen., Confed. Army officer) and their families, 1754-1901 (23 vols. and 6,000 pieces); Christopher Gustavus Memminger (S. C.; lawyer, Confed. Sec. Treas., public school leader), 1803-1915 (1 vol. and 2,000 pieces); William Porcher Miles (S. C.; U. S. and Confed. Rep., Univ. of S. C. pres.), 1782-1907 (31 vols. and 3,263 pieces); James Lawrence Orr (S. C.; U. S. Rep., Confed. Sen., Gov., Minister to Russia), 1779-1892 (2 vols. and 350 pieces); Benjamin Franklin Perry (S. C.; lawyer, journalist, Gov.), 1822-72 (4 vols., 22 pieces, and 480 microfilm frames); James Louis Petigru (S. C.; lawyer, Union Party leader), 1832-63 (50 pieces and 59 pieces on microfilm); Francis Wilkinson Pickens (S. C.; U. S. Rep., Minister to Russia, Gov.) and his family, 1800-89 (170 pieces); Robert Barnwell Rhett (S.C.; planter, editor, U. S. Rep. and Sen.) and his sons, 1835-80 (377 pieces); John Rutledge, Jr. (S. C.; lawyer, U.S. Rep.), 1782-1819 (1 vol. and 480 pieces); William Dunlap Simpson (S. C.; Confed. Army officer, Gov., State chief justice) and his family, 1824-99 (260 pieces); William Smith (S. C.; U. S. Rep. and Sen.) and his family, 1768-1906 (100 pieces); William Francis Stevenson (S. C.; U. S. Rep.), 1861-1924 but chiefly 1916-22 (1,525 pieces); and Waddy Thompson (S. C., Fla.; U. S. Rep. from S. C., Minister to Mexico), 1823-51 (80 pieces).

Papers of Georgians who held public office include papers of Augustus Octavius Bacon (Ga.; lawyer, Confed. Army officer, U. S. Sen.), 1853-79 (microfilm of 3 vols. and 2 pieces); John MacPherson Berrien (Ga.; U. S. Sen. and Attorney Gen., State supreme court justice), 1778-1938 (4 vols. and 1,500 pieces); James Conquest Cross Black (Ga.; lawyer, U. S. Rep.), 1864-99 (7 vols.); William Bellinger Bulloch (Ga.; lawyer, banker, U. S. Sen.)

and his family, 1784-1929 (3 vols. and
500 pieces); Tomlinson Fort (Ga.; physician, banker, U.S. Rep.), 1812-83
(88 pieces on microfilm); James Mathew Griggs (Ga.; U.S. Rep.), 1892-
1913 (1,000 pieces); Henry Jackson
(Ga.; Univ. of Ga. prof., Chargé d'Affaires in France) and his son, Henry
Rootes Jackson (Ga.; Mexican War and
Confed. Army officer, Minister to Austria and Mexico), and their family,
1784-1923 (14 vols. and 2,910 pieces);
Thomas Butler King (Ga.; U.S. Rep.,
Confed. commissioner in Europe) and
his family (8 vols. and 4,000 pieces);
Alexander Robert Lawton (Ga.; lawyer, Confed. Army officer, Minister
to Austria), 1776-1907 (9 vols. and
550 pieces); Eugenius Aristides Nisbet
(Ga.; U.S. Rep., State supreme court
judge) and his family, 1752-1936
(1,800 pieces); George Welshman
Owens (Ga.; lawyer, U.S. Rep.), 1814-
65 (microfilm of 65 pieces); Alexander
Hamilton Stephens (Ga.; U.S. Rep.,
Confed. Vice Pres., Gov.), 1834-72
(microfilm of 3,000 pieces); William
Henry Stiles (Ga.; U.S. Rep., Chargé
d'Affaires in Austria) and his family,
1762-1899 (43 vols. and 3,200 pieces);
Nelson Tift (Ga.; merchant, railroad
promoter, U.S. Rep.), 1835-56 (microfilm of copy of diary, 175 pages);
Thomas Edward Watson (Ga.; U.S.
Rep. and Sen., People's Party presidential candidate), 1870-1922 (37 vols.
and 15,000 pieces); and Benjamin Cud-
worth Yancey (S.C., Ala., Ga.; newspaper editor, Minister to Argentina,
Confed. Army officer) and his family,
1800-1931 (31 vols. and 3,300 pieces).

Papers of Alabamians who held
public office include papers of John
Bragg (Ala.; State circuit court judge,
U.S. Rep.), 1851-87 (610 pieces);
Frederick G. Bromberg (Ala.; lawyer, U.S. Rep.), 1738-1930 (11,815
pieces); John Archibald Campbell
(Ala., La.; U.S. Supreme Court Justice, Confed. Asst. Sec. War) and his
family, 1781-1927 (4 vols. and 706

pieces); Braxton B. Comer (Ala.;
planter, businessman, Gov., U.S.
Sen.), 1908-27 (7 vols. and 20,000
pieces); Nathaniel H. R. Dawson
(Ala.; lawyer, banker, U.S. Commissioner of Education), 1851-1917
(555 microfilm exposures); Benjamin
Fitzpatrick (Ala.; planter, Gov., U.S.
Sen.) and son, 1819-92 (208 pieces);
John Gayle (Ala.; State supreme
court justice, Gov., U.S. Rep.),
1821-35 (200 pieces, copies); Hilary
A. Herbert (Ala.; U.S. Rep., Sec.
Navy), 1892-1931 (14 vols. and 300
pieces); Edward A. O'Neal (Ala.; lawyer, Confed. Army officer, Gov.),
1833-93 (10 vols. and 500 pieces);
Philip Phillips (S.C., Ala., D.C.;
lawyer, U.S. Rep. from Ala.) and his
family, 1804-1923 (13 vols. and 1,000
pieces); Israel Pickens (N.C., Ala.;
U.S. Rep. from N.C., Gov. of and U.S.
Sen. from Ala.), 1812-27 (65 pieces);
Thomas D. Samford (Ala.; U.S. dist.
attorney, Democratic Party leader),
1901-46 (microfilm of 4 vols.); William J. Samford (Ala.; U.S. Rep.,
Gov.), 1884-99 (1 vol. on microfilm);
Jesse F. Stallings (Ala.; lawyer, insurance businessman, U.S. Rep.),
1892-1916 (1,200 pieces); and William
L. Yancey (Ala.; U.S. Rep., Confed.
Sen.), 1837-63 (50 pieces).

Papers of Tennesseans who held
public office include papers of John
Bell (Tenn.; U.S. Rep. and Sen., Sec.
War), 1849-61 (90 pieces); John M.
Bright (Tenn.; lawyer, U.S. Rep.),
1854-1911 (5 vols. and 500 pieces);
Edward Ward Carmack (Tenn.; lawyer, newspaper editor, U.S. Rep.
and Sen.), 1850-1942 (15 vols. and
2,200 pieces); Robert L. Caruthers
(Tenn.; U.S. Rep., State supreme
court justice), 1823-70 (1,575 pieces); Joseph Smith Fowler (Tenn.;
lawyer, U.S. Sen.), 1863-1902 (155
pieces); Felix Grundy (Tenn.; U.S.
Rep. and Sen., Attorney Gen.), 1807-
89 (68 pieces); Gustavus Adolphus
Henry (Tenn.; lawyer, planter, Con-

fed. Sen.), 1804-71 (660 pieces); Howell E. Jackson (Tenn.; U. S. Sen., U. S. Supreme Court Justice) and his family, 1826-1911 (16 vols. and 478 pieces); George W. Jones (Tenn.; U. S. and Confed. Rep.), 1835-84 (240 pieces); David M. Key (Tenn.; Confed. Army officer, U. S. Sen., Postmaster Gen., U. S. dist. court judge), 1839-1901 (2 vols., 22 pieces, and 2 microfilm reels); Samuel D. McReynolds (Tenn.; U. S. Rep., State judge), 1891-1940 (7 vols. and 250 pieces); John Overton (Tenn.; State supreme court justice, political leader), 1790-1840 (7 pieces and microfilm of 461 pieces); and Lawrence D. Tyson (Tenn.; U. S. Army officer, newspaper publisher, U. S. Sen.), 1917-29 (2,900 pieces).

Papers of Mississippians and Louisianians who held public office include papers of James L. Alcorn (Miss.; U. S. Sen., Gov., Confed. Army officer), 1850-76 (3 vols. and 31 pieces); Taylor Beatty (La.; Confed. Army officer, sugar planter, judge), 1861-1917 (10 vols. of diary); Donelson Caffery (La.; planter, Confed. Army officer, U. S. Sen.) and his family, 1838-1924 (350 pieces); John F. H. Claiborne (Miss., La.; lawyer, journalist, historian, U. S. Rep. from Miss.) and his family, 1794-1910 (7 vols. and 880 pieces); Edward J. Gay (Mo., La.; planter, manufacturer, U. S. Rep. from La.), 1842-89 (9 vols. and 360 pieces); Randall Lee Gibson (La.; Confed. Army officer, planter, U. S. Rep. and Sen.) and his family, 1846-1919 (200 pieces); James T. Harrison (Miss.; lawyer, Confed. Rep.), 1770-1878 (250 pieces); Jason Niles (Miss.; lawyer, U. S. Rep., newspaper editor), 1836-90 (37 vols. of diary); Jehu A. Orr (Miss.; U. S. dist. attorney, Confed. Army officer, Confed. Rep., State circuit court judge), 1809-1917 (46 vols. and 344 pieces); John M. Parker (La.; cotton merchant, Progressive Party leader, Gov.), 1902-20 (4 vols. and 3,500 pieces); John Perkins, Jr. (La.; lawyer, cotton planter, U. S. Rep., Confed. Sen.), 1822-85 (550 pieces); Andrew Price (La.; lawyer, planter, U. S. Rep.), 1878-1926 (6 vols. and 1,000 pieces); John A. Quitman (Miss.; Mexican War officer, Gov., U.S. Rep.), 1784-1858 (5 vols. and 2,200 pieces); and Henry C. Warmoth (La.; Civil War officer, Gov.), 1860-1930 (77 vols. and 3,500 pieces).

Papers of office holders of other States and the District of Columbia include papers of Richard Keith Call (Fla.; lawyer, Terr. Delegate to Cong., Terr. Gov.) and his family, 1804-1905 (6 vols. and 330 pieces); Louis A. Dent (Md., D. C.; lawyer, U. S. consul in Jamaica), 1717-1946 (9 vols. and 2,500 pieces); Asbury Dickins (D. C.; Treas. Dept. and State Dept. official, sec. of U. S. Senate) and his family, 1713-1934 (38 vols. and 2,300 pieces); Henry H. Glassie (D. C.; special asst. to U. S. Attorney Gen.), 1833-1937 (8 vols. and 466 pieces); Arthur Pue Gorman (Md.; pres. of Chesapeake and Ohio Canal Co., U. S. Sen.), 1875-1909 (64 scrapbooks); James Guthrie (Ky.; Sec. Treas., U. S. Sen.), 1857-62 (53 pieces); Peter Hagner (Pa., D.C.; Third Auditor of the Treasury) and his family, 1730-1940 (5 vols. and 3,600 pieces); James K. Jones (Ark.; planter, lawyer, U. S. Sen. and Rep.) and his family, 1900-21 (21 vols. and 6,500 pieces); Stephen R. Mallory (Fla.; lawyer, U. S. Rep., Confed. Sec. Navy), 1858-72 (2 vols. and microfilm of 69 pieces); Isidor Rayner (Md.; lawyer, U. S. Rep. and Sen.), 1866-1921 (11 vols. and 75 pieces); Ethelbert Stewart (Ill., D.C.; Chief of Bureau of Labor Statistics), 1884-1933 (300 pieces); Robert E. Thomason (Tex.; U. S. dist. court judge, U. S. Rep.), 1931-47 (80 pieces); and William Wirt (Va., Md.; U.S. Attorney Gen.) and his family, 1802-67 (170 pieces).

Papers of Army officers include those of Edward Porter Alexander (Ga.; U. S. and Confed. Army officer, prof. at U. S. Military Academy and S. C. Univ., pres. of Ga. Railroad and Banking Co.), 1820-1923 (3 vols. and 3,500 pieces); Henry L. Benning (Ga.; lawyer, Confed. Army officer), 1795-1897 (microfilm of 100 pieces); Herman Biggs (N. Y.; U. S. Army officer), 1837-82 (3 vols. and 145 pieces); Benjamin Franklin Cheatham (Tenn.; Mexican War and Confed. Army officer), 1834-93 (microfilm of 134 pieces); Thomas L. Clingman (N. C.; U.S. Rep. and Sen., Confed. Army officer), 1862-65 (790 pieces); Raleigh Edward Colston (Va., N. C.; Va. Military Institute prof., Confed. Army officer, Egyptian Army officer), 1842-1906 (10 vols. and 743 pieces); Philip St. George Cooke (Va.; U. S. Army officer, author) and his son, John R. Cooke (Va.; engineer, U. S. and Confed. Army officer), 1837-1942 (280 microfilm frames); Samuel Cooper (Va.; U. S. and Confed. Army officer) and his family, 1783-1899 (microfilm of 88 pieces); Richard Stoddert Ewell (U. S. and Confed. Army officer), 1856-72 (150 pieces); Harley B. Ferguson (N. C., Miss.; U. S. Army officer, engineer, pres. of the Miss. River Commission), 1892-1941 (27 vols. and 3,000 pieces); Robert C. Foster (Tenn.; lawyer, Mexican War and Confed. Army officer), 1837-67 (150 pieces); William M. Gardner (Ga.; U. S. and Confed. Army officer), 1818-1915 (54 pieces); Jeremy F. Gilmer (N. C., Ga.; U. S. and Confed. Army officer), 1769-1895 (5 vols. and 2,070 pieces); William W. Gordon (Ga.; Confed. Army and Spanish-American War officer, cotton merchant), 1745-1912 (7,500 pieces); Daniel C. Govan (Miss., Ark., Wash.; planter, Confed. Army officer, U. S. Indian agent), 1861-1908 (97 pieces); Bryan Grimes (N. C.; planter, Confed. Army officer) and his family, 1792-1917 (2 vols. and 1,100 pieces);

Henry W. Harrington (S. C., N. C.; Rev. War officer, planter), 1775-1848 (70 pieces); Daniel Harvey Hill (Va., N. C., Ark.; U. S. and Confed. Army officer, college prof., Univ. of Ark. pres.), 1846-85 (4 vols. and 60 pieces); Chiliab Smith Howe (Mass., Ala., Miss.; U. S. Army officer, planter, merchant), 1828-99 (450 pieces), relating primarily to Cherokee removal from North Carolina and Tennessee; Edmund Kirby-Smith (Fla., Tenn.; U. S. and Confed. Army officer, Univ. of Nashville pres.) and his family, 1776-1902 (2,070 pieces); Evander McIvor Law (S. C., Fla.; Confed. Army officer), 1860-64 (microfilm of 479 pieces); Edwin G. Lee (Va.; lawyer, Confed. Army officer, Confed. agent), 1864-65 (microfilm of 1-vol. diary kept in Canada); Stephen D. Lee (Miss.; U. S. and Confed. Army officer, pres. of Miss. Agricultural and Mechanical College) and his family, 1784-1929 (1 vol. and 270 pieces); and William Lenoir (N. C.; Rev. War officer) and his family, 1755-1929 (17 vols. and 13,000 pieces).

Papers of other Army officers include those of William G. Lewis (N.C.; Confed. Army officer, civil engineer), 1855-1911 (72 pieces); Samuel H. Lockett (Ala., Tenn.; U. S. and Confed. Army officer, Egyptian Army officer, Univ. of Tenn. prof.), 1861-88 (3 vols. and 175 pieces); George W. Logan (La.; Confed. Army officer), 1861-65 (4 vols. and 1,800 pieces); Thomas M. Logan (S. C., Va.; Confed. Army officer, lawyer, organizer of the Southern Railway) and his family, 1846-1938 (4 vols. and 120 pieces); William W. Mackall (Va.; U. S. and Confed. Army officer), 1839-91 (2 vols. and 400 pieces); Lafayette McLaws (Ga.; U. S. and Confed. Army officer, insurance businessman), 1836-97 (800 pieces); James G. Martin (N. C.; U. S. and Confed. Army officer, lawyer) and his family, 1812-1942 (5 vols. and 275 pieces); John

H. Morgan (Ky.; Confed. cavalry officer), 1840-70 (650 pieces); Frank Parker (Ill.; U.S. Army officer, Military Commander of the Philippines, Asst. Chief of Staff), 1890-1946 (34 vols. and 11,000 pieces); Alden Partridge (N.Y., Vt.; U.S. Army officer, Supt. of the U.S. Military Academy), 1807-54 (3 microfilm reels); William Dorsey Pender (N.C.; U.S. and Confed. Army officer), 1860-63 (200 pieces); William Nelson Pendleton (Md., Va.; U.S. and Confed. Army officer, Episcopal clergyman) and his family, 1798-1889 (2,391 pieces); James Johnston Pettigrew (S.C.; lawyer, Confed. Army officer) and his family, 1685-1926 (56 vols. and 14,000 pieces); Felix P. Poché (La.; lawyer, Confed. Army officer), 1863-65 (10 vols. on microfilm); Leonidas Polk (Tenn., La., N.C.; Episcopal bishop, Confed. Army officer) and his family, 1767-1934 (4 vols., 300 pieces, and 3 microfilm reels); Trusten Polk (Mo.; Gov., U.S. Sen., Confed. Army officer), 1861-65 (1 vol. and 6 pieces); William Polk (N.C.; Rev. War officer, pres. of N.C. State Bank), 1773-1834 (8 vols. and 500 pieces); Stephen D. Ramseur (N.C.; Confed. Army officer), 1853-1940 (325 pieces); Jethro Sumner (N.C.; Rev. War officer), 1775-97 (400 pieces); William Booth Taliaferro (Va.; U.S. and Confed. Army officer, State legislator) and his family, 1805-1901 (840 microfilm frames); Zachary Taylor (Ky.; U.S. Army officer, U.S. Pres.), 1841-50 (126 pieces on microfilm); M. Jeff Thompson (Mo.; surveyor, Confed. Army officer), 1860-74 (3 vols. and 140 pieces); Charles S. Venable (Va., S.C.; mathematician, Confed. Army officer, aide to Robert E. Lee), 1861-65 (475 pieces); John H. Winder (Md.; U.S. and Confed. Army officer), 1808-89 (41 pieces); John Ellis Wool (U.S. Army officer), 1836-37 (50 pieces); and Marcus J. Wright (Tenn., D.C.; Confed. Army officer, military historian),

1792-1945 (700 pieces).

Papers of naval and Marine Corps officers include those of Edwin Alexander Anderson (N.C.; U.S. naval officer), 1878-1939 (800 pieces); George B. Balch (U.S. naval officer, Supt. of U.S. Naval Academy), 1830-1924 (3 vols. and 410 pieces); James Barron (U.S. naval officer), 1835-84 (2 vols. and 1,540 pieces); Franklin Buchanan (U.S. naval officer, Supt. of U.S. Naval Academy, Confed. naval officer), 1829-32, 1862-63 (2 vols.); Harrison H. Cocke (U.S. naval officer), 1762-1876 (5 vols. and 175 pieces); Lyman A. Cotten (U.S. naval officer, naval attaché in Japan), 1886-1936 (29 vols. and 7,000 pieces); William C. Harllee (U.S. Marine Corps officer, Director of Marine Corps Institute), 1685-1944 (4,000 pieces); William L. Hudson (U.S. naval officer), 1840-42 (microfilm of log, 558 pages); Rufus Z. Johnston (U.S. naval officer), 1895-1950 (470 pieces); Andrew T. Long (U.S. naval officer), 1887-1943 (2 vols. and 1,000 pieces); Newton A. McCully (U.S. naval officer), 1923-24 (325 pieces); John N. Maffitt (N.C.; U.S. and Confed. naval officer), 1833-1911 (3 vols. and 200 pieces); A. Stanton Merrill (U.S. naval officer), 1912-48 (35 vols. and 300 pieces); Edward Middleton (U.S. naval officer), 1810-93 (204 pieces); Richard L. Page (Va.; U.S. and Confed. naval officer, Confed. Army officer), 1825-64 (microfilm of 5 vols.); Archibald H. Scales (U.S. naval officer), 1883-1929 (1,110 pieces); Adolphus Staton (U.S. naval officer), 1907-36 (4,400 pieces); James H. Tomb (Fla.; Confed. naval officer) and his son, William V. Tomb (U.S. naval officer), 1855-1936 (350 pieces); William P. Upshur (U.S. Marine Corps officer), 1898-1928 (600 pieces); William Conway Whittle (Va.; U.S. and Confed. naval officer) and his family, 1826-1919 (805 pieces); and John Taylor Wood (La., Nova Scotia; U.S. and Confed. naval officer, aide to Jefferson Davis) and his family, 1858-1915 (3 vols. and 198 pieces).

Papers of educational leaders include those of Kemp Plummer Battle (N. C.; lawyer, pres. of Univ. of N.C.) and his family, 1765-1919 (3,000 pieces); William James Battle (Tex.; prof. and dean at Univ. of Tex.) and his family, 1876-1955 (6,000 pieces); Launcelot Minor Blackford (Va.; Confed. Army officer, headmaster Episcopal High School), 1847-1913 (39 vols. of diary); Albert P. Bourland (Tenn.; prof. at George Peabody College, executive sec. of Southern Education Board), 1899-1922 (3,000 pieces); Eugene C. Branson (N. C.; rural economist, Univ. of N. C. prof.), 1899-1923 (4,000 pieces); William Le Roy Broun (Va., Ga., Ala., Tenn., Tex.; scientist, prof. at Univ. of Ga. and elsewhere, Confed. Army officer), 1838-1902 (9 vols. and 4,500 pieces); Harry Woodburn Chase (N. C., Ill., N. Y.; univ. prof., pres. Univs. of N. C. and Ill., chancellor New York Univ.), 1924-55 (175 pieces); Charles Lee Coon (N. C.; public school administrator, sec. N. C. Child Labor Committee), 1695-1927 (14 vols. and 5,000 pieces); Charles W. Dabney (Va., N. C., Tenn., Ohio; pres. of Univs. of Tenn. and Cincinnati, member of Southern Education Board) and his family, 1744-1945 (32 vols. and 6,000 pieces), with 10,000 pieces relating to the Southern Education Board; John Rose Ficklen (La.; historian, Tulane Univ. prof.), 1864-1907 (13 vols. and 175 pieces); Joseph Grégoire de Roulhac Hamilton (N. C.; historian, Univ. of N. C. prof., director of the Southern Historical Collection), 29 boxes, unarranged; Lewis L. Hobbs (N. C.; Guilford College pres., Society of Friends leader) and his family, 1787-1949 (37 vols. and 625 pieces); Charles W. Hutson (La., Miss., Tex.; univ. prof., editor, painter), 1860-1949 (600 pieces); John L. Johnson (Va., Miss., Tenn.; Baptist minister, Univ. of Miss. prof., Mary Sharpe College pres.), 1850-1910

(1 vol. and 700 pieces); William Preston Johnston (Va., La.; pres. of La. State and Tulane Univs.), 1853-99 (50 pieces); James Y. Joyner (N.C.; State supt. of public instruction, member of Southern Education Board), 1900-19 (2,000 pieces); John Kimberly (N. C., Tenn.; Univ. of N. C. prof.) and his family, 1821-78 (12 vols. and 1,760 pieces); John McLaren McBryde (Va., S. C., Tenn.; agriculturist, pres. of S. C. College and Va. Polytechnic Institute) and his son, John M. McBryde, Jr. (Va., N. C., La.; college prof.), 1856-1940 (1,200 pieces); Alexander McIver (N.C.; Davidson College and Univ. of N.C. prof., State supt. of public instruction) and his family, 1884-1929 (300 pieces); Nathaniel R. Middleton (S. C.; College of Charleston pres.), 1830-90 (1,200 pieces); Elisha Mitchell (N. C.; geologist, botanist, Univ. of N. C. prof.) and his family, 1818-78 (50 pieces); Samuel C. Mitchell (S. C., Del., Va.; pres. of Univ. of S. C. and Del. College, history prof. at Richmond Univ.), 1912-46 (1 vol. and 4,200 pieces); Howard W. Odum (N. C.; sociologist, Univ. of N. C. prof.), 1920-52 (250,000 pieces); Charles Phillips (N. C.; Univ. of N. C. and Davidson College prof., Presbyterian minister), 1856-89 (140 pieces); Ulrich B. Phillips (Mich., Conn.; historian, Univ. of Mich. and Yale prof.), 1900-37 (39 pieces and 167 typed copies); Franklin L. Riley (Miss., Va.; history prof. at Univ. of Miss. and Washington and Lee Univ.), 1843-1930 (1,600 pieces); William N. Sheats (Fla.; State supt. of public instruction), 1872-1949 (5 vols. and 1,800 pieces); Calvin H. Wiley (N. C.; State supt. of schools, author) and his family, 1770-1951 (2,300 pieces); and Louis Round Wilson (N. C., Ill.; Librarian, Director of Press and of Extension Bureau at Univ. of N. C., dean of Graduate School of Library Science at Univ. of

Chicago), 1901-50 (10,000 pieces).

Papers of religious leaders include those of James Atkins (N. C.; college pres., Methodist bishop) and his family, 1874-1931 (8 vols. and 1,600 pieces); John W. Beckwith (Ga.; Episcopal bishop, Confed. chaplain), 1852-89 (1 vol. and 64 pieces); Nathan S. S. Beman (Ga., N. Y.; Presbyterian minister, pres. of Renssalaer Polytechnic Institute, abolitionist leader), 1834-39 (50 pieces); William Carey (England, India; Baptist missionary, philologist, botanist), 1793-1825 (microfilm of 52 pieces); Joseph Blount Cheshire (N.C.; Episcopal bishop), 1863-1932 (8 vols. and 3,670 pieces); George S. Dickerman (Conn.; Congregational minister, associate sec. of the Southern Education Board), 1900-31 (8 vols. and 2,500 pieces); Edward Dromgoole (Va.; Methodist minister), 1770-1822 (4 vols. and 350 pieces); Edward Owings Guerrant (Ky.; Confed. Army officer, physician, Presbyterian minister), 1856-1917 (135 vols. and 30 pieces); Henry C. Lay (Ala., Ark., Md.; Episcopal bishop) and his family, 1844-1908 (28 vols. and 3,600 pieces); Silas McBee (N.Y.; Episcopal writer, editor of the Churchman), 1872-1923 (12,500 pieces); Basil Manly, Jr. (S. C., Ky.; Baptist minister, prof. at Southern Baptist Theological Seminary), 1842-93 (150 pieces and microfilm of 22 vols.); Nereus Mendenhall (N. C., Pa.; physician, civil engineer, teacher) and his family, 1787-1949 (37 vols. and 625 pieces); Robert H. Morrison (N. C.; Presbyterian minister, Davidson College pres.) and his family, 1820-82 (375 pieces); Edgar G. Murphy (Ala.; Episcopal clergyman, author, executive sec. of the Southern Education Board), 1893-1913 (2 vols. and 210 pieces); James H. Otey (Tenn.; Episcopal bishop), 1823-84 (15 vols. and 80 pieces); Charles Pettigrew (N. C.; Episcopal clergyman), 1771-1807 (200 pieces); Edwin McNeill Poteat (N. C., N. Y.; Baptist missionary to

China, pres. of Colgate-Rochester Divinity School, preacher at Raleigh, N. C.), 1925-56 (4,000 pieces); Charles Todd Quintard (Tenn.; physician, Episcopal bishop, Confed. chaplain), 1864-98 (7 microfilm reels); John Rogers (Ky.; Disciples of Christ evangelist), 1800-63 (3 vols.); and John F. Young (Fla.; Episcopal bishop, 1856-58 (54 pieces).

Papers of authors and editors include those of Sherwood Anderson (Ill., Va.; novelist, poet), 1926-35 (52 pieces); Peter Force (D. C.; historian, editor), 1775-1875 (1 vol. and 54 pieces); Joseph Gales (England, N. C.; reformer, newspaper editor), 1815-39 (1 vol. and 4 pieces); Kahlil Gibran (Syria, U. S.; poet, artist), 1904-31 (250 pieces); Narciso Gener Gonzales (S. C.; newspaper editor) and his family, 1698-1898 (26 vols. and 5,000 pieces); Duff Green (Mo., D. C., Ga.; journalist, political leader, industrial promoter) and his family, 1810-1902 (29 vols. and 3,600 pieces); Wade H. Harris (N. C.; newspaper editor), 1909-35 (5 vols. and 500 pieces); Henry Harrisse (N. Y., France; lawyer, bibliographer, historian), 1853-1910 (228 pieces and copies of 75 pieces); Caroline Lee Whiting Hentz (Ala., Fla.; author) and her family, 1810-1918 (12 vols., 100 pieces, and 23 pieces on microfilm); John B. Jones (Md., Va.; periodical editor, author) and his family, 1794-1894 (1 vol. and 180 pieces); Grace Elizabeth King (La.; short-story writer, novelist) and her family, 1833-1933 (microfilm of 2 vols. and 970 pieces); Henry Louis Mencken (Md.; author, editor, critic), 1927-52 (500 letters) not open for use until 1978; Margaret Junkin Preston (Va.; poet and prose writer), 1842-92 (150 pieces); James Gettys McGready Ramsey (Tenn.; physician, author), 1789-1883 (1 vol. and 50 pieces); James Ryder Randall (Md., La., Ga.; poet, journalist), 1855-64 (117 pieces); Elmer Roberts (Ind.,

Fla.; foreign correspondent), 1860-
1937 (2 vols. and 2,300 pieces); Edmund Ruffin (Va.; agriculturist, publisher and editor of the Farmer's
Register, Confed. leader), 1823-65
(5 vols. and 940 pieces); William L.
Saunders (N.C.; lawyer, Confed. Army
officer, N. C. sec. state, historical
editor), 1712-1907 (600 pieces); Randolph Shotwell (N. C.; newspaper editor), 1868-85 (100 pieces); Cornelia
Phillips Spencer (N. C.; author) and
her family, 1830-1930 (71 vols. and
1,500 pieces); Samuel A. Tannenbaum
(N. Y.; physician, psychiatrist, Shakespearean scholar), 1908-42 (800
pieces); and Josiah Turner (N. C.; Confed. Rep., newspaper editor), 1805-
1918 (800 pieces).

Papers of scientists and physicians
include those of Harry A. Allard
(Mass., D. C.; naturalist, U.S. Dept. of
Agriculture specialist), 1880-1953 (15
vols. and 5,000 pieces); Richard D. Arnold (Ga.; physician, prof. at Savannah
Medical College), 1849-76 (1 vol. and
89 pieces); Robert Ervin Coker (N. C.;
prof. of zoology at Univ. of N. C., expert in fisheries and marine life),
1906-56 (7,000 pieces); William Chambers Coker (N. C.; botanist, prof. Univ.
of N. C.), 1912-51 (25,000 pieces);
Moses Ashley Curtis (N. C., S. C.;
Episcopal clergyman, botanist) and
his family, 1825-1929 (14 vols. and
3,200 pieces); Richard P. Daniel (Fla.;
physician, U. S. Navy surgeon), 1855-
58 (microfilm of medical log); Joseph
Goldberger (D. C.; physician, U. S.
Public Health Service official, pella-
gra specialist), 1891-1949 (2 vols.
and 2,400 pieces); James K. Hall (N.C.,
Va.; physician psychiatrist) and his
family, 1751-1949 (15 vols. and 32,000
pieces); Calvin Jones (N. C., Tenn.;
physician) and his family, 1797-1929
(24 vols. and 1,100 pieces); Joseph Le-
Conte (Ga., Calif.; geologist, univ.
prof.) and his family, 1809-1931
(2 vols. and 230 pieces); William de B.
MacNider (N. C.; pharmacologist, dean

of Univ. of N. C. Medical School),
1905-51 (30,000 pieces); William H.
Morgan (Tenn.; dentist, dean of Vanderbilt Univ. School of Dentistry),
1836-93 (1,685 pieces); Joseph H.
Pratt (N. C.; geologist, engineer,
Univ. of N. C. prof.), 1900-40 (8,000
pieces); George W. Rains (N.Y., Ga.;
U. S. and Confed. Army officer, inventor, chemist, dean of Medical
College of Ga.), 1843-79 (50 pieces);
Charles Wilkins Short (Ky.; physician, botanist, prof. at Transylvania
Univ. and Medical Institute of Louisville), 1784-1880 (455 pieces); James
Marion Sims (Ala., N. Y.; gynecologist, founder of Woman's Hospital in
N. Y., inventor of surgical instruments), 1835-84 (107 pieces); Samuel H. Stout (Tenn., Ga., Tex.; physician, Confed. Army officer), 1847-
1903 (microfilm of 900 pieces); and
William C. Stubbs (La.; agriculturist,
director of the State sugar experiment
station), 1881-1925 (200 pieces).

Among papers of other individuals
are those of Alexander Boyd Andrews
(N. C.; Confed. officer, railroad promoter), 1859-91 (3,000 pieces); Daniel Dudley Avery (La.; sugar planter,
broker, lawyer, salt miner) and the
Avery and Marsh families, 1796-1916
(1,000 pieces); George J. Baldwin
(Ga.; engineer, financier, leader in
mining, railroad, and utility development), 108 boxes, unarranged; Willis
Grandy Briggs (N. C.; lawyer, Republican Party leader), 1764-1954 (2,400
pieces); Julian S. Carr (N. C.; tobacco
and textile manufacturer, banker,
philanthropist), 1895-1923 (8 vols.
and 750 pieces); John Hartwell Cocke
(Va.; planter, War of 1812 officer,
publicist, temperance advocate) and
his son, 1804-83 (microfilm of 750
pieces); William Elliott (S. C.; planter, agricultural reformer, writer)
and his family, 1698-1898 (26 vols.
and 5,000 pieces); Peter Spence Gil-
christ (N. C.; chemical engineer),
1904-10 (3,300 pieces); Thomas J.

Green (N. C., Fla., Tex., Calif.; Tex. Army officer, Southern Pacific Railroad director), 1820-65 (1,288 pieces); John Davis Hawkins (N. C.; lawyer, landowner, legislator) and other members of the family, especially his sons, William Joseph (railroad pres.) and Philemon Benjamin (phosphate co. pres.), 1740-1898 (233 vols. and 4,567 pieces); Robert F. Hoke (N. C.; Confed. Army officer, planter, N. C. Railroad Co. director), 1865-1943 (2 vols. and 90 pieces); John Janney (Va.; lawyer, pres. of Va. secession convention) and his family, 1731-1938 (5 vols. and 2,400 pieces); Edward M. L'Engle (Fla.; lawyer, Confed. Army officer, railroad pres.), 1852-97 (5,140 pieces); Juliette Gordon Low (England, Scotland, Ga.; founder of Girl Scouts of America), 1866-1927 (700 pieces); Archibald De Bow Murphey (N. C.; reformer, State superior court judge), 1793-1830 (50 pieces); John Screven (Ga., Confed. Army officer, railroad official) and his family, 1779-1922 (2,400 pieces); Charles O. Sherrill (N.C., D.C., Ohio; engineer, U. S. Army officer, director of buildings and parks in D. C., city manager of Cincinnati), 1926-51 (400 pieces); William Thomas Sutherlin (Va.; tobacconist, banker, Confed. quartermaster), 1842-92 (1,150 pieces); Daniel Augustus Tompkins (S. C., N. C.; industrial leader, newspaper publisher), 1867-1919 (13 vols. and 30,000 pieces); and James Wallace (Nova Scotia, Ga.; British vice consul and merchant at Savannah) and his family, 1787-1826 (microfilm of 100 pieces).

Eighteenth-century manuscripts include material on colonial history, photostats of selected material from the Public Record Office in London, and a significant quantity of material relating to the American Revolution and the early national period. All periods of the 19th and 20th centuries are covered in groups of manuscripts related to a variety of topics: law and politics; the military services in war and peace; railroads, banking, manufacturing, shipping, and other business activity; and education, religion, literature, and social customs. Included in the great quantity of ante bellum records are letters of planters and their families, diaries and plantation journals, business records and accounts, and the records of merchants and factors. Among the materials of the Civil War period, in addition to the papers of officials and military leaders, are letters and diaries of enlisted men and junior officers of both United States and Confederate armies, medical and personnel records, many reminiscences, and letters and diaries of civilians. The Reconstruction period, the later 19th century, and the 20th century are covered in a number of large and important groups of papers.

The Manuscripts Department also administers the Archives of the University of North Carolina, 1792-1955 (530 vols. and 150,000 pieces), containing official minutes of the board of trustees and of the faculty, records and papers of the University administration, and records and papers of student organizations. Personal papers of many of the University's faculty are included in the Southern Historical Collection.

See Hist. Records Survey, Guide to the Manuscripts in the Southern Historical Collection of the University of North Carolina (1941. 204 p.); and annual lists of acquisitions in Journal of Southern History.

CHARLOTTE 2

Public Library of Charlotte and Mecklenburg County. 310 North Tryon St. Mary Louise Phillips, Head, Carolina Collection.

Holdings: A small collection

relating to Charlotte, Mecklenburg
County, North Carolina, and South
Carolina. The Library is the depository for historical manuscripts collected by or belonging to the Mecklenburg Historical Association.

See Hist. Records Survey, Guide
for N. C., p. 10.

DAVIDSON

Davidson College Library. Chalmers
G. Davidson, Director.

Holdings: Chiefly (1) the Davidson
College History Collection, including
faculty minutes from 1820, trustees
minutes from 1836, literary society
minutes, 1837-1900, and student letters, addresses, and notebooks, 1837-
75; and (2) the Peter S. Ney Collection,
19th-20th centuries (4 vols. and many
photographs), including holograph poems by Ney (N. C.; French emigré, reported to have been Napoleon's Marshal
Ney), a mathematics notebook in his
hand, scrapbooks of clippings about
him, chiefly 20th century (2 vols.), and
several books with his marginalia; and
(3) material on Woodrow Wilson (N.J.;
U. S. Pres.), including 4 scrapbooks,
and 4 signed letters and reproductions
of several other letters.

DURHAM

Duke Hospital Library, Duke University. (Mrs.) Rachel Chester Roth,
Curator of the Trent Collection.

Holdings: An important assemblage of manuscripts in the Josiah C.
Trent Collection in the History of
Medicine, 15th-20th centuries (60
vols. and 2,500 items). Among the
earliest manuscripts are two German
calendars, ca. 1435, giving medical
instructions; a copy of the Regimen
of Magninus of Milan, 15th century,

and one of the Regimen Sanitatis Sa-
lernitanum, 16th century; an inventory of the property of a hospital in
Perugia, ca. 1550; and a copy of the
Persian treatise on anatomy by Man-
sur ibn Muhammad ibn Ahmad, 16th
century.

Among the papers of a later date
are many small collections and famous autographs. The larger or
more important collections include
papers of John Adams (U. S. Pres.)
and his wife Abigail, 1797-1801
(8 items); Louis Agassiz (Switzerland, Mass., S. C.; zoologist) and his
family, 1861-1910 (12 items); Rudolph
Bergh (Denmark; physician, zoologist),
1853-1907 (110 items); Pliny Earle,
Jr. (Mass.; physician, psychiatrist),
1806-97 (59 items); William Stump
Forwood (ethnologist, historian),
1857-63 (70 items); Lee Griggs (Va.;
physician), 1823-31 (2 vols. and 7
items); Oliver Wendell Holmes (Mass.;
poet, essayist, physician), 1850-85
(7 items and 56 letters in the Silas
Weir Mitchell papers); Edward Jenner (England; physician, father of
vaccination), 1800-22 (64 items);
Howard A. Kelly (Md.; prof. of gynecology), 1888-1933 (110 items), including 43 letters from William Henry Welch (Md.; physician, prof. at
Johns Hopkins Univ.); Alexander J.
G. Marcet (Swiss refugee physician),
1802-23 (83 items); Hugh Mercer
(Pa., Va.; physician, Rev. War officer), 1771-75 (1 vol.); Samuel Meredith (Pa.; Rev. War officer, Member
Continental Cong., U. S. Treasurer),
1775-1805 (22 items); and John Kearsley Mitchell (Pa.; physician, Jefferson
Medical College prof.), 1827-49, and
Silas Weir Mitchell (Pa.; physician,
neurologist, poet, novelist), 1854-
1915 (721 items).

Additional papers of similar character are those of Sir William Osler
(Canada, Md., England; physician,
prof. at Johns Hopkins and Oxford
Univs.), 1902-19 (4 items and 17 let-

ters in the Silas Weir Mitchell papers); D'Arcy Power (England; physician, medical historian), 1906-13 (1 vol.); Sir Humphrey Davy Rolleston (England; physician), 1882-1937 (34 items); Benjamin Rush (Pa.; physician, Member Continental Cong., prof. at Univ. of Pa.), 1766-1845 (11 vols. and 241 items); John Jervis, Earl of St. Vincent (British admiral), 1796-1800 (60 items); Marcus Aurelius Severinus (Italy; physician), 1638-46/47 (5 items); the Shattuck family (Mass.; Boston physicians), 1822-1928 (31 items); Sir James Young Simpson (Scotland; obstetrician), 1838-1911 (103 items); Robert King Stone (D. C.; Pres. Lincoln's family physician), 1863-90 (4 vols. and 1 item); John Torrey (N. Y.; botanist, chemist), 1818-62 (57 items); Alexander von Humboldt (Germany; naturalist), 1816-55 (23 items); Benjamin Waterhouse (Mass.; physician), 1754-1846 (52 items and 2 vols., photostats); and Charles Knickerbocker Winne (U. S. Army surgeon), 1864-65 (1 vol.). There are also admission and instruction cards of early U. S. medical schools, 1811-80 (89 items).

—oOo—

Duke University Libraries. Benjamin E. Powell, Librarian; Mattie Russell, Curator of Manuscripts.

Holdings: Thousands of volumes of diaries, journals, account books, letterpress books, and other bound manuscripts and 2,650,000 items, dated from the 10th to the 20th centuries but mainly from the American Revolution to recent years, and relating chiefly to the Southern States. Of first importance are papers pertaining to the Civil War, including official records of the Confederate and State governments, papers of many military and naval officers, and letters and diaries of soldiers and civilians (in over 500 collections) for the war and reconstruction periods. Other papers relate to national politics and government, the U. S. Army and Navy, foreign affairs and Indian relations, and Southern agriculture, business of many kinds, education, and religious life.

Among the older holdings are medieval and Renaissance manuscripts, 10th-17th centuries (44 items), chiefly lectionaries and other New Testament manuscripts; transcripts of documents in the Mexican archives concerning the early history of the University of Mexico, 1553-1830 (340 folios); and a collection of Peruvian manuscripts, 1580-1872 (22 vols. and 23 items), on commerce and industry, literary activity, and religious and social history.

Papers of British origin include those of Edgar Alfred Bowring (England; Board of Trade official, Member of Parliament, author), 1841-47 (14 vols. of journals); Adam Clarke (England; Methodist minister, classical and Biblical scholar), 1743-1875 (299 items); Joseph Conrad (England; novelist), 1897-1922 (147 items); Sir John Easthope (England; financier, newspaper owner, Member of Parliament), 1809-1957 (499 items); Stephen Fuller (England; colonial agent for Jamaica), chiefly 1786-96 (2 vols. and 42 items); George Jacob Holyoake (England; social reformer, author), 1873-1931 (355 items); John Mitchell Kemble (England; philologist, historian), 1829-57 (2 vols. and 49 items); Lord Richard Bickerton Pemell Lyons (England; Minister to the U. S. and to France), 1857-62 (44 items); Sir John Newport (Ireland; Member of Parliament), 1792-1834 (68 items); Edward Lacon Ommaney (England, India; British Army officer), 1810-58 (177 items); Arthur William Edgar O'Shaughnessy (England; poet), 1859-81 (172 items); Dante Gabriel Rossetti (England; poet, painter) and his brother, William Michael Rossetti (England; art critic), 1840-1912 (420 items); Emma Juliana (Gray) Smith and John P. George Smith (England, Brazil; naturalists), 1843-45 (61 letters); William Smith (England; Member of Parliament, abolitionist), 1785-1834 (240 items); Sir Edward John Stanley (England; "liberal" reformer, Member of Parliament), 1835-37 (49 items); Alfred, Lord Tennyson (England; poet) and his family, 1831-98 (90 items); Arthur Wellesley, first Duke of Wellington (British Army officer, Prime Minister), 1704-1877 (1 vol. and 73 items); William Wilberforce (England; philanthropist, Member of Parliament, abolitionist), 1796-1851 (159 items); and John Wolcot (England; poet), 1790-1820 (352 items, of which 297 are photostatic copies). There are also some papers of the Levant Co., 1768-1902 (3 vols. and 134 items); a Jamaica plantation, 1766-1873 (9 vols. and 235 items); and the British Consulate in Georgia, 1816-75 (466 items).

Papers of North Carolina political leaders include those of Josiah William Bailey (N. C.; editor of Biblical Recorder, U. S. Sen.), 1833-1948 (671,500 items); Asa Biggs (N. C., Va.; U. S. Rep. and Sen., U. S. and Confed. judge), 1827-85 (1 vol. and 164 items); Lawrence O'Bryan Branch (N. C.; U. S. Rep., Confed. Army officer) and his family, 1813-95 (6 vols. and 793 items); John Heritage Bryan (N. C.; U. S. Rep.) and his family, 1798-1921 (63 items); Tod Robinson Caldwell (N. C.; Gov.), 1839-74 (175 items); Henry Toole Clark (N. C.; State legislator, Gov.), 1757-1885 (1,341 items); Locke Craig (N. C.; State legislator, Gov.), 1880-1924 (1 vol. and 125 items); William Alexander Graham (N. C.; U. S. and Confed. Sen., Gov., Sec. Navy), 1846-96 (71 items); Edwin Clarke Gregory (N. C.; lawyer, political leader), 1877-1948 (3,699 items); Clyde R. Hoey (N. C.; Gov.,

U. S. Rep. and Sen.), 1944-54 (89,500 items); James Iredell (N. C.; U. S. Supreme Court Justice) and James Iredell, Jr. (N. C.; War of 1812 officer, Gov., U. S. Sen.), 1767-1856 (125 items); Angus Wilton McLean (N. C.; Asst. Sec. Treas., Gov., Director of War Finance Corp.), 1915-33 (microfilm of 2 vols. of numerous letters); Willie Person Mangum (N.C.; U. S. Rep. and Sen.), 1763-1861 (1 vol. and 142 items); Robert Newton Page (N. C.; banker, U. S. Rep.), 1892-1930 (1 vol. and 3,541 items); David S. Reid (N. C.; Gov., U. S. Rep. and Sen.), 1827-81 (75 items); Romulus Mitchell Saunders (N. C.; U. S. Rep., Gov.), 1833-66 (64 items); Furnifold McLendel Simmons (N. C.; U. S. Rep. and Sen.), 1890-1931 (75,000 items); and John Humphrey Small (N. C.; U. S. Rep.), 1720-1946 (9,707 items).

Papers of South Carolina political leaders include those of Armistead Burt (S. C.; U. S. Rep.), 1825-90 (5,641 items); John C. Calhoun (S.C.; U. S. Rep. and Sen., Vice Pres., Sec. War, Sec. State) and his family, 1765-1892 (343 items); James Chesnut (S. C.; lawyer, Confed. Army officer, U. S. Sen.), 1831-63 (102 items); Henry W. De Saussure (S. C.; director of U. S. Mint, State judge) and his grandson, Wilmot Gibbes De Saussure (S. C.; State legislator, Confed. Army officer), 1800-1916 (119 items); Nathaniel Barksdale Dial (S. C., D. C.; industrial promoter, U. S. Sen., lawyer), 1915-35 (2,662 items); Samuel Dibble (S. C.; U. S. Rep.), 1779-1910 (1,672 items); John P. Grace (S. C.; editor, mayor of Charleston), 1906-40 (3 vols. and 12,077 items); George McDuffie (S.C.; U. S. Rep. and Sen., Gov.), 1819-70 (250 items); John Jackson McSwain (S. C.; U. S. Rep.), 1910-41 (15 vols. and 11,903 items); Samuel Jones Nicholls (S. C.; U. S. Rep.), 1915-21 (4,000 items); Francis Wilkinson Pickens (S. C.; U. S. Rep., Minister to Russia, Gov.) and his family, 1778-1900 (1 vol. and 439 items); Charles Cotesworth Pinckney (S. C.; Rev. War officer, Member U. S. Constitutional Convention, Minister to France) and his family, 1744-1887 (1 vol. and 1,180 items); John Rutledge, Jr. (S.C.; lawyer, U. S. Rep., U. S. Army officer), 1760-1862 (2 vols. and 117 items); and William Dunlap Simpson (S. C.; Confed. Army officer, Gov., State chief justice), 1798-1914 (3,660 items).

Papers of Virginia and West Virginia political leaders include those of Alexander Robinson Boteler (Va., W. Va.; U. S. and Confed. Rep., Confed. Army officer), 1776-1898 (1,578 items); David Campbell (Va.; War of 1812 officer, Gov.) and William Bowen Campbell (Tenn.; lawyer, banker, Gov., U. S. Rep.) and their families, 1773-1908 (32 vols. and 8,041 items); John Clopton (Va.; Rev. War officer, U. S. Rep.) and Charles Montriou Wallace, Sr. (Va.; merchant) and their families, 1629-1915 (19 vols. and 11,728 items); John Warwick Daniel (Va.; Confed. Army officer, U. S. Rep. and Sen.), 1849-1910 (483 items); James D. Davidson (Va.; lawyer, political leader, educator), 1829-78 (317 items); George Coke Dromgoole (Va.; lawyer, U. S. Rep.), 1767-1920 (6 vols. and 4,545 items); Charles James Faulkner (Va., W. Va.; U. S. Rep., Minister to France, Confed. Army officer), 1815-83 (364 items); Charles James Faulkner, Jr. (W. Va.; lawyer, U. S. Sen.), 1876-97 (1 vol. and 144 items); William Henry Harrison Fiske (W. Va.; political leader), 1792-1894 (1,793 items); John Buchanan Floyd (Va.; Gov., Sec. War, Confed. Army officer), 1836-62 (257 items); Frederick William Mackey Holliday (Va.; Confed. Army officer, Confed. Rep., Gov.), 1846-99 (20 vols. and 2,171 items); Thomas Jefferson (Va.; Gov., Minister to France, Sec. State, U. S. Pres.), 1781-1828 (33

items); Francis Rives Lassiter (Va.; U. S. dist. attorney, U. S. Rep.) and his family, 1832-1927 (3 vols. and 21,740 items); Edward Lucas (W. Va.; U. S. Rep.), 1821-68 (138 items); James McDowell, Jr. (Va.; Gov., U. S. Rep.), 1767-1888 (736 items); William Mahone (Va.; Confed. Army officer, railroad pres., U. S. Sen.), 1856-95 (100,000 items); John Rutherfoord (Va.; Gov.), 1754-1931 (33 vols. and 2,712 items); Claude Augustus Swanson (Va.; U. S. Rep. and Sen., Gov., Sec. Navy), 1867-1935 (62 items); John Tyler (Va.; Gov., U. S. Rep., Sen., and Pres.), 1828-72 (44 items); and George Washington (Va.; Rev. War Commander in Chief, U. S. Pres.) and his family, 1760-1859 (99 items).

Papers of other Southern political leaders include those of Thomas Bibb (Ala.; Gov.), 1823-92 (180 items); Clement Claiborne Clay (Ala.; U. S. Sen., Confed. Sen. and diplomat) and Clement Comer Clay (Ala.; U. S. Rep. and Sen., Gov.) and their families, 1811-1925 (25 vols. and 8,546 items); Henry Clay (Ky.; U. S. Rep. and Sen., Sec. State), 1802-52 (138 items); Howell Cobb (Ga.; Gov., U. S. Rep., Sec. Treas., Confed. Army officer), 1843-68 (53 items); Benjamin Conley (Ga.; Gov.), 1876-87 (84 items); William Harris Crawford (Ga.; U. S. Sen., Minister to France, Sec. War, Sec. Treas.), 1790-1867 (120 items); John Jordan Crittenden (Ky.; U. S. Sen. and Rep., U. S. Attorney Gen., Gov.), 1786-1932 (3 vols. and 1,054 items); Jefferson Davis (Miss.; U. S. Rep. and Sen., Sec. War, Confed. Pres.), 1851-1938 (688 items); Herbert Jackson Drane (Fla.; U. S. Rep.), 1863-1947 (23 vols. and 1,204 items); George Smith Houston (Ala.; U. S. Rep. and Sen., Gov.), 1831-99 (3 vols. and 461 items); Andrew Jackson (Tenn.; U. S. Pres.), 1796-1843 (47 items); Andrew Johnson (Tenn.; U. S. Pres.), 1859-68 (42 items);

Herschel Vespasian Johnson (Ga.;
judge, Gov., Confed. Sen.), 1812-80
(31 vols. and 829 items); Seaborn
Jones (Ga.; lawyer, U.S. Rep.), 1761-
1847 (167 items); James McHenry
(Md.; Rev. War officer, Member Continental Cong., Sec. War), 1797-99
(53 items, typed copies); Eugenius
Aristides Nisbet (Ga.; U.S. Rep.,
State supreme court judge) and his
family, 1799-1934 (6 vols. and 15,903
items); Pierre Soulé (La.; lawyer,
U.S. Sen., Minister to Spain), 1841-64
(44 items); Alexander Hamilton Stephens (Ga.; U.S. Rep., Confed. Vice
Pres., Gov.), 1822-1911 (3 vols. and
2,981 items); Edward Telfair (Ga.;
planter, Member Continental Cong.,
Gov.), 1762-1831 (2 vols. and 890
items); and Joseph Wheeler (Ala.;
Confed. and U.S. Army officer, U.S.
Rep.), 1864-89 (57 items).

Papers of political leaders and
public officials from other States include those of James Martin Bell (Pa.;
Whig leader, State sen., banker, railroad promoter), 1768-1870 (47 vols.
and 13,557 items); Samuel Calvin (Pa.;
U.S. Rep.), 1792-1929 (1 vol. and
2,755 items); Alfred Cumming (Ga.,
Utah; Terr. Gov. of Utah) and his family, 1792-1889 (9 vols. and 755 items),
containing information about the "Mormon War," frontier life, and the Indians; George Brinton McClellan Harvey (N.J., N.Y.; political journalist,
editor of Harper's Weekly, Ambassador to Great Britain), 1878-1909 (138
items); Franklin Delano Roosevelt
(N.Y.; Gov., U.S. Pres.) and his family, 1913-48 (26 items); Theodore
Roosevelt (N.Y.; Gov., U.S. Pres.)
and his family, 1888-1939 (43 items);
Francis Thomas (Md.; U.S. Rep., Gov.,
Minister to Peru), numerous letters;
and Garret Dorset Wall (N.J.; U.S.
Sen.), 1745-1845 (125 items).

Papers of military and naval officers include those of Turner Ashby
(Va.; Confed. Army officer), 1861-63
(2,196 items); Pierre G. T. Beauregard

(La.; U.S. and Confed. Army officer,
railroad pres.), 1844-93 (339 items);
Stephen Gano Burbridge (Ky.; Civil
War officer), 1864 (1,364 items);
Richard G. M. Dunovant (S.C.; Con-
fed. Army officer), 1861 (145 items);
Robert L. Eichelberger (U.S. Army
officer), 1919-48 (25,000 items); Nathan Bedford Forrest (Tenn.; Confed.
Army officer), 1862-66 (393 items);
Louis M. Goldsborough (U.S. naval
officer, Naval Academy Supt.), 1827-
77 (1 vol. and 518 items); Nathanael
Greene (R.I., Ga.; Rev. War officer,
planter), 1778-99 (110 items); John
Francis Hamtramck (Mo., W. Va.;
Osage Indian agent, Mexican War officer) and his family, 1757-1862
(3 vols. and 2,619 items); Thomas
Jonathan Jackson, known as Stonewall Jackson (Va.; prof. at Va. Military Institute, U.S. and Confed. Army officer), 1855-1906 (2,582 items);
Bradley Tyler Johnson (Md., Va.;
lawyer, Confed. Army officer), 1851-
1909 (920 items); Thomas Jordan
(S.C.; U.S. and Confed. Army officer,
journalist), 1861-65 (234 items); and
John McIntosh Kell (Ga.; U.S. and
Confed. naval officer), 1841-65 (3 vols.
and 110 items).

Papers of other military and naval officers include those of Campbell
King (U.S. Army officer), 1917-33
(1 vol. and 259 items); Robert E. Lee
(Va.; U.S. and Confed. Army officer,
pres. of Washington College) and his
family, 1749-1939 (4 vols. and 168
items); James Longstreet (La.; U.S.
and Confed. Army officer, U.S. Railroad Commissioner), 1821-1904 (72
items, 16 on microfilm); Samuel Mc-
Gowan (U.S. naval officer), 1910-35
(228 items); Alfred Thayer Mahan
(U.S. naval officer, historian), 1856-
1930 (91 items); Matthew Fontaine
Maury (Va.; U.S. and Confed. naval
officer, Naval Observatory Supt.,
oceanographer), 1829-71 (163 items);
John Singleton Mosby (Va.; Confed.
ranger, lawyer), 1862-1912 (63 items);

William Nelson Pendleton (Md., Va.; U. S. and Confed. Army officer, Episcopal clergyman), 1861-62 (174 items); Alfred Landon Rives (Va.; U. S. and Confed. Army engineer, railroad official), 1839-88 (1,205 items); James Henry Rochelle (Va.; U. S. and Confed. naval officer) and his family, 1781-1907 (964 items); Daniel Ruggles (Mass., Va.; U. S. and Confed. Army officer), 1847-65 (2 vols. and 158 items); and Charles Steedman (U. S. naval officer), 1835-90 (2 vols. and 170 items).

Papers of American literary figures include those of James Lane Allen (Ky., N. Y.; novelist, short-story writer), 1889-1911 (64 items); William Cullen Bryant (Mass., N. Y.; poet, newspaper editor), 1839-95 (40 items); George Washington Cable (La., Mass.; short-story writer, novelist), 1879-1917 (105 items, 58 microfilmed); Thomas Holley Chivers (Ga.; poet), 1833-59 (634 items); John Esten Cooke (Va.; novelist), 1840-96 (7 vols. and 297 items); Caroline Danske Bedinger Dandridge (W. Va.; author), 1752-1954 (150 vols. and 5,506 items); John William Fox, Jr. (Ky., Va.; novelist), 1890-1901 (66 items); Edwin Wiley Fuller (N. C.; poet, novelist), 1858-72 (535 items); Paul Hamilton Hayne (S. C., Ga.; poet) and his family, 1815-1944 (31 vols. and 4,569 items); Henry James (Mass., England; novelist), 1888-1915 (43 items); Robert Underwood Johnson (N. Y.; editor of Century Magazine, author, Ambassador to Italy), 1881-1929 (99 items); Sidney Lanier (Ga., Md.; poet), 1801-1942 (83 items, copies); James Russell Lowell (Mass.; poet, essayist, Harvard College prof., Minister to Spain and Great Britain), 1855-90 (50 items); Clara Victoria Dargan Maclean (S. C.; poet, short-story writer), 1849-1913 (19 vols. and 625 items); Thaddeus Kosciuszko Oglesby (Ga.; author), 1876-1918 (2,152 items); Thomas Nelson Page (Va., D. C.; lawyer, author,

Ambassador to Italy) and his family, 1739-1926 (2 vols. and 9,291 items); Walter Hines Page (N. C., N. Y.; journalist, Ambassador to Great Britain), 1892-1917 (100 items); Thomas Sergeant Perry (Mass.; author, English prof. at Univ. of Keiogijiku, Japan), 1859-1929 (42 vols. and 3,000 items on microfilm); Emma Dorothy Eliza Nevitte Southworth (D. C.; novelist), 1857-90 (277 items); Mary Virginia Hawes Terhune, known as Marion Harland (Va., N. J., Mass., N. Y.; novelist, writer on household management), 1843-1920 (69 items); and Walt Whitman (N. Y., D. C., N. J.; poet), 1845-92 (400 letters and 200 literary manuscripts). There is also a collection of various papers of American writers, 1814-1930 (94 items).

Among papers of clergymen and educators are those of Charles Wesley Andrews (W. Va.; Episcopal clergyman), 1808-1901 (3,637 items); Edward Earle Bomar (S. C.; Baptist minister), 1757-1842 (12 vols. and 548 items); William K. Boyd (N. C.; prof. of history at Duke), 20th century; Eugene Clyde Brooks (N. C.; Trinity College prof. of education, State supt. of public instruction), 1894-1946 (12 vols. and 2,050 items); James Cannon, Jr. (Va., D. C.; Methodist bishop), 1869-1948 (8 vols. and 11,353 items); Flavius Josephus Cook, known as Joseph Cook (Mass.; Congregational minister, lecturer), 1847-1916 (12 vols. and 812 items); Charles Abram Ellwood (Mo., N. C.; sociologist, prof. at Univ. of Mo. and Duke Univ.), 1890-1946 (3,552 items); Edwin Milton Fairchild (D. C.; chairman of Character Education Institution), 1866-1922 (120 items); Albert Bushnell Hart (Mass.; historian, Harvard Univ. prof.), 1890-1924 (103 items); Eugene Russell Hendrix (Mo.; Methodist bishop), 1764-1914 (160 items); Thomas Wentworth Higginson (Mass.; Unitarian clergyman, author,

social reformer), 1868-1906 (63 items);
George Frederick Holmes (Va.; prof. of
history and literature at Univ. of Va.,
writer) and his family, 1815-1931 (65
vols. and 3,152 items); John Carlisle
Kilgo (N. C.; Trinity College pres.,
Methodist bishop), 1891-1944 (2,880
items); Charles Todd Quintard (Tenn.;
physician, Episcopal bishop, Confed.
chaplain), 1857-99 (346 items); Benjamin Leonard Covington Wailes (Miss.;
agriculturist, geologist, prof. at Univ.
of Miss.), 1843-59 (29 vols. and 126
items); William Rollinson Whittingham
(N. Y., Md.; Episcopal clergyman,
Bishop of Md.), 1823-79 (12,471 items);
and Marquis Lafayette Wood (N. C.;
Methodist minister, missionary, pres.
of Trinity College), 1857-85 (21 vols.
of diaries).

Papers of other professional men
include those of John Franklin Crowell
(D. C., N. Y.; economist, statistician),
1895-1924 (256 items); John Berkley
Grimball (S. C.; judge), 1727-1930
(5 vols. and 1,583 items); George B.
Harrison (Va.; lawyer), 1821-1924
(79 vols. and 13,419 items); Charles
Colcock Jones, Jr. (Ga., N. Y.; lawyer, Confed. Army officer, historian),
1763-1926 (66 vols. and 844 items);
Charles Edgeworth Jones (Ga.; lawyer, author), 1802-1924 (417 items);
W. Robert Leckie (D. C., Va.; military engineer) and William Hendrick
(Va.; planter) and their families, 1768-
1906 (18 vols. and 1,872 items); Richmond Mumford Pearson (N. C.; State
chief justice), 1862-64 (164 items);
William Laurence Saunders (N. C.;
lawyer, Confed. Army officer, historical editor), 1792-1905 (3 vols. and
381 items); Harry A. Slattery (S. C.,
D. C.; lawyer, Under Sec. Interior,
Rural Electrification Administrator),
1901-53 (243 vols. and 51,279 items);
Daniel Augustus Tompkins (S. C., N.C.;
industrial leader, newspaper publisher), 1860-1926 (630 items); George
Van Metre and William Ferrel (Ky.,
Mass., D. C.; meteorologist), 1732-

1937 (8 vols. and 1,614 items); and
Charles Cecil Wyche (S. C.; judge),
1902-24 (9,736 items).

Among many groups of personal
papers are those of William Watts
Ball (S. C.; newspaper editor), 1805-
1952 (116 vols. and 26,721 items);
Francis Preston Blair (Ky., D. C.;
editor of the Washington Globe), 1831-
77 (87 items); William Bradford (Pa.;
printer, publisher), 1789-1901 (212
items); William Garrott Brown (Mass.,
N. Y.; historian, essayist), 1898-1917
(630 items); John Buford (Va.; businessman), 1804-98 (604 items); Robert Burton (N. C.; planter, Rev. War
officer, Member Continental Cong.)
and his family, 1771-1925 (1 vol. and
100 items), relating in part to the
Transylvania Land Co.; Charles
Campbell (Va.; historian, antiquarian, editor), 1770-1935 (5 vols. and
1,360 items); J. Elwood Cox (N. C.;
manufacturer, banker), 1889-1928
(46,000 items); James Dunwoody
Brownson De Bow (La.; editor of De
Bow's Review, U. S. Census Supt.),
1779-1915 (3 vols. and 1,613 items);
James Calvin Hemphill (S. C.; journalist, newspaper editor) and his
family, 1791-1933 (12,371 items);
Joseph F. A. Jackson (Pa.; newspaper editor, author), 1829-1944 (250
items); Marshall MacDonald (Va.,
D. C.; Confed. Army officer, U. S.
Commissioner of Fish and Fisheries)
and his family, 1798-1926 (3,838
items); Lucy Randolph Mason (Va.;
Southern field representative of the
Congress of Industrial Organizations),
1916-53 (11 vols. and 6,472 items);
James Ford Rhodes (Mass.; historian), 1911-19 (60 items); James Augustus Thomas (N. C., N. Y.; tobacco
merchant, philanthropist), 1905-41
(28,488 items); Thomas Willis White
(Va.; founder and editor of the Southern Literary Messenger), 1835-42
(50 items); James Howard Whitty (Va.;
author, collector of Poeana, editor),
1792-1943 (4 vols. and 11,606 items);

and Marcus J. Wright (Tenn., D. C.; military historian), 1864-1913 (128 items).

There are many papers of merchants, planters, traders, and manufacturers. Among the most voluminous of these are the papers of a South Carolina rice planter, 1773-1833 (26 vols. and 3,211 items); a Virginia tobacco planter and iron manufacturer, 1772-93 (3,135 items); a North Carolina merchant, 1878-1918 (118 vols. and 3,517 items); a tobacco exporter in Virginia, 1789-1894 (8 vols. and 4,924 items); a South Carolina cotton planter, 1827-1913 (8 vols. and 4,250 items); a North Carolina lumber company, 1832-1954 (22 vols. and 16,000 pieces); and a Virginia tobacco manufacturer, 1850-79 (14,086 items). Other papers deal with general mercantile operations, export and import trade, land speculations, the slave trade, lumber and naval store dealings, and many aspects of plantation operations. Records of business concerns include those of several banks; and a Durham, N. C., cotton manufacturing company, 1910-34 (95 vols. and 34,236 items).

Records of or relating to governmental units include a collection of papers on the Confederate States of America, 1861-65 (37 vols. and 3,103 items), among them army, hospital, and financial papers; records of the United States and Confederate court for eastern North Carolina, chiefly 1861-65 (3,390 items); records of various towns and counties, among them Washington County, Tenn., 1774-1859 (3,713 items); records of the U.S. collector of customs, Savannah, Ga., 1754-1920 (2 vols. and 5,577 items); and original schedules of the U. S. censuses of agriculture, manufacturing, and social statistics, 1850-80, in whole or in part for Colorado, District of Columbia, Georgia, Kentucky, Louisiana, and Tennessee.

Other papers include a collection of Methodist Episcopal Church, South, records, 1759-1938 (338 vols. and 4,650 items), principally records of conferences and churches in North Carolina; papers of a Charleston, S. C., law firm, 1720-1932 (200 vols. and 100,000 items); minutes and proceedings of the Democratic National Convention (Charleston, S. C.), 1860 (172 items); records of a North Carolina and of a South Carolina local unit of the Patrons of Husbandry, 1873-90 (7 vols. and 168 items); official files of the Socialist Party of America, 1900-52 (23 vols. and 154,812 items); the Southern Labor Archives, 1854-1953 (23 vols. and 151,000 items), including records of early typographical unions and of the American Federation of Labor and Congress of Industrial Organizations; and papers of the Alliance for the Guidance of Rural Youth, Richmond, Va., 1917-48 (35 vols. and 23,081 items).

See Nannie M. Tilley and Noma L. Goodwin, Guide to the Manuscript Collections in the Duke University Library (1947. 362 p.); and Forest History Sources, pp. 87-90.

EDENTON

Cupola House Museum.

Holdings: 25 cu. ft., 1700-1868, relating chiefly to Edenton, Chowan County, and the Albemarle region. Included are the archives of the town of Edenton, 1783-1860; case rolls of the Edenton District Superior Court of Equity, 1790-1806, and of the Chowan County Superior Court of Equity, 1807-68; and some letters, deeds, and wills of persons of the locality.

See Hist. Records Survey, Guide for N. C., p. 12.

GREENSBORO

Bennet College Library. (Mrs.) Constance Hill Marteena, Librarian.

Holdings: A small collection relating chiefly to Negro education and progress in the South. Included are papers of Norris Wright Cuney (Tex.; Republican Party leader, collector of the Port of Galveston), 1883-96 (3 scrapbooks of clippings and manuscripts and 33 pieces); papers relating to the history of the College, from 1873; and miscellaneous materials on the achievements of Afro-American women in the United States.

—oOo—

Guilford College Library. Guilford College Branch. (Mrs.) Treva W. Mathis, Assistant Librarian in charge of Quaker Room.

Holdings: 409 vols., 1680 to date, consisting chiefly of records of the Society of Friends. Included are minutes of meetings of the society in North Carolina, Georgia, and Tennessee (300 vols.); records of births, marriages, and deaths (56 vols.); and other miscellaneous materials (53 vols.).

See Louis R. Wilson and R. B. Downs, "Special Collections for the Study of History and Literature in the Southeast," in Bibliographical Society of America, Papers, 28:112-113 (1934); and Hist. Records Survey, Guide for N. C., p. 12.

—oOo—

Woman's College Library, University of North Carolina. Charles M. Adams, Librarian.

Holdings: Several collections that relate chiefly to the College and to North Carolina. The College Collection, 1892 to date, contains the archives of the College, including the official correspondence of the first two presidents, Charles Duncan McIver and Julius I. Foust; private papers of Dr. McIver; and various records of activities of faculty members and students. The Woman's Collection contains a few boxes of papers relating to the activities of women in the State. There are also 41 literary manuscripts by 14 authors associated with North Carolina, and 110 pieces of music manuscripts by North Carolina composers.

HIGH POINT

High Point College Library. Marcella Carter, Librarian.

Holdings: Journals of the North Carolina Conference of the Methodist Protestant Church, 1852-65 (1 vol.).

MONTREAT

Historical Foundation of the Presbyterian and Reformed Churches. Thomas H. Spence, Jr., Executive Director.

Holdings: 7,500 vols. and 175 linear ft., 1638-1959, consisting of records of the Presbyterian and Reformed churches of the world, particularly in the United States and, more especially, in the South. Included are records of synods and presbyteries of the Presbyterian, Associate Presbyterian, and Cumberland Presbyterian Churches of the South Atlantic, Southern, and certain other States. There are also records of Presbyterian organizations in Brazil, Canada, China, England, France, Japan, Korea, Mexico, The Netherlands, Northern Ireland, and Scotland; some papers relating to Greece and Asia Minor during the 19th century; and papers concerning early missionary activities in China and Mexico. Numerous items are associated with the organization of the Presbyterian Church, U.S., in 1861. A 2,000-volume manuscript history covers the congregations and other organizations of the Presbyterian Church, U.S. Personal papers include collections pertaining to W. A. Alexander (Miss., Tenn.; Presbyterian clergyman); Wilma Jacobs Brown (Mexico;

missionary); Robert F. Campbell (Va., N.C.; Presbyterian clergyman); Robert L. Dabney (Va., Tex.; Presbyterian theologian, prof. at the Va. Union Theological Seminary and the Univ. of Tex.); George W. Harlan (Mo.; Congregational and Presbyterian clergyman); Moses D. Hoge (Va.; Presbyterian clergyman); Walter L. Lingle (Ga., S.C., Va., N.C.; Presbyterian clergyman, president of Davidson College); Francis McFarland (Va.; Presbyterian clergyman); William S. Plumer (Va., Pa., S.C.; Presbyterian theologian, prof. at Columbia Theological Seminary); William S. Red (Tex.; Presbyterian clergyman); William H. Ruffner (Va.; Presbyterian clergyman, State supt. of education); Thomas Smyth (S.C.; Presbyterian clergyman); and James H. Thornwell (S.C.; Presbyterian theologian, pres. of S.C. College, prof. in Columbia Theological Seminary).

See Hist. Records Survey, Guide for N.C., p. 13; and Thomas H. Spence, Jr., Survey of Records and Minutes in the Historical Foundation of the Presbyterian and Reformed Churches (1943. 46 p.), and The Historical Foundation and Its Treasures, pp. 61-75 (1956).

RALEIGH

North Carolina State College Library.

Holdings: Papers of Carl Alwyn Schenck (Germany, N. C.; forester), and records of the Biltmore Forest School, Biltmore, N. C.

—oOo—

State Department of Archives and History. Christopher Crittenden, Director; H. G. Jones, State Archivist.

Holdings: 5,070 cu. ft., 1535-1957, consisting of (1) noncurrent official records, 4,285 cu. ft., 1535-1954, held by the Department as the State's archival agency, and (2) other manuscripts, 785 cu. ft., 1657-1957, chiefly unofficial and private papers relating primarily to North Carolina and neigh-

boring States but containing also much information at the national level of interest. (The Department was formerly known as the North Carolina Historical Commission.)

Official records of the Colony and State of North Carolina consist of journals and other legislative records, 1689-1917 (250 cu. ft.); executive records, 1663-1954 (1,500 cu. ft.); and judicial records, 1690-1939 (50 cu. ft.). Among the executive records are papers of the governors, since 1694; the secretary of state, since 1663, including records of land grants and surveys, and Revolutionary War military papers; the treasurer, since 1775; and customs officers, 1732-90. Judicial records consist of minutes and dockets of the General Court, 1690-1767 (3 cu. ft.); of certain district courts, 1741-1841 (9 cu. ft.); and of the Superior Court, 1807-1939 (37 cu. ft.). The Department has noncurrent records of 95 existing counties, 5 extinct ones, and 5 counties now in Tennessee, and microfilm copies of records of most North Carolina counties and 8 counties once in North Carolina but now in Tennessee. These records include such materials as wills, inventories of estates, deeds, county court minutes, marriage bonds, lists of taxables, and school reports. The Department also has a collection of original papers of North Carolina under the Lords Proprietors, 1664-74 ($1/2$ cu. ft.).

Other materials are photographic copies of some U.S. archives relating to North Carolina, among them 2,000 petitions for amnesty and pardon following the Civil War, and census schedules, 1800-70; and certain original U.S. census schedules of 1850-80. (The 1880 census schedules are not available to the public because of their condition.) Copies of foreign archives are extensive, among them records in British depositories, chiefly the Public Record Office, relating to North Carolina, 1663-1783 (6 cu. ft.), and records in Spanish archival depositories relating to Flori-

da and what is now the Southeastern
United States, 1535-1802 (14 cu. ft.).
There are also copies of many manuscripts in various U. S. depositories
that relate to North Carolina.

Papers of persons who served the
United States in Congress or in the
executive or judicial branches include
those of Lawrence O'Bryan Branch
(N.C.; lawyer, U.S. Rep., Confed. Army officer) and his family, 1770-1884
($5/8$ cu. ft.); John Herritage Bryan
(N.C.; lawyer, U.S. Rep.), 1773-1906
(3 cu. ft.); Thomas Burke (N. C.; lawyer, Member Continental Cong., Gov.),
1769-82 ($3/8$ cu. ft.); William Alexander
Graham (N.C.; lawyer, U.S. Sen., Gov.,
Sec. Navy, Confed. Sen.), 1779-1918
(2 cu. ft.); James Iredell (N. C.; U. S.
Supreme Court Justice), 1770-1829
($1/4$ cu. ft.); Nathaniel Macon (N. C.;
U.S. Rep. and Sen.), 1804-37 ($1/4$ cu.
ft.); Willie Person Mangum (N. C.;
lawyer, U. S. Rep. and Sen.), 1809-94
($1\frac{1}{2}$ cu. ft.); William H. Polk (Tenn.;
Mexican War officer, U.S. Rep.) and
his family, 1730-1897 ($1\frac{1}{2}$ cu. ft.);
David S. Reid (N.C.; Gov., U. S. Rep.
and Sen.), 1803-80 (3 cu. ft.); John
Steele (N.C.; U.S. Rep., Comptroller
of Treas.), 1777-1831 ($1/2$ cu. ft.);
Montfort Stokes (N.C.; U.S. Sen., Gov.),
1790-1811 ($1/8$ cu. ft.); and Zebulon
Baird Vance (N.C.; lawyer, Gov.,
U.S. Sen.), 1827-1928 (6 cu. ft.).

Papers of other persons holding
high public office include those of
Charles Brantley Aycock (N. C.; law-
yer, Gov.), 1899-1912 ($5/8$ cu. ft.);
Robert Gregg Cherry (N.C.; lawyer,
Gov.), 1912-57 (35 cu. ft.); Walter
Clark (N. C.; Confed. Army officer,
State chief justice), 1783-1920 ($2\frac{1}{2}$
cu. ft.); William Richardson Davie
(N. C.; Rev. War officer, Gov.), 1778-
1817 ($1/2$ cu. ft.); William W. Holden
(N. C.; newspaper editor, Gov.), 1852-
89 ($1/8$ cu. ft.); Archibald De Bow
Murphey (N. C.; reformer, State su-
perior court judge), 1797-1852 ($1/2$
cu. ft.); Thomas Pollock (N. C.; Gov.),

1706-61 ($1/8$ cu. ft.); William B. Rodman (N. C.; State attorney gen.) and
his family, 1836-1931 (4 cu. ft.);
David Lowry Swain (N. C.; lawyer,
Gov., pres. of Univ. of N. C.), 1763-
1895 ($1\frac{1}{2}$ cu. ft.); Calvin H. Wiley
(N. C.; State supt. of schools, author),
1785-1902 (2 cu. ft.); and Jonathan
Worth (N. C.; lawyer, planter, Gov.),
1831-76 (2 cu. ft.).

Records of military leaders, in
addition to some mentioned elsewhere, include those of Pierre G. T.
Beauregard (La.; Confed. Army officer), 1862-69 ($1/8$ cu. ft.); Joseph
Graham (N. C.; Creek War officer),
1813-36 ($1/4$ cu. ft.); Daniel Harvey
Hill (Va., N. C., Ark.; U. S. and Confed. Army officer, college prof.,
pres. of Univ. of Ark.), 1816-89 ($5/8$
cu. ft.); Stephen D. Ramseur (N. C.;
Confed. Army officer), 1860-1920
($1/8$ cu. ft.); and James Iredell Waddell (Md.; U. S. and Confed. naval officer, Commander of the Shenandoah)
and his family, 1755-1919 ($1/4$ cu.
ft.).

Papers of other persons include
those of Samuel A'Court Ashe (N. C.;
lawyer, newspaper editor, historian), 1706-1934 (1 cu. ft.); John Gray
Blount (N. C.; merchant, planter,
land speculator), 1770-1931 (11 cu.
ft.), among them substantial quantities of letters by William Blount
(N. C., Tenn.; Member Continental
Cong., land speculator, Gov. of Southwest Terr., U. S. Sen. from Tenn.)
and Willie Blount (Tenn.; Gov.); Joseph Blount Cheshire (N. C.; Episcopal bishop), 1724-1911 (7 cu. ft.);
Reginald A. Fessenden (Canada, N.Y.,
N. J., Pa., N. C.; inventor, physicist), 1890-1926 (56 cu. ft.); Edward
Jones Hale (N. C.; newspaper editor),
1850-67 ($1/2$ cu. ft.); Daniel Harvey
Hill, Jr. (N. C.; college pres., historian), 1890-1924 (1 cu. ft.); Charles
Pettigrew (N. C.; Episcopal clergyman)
and his family, 1772-1900 (4 cu. ft.);
and Cornelia Phillips Spencer (N. C.;

author), 1859-1905 ($\frac{1}{2}$ cu. ft.).

Papers that provide information for many aspects of economic history are numerous. Included are hundreds of account books dating from the 18th to the 20th centuries. For agriculture there are records of the North Carolina Farmers' State Alliance, 1887-1929 (5 cu. ft.), and the North Carolina Farmers' Union, 1912-28 (8 cu. ft.), as well as records of plantation operations. Other papers pertain to banking, commerce, lands, manufacturing of textiles and tobacco, and railroads.

The Department also has papers relating to all wars in which the United States has been engaged, including Civil War pension records (11 cu. ft.), an index to Moore's Roster of North Carolina Troops in the War Between the States, a large collection on North Carolina's participation in World War I, 1914-33 (95 cu. ft., of which 28 cu. ft. are individual service records), and World War II records (57 cu. ft., including 41 cu. ft. of individual service records).

See lists of accessions in the Biennial Reports of the N. C. Hist. Commission (1906-8 to 1942-44), and the N. C. Department of Archives and History (1942-44 to 1952-54); the Commission's Calendars of Manuscript Collections (1926. Vol. 1. 351 p.) and "Materials in the Commission's Archives," pp. 62-86, in its Forty Years of Public Service (1942); and Hist. Records Survey, The Historical Records of North Carolina: the County Records (1938-39. 3 vols.), and Guide to the Manuscript Collections in the Archives of the North Carolina Historical Commission (1942. 216 p.).

SALISBURY

Catawba College Library. Lulu Ruth

Reed, Librarian.

Holdings: 3 vols. and 6 pieces, 1770-1893, relating chiefly to the College and to the German Reformed Church in North Carolina.

See Hist. Records Survey, Guide for N. C., p. 16.

WINSTON-SALEM

Moravian Archives. 4 East Bank St. (P.O. Box 115, Salem Station.) Grace L. Siewers, Acting Archivist.

Holdings: 2,000 vols. and 10,000 pages of manuscripts, 1753 to date, relating chiefly to the Moravian settlement in North Carolina (known as Wachovia). Included are church registers, account books, minute books, diaries, memoirs, letters, and manuscript music. Much of this material has been published by the State Department of Archives and History.

See Allison, Inventory, p. 212; and Hist. Records Survey, Guide for N. C., p. 17.

—oOo—

Smith Reynolds Library. Wake Forest College. Carlton P. West, Librarian.

Holdings: 300 pieces, since 1790, consisting chiefly of record books of a number of Baptist churches in North Carolina and papers relating to Wake Forest College.

See Hist. Records Survey, Guide for N. C., p. 16.

BISMARCK

State Historical Society of North Dakota. Russell Reid, Superintendent; Margaret Rose, Librarian.

Holdings: 520 ft., relating chiefly to Dakota Territory, the State of North Dakota, and the Indians of the area. Archival materials include official papers of the Territorial Governors and secretaries of state. Other papers are those of Isaac P. Baker (N. Dak.; banker, owner of a steamship line on the Missouri); A. M. Christianson (N. Dak.; State supreme court justice); Charles Lemon Hall (N. Dak.; Congregational missionary on the Ford Berthold Reservation); Orin G. Libby (N. Dak.; historian, prof. at the Univ. of N. Dak., sec. of State Historical Society); Alexander McKenzie (N. Dak.; lawyer, political leader); Burleigh F. Spalding (N. Dak.; U. S. Rep., chief justice of State supreme court); and E. A. Williams (N. Dak.; surveyor-gen., political leader). There are also papers of a land company, the U. S. General Land Office in North Dakota, the North Dakota World War I History Commission, and the WPA Historical Records Survey. Included too are diaries, journals, and reminiscences of post traders, early settlers, and prominent citizens; Civil War letters; minute books of societies, clubs, and organizations; hotel registers; and autograph albums.

BOTTINEAU

North Dakota School of Forestry. George P. Hynes, Librarian.

Holdings: Records of the Turtle Mountain Woodland Association, a forestry cooperative; and a collection of papers resulting from research in horticulture, agricultural economics, and statistics.

See Forest History Sources, p. 92.

GRAND FORKS

University of North Dakota Library. Donald J. Pearce, Head Librarian.

Holdings: 70,000 pieces, of the 19th and 20th centuries. Included are papers of Usher L. Burdick (N. Dak.; U. S. Rep.); John Burke (N. Dak.; Gov., Treas. of U. S.); John M. Gillette (N. Dak.; sociologist, Univ. of N. Dak. prof.); Otto Krueger (N. Dak.; U. S. Rep.); William Langer (N. Dak.; U. S. Sen.), 734 containers; William Lemke (N. Dak.; U. S. Rep.); John Moses (N. Dak.; Gov.); J. F. T. O'Connor (N. Dak.; Treas. of U. S.); George Shafer (N. Dak.; Gov.); Edwin White (N. Dak.; Chief Engineer, Federal Communications Commission); and Frank White (N. Dak.; Gov., Treas. of U. S.) and other members of the White family.

There are 12 manuscripts of Maxwell Anderson (N. Dak., N. Y.; playwright), including 2 unpublished plays; and manuscripts and other papers of Gottfried Hult (N. Dak.; Univ. of N. Dak. prof., translator of Ibsen). Included too are some 20 small collections of letters and other papers of Dakota pioneers; complete papers of the North Dakota–Montana Wheat Growers Association, a marketing pool, 1922-31; and a set of Nuremberg Trial papers, 225 ft.

See North Dakota Quarterly, summer 1956, pp. 91 ff.

AKRON 17

Archives and Library, Firestone Tire and Rubber Company. William D. Overman, Archivist.

Holdings: 560,000 documents, 150,000 photo negatives, several thousand feet of microfilm copies, and 400 recordings of speeches and company activities, comprising (1) personal papers of Harvey S. Firestone (Ohio; manufacturer) and his family, dating from the late 18th century, and (2) noncurrent records of the company of lasting value, dating from 1900.

See William D. Overman, "The Firestone Archives and Library," in Am. Archivist, 16:305-309 (Oct. 1953); and "The Pendulum Swings," ibid., 22:3-10 (Jan. 1959).

BEREA

Greater Cleveland Methodist Historical Society. Library of Baldwin-Wallace College. Arthur C. Boggess, President.

Holdings: 86 vols., relating chiefly to Ohio Methodism with some emphasis on nationwide German Methodism. Included are minutes of annual conferences, letters, and church records.

BLUFFTON

Mennonite Historical Library, Bluffton College. Delbert L. Gratz, Librarian.

Holdings: 3,000 frames of microfilm copies of papers, 1525-1900, re-

lating chiefly to the Bernese Anabaptists, predecessors of the Mennonites in America; and originals or microfilm copies of various other Mennonite Church records.

BOWLING GREEN

Bowling Green State University Library. Paul F. Leedy, Librarian.

Holdings: Records of the U.S. Military Prison, Johnson's Island, Ohio, consisting of ledgers containing the accounts of some 3,770 Confederate prisoners of war with the sutler at the prison, 1862-64 (7 vols.).

CHILLICOTHE

Ross County Historical Society. 24 West Second St.

Holdings: Manuscripts relating to Ohio and the Northwest Territory. Included are undetermined quantities of papers of Duncan McArthur (Ohio; War of 1812 officer, U.S. Rep., Gov.); Arthur St. Clair (Pa., Ohio; Rev. War officer, Gov. of Northwest Terr.); Edward Tiffin (Ohio; Gov., U.S. Sen.); and Thomas Worthington Ohio; U.S. Sen., Gov.).

See Autograph Collector's Journal, 5 (no. 3):52 (spring 1953).

CINCINNATI 20

American Jewish Archives. 3101 Clifton Ave. Jacob R. Marcus, Director.

Holdings: 250,000 items, 1654-

1955, relating chiefly to Jews in the United States. A considerable part of the holdings consists of photographic and typewritten copies, but there are extensive collections of originals, especially of personal papers.

Outstanding collections of personal papers include those of Benjamin N. Cardozo (N.Y., D.C.; U.S. Supreme Court Justice, author), 1920-37 (65 pieces); Albert Ehrehfried (Mass.; surgeon, author), 7 vols.; Rebecca Gratz (Pa.; philanthropist, founder of the Hebrew Sunday School Society), 1797-1863 (photostatic copies of 933 pieces); Lazard Kahn (Tenn., Ala., Ohio; stove manufacturer), 1866-71 (100 pieces); Jacob Moritz Loeb (Ill.; insurance executive, philanthropist), 1898-1935 (37 vols.); Louis Marshall (N.Y.; lawyer, publicist), 1891-1930 (66 vols.); Annie Nathan Meyer (N.Y.; founder of Barnard College, author), 1890-1950 (20 vols.); Adolph S. Ochs (Tenn., N.Y.; newspaper publisher), 1893-1939 (153 pieces); Edward Rosewater (Ohio, Nebr.; Civil War telegrapher, newspaper publisher) and his family, 1841-1940 (4,500 pieces); Jacob H. Schiff (N.Y.; financier, philanthropist), 1914-26 (35 vols.); Philip Louis Seman (N.Y., Ill.; social worker), 1897-1957 (9 vols.); Samuel Untermyer (N.Y.; lawyer), 1899-1920 (18 vols.); Felix M. Warburg (N.Y.; financier, philanthropist), 1910-37 (211 vols.); and Frank L. Weil (N.Y.; lawyer), 1936-48 (6 vols.). There are extensive collections of the personal and business papers of the Myers family of Norfolk, Va., 1785-1861, and of the Minis family of Georgia, 1840-70.

Papers of religious and education leaders include those of Abraham Cronbach (Ind., Ill., Ohio; rabbi, prof. at Hebrew Union College), 1910-53 (7 vols.); Gotthard Deutsch (Ohio; prof. at Hebrew Union College, author, editor), 1892-1921 (5 vols. and 1,072 pieces); David Einhorn (N.Y.;

rabbi, author), 1869-79 (70 pieces); Hyman G. Enelow (Ky., N.Y.; rabbi, author, editor), 1906-33 (54 vols.); Louis Grossman (Mich., Ohio; rabbi, prof. at Hebrew Union College, editor, author), 1880-1922 (4 vols.); Maximilian Heller (Ohio, Ill., Tex., La.; rabbi, prof. of Hebrew at Tulane Univ., editor); David Philipson (Md., Ohio; rabbi, prof. at Hebrew Union College), 1883-1946 (12 vols. and 346 pieces); Isaac M. Wise (Ohio; rabbi, pres. of Hebrew Union College), 1849-98 (72 pieces); Stephen S. Wise (N.Y.; rabbi, author), 1912-48 (2 vols. and additional material); and Louis Wolsey (Pa.; rabbi, founder of American Council for Judaism), 1942-48 (3 vols.).

Included also are records of the Central Conference of American Rabbis, 1893-1937 (24 vols.); the Dickstein Committee, to investigate Nazi activities in the United States, 1934-39 (39 vols.); Hebrew Union College, 1904-25 (60 vols.); the Jewish Institute of Religion, 1921-49 (47 vols.); the Pro-Falasha Committee, on the condition of Jews in Abyssinia, 1923-49 (7 vols.); and the Union of American Hebrew Congregations, 1873-1917 (93 vols.). There are extensive collections of minute books and other official records of Jewish congregations throughout the United States, 1729-1936 (661 vols.), and of societies, clubs, lodges, sisterhoods, and other organizations,, 1786-1951 (184 vols.). Miscellaneous collections include diaries, a wide variety of 18th- and 19th-century correspondence, early American Hebrew marriage certificates, genealogical data of American families of Jewish origin, and a considerable amount of material for local history. There are microfilm copies of minutes of the Jewish Community Federation and the Jewish Community Council, both of Cleveland, Ohio, 1902-58 (16 reels). There is also a collection of 243 manuscript plays in Yiddish, many of them original acting copies used during the heyday of the Yiddish theater in New York City.

See annual reports on "Acquisitions," in American Jewish Archives, 1948 to date.

—oOo—

Hebrew Union College Library. Herbert C. Zafren, Librarian.

Holdings: 1,500 volumes and 4,000 pieces, dating from before the 10th century to the present, relating chiefly to Judaica and Hebraica in their various aspects. Included are an exceptionally valuable collection of Jewish liturgical music, 125 Biblical scrolls (of which 59 are illuminated), 31 vols. of biblical codices, 59 vols. of Chinese-Jewish origin, a number of texts of published and unpublished Jewish literature, and some communal records.

CINCINNATI 21

Historical and Philosophical Society of Ohio. University of Cincinnati Library Bldg. (Mrs.) Alice Palo Hook, Librarian.

Holdings: 110,000 vols. and items, 1765 to date, relating chiefly to the military, political, social, economic, business, and personal history of the Ohio Valley region.

Personal papers include those of Warner M. Bateman (Ohio; State sen. and dist. attorney), 1857-97 (16 vols. of diary and 56 letters); Salmon Portland Chase (Ohio; Gov., U. S. Sen., Sec. Treas., U. S. Chief Justice), 1849-78 (218 letters); David Wasgatt Clark (Ohio; Methodist bishop, publisher of Ladies' Repository), 1850-70 (440 letters); William Cranch (D. C.; chief justice of U. S. circuit

court), 1800-50 (63 items); Oran Follett (N. Y., Ohio; newspaper editor, State legislator), 1825-89 (253 items); Joseph Benson Foraker (Ohio; Gov., U. S. Sen.), 1884-1917 (11,000 items); Miles Greenwood (Ohio; ironmaster), 1861-65 (30 letters and documents), on Civil War guns; Murat Halstead (Ohio, N. Y.; newspaper editor), 1851-1906 (3,526 items); Judson Harmon (Ohio; Gov., U. S. Attorney Gen.), 1908-12 (32 letter-file boxes); John Johnston (Ohio; U. S. Army officer, Indian agent), 1806-60 (4 boxes of business papers and 222 letters); Timothy Kirby (Ohio; Bank of the U. S. agent), 1817-59 (28 folio vols. and 8,000 items), primarily on Second Bank of the U. S. in Cincinnati, its records, and settlement of its affairs; Alexander Long (Ohio; lawyer, U. S. Rep.), 1840-96 (4,050 political and personal letters), with emphasis on Democratic party activities and Civil War sympathies; Joseph Pitcairn (U. S. consul at Paris and Hamburg), 1796-1814, 1821 (193 letters); Hiram Powers (Ohio, Italy; sculptor), 1829-69 (722 letters to and from Cincinnatians); John Smith (Ohio; U. S. Sen.), 110 items concerning his relationship to the Burr-Blennerhassett affair; Thomas B. Stevenson (Ky., Ohio; newspaper editor), 1813-77 (304 letters from notable persons); John Cleves Symmes (N. J., Ohio; Member Continental Cong., Northwest Terr. judge), including correspondence with Jonathan Dayton (N. J.; Rev. War officer, U. S. Rep. and Sen.), 98 items, and letters to Robert Morris (N. J.; State chief justice, U. S. dist. court judge), 43 items; Charles Stewart Todd (Ky.; lawyer, War of 1812 officer, Minister to Russia), 87 letters; and Timothy Walker (Mass., Ohio; lawyer, editor, author), 1825-55 (journal and 108 letters received). There are also collections of letters from 9 Civil War soldiers; and papers of a Methodist minister, a steamboat captain, a Cincinnati financier and philanthropist, and other local leaders.

There are papers of numerous family groups. One of those is the Lytle family, the papers of which (5,200 items) include correspondence and other documents of William Lytle (Ky., Ohio; pioneer land speculator, Surveyor-Gen. of Northwest Terr.), Robert Todd Lytle (Ohio; lawyer, U.S. Rep.), and William Haines Lytle (Ohio; Civil War officer, poet). There is a considerable collection of King family papers, 1785-1889, primarily papers of Rufus King (Ohio; lawyer), but containing 115 letters of Rufus King (Mass., N.Y.; U.S. Sen. from N.Y., Minister to Great Britain) and letters of other persons. Papers collected by Robert Clarke (Ohio; publisher, author), 757 items, include manuscripts on Illinois Territory and the War of 1812 and on John Cleves Symmes and the Miami purchase. The Torrence Collection, 1790-1857 (2,056 letters and 115 other documents), relates to the settlement of Cincinnati and vicinity and consists primarily of papers of James Findlay (Ohio; War of 1812 officer, mayor of Cincinnati, U.S. Rep.). Another group of family papers, 1805-99 (173 personal letters, 1,500 business letters, and 19 boxes of legal notes), contains those of James H. Thompson (Ky., Ohio; lawyer, judge of common pleas) and his wife Eliza Jane (Trimble) Thompson (Ohio; temperance leader).

In addition to extensive collections of manuscripts there are many separate letters and documents or volumes of historical value. Among these are found early church and cemetery records; tax, census, voting, and military lists; journals and diaries of early settlers and others; Civil War correspondence and documents; business records; family histories and records; histories and minutes of societies, clubs, and institutions; and county, township, and city documents of various kinds.

CINCINNATI 2

Lloyd Library and Museum. 309 West Court St. (Mrs.) Corinne Miller Simons, Librarian.

Holdings: Some correspondence and other manuscripts, in addition to many books and pamphlets, relating chiefly to botany, pharmacy, and eclectic medicine. Included are papers of Curtis Gates Lloyd (Ohio; mycologist), 1884-1926 (25 boxes); John Uri Lloyd (Ohio; manufacturing pharmacist, prof. of chemistry at Eclectic Medical College and prof. of pharmacy at Cincinnati College of Pharmacy), 1870-1936 (54 boxes); and James Pattison Walker (England; Surgeon-General of the British Army), 1848-1906 (529 vols.), pertaining to eclectic medical methods, techniques, and case histories in Europe; and minutes, students' records, and other archives of the Eclectic Medical College, 1845-1939 (4 file cabinets).

See the following articles by Corinne M. Simons in National Eclectic Medical Quarterly, vols. 41-43 (Mar. 1950-Dec. 1951): "Eclectic College Records in Lloyd Library," "Walker's Eclectic Collection in Lloyd Library," "John Uri Lloyd and the Lloyd Library," and "Curtis Gates Lloyd, Mycologist, 1859-1926."

—oOo—

Public Library of Cincinnati and Hamilton County. Eighth and Vine Sts. Ernest I. Miller, Director.

Holdings: A considerable collection relating chiefly to Ohio and water navigation in the Ohio River region. Included are letters and other papers of Otway Curry (Ohio; poet, editor,

State legislator), 140 pieces; personal papers of Alice Archer Sewall James (Ohio; artist, poet), 1880-1950; and a few letters of Frances Wright (England, N. Y., Ohio; reformer). Included also are the journal of a Nantucket whaler in the South Pacific, 1791-94; a meteorological diary kept in Cincinnati, 1834-50; the daily memorandum book of a river merchant of Cincinnati, 1844-55 (photostatic and microfilm copies); a group of letters descriptive of Cincinnati before 1860; the diary of an emigrant from Germany to Ohio, 1830-35; business papers of a carriage dealers' firm in Indiana, 1880-1910, and of steamboat builders in Pittsburgh, 1857-1927; diaries of 2 Ohio River captains and an Ohio River pilot, 1843-1941; account books, freight books, landing lists, lock books, logbooks, passenger lists, wharfboat books and logs, and other records of various steamboats, packet lines, and individuals, 1811 to date; and papers of several Ohio families.

CINCINNATI 21

University of Cincinnati Library. Arthur T. Hamlin, Librarian.

Holdings: 300 pieces, 1915-48, relating chiefly to D. H. Lawrence. Included are papers of D. H. Lawrence (England; poet, novelist) and his wife, Frieda, 1924-30 (161 pieces); and John Middleton Murry (England; author, literary critic, editor), 1916-48 (70 pieces).

CLEVELAND 14

Cleveland Public Library. 325 Superior Ave. Raymond C. Lindquist, Director.

Holdings: Included are several medieval manuscripts; a collection of

musical manuscripts; about 1,000 chess manuscripts in several languages, chiefly Western; 25 Persian manuscripts, largely historical; papers relating to British India, 1750-1850 (250 pieces); an almost complete collection of facsimiles of Mexican and Maya codices; and letters and other documents relating to Cleveland and vicinity.

CLEVELAND 6

Western Reserve Historical Society. Meredith B. Colket, Jr., Director; Alene Lowe White, Librarian.

Holdings: 1,000,000 pieces, 1750-1956, relating chiefly to Ohio but containing much of wider interest. Included are quantities of personal papers; several large and unusual special collections; records of business houses and associations; materials on railroad, canal, and lake transportation; local township and church records; unpublished genealogies; and many other collections dealing with almost every phase of historical development.

Among papers of individuals are those of Warner M. Bateman (Ohio; State sen. and dist. attorney), 1855-97, including correspondence with Salmon Portland Chase (Ohio; Gov., U. S. Sen., Sec. Treas., U. S. Chief Justice), Thomas Corwin (Ohio; Gov., U. S. Rep. and Sen., Sec. Treas.), and Rutherford B. Hayes (Ohio; Civil War officer, U. S. Rep., Gov., U. S. Pres.), and a large number of letters from John Sherman (Ohio; U. S. Rep. and Sen., Sec. Treas., Sec. State). There are also papers of Theodore E. Burton (Ohio; banker, U. S. Rep. and Sen.), 42 large packages; George W. Crile (Ohio; surgeon), including materials concerning his service in the Spanish-American War and World War I (30 ft.); Myron T. Herrick (Ohio; Gov., Minister to France), 4

filing drawers and 16 large packages;
Peter Hitchcock (Ohio; War of 1812 officer, U. S. Rep., State supreme court
judge) and Reuben Hitchcock (Ohio;
lawyer, receiver for the Atlantic and
Great Western Railway) and their fam-
ily (10 ft. and 1 large box); William
McKinley (Ohio; Gov., U. S. Rep. and
Pres.), a large file of letters, military papers, and family materials; Albert G. Riddle (Ohio; U. S. Rep., consul at Matanzas, Cuba, prosecutor of
John H. Surrat), 6 packages, including correspondence with Salmon Portland Chase (Ohio; Gov., U. S. Sen.,
Sec. Treas., U. S. Chief Justice),
Joshua Reed Giddings (Ohio; U. S.
Rep., consul gen. in Canada), and
Horace Greeley (N. Y.; editor of New
York Tribune, political leader); Allen
Trimble (Ohio; Gov., agriculturist),
6 packages; Jeptha H. Wade (Ohio; financier, philanthropist), 500 items,
including correspondence on telegraph
companies; and Elisha Whittlesey
(Ohio; War of 1812 officer, U. S. Rep.,
Comptroller of Treas.), 90,000 let-
ters, chiefly political.

There are several groups of papers
relating to military affairs. For the
French and Indian War and the Revolutionary War there is a small body of
material, 1750-95, including letters
of Samuel H. Parsons (Conn., Ohio;
Rev. War officer), 1773-87 (166
pieces). War of 1812 materials include a journal of an officer of the
Royal Marines, 1813-14; an account
of the Raisin River massacre; a diary
kept at Upper Sandusky and Fort
Meigs, 1812-14; records of Gleason
Lewis (Ohio; pension agent), concerning claims from the Revolutionary War
and the War of 1812 (3 vols.); papers
of Simon Perkins (Ohio; War of 1812
officer, agent for the Erie Land Co.),
10 boxes; legal and military papers of
George Tod (Ohio; State supreme
court judge, War of 1812 officer), 3
boxes; and various commissary reports, soldiers' letters, and personal

narratives. For the Civil War period there is much material, the nucleus of which is the William P. Palmer Collection, covering both sides
and including letters and papers on
slavery, abolition, the Underground
Railway, and various campaigns in
the war; regimental histories; and
personal narratives (75 ft.). There
are papers of Braxton Bragg (La.,
Tex.; U. S. and Confed. Army officer),
45 ft.; and Franz Sigel (Mo., N. Y.;
Civil War officer), 12 ft.; and records
of the U. S. Sanitary Commission of
Cleveland (40 ft.).

The Society has also a large and
valuable collection of records pertaining to lands. Records of the Connecticut Land Co. include headquarters records and field notes, maps,
and other papers of early surveyors
of the Western Reserve and Fire-
lands (23 vols., 11 letter files, 500
original surveys, 3 rolls of microfilm, and many separate pieces).
Among these are papers of Moses
Cleaveland (Conn.; Rev. War officer,
founder of Cleveland, Ohio); Samuel
Huntington (Ohio; State supreme court
judge, Gov.); Turhand Kirtland (Conn.,
Ohio; agent for the Connecticut Land
Co., judge); and Ephraim Root (Conn.;
sec. of the Connecticut Land Co.).
Records of the Erie Land Co., 25
vols. and 72 boxes, include much
correspondence of Simon Perkins
(Ohio; War of 1812 officer, agent for
the company). There are also records of the Virginia Military Land
District, 1787-1802 (7 vols. and 5
packages); and letters of three directors of the Ohio Land Co.; Samuel
Holden Parsons (Conn., Ohio; Rev.
War officer), Rufus Putnam (Mass.,
Ohio; Rev. War officer, judge for
Northwest Terr.), and James M. Var-
num (R. I., Ohio; Rev. War officer,
judge for Northwest Terr.).

The Wallace H. Cathcart Collection of Shaker records, dating from
1776 (6,000 vols., 384 hymnals, 125

ft., and 28 letter files), includes records of 19 Shaker communities in 8 States.

CLEVELAND

Western Reserve University Library. Lyon N. Richardson, Librarian.

Holdings: Several collections relating chiefly to the University and persons associated with it. Included are papers of or about Newton D. Baker (Ohio; lawyer, mayor of Cleveland, Sec. War), 1 box; John H. Clarke (Ohio; U. S. Supreme Court Justice), 3 boxes, consisting mainly of letters received from Newton D. Baker, William H. Taft, Woodrow Wilson, and Willis Van Devanter; Benedict Crowell (Ohio; Asst. Sec. War), 1918-20 (20 boxes); Charles Backus Storrs (Ohio; Congregational and Presbyterian clergyman, first pres. of Western Reserve College); Charles F. Thwing (Mass., Ohio; Congregational clergyman, author, pres. of Western Reserve Univ.), 68 boxes; and Elizur Wright (Ohio, Mass.; prof. at Western Reserve College, editor of abolitionist periodicals, actuary). There are also a collection of manuscript material on the history of Western Reserve College, 1831-58; typed copies of some letters of a Civil War officer; and 37 musical manuscripts, 13th-17th centuries. Among business records are those of a Cleveland company manufacturing steamboilers, 1868-1930 (323 vols., 172 boxes, and 327 pieces); and a Cleveland printing firm, 1885-1939 but chiefly 20th century (53 vols., 139 bundles, and 79 envelopes).

See Hist. Records Survey, Inventory of Business Records: The D. Connelly Boiler Company; the J. B. Savage Company (1941. 104 p. Processed).

COLUMBUS 10

Ohio Historical Society. (Formerly Ohio State Archaeological and Historical Society.) 1813 North High St. Elizabeth R. Martin, Librarian; Kenneth W. Duckett, Curator of Manuscripts.

Holdings: 1,000,000 pieces, 1750-1960, consisting of papers relating chiefly to Ohio but including some of national interest. Official noncurrent records of the State of Ohio are located in the Ohio Archives Division of the Ohio Historical Society. The official files of Ohio's Governors, 1803-1958, have been microfilmed through 1882.

Papers of Presidents of the United States, Cabinet officers, Supreme Court Justices, and diplomats include those of George Sewall Boutwell (Mass.; lawyer, U. S. Rep. and Sen., Sec. Treas.), 1869-92 (1 box); Henry Clay (Ky.; U. S. Rep. and Sen., Sec. State), 1811-46 (7 boxes, copies); William T. Coggeshall (Ohio; journalist, Minister to Ecuador), 1847-80 (8 boxes); Thomas Corwin (Ohio; Gov., U. S. Rep. and Sen., Sec. Treas.), 1832-55 (1 box); Thomas Ewing (Ohio; U. S. Sen., Sec. Treas., Sec. Interior) and his family, 1820-1934 (4 boxes); James A. Garfield (Ohio; Civil War officer, U. S. Rep. and Pres.), 1853-85 (1 box); Warren G. Harding (Ohio; U. S. Sen. and Pres.), 1910-23 (2 boxes); William Henry Harrison (Ohio; War of 1812 officer, U. S. Rep. and Sen., U. S. Pres.), 1796-97 (16 pieces); Friederich Hassaurek (Ohio; journalist, Minister to Ecuador), 1849-81 (7 boxes); Rutherford B. Hayes (Ohio; lawyer, Civil War officer, U. S. Rep., Gov., U. S. Pres.), 1849-92 (8 boxes); William McKinley (Ohio; Gov., U. S. Rep. and Pres.), 1879-86 (2 letter books); John McLean (Ohio; U. S. Rep., Postmaster Gen., U. S. Supreme Court Justice),

1846-56 (1 box); Return Jonathan
Meigs, Jr. (Ohio; State chief justice,
U. S. Sen., Gov., Postmaster Gen.),
1801-18 (1 box); John Sherman (Ohio;
U. S. Rep. and Sen., Sec. Treas., Sec.
State), 1841-43, 1854-59 (1 vol. and 1
box); Henry Stanbery (Ohio; U.S. Attor-
ney Gen.), 1858-92 (49 pieces); Noah
Haynes Swayne (Ohio; U. S. Supreme
Court Justice), 1823-62 (1 box); and
William Howard Taft (Ohio; U. S.
Pres.), 1908-20 (35 letters).

Papers of Members of Congress
include, in addition to the above, those
of John A. Bingham (Ohio; lawyer, U.S.
Rep., Minister to Japan), 1867-83
(1 vol. and 28 pieces); John W. Brick-
er (Ohio; Gov., U. S. Sen.), 1938-56
(150 cu. ft.); Ethan Allen Brown (Ohio;
Gov., U. S. Sen.), 1807-36 (1 box);
James Edwin Campbell (Ohio; lawyer,
Gov., U. S. Rep.), 1843-1924 (16 boxes); George Leroy Converse (Ohio;
lawyer, U. S. Rep.), 1802-92 (8 boxes); Eleutheros Cooke (N. Y., Ind.,
Ohio; lawyer, U. S. Rep.), 1804-56
(1 box); Robert Crosser (Ohio; U. S.
Rep.), 1914-48 (42 boxes); Martin Luther Davey (Ohio; Gov., U. S. Rep.),
1936-44 (1 box); Charles W. F. Dick
(Ohio; U. S. Rep. and Sen.), 1900-15
(44 boxes); Simeon D. Fess (Ohio;
pres. of Antioch College, author, editor, U. S. Rep. and Sen.), 1912-34 (56
boxes and 11 scrapbooks); Samuel
Galloway (Ohio; lawyer, U. S. Rep.),
1840-70 (2 boxes); Joshua Reed Giddings (Ohio; lawyer, abolitionist,
U. S. Rep., consul gen. in Canada),
1821-64 (10 boxes); William Forrest
Hunter (Ohio; U. S. Rep., Civil War
officer), 1851-67 (1 vol. and 1 box);
Joseph Warren Keifer (Ohio; lawyer,
Civil War officer, U. S. Rep.), 1860-
70 (1 box); Joseph Kerr (Pa., Ohio;
War of 1812 officer, U. S. Sen.), 1787-
1829 (3 boxes); James Kilbourn (Ohio;
War of 1812 officer, U. S. Rep.), 1810-
49 (4 boxes); Daniel Kilgore (Ohio;
merchant, U. S. Rep.), 1818-51 (8 boxes of business papers); Frank John

Lausche (Ohio; Gov., U. S. Sen.),
1945-46, 1949-56 (75 file drawers);
Allen G. Thurman (Ohio; U. S. Rep.
and Sen.), 1833-87 (2 boxes); Edward Tiffin (Ohio; Gov., U. S. Sen.),
1796-1813 (1 box); Joseph Vance
(Ohio; War of 1812 officer, Gov., U.S.
Rep.), 1800-37 (1 box); John Martin
Vorys (Ohio; U. S. Rep.), 1939-58
(48 file drawers and 8 boxes); George
White (Ohio; Gov., U. S. Rep.), 1920-
53 (80 cu. ft.); Frank B. Willis (Ohio;
Gov., U. S. Rep. and Sen.), 1908-28
(20 cu. ft.); and Thomas Worthington
(Ohio; U. S. Sen., Gov.) and his family, 1790-1920 (69 boxes).

Papers of Ohio Governors and
other State officials and political
leaders, in addition to some of those
named above, include those of Arthur L. Garford (Ohio; industrialist,
Progressive Party leader), 1900-30
(13 vols. and 90 boxes); Andrew L.
Harris (Ohio; State legislator, Gov.),
1858-98 (1 box); Samuel Huntington
(Ohio; State supreme court judge,
Gov.), 1778-1942 (1 box and 1 package); John Hancock Klippart (Ohio;
sec. of State Board of Agriculture),
1833-1931 (95 boxes); John and Joseph H. Larwill (Ohio; State legisla-
tors), 1804-80 (76 boxes); Mary
Brown Lee (Ohio; political leader),
1900-48 (24 boxes); George A. Myers
(Ohio; Negro political leader, ally of
Marcus A. Hanna), 1893-1929 (21 boxes); John Russell (Ohio; State sec. of
state), 1847-68 (3 boxes); Winthrop
Sargent (Mass., Ohio, Miss.; Rev.
War officer, Sec. of Northwest Terr.,
Gov. of Miss. Terr.), 1778-1865
(21 boxes); and Allen Trimble (Ohio;
Gov., agriculturist) and his family,
1783-1900 (20 boxes), including pa-
pers of William Allen Trimble (Ohio;
War of 1812 officer, U. S. Sen.).

Papers of authors and scientists
include those of Paul Laurence Dunbar (Ohio; poet), 1890-1928 (26 boxes); Frank A. Hardy (Ohio; novelist),
1850-85 (1 box); Increase Allen

Lapham (Ohio, Wis.; botanist, geologist), 1834-75 (3 boxes); John Patterson MacLean (Ohio; archeologist, author), 1888-1926 (34 boxes); William Corless Mills (Ohio; archeologist), 1913-28 (14 boxes); Warren King Moorehead (Ohio, Mass.; archeologist, author, member of U.S. Board of Indian Commissioners), 1907-33 (114 boxes); Wilbur Henry Siebert (Ohio; historian), 1890-1950 (134 boxes), consisting chiefly of notes on loyalists in the American Revolution and on the underground railroad; William S. Sullivant (Ohio; botanist, bryologist) and his family, 1797-1929 (14 boxes); Jeannette Bell Thomas (Ohio; folklorist), 1927-40 (15 boxes); and William Henry Venable (Ohio; teacher, poet), 1838-1920 (74 boxes).

Other personal papers include those of John Brown (Ohio, Pa., Kans.; abolitionist) and his family, 1830-1914 (9 boxes); Albert Gallatin Byers (Ohio; physician, minister) and his son, Joseph Perkins Byers (Ohio, N.J., N.Y.; penologist), 1833-1949 (8 boxes); James M. Comly (Ohio; journalist, Civil War officer) and his family, 1800-1900 (34 boxes); Jay Cooke (Pa.; banker, financier), 1845-96 (44 boxes); Washington Gladden (N.Y., Mass., Ohio; Congregational clergyman, advocate of the "Social Gospel"), 1852-1921 (84 boxes); Charles Hammond (Ohio; lawyer, journalist, legislator), 1812-40 (6 boxes); John Wesley Henley (Ohio; sec. of Ohio Universalist Association), 1840-1900 (43 vols.); Thomas D. Jones (Ohio; sculptor), 1839-1921 (4 boxes); Samuel Medary (Ohio; journalist, Terr. Gov. of Minn. and Kans.), 1841-68 (2 boxes); John Mouk (Ohio; Mennonite bishop), 1863-1903 (6 vols. of diaries); William Tecumseh Sherman (U.S. Army officer) and his family, 1839-91 (17 boxes); Thomas C. H. Smith (Mass., Ohio; Civil War officer), 1862 (9 boxes), on General Pope's Virginia campaign; and William Henry Smith (Ohio, Ill.;

newspaper editor, general manager of Associated Press, historian), 1854-1922 (44 boxes).

Business papers include records of the Scioto Valley Traction Co., 1900-28 (200 vols. and 24 boxes); the Baltimore, Pittsburgh and Chicago Railway, 1859-76 (10 vols.), the Lake Shore Electric Railway Co., 1914-49 (112 boxes), and other railroads; a number of iron furnaces in Jackson County, 1854-1919 (221 boxes); Darius Tallmadge stagecoach records, 1817-52 (35 boxes); and the Urbana Banking Co., 1830-50 (24 boxes).

Records of other organizations in Ohio include those of the Columbus Academy of Medicine, 1879-83 (1 vol.); Society of Friends in various localities throughout the State, 1807-92 (9 vols. and 1 box); Freewill Baptists, 1815-1915 (7 vols.); Governors' Conference of 1943 (1 box); Methodist Church, 1814-1916 (7 vols. and 4 boxes); National Glass Workers of America, 1900-50 (17 boxes); Ohio Federation of Women's Clubs, 1909-15 (1 vol.); Ohio Historical Commission, 1917-19 (3 boxes), relating to Ohio in World War I; Ohio State Dental Association, 1866-1930 (2 vols.); Ohio Universalist conventions, 1869-1914 (14 vols.); Perry's Victory and International Peace Centennial Commission, 1909-32 (65 boxes); Presbyterian churches, 1806-1940 (28 boxes); United Society of Believers [Shakers], 1824-87 (46 boxes); Woman's Christian Temperance Union, 1900-30 (4 boxes); and Society of Separatists of Zoar, 1830-1900 (130 vols. and 16 boxes).

There are also some transcripts and originals of records of the Northwest Territory, 1788-1803; scattered county records; records of various U.S. Army units; numerous Civil War letters and diaries and similar materials for the Mexican War and World Wars I and II; a collection of meteorological registers, 1804-39; papers

relating to the early settlement of
Marietta and Sandusky, Ohio (20 boxes), to the Burr Conspiracy (1 box),
and to the Lincoln Highway (13 boxes);
and copies of the correspondence of
British consuls in the United States,
1797-1818 (6 boxes).

See Elizabeth C. Biggert, Guide
to the Manuscript Collections in the
Library of the Ohio State Archaeological and Historical Society (1953.
153 p.).

COLUMBUS 15

Ohio State Library. Walter Brahm,
State Librarian.

Holdings: 3,417 pieces, 1763-1836,
relating chiefly to Ohio. Included are
papers of Ethan Allen Brown (Ohio;
Gov., U.S. Sen.), 1802-36 (497 pieces);
Daniel D. Emmett (Ohio; composer of
popular songs), uncataloged; Samuel
Huntington (Ohio; State supreme court
judge, Gov.), 1785-1826 (388 pieces);
Return Jonathan Meigs, Jr. (Ohio;
U.S. Sen., Gov., Postmaster Gen.),
1811-15 (269 pieces); Arthur St. Clair
(Pa., Ohio; Rev. War officer, Pres. of
Continental Cong., Gov. of Northwest
Terr.), 1763-1818 (1,144 pieces); and
Thomas Worthington (Ohio; U.S. Sen.,
Gov.), 1798-1826 (1,119 pieces).

COLUMBUS 10

Ohio State University Libraries.
1858 Neil Ave.   Eleanor F. Matthews,
Librarian, English and Speech Graduate Library.

Holdings: Papers of or relating to
Werrett Wallace Charters (Minn., Mo.,
Ill., Ohio; education prof. at several
universities, director of Bureau of
Education Research at Ohio State
Univ.), 1875-1952 (58 boxes); letters
and post cards from Hart Crane (Ohio;

poet, journalist), 1919-28 (125 pieces); unpublished recollections of the
Civil War, by an Ohio volunteer; and
archives of Ohio State University,
1883-1952 (19 file drawers), including manuscripts and other papers of
its presidents, William Oxley Thompson, James H. Canfield, William
Henry Scott, and George W. Right-
mire.

DAYTON 2

Dayton and Montgomery County
Public Library.   215 East Third
St.   Elizabeth Faries, Librarian
for the Dayton Room.

Holdings: 150 vols. and 3,000
pieces, 1728-1945, relating chiefly
to Dayton and Ohio. (Some of these
formerly belonged to the Dayton
Historical Society.) Included are papers of W. D. Bickham (Ohio; Civil
War correspondent, newspaper editor), chiefly letters to Bickham
from political and military leaders,
1860-1919 (127 pieces), and papers
relating to the Dayton Journal, 1863-
1936 (123 pieces); John W. Lowe
(Ohio; Mexican War and Civil War officer), 1847-61 (1 vol. and 217 pieces), containing a diary and 77 letters
written during the Mexican War;
Benjamin Van Cleve (Ohio; Hamilton
County surveyor), 1801-13 (2 vols.
and photostats of 132 letters and documents); and John W. Van Cleve (Ohio;
geologist, botanist), 1835-58 (2 vols.
and some 60 pieces), including letters
from important American scientists,
1835-49, and materials on Lake Superior copper resources, 1856-57.
There are also 2,100 other letters,
chiefly of family interest; diaries and
travel notes, 1848-1941 (21 vols.);
church records, 1817-22 and 1893-
1904 (3 vols. and 4 pieces); minutes
of a medical society, 1848-98 (2 vols.);
a collection of miscellaneous deeds

and other documents pertaining to land, 1728-1861 (93 pieces); ledgers, letter books, and other business records, 1805-1918 (46 vols. and 462 pieces), chiefly relating to Dayton firms and including material concerning supply during the War of 1812; and miscellaneous county and other governmental records, 1795-1945. A recent accession is the Henry Brown—Robert Patterson Collection, 1797-1839 (500 pieces), largely concerned with supplying the U.S. Army in the Northwest, 1797-1815.

DAYTON 6

Historical Society of The Evangelical United Brethren Church. Memorial Library, United Theological Seminary. 1810 Harvard Blvd. Rev. John H. Ness, Jr., Curator and Secretary.

Holdings: Historical records, 1784 to date, of The Evangelical United Brethren Church and its predecessors; the Evangelical Association, the United Evangelical Church, the Evangelical Church, and the Church of the United Brethren in Christ. The records include 3,500 journals (handwritten, printed, and/or microfilmed) of Annual Conferences from 1800 to the present; 50 quadrennial journals of General Conferences from 1815 to the present (handwritten and printed); 125 annual yearbooks (1866-1960); 65 Disciples (1809-1960); minutes and records of general offices, colleges, seminaries, mission boards and fields, orphanages, old people's homes, and hospitals (600 items); and diaries, sermons, and manuscripts of church leaders (2,500 items).

DELAWARE

Ohio Wesleyan University Library. J. H. Lancaster, Director.

Holdings: A quantity of papers relating chiefly to the Methodist Church in Ohio, some of which were collected by the Ohio Methodist Historical Society. Included are minutes of the Ohio Conference of the Methodist Episcopal Church, 1800-72; records of some early circuits, a few individual churches, and other Methodist organizations; diaries, letters, sermons, and other papers of early Methodist clergymen; and records of the Ohio Methodist Historical Society (22 folders). Papers of individuals include sermons, addresses, and correspondence of James Bradley Finley (Ohio; Methodist clergyman, missionary to the Wyandot Indians), 1814-53 (5 vols. and 1,480 pieces); some papers of George W. Maley (Ohio; Methodist circuit rider), 1821-40; a journal of Adam Poe (Ohio; Methodist clergyman), 1829-46; reminiscences and correspondence of Samuel Williams (Ohio; Methodist clergyman), 1844-54; and papers of Edward Thomson (Ohio, N.Y.; Methodist bishop, pres. of Ohio Wesleyan Univ.), 1834-64 (4 vols.). A collection of materials relating to Walt Whitman (N.Y., D.C., N.J.; poet) includes some correspondence of his intimate acquaintances. There are also some Renaissance manuscripts (6 vols.).

FREMONT

Rutherford B. Hayes Library. Watt P. Marchman, Director.

Holdings: 500,000 pieces, 1775-1954, relating chiefly to the United States in the second half of the 19th century. In addition to the manuscripts themselves there are microfilm copies of many manuscripts in the Library of Congress, the National Archives, and other depositories.
    The nucleus of the holdings is a group consisting of the main body of

papers of Rutherford B. Hayes (Ohio; lawyer, Civil War officer, U.S. Rep., Gov., U.S. Pres.), 1822-93 (293 vols. and 77,425 pieces), and papers of members of his family. Included are Hayes' diary, 1834-93 (34 vols.); drafts and recipients' copies of letters by him, 1834-93 (6,385 pieces); letters received by him, 1834-93 (60,000 pieces); his messages and speeches (2,500 pieces); and his business papers, 1838-92 (37 vols. and 2,420 pieces). The family papers include those of his wife, Lucy Webb Hayes, 1841-93 (7,500 pieces); his mother, Sophia Hayes, 1811-66 (6 vols. of diaries and journals, and 213 other pieces); his son, Webb C. Hayes, 1862-1934 (20,000 pieces); and other members of the family (50,000 pieces).

Papers of other Presidents and of Vice Presidents include those of Chester A. Arthur (N.Y.; U.S. Vice Pres. and Pres.), 1881-84 (16 pieces); James Buchanan (Pa.; U.S. Pres.), 1857-60 (14 pieces); Schuyler Colfax (Ind.; U.S. Vice Pres.), 1855-76 (34 pieces); James A. Garfield (Ohio; U.S. Pres.), 1856-81 (30 pieces); Ulysses S. Grant (U.S. Army officer, U.S. Pres.), 1864-83 (255 pieces); Benjamin Harrison (Ind.; U.S. Pres.), 1877-99 (42 pieces); Andrew Johnson (Tenn.; U.S. Vice Pres. and Pres.), 1865-68 (158 pieces); and Abraham Lincoln (Ill.; U.S. Pres.), 1861-65 (180 pieces). There are a special collection of White House correspondence of Presidents, 1860-1953 (500 pieces); and "diaries," 1898-1902 (7 vols.), left at the White House for the daily information of Presidents William McKinley and Theodore Roosevelt, recording important telegraphic and other messages received and sent and concerning chiefly the Spanish-American War, the Boxer Rebellion, and the Philippine Insurrection.

Papers of other persons in high positions in the U.S. Government include those of Benjamin Helm Bristow

(Ky., N.Y.; Civil War officer, U.S. Solicitor Gen., Sec. Treas.), 1868-84 (182 pieces); William Claflin (Mass.; Gov., U.S. Rep.) and Mary Buckland Davenport Claflin (Mass.; author), 1790-1905 (8,500 pieces); Benjamin Franklin Coates (Ohio; physician, Civil War officer, U.S. collector of internal revenue), 1860-81 (201 pieces); William E. Haynes (Ohio; Civil War officer, merchant, banker, U.S. Rep.), 1888-94 (1,200 pieces); John Little (Ohio; lawyer, State legislator, U.S. Rep.), 1875-96 (128 pieces); Stanley Matthews (Ohio; U.S. Sen., Supreme Court Justice) and his family, 1803-81, principally correspondence with his wife, 1843-81, and other members of his family; Oliver H. P. T. Morton (Ind.; lawyer, Gov., U.S. Sen.), 1862-77 (40 pieces); Warren Perry Noble (Ohio; lawyer, U.S. Rep.), 1862-71 (238 pieces); John B. Rice (Ohio; physician, U.S. Rep.), 1878-83 (1,800 pieces); and John Sherman (Ohio; U.S. Rep. and Sen., Sec. Treas., Sec. State), 1848-99 (150 pieces).

Other papers include those of Mary Clemmer Ames (N.Y., D.C.; novelist, poet, newspaper correspondent), 1859-81 (145 pieces); Henry Washington Benham (U.S. Army officer, engineer), 1861-84 (70 pieces, including 2 vols. of letters sent and photographs of Civil War military installations); Peleg Whitman Chandler (Mass.; lawyer, author), 1870-80 (202 pieces); Arthur L. Conger (Ohio; Civil War officer, industrialist, political leader), 1878-98 (15 vols. and 15,000 pieces); George William Curtis (N.Y.; author, editor, orator), 1850-92 (279 pieces); James Bradley Finley (Ohio; Methodist clergyman, missionary to the Wyandot Indians), 1820-38 (54 pieces); William Dean Howells (Ohio, Mass., N.Y.; novelist, literary critic, editor of Atlantic Monthly), 1857-1918 (323 pieces); Charles O'Neil (Mass.; U.S. naval officer),

1895-99 (408 pieces); William King Rogers (Ohio, Minn.; lawyer, land developer, private secretary to Pres. Hayes), 1849-1922 (3,018 pieces); William Tecumseh Sherman (U. S. Army officer), 1862-88 (25 pieces); William Henry Smith (Ohio, Ill.; newspaper editor, Associated Press general manager, historian), 1864-95 (60 pieces, including portions of an unpublished manuscript on history of slavery); and Charles R. Williams (Ill., Ind.; newspaper editor, biographer), 1892-1927 (7 vols. and 65 pieces).

Scattered among one or more groups are papers of Henry Ward Beecher (N. Y.; Congregational clergyman), 1867-86 (87 pieces); George Frisbie Hoar (Mass.; U. S. Rep. and Sen.), 1869-1904 (65 pieces); Harriet Beecher Stowe (Ohio, Mass., Conn.; author, abolitionist), 1872-90 (68 pieces); Adin Ballou Underwood (Mass.; lawyer, U. S. Army officer, surveyor of customs), 1865-80 (48 pieces); John Greenleaf Whittier (Mass.; poet, abolitionist), 1872-89 (81 pieces); Henry Wilson (Mass.; U. S. Sen. and Vice Pres.), 1856-72 (1 vol. and 37 pieces); and Robert Charles Winthrop (Mass.; U. S. Rep. and Sen.), 1876-92 (33 pieces).

In addition to papers identified as those of particular persons, the holdings include original opinions of the Attorney General of the United States, 1842-46 (1 vol.); official letter books and some correspondence of George Crook (Indian Wars officer, commander of the Dept. of the Platte and the Division of the Missouri), 1871-90 (2 vols. and 20 pieces), 1864-87; and the manuscript journal of the executive proceedings of the U. S. Senate, 1877-80 (6 vols.). The Library has also many papers relating to the Civil War, including muster rolls, diaries, letters written by soldiers, and reminiscences of battles and campaigns. There is a considerable quantity of records of or pertaining to the town of

Fremont and Sandusky County, Ohio, among them business papers, records of the Episcopal Church in Fremont, family papers, and records of a temperance society and other local organizations.

There are papers containing information on the "reconstruction" of the Southern States, civil service reform, currency and monetary problems, prison reforms, education, Indians, Negroes, the Spanish-American War, and many other subjects.

See Ohio State Archaeological and Historical Society, An Index and List of the Letters and Papers of Rutherford Birchard Hayes ([1933.] 42 p.); the Library's Annual Report, 1939-40 and 1940-41; and Watt P. Marchman, "The Rutherford B. Hayes Memorial Library," in College and Research Libraries, 17:224-227 (May 1956).

GAMBIER

Kenyon College Library. Edward C. Heintz, Librarian.

Holdings: Included are papers of Philander Chase (Conn., Ohio, Ill.; Episcopal bishop, founder of Kenyon College); and two autograph collections of papers, one with signatures of Presidents of the United States, and the other with signatures of 20th-century political and literary leaders in the United States.

HIRAM

Hiram College Library. Thelma R. Bumbaugh, Librarian.

Holdings: Chiefly an uncataloged collection of letters and other manuscripts of Burke Aaron Hinsdale (Ohio, Mich.; pres. of Hiram College, prof. of education at Univ. of

Mich.); and letters of and to Edmund Burritt Wakefield (Ohio, N. Y.; prof. and acting pres. of Hiram College).

MARIETTA

Campus Martius Museum of the Ohio Historical Society. (Mrs.) Catherine B. Remley, Curator.

Holdings: A considerable collection, dating from the late 18th century and relating chiefly to Marietta and the early history of Ohio. Included are some maps and other records of the Ohio Co. before 1800; court and other records of Washington County, 1788-1803; census records made in 1800 and 1803; some Civil War letters; and various church records, journals, diaries, and family papers. There are collections of papers of Harman Blenner-hassett (Ohio; associate of Aaron Burr); Manasseh Cutler (Mass.; Congregational clergyman, an organizer of the Ohio Co., U.S. Rep.); Return Jonathan Meigs, Jr. (Ohio; State chief justice, Gov., U.S. Sen., Postmaster-Gen.), 100 pieces; Rufus Putnam (Mass., Ohio; Rev. War officer, an organizer of the Ohio Co.); and Lili Martin Spencer (Ohio; artist), 100 letters and other documents. In a display by the Sons and Daughters of Pioneer Rivermen are 5,000 photographs and many records pertaining to early river history.

There has recently been acquired a large autograph collection gathered by Charles Slack of Marietta, including letters and other documents bearing the autographs of founders and proprietors of American Colonies, signers of the Declaration of Independence, Revolutionary generals, members of the Federal Constitutional Convention, Presidents of the Continental Congress, Presidents and Vice Presidents of the United States, statesmen and soldiers of the Civil War period, and many other persons.

Marietta College Library. Richard K. Gardner, Librarian.

Holdings: 10,000 items, chiefly 1760-1860, relating for the most part to the Northwest Territory and Ohio, especially the Marietta region, but including also much of broader interest. One of the most important groups consists of records of the Ohio Co., dating from 1786 and comprised of minutes of directors, records of deeds granted, survey plats, surveyors' notes, and letters received. Papers of and assembled by Samuel Prescott Hildreth (Ohio; physician, naturalist, historian) include documents on the history of the Ohio Valley, 1787-1847 (1 vol.); letters from the correspondence of Paul Fearing (Ohio; lawyer, U.S. Rep.), 1785-1820 (1 vol.); letters on science, natural history, and civil history, 1809-56 (3 vols.); meteorological records and journals of disease, 1831-54 (3 vols.); and Washington County, Ohio, court records, 1788-1802. Personal papers include those of Ephraim Cutler (Ohio; Terr. and State legislator) and his son William Parker Cutler (Ohio; State legislator, railroad builder), 1795-1889 (1,500 pieces); and Rufus Putnam (Mass., Ohio; Rev. War officer, an organizer of the Ohio Co., judge for Northwest Terr.), 1775-1824 (3 vols.). Included also are records of a Marietta bank, 1811-47; an autograph collection containing letters and other papers signed by signers of the Declaration of Independence and of the Constitution, U.S. Presidents, and other prominent persons, 1475-1954 (1,100 items); and the Marietta College Archives.

See Hortense Foglesong, "The Charles G. Slack Collection of Manuscripts, Marietta College," in Ohio Valley Hist. Assn., Annual Report for 1908, pp. 20-25; and Marietta College Bulletin, 51, no. 4 (1953).

MARION

Harding Memorial Association.

Holdings: An undetermined quantity of the private papers of Warren G. Harding (Ohio; newspaper editor, U. S. Sen. and Pres.) and some subsidiary documents. (These are not open to the public.)

MILAN

Edison Birthplace Association, Inc. Mrs. John E. Sloane, President. Llewellyn Park. West Orange, N. J.

Holdings: Included are some personal letters, notes, and sketches of Thomas A. Edison (N. J.; inventor); many rare photographs; and 2 ledgers from a Milan store showing transactions with the Edison family about 1840.

NORWALK

Fire Lands Historical Society. Case Ave. Mrs. Seville S. Young, Librarian.

Holdings: An undetermined quantity of manuscripts relating chiefly to the early history and development of the "Fire Lands." Included are notes, diaries, deeds, indentures, genealogical materials, the final record book of the Fire Sufferers Land Society, Mexican War and Civil War muster rolls and other papers, records of a plank road company, and some papers of Elisha Whittlesey (Ohio; War of 1812 officer, U. S. Rep., Comptroller of Treas.).

OBERLIN

Oberlin College Library. Eileen Thornton, Librarian.

Holdings: 30,000 pieces, 1804-1921, relating chiefly to American social and political history. Included are papers of Dan Beach Bradley (Ohio, Siam; missionary to Siam), 1804-73 (25 vols.), journals; Jacob Dolson Cox (Ohio; Civil War officer, Gov., Sec. Interior, U. S. Rep., pres. of Univ. of Cincinnati), 1861-98 (560 pieces); James H. Fairchild (Ohio; pres. of Oberlin), 1852-1903 (7,500 pieces); Charles Grandison Finney (N. Y., Ohio; evangelist, pres. of Oberlin), 1817-75 (2,425 pieces); Henry Churchill King (Ohio; Congregational clergyman, pres. of Oberlin, member of Inter-allied Commission on Mandates in Turkey following World War I), a considerable quantity; James Monroe (Ohio; Oberlin prof., U. S. Consul at Rio de Janeiro, U. S. Rep.), 1841-98 (6,075 pieces); and George Frederick Wright (Mass., Ohio; Congregational clergyman, geologist, Oberlin prof.), 1850-1921 (12,300 pieces). Included also are records of various Congregational churches in Ohio and related organizations, 19th century, that formerly belonged to the Ohio Church History Society.
See Allison, Inventory, p. 145.

OXFORD

Miami University Library. Leland S. Dutton, Librarian.

Holdings: Included are contemporary manuscript copies of journals of the House of Representatives of the Northwest Territory, 1799-1802 (4 vols.); manuscript diaries, 1832-60 (10 vols.); and a collection of papers relating to the University (7,000 items). Personal papers include those of Robert Hamilton Bishop (Ohio; Presbyterian minister, antislavery advocate, pres. Miami Univ.),

1836-53 (6 linear ft.); Samuel Fulton
Covington (Ohio; insurance executive,
newspaper editor), 1840's–1880's
(3 linear ft.); Burton Lee French (Idaho, Ohio; U.S. Rep. from Idaho, prof.
of government at Miami Univ.), 1903-
53 (30 linear ft.); John Hough James
(Ohio; banker, newspaper editor, railroad builder), 1814-81 (185 small
vols.); and William Holmes McGuffey
(Ohio, Va.; univ. prof. and pres., compiler of school readers), 1826-70 (175
pieces), among them letters from political and other leaders.

TOLEDO 2

Toledo Museum of Art. Otto Witt-
mann, Director.

Holdings: The George W. Stevens
Collection relating to the arts of writing, inscription, illumination, calligraphy, printing, and bookbinding from
Egyptian times to the present. The
earliest examples are Egyptian stelae
and papyri, Babylonian cuneiform
cylinders, and Roman tablets and papyri. There are many examples of
medieval and Near Eastern illumination and calligraphy.

—oOo—

Toledo Public Library. 325 Michigan
St. Robert D. Franklin, Director;
(Mrs.) Irene McCreery, Local His-
tory Librarian.

Holdings: A few hundred items,
1810-1932, consisting chiefly of personal papers of local and State interest. Included are papers of William
W. Jones (Ohio; physician, mayor of
Toledo), 1871-78, among them reminiscences of the cholera epidemic of
1850; Jesup W. Scott (Ohio; lawyer,
author, founder of Univ. of Toledo),
1828-69 (34 pieces); and Clark Wag-
goner (Ohio; journalist, historian),

1877-1902 (41 vols.). There are also account books, 1832-74 (11 vols.),
chiefly of general stores; records of
a Presbyterian church, 1836-66; a
few muster rolls and other military
records, 1810-12; and some school
records, 1817-54. Also in the Local
History Room with the above materials are a few manuscripts belonging to the Historical Society of Northwestern Ohio and relating chiefly to
the Old Northwest Territory and especially the Maumee River Valley.

WESTERVILLE

Otterbein College Library. (Mrs.)
Mary W. Crumrine, Librarian.

Holdings: A collection of manuscript and archival materials relating
to Otterbein College, the Evangelical
United Brethren Church, and Benjamin Russel Hanby (Ohio; United
Brethren pastor, song writer).

WRIGHT-PATTERSON AIR
FORCE BASE

Air Force Museum. Royal D. Frey,
Chief, Reference and Research Division.

Holdings: 500,000 documents,
1783 to the present, relating chiefly
to the history and technology of military aviation. Included are letters
of persons prominent in aviation and
voluminous technical reports and orders.

YELLOW SPRINGS

Antioch College Library. Bessie
Totten, Curator of Antiochiana.

Holdings: Chiefly (1) an exten-

sive collection of papers of and relating
to Horace Mann (Mass., Ohio; educator,
U. S. Rep. from Mass., pres. of Antioch
College), including 100 original letters
by him, 1824-59, and several hundred
to him; (2) copies of letters of the
Peabody, Mann, and related families
(some from originals in private possession), 1790-1953 (7 vols.); and (3)
minutes of trustees and faculty, records of College organizations, and
other records of or about the College,
1852-1956.

YOUNGSTOWN 3

Public Library of Youngstown and
Mahoning County.   Martha Goodman, Head of Reference Department.

Holdings: Copies of early cemetery inscriptions and names of early
settlers of Mahoning County and nearby counties in Ohio and Pennsylvania
(76 notebooks); some typewritten copies of old church records; original
U.S. census of Mahoning County, 1860
(1 vol.); and miscellaneous papers,
chiefly of local interest (1 file drawer).   In the Library also are papers
belonging to the Mahoning Valley Historical Society (4 file drawers), including deeds, voters' lists, surveyors' maps, and other papers relating
to Mahoning and Trumbull Counties,
Ohio.

NORMAN

Division of Manuscripts, University of Oklahoma Libraries. A. M. Gibson, Head.

Holdings: 5,000 cu. ft., 1800-1959, relating chiefly to Oklahoma and the Southwest.

Papers of Oklahoma Governors covering both the Territorial and statehood periods include those of Charles N. Haskell, Lee Cruce, J. B. A. Robertson, Jack Walton, Henry Johnston, William H. Murray, Leon Phillips, Robert S. Kerr, and Johnston Murray. Records of proceedings of the Oklahoma Constitutional Convention plus papers of various convention members are also in this section.

Labor history is chronicled in the complete files of the Oklahoma Federation of Labor, and the papers of Charles L. Daugherty and Jim Hughes (Okla.; commissioners of labor). For Indian history there are the Indian-Pioneer Papers (116 vols. of interviews); official papers of the Five Civilized Tribes, as well as private papers of Elias Boudinot (Ga., Indian Terr.; Cherokee Indian leader, editor), John Ross (Tenn., Indian Terr.; Cherokee chief), Stand Watie (Ga., Indian Terr.; Cherokee chief, Confed. Army officer), and George Washington Grayson (Indian Terr.; Creek chief). Literary materials are in the extensive University of Oklahoma Press files and the papers of Walter Campbell, known as Stanley Vestal (Okla.; writer, Univ. of Okla. prof.). Relating to science are the papers of Charles N. Gould (Okla.; director of State geological survey), C. E. Decker (Okla.; prof. of paleontology at Univ. of Okla.), and Arthur I. Ortenburger (Okla.; prof. of zoology at Univ. of Okla.), and records of the Oklahoma Geological Survey. Law and order papers are represented by those of William Tilghman and Charles B. Rhodes (Okla.; U. S. deputy marshals), and Isaac C. Parker, known as the "Hanging Judge" (Indian Terr.; U. S. dist. court judge).

Papers of men who served in the U. S. Congress include those of Andrew J. Biemiller (Wis.; U. S. Rep.), 1949-50; Lyle H. Boren (Okla.; U. S. Rep.), 1934-46; Wilburn Cartwright (Okla.; U. S. Rep.), 1910-42; Helen Gahagan Douglas (Calif.; actress, U.S. Rep.), 1926-51; Milton C. Garber (Okla.; newspaper editor, U. S. Rep.), 1923-48; Percy Lee Gassaway (Okla.; U. S. Rep., State judge), 1926-42; Lorraine M. Gensman (Okla.; lawyer, U. S. Rep.), 1917-23; Thomas P. Gore (Okla.; lawyer, U. S. Sen.), U. S. Sen.), 1890-1948; Jed Joseph Johnson (Okla.; lawyer, U. S. Rep.), 1927-47; Robert S. Kerr (Okla.; oil businessman, Gov., U. S. Sen.), 1909-46; Dick T. Morgan (Ind., Okla.; lawyer, U. S. Rep.), 1880-1920; Toby Morris (Okla.; lawyer, U. S. Rep.), 1947-53; John C. Nichols, known as Jack Nichols (Okla.; lawyer, U. S. Rep.), 1936-45; Preston E. Peden (Okla.; lawyer, U. S. Rep.), 1947-49; William Bliss Pine (Okla.; oil producer, U. S. Sen.), 1925-31; George Blaine Schwabe (Okla.; lawyer, U. S. Rep.), 1945-49; Paul Stewart (Okla.; lawyer, newspaper editor, U. S. Rep.), 1943-47; William G. Stigler (Okla.; lawyer, U. S. Rep.), 1944-52; John William Elmer Thomas (Okla.; lawyer, U. S. Rep. and Sen.), 1926-50; Claude Weaver (Okla.; lawyer, U. S. Rep., State judge), 1885-1945; Victor E. Wickersham (Okla.; U. S. Rep.), 1941-

48; and George Howard Wilson (Okla.; lawyer, U. S. Rep.), 1949-51.

Papers of other persons include those of William C. Austin (Okla.; banker, political leader, member of Oklahoma Planning and Resources Board), 1920-43; Bower Broaddus (Okla.; lawyer, Federal judge), 1930-49; Orel Busby (Okla.; lawyer, political leader, State supreme court justice), 1916-50; Charles C. Colcord (Okla.; U. S. deputy marshal, banker, oilman), 1859-1934; James William Denver (Calif.; lawyer, U. S. Rep., Gov. of Kans. Terr.), 1850-89; Elsbeth Freudenthal (N. Y., N. Mex.; author), 1941-52; Edith C. Johnson (Okla.; journalist, civic leader), 1915-51; Edward B. Johnson (Okla.; banker, stockman), 1882-1929; Gordon W. Lillie, known as Pawnee Bill (Okla.; rancher, manager of Wild West show), 1911-43; John A. Simpson (Okla.; National Farmers' Union pres.), 1889-1937; and Harrington Wimberly (Okla.; newspaper publisher, member Federal Power Commission), 1924-48.

There are business papers relating to oil; gold, lead, zinc, and coal mining; farming; livestock production; banking; and merchandising. Included are records of the Kali-Inla Coal Co., 1903-44, a bank in Oklahoma City, 1905-26, and some 25 other banks representing both rural and metropolitan finance; the 101 Ranch and Wild West Show, 1892-1935; an Indian Territory trading company, 1875-1926, and other hardware, farm, and mining supply firms; a mercantile company, 1870-1908; a cotton ginning concern, 1940-46; a milling company, 1897-1950; and the National Research Council's Committee on Ecology of Gresslands, 1933-47 (150 pieces).

The evolution of Oklahoma Territory is documented by settlers' diaries, correspondence, and journals. The Division of Manuscripts has upward of 200,000 glass plate negatives and prints depicting land runs, Indians, metamorphosis of Oklahoma towns from tents through modern brick and steel structures, hunting scenes, and wildlife. Well over 2,000 maps of Indian Territory, Oklahoma Territory, and the Southwest are included.

See Oklahoma; a Guide to Holdings of Regional Manuscripts (Preliminary draft, 1952. 114 p. Processed). A new guide is in manuscript and will be published during 1960.

OKLAHOMA CITY 5

Archives Division, Oklahoma State Library. Ralph Hudson, State Librarian and State Archivist.

Holdings: A large amount of material, consisting of (1) official records of the State and Territory of Oklahoma, held by the Division as the State's archival agency, and (2) some other papers of value for the history of Oklahoma. In the first category the most significant parts comprise the records of the Governor's office (9 ft.); and records of the Territory's Confederate pension agency. In the second category there are records of U. S. land offices in Oklahoma and Indian Territories. There is also a large quantity of records on microfilm.

—oOo—

Oklahoma Historical Society. Elmer L. Fraker, Administrative Secretary; Rella Looney, Archivist of Indian Archives Division.

Holdings: A large collection, 1831-1952, relating to Oklahoma and the Southwest, especially to Indian affairs.

Papers in the main library in-

clude those of Thomas G. Andrews
(Okla.; State supreme court judge),
20th century (95 letters); S. Frederick Barde (Okla.; journalist, historian), 1898-1916 (30 vols. and 12 filing
drawers); E. H. Kelley (Okla.; State
bank commissioner), 1886-1954 (4 filing drawers), a collection on banks
and banking in Oklahoma; C. W. Kirk
(Okla.; missionary, educator of Indians), 1878-92 (90 items); Joseph B.
Thoburn (Okla.; historian, archeologist, Univ. of Okla. prof., curator of
Okla. Hist. Soc.), 1899-1941 (1 filing
case); Amiel Weeks Whipple (U. S. Army officer, topographical engineer),
1851-54 (31 notebooks and 134 other
items), concerning the Mexican Boundary Survey and the Pacific Railroad
Survey, and including maps, original
drawings, and paintings; and Robert
L. Williams (Okla.; Gov., U. S. dist.
court judge), 1896-1919 (25 vols. and
98,000 pieces). There are also
church collections (4 filing drawers),
including 3 drawers on Baptist and
Indian Baptist associations.

In the Indian Archives Division
are papers of Gilbert Duke (Okla.;
Choctaw chief), 1882-1915 (1,275
pages); papers of Grant Foreman (Okla.; lawyer, author), 1898-1952 (20
filing drawers), including some papers of John Robert Thomas (Ill., Okla.; U. S. Rep. from Ill., U. S. judge in
Indian Terr.); and legal documents in
contested cases before the Dawes
Commission (see below), collected by
Foreman and Thomas (1 filing drawer). There are also business papers
of Frederick B. Severs (Okla.; trader
and storekeeper), 1869-1900 (2,562
account books and 1 filing drawer);
and papers of Edwin Ludlow (Okla.;
mining engineer), 1890-1924 (3 filing
drawers), relating to mining areas in
the United States, Canada, and elsewhere.

U. S. Government field records relating to Indians in Oklahoma, deposited in the Indian Archives Division, are

voluminous. Records relating to the
Five Civilized Tribes, from the agency at Muskogee, include papers on
the Cherokee, 1867-1914 (740 vols.,
72,309 pages, and 28 filing drawers);
the Chickasaw, 1866-1906 (99 vols.
and 17,510 pages); the Choctaw, 1831-
1907 (499 vols. and 54,083 pages);
the Creeks, 1852-1910 (73 vols. and
55,973 pages); and the Seminoles,
1897-1907 (11 vols. and 228 pages).
Included also are records of and concerning the Dawes Commission, otherwise known as the Commission to
the Five Civilized Tribes, headed by
Henry Laurens Dawes (Mass.; U. S.
Rep. and Sen.), 1890-1913 (343 vols.
and 21 filing drawers). Records of
other Indian agencies or subagencies
in Oklahoma include those of the
Cheyenne and Arapahoe agency, 1869-
1933 (886 vols. and 566,686 pages);
the Kiowa agency, 1861-1927 (519
vols. and 749,335 pages); the Pawnee
agency, 1870-1932 (907 vols. and
211,200 pages); the Quapaw agency,
1848-1909 (26,089 pages); and the
Sac and Fox agency and the Shawnee
agency, 1840-1932 (623 vols. and
485,362 pages).

SHAWNEE

Oklahoma Baptist University Library.
Lee Bowen Spencer, Librarian.

Holdings: Several hundred manuscripts, 1875 to date, in the Baptist
History Collection. Included are the
papers of James Burley Rounds (Okla.; pioneer missionary and Baptist
leader). There are also archives of
the Baptist General Convention of Oklahoma and minutes of Oklahoma Baptist associations and conventions,
1883-1956.

TAHLEQUAH

Northeastern State College Library.

Sue B. Thornton, Librarian.

Holdings: Manuscripts relating chiefly to the Cherokee Indians. Included are business and other papers of Andrew Nave (Indian Terr.; merchant), 1839-65, among them some 100 John Ross (Tenn., Indian Terr.; Cherokee chief) items.

See T. L. Ballenger, "The Andrew Nave Letters," in Chronicles of Okla., 30:2-5 (spring 1952).

TULSA

Thomas Gilcrease Institute of American History and Art. P.O. Box 2419. Martin A. Winger, Archivist.

Holdings: A substantial quantity of manuscripts, dating from the early 16th century and relating chiefly to the Five Civilized Tribes, Oklahoma, the Southwest, and Mexico.

Papers of individuals include those of Frederick W. Benteen (U. S. Army officer), 1891-96 (44 letters), regarding the Battle of the Little Big Horn; Jean Luis Berlandier (France, Mexico; engineer), 1827-30 (4 vols.), journals while on Northern Boundary survey; Andre Bernaldez (Spain; historian), a 1511 manuscripts containing a narrative of Columbus; William Burnet (England, N. Y.; Gov. of N. Y.), 1726-28 (14 letters); Cyrus Byington (Mass., Miss.; missionary to the Choctaw), 1819-68 (2 vols. of manuscripts on linguistics and 338 letters); John C. Casey (U. S. Army officer), 1825-59 (5 notebooks and 150 letters); John Perceval, 1st Earl of Egmont (England; Ga. colony trustee), "The Proceedings of the Trustees for the Establishment of Georgia, 1732-38" (1 vol.); Luke Foxe (England; navigator), 1631 (2 vols.), journal and logbook of the ship Charles which he commanded on an expedition seeking the Northwest Passage; Josiah Gregg (Mo., N. Mex.; Santa Fe trader, author), 1846-49 (8 vols. of diaries and 6 letters); Francis Gwyn (England; Under Secy. of State), 1684-89 (1 vol.), regarding Indian treaties and French-English diplomacy relating to New York and Canada; Frederick Haldiman (England; army officer), 1770-94 (58 letters and other documents), relating to Indian affairs in New York and Canada; Ethan Allen Hitchcock (U. S. Army officer, author), 1826-94 (91 vols. of diaries and 86 folders of other papers); Andrew Jackson (Tenn.; U. S. Army officer and Pres.), 1813-36 (10 letters); and Charles J. Latrobe (England; naturalist), 1832-34 (1-vol. diary).

Other papers of individuals include those of Ranald S. Mackenzie (U. S. Army officer), 1873-83 (1-vol. letter book and 10 letters); Samuel Bell Maxey (Tex.; Confed. Army officer, U. S. Sen.), 1861-65 (237 letters); Alfred J. Miller (Md.; landscape painter), 1837, manuscript notes of sketches made on trip to Rocky Mountains; Thomas Moran (Pa., N. Y.; landscape painter, etcher), 1870-1930 (12 vols. and 123 folders), sketch books, notes, and other papers; William A. Phillips (Kans., D. C.; Civil War officer, lawyer, U. S. Rep.), 1883-93 (46 pieces), pertaining to the Cherokee Indians; Peter Perkins Pitchlynn (Indian Terr., D. C.; lawyer, Choctaw chief), 1797-1929 (3,000 folders), letters and documents of both personal and official Cherokee matters; Alexander Lawrence Posey (Okla.; Creek poet, journalist), 1888-1945 (2 scrapbooks and 169 pieces), manuscript poems and letters; and John Ross (Tenn., Indian Terr.; Cherokee chief), 1814-70 (1,400 folders), letters and documents of both personal and official Cherokee matters.

Included also is a large collection of 16th-18th century documents relating to Mexico, the Mexican Inquisition, and the Southwest. There are also groups of papers relating to each of the Five Civilized Tribes.

TULSA 4

University of Tulsa Library. Eugenia Maddox, Librarian.

Holdings: 2,250 pieces, relating chiefly to missions in Indian Territory, the Cherokee and Creek Indians, and the political career of Alice Mary Robertson (Okla.; teacher and social worker with the Creeks, U.S. Rep.). In addition to letters of Alice Mary Robertson there are letters of her father, William Schenck Robertson (Okla.; pioneer educator with the Creeks); Robin McGill Loughridge (Ala., Okla., Tex.; Presbyterian missionary, educator with the Creeks); Walter Lowrie (Pa., N.Y.; U.S. Sen. from Pa., sec. of the Board of Foreign Missions of the Presbyterian Church); James C. Pilling (D.C.; ethnologist, bibliographer); and Samuel Austin Worcester (Ga., Okla.; Congregational clergyman, missionary to the Cherokee, translator).

OREGON

BEND

Deschutes County Library. Ivy Grover, Librarian.

Holdings: 40 items, 1863-1900, consisting of papers relating to Confederate Army equipment and supplies, 1863-69; a diary of a journey from St. Louis to Montana, 1866; and miscellaneous papers, chiefly of local interest, 1887-1900.
See Hist. Records Survey, Guide for Oreg.-Wash., p. 3.

CRATER LAKE

Crater Lake National Park. Box 672, Medford, Oreg. The Superintendent.

Holdings: 11 scrapbooks (containing manuscript letters interspersed with clippings) and 300 letters, 1885-1934, constituting a collection relating chiefly to the park. Included are some scattered letters from persons of prominence.

EUGENE

University of Oregon Library. Martin Schmitt, Curator.

Holdings: In the Department of Special Collections, 132,439 manuscripts, 19th and 20th centuries, relating chiefly to Oregon and the Pacific Northwest. Personal papers include those of Eric William Allen (Oreg.; dean of School of Journalism of Univ. of Oreg.), 1917-34 (562 letters); Jonathan Bourne (Oreg.; lawyer, U. S. Sen.), 1883-1940 (51,000 letters); Luella Clay Carson (Oreg., Calif.; dean of women at Univ. of Oreg., pres. of Mills College), 1889-1916 (281 letters); William B. Greeley (D. C., Wash.; forester, sec. and manager of West Coast Lumbermen's Association), 1929-55 (a large quantity); Ernest Haycox (Oreg.; novelist, short-story writer), 1930-47 (42 letters); Nan Wood Honeyman (Oreg.; State legislator, U. S. Rep.), 1932-50 (114 letters); Charles Samuel Jackson (Oreg.; newspaper publisher), 1902-6 (79 letters); Charles Linza McNary (Oreg.; lawyer, U. S. Sen.), 1921-41 (8 boxes); Joel Palmer (Ind., Oreg.; author, supt. of Indian affairs for Oreg. Terr.), 1851-79 (548 letters); Walter Marcus Pierce (Oreg.; lawyer, Gov., U. S. Rep.), 1933-43 (46 vols. and 216 boxes); Henry Davidson Sheldon (Oreg.; prof. of philosophy and education at Univ. of Oreg.), 1890-1948 (30 boxes, including 5,163 letters); and John Whiteaker (Oreg.; Gov., U. S. Rep.), 1859-78 (3 vols.). There are also some 200 collections of business records, organization papers, personal reminiscences, and autobiographies. Among these are records of the International Association of the Congo, 1881-83, which includes correspondence of Henry M. Stanley (England; journalist, explorer). There are papers concerning the American Pioneer Trails Association, 1923-42 (6 vols. and 6 boxes); and a file of the U. S. Military Tribunal No. IV, Case No. 11, Nuremberg, Germany, 1947-49 (808 vols.).

FOREST GROVE

Pacific University Library. Elsie M. Lundborg, Librarian.

Holdings: Miscellaneous diaries, journals, and letters of early pioneers; and other materials, including scrapbooks, relating chiefly to the locality.

See Hist. Records Survey, Guide for Oreg.-Wash., p. 5.

HILLSBORO

Washington County Historical Society Museum. 212 N. Second St. Violet Rush, Curator.

Holdings: A collection containing photographs and records of pioneer families of Washington County, early church and school records, and papers on the history of Oregon Territory.

See Hist. Records Survey, Guide for Oreg.-Wash., p. 6.

PORTLAND 5

Library Association of Portland. 801 SW. Tenth Ave. Elizabeth Anne Johnson, Head, Literature and History Department.

Holdings: Medieval and Renaissance manuscripts (9 vols.); meteorological observations taken at the library, 1870-74; papers on the Russo-American Telegraph Expedition, 1865-67 (200 pages); official records of the Lewis and Clark Centennial Exposition of 1905 (28 vols.); and transcripts of evidence on fishing rights of the Indians, 1916 (3 vols.).

See De Ricci, Census, p. 1982; Charles W. Smith, A Union List of Manuscripts in Libraries of the Pacific Northwest, passim (1931. 57 p.); and Hist. Records Survey, Guide for Oreg.-Wash., p. 11.

PORTLAND 1

Oregon Historical Society. 235 SW.

Market St. Thomas Vaughan, Director.

Holdings: 100,000 items, 1826-1960, relating chiefly to Oregon and the Pacific Northwest.

Papers of men who held Territorial, State, or Federal office include those of George Abernethy (Oreg.; merchant, Provisional Gov.), 2 vols. and 18 items; Matthew P. Deady (Oreg.; U. S. dist. judge), 1851-91 (10 vols. of diary and 3,180 letters); Stephen Johnson Field (Calif.; U. S. Supreme Court Justice), 1865-93 (174 items); Edward R. Geary (Oreg.; Supt. of Indian Affairs for Oreg. and Wash.), 1859-60 (1 large box); Addison C. Gibbs (Oreg.; lawyer, Gov.), 1846-74 (57 folders); Joseph Lane (Ind., Oreg.; Mexican War officer, Gov. of Oreg. Terr., U. S. Sen.), 1846-81 (2,000 items); Lewis A. McArthur (Oreg.; historian, Oreg. Geographic Board member), 1925-48 (23 vols. and 2 filing drawers); John Minto (Oreg.; State legislator, sheep breeder, conservation advocate), 15 folders; James W. Nesmith (Oreg.; Supt. of Indian Affairs for Oreg. and Wash., U. S. Rep. and Sen.), 1845-85 (344 items); Benjamin Stark (Oreg.; U. S. Sen.), 1845-64 (1,400 items); and Samuel R. Thurston (Oreg.; lawyer, Terr. Delegate to Cong.), 1838-51 (80 items).

Papers of other individuals include those of Jesse Applegate (Oreg.; political leader), 1845-86 (240 items); Asahel Bush (Oreg.; newspaper publisher, politician, banker), 1847-1914 (977 letters, including 685 transcripts); Charles H. Carey (Oreg.; municipal judge), 1890-1930 (2 filing cases); Eva Emery Dye (Oreg.; author), 1890-1942 (30 boxes); Thompson Colt Elliott (Wash.; investment banker, historian, director of Oreg. Historical Society), 40 folders, relating largely to early fur trade and traders in the Pacific Northwest;

Seth Luelling (Oreg.; horticulturist), 1854-75 (diaries); Cincinnatus Hiner Miller, known as Joaquin Miller (Oreg., Calif.; poet, playwright), 1866-70 (4 vols.), copies of ledgers; Seth Luen Pope (Oreg.; sea captain, industrialist) and his family, 1710-1912 (70 vols. and 365 pieces), including several ship's logs; Omar C. Spencer (Oreg.; lawyer), 1940-51 (56 folders of correspondence), concerning drainage and soil reclamation and conservation; and Marcus Whitman (Oreg.; missionary, pioneer), 1835-47 (58 items).

There are also many small collections of personal and other papers; papers relating to the Hudson's Bay Co. in Oregon Territory, 1826-63; Fort Hall account books, 1834-38 (3 vols.); military papers of officers in the Yakima and other Indian wars; the Oregon Indian wars pension application file, 1896-1905 (papers, including letters, for 2,750 applications); the Francis Seufert collection of ledgers and papers relating to middle Columbia fishing and canning operations, 1886-1955; a southern Oregon collection on mining, banking, and Wells Fargo shipping accounts, 1852-1914; a collection of letters, diaries, and ledgers on Pacific Northwest steamboat and coastal shipping history; additional records of businesses and banks, 1835-1940; correspondence of a Methodist mission in Oregon, 1838-53; minutes and other records of two temperance organizations, 1847-59; records of various churches, including photostats of records of early Catholic missions in the area; records of a Portland cemetery, 1850-1950; and microfilmed records relating to deaths, wills, and estates of Oregon pioneers, collected by the Daughters of the American Revolution (27 reels). Other records reproduced from sources elsewhere include copies of many diaries and journals; records of the Provisional and Territorial Governments of Oregon,

1843-59 (28 microfilm reels); Astoria Customhouse records, 1848-68 (6 reels); transcripts of selected correspondence of the American board of Commissioners for Foreign Missions, 1828-59 (432 letters); and the U. S. Engineers civil files, Portland, 1872-1927 (400 microfilm reels). Records entirely of the 20th century include those of the Lewis and Clark Centennial Commission and Exposition, 1905, Portland (100 boxes); reports of the Portland Public Works Commission, 1914-37 (22 folders); papers of the World War II history project for Oregon (24 filing drawers); records of the U. S. Federal Writers' Project for Oregon (73 folders); records of Oregon war public service projects of the U. S. Federal Works Agency, 1942-47 (88 folders); and files of the Western Forestry and Conservation Association, 1909-45 (150 folders).

See Charles W. Smith, A Union List of Manuscripts in Libraries of the Pacific Northwest, passim (1931. 57 p.); John Van Male, Resources of Pacific Northwest Libraries, p. 163 (1943); and Hist. Records Survey, Guide to the Manuscript Collections of the Oregon Historical Society (1940. 133 p. Processed).

PORTLAND 2

Reed College Library. Luella R. Pollock, Librarian.

Holdings: 17,229 pieces, 1864-1907, consisting of the papers of Simeon Gannett Reed (Oreg.; capitalist), 1864-1907 (15,000 pieces), and the minutes of and letters about the Oregon Steam Navigation Co., 1865-95 (229 pieces). The Reed papers relate chiefly to the breeding of livestock, mining, the development of rail and water transportation, finance, and real estate in the

Pacific Northwest.

See Hist. Records Survey, Guide for Oreg.-Wash., p. 12; and Dorothy O. Johansen, "The Simeon G. Reed Collection of Letters and Private Papers," in Pacific Northwest Quarterly, 27:54-65 (Jan. 1936).

SALEM

Oregon Collection, Oregon State Library. Eloise Ebert, State Librarian.

Holdings: 1,211 ft. of private manuscripts, photographs, negatives, and microfilm. The collection relates to the State with particular emphasis on the Salem area, but it is not being added to and eventually portions may be transferred to other libraries. The Oregon State Archives, administratively a unit of the Oregon State Library, is separately described below.

The Oregon Collection includes papers of Asahel Bush (Oreg.; newspaper publisher, politician, banker) and his family, 1837-1938; papers of John Minto (Oreg.; State legislator, sheep breeder, conservation advocate), 1864-1912; papers of a survey of race relations on the Pacific Coast, consisting of the files of William Carlson Smith (Calif., Hawaii, Oreg.; sociology prof.), 1924-27; business and family papers associated with Salem enterprises, the Capitol National Bank, 1885-1922, and the Capitol Lumbering Company, 1853-1934; and records of the Oregon Voter, Portland, 1917-47. The photographic collection includes records of two Salem studios, 1891-1946; negatives of the Albertype Co., Brooklyn, N.Y., for Oregon; and private pictures taken by members of the Asahel Bush family, 1900-14. The Library administers archives of the Oregon units of the American Association of University Women, 1923-58, the Business and Professional Women's Clubs, 1921-54, the Daughters of the American Revolution, 1917-58, the Grand Army of the Republic, 1881-1914, and the League of Women Voters, 1930-53. It is also the repository for microfilm copies of records of the Missionary District of Eastern Oregon of the Episcopal Church, 1870-1956.

See Mirpah G. Blair, Some Rarities in the Oregon State Library, pp. 16-18 (1955).

—oOo—

Oregon State Archives, Oregon State Library. Eloise Ebert, State Librarian; David C. Duniway, State Archivist.

Holdings: 10,000 ft. of official records. The earliest are the files of the Oregon Provisional and Territorial Governments, 1843-59, for the Governor, Secretary of the Territory, Treasurer, Auditor, Recorder, and Legislature, and include records of the Willamette Cattle Co. beginning in 1837. Record groups of 54 State agencies include those of the Governors, 1894-99, 1935-58, Legislative Assembly, 1859-74, 1923-59, Secretary of State, 1859-1954, Attorney General, 1907-45, Board of Control, 1903-58, Treasurer, 1859-1951, and various appointive agencies. There are also records of 22 defunct State agencies, such as the World War Veterans State Aid Commission, 1921-44, State Planning Board, 1933-39, Capitol Reconstruction Commission, 1935-39, and Defense Council, 1941-45. The records of 23 counties and 4 cities, 1845-1958, are represented, including records of the County Court, Circuit Court, Clerk, Assessor, Auditor, Treasurer, School Superintendent, Justices of the Peace, Sheriff, and Tax Collector. Federal Records deposited in the Archives include those of the Oregon Federal Writer's Project, 1935-40; and U.S.

census schedules other than population for 1850, 1860, and 1870, and schedules including population for 1880.

See Oregon State Archives, First Biennial Report, 1944-46, and "Checklist of Records Relating to Legislation" in Oregon's Public Records ([8 p.] 1959).

—oOo—

Willamette University Library. Brooks A. Jenkins, Librarian.

Holdings: 6 linear ft., since 1839, consisting chiefly of records of the Oregon Conference of the Methodist Church and letters, journals, and diaries of early missionaries in Oregon. Present also is the logbook of a trader to China, Lower California, and the Columbia River region, 1855-56.

See Hist. Records Survey, Guide for Oreg.-Wash., p. 15; and John Van Male, Resources of Pacific Northwest Libraries, p. 177 (1943).

THE DALLES

Wasco County Library. 4th and Washington Sts. Mary Frances Gilbert, Librarian.

Holdings: A small collection of letters of pioneers and miscellaneous papers, 1856-91, chiefly of local interest. Included are the holdings of the defunct Old Fort Dalles Historical Society.

See Hist. Records Survey, Guide for Oreg.-Wash., p. 17.

TILLAMOOK

Tillamook County Pioneer Museum. 2106 2d St. Rosaline R. Walker, Custodian.

Holdings: A small collection of interest for local and State history. There are a few papers of early settlers in the county, a large number of early photographs, some old family Bibles, and some maps.

See Hist. Records Survey, Guide for Oreg.-Wash., p. 18.

ALLENTOWN

Lehigh County Historical Society.
Fourth and Walnut Sts. Melville J.
Boyer, Curator and Secretary.

Holdings: 1,200 items, relating
chiefly to Lehigh County. Included are
a letter book of a deputy quartermaster
general, 1778-81; a few Civil War letters; and some church records.

—oOo—

Muhlenberg College Library. John S.
Davidson, Librarian.

Holdings: A journal of Frederick
Augustus Conrad Muhlenberg (Pa.;
Lutheran clergyman, U.S. Rep.), 1770
(1 vol.); papers relating to Muhlenberg
College, 1867-1948 (37 vols.); a collection of Pennsylvania-German dialect writings (34 vols.); and a number
of miscellaneous papers.
See Hist. Records Survey, Guide
for Pa., p. 1.

ALTOONA

Blair County Historical Society.
Baker Mansion Library. J. J. Hauser,
Secretary, Curator.

Holdings: Chiefly records of or
relating to the Allegheny Portage Railroad, operated between Hollidaysburg
and Johnstown, Pa., 1834-57 (1,000
items); and some day books, cash
books, and payroll books of Allegheny
Furnace, 1840-75.

AMBRIDGE

Old Economy, Pennsylvania Historical
and Museum Commission. Lawrence
Thurman, Curator.

Holdings: 500,000 items, 1804-
1905, consisting of business and personal letters, ledgers, and other records of the Harmony Society, a social, economic, and religious group.
There are many papers of or relating
to George Rapp (Pa., Ind.; religious
leader, founder and head of the society).

ANNVILLE

Lebanon Valley College Library.
Helen E. Myers, Librarian.

Holdings: 200 items, 1727 to
date, consisting chiefly of a few Revolutionary War letters; some early
school records; letters regarding
early furnaces; day books and account books for three generations of
local physicians; a fairly large group
of day books and account books of local stores, flour mills, and taverns;
a small collection of letters of the
family of Lloyd Mifflin (Pa.; painter,
poet); and a group of Lebanon Valley
College manuscripts.

ATHENS

Tioga Point Museum and Historical
Society. 724 South Main St. Elsie
Murray, Historian.

Holdings: 3,200 items, 1786-
1875 for the most part, but with
some of earlier and later dates.
They consist of letters, diaries,
account books, deeds, patents, surveys and maps, and other documents

that relate chiefly to early local history. Included are papers pertaining to the conflicting claims of Pennsylvania and Connecticut to lands along the Susquehanna River, 1780-1840 (several hundred items); a number of items concerning the Asylum Co. and the French colony of Azilum; account books of pioneer Susquehanna merchants; canal and railroad papers illustrating the development of transportation in northern Pennsylvania and southern New York, 1825-78 (500 items); records of the Athens Academy, 1797-1876 (80 items); some church records; a diary of a missionary journey to the Cherokee Indians, 1820; letters from a Civil War soldier; and a journal of a gold-seeking trip to the Yukon, 1898.

See Hist. Records Survey, Guide for Pa., p. 3.

BETHLEHEM

Archives of the Moravian Church. Main St. at Elizabeth Ave. Kenneth G. Hamilton, Archivist.

Holdings: 7,300 vols. and 58,000 pieces, 1457 to date, consisting of letters, reports, diaries, and other papers relating chiefly to the Moravian Church in the Western Hemisphere, particularly in North America. A great deal of the material relates to activities in Pennsylvania, but importantly represented also are church organizations in Canada, Connecticut, Illinois, Iowa, Kansas, Maryland, New Jersey, New York, North Carolina, Ohio, and Rhode Island. Papers of individuals include extensive quantities of papers of John Ettwein (N. C., Pa.; Moravian missionary to the Indians, bishop), 1772-97; John Gottlieb Ernestus Heckewelder (Pa., Ohio; Moravian missionary to the Indians, author), 1765-1823; Augustus Gottlieb Spangenberg (Pa., N. C.; Moravian bishop, overseer of the Bethlehem settlement of Moravians, missionary), 1744-60; and David Zeisberger (Pa., Ohio; Moravian missionary to the Indians, author), 1745-98. There is much material relating to Indians and Indian missions, including a large number of papers of the Society for Propagating the Gospel Among the Heathen, 1735-1811. Included also are manuscripts of religious music, 1710-1850 (900 pieces); and archives of the Moravian College, Bethlehem, 1840 to date.

See Allison, Inventory, pp. 147-165; Hist. Records Survey, Guide for Pa., p. 5; and Paul A. W. Wallace, "The Moravian Records," in Ind. Magazine of History, 48:141-160 (June 1952).

—oOo—

Bethlehem Public Library. 11 West Market St. Harriet T. Root, Librarian.

Holdings: 54 vols. of typed transcriptions of original church, pastoral, and cemetery records in the Bethlehem area of Northampton and Lehigh Counties, Pa.

—oOo—

Lehigh University Library. James D. Mack, Librarian.

Holdings: Miscellaneous collections, including a composition by Johann Sebastian Bach (Germany; composer), 3 pages; papers of John Russell Bartlett (R. I., N. Y.; antiquarian, bibliographer, author), 197 documents relating to Rhode Island's part in the Civil War and to the dedication of the national cemetery at Gettysburg; journals of Harvey M. Bassler (geologist), comprising records of expeditions along the Amazon River, 1921-30 (9 vols.), together with holograph maps; letters and brief literary works of James Fenimore Cooper (N. Y.; novelist), 23 items; correspondence of Richard Harding Davis (Pa., N. Y.; journalist, author), 1887-1916 (405 pages); notes, drafts, and certified transcripts pertaining to the work of Lawrence H. Gipson (Idaho, Ind., Pa.; historian), 20th century; unpublished letters of Washington Irving (N. Y.; author, U.S. Minister to Spain), 19 items; and miscellaneous documents relating to Asa Packer (Pa.; railroad builder, U. S. Rep., philanthropist, founder of Lehigh Univ.). There are also documents relating to charges of corruption made by James Monroe against Alexander Hamilton, 1792-97 (30 pages); records of an iron company at Easton, Pa., 1854-1916 (4 vols. and some miscellaneous papers); and a collection of miscellaneous autograph letters and documents, including personal correspondence of every American President and of other political leaders, American and foreign scientists, and American and foreign literary figures (423 items).

BRYN ATHYN

Academy of the New Church Library. Lois E. Stebbing, Librarian.

Holdings: 15,500 pieces, consisting of (1) the Swedenborgian Collection (50 vols.), containing a few original items and numerous photographic copies of the original writings of Emanuel Swedenborg (Sweden; philosopher, religious writer); and (2) the Archives Collection, containing lectures and notes by members of the Academy's faculty; correspondence, sermons, and other papers of several Swedenborgian leaders; and other materials relating to the New Church, since 1800, and to the Academy, since 1876.

See Hist. Records Survey, Guide

for Pa., p. 9.

CARLISLE

Dickinson College Library. Charles Coleman Sellers, Librarian.

Holdings: 35,000 pieces, of which the College archives constitute the largest group. Included in this group are letters of founders and alumni, among them John Armstrong (Pa.; Rev. War officer, Member Continental Cong.), Moncure D. Conway (Ohio, Mass., England; Unitarian and Congregational clergyman, author), John Dickinson (Pa., Del.; Member Continental Cong., Pres. of Del. and of Pa.), Horatio C. King (N. Y.; Civil War officer, lawyer, newspaper editor), Charles Nisbet (Pa.; Presbyterian clergyman, first pres. of Dickinson College), Benjamin Rush (Pa.; physician, Member Continental Cong., prof. at Univ. of Pa.), and Roger Brooke Taney (Md.; U. S. Attorney Gen., Sec. Treas., U. S. Chief Justice).

There are also personal papers of Robert Bridges (Pa., N. Y.; author, editor of Scribner's Magazine), 1,200 items; the Buchanan Collection, containing 300 letters, speeches, and other papers of James Buchanan (Pa.; U. S. Rep. and Sen., Minister to Russia and to Great Britain, Sec. State, U. S. Pres.) and an equal number of papers of contemporary political figures; some letters and literary manuscripts of John Drinkwater (England; poet, playwright); papers of Marion Dexter Learned (Pa.; college prof. and author), 3,200 items mostly relating to the German-American cultural alliance preceding World War I; and a collection on political and military affairs in Pennsylvania, 1855-66 (3,500 items), mostly the papers of Eli Slifer (Pa.; Sec. of the Commonwealth).

Hamilton Library and Historical Association of Cumberland County. 21 North Pitt St. D. W. Thompson, Secretary.

Holdings: 1,000 pieces relating to Cumberland County since 1750. Included are letters, account books, Revolutionary loyalty oaths, treasury vouchers of the county, Civil War draft records, and Carlisle borough minutes from 1845.

See Hist. Records Survey, Guide for Pa., p. 10.

CHESTER

Delaware County Historical Society. (Mrs.) Elsie M, Jones, Curator.

Holdings: A small collection, 1715-1876, consisting of letters, diaries, account books, church records, and miscellaneous manuscripts relating chiefly to Delaware County. Included are papers of Edward Darlington (Pa.; lawyer, U.S. Rep.).

See Hist. Records Survey, Guide for Pa., p. 12.

COATESVILLE

Presbyterian Historical Society of Coatesville, Pennsylvania. C. Hans Evans, Pastor.

Holdings: 700 pieces and 44 vols., consisting chiefly of minutes, sermons, marriage and death records, correspondence of ministers, and other materials relating to the Coatesville Presbyterian Church, 1825-1927.

See Hist. Records Survey, Guide for Pa., p. 12.

COUDERSPORT

Potter County Historical Society.

(Mrs.) Mary E. Welfling, Secretary.

Holdings: Several hundred pieces, dating from as early as 1803, and relating chiefly to Potter County. Included are diaries, letters, and account books; and records of a turnpike, of some schools, and of various local organizations.

DOYLESTOWN

Bucks County Historical Society Library. Mrs. Paul Niemeyer, Librarian.

Holdings: 8,000 vols. and 20,000 pieces, 1681 to date, relating chiefly to Bucks County and its vicinity, but containing some materials that relate to a larger area. Included are Durham Furnace records, 1779-94; records of the Delaware and Raritan Canal Co., 1831-97; account books and other records of numerous business establishments and individuals; records of various courts, schools, and other governmental organizations, dating from 1681; an extensive collection of church records, 18th and 19th centuries; and a small collection of material on early technology.

EASTON

Easton Public Library. (Mrs.) Jane S. Moyer, Librarian.

Holdings: 150 vols., relating chiefly to Easton and vicinity. Included are 50 vols. of 17th-19th century church and cemetery records, 4 vols. of records of an iron company, and some Civil War diaries.

See Hist. Records Survey, Guide for Pa., p. 15.

Kirby Political Science Museum,
Lafayette College.   Eugene P. Chase,
Director.

Holdings: 350 items, consisting
mainly of English and American legal
documents. Included are a collection
of autograph letters and other documents of numerous persons important
in American political and literary history; and a few medieval manuscripts.
See Hist. Records Survey, Guide
for Pa., p. 16.

—oOo—

Lafayette College Library.   Clyde L.
Haselden, Librarian.

Holdings: Included are several
medieval manuscripts; an autograph
collection of letters by English literary figures, 18th century (30 items);
letters by the Marquis de Lafayette
(France; American Rev. War officer),
1777-1834 (200 items), of which 171
are to George Washington (Va.; U. S.
Pres.); Lafayette College items,
chiefly relating to student activities;
a few literary manuscripts; and business records of a local slate industry,
late 19th century (15 vols. and 20 file
boxes).
See Hist. Records Survey, Guide
for Pa., p. 15; and De Ricci, Census,
p. 2000.

—oOo—

Northampton County Historical and
Genealogical Society.   101 South
Fourth St.   Russell S. Bauer,
Secretary.

Holdings: 500 pieces, including
some Durham Furnace records,
1750-1800, a few day books, some
Revolutionary War and Civil War
material, numerous genealogies,
and other papers mainly of local
interest.
See Hist. Records Survey, Guide
for Pa., p. 16.

EBENSBURG

Cambria County Historical Society.
Y. M. C. A. Building. Edna Lehman,
Curator.

Holdings: 160 pieces, 1795-1954,
consisting of personal and business
letters, deeds and other legal papers,
and other items of local interest.

ERIE

Erie County Historical Society.   407
State St.   John W. Ray, Executive
Secretary.

Holdings: 1,500 items relating
to northwestern Pennsylvania. Included is a journal of the Erie Canal
Co.

—oOo—

Erie Public Museum.   356 West
Sixth St.   John V. Alexick, Director.

Holdings: 6,000 pieces, relating
chiefly to Erie and northwestern
Pennsylvania.   Included are a letter
book of the collector of the port of
Erie, 1796, and a collection of autograph letters of Presidents and other
American leaders (85 pieces).
See Hist. Records Survey, Guide
for Pa., p. 18.

FORT WASHINGTON

Historical Society of Fort Washington.   Clifton House.

Holdings: Several hundred
pieces, mainly of local interest,
including letters, diaries, and records of gristmills and sawmills
and of other business enterprises.
See Hist. Records Survey, Guide
for Pa., p. 19.

GETTYSBURG

Lutheran Historical Society Library.
West Confederate Ave.   Herbert H.
Schmidt, Librarian.

Holdings: 25,500 pieces, relating
chiefly to the Lutheran Church, especially in Pennsylvania.   Personal papers include those of Justus H. C. Helmuth (Pa.; Lutheran clergyman, prof.
of German at Univ. of Pa.); Samuel S.
Schmucker (Va., Pa.; Lutheran clergyman, pres. of Gettysburg College),
1727-1869; and Martin Luther Stoever
(Pa.; prof. of history and Latin at
Gettysburg College, author), 1838-70.
Included also are records of the General Synod, many of the district synods
and their conferences, records of congregations, and minutes of ecclesiastical committees.
  See Allison, Inventory, pp. 165-
173; A. R. Wentz, "Collections of the
Lutheran History Society," in Pa. History, 3:66-69 (Jan. 1936); and Hist.
Records Survey, Guide for Pa., p. 20.

—oOo—

Lutheran Theological Seminary Library.   Herbert H. Schmidt, Librarian.

Holdings: 6 vols. and 26 pieces of
medieval and Renaissance manuscripts;
and a collection of diaries, sermons,
and Lutheran church records.
  See De Ricci, Census, p. 2001.

HARRISBURG

Historical Society of Dauphin County.
219 South Front St.   (Mrs.) Cornelia
F. Tillman, Curator.

Holdings: 20,000 pieces, from as
early as 1734, relating chiefly to Dauphin County.   Included are some early
court records of Dauphin, Lancaster,

and Cumberland Counties; various
business records, including those of
Frederick Kelker (Pa.; pioneer businessman in Harrisburg), 1794-1906;
papers of Simon Cameron (Pa.; Minister to Russia, U. S. Sen., Sec. War),
1836-92 (4,100 pieces); papers of
William R. De Witt (Pa.; surgeon,
Civil War officer), 1862-71; and an
extensive collection of genealogical
data.

—oOo—

Pennsylvania Historical and Museum
Commission.   Sylvester K. Stevens,
Executive Director.

Holdings: An extensive body of
official and other records relating
chiefly to Pennsylvania.   Most of
these are administered by the two
Divisions in Harrisburg described
immediately below.   Others are in
two of the Commission's historical
properties, which are described under the names of the places where
they are located: (1) Old Economy,
at Ambridge, Pa., and (2) Drake
Museum, Drake Well Museum Park,
near Titusville, Pa.
  See Preliminary Guide to the Research Materials of the Pennsylvania
Historical and Museum Commission,
58 p. (1959).

Division of Public Records.   221
Education Bldg.   Henry Howard
Eddy, State Records Officer.

Holdings: 3,500 cu. ft. of records, 1,758 reels of microfilm,
2,000 photographs, and 1,500 maps,
held as the State's archival agency.
These consist almost exclusively of
records created by the legislative
and executive branches in conducting
the official affairs of Pennsylvania.
Strongly represented are the following officers and agencies: The Provincial Council, 1682-1775; General

Assembly, 1700-1909; Port of Philadelphia, 1727-1907; Committee of Safety and Council of Safety, 1775-77; Supreme Executive Council, 1777-90; Council of Censors, 1784; Secretary of the Commonwealth, 1790-1943; and Attorney General, 1875-1907. On the fiscal side there are the principal series of records of the General Loan Offices of 1773, 1785, and 1793; State Treasurer, 1775-1930; Comptroller General, 1775-1809; Register General, 1789-1809; Receiver General, 1787-1809; Auditor General, 1809-1939; and Loan and Transfer Agent of the Commonwealth, 1835-1919. Included are basic charters, constitutions, and Indian deeds and treaties, 1679-1838; minutes of the executive (council or governor), 1682-1943; original engrossed laws, 1700-1867; minutes of the wardens of the port of Philadelphia, 1766-1869; military orders, reports, and accounts, chiefly 1775-1861; public debt accounts, 1780-1919; patronage papers, 1776-1840; clemency and conviction papers, 1777-1899; minutes, journals, and dockets of State penitentiaries, 1818-1931; and documentation of public works and improvements (capitols, stream clearance, canals, highways, and turnpikes), 1706-1929.

    Incidental holdings from private sources include the sequestered records of the partnership of Baynton, Wharton, and Morgan, western traders, 1723-94 (68 vols. and 20 cu. ft.); also those of Joshua and Thomas Gilpin, paper manufacturers, 1790-1854 (62 vols. and 1 cu. ft.). There are also papers of James Buchanan (Pa.; U.S. Rep. and Sen., Minister to Russia and to Great Britain, Sec. State, U.S. Pres.), 1815-63 (50 items); George Mifflin Dallas (Pa.; U.S. Sen., Minister to Russia and to Great Britain, U.S. Vice Pres.), 1817-63 (63 items); Lavinia Dock (Pa., N.Y.; nurse, author) and Mira Dock (Pa.; conservationist) and their family, 1865-1951 (7 cu. ft.); J. Horace McFarland (Pa.;

conservationist, city planner), 1901-48 (15 cu. ft.); John Tod (Pa.; U.S. Rep., State supreme court justice), 1788-1835 (5 cu. ft.); and Jasper Yeates (Pa.; State supreme court justice), 1776-1807 ($1/2$ cu. ft.).

Division of Research and Publications. State Museum Bldg. Donald H. Kent, Chief.

    Holdings: 1,324 cu. ft. of original sources, 260 cu. ft. of transcripts, 495 reels of microfilm (exclusive of more than 3,000 reels of copies of newspapers), 6,410 photostats, 7,746 photographs, 95 original maps, and 915 photostats and tracings of maps, 1544-1875. These consist entirely of materials collected for research on Pennsylvania history and for publications of the Commission. The original sources include 1,050 cu. ft. of papers dealing with canal, railroad, and coal-mining operations. There are 154 cu. ft. of records inventories and checklists made under the auspices of the Works Projects Administration, and 120 cu. ft. of business, family, and personal papers, 1786-1903. Among the latter are papers of Edward Camphausen (Pa.; businessman, U.S. consul at Naples), 1882-1903 (3 letter books).

    The microfilm collection includes 70 reels on the French and Indian War, and the Revolutionary and post-Revolutionary periods; 45 reels of papers of William Jackson Palmer (Pa., Colo.; Civil War officer, railroad executive) and James Harrison Wilson (U.S. Army officer, civil engineer); 10 reels of papers of Simon Cameron (Pa.; Minister to Russia, U.S. Sen., Sec. War); 55 reels of other Pennsylvania material in various depositories; and 220 reels of diaries, journals, business records, and legal and other papers, from 1750. The photostats range from 1725 to 1875 and include 5,266 pages from manuscripts in other depositories and 1,144 pages of diaries, journals, and miscellaneous papers. The transcripts consist chiefly of material from British, Canadian, and French archives, and of current history files on the State government's administrative and departmental policies.

HAVERFORD

Haverford College Library. John A. Lester, Jr., Librarian.

Holdings: Chiefly the following groups, some of which were formerly in Roberts Hall of Haverford College: (1) The J. Rendel Harris Collection of Ancient and Oriental Manuscripts, containing over 60 Hebrew, Greek, Latin, Arabic, Syriac, and Ethiopian rolls and codices; (2) the Charles Roberts Autograph Collection, containing letters of the signers of the Declaration of Independence, U.S. Presidents, Members of Congress, Cabinet officials, governors, authors, scientists, ecclesiastics, and others (20,000 items); (3) the William Pyle Philips Autograph Collection, consisting of autographs of signers of the Declaration of Independence and 12 letters by U.S. Presidents; (4) a selection of 200 letters and memoranda from the files of Christopher Morley (Pa., N.Y.; author, editor); and (5) the Quaker Manuscript Collection (40,000 items), pertaining to Quaker history and biography and containing letters of numerous Quaker leaders, papers of Quaker families, many diaries and journals, and a collection of records and other papers relating to the founding and administration of Haverford College. The archives of the American Friends Service Committee, 1917 to date (several hundred cubic feet), are deposited in the Haverford College Library building.
See Hist. Records Survey,

Guide for Pa., pp. 23-25.

HONESDALE

Wayne County Historical Society. 810 Main St. Grace K. Bentley, Secretary.

Holdings: 1,000 items, 1794-1865, relating chiefly to Wayne County. Included are papers concerning Philip Hone (N.Y.; businessman) and the Delaware and Hudson Canal; papers about a gravity railroad; and some diaries, letters, and miscellaneous manuscript materials.
See Hist. Records Survey, Guide for Pa., p. 25.

HOPEWELL FURNACE (R.D. 1, Elverson).

Hopewell Village National Historic Site. The Superintendent.

Holdings: 62 vols. and 1,500 pieces, 1799-1858, relating chiefly to business of Hopewell Furnace in making pig iron and iron castings and operation of a company store.

HUNTUNGDON

Juniata College Library. Mrs. S.S. Hettinger, Librarian.

Holdings: A few 18th-century manuscripts relating chiefly to the early history of the Church of the Brethren in America; 2 vols. of original hymns by Johann Conrad Beissel (Pa.; founder of the Solitary Brethren of the Community of Seventh Day Baptists); and several hundred letters and other papers of Martin G. Brumbaugh (Pa.; pres. of Juniata College, supt. of schools in Philadelphia, Gov.), 1890-1927,

mostly on education or Church of the
Brethren subjects.

KENNETT SQUARE

Bayard Taylor Memorial Library.
Mrs. L. J. Ficcio, Librarian.

Holdings: A small quantity of
letters, literary manuscripts, and
watercolor sketches by Bayard Taylor (Pa.; author, traveler).

—oOo—

Longwood Library. Charles W. David,
Director.

Holdings: Some 700,000 manuscript pieces, 1588-1954, relating
chiefly to the personal, business, and
other interests of the Du Pont family,
and consisting of the three groups
described below.

The Longwood Manuscripts include
the Du Pont Family Papers, 1780-1906
(30,000 items), consisting of papers of
Pierre Samuel du Pont de Nemours
(France; economist, statesman, author) and his second wife, 1780-1818
(1 box); Victor Marie du Pont (France,
Del.; French diplomat, manufacturer)
and his wife, 1790-1827 (3 boxes);
Eleuthère Irénée du Pont (Del.; manufacturer, founder of E. I. du Pont de
Nemours and Co.) and his wife, 1785-
1838 (11 boxes); and other members
of the Du Pont family and their relatives, 1768-1906 (5 boxes), among
them papers of Alfred Victor du Pont
(Del.; manufacturer, pres. of E. I. du
Pont de Nemours and Co.). Among
these family papers are records of
Du Pont, Bauduy and Co., and two
other textile firms, 1809-56 (5 boxes); and records of E. I. du Pont de
Nemours and Co., 1800-1902 (44 boxes). The Longwood Manuscripts also
include papers of Pierre Samuel du
Pont (Del.; manufacturer, financier,

philanthropist, pres. of E. I. du Pont
de Nemours and Co. and of General
Motors Corp.), 1893-1954 (500,000
items), closed until further notice.

A second large group in the Longwood Library is The Henry Francis
du Pont Winterthur Collection of
Manuscripts, presented by Henry
Francis du Pont (Del.; director of
E. I. du Pont de Nemours and Co.
and of General Motors Corp.), and
consisting chiefly of personal and
business papers of various members
of the Du Pont family, 1588-1926
(150,000 items). Included are papers
of Henry Algernon du Pont (Del.; U.S.
and Civil War officer, railroad pres.,
U.S. Sen.) and his wife, chiefly 1843-
1900 (192 boxes); Samuel Francis du
Pont (Del.; U.S. naval officer) and
his wife, 19th century (197 boxes);
and other persons mentioned in the
preceding paragraph. Also in this
group are papers with autographs of
famous figures in Europe and America, including those of the French
Revolution and Napoleonic Era
(3 vols.).

A third major group consists of
Additional Manuscripts, acquired by
the Library since 1954. Included is
an important collection of early records of E. I. du Pont de Nemours
and Co., 1799-1834 (1,835 items);
records of the Lukens Steel Co., of
Coatesville, Pa., 1799-1895 (70 vols.
and 315 boxes); papers of a gas company in Philadelphia; a collection of
Belin-d'Andelot family papers, 16th-
20th centuries (10 boxes), restricted
access; facsimiles of selected materials relating to Du Pont de Nemours
and Victor Marie du Pont in several
depositories in France; and various
records of mercantile and other business activities in Philadelphia, Wilmington, Del., and Chester County,
Pa., 18th-19th centuries.

(Note: It is planned that by early
1961 the Longwood Library will be
merged with the Hagley Museum

Library, of the Eleutherian Mills—Hagley Foundation (see earlier in this volume under Wilmington, Del.). The combined library, to be known as the Eleutherian Mills Historical Library, will occupy a new building near Greenville, Del.)

LANCASTER

Franklin and Marshall College Library. Herbert B. Anstaett, Librarian.

Holdings: 700 pieces, 1774-1954, consisting chiefly of a group of letters from James Buchanan (Pa.; U.S. Pres.) to members of the Reynolds family, 1822-62 (51 pieces); diaries of Jonathan M. Foltz (Pa.; Surgeon-Gen. of U.S. Navy), 1831-77 (40 vols.); literary manuscripts of Lloyd Mifflin (Pa.; painter, poet); diaries of William Reynolds (Pa.; U S. naval officer), 1838-42 (7 vols.), kept while a member of the Wilkes Expedition; letters of John Fulton Reynolds (Pa.; Civil War officer) to his family, 1849-63 (1 vol.); messages regarding the Pennsylvania militia, Sept. 13-25, 1862 (1 small box); and a collection of official records and other papers relating to the College and its predecessors (Franklin College and Marshall College), from 1785.

—oOo—

Historical Society of the Evangelical and Reformed Church. Herbert B. Anstaett, Librarian.

Holdings: 100 folio boxes, 1699 to date, containing (1) correspondence, diaries, and sermons of ministers of the Reformed Church in the United States, (2) papers relating chiefly to the Reformed Church in the United States (German Reformed), (3) copies of the official archives of the Synod of Holland, 1730-1810, relating to

the Reformed Church in the United States, and (4) official publications of the Reformed Church in the United States, 1734 to date. (In 1934 the Reformed Church in the United States merged with the Evangelical Synod of North America to form the Evangelical and Reformed Church; the present Society was formerly the Historical Society of the Reformed Church in the United States.)

See Allison, Inventory, pp. 175-177; and Hist. Records Survey, Guide for Pa., p. 28.

—oOo—

Lancaster County Historical Society. 307 North Duke St. M. Luther Heisey, Corresponding Secretary.

Holdings: 2,000 items, 1720-1930, relating chiefly to Lancaster County and Pennsylvania. Included are a Lancaster County collection containing legal papers, church records, military papers, election returns, and other materials, 1720-1930; some 200 letters to and from James Buchanan (Pa.; U.S. Pres.), 1822-62; papers of Andrew and James Hamilton (Pa.; lawyers and political leaders) and family, 1749-1840 (200 items); business papers of Harrisburg merchants, 1825-40; and some German Fractur materials, 1738-1930.

See Hist. Records Survey, Guide for Pa., p. 29.

—oOo—

Pennsylvania Farm Museum of Landis Valley. R.D. 5.

Holdings: Several hundred manuscripts (with a large number of museum objects), including business records, diaries, Fractur work, and other material relating chiefly to Lancaster County and vicinity.

See Hist. Records Survey,

Guide for Pa., p. 30.

LATROBE

St. Vincent Archabbey.   Rev. F. Felix
Fellner, Archivist.

Holdings: Papers of Boniface
Wimmer (Germany, Pa.; Roman Catholic archabbot, founder of the Benedictine Order in the U.S.); papers of Innocent Wolf (Pa., Kans.; Roman Catholic
abbot); some other papers relating to
the Benedictine Order; and some Renaissance manuscripts (2 vols. and 2
pieces).
See De Ricci, Census, p. 2007.

LEBANON

Lebanon County Historical Society.
601 Walnut St.   Helen Sprecher,
Secretary.

Holdings: 647 vols., 1791-1940,
consisting chiefly of day books, ledgers, journals, and other records of
several iron furnaces at Cornwall,
Lebanon County, Pa.   Included also
are some records of related flour
mills, farms, and other business
operations.

LINCOLN UNIVERSITY

Vail Memorial Library, Lincoln University.   Donald C. Yelton, Librarian.

Holdings: 33 vols. and 148 pieces,
including records of and pertaining to
the University, since 1853; some
church records, 1829-1936; papers
relating to Negro schools, 1814-66;
correspondence, sermons, diary, and
other papers of John Miller Dickey
(Presbyterian minister, founder of
the University), 1807-78; manuscripts

of published works of Robert Hamill
Nassau (Presbyterian missionary to
Africa); and minutes of the Pennsylvania Colonization Society, 1864-77,
1898-1913.   There is also a collection relating to slavery and the Negro
that was formerly in the Home for
Aged and Infirm Colored Persons,
Philadelphia.
See Hist. Records Survey, Guide
for Pa., p. 31.

McCONNELLSBURG

Fulton County Historical Society.
Walter R. Sloan, President.

Holdings: 100 items, consisting
of some records of 2 local churches,
Presbyterian and Reformed, and other papers relating to Fulton County.
See Hist. Records Survey, Guide
to Pa., p. 34.

MEADVILLE

Crawford County Historical Society.
Meadville Public Library.   Sara L.
Miller, Curator and Secretary.

Holdings: A few thousand pieces,
consisting of letters, ledgers, day
books, and other papers relating
chiefly to Meadville, Crawford County, and Pennsylvania.

—oOo—

Reis Library, Allegheny College.
Philip M. Benjamin, Librarian.

Holdings: A considerable quantity
of manuscripts, chiefly 19th century,
and consisting of several groups of
widely varied content.   The oldest
manuscripts are four 15th-century
manuscripts on vellum.   The Alle-
gheniana collection (500 items) relates to the founding and early history

of the College and is composed largely of correspondence of Timothy Alden (N. H., Pa.; Congregational clergyman, first pres. of Allegheny College). A collection of materials on John Brown (Pa., N. Y., Kans.; abolitionist) consists largely of photostats of documents for the period of his life in Crawford County, Pa., 1815-26. Papers of Ida M. Tarbell (Pa., N. Y.; author), 1896-1944, include literary manuscripts and 11,000 letters relating to her writings on Abraham Lincoln and to her other activities. There are journals kept by James Mills Thoburn (India, Pa.; Methodist missionary bishop), 1858-1916 (30 vols.); and 600 manuscript sermons of James Matthew Thoburn (India, Mich., Pa.; Methodist minister), 1879-1935. The library also has a special collection relating to the founders of Meadville, 1800-60 (1,000 items), including correspondence dealing with the Atlantic and Great Western Railway.

MECHANICSBURG

Federal Records Center, GSA. Bldg. 308, Naval Supply Depot. Chief.

Holdings: A large quantity of noncurrent and semicurrent records, chiefly of recent date, consisting of (1) records of U. S. Navy and Marine Corps Fleet Commands ("Flag Files"), from 1941; and (2) records of nonmilitary agencies of the U. S. Government in western Pennsylvania.

MEDIA

Delaware County Institute of Science. 11 South Ave.

Holdings: 150 items of miscellaneous character, 1681-1860, relating chiefly to Delaware, Chester, and Montgomery Counties. Included are weather observations, 1849-57; papers relating to road construction; and minutes of the Institute.

See Hist. Records Survey, Guide for Pa., p. 35.

MILFORD

Pike County Historical Society. Broad and Harford Sts.

Holdings: 200 items, including 17 vols., 1790-1904, relating chiefly to Pike County. Among family papers are some account books and business records.

See Hist. Records Survey, Guide for Pa., p. 36.

MONTROSE

Susquehanna County Historical Society. Leo Lamb, Chairman of Historical Committee.

Holdings: 15 vols. and 1,000 pieces, 1815-1900, relating chiefly to Susquehanna County. Included are some papers of Galusha A. Grow (Pa.; lawyer, U. S. Rep.); miscellaneous business papers, county archives, and church records; papers relating to Susquehanna County in the Civil War; and manuscripts of genealogical interest.

See Hist. Records Survey, Guide for Pa., p. 37.

MUNCY

Muncy Historical Society. Marshall R. Anspach, Archivist. 1200 Campbell St., Williamsport, Pa.

Holdings: Papers relating chiefly to north central Pennsylvania. Included are microfilm copies of the

papers of Samuel Wallis (Pa.; survey-
or), 1765-98 (10,000 documents), consisting of business and personal letters
concerning land transactions. There
are also copies of 500 Revolutionary
War pension claims of persons resid-
ing in Lycoming, Union, Northumberland, and adjacent counties.

See Hist. Records Survey, Guide
for Pa., p. 37.

NAZARETH

Moravian Historical Society.

Holdings: 5,000 items, including
100 vols., 1740-1929, relating to the
Moravian Church in America. Included are correspondence of missionaries
to the Indians and diaries and other records of various Moravian congregations.

See Hist. Records Survey, Guide
for Pa., p. 38.

NEW CASTLE

New Castle Public Library.

Holdings: Correspondence of Oscar L. Jackson (Pa.; U.S. Rep.),
1875-79 (1 vol.); some Civil War letters, 1861-64 (1 vol.); and a few miscellaneous papers, chiefly of local
interest.

See Hist. Records Survey, Guide
for Pa., p. 38.

NORRISTOWN

Historical Society of Montgomery
County. 1654 DeKalb St. Mrs.
LeRoy Burris, Librarian.

Holdings: 1,500 vols. and 2,000
other pieces, 1700-1900, relating
chiefly to Montgomery County. Included are records of bridge, horse, and

turnpike companies; photostats of
court of quarter session records
prior to 1784; many original dockets,
ledgers, and journals; church and
family histories; and tax assessments.

PENNSBURG

Schwenkfelder Library.

Holdings: 100,000 items, chiefly
1550-1850, relating (1) to the history
of Schwenkfelder churches and their
members in Europe and America,
and (2) to the Perkiomen region of
Pennsylvania. Included are some
200 mathematical copy books, 1731-
1872, and some Fractur work.

See Hist. Records Survey, Guide
for Pa., p. 39; and A. Day Bradley,
"The Mathematical Manuscripts in
the Schwenkfelder Historical Library," in Scripta Mathematica, 7;49-58
(1940).

PHILADELPHIA 3

Academy of Natural Sciences of
Philadelphia. 19th St. and the Park-
way. (Mrs.) Venia T. Phillips,
Librarian.

Holdings: 300 vols., 280 bundles,
and 68,000 pieces, 1795-1940, relating chiefly to the natural sciences.
They include minute books of the
Academy and its various sections and
affiliated societies, papers presented
at meetings, and other organizational
records. There are numerous personal collections of letters, journals,
speeches, biographies, notebooks,
and diaries. Two very large series
are general correspondence of the
Academy, 1812-1920 (18,000 pieces);
and correspondence of the American
Entomological Society, 1866-1920
(7,713 pieces).

Special collections include letters to and from and, where indicated, other papers of the following: Homer Franklin Bassett (Conn.; entomologist, librarian), 1864-89 (1,381 letters and journals); Jacob Cist (Pa.; anthracite coal pioneer, industrialist, inventor, naturalist), 1800-25 (20 bundles), including account books, notebooks, and other papers; Zaccheus Collins (Pa.; merchant, philanthropist, botanist), 1805-27 (296 pieces); Samuel Stehman Haldeman (Pa.; entomologist, conchologist, philologist, prof. at the Univ. of Pa.), 1842-80 (513 pieces), largely letters from early naturalists; Isaac Lea (Pa.; malacologist, publisher, author), 1818-84 (253 letters); John Lawrence LeConte (Pa.; entomologist, physician), 1845-83 (253 letters); Joseph Leidy (Pa.; physician, naturalist, paleontologist, prof. at Univ. of Pa.), 1852-90 (2,893 pieces of correspondence, 2 cartons and 4 vols. of other papers); William Samuel Waithman Ruschenberger (Pa., N.Y.; naturalist, physician, medical director U.S. Navy), 1871-94 (369 letters, 2 vols., and 22 other papers); Thomas Say (Pa., Ind.; entomologist, conchologist, prof. at Univ. of Pa.), 1813-25 (34 letters and some memoranda and other papers); Lewis David von Schweinitz (Pa.; Moravian clergyman, botanist, pioneer mycologist), 1817-33 (353 letters and 18 vols. of notebooks, catalogs, and other papers); Witmer Stone (Pa.; naturalist, director of Academy of Natural Sciences), 1884-1936 (24,875 letters to him and 22 by him); Herman Strecker (Pa.; entomologist, sculptor), 1888-1902 (131 letters), some relating to the disposition of his Lepidoptera collection; John Torrey (N.Y.; botanist, chemist, college prof.), 1795-1853 (283 autographs from 240 scientists, collected chiefly by Torrey, and 47 letters signed by him); and John Kirk Townsend (Pa.; ornithologist, explorer), 1834-36 (20 letters and journals), relating chiefly to a journey to the Columbia River.

Listed below are some of the scientists for whom there are letters, and sometimes, other papers among the Academy's manuscripts. The quantity given refers to the number of autographed letters by the scientist unless otherwise indicated. Included are Charles Baker Adams (Mass., Vt.; naturalist, geologist, conchologist, prof. at Amherst College), 1840-52 (38); Louis Agassiz (Switzerland, Mass., S.C.; zoologist, prof. at Harvard and the Medical College of S.C.), 1837-70 (20); John Merton Aldrich (Idaho, D.C.; dipterist, entomologist, prof. at Univ. of Idaho, curator of insects at U.S. National Museum), 1900-32 (48); Glover Morrill Allen (Mass.; mammalogist, ornithologist, curator of mammals at Harvard Museum of Comparative Zoology), 1899-1937 (82); Joel Asaph Allen (Mass., N.Y.; zoologist), 1868-1919 (307); John Gould Anthony (Ohio, Mass.; conchologist), 1833-75 (60); William Harris Ashmead (Fla., D.C.; entomologist), 1880-1903 (58); Spencer F. Baird (Pa., D.C.; zoologist, Dickinson College prof., Sec. of Smithsonian Institution, U.S. Commissioner of Fish and Fisheries), 1841-86 (238); Samuel Prentiss Baldwin (Ohio; botanist), 1920-33 (126); Outram Bangs (Mass.; ornithologist), 1894-1930 (86); Nathan Banks (D.C., Mass.; entomologist, curator of insects at Harvard Univ. Museum of Comparative Zoology), 1890-1929 (52); Thomas Barbour (Mass.; naturalist, zoologist, author, director of Harvard Univ. Museum of Comparative Zoology), 1901-19 (95); William Bartram (Pa.; naturalist, traveler), a diary and fragments of a publication on botany; William Beutenmuller (N.J.; entomologist, curator at American Museum of Natural History), 1891-1907 (81); Ezra Brainerd (Vt.; botanist, geologist, pres. of Middlebury Col-

lege), 1904-12 (34); William Brewster
(Mass.; ornithologist), 1890-1916 (60);
Daniel Garrison Brinton (Pa.; surgeon,
ethnologist, prof. at Univ. of Pa.),
1868-98 (34); Nathaniel Lord Britton
(N. Y.; botanist, geologist, director of
New York Botanical Garden), 1890-
1921 (125); and Arthur Erwin Brown
(Pa.; zoologist, curator at Academy of
Natural Sciences), 1880-1910 (83).

Other scientists include William
Marriott Canby (Pa., Del.; botanist,
banker), 1861-95 (50); John Cassin
(Pa.; ornithologist), 1843-67 (32 letters and catalogs); Frank Michler
Chapman (N. Y.; ornithologist, curator
at American Museum of Natural History), 1890-1937 (481); Henry Cadwalader Chapman (Pa.; physician,
naturalist, prof. at Univ. of Pa. and
Jefferson Medical College), 1875-99
(62); Theodore Dru Alison Cockerell
(N. Mex., Ariz., Colo.; zoologist, prof.
at Univ. of Colo.), 1892-1933 (140);
John Henry Comstock (N. Y.; entomologist, prof. at Cornell Univ.), 1877-
1907 (17); Edwin Grant Conklin
(Ohio, Pa., N. J.; zoologist, univ.
prof.), 1898-1922 (53); George Hammell Cook (N. J.; prof. at Rutgers College, State geologist), 1856-83 (33);
Edward Drinker Cope (Pa.; biologist,
paleontologist, prof. at Univ. of Pa.),
1860-97 (82); Charles Barney Cory
(Mass., Ill.; ornithologist), 1878-1921
(48); Elliott Coues (D. C.; ornithologist, U. S. Army surgeon), 1857-99
(89); Ezra Townsend Cresson (Pa.;
entomologist), 1859-1909 (37); William
Healey Dall (D. C.; naturalist, Geological Survey paleontologist, curator of
mollusks in National Museum), 1864-
1927 (120); James Dwight Dana (D. C.,
Conn.; mineralogist, geologist, zoologist, prof. at Yale), 1845-87 (70);
William Darlington (Pa.; physician,
botanist, U. S. Rep.), 1819-54 (33);
Ruthven Deane (Mass., Ill.; ornithologist), 1891-1935 (483); Samuel Gibson
Dixon (Pa.; bacteriologist, prof. at
Univ. of Pa., State Commissioner of

Health), 1885-1917 (134); William
Dutcher (N. J.; ornithologist), 1896-
1919 (52); Harrison Gray Dyar (D.C.;
entomologist), 1891-1912 (52); and
Jonathan Dwight (N. Y.; ornithologist),
1891-1928 (433).

Still other scientists include William Henry Edwards (N. Y., W. Va.;
lawyer, railroad executive, entomologist), 1847-90 (59); Daniel Giraud
Elliott (N. Y., Ill.; zoologist), 1860-
1915 (89 pieces); Job Bicknell Ellis
(N. Y., N. J.; botanist, mycologist),
1875-97 (77); Barton Warren Evermann (Ind., Calif.; ichthyologist,
author, ornithologist), 1883-1932
(49); Henry Clinton Fall (Mass.; entomologist), 1883-1913 (78); Ephraim
P. Felt (N. Y.; State entomologist),
1898-1925 (38); Henry Torsey Fernald (Pa., Mass.; entomologist, State
zoologist of Pa.), 1896-1917 (56);
Adele Fielde (N. Y., Wash.; Baptist
missionary, naturalist), 1884-1916
(57); Albert Kendrick Fisher (D. C.;
U. S. Biological Survey zoologist,
ornithologist), 1884-1937 (209); Edward Howe Forbush (Mass.; ornithologist), 1898-1929 (73); Persifor
Frazer (Pa.; geologist, prof. at Univ.
of Pa.), 1878-1908 (72); Louis Agassiz Fuertes (N. Y.; ornithologist, artist), 1899-1926 (61); Theodore
Nicholas Gill (D. C.; zoologist, prof.
at George Washington Univ.), 1861-
1912 (50); Augustus Addison Gould
(Mass.; physician, conchologist),
1833-63 (43); Asa Gray (N. Y., Mass.;
botanist, prof. at Harvard Univ.),
1828-86 (65); James Hall (N. Y.; geologist, paleontologist), 1841-42 (47);
Ferdinand Vandeveer Hayden (Pa.,
D. C.; geologist on surveys in the
West, Civil War surgeon, Univ. of
Pa. prof., U. S. Geological Survey official), 1854-86 (257); Angelo Heil-
prin (Pa.; geologist, explorer, geographer), 1880-99 (54 letters and journals); Joseph Henry (N.Y., N.J., D.C.;
physicist, prof. at College of N.J.,
Sec. of Smithsonian Institution, pres.

of National Academy of Sciences), 1846-78 (64); Henry Wetherbee Henshaw (Mass., D. C.; ornithologist, ethnologist, Chief of U. S. Biological Survey), 1884-1923 (57); William Jacob Holland (Pa.; naturalist, educator, clergyman), 1882-1931 (141); George Henry Horn (Pa.; physician, entomologist), 1864-97 (36); Leland Ossian Howard (D. C.; entomologist, Chief of Bureau of Entomology), 1883-1926 (98); Reginald Heber Howe (Mass.; naturalist, museum curator), 1898-1921 (59); and Arthur Holmes Howell (D. C.; ornithologist, biologist of U.S. Biological Survey), 1900-37 (67).

Also included are David Starr Jordan (Ind., Calif.; naturalist, pres. of Ind. and Stanford Univs.), 1877-1925 (111); William Hypolitus Keating (Pa.; mineralogist, chemist, prof. at Univ. of Pa.), 1821-27 (30); George Frederick Kunz (N. Y.; gem expert, vice pres. of Tiffany and Co.), 1880-1916 (40); Frank Lamson-Scribner (Tenn., D. C.; botanist, prof. at Univ. of Tenn., U. S. Agriculture Dept. official), 1884-99 (108 pieces); Isaac Lea (Pa.; malacologist, publisher, author), 1843-81 (62); John Lawrence LeConte (Pa.; entomologist, physician), 1843-81 (58); Joseph Peter Lesley (Pa.; geologist, prof. at Univ. of Pa.), 1871-93 (40); Leo Lesquereux (Switzerland, Ohio; paleobotanist), 1857-84 (34); Charles Alexandre Lesueur (France, Pa., Ind.; naturalist, artist), 1821-45 (17 letters and memoranda); Frederick Augustus Lucas (Mass., D. C., N. Y.; paleontologist, museum administrator), 1891-1921 (39); Waldo Lee McAtee (D. C.; ornithologist, U. S. Biological Survey official), 1911-37 (306); Henry Christopher McCook (Pa.; Presbyterian clergyman, Civil War officer, naturalist, entomologist), 1871-1911 (131); Edward Avery McIlhenny (La.; naturalist, ornithologist), 1899-1937 (97); Othniel Charles Marsh (Conn.; paleontologist, prof. at Yale Univ.), 1867-94 (58); Thomas Meehan (Eng-

land, Pa.; botanist, horticulturist), 1860-1900 (226); Gerrit Smith Miller (N. Y.; farmer, mammalogist), 1892-1931 (173); Thomas Harrison Montgomery (Pa., Tex.; zoologist, prof. at Univs. of Pa. and Tex.), 1891-1912 (79); Clarence Bloomfield Moore (Pa.; archeologist, explorer), 1893-1918 (96); John Gottlieb Morris (Md.; Lutheran clergyman, entomologist), 1840-81 (48); and Gotthilf Henry E. Muhlenberg (Pa.; Lutheran clergyman, botanist), 1792-1815 (61).

Other scientists are Edward William Nelson (D. C., Calif.; naturalist, research associate at Smithsonian Institution); 1898-1934 (151); Thomas Nuttall (Pa., Mass., England; botanist, ornithologist), 1816-50 (16 letters and memoranda); Henry Fairfield Osborn (N. Y., N. J.; paleontologist, prof. at Princeton and Columbia Univs.), 1881-1927 (80); Theodore Sherman Palmer (D. C.; ornithologist, official of U. S. Biological Survey), 1890-1937 (788); Richard Alexander Fullerton Penrose (Pa., Ill.; geologist, philanthropist, prof. at Univ. of Chicago), 1902-25 (72); William Pepper (Pa.; physician, prof. at Univ. of Pa.), 1868-91 (50); John Charles Phillips (Mass.; physician, ornithologist, curator of birds at Harvard Museum of Comparative Zoology), 1912-30 (95); Charles Pickering (Pa.; physician, naturalist, curator of Academy of Natural Sciences), 1826-51 (2 vols. of diary and 15 letters); Thomas Conrad Porter (Pa.; German-Reformed clergyman, botanist, college prof.), 1853-91 (258); Samuel N. Rhoads (Pa., N. J.; zoologist), 1890-1934 (208); Charles Wallace Richmond (D. C.; ornithologist, curator of birds in U. S. National Museum), 1890-1931 (520); Robert Ridgway (D. C.; ornithologist, curator of birds in U. S. National Museum), 1874-1929 (129); Charles Valentine Riley (Ill., Mo., D. C.; entomologist, U. S. Dept. of Agriculture official), 1865-95

(72); and Thomas Sadler Roberts (Minn.; physician, ornithologist, prof. at Univ. of Minn.), 1895-1936 (65).

Still other scientists include John Hall Sage (Conn.; banker, ornithologist), 1890-1925 (341); Samuel Scoville (N.Y.; lawyer, ornithologist), 1908-29 (63); Samuel Hubbard Scudder (Mass.; entomologist), 1867-1901 (47); Robert Wilson Shufeldt (N.Y., D.C.; U.S. naval officer, naturalist), 1885-1924 (195); Benjamin Silliman (Conn.; prof. of chemistry and natural history at Yale College), 1818-64 (49); Henry Skinner (Pa.; entomologist), 1884-1925 (55); John Bernhard Smith (N.Y., D.C., N.J.; entomologist, prof. at Rutgers College), 1889-1910 (182); Leonhard Hess Stejneger (D.C.; zoologist, curator of biology at U.S. National Museum), 1890-1926 (51); Charles Wardell Stiles (D.C.; zoologist, prof. at Georgetown Univ.), 1867-1941 (64); William Stimpson (D.C., Ill.; naturalist, director of Chicago Academy of Sciences), 1851-71 (32); Harvey Adam Surface (N.Y., Pa.; mammalogist, prof. at Pa. State College), 1898-1932 (62); Walter Edmond Clyde Todd (Pa.; ornithologist, curator at Carnegie Museum, Pittsburgh), 1891-1936 (144); Spencer Trotter (Pa.; zoologist, geographer, college prof.), 1876-1931 (122); Frederick William True (D.C.; zoologist, curator of Dept. of Biology of U.S. National Museum), 1882-1914 (55); Lardner Vanuxem (Pa., S.C.; geologist, prof. at South Carolina College), 1821-47 (53); Arthur Trezevant Wayne (S.C.; ornithologist), 1899-1928 (109); and Francis Wolle (Pa.; botanist, inventor), 1877-91 (31).

See Richard H. Heindel, "Historical Manuscripts in the Academy of Natural Sciences, Philadelphia," in Pa. History, 5:30-32 (Jan. 1938).

PHILADELPHIA 31

American Catholic Historical Society

Library. St. Charles' Seminary. Rev. Joseph A. Ward, Curator.

Holdings: A collection of manuscripts, quantity and inclusive dates unknown, relating to American Catholic history. Included are a few papers of Thomas Lloyd (Pa.; shorthand reporter).

PHILADELPHIA 6

American Philosophical Society Library. 105 South Fifth St. Richard H. Shryock, Librarian.

Holdings: 190,000 pieces, 1529 to date, relating chiefly to America during the colonial period, the Revolution, and the early years of the Republic. Special attention is given to the history of science.

Papers of persons who held important public office include papers of George Clymer (Pa.; merchant, Member Continental Cong., U.S. Rep.), 1785-1848 (26 pieces); Benjamin Franklin (Pa.; printer, scientist, diplomat, Member Continental Cong.), 1642-1874 (16,000 pieces); Ebenezer Hazard (N.Y., Pa.; editor of historical documents, Postmaster Gen.), 1764-1813 (33 pieces), including some records of the post office at Philadelphia, 1764-68; Francis Hopkinson (N.J., Pa.; Member Continental Cong., judge of Pa. admiralty court), 1778-90 (47 pieces); Thomas Jefferson (Va.; Gov., Sec. State, U.S. Pres.), 1776-1824 (300 pieces); Arthur Lee (Va.; diplomat, Member Continental Cong.), 1776-81 (75 pieces); Richard Henry Lee (Va.; Pres. of Continental Cong., U.S. Sen.), 1774-1823 (150 pieces); James Logan (Pa.; colonial official, scholar), 1714-44 (4 vols. of copies of letters and 30 miscellaneous pieces); James Madison (Va.; U.S. Pres.), 1784-93 (2 vols. of meteorological journals); John Marshall (Va.; U.S. Chief Justice), 1803-31 (63 pieces), drafts of judicial opinions; William Penn (England, Pa.; founder and proprietor of Pa.), 1665-1797 (150 pieces); Benjamin Rush (Pa.; physician, Member Continental Cong., prof. at Univ. of Pa.), 1776-1813 (35 pieces); William Short (Va., Pa.; diplomat), 1787-1838 (230 pieces), consisting of his correspondence with Madame de la Rochefoucauld; Benjamin Vaughan (England, Maine; diplomat, political economist, agriculturist), 1746-1830 (1,500 pieces); and George Washington (Va.; U.S. Pres.), 1774-81 (30 pieces).

Papers of scientists include those of John James Audubon (Pa., Ky., La., N.Y.; ornithologist, artist), 1822-45 (200 pieces); Benjamin Smith Barton (Pa.; physician, naturalist, prof. at Univ. of Pa.), 1790-1815 (40 pieces); Giambatista Beccaria (Italy; physicist), 1766-80 (64 pieces); Albert F. Blakeslee (Mass., Conn., N.Y.; botanist), 1904-54 (15,000 leaves); Franz Boas (N.Y.; anthropologist, philologist, prof. at Columbia Univ.), 1872-1934 (12,000 pieces), consisting in part of papers on American Indian languages; Charles Lucien Bonaparte (France; naturalist), 1825-57 (60 pieces); Sir Humphry Davy (England; chemist), 1803-82 (26 pieces); Henry Donaldson (Ill., Pa.; neurologist, prof. at Univ. of Chicago and Wister Institute of Anatomy and Biology), 1890-1938 (49 vols. of diaries); John Fries Frazer (Pa.; scientist, prof. at Univ. of Pa.), 1834-70 (600 pieces); Persifor Frazer (Pa.; geologist, prof. at Univ. of Pa.), 1883-85 (200 pieces); Asa Gray (N.Y., Mass.; botanist, prof. at Harvard Univ.), 1838-87 (70 pieces); Alexander von Humboldt (Germany; naturalist), 1793-1859 (50 pieces); Herbert Spencer Jennings (Md., Calif.; zoologist, prof. at Johns Hopkins Univ.), 1898-1945 (864 pieces); Lorenzo Lorraine Langstroth (Pa., Ohio; apiarist), 1852-95 (200

pieces); John Eatton LeConte (Pa.; entomologist), 1858 (4,000 entomological drawings); John Lawrence LeConte (Pa.; entomologist, physician), 1830-81 (1,500 pieces); J. Peter Lesley (Pa.; geologist, prof. at Univ. of Pa.), 1838-93 (3,000 pieces); and Benjamin Smith Lyman (Pa.; geologist, mining engineer), 1850-1918 (6,000 pieces).

Papers of other scientists include those of André Michaux (France, S.C.; explorer, botanist), 1787-96 (8 notebooks and a few miscellaneous pieces); François André Michaux (France; botanist, traveler), 1852-98 (200 pieces), largely about the Michaux legacy to the American Philosophical Society; Samuel G. Morton (Pa.; physician, naturalist), 1819-50 (486 pieces); Gotthilf H. E. Muhlenberg (Pa.; Lutheran clergyman, botanist), 1786-1815 (20 vols.); George Ord (Pa.; naturalist, ornithologist, philologist), 1832-58 (50 pieces); Elsie C. Parsons (N.Y.; anthropologist), 1920-45 (300 pieces); Robert Patterson and his son, Robert Maskell Patterson (Pa.; mathematicians, prof. at Univ. of Pa.), 1775-1854 (275 pieces); Joseph Priestley (England, Pa.; chemist, theologian), 1774-1803 (52 pieces); Constantine S. Rafinesque (Ky., Pa.; botanist, ichthyologist, prof. at Transylvania Univ.), 1808-48 (255 pieces); David Rittenhouse (Pa.; astronomer, mathematician), 1772-96 (50 pieces); Thomas Say (Pa., Ind.; entomologist, conchologist, prof. at Univ. of Pa.), 1824-33 (200 pieces); Erwin Frink Smith (D.C.; botanist, bacteriologist, plant pathologist), 1880-1920 (2,000 pieces); Frank G. Speck (Pa.; anthropologist, prof. at Univ. of Pa.), 1904-50 (300 pieces); Jacob Stauffer (Pa.; patent lawyer, naturalist), 1850-79 (235 pieces); and John Warner (Pa.; amateur mathematician), 1850-64 (255 pieces).

Of value also for the history of science are correspondence of Walter

B. Cannon (Mass.; physiologist, prof. at Harvard Medical School) and William W. Keen (Pa.; surgeon, prof. of artistic anatomy at Pa. Academy of Fine Arts), 1905-28 (658 pieces); a collection of papers of Peter Collinson (England; naturalist) and John Bartram (Pa.; botanist), 1732-72 (35 pieces); an autograph collection of papers of scientists assembled by John Edward Gray (England; zoologist), 1783-1884 (600 pieces); a collection by Sir James Paget (England; surgeon extraordinary to Queen Victoria), 1784-1932 (200 pieces), containing papers of 19th-century English scientists; and the Darwin and Evolution Collection, 1826-84 (1,500 pieces), consisting of correspondence of Charles Robert Darwin (England; naturalist, author), Sir Charles Lyell (England; geologist), Thomas H. Huxley (England; biologist), Sir Richard Owen (England; biologist), George John Romanes (England; biologist), and others.

Papers of other persons include those of Benjamin Franklin Bache (Pa.; journalist) and the Bache family, 1770-1873 (150 pieces), including letters of Franklin Bache (Pa.; chemist, physician) and Alexander Dallas Bache (Pa., D. C.; physicist, Girard College pres., Supt. of U. S. Coast Survey); the Duane family, 1770-1907 (86 pieces), including William Duane (Pa.; journalist, editor of the Aurora) and his son William John Duane (Pa.; lawyer, State legislator); Nathanael Greene (R. I., Ga.; Rev. War officer), 1778-80 (1,200 pieces); Timothy Horsfield (Pa.; Indian agent), 1733-71 (200 pieces); Michael Jacobs (Pa.; educator), 1839-65 (248 pieces); John Frederick Lewis (Pa.; lawyer, philanthropist), 1883-1930 (23,000 pieces); Thomas L. McKenney (D. C.; Commissioner of Indian Affairs, author), 1827 (3 vols.); John Neagle (Pa.; portrait painter), 1825-50 (5 notebooks), concerning art and painting; Ely Samuel Parker (N. Y.,

Ill.; Seneca sachem, civil engineer, Civil War officer), 1794-1946 (300 pieces); Charles Willson Peale (Md., Pa.; portrait painter, naturalist) and family, 1728-1907 (3,370 pieces); Zebulon M. Pike (U. S. Army officer, explorer), 1805-6 (1 vol. and 56 pieces); Richard Price (England; Nonconformist minister, writer), 1767-90 (90 pieces); Robert Rogers (N. H., England; colonial ranger), 1766-67 (100 pieces); Frederick Smyth (England, N. J.; lawyer), 1756-1813 (56 pieces); William Strahan (Scotland, England; Member of Parliament, printer, publisher), 1751-77 (4 vols.), accounts, and journals of trips to Scotland from London; Elihu Thomson (Mass.; inventor, General Electric Co. official), from 1870 (35,000 pieces); William Tilghman (Md., Pa.; chief justice of Pa.), 1771-1837 (55 pieces); John Vaughan (Pa.; merchant, sec. and librarian of American Philosophical Society), 1798-1840 (200 pieces); and George Weedon (Va.; Rev. War officer), 1777-86 (153 pieces). There are also papers of the Shippen family of Pennsylvania, 1742-88 (600 pieces).

Among other holdings of the Society are the originals of the laws of Pennsylvania, 1693-1700 (1 vol.); minutes of the Provincial Council of Pennsylvania, 1693-1716 (3 vols.); records of the commission to determine the boundary line between Maryland and Pennsylvania (the Mason and Dixon line), 1760-68 (2 vols.); papers concerning quit rents on estates of the Penn family in Pennsylvania, 1788-1893 (1 vol.); journals of Meriwether Lewis and William Clark, 1803-6 (22 codices and miscellaneous pieces); journal of John Ordway, a member of the Lewis and Clark expedition, 1804-6 (4 notebooks); the Independence Hall Collection, pertaining chiefly to the various restorations of the Hall, 1794-1900 (300 pieces); reports of archeological research expeditions in Pennsylvania, 1938-41 (44 pieces); and Indian vocabularies and other papers relating to the American Indians. The American Philosophical Society Archives, 1758 to date (several thousand pieces), contain minutes, reports of committees, correspondence, and other papers, many of them valuable for the history of American science.

See the Society's Calendar of the Correspondence Relating to the American Revolution of Brigadier-General George Weedon, Hon. Richard Henry Lee, Hon. Arthur Lee, and Major-General Nathanael Greene in the Library of the American Philosophical Society (1900. 255 p.); I. Minis Hays, Calendar of the Papers of Benjamin Franklin in the Library of the American Philosophical Society (1908. 5 vols.); Edwin G. Conklin, "The American Philosophical Society and the Founders of Our Government," in Pa. History, 4:235-240 (Oct. 1937); Hist. Records Survey, Guide for Pa., p. 41; William E. Lingelbach, "The Library of the American Philosophical Society," in William and Mary Quarterly, ser. 3, 3:48-69 (Jan. 1946); and "The Library of the American Philosophical Society, 1942-1952, Decade Report by the Chairman of the Committee on Library" (17 p. Processed). The Society's Library Bulletin contains special articles on the papers of Franz Boas, Charles Darwin, Benjamin Franklin, Ebenezer Hazard, Charles Lyell, Charles Willson Peale and family, William Penn, Benjamin Rush, Frank G. Speck, Elihu Thomson, and Benjamin Vaughan, and the originals of the laws of Pennsylvania, 1693-1700, and other information about accessions.

PHILADELPHIA 3

American Sunday School Union Library. 1816 Chestnut St. William J.

Jones, Editor of Publications.

Holdings: 2,500 items, 1817-1954, consisting of the official records of the Union and related organizations. Included are periodic reports of missionaries of the Union, 1825-1908 (485 vols.); and some letters involving the slavery controversy.

See Allison, Inventory, p. 186.

PHILADELPHIA 45

American Swedish Historical Museum. 1900 Pattison Ave. Marna Feldt, Administrative Assistant.

Holdings: 20,000 pieces and 20,000 ft. of microfilm, relating chiefly to early Swedish settlers in America. Included are extensive microfilm copies of records in the Swedish Royal Archives and the British Public Record Office; a large quantity of papers of John Ericsson (N.Y.; engineer, inventor, designer of the Monitor and other naval vessels); letters and other papers relating to Jenny Lind (Sweden; singer), 1840-87 (300 pieces); a collection of autographs of Swedish kings, diplomats, churchmen, statesmen, scientists, and explorers, from 1620 (100 pieces); and various church and town records, letters, and other papers dating largely from the 17th century.

PHILADELPHIA 6

Christ Church Library. 20 North American St. William W. Montgomery, Librarian.

Holdings: 90 vols. and 110 other items, 1694-1939, chiefly records of or relating to this Episcopal church. Included are many sermons by William White (Pa.; Bishop of Pa.).

See Hist. Records Survey, Guide
for Pa., p. 46.

PHILADELPHIA 3

College of Physicians of Philadelphia
Library.   19 South 22d St.   W. B.
McDaniel 2d, Curator of Historical
Collections.

Holdings: 927 cataloged medical
items, 14th-20th centuries, classed
as manuscripts and consisting of
texts, lectures, diaries, commonplace and recipe books, correspondence, ledgers, and miscellaneous
private papers. In addition, there
are thousands of letters and miscellaneous small items cataloged only
under the author or issuing institution. Coverage is international, with
special emphasis on medicine in Philadelphia and Pennsylvania. Included
is an extensive collection of letters
written to Joseph Leidy (Pa.; physician, paleontologist, Univ. of Pa.
prof.).
    See De Ricci, Census, p. 2009;
and Hist. Records Survey, Guide for
Pa., p. 47.

—oOo—

Curtis Institute of Music.   Rittenhouse Sq.   J. L. Gotlobe, Librarian.

Holdings: Musical manuscripts
and related papers, 1448-1951. Included are the Burrell Collection (528
items) of letters and some musical
manuscripts of Richard Wagner (Germany; composer); and holograph musical signatures, 1951, from various
composers to Mary Louise Curtis Bok
Zimbalist (Pa.; pres. and founder of
the Curtis Institute of Music). There
are also other musical manuscripts
and letters of European and American
composers.
    See De Ricci, Census, p. 2011;

and Otto Edwin Albrecht, A Census
of Autograph Music Manuscripts of
European Composers in American
Libraries, p. 317, and passim (1953).

PHILADELPHIA 6

Department of Records, Society of
Friends of Philadelphia.   302 Arch
St.   Howard H. Brinton, Custodian.

Holdings: 1,820 vols. and 9,880
pieces, 1676-1955, relating chiefly
to the Society of Friends in Pennsylvania and New Jersey. Included are
minutes of meetings and other records of Friends communities, 1681-
1954; papers relating to the opposi-
tion of Friends to wars of the Colonies and the United States; records of
educational work among Negroes,
American Indians, and Japanese; records of Friends schools, 1695-1954;
and correspondence, reports, treaties, and other papers relating to Indian affairs, 1725-1903. On deposit
are some records of the Association
of Friends for the Instruction of Adult
Colored Persons, 1789-1904, and of
the Friends Freedmen's Association,
1863-1935.
    See Hist. Records Survey, Guide
for Pa., p. 47; and Hist. Records
Survey, Inventory of Church Archives: Society of Friends in Pennsylvania (1941. 397 p. Processed).

PHILADELPHIA 32

Dropsie College for Hebrew and
Cognate Learning.   Broad and York
Sts.   Maxwell Whiteman, Libra-
rian.

Holdings: 50,000 items, including a collection of Genizah Fragments, 988-1835 (450 items); a collection of Oriental manuscripts (256
vols.); and correspondence relating

to religious, social, and literary activities in the United States, the West Indies, and American territories, 1800-1925.

See Hist. Records Survey, Guide for Pa., p. 49.

PHILADELPHIA

Edgar Allan Poe House and Museum. 530 North Seventh St. Col. Richard Gimbel, c/o Yale University Library, New Haven, Conn.

Holdings: An undetermined quantity of letters and other manuscripts in a large collection of first editions, illustrations, newspapers, and other materials by and relating to Edgar Allan Poe (Va., Md., Pa., N.Y.; poet, critic, short-story writer), 1800 to date (50,000 items).

See Hist. Records Survey, Guide for Pa., p. 50.

—oOo—

Federal Records Center, GSA. 5000 Wissahickon Ave. Chief.

Holdings: A quantity of noncurrent or semicurrent records, chiefly of recent date, of some of the nonmilitary agencies of the U. S. Government in eastern Pennsylvania. Most of these records have been appraised for disposal after specified periods of time, but some will be preserved because of their enduring value. Included in the latter category are records of the Bureau of Customs, from 1789; and 19th-century records of the U. S. Mint.

PHILADELPHIA 3

Free Library of Philadelphia. Logan Square. Emerson Greenaway, Director.

Holdings: 2,900 cuneiform tab-

lets, 23d-5th centuries B. C., and some 13,500 manuscripts, including European illuminated manuscripts, 9th-18th centuries (250 vols. and 2,000 individual leaves); Oriental manuscripts, 15th–early 19th centuries (155 vols. and 1,200 miniatures); 200 vols., 13th-18th centuries, illustrating the history of the Common Law; 2,850 letters of English and American political and legal figures; 100 American historical and diplomatic letters and documents, 1795-1865; minutes of the Common Council of Philadelphia, 1704-76 (6 vols.); 3,700 documents and letters, 15th-19th centuries, assembled by D. N. Carvalho for the study of inks, paper, and handwriting; 85 manuscripts of the 18th-century Pennsylvania Germans (including musical manuscripts), and 1,000 of their decorative manuscripts in Fraktur (ca. 1760-1860); 575 19th-century letters and documents of the Society of Seventh Day Baptists of Ephrata; 800 letters of Charles Dickens, and some few letters and manuscripts of other English and American authors; 1,000 letters of engravers, chiefly Englishmen of the 18th and early 19th centuries; and 375 autographs of American and international leaders in World War II.

See Hist. Records Survey, Guide for Pa., p. 51, and references cited there; and De Ricci, Census, pp. 2012-2084.

PHILADELPHIA 7

Genealogical Society of Pennsylvania. 1300 Locust St. Katherine M. Taylor, Executive Secretary.

Holdings: 2,000 vols., 1672-1920, consisting of county, State, church, and other records that provide information about births, marriages, and deaths and other information of genealogical interest. They relate chiefly to Pennsylvania and to a less extent to neighboring States.

See "Collections of the Genealogical Society of Pennsylvania," in the Society's Publications, 6:309-318 (Mar. 1917); and Hist. Records Survey, Guide for Pa., p. 54.

PHILADELPHIA 23

German Society of Pennsylvania. Spring Garden and Marshall Sts. Lidy Pohl, Librarian.

Holdings: 40 items on German culture in the United States, including a few relating to Henry Melchior Muhlenberg (Pa.; Lutheran clergyman).
See Hist. Records Survey, Guide for Pa., p. 55.

PHILADELPHIA

Germantown Historical Society. 5214 Germantown Ave.   Edward W. Hocker, Librarian.

Holdings: Several scrapbooks and 100 boxes, 1689-1960, relating to Germantown. Included are papers pertaining to the Battle of Germantown, the founding of Germantown, the Wissahickon Valley, and the Civil War; and journals, account books, and family papers.
See Hist. Records Survey, Guide for Pa., p. 55.

PHILADELPHIA 21

Girard College Library.   Corinthian and Girard Aves.   Margaret E. McFate, Librarian.

Holdings: 1,000 vols. of ledgers, journals, account books, ships' logs, sea charts, and maps used by Stephen Girard (Pa.; merchant, financier,

philanthropist, founder of Girard College); and 75,000 cataloged letters and 36 boxes of uncataloged material, 1772-1831, comprising shipping, banking, and personal papers of Girard.
See Hist. Records Survey, Guide for Pa., p. 56.

PHILADELPHIA

Graphic Sketch Club.   711-719 Catharine St.

Holdings: Several Hebrew scrolls and a 16th-century illuminated missal.
See Hist. Records Survey, Guide for Pa., p. 58.

PHILADELPHIA 24

Historical Society of Frankford. 1507 Orthodox St.

Holdings: 2,000 vols. and 1,300 other pieces, 1681-1956, relating to the Frankford section of Philadelphia. Included are school records; account books of a building and loan association, 1831-63, and of various other business organizations; and some Civil War records.
See Hist. Records Survey, Guide for Pa., p. 58.

PHILADELPHIA 7

Historical Society of Pennsylvania. 1300 Locust St.   Richard N. Williams 2d, Director.

Holdings: 4,000,000 items, 14th-20th centuries, dealing primarily with Philadelphia and Pennsylvania but containing 200,000 foreign items of considerable importance and a much larger quantity of papers that provide information of significance about national aspects of the history of the United States. Many of the holdings are in the form of "collections" that consist of letters and other manuscripts assembled from many sources and organized by previous owners or by the Society itself into artificial groups. These are described first below. Then follow family papers, personal papers in various occupational categories, records of governmental units, and records of nongovernmental organizations. These groups, established for purposes of summary description, are not mutually exclusive.

The Gratz Collections, 1383-1921 (175,000 items), presented by Simon Gratz (Pa.; lawyer, autograph collector, member of the Philadelphia Board of Education), consist of a number of artificially established groups. The European Section, 1383-1916 (189 boxes), includes groups of letters and other papers signed by British authors, bishops and other clergymen, dramatists, jurists, and statesmen, and by continental European actors and actresses, military and naval officers, musicians and composers, painters and sculptors, scientists and physicians, and royalty. Also in this section are groups of papers relating to the Reformation, the Thirty Years' War, and the French Revolution. The American Section contains subsections of papers on American political subjects (120 boxes), American wars (82 boxes), jurists (26 boxes), churches and clergymen (95 boxes), arts and sciences (101 boxes), Indian affairs (7 boxes), commercial subjects (21 boxes), and other matters. Included in this section are letters by Presidents and Cabinet members (15 boxes), colonial governors (3 boxes), U.S. Senators (13 boxes), Members of the Continental Congress (10 boxes), and Revolutionary War officers (8 boxes); and correspondence of John Dickinson (Pa., Del.; Member Continental

Cong., Pres. of Del. and of Pa.), 1775-98 (2 boxes); Albert Gallatin (Pa., N.Y.; U.S. Rep. from Pa., Sec. Treas.), 1801-11 (3 boxes); Stephen Girard (Pa.; merchant, financier, philanthropist, founder of Girard College), 1794-1811 (1 box); William Maclay (Pa.; U.S. Sen.), 1767-92; Baron Friedrich Wilhelm von Steuben (Prussia, N.Y.; Rev. War officer), 1782-93 (1 box); Charles Thomson (Pa.; Sec. Continental Cong.), 1754-1824 (4 boxes); and Benjamin West (Pa., England; historical painter), 1789-1824 (1 box). The Miscellaneous Section, 1533-1910 (50,000 items), contains, in an alphabetically arranged file, a small number of papers of each of a large number of persons of importance in American and European history. The Society also has correspondence of Simon Gratz, 1858-1923 (6,000 items).

The Dreer Collection, 1492-1917 (40,000 items), was assembled as an autograph collection and presented by Ferdinand Julius Dreer (Pa.; capitalist, philanthropist). It contains many series of letters and other papers of persons prominent in the political, military, literary, religious, scientific, musical, artistic, and business history of the United States and, in less degree, of Europe. Papers of prominent persons include those of Nicholas Biddle (Pa.; statesman, financier), 1813-36 (2 vols.), correspondence as president of the Second Bank of the United States; John Brown (Pa., N.Y., Kans.; abolitionist); George Clymer (Pa.; merchant, Member Continental Cong., U.S. Rep.), 1779-1812 (120 items); Robert Fulton (N.Y. civil engineer, inventor), 1813-46 (1 vol.); Henry D. Gilpin (Pa.; U.S. Attorney Gen., author, editor), 1833-46 (3 vols. of letter books); Leigh Hunt (England; essayist, poet), 1843-61 (1 vol.); Thomas Jefferson (Va.; U.S. Pres.), 1774-1825 (1 vol.); Elisha K. Kane (Pa.; U.S. naval officer,

physician, explorer), 1853-56 (2 vols.);
John Lacey (Pa., N. J.; Rev. War officer), 1776-77 (1 vol.); the Marquis de
Lafayette (France; American Rev. War
officer), 1781-1832 (1 vol.); Humphrey
Marshall (Pa.; botanist), 1772-1803;
Robert Morris (Pa.; financier, Member Continental Cong., U. S. Sen.),
1776-79 (1 vol.); William Penn (England, Pa.; Quaker statesman, founder
of Pa.) and his family, 1666-1703
(3 vols.); Gideon J. Pillow (Tenn.; Mexican War and Confed. Army officer),
1846-61 (1 vol.); Sir John Ross (England; British naval officer, Arctic explorer), 1834 (1 vol.); Benjamin Rush
(Pa.; physician, Member Continental
Cong., prof. at Univ. of Pa.), 1739-
1813 (1 vol.); Jared Sparks (Mass.;
historian), 1835-53 (1 vol.); and
George Washington (Va.; Rev. War
Commander in Chief, U.S. Pres.),
1749-1839 (1 vol.).

Other collections include the American Negro Historical Society Papers,
1790-1901 (3,000 items), among them
correspondence of Frederick Douglass
(Mass., N. Y., D. C.; Negro abolitionist, reformer, journalist), 1870-95,
records of the Pennsylvania State
Equal Rights League, 1864-72, papers
relating to Negro baseball clubs, and
other papers relating to the cultural
and economic advancement and the
struggle for freedom of the American
Negro; and the Autograph Collection of
the Historical Society of Pennsylvania,
1671-1939 (38,000 items), including
papers of William Penn (England, Pa.;
founder of Pa.) and his family, 1671-
1866 (2 boxes), and smaller quantities
of papers of many prominent American
and foreign persons. The Miscellaneous Collection of the Society, 1661-
1931 (7,500 items), relates chiefly to
the political and military history of
the colonial period and includes Board
of War papers, 1775-79; Federal Congress papers, 1789-1811; Georgia,
New York, and Virginia Assembly papers, 1698-1759; Indian affairs papers,

1661-1930; Continental Congress papers, 1777-81; papers concerning
Civil War volunteers from Pennsylvania, 1862-68; and papers relating
to railroads, 1818-1902. There are
also a collection of business, professional, and personal account
books, chiefly for the Philadelphia
area, 1676-1936 (650 vols.); a collection of records of various associations, clubs, and societies, 1764-
1937 (110 vols.); a church and meeting collection, 1692-1910 (100 vols.),
consisting of miscellaneous materials
for church history; a collection of
music books, 1800-65 (6 vols.); and a
collection of autograph collections
not mentioned elsewhere, 1813-1904
(27 vols.).

Other collections include the Etting Collection, 1558-1917 (20,000
items), which consists of an autograph collection of manuscripts of
distinguished Americans and Europeans, 1558-1887; a group of family
papers, 1739-1847, pertaining largely to commercial and related activities of the colonial and early national
periods; and a group of papers concerning civic, social, and professional activities in which Frank M. Etting
(Pa.; Civil War officer, civic leader,
chairman of Centennial Exposition of
1876) was interested. Included in
this collection are letters of early
Quakers, 1650-1815 (1 vol.), governors of the States, 1675-1852 (2 vols.),
officers of the American and British
armies and navies, 1740-1887 (5
vols.), and U. S. Presidents, Vice
Presidents, and Cabinet members,
1789-1861 (4 vols.). Included also
are records of the Ohio Co., 1753-
1817 (2 vols.), and of the United
States Bank of America, 1791-1836
(4 vols.); and papers relating to Independence Hall and its restoration,
1871-76 (3 vols. and 4 boxes). The
Gilbert Cope Historical and Genealogical Collection, 1682-1924 (30,000
items), pertains chiefly to Chester

County, Pa., and contains Quakeriana, official records of the county, records of commercial and industrial enterprises, and genealogical and family papers. The Logan Collection, 1664-1871 (12,000 items), contains papers of James Logan (Pa.; scholar, colonial official), 1681-1769 (24 vols. and 150 letters); George Logan (Pa.; physician, U.S. Sen.) and his family, 1730-1836 (6 vols. and 1 box); and John Dickinson (Pa., Del.; Member Continental Cong., Pres. of Del. and of Pa.) and his family, 1664-1847 (8 vols. and many other items); and a large quantity of official records of the colony of Pennsylvania. Papers collected by James T. Mitchell (Pa.; State chief justice), 1659-1911 (12,000 items), include, in addition to his personal papers, autograph letters and other documents by distinguished jurists and other prominent persons. A collection of land and legal papers, 1762-1835 (8,000 items), includes papers of William Smith (Pa.; Anglican and Episcopal clergyman), chiefly relating to lands in Maryland, Pennsylvania, and New York but including some land notes on sections of Maine and Nova Scotia. The Hamilton Collection, 1750-1850 (7,500 items), includes legal papers of James Hamilton (Pa.; lawyer) and James Wilson (Pa.; Member Continental Cong., U.S. Supreme Court Justice) and has much material on western Pennsylvania. The Cox-Parrish-Wharton Papers, 1600-1900 (5,000 items), relate to religious, humanitarian, social, and economic influences of Quakers in American life. The collection of John William Wallace (Pa.; legal scholar, author), 1725-1854 (1,700 items), contains, in addition to family papers, papers of William Bradford (Pa.; U.S. Attorney Gen.), 1772-96, and of Thomas Willing (Pa.; financier), 1771-1854 (1 vol.). The Sartain Collection, 1771-1929 (1,100 items), includes correspondence and

other papers of John Sartain (Pa.; engraver, publisher) and drawings and engravings by Sartain, his son, and others; there are 122 drawings by Thomas Birch (Pa.; landscape and marine painter) and notes and miscellaneous papers of Rembrandt Peale (Pa.; portrait and historical painter). A collection assembled by H. L. Carson (Pa.; State attorney gen.), 1690-1929 (4,000 items), consists of papers and portraits of lawyers, judges, and other persons concerned with the administration of law, especially in Pennsylvania. An autograph collection assembled by Washington Townsend (Pa.; U.S. Rep.), 1716-1863 (262 items), contains letters to Isaac Dutton Barnard (Pa.; lawyer, War of 1812 officer, U.S. Sen.), 1812-32 (100 items).

The Penn Manuscripts, 1606-1874 (25,000 items), constitute one of the Society's most important groups of family papers. Included in this group are papers of Sir William Penn (England; naval officer), 1644-60 (2 vols.), letters and a journal; papers of William Penn (England, Pa.; Quaker statesman, founder of Pa.) and some of his descendants, 1654-1855 (15 vols.); records of and relating to the proprietary government of Pennsylvania, 1629-1874 (59 vols. and 2 boxes); Penn family papers, 1653-1834 (27 vols. and 1 box); and papers relating to the boundary disputes between the Penns and Lord Baltimore, 1606-1775 (38 vols.).

There are many other groups of family papers. The Cadwalader family collection, 1630-1900 (100,000 items), has in it papers of George Croghan (Pa.; Indian trader and agent, land speculator), 1744-82 (9 boxes); Phineas Bond (Pa.; British consul, lawyer), 40 boxes; John Cadwalader (Pa.; Rev. War officer); Thomas Cadwalader (Pa.; lawyer, War of 1812 officer, manager of Penn family affairs in America); John Cad-

walader (Pa.; U. S. Rep., U. S. dist.
court judge), 1830-59 (128 boxes and
23 letter books); and George Cadwalader (Pa.; lawyer, Mexican War and
Civil War officer).   Papers of the
Drayton family, 1796-1896 (2,500
items), include papers of William
Drayton (S. C., Pa.; U. S. Rep. from
S. C., Pres. of Bank of U. S.), 1817-46;
and Percival Drayton (Pa.; U. S. naval
officer), 1840-66.   The Edward Carey
Gardiner Collection of papers of the
Baird, Carey, Gardiner, and Penning-
ton families, 1632-1939 (12,000 items),
contains papers of Henry Carey Baird
(Pa.; publisher, economic writer);
Mathew Carey (Pa.; publisher, economist) and Henry C. Carey (Pa.; publisher, economist); and Edward Pen-
nington (Pa.; Quaker pamphleteer,
surveyor-gen. of Pa.).   The Gilpin
family papers, 1727-1872 (20,000
items), include not only papers of Henry D. Gilpin (Pa.; U. S. Attorney Gen.,
author, editor) and his family, but also some papers of James Brown (La.;
U. S. Sen., Minister to France), 1824-
35 (40 letters); Joel Roberts Poinsett
(S. C.; U. S. Rep., Minister to Mexico,
Sec. War), 1794-1850 (700 items);
and William Short (Va., Pa.; diplomat), 1786-1801; and papers in the
case of James Wilkinson (U. S. Army
officer, Gov. of La. Terr.) v. Daniel
Clark (La.; merchant, Terr. Delegate to Cong.), 1788-1808 (300 items).
Papers of the merchant family of
Hollingsworth, 1748-1887 (165,000
items), relate chiefly to trade in
America, the West Indies, and Europe, political and economic conditions, and local, domestic, and social
affairs.   The Maitland family papers,
1729-1898 (222 items), include papers
of Thomas Fitzsimons (Pa.; merchant,
U. S. Rep.), 1784-1811; and John J.
Maitland (Pa., Va.; Confed. Army officer).

   Papers of four generations of the
Meredith family, 1760-1888 (150
vols. and 50,000 items), include pa-

pers of Joseph Dennie (N. H., Pa.;
essayist, editor), David B. Ogden
(N. J., N. Y.; lawyer, Federalist
leader), and William M. Meredith
(Pa.; lawyer, Sec. Treas.).   There
are also papers of Isaac Norris (Pa.;
merchant, mayor of Philadelphia),
his son Isaac (Pa.; merchant, Quaker party leader), and their families,
1742-1860 (70 vols. and 16 boxes),
including papers relating to the administration of the General Loan Office of Pennsylvania; Israel Pemberton, Jr. (Pa.; Quaker merchant,
philanthropist), James Pemberton
(Pa.; Quaker merchant, philanthropist), John Pemberton (Pa.; Quaker
preacher), and their families, 1641-
1880 (15,000 items); other members
of the Pemberton family, 1800-1900
(10,000 items), including papers of
Henry Pemberton (Pa.; chemist, inventor, salt manufacturer) and John
C. Pemberton (Pa., Va.; U. S. and
Confed. Army officer); Andrew Porter (Pa.; Rev. War officer, State surveyor-gen.), 1773-1813, his son,
David Rittenhouse Porter (Pa.; iron
manufacturer, Gov.), 1829-67, and
their families, 1770-1880 (350
items); Samuel Powel (Pa.; merchant, mayor of Philadelphia), John
Hare Powel (Pa.; U. S. Army officer,
agriculturist), and their families,
1700-1925 (50,000 items); and Francis Rawle (Pa.; merchant, political
economist, member of the provincial
assembly of Pa.), William Rawle
(Pa.; lawyer, philanthropist), and
their families, 1683-1915 (6,000
items).   The George Washington Collection, 1675-1883 (6 vols.), includes
a few letters of Washington (Va.; U.S.
Pres.), and documents relating to
his family.   Other family papers are
in some of the groups identified in
the following paragraphs of this entry.

   Papers of persons who held public office include papers of John Adams (Mass.; Member Continental

Cong., diplomat, U. S. Pres.), 1781-1829 (150 items), consisting of letters to Francis Adrian van der Kemp (Dutch scholar and preacher); William Bigler (Pa.; Gov., U. S. Sen.), 1836-80 (5,000 items); William Bingham (Pa.; land speculator, Member Continental Cong., U. S. Sen.), 1777-1917 (2 vols. and 40,000 items), largely relating to Maine, New York, and Pennsylvania lands; Rudolph Blankenburg (Pa.; Philadelphia mayor), 1881-1918 (150 items); Elias Boudinot (N. J.; Rev. War officer, Member Continental Cong., U. S. Rep., Director of U. S. Mint) and his family, 1716-1828 (500 items); John Martin Broomall (Pa.; U. S. Rep.), 1867-68 (300 items); George Bryan (Pa.; political leader, State supreme court judge), 1756-1829 (1,250 items); James Buchanan (Pa.; U. S. Rep. and Sen., Minister to Russia and Great Britain, Sec. State, U. S. Pres.), 1775-1868 (25,000 items); Pierce Butler (S. C.; Member Continental Cong., U.S. Sen.) and his family, 1771-1900 (3,000 items); Samuel Calvin (Pa.; lawyer, U. S. Rep.), 1848-64 (1,000 items); Salmon Portland Chase (Ohio; Gov., U. S. Sen., Sec. Treas., U. S. Chief Justice), 1824-81 (15,000 items); Edward Coles (Ill.; sec. to Pres. Madison, abolitionist, Gov.), 1762-1887 (600 items); George Mifflin Dallas (Pa.; U. S. Sen., Minister to Russia and Great Britain, U. S. Vice Pres.), 1791-1880 (1-vol. diary and 1,400 items), including 180 items of correspondence of his father, Alexander James Dallas (Pa.; Sec. Treas.); William Morris Davis (Pa.; U. S. Rep.), 1853-79 (200 items); John Dickinson (Pa., Del.; Member Continental Cong., Pres. of Del. and of Pa., 1760-72 (8 vols.); Benjamin Franklin (Pa.; printer, scientist, Member Continental Cong., diplomat), 1747-94 (13 vols.); James Hamilton (Pa.; Lt. Gov.), 1733-83 (60 items); Israel Jacobs (Pa.; U. S. Rep., agriculturist) and his family, 1681-1838 (500 items); Josiah

Stoddard Johnston (La.; U. S. Rep. and Sen.), 1821-39 (5,000 items), including 50 letters from Henry Clay (Ky.; U. S. Rep. and Sen., Sec. State), 1824-33; William Jones (Pa.; U. S. Rep., Sec. Navy, pres. of Bank of U. S.), 1792-1839 (1,000 items), as well as other Jones Papers, 1794-1827, collected for a projected biography by Uselma C. Smith (Pa.; lawyer) and Smith's own papers (500 items); Henry Laurens (S. C.; merchant, planter, Pres. of Continental Cong.), 1762-80 (1,500 items), including one letter book, 1762-66; and Ellis Lewis (Pa.; State chief justice), 1810-71 (100 items).

Papers of other persons who held public office include papers of Thomas McKean (Del., Pa.; Pres. of Continental Cong., Pres. of Del., chief justice and Gov. of Pa.), 1759-1847 (650 items); Isaac Wayne MacVeagh (Pa.; lawyer, diplomat, U. S. Attorney Gen.), 1833-1950 (3,500 items), including many letters from his father-in-law, Simon Cameron (Pa.; U. S. Sen., Sec. War, Minister to Russia); James Madison (Va.; U. S. Rep., Sec. State, U. S. Pres.), 1794, 1801-36 (2 vols.); Joseph Hampton Moore (Pa.; U. S. Rep., mayor of Philadelphia), 1884-1949 (20,000 items); Robert Morris (Pa.; financier, Member Continental Cong., U. S. Sen.), 1769-1836 (250 items), relating chiefly to his speculation in western lands; Leonard Myers (Pa.; U. S. Rep.), 1854-1905 (150 items), including 2 vols. of autographs of Members of Congress, 1865-75; Richard Peters (Pa.; provincial official, Episcopal clergyman), 1697-1845 (1,500 items); Richard Peters (Pa.; Member Continental Cong., U.S. dist. court judge, agricultural scientist) and his family, 1687-1871 (1,300 items); Joel Roberts Poinsett (S. C.; U. S. Rep., Minister to Mexico, Sec. War), 1785-1851 (4,250 items); Condy Raguet (Pa.; U. S.

Chargé d'Affaires in Brazil), 1824-28 (2 vols.); George Read (Del.; Member Continental Cong., U.S. Sen., State chief justice) and his family, 1716-1872 (250 items); Jonathan Roberts (Pa.; U.S. Rep. and Sen.), 1780-1930 (3,000 items), relating particularly to State and national political history during the Jefferson, Madison, and Monroe administrations; Thomas Rodney (Del., Miss.; Member Continental Cong., U.S. judge for Miss. Terr.), 1796-97 (1 vol.), journal; Richard Rush (Pa.; U.S. Attorney Gen., Sec. State, diplomat), 1812-57 (1 vol. and 83 letters); Winthrop Sargent (Mass., Ohio, Miss.; Rev. War officer, Sec. of Northwest Terr., Gov. of Miss. Terr.), 1754-1807 (100 items); John Sergeant (Pa.; U.S. Rep.), 1783-1897 (1,200 items); William Shaler (U.S. consul in Barbary States and Cuba) and his family, 1794-1903 (1,700 items); Alexander Hamilton Stephens (Ga.; U.S. Rep., Confed. Vice Pres., Gov.), 1858-82 (300 letters); Charles Thomson (Pa.; Sec. Continental Cong.), 1774-1811 (9 vols.); William Tilghman (Md., Pa.; circuit court judge, chief justice of Pa.), 1772-1827 (8,500 items); Richard Vaux (Pa.; lawyer, penologist, mayor of Philadelphia, U.S. Rep.) and his family, 1686-1893 (4,500 items), containing much on social and political reform; John Welsh (Pa.; merchant, philanthropist, Minister to Great Britain), 1837-78 (1,500 items); James Wilson (Pa.; Member Continental Cong., U.S. Supreme Court Justice), 1718-1857 (1,500 items); William Bauchop Wilson (Pa.; labor leader, U.S. Sen., Sec. Labor), 1913-21 (15,000 items); George Wolf (Pa.; U.S. Rep., Gov.), 1829-36 (1,200 items); and Jaspar Yeates (Pa.; State supreme court justice) and his family, 1718-1876 (7,500 items).

Papers of Army and Navy officers include those of Joshua Barney (U.S. naval officer), 1782-1818 (150 items); William Bradford (Pa.; printer, pub-lisher, Rev. War officer) and his family, 1682-1863 (1,000 items); Daniel Brodhead (Pa.; Rev. War officer), 1780-85 (1 vol.), letter book; John Rutter Brooke (U.S. Army officer, Military Gov. of Puerto Rico and Cuba), 1753-1903 (10,000 items); Charles Henry Tucker Collis (Pa.; Civil War officer), 1863-68 (3 vols.); Stephen Decatur (Pa.; U.S. naval officer), 1801-5 (1 vol.), letter book; Comte D'Estaing (France; vice-admiral), 1778-79 (1 vol.), journal; Edward Hand (Pa.; physician, Rev. War officer, Member Continental Cong.), 1771-1807 (425 items); Andrew Atkinson Humphreys (U.S. Army officer, Chief of the Corps of Engineers), 1827-1901 (16,000 items); Thomas Hutchins (Pa.; military engineer, geographer, surveyor), 1759-88 (300 items); William Irvine (Pa.; Rev. War officer, U.S. Rep.), 1768-1834 (2,000 items); John Laurens (S.C.; Rev. War officer, envoy to France), 1779 (1 vol.), commonplace book; George Gordon Meade (U.S. Army officer) and his family, 1793-1896 (33 vols. and 2,500 items); Daniel Parker (U.S. Army Adjutant and Inspector Gen.), 1761-1846 (22,000 items), a large part being official correspondence of the War Department and another part being papers of Zaccheus Collins (Pa.; merchant, philanthropist, promoter of the advancement of botany and other natural sciences); Zebulon Montgomery Pike (U.S. Army officer, explorer), 1805-6 (1 vol.), journal; George C. Read (Pa.; U.S. naval officer), 1836-40 and 1845-47 (7 vols.), journals and correspondence; John Rodgers (U.S. naval officer, head of Board of Navy Commissioners) and his family, 1791-1885 (168 vols. and 763 manuscripts); Persifor Frazer Smith (U.S. Army officer), 1770-1873 (300 items); Thomas Truxtun (U.S. naval officer), 1797-1801 (7 vols.); and Anthony Wayne (Pa.; Rev. War officer) and his family,

1765-1890 (6,500 items).

Papers of religious leaders include those of John Christopher Frederick Cammerhoff (Pa.; Moravian missionary and bishop), 1747-48 (1 vol.), letters relating to early Moravian settlements in Pennsylvania; John Gottlieb Ernestus Heckewelder (Pa., Ohio; Moravian missionary to the Indians, author), 1755-1822 (150 items); M. Kunze (Pa.; pastor of Lutheran Zion Church in Philadelphia), 1774-76 (1 vol.), manuscript sermons; Frederick Adolphus Packard (Mass., Pa.; editor of Sunday School publications), 1829-85 (600 items); William Smith (Pa.; Episcopal clergyman, educator), 1690-1869 (6 vols.); William White (Pa.; Episcopal bishop), 1765-1865 (3 vols. and 100 items); and John Woolman (N.J., Pa.; Quaker minister, abolitionist) and his family, 1652-1830. Also among the Historical Society's holdings are records of the Society for the Propagation of the Gospel, 1732-79 (130 pages), consisting of letters of missionaries and ministers relating to Pennsylvania; records of the Universalist Church, 1820-1920 (7 vols.), and of various Universalist Church organizations in Philadelphia, 1810-1934 (50 vols.); and a small collection of other church records, 1737-1847 (11 vols.).

Papers of artists, musicians, and authors include papers of George Allen (Vt., Del., Pa.; prof. of languages at Del. College and Univ. of Pa., author), 1828-43 (3 vols.); A. Margaretta Archambault (Pa.; artist, author), 1876-1945 (1,000 items); William G. Armstrong (Pa.; writer, engraver), 1851-88 (38 vols.), diaries; Thomas Willing Balch (Pa.; author, specialist in international arbitration) and his family, 1699-1923 (22 vols. and 2,000 items), including papers relating to the arbitration of the Alabama claims, 1864-72 (1 vol.), and material on Alaskan boundaries, 1854 (2 vols.); Charles Brockden Brown (Pa., N.Y.; novelist, journalist), 1715-1824 (14 vols.);

Peter S. Du Ponceau (France, Pa.; lawyer, author), 1633-1844 (2 vols. and 8 boxes); Albert J. Edmunds (England, Pa.; Biblical scholar, author), 1861-1941 (7,500 items); Sydney George Fisher (Pa.; lawyer, author), 1834-70 (65 vols.), diaries; Joseph F. A. Jackson (Pa.; editor, author), 1798-1941 (242 items); Charles Godfrey Leland (Pa., England, Italy; humorist, poet, essayist), 1835-1906 (5,000 items); George Horace Lorimer (Pa.; editor, author), 1900-37 (2,000 items); T. Chalkley Matlack (Pa.; artist, writer), 1912-39 (9 vols.), literary manuscripts; Ellis Paxson Oberholtzer (Pa.; historian), 1735-1931 (3,500 items); William Rudolf O'Donovan (N.Y.; sculptor, painter), 1861-1920 (150 items); Francis Daniel Pastorius (Germany, Pa.; lawyer, author, founder of Germantown), 1683-1721 (4 vols. and 36 papers); Charles Willson Peale (Md., Pa.; portrait painter, naturalist), Rembrandt Peale (Pa., N.Y., Mass.; portrait and historical painter), and Titian R. Peale (Pa.; naturalist, artist), 1794-1854 (250 items); Joseph Pennell (Pa., England, N.Y.; etcher, author) and Elizabeth Robins Pennell (Pa., England, N.Y.; author), 1917-33 (75 letters); Robert Proud (Pa.; schoolmaster, historian), 1681-1811 (43 vols. and 4 boxes), consisting mainly of original manuscripts of histories and other literary works, and of official papers and letters gathered by him; Winthrop Sargent (Pa., Miss., N.Y.; author, lawyer), 1845-68 (5 vols.); Richard Penn Smith (Pa.; dramatist, essayist, lawyer), 1785-1856 (5 vols.), literary manuscripts; Charles Janeway Stillé (Pa.; prof. of literature and belles-lettres at Univ. of Pa., historian), 1845-93 (500 items); Bayard Taylor (Pa.; author, traveler), 1845-46 (1 vol.), sketchbook of views in Italy and France; Benjamin West (Pa., England; historical painter), 1790-1811 (4 vols.), drawings and account books; Anne Hollingsworth Wharton (Pa.; author), 1852-1926 (80,000 items); and Septimus Winner (Pa.; composer), 1845-1902 (41 vols.), diaries, letters, and music notebooks.

Papers of scientists and physicians include those of Franklin Bache (Pa.; chemist, physician), 1818-60 (500 items); Benjamin Smith Barton (Pa.; naturalist, prof. of medicine at College of Philadelphia), 1778-1813 (200 items), journals and correspondence; John Bartram (Pa.; first native American botanist) and his son, William Bartram (Pa.; naturalist, traveler), 1738-1810 (14 vols.), including diaries, journals, and correspondence; Benjamin Smith Lyman (Mass., Pa.; geologist, mining engineer), 1851-1918 (1,500 items); Charles K. Mills (Pa.; neurologist, prof. at Univ. of Pa.), 1864-1931 (4,000 items); John Morgan (Pa.; physician, founder of Univ. of Pa. Medical School, medical director of Continental Army), 1764 and 1781-84 (2 vols.), journals; Gotthilf Henry E. Muhlenberg (Pa.; Lutheran clergyman, botanist), 1781-1815 (400 items), correspondence relating chiefly to herbs and plants; Jonathan Potts (Pa.; physician, Rev. War medical officer), 1766-80 (500 items); and Benjamin Silliman (Conn.; prof. of chemistry and natural history at Yale College), 1785-1867 (700 items). The Society also has medical notes on lectures by Benjamin Rush (Pa.; physician, Member Continental Cong., prof. at Univ. of Pa.) and Joseph Black (Scotland; chemist, prof. of anatomy at Glasgow Univ., chemistry prof. at Univ. of Edinburgh), 1785-86 (6 vols.).

Papers of business leaders include those of Clement Biddle (Pa.; Rev. War officer, merchant) and his family, 1743-1896 (1 vol. and 847 items); Samuel Coates (Pa.; merchant, philanthropist) and his family, 1722-1847 (12,000 items), chiefly business papers; Jay Cooke (Pa.; banker, financier), 1842-80 (106 boxes of correspondence and

6 letter books); Henry Drinker (Pa.; Quaker merchant), 1739-1869 (25,600 items), containing much material on land dealings on the frontier, and some on the tea importation controversy and other preliminaries of the Revolutionary War, together with the diary of his wife, Elizabeth Drinker (Pa.; prominent Quaker), 1758-1807 (33 vols.); Josiah Humphreys (Pa.; shipbuilder, naval architect), 1682-1835 (20 vols.); William David Lewis (Pa.; merchant, banker), 1815-81 (several vols. and 10,000 letters received); John Nicholson (Pa.; State comptroller gen., land-company promoter), 1775-98 (7 vols.), letters relating to real estate, financial, and legal matters; John Nixon (Pa.; Revolutionary patriot, merchant, banker), 1707-1845 (1,500 items); Uriah Hunt Painter (Pa., D. C.; newspaperman, entrepreneur), 1855-1936 (75 vols. and 10,000 items); John Meredith Read (Pa.; lawyer, State supreme court justice) and his father, John Read (Pa.; lawyer, director of the Philadelphia Bank), 1797-1871 (1,000 items); John Reed and Standish Forde (Pa.; Philadelphia merchants), 1759-1823 (8,000 items), relating mainly to foreign commerce, and including some papers of Robert Morris (Pa.; financier, Member Continental Cong., U. S. Sen.), 1795-1802 (100 items), dealing with his financial difficulties; James M. Swank (Pa.; executive sec. of American Iron and Steel Association), chiefly 1871-98 (250 items); Robert Waln (Pa.; merchant, U. S. Rep.), 1792-1823 (500 items), most of which relate to the East India and China trade; and Thomas Wharton (Pa.; merchant, Pres. of Pa.) and his family, 1679-1834 (2,000 items).

Papers of other individuals include those of Thomas Bradford (Pa.; printer, publisher, Rev. War officer), 1760-1862 (3,500 items); Mathew Carey (Pa.; publisher, economist),

1787-1822 (50,000 items); Hampton L. Carson (Pa.; lawyer), 1874-1927 (2,392 items), including papers of the Commission on Revision of the Constitution of Pennsylvania, 1919-20; Elihu Embree (Tenn.; abolitionist), 1814-25 (50 items); Samuel Morse Felton (Mass., Pa.; civil engineer), 1861-65 and 1886-87 (486 items), relating chiefly to transportation of troops and supplies during the Civil War, and including some papers of Allan Pinkerton (Scotland, Ill.; detective), 1861; Christian Gobrecht (Pa.; engraver), 1795-1844 (100 items); John Harris (Pa.; Indian trader, founder of Harrisburg) and his family, 1687-1915 (500 items); Peter McCall (Pa.; law prof. at Univ. of Pa.), 1773-1879 (1,500 items); George Morgan (Pa., Ill.; land speculator, Indian agent), 1767-68 (1 vol.), letter book; John Fanning Watson (Pa.; antiquarian, publisher), 1693-1855 (16 vols.), relating largely to the history of Pennsylvania; Johann Conrad Weiser (Pa.; Indian agent), 1741-66 (225 items); Herbert Welsh (Pa.; publicist, reformer), 1858-1934 (50,000 items), including papers on Indian rights, 1877-1934 (11 boxes), on National Civil Service Reform League, 1881-1929 (4 boxes), and on the Philippines, 1892-1925 (5 boxes); Thomas I. and Henry Wharton (Pa.; lawyers), 1825-75 (20,000 items), chiefly legal papers and correspondence; and Thomas Willing (Pa.; financier) and his family, 1761-1866 (1,000 items).

Papers of various nongovernmental organizations include those of the Academy of Fine Arts, 1794-1830 (3 vols.); American Institute of Architects, Philadelphia Chapter, 1845-1940 (18 vols. and 1,000 drawings and blueprints); American Red Cross, Pennsylvania-Delaware Division, 1917-19 (240 items); Apprentices Library, 1813-45 (23 vols. and 7 boxes); Asylum Co., 1793-1851 (350 items); Bureau of Unemployment Relief, 1930-32 (2,000 items); Centennial Exposition (Philadelphia), 1876 (12 vols. and 3,000 items); Citizen's Bounty Fund Committee, 1862-66 (5,000 items); Citizens' Permanent Relief Committee (an organization that provided relief for sufferers from disasters), 1885-99 (10,000 items); Indian Rights Association, 1883-1937 (25,000 items); Indigent Widows and Single Women's Society of Philadelphia, 1823-62 (400 items); Malta Boat Club (a Philadelphia athletic and social club), 1870-1912 (3,000 items); Mask and Wig Club (a dramatic organization at Univ. of Pa.), 1889-1937 (5,000 items); Pennsylvania Civil Service Reform League, 1881-1935 (4,000 items); Pennsylvania Population Land Co., 1792-1834 (1,000 items); Pennsylvania Society for Promoting the Abolition of Slavery, 1748-1916 (12,000 items); Philadelphia Board of Trade, 1801-1942 (7 vols. and 19 boxes); Philadelphia fire companies, 1758-1872 (170 vols.); Philadelphia General Hospital (Blockley), 20th century (6,000 items); Society for the Relief of Poor and Distressed Masters of Ships, Their Widows and Children, 1765-1923 (54 vols.); Stage Door Canteen (Philadelphia branch of the American Theater Wing of United Service Organizations), 1942-46 (2,500 items); Union League, 1896-1909 (300 items); Union Volunteer Refreshment Saloon (an organization that cared for Union soldiers as they passed through Philadelphia), 1861-65 (3,000 items); United States Constitutional Centennial Commission, 1886-87 (2,200 items); United States Sanitary Commission, Philadelphia Association, 1861-73 (3,500 items); and Women's Dental Association of the United States, 1892-1921 (2 vols.).

The Society has many official records of governmental units. Records of the Province of Pennsylvania include Assembly papers, 1682-1783 (300 items), and minutes, 1724-25

(1 vol.); Council papers, 1684, 1714-1823 (150 items); and letters written by various Provincial delegates in England and elsewhere. There are records of the admiralty court at Philadelphia, 1770-1804 (8 boxes); and records of a number of other courts, 1676-1818 (67 vols.). Records of Pennsylvania counties are numerous, among them various records of Berks and Montgomery Counties, 1693-1869 (250 items); Bucks County, 1682-1850 (600 items); Chester County, 1684-1847 (1 vol. and 600 items); Northampton County, 1682-1887 (25,000 items); Northumberland County, 1767-1899 (7,000 items); Philadelphia County, 1671-1855 (600 items); and other counties, 1708-1882 (1,500 items). There are also tax and assessment books, chiefly of Philadelphia and Montgomery Counties, 1762-1855 (725 vols.); and Philadelphia tax books, 1803-53 (266 vols.). Official maritime records include papers of the port of Philadelphia, 1716-1855 (3 vols. and 650 items); ship registers of the Province of Pennsylvania, 1722-76 (21 vols.); and Philadelphia customhouse papers, 1704-1929 (16,000 items). Records of U. S. agencies include a report of the committee of the Board of the Treasury on the financial condition of the United States, 1781-83 (1 vol.); a receipt book of the Continental Loan Office in Philadelphia, 1786-90 (1 vol.); a U. S. passport register, 1809-25 (1 vol.); Navy Department papers, 1831-77 (2 vols. and 150 items); Pennsylvania Committee of Public Safety papers, 1917-18 (2 vols.); and draft board papers for the Ninth District of Philadelphia, 1917-18 (2,000 items).

Among the Society's extensive holdings of business records are records of or relating to a number of banks, among them the Bank of North America, 1780-1923 (620 vols. and many other papers); the Bank of the United States, 1797-1850 (2,200 items);

the Bank of the United States of Pennsylvania, 1840-55 (35 vols. and 7 boxes); and the Federal Reserve Bank of Philadelphia, 1914-36 (12 vols.). Other records are those of the Dutch West India Co., 1626-1834 (500 items); the Principio Iron Works, 1724-1903 (31 vols.); the Union Canal, 1791-1922 (10 vols. and 8 boxes); the North American Land Co., 1793-1880 (90 vols., 2 boxes, and 405 other items), and several other land companies; the Baldwin Locomotive Works, 1834-68 (175 vols.); the Baltimore and Philadelphia Steamship Co., 1844-1936 (50 vols. and 3,000 items); the Lehigh Valley Railroad Co., 1858-96 (48 vols.); and the Isabella Furnace (one of the last charcoal-burning furnaces in the United States), 1880-1921 (173 boxes). Included also are records of a Philadelphia company engaged in international trade in sugar, groceries, and the like, 1787-1913 (702 vols.); a Wilmington, Del., firm that specialized in railroad equipment, 1817-1929 (70,000 items); a firm of lumber merchants of Columbia, Pa., and Philadelphia, 1847-81 (36 vols.); several building and loan associations, 1871-1909 (20 vols.); a Philadelphia streetcar and bus manufacturer, 1876-1940 (10,000 items); and a coal mining company, 1880-1939 (19 vols.). There are collections of papers relating to the early manufacture of paper in America, 1724-1858 (1,100 items); account and other record books of forges and furnaces in Pennsylvania, 1726-1832 (250 vols.); insurance papers, chiefly on Philadelphia properties, 1726-1900 (1,500 items); business papers of Philadelphia chemists, 1818-53 (20,000 items); and records of a company of commission merchants in Philadelphia and of various manufacturing companies, 1828-1910 (50,000 items).

Other papers include copies of British Board of Trade papers, 1675-

1782 (146 vols.); Mason and Dixon Line papers, 1701-68 (2 vols. and 1 folio); a colonial and Continental Congress paper money collection, 1714-86 (2 vols. and 1,000 items); documents relating to the construction and outfitting of the frigate Confederacy, 1776-79, 1786 (525 items); correspondence and notes on songs of the Revolution (250 items); various military records, including American orderly books, 1775-1861 (42 vols.), and muster rolls, 1776-1865 (26 vols.); English and German songs in vogue in Pennsylvania, 1796-1823 (6 vols.); meteorological record books kept at Philadelphia, 1854-1930 (7 vols.); miscellaneous Civil War papers, 1861-65 (2,000 items); and a World War II collection, 1939-45 (30,000 items). The Society has a large number of diaries, 16th-20th centuries, only a few of which are specifically mentioned above.

See the Society's Guide to the Manuscript Collections of the Historical Society of Pennsylvania (2d ed. 1949. 1 vol., unpaged).

PHILADELPHIA 6

Historical Society of the Philadelphia Annual Conference of the Methodist Episcopal Church. 326 New St. Frederick E. Maser, Librarian.

Holdings: 7,000 vols. and 325 other items, 1557-1956, relating chiefly to the Methodist Episcopal Church in the United States and especially in Philadelphia. Included are journals of the Philadelphia Annual Conference, 1773-1956; records of missionary activities; records of 167 churches in 14 counties in southeastern Pennsylvania, 1834-1956; and a few personal diaries and a collection of letters, 1757-1883, of Methodist leaders.

See Hist. Records Survey, Guide for Pa., p. 60; and Allison, Inventory, pp. 197-199.

—oOo—

Independence National Historical Park Project. 420 Chestnut St. Superintendent.

Holdings: 6 vols. and 235 pieces, 1643-1845, chiefly an autograph collection. Included are letters by Members of the Continental Congress, the Federal Constitutional Convention, officers (including foreign) of the American Revolution, and Members of early Federal Congresses, 1789-1820. Included also are legal and business correspondence and deeds relating to Philadelphia and the proprietary government of Pennsylvania.

PHILADELPHIA 1

Insurance Company of North America. 1600 Arch St.

Holdings: Manuscripts, 1584-1936, consisting of the archives of the Insurance Company of North America, the earliest dated 1792, and other papers relating chiefly to fire and marine insurance.

See M. J. McCosker, The Historical Collection of the Insurance Company of North America (1945. 173 p.).

PHILADELPHIA 3

Inter-Church Child Care Society. 125 South 22 St. Hugh M. Trantum, Executive Director.

Holdings: 150 vols. and 115 boxes, relating chiefly to relief and religious work with the poor in Philadelphia since about 1835.

See Hist. Records Survey, Guide for Pa., p. 61.

PHILADELPHIA 47

Library Company of Philadelphia.
Broad and Christian Sts. Edwin
Wolf 2d, Librarian; Barney Ches-
nick, Curator.

Holdings: 140,000 pieces, 1682-
1937, relating chiefly to Pennsylvania
and especially to Philadelphia. All
manuscripts formerly housed at Juniper and Locust Streets are now at
Broad and Christian Streets.

Papers of individuals include those
of George Allen (Vt., Del., Pa.; Episcopal clergyman, prof. of languages at
Del. College and Univ. of Pa.), 1763-
1859 (264 items); John Dickinson (Pa.,
Del.; Member Continental Cong., Pres.
of Pa. and of Del.), 1732-1808 (21 boxes); William Henry Fry (Pa.; musician,
composer,journalist), 1815-64 (50 manuscripts); Michael Gratz (Pa.; merchant),
1740-1811 (5 boxes); Stephen Grellet
(Pa., N.Y., N.J.; minister of the Society of Friends), 1701-81 (5 vols.);
James Barton Longacre (Pa.; engraver), 1794-1869 (7 boxes); Samuel
George Morton (Pa.; physician, naturalist), 1799-1851 (6 boxes); Samuel
Powel (Pa.; merchant, mayor of Philadelphia) and John Hare Powel (Pa.;
U. S. Army officer, agriculturist),
1786-1856 (50 vols. and 2 boxes); Robert Proud (Pa.; schoolmaster, historian), 1728-1813 (5 boxes); John
Read (Pa., N.J.; lawyer, director of
the Philadelphia Bank), 1769-1854,
John Meredith Read (Pa.; lawyer,
State supreme court justice, judge),
1797-1874, and John Meredith Read,
Jr. (Pa., N.Y.; lawyer, diplomat),
1837-96 (40 vols., 40 boxes, and 77
albums); Benjamin Rush (Pa.; physician, Member Continental Cong., prof.
at Univ. of Pa.), 1760-1813 (71 vols.);
James Rush (Pa.; physician, psychologist), 1814-60 (20 boxes); and Thomas Truxton (Pa.; U. S. naval officer),
1755-1822, together with those of
Charles Biddle (Pa.; U. S. naval offi-

cer), 1745-1821 (115 items). Also
included are miscellaneous manuscripts collected by Pierre Eugene
du Simitière (Pa.; painter, antiquarian, naturalist), 10 vols.; and the archival material of the Library Company of Philadelphia and the Loganian
Library, 1731-1955 (20 vols. and 10
boxes).

See Hist. Records Survey's Descriptive Catalogue of the Du Simitière
Papers in the Library Company of
Philadelphia (1940. 196 p. Processed).

PHILADELPHIA 19

Lutheran Theological Seminary
Library. 7301. Germantown Ave.
Henry H. Scherer, Librarian.

Holdings: Several thousands of
pieces, 1730 to date, relating chiefly to the Lutheran Church in the
United States. In some cases the
quantities given below are approxi-
mations and, as it is not feasible to
distinguish between pieces and volumes, the quantity given in pieces
sometimes includes volumes.

Papers of Lutheran clergymen
include those of Justus Henry Christian Helmuth (Pa.; prof. of German
at Univ. of Pa., author), 1767-1810
(75 pieces), consisting of sermons,
reports, and diary; Paul Henkel (Pa.,
Va.), 1754-1824 (6 pieces), reports
and diary; Charles Michael Jacobs
(Pa.; prof. at Lutheran Theological
Seminary), 1864-1920 (50 pieces),
lectures and notes; Henry Eyster Jacobs (Pa.; theology prof. at and pres.
of Lutheran Theological Seminary),
1864-1920 (98 pieces), lectures,
notes, and reports; Charles Porter-
field Krauth (Md., Va., Pa.; prof. at
Lutheran Theological Seminary and
Univ. of Pa., editor), 1843-81
(84 pieces); John Christopher Kunze
(Pa., N.Y.; prof. at Univ. of Pa. and

Columbia College), 1770-1802 (many pieces); William Julius Mann (Pa.; prof. of German at Lutheran Theological Seminary, author), 1851-92 (81 pieces); Frederick Augustus Conrad Muhlenberg (Pa.; Member Continental Cong., U. S. Rep.), 1770-1820; Henry Melchior Muhlenberg (Pa.), 1733-85 (54 pieces), including a journal; Charles Frederick Schaeffer (Pa., Md., Ohio, N. Y.; prof. at Gettysburg Theological Seminary and Lutheran Theological Seminary), 1829-66 (40 pieces); Theodore Emanuel Schmauk (Pa.; editor of the Lutheran Church Review and other periodicals, author), 1883-1920 (34 pieces); Beale Melanchthon Schmucker (Pa.), 1848-86 (48 pieces); Joseph Augustus Seiss (Md., Pa.; Lutheran clergyman, author), 19th century (19 items); and Adolph Theodor Spaeth (Pa.; prof. at Lutheran Theological Seminary, author), 1887-95 (50 pieces), including a diary. Also included are diaries of 18th-century clergymen and a chaplain in the Revolutionary Army.

There are records of the Evangelical Lutheran Ministerium of Pennsylvania, 1748 to date (10 cartons and 3,442 pieces); the Lutheran Theological Seminary at Philadelphia, 1864 to date (264 pieces); and the United Lutheran Church in America, 1917 to date (200 pieces). The holdings include records of the earliest Lutheran church organization in America; of churches from 1730 to date; and of the General Council of the Evangelical Lutheran Church in North America, 1866-1918. Also included are records of the Lutheran Church in British Guiana, 1742-1850.

See Hist. Records Survey, Guide for Pa., p. 65.

PHILADELPHIA 7

Municipal Archives, City of Philadelphia. 156 City Hall. Charles E.

Hughes, Jr., City Archivist.

Holdings: A large quantity of official records of the city and county of Philadelphia, 1683-1956 but chiefly of the 19th and 20th centuries. Archives of the city of Philadelphia, 1683-1956, include minutes and journals of the city councils, 1704-1955 (352 vols.); annual messages of the mayor, with reports of the city departments, 1870-1933 (121 vols.); wills and letters of administration and related papers, 1682 to date; and many records relating to assessments and taxes. There are also archives of boroughs, districts, and townships that have been consolidated with the city; these records, 1779-1885, consist chiefly of minutes of various governing boards and financial records. Archives of the county of Philadelphia, 1683-1943, include the records of several county courts, 1793-1935 (290 vols. and 124 boxes); deed books, 1683-1863 (1,342 vols.); survey returns, 1683-1870 (6 vols.); and marriage records, 1860-85. Many of the earlier city and county records, including deeds to Independence Square, 1683-1820 (1 ft.), the city charter of 1701, and assessment records, which are now in the Municipal Archives, were formerly in the custody of the Historical Society of Pennsylvania. Other records include those of the Centennial Commission, 1873-77.

See Charles E. Hughes, Jr., and Allen Weinberg, Guide to the Municipal Archives of the City and County of Philadelphia (1957. [64] p.).

—oOo—

Pennsylvania Hospital Medical Library. Eighth and Spruce Sts. H. Robert Cathcart, Administrator.

Holdings: 2,000 pieces of minute books, correspondence, and business

records, 1751-1895, relating to the
history of the Pennsylvania Hospital.
Included are some autograph letters
of Benjamin Franklin, Stephen Girard, and medical personalities of the
colonial period.

 See Hist. Records Survey, Guide
for Pa., p. 66.

—oOo—

Pennsylvania Prison Society. 311
South Juniper St. G. Richard Bacon,
Executive Secretary.

 Holdings: 18 vols., 1787-1920,
relating to the Philadelphia Society for
Alleviating the Miseries of Public Prisons, now the Pennsylvania Prison Society. Included are minutes of the Society, 1787-1832, 1852-1920 (5 vols.);
minutes of the Acting Committee,
1798-1918 (10 vols.); and minutes of
the Visiting Committee to the Eastern
State Penitentiary, 1854-85 (3 vols.).

PHILADELPHIA 1

Philadelphia Museum of Art. Parkway
at Fairmount Ave. Marjorie E. Lyons,
Librarian; Carl Zigrosser, Curator of
Prints.

 Holdings: In the Library there are
38 illuminated medieval and Oriental
manuscripts (French, Flemish, Spanish, German, Armenian, Persian, and
Indian), 14th-19th centuries; formulas,
kiln drawings, letters, and pattern
books of Thomas Tucker (Pa.; maker
of porcelain), 19th century; and noncurrent administrative papers of the
Museum, 1864-1955. The Archives of
American Art comprise 2,300 pieces,
19th-20th centuries, relating to American artists, among them letters to,
from, or about artists, and artists'
notebooks, account books, and other
papers.

 See De Ricci, Census, p. 2101; and

Hist. Records Survey, Guide for Pa.,
p. 69.

PHILADELPHIA 7

Presbyterian Historical Society.
520 Witherspoon Building, Juniper
and Walnut Sts. William B. Miller,
Acting Executive Secretary.

 Holdings: 400,000 manuscripts,
1600 to date, relating to the Presbyterian Church in the United States of
America. Included are official records and transcripts of records of
the annual General Assembly since
1789, and of synods, presbyteries,
and other church organizations in
many parts of the United States; official documents of the first presbytery organized in Philadelphia, beginning with the minutes in 1706 and con-
tinuing to date, with a few gaps; minutes of local churches (3,000 vols.);
letters from missionaries among the
American Indians, 1833-90 (14,000
pieces); letters from domestic missions in America, particularly in
the West, 1832-1900 (50,000 pieces);
microfilm copies of letters written
by missionaries to the Board of Foreign Missions (250,000 pieces); papers of Sheldon Jackson (Presbyterian missionary in Rocky Mountain
States and Alaska, Supt. of Public
Instruction in Alaska, author), 1856-
1908 (8,000 pieces); and part of the
John D. Shane Collection, 1716-1860
(33 vols. and 5,128 pieces), pertaining mainly to activity of the Presbyterian Church in Kentucky, Tennessee, and other areas of the Mississippi Valley (the other part being
among the Draper Manuscripts in the
State Historical Society of Wisconsin).

 See Allison, Inventory, pp. 199-
205; Otto A. Rothert, "Shane, the
Western Collector," in Filson Club
Hist. Quarterly, 4:1-16 (Jan. 1930);

the Society's Primary Source Materials on Western Life in America at the Presbyterian Historical Society (1948. 4 p. Processed), and its Annual Reports; and the following articles in the Presbyterian Hist. Society Journal: Joseph B. Turner, "A Catalogue of Manuscript Records in the Possession of the Presbyterian Historical Society," 8:13-22 (Mar. 1915); Edward B. Shaw, "Calendar of the Shane Papers; a Preliminary Report," 19:183-192 (Dec. 1940); Harrison A. Brann, "Bibliography of Sheldon Jackson Collection," 30:139-164 (Sept. 1952); and Charles A. Anderson, "Index of American Indian Correspondence," 31:63-70 (Mar. 1953).

PHILADELPHIA

R. W. Grand Lodge of Pennsylvania Free and Accepted Masons. Broad and Filbert Sts. William J. Paterson, Librarian and Curator.

Holdings: 95 vols. and 47 other pieces, relating mainly to Free Masonry in the United States, especially in Pennsylvania, since 1761. Included are records of several lodges no longer in existence; 11 letters from George Washington (Va.; U. S. Pres.), 1792-97; and a volume of letters from various persons of prominence in the United States, 1759-1916.
See Hist. Records Survey, Guide for Pa., p. 70.

PHILADELPHIA 22

Temple University Libraries. Park Ave. and Berks St. Walter Hausdorfer, Librarian.

Holdings: 923 vols. and 7,433 items, 1378/79–1959, relating mainly to Temple University. Included are archives of the University, 1887-1959

(823 vols. and 6,293 items); letters, prayers, and sermons of Russell H. Conwell (Mass., Minn., Pa.; Civil War officer, Baptist clergyman, founder of Temple Univ.), 1862-1925 (88 vols. and 639 items); letters and other manuscripts of Walter John De La Mare (England; poet, novelist), 1918-56 (133 items), including 128 letters and typewritten manuscripts of 4 poems; and undated manuscripts of Late Harvest (published 1946) by Norman Douglas (England; novelist, scientist), 12 vols., including 2 vols. of index. There is also a collection of manuscript documents in business history, 1378/79–1873 (368 items).

PHILADELPHIA 2

Union League of Philadelphia. 140 South Broad St.

Holdings: 11 vols. and 16 other items, relating chiefly to the development of the Union League. There is a small collection of letters by American leaders and a shorthand record of testimony about the assassination of Abraham Lincoln.
See Hist. Records Survey, Guide for Pa., p. 77.

PHILADELPHIA 4

University of Pennsylvania Industrial Research Unit. 3440 Walnut St. Miriam Hussey, Research Associate.

Holdings: 800 items, 1762-1932, relating chiefly to a hardware and paint-manufacturing business and to woolen mills. Included are records, 1785-1932, of the firm founded by Samuel Wetherill (Pa.; Quaker, Rev. War soldier) and continued by his direct descendants, including his great grandson Samuel Wetherill (Pa.;

chemical manufacturer); most of the records consist of daybooks, ledgers, letter books, and books of account from the years before 1872, at which time the retail business was discontinued. There is also, on permanent loan, a collection of daybooks, ledgers, and cash books of a woolen milling concern, 1864-1913 (77 vols.).

See Hist. Records Survey, Guide for Pa., p. 75; and the Industrial Research Department's published catalog of the Wetherill papers (1942. 121 p. Processed).

—oOo—

University of Pennsylvania Law School Library. Carroll C. Moreland, Librarian.

Holdings: 46 vols. and 305 other items, 1377-1860, containing English deeds, indentures, and other legal documents, Law School lecture notes, and miscellaneous legal manuscripts.

See Hist. Records Survey, Guide for Pa., p. 76; and De Ricci, Census, p. 2109.

—oOo—

University of Pennsylvania Library. 34th and Woodland Ave. Kenneth M. Setton, Director of Libraries; Neda M. Westlake, Assistant Curator, Rare Book Collection; Leonidas Dodson, University Archivist.

Holdings: 18,000 ft. of manuscripts, 12th-20th centuries, relating chiefly to Philadelphia, Pennsylvania, United States history to 1870, American literature and science, and medieval history. (Holdings of the Industrial Research Unit, Law School Library, and Museum are described separately.) Included are Sanskrit manuscripts, 16th-19th centuries (138 boxes); and European manuscripts, described below, in the Henry

Charles Lea Library. There are also papers relating to Spanish colonial and foreign relations, 17th-19th centuries (10 boxes).

Papers of political and cultural leaders include those of John Quincy Adams (Mass.; U. S. Sen. and Rep., diplomat, Sec. State, U. S. Pres.), 1818-22 (60 items); Thomas H. Burrowes (Pa.; State legislator, advocate of a free school system), 1836-39 (199 pieces); George Mifflin Dallas (Pa.; U. S. Sen., Minister to Russia and to Great Britain, U. S. Vice Pres.), 1837-39, 1856-60 (2 vols.); Benjamin Franklin (Pa.; printer, scientist, Member Continental Cong., diplomat), 1777-88 (11 vols.); Sir George Macartney (England; diplomat, colonial gov. in India), 1781-85 (21 boxes); James Monroe (Va.; Member Continental Cong., U. S. Sen., Gov., diplomat, Sec. State, U. S. Pres.), 1817-25 (29 items); Francis Daniel Pastorius (Germany, Pa.; lawyer, author, founder of Germantown), 1696-1719 (2 vols.); William Pepper (Pa.; physician, Univ. of Pa. prof. and provost), 1876-1900 (12 vols.); Samuel Jackson Randall (Pa.; Civil War officer, U. S. Rep., Speaker of the House), 1844-90 (270 boxes); and Benjamin Rush (Pa.; physician, Member Continental Cong., prof. at Univ. of Pa.), 1769-91 (10 vols. and 2 pieces), of which the volumes are student notebooks on his lectures. The Library also has a few items by each of many other important Americans and Europeans; papers of German-Hessian-American military history, 1775-1865 (10 boxes); lectures given at the Medical School of the University, and students' notes, 1760-1860; and records of the Pennsylvania Society for Promoting Agriculture.

Papers of writers include those of Robert Montgomery Bird (Pa.; physician, playwright, novelist, editor), 1835-50 (25 vols. and 12 boxes); Catherine Drinker Bowen (Pa.; novelist, biographer), 1940-50 (16 boxes); Theodore Dreiser (Mo., N.Y.; editor, novelist), 1890-1945 (4,536 ft., consisting of manuscripts, letters, diaries, clippings, and personal library); James T. Farrell (Ill., N.Y.; journalist, novelist), literary manuscripts; William Clyde Fitch (N.Y.; playwright), 1890-1904 (18 vols.); Waldo Frank (N.Y., Mass.; novelist), 1910-55 (24 boxes); James A. Herne (N.Y.; playwright, actor), 1880-90 (3 manuscripts); William Dean Howells (Mass., N.Y. novelist, literary critic, editor), 1872-1919 (27 items); Joseph F. A. Jackson (Pa.; editor, author), 1867-1943 (1 box); Josephine Lawrence (N.Y.; novelist, writer of juvenile fiction), 1952 (1 box); Charles Godfrey Leland (Pa., England, Italy; humorist, poet, essayist), 1875-1900 (3 manuscripts); James Russell Lowell (Mass.; poet, essayist, Minister to Spain and to Great Britain), 1858-90 (20 letters and 1 literary manuscript); Edgar Lee Masters (Ill., N.Y.; poet, dramatist), 1912-40 (10 folders); Henry Louis Mencken (Md.; author, editor, critic), 1910-45 (32 folders); Silas Weir Mitchell (Pa.; physician, neurologist, poet, novelist), 1890-1910 (85 letters and 18 literary manuscripts); Ezra Pound (N.Y., Europe; poet), 1915-46 (34 items); Henry Hope Reed (Pa.; literary critic, Wordsworth authority), 1840-50 (20 lectures); Felix Emanuel Schelling (Ind., Pa.; critic, English prof. at Univ. of Pa.), 1875-1937 (33 folders); George Seldes (N.Y., Conn.; journalist, author), 1930-55 (8 boxes); and Walt Whitman (N.Y., D.C., N.J.; poet), 1860-91 (3 boxes and many autograph notes in books). There are also small quantities of papers of other important literary figures; writers, both American and English; and autograph collections and papers of theatrical managers, 1830-1900 (75 vols.).

In the Edgar Fahs Smith Memorial Collection are a few original letters from seven signers of the Declaration of Independence; many letters from men prominent in early American history; and approximately 1,400 manuscripts of famous chemists of various nationalities.

In the Henry Charles Lea Library and the Rare Book Collection are 225 manuscripts of the 12th-19th centuries, written in English, French, German, Italian, Spanish, Rhaeto-Roman, Greek, and Latin. Among the more important groups are Italian statutes, plays and literary miscellanies, classical works in original tongues and translations, and texts relevant to the study of church history. Included are "Blancardin," Chansonnier, 1400; letters of the Avignon popes, 1420; a pseudo-Aristotle "De Mundo," translated by Argyropoulos; and a dramatized version of the story of Aristotle and Phyllis, in German, ca. 1450. In addition, the Library has photostatic copies of some important manuscript materials: the Misti from the Venetian Archives, and microfilm copies of the letters and manuscripts of Gottfried Wilhelm von Leibniz (Germany; philosopher), 100,000 pieces.

In the University Archives are 1,800 ft. of records, 1740-1955. The General Archives include records accumulated in the office of the Secretary, 1749-1940 (56 ft.); selected University papers mounted in albums, 1740-1835 (4 ft.); minute books of committees of the Trustees, 1857-1932 (4 ft.); and correspondence of Charles Custis Harrison (Provost), 1894-1910 (4 ft.), and of Josiah H. Penniman (Provost), 1921-30 (12 ft.). The Central File includes papers of the President, Provost, and Vice Presidents, 1930-40 (20 ft.); and financial records, 1749-1951 (700 ft.).

Records of the schools and divisions of the University include minute books, correspondence, and student records, as follows: records of the College, 1792-1953 (115 ft.); college collateral courses, 1903-50 (17 ft.); summer school, 1904-49 (9 ft.); School of Fine Arts, 1890-1950 (70 ft.); Wharton School, 1881-1951 (58 ft.); Graduate School, 1885-1950 (147 ft.); Moore School, 1943-53 (31 ft.); Office of Student Affairs, 1921-54 (50 ft.); Development Fund, 1925-45 (90 ft.); General Alumni Society, 1903-6 (4 ft.); alumni (biographical folders), 1757-1955 (62 ft.); School of Education, 1914-52 (120 ft.); Law School, 1852-98 (1/2 ft.); Medical School, 1768-1950 (127 ft.); Graduate School of Medicine, 1921-50 (86 ft.); University Hospital, 1862-1920 (1 ft.); Orthopedic Hospital, 1867-1934 (1/2 ft.); Gynecean Hospital, 1887-1939 (1/2 ft.); Medico-Chirurgical College, 1888-1917 (3 ft.); Dental School, 1878-1952 (75 ft.); Veterinary School, 1904-49 (82 ft.); and Towne Scientific School, 1872-1949 (6 ft.).

Personal papers of members of the faculty include those of George Frederick Barker (Conn., Pa.; chemist and physicist, Yale and Univ. of Pa. prof., editor of American Journal of Science), 1/2 ft.; George A. Barton (Pa.; Semitic scholar), 1 ft.; Edward P. Cheyney (Pa.; historian), 7 ft.; William E. Lingelbach (Pa.; historian), 3 ft.; and Robert Tait McKenzie (Canada, Pa.; sculptor, physician, director of physical education), 1887-1938 (9 ft.).

See De Ricci, Census, pp. 2106-2108. The Library plans to prepare a catalog of its medieval and early modern manuscripts. See also the University's Calendar of the Papers of Benjamin Franklin in the Library of the University of Pennsylvania (1908. [147] p.); Hist. Records Survey, Guide for Pa., p. 73; and University of Pa. Library Chronicle, vols. 10-20 (1942-54), in which there are special articles on the papers of Robert M. Bird, Thomas H. Burrowes, Theodore Dreiser, James

Monroe, and Walt Whitman, and on the collection in the Henry Charles Lea Library.

—oOo—

University of Pennsylvania Museum. 33d and Spruce Sts. Cynthia Griffin, Librarian.

Holdings: More than 20,000 Sumerian, Babylonian, and Assyrian tablets and fragments; 600 papyri; 7 Persian and Arabic manuscripts, 12th-16th centuries; and some manuscripts in the Daniel Garrison Brinton Library of aboriginal linguistics and ethnology.

See Hist. Records Survey, Guide for Pa., p. 76.

PHILADELPHIA 21

Wagner Free Institute of Science. 17th St. and Montgomery Ave. Robert Chambers, Jr., Director.

Holdings: 12 wooden chests of business and personal letters and other papers of William Wagner (Pa.; merchant, scientist, founder of the Institute), 1819-84. Included is Wagner's journal, 1855-84.

PHILADELPHIA 18

Westminster Theological Seminary. Willow Grove Ave. and Church Rd., Chestnut Hill.

Holdings: 42 vols., 24 filing drawers, and 24 boxes, plus a collection of facsimiles, relating chiefly to Biblical and Presbyterian church history. Included are lectures by William Brenton Greene, Jr. (Mass., Pa., N.J.; Presbyterian minister, prof. at Princeton Theological Sem.), 1899-1914 (42 vols.); and papers of

John Gresham Machen (N. J., Pa.; fundamentalist Presbyterian theologian, founder of Westminster Theological Sem.), 1910-37 (24 filing drawers and 24 boxes). Facsimiles, made in the 20th century, are of Biblical papyri, Greek miniscule manuscripts, and Greek New Testament texts (15 vols. and 7 folders).

See Hist. Records Survey, Guide for Pa., p. 78.

PHOENIXVILLE

Public Library. Main St. and Second Ave. Ruth L. Peters, Librarian.

Holdings: 31 vols. and 3 other pieces, consisting chiefly of diaries of Esther G. Leggett (Pa.; Phoenixville civic leader and world traveler), 1902-27.

PITTSBURGH 12

Allegheny Regional Branch Library. Federal and East Ohio Sts. Anthony A. Martin, Chief Librarian.

Holdings: 2 vols. of minutes of Old Allegheny Borough, 1821-40.

PITTSBURGH 13

Carnegie Library of Pittsburgh. Forbes St. at Schenley Park. H. Dorothy English, Librarian, Pennsylvania Division.

Holdings: 40 vols. and 5,000 letters, relating chiefly to Pittsburgh and Western Pennsylvania. The main part is the Craig Collection, which includes papers of Isaac Craig (Pa.; U. S. Army officer); George Croghan (Pa.; Indian trader and agent, land speculator), 1765 (1-vol. journal); George Morgan (Pa., N. J.; land

speculator, Indian agent, Rev. War officer), 1774-78 (3 letter books); and John Neville (Va., Pa.; Rev. War officer, Whiskey tax inspector). Also included are papers relating to the Whiskey Rebellion, 1791-94.

See Hist. Records Survey, Guide for Pa., p. 80.

—oOo—

Darlington Memorial Library, University of Pittsburgh. Ruth Salisbury, Librarian.

Holdings: 3,628 items, 1759-1858, relating chiefly to the Pittsburgh region. Included are papers of Henry M. Brackenridge (Pa.; judge, U. S. Rep., author), 1816-58 (1 vol., containing 125 letters received); Joseph Leger d'Happart (France, Pa.; soldier, businessman), 1797-1815 (2,000 letters and papers); Robert McKnight (Pa.; lawyer, U. S. Rep.), 1842-47 (2 vols. of diaries); George Morgan (Pa., N. J.; land speculator, Indian agent), 1771 (1 letter book); Charles Nisbet (Pa.; Presbyterian clergyman, pres. of Dickinson College), 1786-1803 (56 letters); and Robert J. Walker (Pa., Miss.; U. S. Sen. from Miss., Sec. Treas.), 1832-48 (354 pieces of private correspondence).

PITTSBURGH 19

Duquesne University Library. Eleanor McCann, Librarian.

Holdings: Included are a small collection of papers of the Catholic Historical Society of Western Pennsylvania; and some papers concerning the family of George Bowen (Vt., India; missionary in Bombay).

PITTSBURGH 13

Foster Hall Collection, University of

Pittsburgh. Fletcher Hodges, Jr.,
Curator.

Holdings: 250 items, 1845-65, including manuscripts of 70 songs and
24 letters by Stephen Collins Foster
(Pa., N.Y.; composer).

—oOo—

Historical Society of Western Pennsylvania. 4338 Bigelow Blvd. Prudence B. Trimble, Librarian-Editor.

Holdings: A collection of papers,
mainly of the 18th and 19th centuries,
relating chiefly to western Pennsylvania. Papers of individuals include
those of Robert Ayers (Methodist circuit rider, Episcopal clergyman),
1785-1828 (1 box of diaries); Henry
Bouquet (England; Army officer in
western Pa.), 1759-61 (2 boxes of
transcripts); Henry M. Brackenridge
(Pa.; judge, U.S. Rep.), author), 1821-
68 (2 boxes); William A. Coffin (N.Y.;
painter, art critic), 1872-89 (1 box);
John Covode (Pa.; U.S. Rep.), 1853-
70 (3 boxes); Isaac Craig (Pa.; U.S.
Army officer), 1745-1826 (1 large
portfolio), consisting of commissions,
certificates, muster rolls, and letters;
Harmar Denny (Pa.; lawyer, U.S. Rep.),
1829-50; John Harper (N.Y.; printer
and publisher), 1831-82 (6 boxes); Alexander Hays (Pa.; engineer, U.S.
Army officer), 1819-64 (6 boxes);
William Jacob Holland (Pa.; naturalist, educator, clergyman), 1848-1932
(70 boxes); Jacob D. Mathiot (Pa.; ironmaster, militia officer, State legislator), 1861-64 (13 boxes); George Morgan (Pa., N.J.; Rev. War officer, Indian agent, land speculator), 1753-1818
(1 folder); James O'Hara (Pa.; Rev.
War officer, glass manufacturer,
banker), 1779-1819 (12 boxes); James
Ross (Pa.; lawyer, U.S. Sen.), 1700-
1837 (1 box); and William Thaw (Pa.;
transportation capitalist, philanthropist), 1818-89 (10 boxes).

Other holdings include a Fort
Pitt daybook, 1765-67; correspondence regarding the Alliance Furnace,
first west of the Allegheny Mountains,
1788-1816 (27 letters); records of
the Pittsburgh chapter of the Daughters of 1812, from 1903 (4 vols. and
2 boxes); letters and other papers relating to the Civil War; papers pertaining to activities of Polish-Amer-
icans of the Pittsburgh region; a
Methodist collection, containing 211
books, some diaries, and other manuscripts; typed manuscripts of original records of 14 churches in Red-
stone Presbytery, 1815-1958 (17 boxes); and a collection of records of
pioneer churches in Somerset County, 1774-1904 (5 boxes), and other
church records. Business records
include those of local iron-manufac-
turing firms, 1827-54 (3 vols.); and
a manufacturer of gas engines, 1923-
24 (3 filing drawers). There are extensive archives of Butler County
(47 vols. and 6 boxes); Westmoreland
County records, 1779-1850 (5 boxes); and some Greene County records
(3 boxes).
     See Inventory of the Manuscript
and Miscellaneous Collections of the
Historical Society of Western Pennsylvania (1933. 11 p. Processed);
and Hist. Records Survey, Guide for
Pa., p. 82.

PITTSBURGH 6

Pittsburgh Theological Seminary Library. 616 North Highland Ave.
Librarian.

Holdings: (1) From the former
Pittsburgh-Xenia Theological Seminary: several hundred pieces relating chiefly to the history of Associate, Associate Reformed, and United Presbyterian churches in the United States, including the diary of John
Cuthbertson (N.Y., Pa.; Reformed

Presbyterian clergyman), 1751-90; papers of John Mitchell Mason (N.Y., Pa.; Associate Reformed Presbyterian clergyman, provost of Columbia College, pres. of Dickinson College); archives of the United Presbyterian Church of North America, dating from 1705 (745 vols. and 42 bundles); and minutes and papers of the synod, presbyteries, and congregations of the Associate Presbyterian Church (85 items), and the Associate Reformed Presbyterian Church, 1793-1856 (40 items); and (2) from the former Western Theological Seminary: 100 items, 1785-1900, relating chiefly to the seminary and to the Presbyterian Church in the Pittsburgh area, including minutes of the Synod of Ohio, the Presbytery of Pittsburgh, the Presbyteries of Clarion and Kittanning, and sessions of some early Presbyterian churches; records of the board of directors and faculty of the seminary; and letters of John McMillan (Pa.; Presbyterian clergyman, prof. at Jefferson College) and of former teachers in the seminary.

See Hist. Records Survey, Guide for Pa., p. 83; and Allison, Inventory, p. 147.

PITTSBURGH 30

United States Steel Corporation. 525 William Penn Place. G. M. Timmis, Supervisor, Archives.

Holdings: 81,000 vols. and 28,000 rolls of microfilms, 1872 to date, relating chiefly to the history of the United States Steel Corporation and predecessor companies. Included are drawings, miscellaneous letters, and various business records.

POTTSVILLE

Historical Society of Schuylkill County. Pottsville City Hall, 14

North Third St. Herrwood E. Hobbs, Secretary.

Holdings: 12,000 items, 1774-1910, relating chiefly to Schuylkill County. Included are papers relating to the Mexican and Civil Wars (including medical activites), churches, politics, mining, merchandising, railroad and other transportation, railroad-labor riots, trade unions, lumber and real estate enterprises, and prisons. Also included are extensive microfilm copies of Schuylkill County cemetery records.

See Hist. Records Survey, Guide for Pa., p. 86.

READING

Historical Society of Berks County. 940 Centre Ave. Mrs. LeRoy Sanders, Director.

Holdings: A substantial collection relating chiefly to the history of Reading and Berks County. Included are account books of early forges and furnaces, records of the Union Canal, early church records and diaries, and some Pennsylvania-German Fractur work. There is also a collection on the theatrical history of Reading.

SCRANTON 10

Lackawanna Historical Society. 232 Monroe Ave. Secretary.

Holdings: 500 vols. and 4,500 other items, relating mainly to Lackawanna County. Included are minutes and other records of several churches, 1830-1935; legal documents and probate court records; records of local business establishments; and papers of James Archibald (Pa.; engineer), 1 box.

See Hist. Records Survey,

Guide for Pa., p. 89.

—oOo—

Scranton Public Library. Leonore
Rice, Reference Librarian.

Holdings: A small collection, consisting of a Baptist association, 1819-
1921 (5 vols.); and papers of Robert
H. McKune (Pa.; mayor of Scranton),
1875-78, some of which relate to the
strike of 1877.

SHIPPENSBURG

Lincoln Library. Henry E. Luhrs,
Director.

Holdings: 65 vols. of records of
local business and professional men;
and 14,000 pieces relating primarily
to Pennsylvania, New York, and New
England from the colonial period.
There are manuscripts relating to
Presidents of the United States and
their administrations, including some
concerning Abraham Lincoln (150
pieces), largely legal writings.

—oOo—

Shippensburg Historical Society.
Henry E. Luhrs, Curator.

Holdings: 428 pieces, consisting
of papers of individuals and organizations and other records relating chiefly to the locality. Included are war
records of residents.

SOMERSET

Mary S. Biesecker Public Library.
230 South Rosina Ave. (Mrs.) Anna
N. Lebda, Acting Librarian.

Holdings: A small collection,
chiefly of local genealogical materials.

Included, however, are a number of
copies of papers of Harmon Husband
(N. C., Pa.; "regulator" in N. C. and
leader of Whiskey Rebellion in Pa.).

STROUDSBURG

Monroe County Historical Society.
Stroud Community House. Mrs.
Nathan G. Meyer, Corresponding
Secretary.

Holdings: A small collection,
1743 to date, relating chiefly to Monroe County. Included are deeds,
docket books, and ledgers; and copies of many Monroe County church
records and cemetery inscriptions.
See Hist. Records Survey, Guide
for Pa., p. 91.

SUNBURY

Northumberland County Historical
Society. John R. Kaufman, Jr.,
Public Library. Charles F. Snyder,
Secretary.

Holdings: 500 pieces, 1756-1901,
relating chiefly to Northumberland
County. Included are records of
coal, iron, canal, and railroad companies, 1835-60; documents on Fort
Augusta, and various military papers; and records of churches
throughout the county.

SWARTHMORE

Friends Historical Library. Swarthmore College. Frederick B. Tolles,
Director.

Holdings: 1,650 vols., 500 boxes, and 2,000 linear ft., 1652-1956,
relating chiefly to the Society of
Friends and to efforts in support of
international peace, the latter com-

prising the Swarthmore College Peace Collection, established as a memorial to Jane Addams.

Papers of individuals include those of Jane Addams (Ill.; social reformer, founder of Hull House in Chicago, advocate of world peace), 1870-1935 (27 ft.); Hannah J. Bailey (Maine; Supt. of Dept. of Peace and International Arbitration, W. C. T. U., advocate of woman's rights), 1887-1923 (22 in.); Bernard Barton (England; poet), 1829-33 (100 pieces); Owen Biddle (Pa.; astronomer, Rev. War officer), 1771-87 (3 boxes); Elihu Burritt (Mass., Conn.; reformer, advocate of world peace, linguist), 1845-56 (10 in.); Corder Catchpool (England, Germany; Quaker relief worker, advocate of peace), 1914-52 (1 box); Ichabod Codding (Ill., Wis.; abolitionist, a founder of Liberty Party), 1832-66 (2 boxes); Elias Hicks (N. Y.; Quaker preacher, leader of the separation in the Society of Friends), 1779-1830 (600 pieces); Edward Hicks (Pa.; Quaker preacher, "primitive" painter), 1816-49 (1 box); William I. Hull (Pa.; prof. of history and international relations at Swarthmore College), 1900-39 (60 boxes); Samuel M. Janney (Va.; historian, Quaker preacher, Indian supt.), 1815-80 (4 boxes); William Ladd (N. H.; founder of the American Peace Society and pioneer in the theory of international organization), 1814-40 (10 in.); Belva Ann B. Lockwood (N.Y., D.C.; lawyer, advocate of woman's suffrage, lecturer), 1887-1917 (5 in.); and Moses Sheppard (Md.; Quaker founder of a mental hospital, abolitionist), 1794-1927 (9 boxes).

Also included are papers of Edwin D. Mead (Mass.; author, lecturer, editor of New England Magazine), 1877-1935 (2 ft.); Lucia Ames Mead (Mass.; author, especially active in the movement for a League of Nations), 1884-1936 (3 ft.); Lucretia Coffin Mott (Pa.; Quaker preacher, abolitionist, feminist), 1834-80 (500 pieces); Robert

Proud (Pa.; schoolmaster, historian), 1776-99 (1 box); Job Scott (R.I.; Quaker preacher), 1777-93 (1 vol.); Anna Garlin Spencer (Mass., N. Y.; journalist, Unitarian minister, advocate of woman's suffrage and other reforms) and family, 1832-1932 ($2^{1}/_{2}$ ft.); Sydney D. Strong (Ill., Wash.; Congregational minister, author), 1895-1940 ($1^{1}/_{2}$ ft.); John Greenleaf Whittier (Mass.; poet, abolitionist), 1828-92 (700 pieces); and John Woolman (N.J.; Quaker preacher, abolitionist), 1756-72 (4 vols.). In the Charles F. Jenkins Autograph Collection there are letters of Members of the Continental Congress, signers of the Constitution, Presidents of the United States, abolitionists and other reformers, poets, and writers.

Records of Friends organizations include those of the American Friends Fellowship Council, 1933-51 (39 boxes); American Friends Service Committee (Civilian Public Service, Prison Service Committee), 1941-47 (225 ft.); Baltimore Yearly Meeting Standing Committee on the Indian Concern, 1813-1900 (2 boxes); Convention of Delegates of the Seven Yearly Meetings Having Charge of the Indians in the Northern Superintendency, 1869-84 (2 boxes); Friends General Conference, 1867-1940 (9 vols.); Friends World Committee for Consultation, 1937-52 (32 boxes); Illinois Yearly Meeting (Hicksite), 1820-1918 (43 vols.); Joint Committee on Indian Affairs of the Four Yearly Meetings (Baltimore, Genesee, New York, Philadelphia), 1836-49 (1 box); Ohio Yearly Meeting (Hicksite), 1813-1922 (100 vols.); and the Philadelphia Yearly Meeting, 1668-1954 (1,550 vols. and 8 ft.).

Records of organizations devoted largely to the preservation of peace include those of the American Peace Society, 1828-1947 ($4^{1}/_{2}$ ft.); Association to Abolish War, 1915-27 (5 in.); Central Organization for a Durable

Peace, 1915-18 (2 ft.); Deutsche
Friedensgesellschaft (German Peace
Society), 1910-47 (1 ft.); International
Federation of League of Nations Asso-
ciations, 1919-34 (5 in.); National
Committee on Conscientious Objec-
tors (of the American Civil Liberties
Union), 1940-46 (11 ft.); National Com-
mittee on the Cause and Cure of War,
1924-47 (13 in.); National Council for
Prevention of War, 1921-47 (200 ft.);
National Service Board for Religious
Objectors, 1940-47 (225 ft.); Pacifist
Research Bureau, 1941-47 (8 in.);
Pennsylvania Committee for Total
Disarmament, 1930-36 (11 ft.); Unit-
ed Peace Chest (of Philadelphia), 1937-
47 (15 in.); Universal Peace Union,
1866-1920 (24 ft.); Women's International League for Peace and Freedom,
1915-47 (205 ft.); and Women's Peace
Union, 1921-41 (18 ft.).

The Library is the official depository for records of meetings belonging
to Philadelphia Yearly Meeting of the
Religious Society of Friends and records of Swarthmore College, 1864-
1954 (46 boxes and 44 vols.). It is
also the official depository for the records of the Fellowship of Reconcilia-
tion, Friends Committee on National
Legislation, National Council for Prevention of War, National Service Board
for Religious Objectors, War Resisters
League, and the Women's International
League for Peace and Freedom.

See Hist. Records Survey, Inven-
tory of Church Archives: Society of
Friends in Pennsylvania (1941. 397 p.
Processed); Ellen S. Brinton and Hi-
ram Doty, Guide to the Swarthmore
College Peace Collection (1947. 72 p.);
Ellen S. Brinton, "The Swarthmore
College Peace Collection," in Am. Ar-
chivist, 10:35-39 (Jan. 1947), and
"Archives of Causes and Movements:
Difficulties and Some Solutions as Il-
lustrated by the Swarthmore College
Peace Collection," in Am. Archivist,
14:147-153 (Apr. 1951); and the Li-
brary's Friends Historical Library

of Swarthmore College (n.d. [8] p.);
and its Check List of the Jane Addams
Papers ([1953.] 4 p. Processed).

TITUSVILLE

Drake Museum. Drake Well Museum
Park.

Holdings: A collection of papers
relating chiefly to the history of the
petroleum industry in northwestern
Pennsylvania. Included are papers
of John H. Scheide (Pa.; oil man,
founder of the Museum), 1860-90
(8 cu. ft.); and papers of Ida M. Tarbell (Pa., N.Y.; author), 5 cu. ft.,
relating to her study of the petroleum
industry.

See Preliminary Guide to the Research Materials of the Pennsylvania
Historical and Museum Commission,
p. 47 (1959).

TOWANDA

Bradford County Historical Society.
Court St. Frances Hall, Secretary.

Holdings: 1,500 pieces, 1770-
1920, relating chiefly to Bradford
County. Included are tax assessment books, 1812-43, for the various
townships and boroughs; decennial
census records, 1850-80; records of
the Susquehannah Co. of Connecticut;
old deeds and other records of real
estate transactions; daybooks and
ledgers of early merchants; a number of Civil War diaries and military
papers; records pertaining to World
Wars I and II; and records relating
to the Susquehanna Collegiate Institute.

See Hist. Records Survey, Guide
for Pa., p. 93.

UNIONTOWN

Public Library. Corner Beeson

Blvd. and Church St. Mabel E. Zearley, Librarian.

Holdings: 500 pieces, 1770-1930, relating chiefly to Fayette and neighboring counties. Included are some Whiskey Rebellion papers; business records of an iron foundry, 1801-12, and of a store, 1811-84; church records, 1770-1930; and scattered official records of Fayette, West Augusta, and Yohogania Counties, 1784-1840.

UNIVERSITY PARK

Pennsylvania State University Library. Ralph W. McComb, Librarian.

Holdings: Many thousands of pieces, 1450-1959, relating chiefly to the University and its predecessor, Pennsylvania State College, and to central Pennsylvania.

In the Pennsylvania Historical Collections are papers of James A. Beaver (Pa.; Civil War officer, Gov., State superior court judge, acting pres. of Pa. State College), 1855-1914 (28 cu. ft.); Philip Benner (Pa.; ironmaster, merchant) and his family, 1830-38 (85 pieces); the Boal family, 1450-1930 (45 cu. ft.), containing correspondence and other persons of a prominent central Pennsylvania family and photographic copies of 15th-century Spanish manuscripts pertaining to Christopher Columbus; Isaac Craig (Pa., U. S. Army officer), 1793-95 (300 pages), typed copies; Ebenezer Denny (Pa.; 1st mayor of Pittsburgh), 1781-99 (287 pages), typed copy of journal; James T. Hale (Pa.; State supreme court justice, U. S. Rep.), 1849-64 (50 pieces); Jacob Hibshman (Pa.; U. S. Rep.), 1804-43 ($2\frac{1}{2}$ cu. ft.); George M. Leader (Pa.; Gov.), 1955-59 (300 cu. ft.), consisting of files of the Governor's office, re-

stricted; Edward Martin (Pa.; Gov., U. S. Sen.), 1955-58 (22 cu. ft.); and James Pollock (Pa.; U. S. Rep., Gov.) and his family, chiefly 1840-45 (33 pieces). Records relating to the history of the University, 1851 to date (20,000 pieces), include papers of the following presidents of Pennsylvania State College: Evan Pugh, 1850-64 (10 ft.); Edwin Erle Sparks, 1879-1924 (5 ft.); George W. Atherton, 1858-1906 (16 ft.); and Ralph Dorn Hetzel, 1917-47 (4 ft.).

Also in the Pennsylvania Historical Collections are store and other business account books, 1784-1891 (19 pieces); records of central Pennsylvania iron furnaces, 1800-74 ($1\frac{1}{4}$ cu. ft.); papers of a turnpike company, 1840-45 (43 cu. ft.); a collection of copies of papers on early American agriculture, 1686-1920 (1 cu. ft.), including copies of the minutes of the Philadelphia Society for the Promotion of Agriculture, 1775-93, 1805-10; and typewritten transcriptions, prepared by the Pennsylvania Historical Survey, of maritime records of the port of Philadelphia, 1776-1937 (24 cu. ft.). There is a collection on naval history, 1834-1925 (1 cu. ft.); and an autograph collection, 1744-1906 (60 pieces), contains papers signed by prominent figures in Europe and the United States.

In the Library but not in its Pennsylvania Historical Collections are papers of Amy Bonner (N. Y.; poet, business representative of Poetry), 1891-1955 (560 pieces), among them 20 diaries and numerous letters from English and American authors; Harvey Flink (Pa.; poet), 1941-50 (226 pieces); Eunice McCloskey (Pa.; poet, painter), 1930-60 (500 pieces); Fred Lewis Pattee (Pa., Fla.; prof. of American literature at Pa. State and Rollins Colleges), 1875-1950 (1,600 pieces), including 47 letters from Hamlin Garland (Mass., Ill., Calif.; novelist) and 59 letters from

Henry Louis Mencken (Md.; author, editor); and small quantities of letters and literary manuscripts of 9 other literary figures.

VALLEY FORGE

Washington Memorial Museum of the Valley Forge Historical Society. Lloyd Eastwood-Seibold, Curator.

Holdings: 1,000 pieces, relating chiefly to Valley Forge before, during, and after the encampment up to the present day, and including also miscellaneous records concerning early colonial days and the Revolutionary War. There are 11 George Washington letters; a few letters and other papers written by other American leaders; and 3 original Valley Forge orderly books.

See Hist. Records Survey, Guide for Pa., p. 94.

VILLANOVA

Villanova University Library. Rev. Daniel P. Falvey, Librarian.

Holdings: Included are 4 manuscripts of works of Saint Augustine, 14th-15th centuries; an Augustinian Rule in Bavarian dialect, 1431 (17 leaves); an account of gods and heroes of pagan mythology (Phillipps Ms. 4200); Legenda aurea . . . per Fratrum Jacobum de Voragine (Phillipps Ms. 12292); Alexandri Strinae de sacramētis libellus, 1567 (20 pages); Regla dela cofradía del traspaso y soledad de Nxa Senora de esta ciud. de Sevilla, 1569; manuscripts in Gaelic, including Ossianic literature and Irish legends and folklore (11 vols.); and Catalogus librorum . . . de rebus hibernicis . . . cura et sumptibus Sheffieldi Grace, 1815 (2 vols.).

Other holdings are theology note-

books of Thomas Matthew Carr (Pa.; Austin friar), kept when a student, 1774-76 (3 vols.); diary and letters to his wife by Alexander M. Thackara (Pa.; manufacturer, consul at Le Havre and consul gen. at Berlin), 1872, 1879-80 (2 vols.); manuscripts of Francis Edward Tourscher (Pa.; Latin prof. and librarian at Villanova Univ.) including translation of some works of St. Augustine (4 vols.), and documents relating to the Hogan schism and trustee troubles in St. Mary's Church, Philadelphia, 1820-29 (3 vols.); photostat of diary of Roger Casement (Ireland; nationalist), March 17–Apr. 8, 1916 (139 leaves); a scrapbook of items relating to restoration of Betsy Ross House and other historical documents; and Villanova College Jug Books (showing penalties for misdemeanors committed by students), 1856-1904 (4 vols.).

See De Ricci, Census, p. 2132; and Hist. Records Survey, Guide for Pa., p. 95.

WASHINGTON

Washington and Jefferson College Historical Collections. W. Russell McWhinney, Reference Librarian.

Holdings: 8,000 pieces of manuscript material, 1740 to date, consisting of two major groups: (1) Washington and Jefferson College Archives, and (2) American History Archives. In the former group are papers of Thaddeus Dod (Pa.; pioneer Presbyterian clergyman), 1781-85 (200 pieces), relating to his school, from which Washington and Jefferson College developed; minutes of the trustees, 1787 to date, and other records of the College; and a collection of literary society records, 1797-1915 (100 vols.). The second group consists largely of manuscripts relating to western Pennsyl-

vania. Included is a collection on the
Revolutionary War in the West (200
pieces); a collection on the settlement
of western Pennsylvania (1,000 pieces);
some minute books and other records
of Virginia courts in what is now
southwestern Pennsylvania, and papers on the boundary controversy between Pennsylvania and Virginia; records of or relating to the North
American Land Co. (400 pieces), and
papers of John Hoge (Pa.; U.S. Rep.),
1804-15 (300 pieces), concerning his
activities as field representative of
the company; records of the Indiana
Land Co. and other papers pertaining
to land matters; and papers of Henry
Willson Temple (Pa.; U.S. Rep.),
chiefly 1913-33 (150 folders). There
are also a large collection on the Whiskey Rebellion of 1794; some records of
early churches and schools; local
material on the War of 1812 and the
Mexican War and a number of Civil
War letters and diaries; and manuscripts documenting activities of the
"Molly Maguires" in the western
Pennsylvania coal fields, 1870-75
(75 pieces), including some letters of
Allan Pinkerton (Ill.; detective).

—oOo—

Washington County Historical Society.
Le Moyne House, 49 East Maiden St.

Holdings: Papers relating chiefly
to Washington County, but including
some of wider interest. Among them
are a number of ledgers and daybooks
of early merchants in Washington and
Washington County; marriage records
of three Washington County justices of
the peace, 1811-44, 1860-87, a Baptist clergyman, 1815-39, and a Presbyterian clergyman, 1841-99; and
original records of the West Augusta
District Court of Virginia, 1775-80
(3 vols.).
See Hist. Records Survey, Guide
for Pa., p. 96.

WASHINGTON CROSSING

Washington Crossing State Park.
William Holland, Curator.

Holdings: 375 items, relating
chiefly to the American Revolution
and consisting largely of the Sol
Feinstone Collection. Included are
several George Washington items.

WAYNESBURG

Greene County Historical Society.
Long Bldg., North Morgan St.
Charles I. Faddis, Curator.

Holdings: A sizable group of
papers, 1769-1925, relating chiefly
to Greene County and other parts of
southwestern Pennsylvania and, less
importantly, to Virginia and West
Virginia. Included are papers of and
pertaining to Christopher Gist (Md.,
N.C., Va.; explorer, soldier, scout);
and the original "Horn Papers," with
material relating to them. There are
also justice of the peace dockets,
1769-1900; sheriffs' records, court
records, and church records, 1795-
1900; many records of businesses in
Greene and Washington Counties, including ledgers and daybooks, 1790-
1900; river logs; and materials pertaining to a local narrow-gage railroad. Papers relating to education
and culture include records of public
schools and teachers in the county,
1848-1925, and of a private academy,
1845-85; literary society minutes and
other records of Monongahela College
(Jefferson, Pa.), 1868-1900, and of
Waynesburg College; records of a
local "Opera House"; and a collection
on traveling Chautauquas in the United
States. Papers pertaining to military
affairs include Civil War letters, a
roster of Greene County men in that
war, and records of Grand Army of
the Republic posts; papers and photo-

graphs pertaining to a local company in the Spanish-American War; and a complete card file of names of men from Greene County in all American wars. There are also genealogical materials (500 vols.); a collection of maps, 1650-1825, including general, colonial, and early State maps; land-patent maps for Greene, Washington, and Fayette Counties; and a large group of photographs, 1865-1900, of Greene County interest.

See Hist. Records Survey, Guide for Pa., p. 98; and Arthur P. Middleton and Douglass Adair, "The Mystery of the Horn Papers," in William and Mary Quarterly, ser. 3, 4:409-445 (Oct. 1947).

WEST CHESTER

Chester County Historical Society. 225 North High St. Bart Anderson, Director.

Holdings: 1,550 cu. ft. of manuscripts and 244 rolls of microfilm, dating from colonial times and relating chiefly to Chester County. Papers of individuals include those of Josiah Harlan (Pa.; soldier-adventurer), relating to his activities in Asia; Isaac I. Hayes (Pa., N.Y.; physician, Arctic explorer); Bayard Taylor (Pa.; author, traveler); Richard Thomas (Pa.; Rev. War officer, U.S. Rep.), 1775-1826; and Constantine S. Rafinesque (Ky., Pa.; botanist, ichthyologist, prof. at Transylvania Univ.), 1808-17, consisting of notes on natural history. County records include tax assessment lists, 1699-1850; tavern papers, 1700-1875; court records; election returns; school records; and many other papers. There is a large quantity of records relating to all post offices that have existed in the county. Business records, dating from the early 18th century, include those of country stores, the

county's oldest bank, nursery businesses, smiths' shops, and mills of various types. Also included are diaries, minute books of various organizations, weather observations, and military records.

See Hist. Records Survey, Guide for Pa., p. 99; and Bart Anderson, "The Chester County Historical Society," in Pa. History, 19:194-197 (Apr. 1952).

—oOo—

State Teachers College Library. Joseph K. Hall, Librarian.

Holdings: 102 vols., 10,100 pieces, and 38 cu. ft., including papers of William Darlington (Pa.; physician, botanist, U.S. Rep.); several letters from pre-Civil War military and political leaders to Persifer F. Smith (U.S. Army officer); letters to and from Anthony Wayne (Pa.; Rev. War officer); some autograph letters of signers of the Declaration of Independence; and a collection of letters of scientists, 1821-98.

See Hist. Records Survey, Guide for Pa., p. 100.

WESTTOWN

Westtown School Historical Library. Anna Hartshorne Brown, Historical Librarian.

Holdings: Several thousand items, 1792-1948, consisting chiefly of records of and relating to this Friends school, and correspondence, diaries, and other papers of local families. There are a few scattered letters of persons of national importance.

See Hist. Records Survey, Guide for Pa., p. 102.

WILKES-BARRE

Wilkes College Library. Mrs. Nada Vujica, Librarian.

Holdings: The Gilbert C. McClintock collection of papers containing autographs of United States Presidents and other Americans of prominence.

—oOo—

Wyoming Historical and Geological Society. 69 South Franklin St. Richmond Dean Williams, Director.

Holdings: 1,300 cu. ft., 1750-1910, relating chiefly to the Wilkes-Barre region of the Susquehanna Valley and the Wyoming Valley region. Papers of individuals include those of Edmund L. Dana (Pa.; lawyer, officer in Mexican and Civil Wars, judge), 1839-65 (210 pieces); Henry M. Hoyt (Pa.; lawyer, Gov., author), 1847-85 (334 pieces); Samuel Meredith (Pa.; Rev. War officer, Member Continental Cong., first U. S. Treasurer), 1771-1842 (50 pieces); Charles Miner (Pa.; U. S. Rep., editor), 1809-63 (457 pieces); Timothy Pickering (Pa., Mass.; Rev. War officer, Postmaster Gen., Sec. War, Sec. State, U. S. Sen. and Rep. from Mass.), 1778-1823 (75 pieces); John Sullivan (N. H.; Rev. War officer, Member Continental Cong., Pres. of N. H.), 1779-86 (22 pieces); and Hendrick B. Wright (Pa.; lawyer, U. S. Rep., author), 1840-81 (50 cu. ft.). Included also are records of the Wilkes-Barre Bridge Co., 1795-1845 (51 pieces); Susquehanna Co., 1750-1810 (photostats of 3,000 pieces); Sharpe, Weiss Coal Co., 1855-1900 (5,000 pieces); and Lehigh and Wilkes-Barre Coal Co., 1878-1910 (4,000 pieces). There are also early township proprietors' books; land records; tax lists; church records; turnpike, canal, and railroad papers; diaries; business and public utility account books; and family papers.

See Hist. Records Survey, Guide for Pa., p. 103.

WILLIAMSPORT

James V. Brown Library. 19 East Fourth St. Katherine W. Bennett, Librarian.

Holdings: A small quantity of diaries, letters, deeds, and other papers, 1790-1919, relating chiefly to Williamsport and Lycoming County. Included are county tax records, 1795-1800; minute books of local fire companies, 1856-74; and some World War I service records.

YORK

Historical Society of York County. 250 East Market St. Daniel R. Porter, Director.

Holdings: 310 vols., 25,000 other pieces, and 190,000 frames of microfilm copies of manuscripts, 1720-1959, relating chiefly to York and Adams Counties and vicinity. Included are local and county records, 1741-1850; church records, 1733-1950; materials on the social and artistic history of the Pennsylvania Germans, the Scotch-Irish, and the Quakers; theatrical collections; account books of merchants and of turnpike and railroad companies; Revolutionary War muster rolls, accounts, and similar documents; and diaries and sermons.

See Hist. Records Survey, Guide for Pa., p. 105; and the Society's Annual Report, 1936 to date.

PUERTO RICO

RIO PIEDRAS

University of Puerto Rico Library.
Thomas S. Hayes, Librarian.

Holdings: Private manuscripts relating primarily to the history and literature of Puerto Rico, but also a large quantity of the correspondence, literary manuscripts, and other papers of Juan Ramón Jiménez (Spain, Puerto Rico; poet), 20th century.

SAN JUAN

Archivo General de Puerto Rico.
Apartado 4184. Luis M. Rodriguez Morales, Director.

Holdings: Records of agencies of the Commonwealth Government, consisting at present chiefly of records of predecessor agencies of the Spanish period received from successor agencies in the present government. Included are (1) records of the Audiencia (19th century), among them civil cases, criminal cases, and records of the Secretary's Office; (2) records of the old Department of Public Works (Obras Publicas), 1848-98 (800 cu. ft.), relating to highways, streets, railroads, bridges, port facilities, water supply systems, schools, hospitals, religious buildings, municipal properties, and other public holdings, with relevant maps and plans; (3) records of a municipal inspection force, the Diputacion Provincial, 1763-1899 (48 cu. ft.); (4) Department of Public Health records, 1881-1931 (785 cu. ft.), mostly the so-called "Registro Demografico," containing records of marriages, births, and deaths; (5) Treasury Department accounts, 1872-90 (80 cu. ft.); (6) Justice Department letterpress books, 1920-30 (8 cu. ft.); (7) holdings of the old "Archivo Historico" (280 cu. ft.), mostly records of the Spanish Governors of Puerto Rico, 1770-1898, emanating from the Fortuleza (a somewhat smaller quantity of records from this same record group is in the National Archives, Washington 25, D.C.); (8) miscellaneous papers from other departments; and (9) the older records of some municipalities.

RHODE ISLAND

KINGSTON

University of Rhode Island Library. F. P. Allen, Librarian.

Holdings: Papers of Caroline Hazard (R. I., Mass.; author, pres. of Wellesley College), letters not yet arranged; Rowland Gibson Hazard (R. I.; manufacturer, writer on philosophical subjects), some letters not yet classified; Elisha Reynolds Potter, Sr. (R. I.; lawyer, farmer, U. S. Rep.), 1710-1834, including business records and diaries, 1798-1829; and Elisha Reynolds Potter, Jr. (R. I.; farmer, State supreme court justice, U. S. Rep.), 1835-82, including business records and letters from William Beach Lawrence (N. Y., R. I.; writer on international law).

NEWPORT

Newport Historical Society. 82 Touro St.

Holdings: 1,700 vols. and 25,000 pieces, 17th-20th centuries, relating chiefly to Rhode Island, especially to Newport. Included are official records of the city of Newport, 1684-1775; and records of town meetings, 1780-1853. Records of churches include Rhode Island Friends records for Portsmouth and Newport, 1683-1931 (28 vols.); Congregational church records for Newport, 1728-1833 (12 vols.); and Baptist church records, 1725-1833 (8 vols.). There are also many ships' logs, including a few logs of whalers; and mercantile records, including business papers of the following Rhode Island

merchants: John Bannister, 1695-1768; James Gould and Son, 1762-1862 (34 vols.); Aaron Lopez, 1752-81 (112 pieces); and William and Samuel Vernon, 1740-82.

PROVIDENCE 12

Annmary Brown Memorial, Brown University. John R. Turner Ettlinger, Curator.

Holdings: 7,900 pieces, 1641-1920. Papers of individuals include those of Rush C. Hawkins (N. Y.; Civil War officer, collector of incunabula), 1851-1920 (7,250 pieces); and George Weedon (Va.; Rev. War officer), 1778-86 (119 pieces). The Samuel Wyllys Papers, a collection of Connecticut legal documents, 1641-1738 (119 pieces), contain 39 documents relating to witchcraft trials, 1662-93, and a number concerning Indian relations, 1667-1714. There are also some Civil War papers, chiefly Confederate (165 pieces).

—oOo—

Brown University Library. David A. Jonah, Librarian.

Holdings: A large quantity of manuscripts, mostly 18th-20th centuries, relating chiefly to Brown University, Rhode Island, and the literary and other aspects of the history of the United States. Holdings of the Annmary Brown Memorial and the John Carter Brown Library are described separately.

Papers of political leaders include those of Samuel Sullivan Cox (Ohio, N. Y.; lawyer, U. S. Rep.,

Minister to Turkey, author), 1853-87
(1,000 pieces); Thomas Wilson Dorr
(R. I.; lawyer, leader of the Dorr Rebellion), 1826-54 (770 pieces); John
Milton Hay (Ill., D. C.; sec. to Pres.
Lincoln and his biographer, diplomat,
poet, Sec. State), 1856-1905 (5,700
pieces), among them journals and literary manuscripts as well as correspondence; Charles Evans Hughes (N.Y.;
Gov., Sec. State, U. S. Chief Justice),
1878-1945 (110 pieces); Abraham Lincoln (Ill.; lawyer, U. S. Rep. and
Pres.), 1825-65 (1,678 pieces), consisting of 865 letters and other manu-
scripts and documents, and 813 letters
to Lincoln by his associates; Charles
Warren Lippitt (R. I.; manufacturer,
Gov.) and his family, 1875-1920 (8,500
pieces); Thomas Rodney (Del., Miss.;
Rev. War officer, Member Continental
Cong., State supreme court justice,
U. S. judge for Miss. Terr.), 1774-
1808 (700 pieces); Jonathan Russell
(R. I., Mass.; merchant, diplomat,
U. S. Rep.), 1795-1832 (7,000 pieces);
William Sprague (R. I.; locomotive
manufacturer, Gov., U. S. Sen.) and
Kate Chase Sprague (Ohio, D.C., R.I.;
political hostess), 1830-1915 (250
pieces); and Eli Thayer (Mass.; edu-
cator, U. S. Rep., organizer of New
England Emigrant Aid Co.), 1841-98
(1,000 pieces), among them some letters from Charles Robinson (Mass.,
Kans.; agent of New England Emigrant Aid Co., Gov. of Kans.).

Papers of persons in the fields of
medicine, science, and technology include those of William Whitman Bailey (R. I.; botanist, poet, prof. at
Brown Univ.), 1857-1907 (20 vols. of
journals, 300 letters, and 1 portfolio
of sketches); Charles Value Chapin
(R. I.; physician, Providence supt. of
health), 1901-40 (3 boxes of correspondence); George Henry Corliss
(R. I.; mechanical engineer, inventor,
manufacturer), 1838-80 (504 pieces);
William Corliss (R. I.; inventor, industrialist), 1856-63 (6 vols. of dia-

ries); Elmer Lawrence Corthell
(N. Y.; civil engineer), 1855-1916
(3 boxes); Solomon Drowne (R. I.;
physician, botanist, prof. at Brown
Univ. Medical School), 1765-1834
(2,100 pieces); James Whitbread Lee
Glaisher (England; mathematician,
astronomer), 1870-84 (275 letters,
chiefly to); Clarence King (D. C.;
geologist, head of U. S. Geological
Survey), 1877-95 (85 letters);
James Joseph Sylvester (England,
Md.; mathematician, prof. at Oxford
and Johns Hopkins Univs.), 1842-97
(107 letters); and Edward Tuckerman
(Mass.; botanist, lichenologist),
1867-74 (52 letters).

Papers of literary figures include those of Henry Adams (Mass.;
historian), 1838-1918 (85 letters);
George Shepard Burleigh (R. I.;
poet, reformer), 1839-90 (29 vols.
and 362 letters and other items);
George Henry Calvert (Md., R. I.;
poet, essayist, mayor of Newport),
1866-83 (106 letters); Harry Crosby
(N. Y., France; poet), 10 vols.;
George William Curtis (R. I., N. Y.;
author, editor), 1852-87 (76 letters,
plus a ledger and other papers);
Maud Howe Elliott (R. I., Mass.; author), 1885-1945 (265 letters and extensive diaries); Richard Watson
Gilder (N. Y.; editor, poet), 1871-
1904 (54 letters); James Albert Harrison (Va.; philologist, author, Univ.
of Va. prof.), 1900-9 (51 letters);
Mellinger E. Henry (N. J.; folklorist),
1910-42 (600 pieces on American
folklore); William Dean Howells
(Mass., N. Y.; novelist, literary
critic, editor), 1896-1919 (113 pieces); John H. Ingram (England; author), 1874-78 (83 letters); Harry
Lyman Koopman (Maine, R. I.; poet,
librarian, bibliography prof. at Brown
Univ.), 1878-1937 (85 boxes); Howard
Phillips Lovecraft (R. I.; novelist, poet), 1897-1937 (16 boxes); Cincinnatus Hiner Miller, known as Joaquin
Miller (Oreg., Calif.; poet, play-

wright), 6 vols. of plays; John George Nicolay (Ill.; private sec. and biographer of Pres. Lincoln), 1864-94 (80 letters); William Douglas O'Connor (Mass., D. C.; journalist, biographer), 1852-86 (79 pieces); Whitlaw Reid (Ohio, N. Y.; Minister to France and to Great Britain, journalist), 1867-98 (130 letters); George Washburn Smalley (Mass., N. Y.; journalist, war correspondent), 1870-97 (58 letters); Benjamin Franklin Mears Sours (Pa.; poet), 1896-1953 (70 vols.); Caroline Ticknor (Mass.; author), 1913-24 (85 letters); Theodore Tilton (N. Y.; newspaper editor, author), 1894-1901 (4 vols. of literary manuscripts); Jones Very (Mass.; transcendentalist, poet, essayist) and his sister, Lydia Very (Mass.; author), 1839-86 (a quantity of sermons, letters, and literary manuscripts); Sarah Helen Whitman (R. I.; poet), 19th century (417 letters); and Emile Zola (France; novelist), 1879-86 (77 letters).

Papers of other persons include those of Lysander Dickerman (Mass., N. H.; clergyman, Egyptologist), 1875-95 (400 pieces); William Herbert Perry Faunce (R. I.; Baptist clergyman, pres. of Brown Univ.), 1875-1913 (27 boxes); John C. Henshaw (U. S. Army officer), 1842-63 (4 vols. and 80 pieces); James Manning (R. I.; Baptist clergyman, pres. of Brown Univ.), 1759-91 (265 pieces); Asa Messer (R. I.; Baptist clergyman, pres. of Brown Univ.), 1791-1826 (6 letter books, 4 vols. of sermons and essays, and 25 letters); Charles King Newcomb (R. I.; transcendentalist, member of Brook Farm community), 1829-70 (445 letters, journals, and other papers); Thomas Ustick (N. Y., Pa.; Baptist clergyman), 1773-1800 (102 letters); Lester Frank Ward (D. C., R. I.; sociologist, prof. at Brown Univ.), 1880-1913 (5,000 pieces); Francis Wayland (R. I.; Baptist clergyman, pres. of Brown Univ.), 1819-65 (2,181 pieces); Henry Wheaton (R. I.,

N. Y.; jurist, diplomat, expounder of international law), 1813-51 (275 pieces), chiefly family letters; and Alva Woods (R. I., Ky., Ala.; Baptist clergyman, univ. pres.), 1794-1887 (4 vols. and 1 box).

Miscellaneous holdings include 54 Indic manuscripts; a collection of 18 letters or other documents of Napoleon I (France; Emperor) and 400 letters by his associates and contemporaries; official manuscript copies of acts and resolves passed by the Rhode Island General Assembly, 1678-1747; a considerable group of manuscript song and music books, late 18th to mid-19th century; a collection of letters by mathematical tablemakers, 1840-1940 (580 pieces); seven collections of Civil War letters (1,200 pieces); and a collection of 4,800 sheet manuscripts of American poets and playwrights, and a large but undetermined number of bound volumes of literary remains of minor poets. Also in the library are records of and manuscripts relating to Brown University and its alumni, 1769 to date (98 linear ft.).

—oOo—

John Carter Brown Library, Brown University. Thomas R. Adams, Librarian.

Holdings: 325,000 pieces, 1150-1900, relating chiefly to North, South, and Central America before 1801.

Papers of individuals include those of John Russell Bartlett (R. I., N. Y.; antiquarian, bibliographer, author), 1846-86 (20 vols.); Elias Boudinot (N. J.; Rev. War officer, Pres. of Continental Cong., U. S. Rep.), 1775-79 (1 vol.); Nicholas Brown (R. I.; merchant, philanthropist) and later members of his family, 1750-1900 (300,000 pieces); John Pory (England, Va.; geographer, traveler, sec. to the Va. council at Jamestown),

1622 (1 vol.); and George Washington
(Va.; Rev. War Commander in Chief,
U.S. Pres.), 1775-99 (3 vols.), con-
sisting of correspondence, 1775-80
(1 vol.), chiefly with Joseph Reed
(N.J., Pa.; lawyer, Rev. War officer,
Member Continental Cong.), and cash
accounts, 1794-99 (2 vols.).

Included also are medieval and
Renaissance illuminated manuscripts
(12 pieces); dictionaries, grammars,
and other manuscript works relating
to the linguistics of aboriginal Latin
America, 1575-1800 (50 vols.); papers relating to the Franciscan Order
of New Spain, 1576-1820 (18 vols.);
other papers relating to New Spain,
1588-1745 (3 vols.); a collection of
autographs of the signers of the Declaration of Independence (50 pieces);
papers of the firm of Samuel G. Arnold and Co., of Providence, Wel-
come Arnold, and Green and Arnold,
1773-1825 (12 boxes); papers of the
Peace Dale Co., woolen manufacturers, 1800 (2 cases); and records of
the Charitable Baptist Society of
Providence, 1774-1800 (40 pieces).

See Damian Van den Eynde, "Cal-
endar of Spanish Documents in the
John Carter Brown Library," in His-
panic Am. Hist. Review, 16:564-607
(Nov. 1936); Lawrence C. Wroth,
"Source Materials of Florida History
in the John Carter Brown Library of
Brown University," in Fla. Hist.
Quarterly, 20:3-46 (July 1941), and
The First Century of the John Carter
Brown Library; a History With a
Guide to the Collections (1946. 88 p.);
and De Ricci, Census, pp. 2143-2152.

PROVIDENCE   6

Moses Brown School.   Mrs. William
Paxton, Librarian.

Holdings: 300 pieces, relating
chiefly to the Society of Friends. Included are records of the Yearly

Meeting of New England, 1683-1902
(9 vols.); Yearly Meeting of Women
Friends, 1764-1875 (7 vols.); Rhode
Island Quarterly Meeting, 1681-1865
(3 vols.); Providence Monthly Meeting, 1783-1800, 1841-69 (2 vols.);
and Abolition Society, 1789-1830
(1 vol.).   Included also are several
papers of and relating to Job Scott
(R.I.; Quaker clergyman), 1751-93.
See Allison, Inventory, p. 206.

PROVIDENCE 3

Providence Public Library.   Stuart
C. Sherman, Librarian.

Holdings: 3 letter-file drawers,
17th-19th centuries, consisting of
miscellaneous letters and other papers relating chiefly to Rhode Island.
Included are letters of Rhode Island
Governors, Revolutionary muster
rolls, letters and orders of Rhode
Island naval and military men, and
papers concerning the French in
Revolutionary Newport; 150 letters
of Daniel Berkeley Updike (Mass.;
printer, typographer), 1900-40; and
miscellaneous letters of U.S. Presidents.   There is also a large collection of over 600 manuscript logbooks
and account books, and miscellaneous
manuscripts relating to the American
whaling industry.

PROVIDENCE 6

Rhode Island Historical Society.
52 Power St.   Clifford P. Monahon,
Director; Clarkson A. Collins III,
Librarian.

Holdings: An extensive collection
of manuscripts, 17th-20th centuries,
relating chiefly to Rhode Island.
Papers of individuals include
those of Moses Brown (R.I.; cotton
manufacturer, philanthropist); Oba-

diah Brown (R. I.; merchant, philanthropist), 1742-59 (20 account books and 3 boxes); William Ellery Channing (Mass.; Congregational and Unitarian minister), 67 letters to Channing, also the Channing-Ellery family papers, 1694-1819 (8 vols.); Nicholas Cooke (R. I.; Rev. War Gov.) and his family, 1732-1811 (2 vols.); Samuel Eddy (R. I.; U. S. Rep., State chief justice); Albert Collins Greene (R. I.; U.S. Sen.) and Richard Ward Greene (R. I.; U. S. dist. attorney, State chief justice) and their family, 1750-1870 (175 vols. and 80 boxes), including 150 account books; William Harris (R. I.; early settler, a proprietor of Providence) and his family, 1638-1846 (6 boxes); Jeremiah Olney (R. I.; Rev. War officer, collector of customs at Providence), 1775-1820 (3 vols.); Richard Ward (R. I.; merchant, colonial Gov.); and Roger Williams (R. I.; clergyman, founder and Pres. of R. I. Colony). The Peck manuscript collection, 1636-1925 (16 boxes), contains letters of Nathanael Greene (R. I., Ga.; Rev. War officer) and of many Rhode Island political leaders and merchants.

Besides personal papers of some Revolutionary patriots, there are other papers relating to the American Revolution, including those pertaining to the war hospital at Providence, 1775-82, and to victualing the British fleet; miscellaneous military papers, 1775-83 (6 vols.); and official papers of Asa Waterman (R. I.; Rev. War deputy commissary), 1775-83 (6 vols. and 2 boxes). Also included are official records of Providence, 1639-1832 (160 vols.), and of other Rhode Island cities and towns; and records of the customhouse at Providence, 1790-1890 (100 vols., 100 boxes, and 8 bundles). Church and related records include those of a number of Six Principle Baptist churches in Rhode Island, 1680-1945 (18 vols.); the Channing Conference of Unitarian Churches,

1867-94; the Rhode Island Sunday School Union, 1825-62 (2 vols.); the First Congregational Church, Providence, 1736-1850 (22 vols. and 21 boxes); the Congregational Pastors' Meeting of Providence and Vicinity, 1873-86 (2 vols.); and various missionary and tract societies, 1815-52. Other manuscripts relating to religious history comprise the collection assembled by Isaac Backus (Conn., Mass.; Baptist minister, historian), 1638-1731 (1 vol.). There are also records of the Providence Association of Mechanics and Manufacturers, 1789-1912 (14 vols. and 4 boxes); records dealing with trade with Europe, the East Indies, the West Indies, and South America, 1750-1823 (20 account books and 40 vols. of correspondence); papers dealing with East India trade, 1800-80 (6 boxes); extensive records of two textile mills, 1797-1954; and records of a privately endowed poor farm of the City of Providence, 1827-1957.

See Bradford F. Swan, "The Providence Town Papers," in R. I. History, 11:65-70 (July 1952); and Earl C. Tanner, "The Providence Federal Customhouse Papers as a Source of Maritime History Since 1790," in New England Quarterly, 26:88-100 (Mar. 1953).

PROVIDENCE 2

Rhode Island State Archives, Department of State. 314 State House. Mary T. Quinn, Assistant for Archives.

Holdings: A considerable quantity of official records, 1638-1954, of the colony and State of Rhode Island, together with a few private papers. Records of the General Assembly, 1638-1954, include acts and resolves (268 vols.), house journals (98 vols.), senate journals (75 vols.), and many related papers, among which are petitions, 1725-1869 (83 vols. and 12 ft.), reports, 1728-1954 (14 vols. and 40 file drawers), and letters, 1730-1886 (65 vols. and 600 pieces). There are also records of colonial courts of equity, 1725-41 (21 vols.), and admiralty, 1726-86 (13 vols.). Papers of the executive branch include correspondence of the secretary of state, 1793-1891 (70 bundles); and his records on corporations, 1790-1954 (218 vols.). Accounts of the general treasurer, 1672-1905, comprise 142 vols.; and correspondence, accounts, and other records of the Public Welfare Department, 1869-1934, occupy 140 ft. and 6 filing cabinets. Included

also are quartermaster records, 1827-1919 (68 vols. and 24 boxes); and miscellaneous military, maritime, and boundary papers (66 vols.).

The private papers consist of papers of Joseph Clarke (R. I.; general treasurer of the colony and State), 1761-77 (34 items); papers of Benjamin Huntington (Conn.; Member Continental Cong., U. S. Rep.), 1772-90 (50 items), which include letters to him from William Ellery (R. I.; Member Continental Cong., State chief justice), 1783-90; and letters and military papers of Asa Waterman (R. I.; Rev. War deputy commissary), 1775-81 (295 items).

SOUTH CAROLINA

CHARLESTON 5

Charleston Library Society. 164 King St. Virginia Rugheimer, Librarian.

Holdings: A miscellaneous collection of letters, diaries, account books, and other papers relating chiefly to South Carolina. Included are some papers of John C. Calhoun (S. C.; U. S. Rep. and Sen., Sec. War, Vice Pres., Sec. State), 1844-50 (18 letters); Wade Hampton 3d (S. C.; Confed. Army officer, Gov., U. S. Sen.), 1898-1900 (25 letters); John Rutledge (S. C.; Member Continental Cong., Gov., U. S. Supreme Court Justice), 1780-82 (25 letters); and George Washington (Va.; U. S. Pres.), 1789-98 (8 letters). There are also an 11th-century Oriental manuscript; minute books of the Carolina Rifle Club, 1869-91 (4 vols.); Charleston tax records, 1859-75 (19 vols.); ledger copies of South Carolina land grants, 1735-52 (2 vols.); and a collection relating to the Huguenots, 16th-18th centuries, containing parish registers, letters, and proceedings of consistories.

CHARLESTON 16

Charleston Museum. Rutledge and Calhoun Sts. E. Milby Burton, Director.

Holdings: 2,042 letters, 1722-1930, and a few other items relating to South Carolina and to natural history. Included are letters to and from the family of John James Audubon (Pa., Ky., La., N. Y.; artist, ornithologist), 1833-71 (111 items); letters by John Bachman (S. C.; Lutheran clergyman, naturalist), 1834-70 (180 items), and

letters to members of his family, 1838-1916 (58 items); journals of William Drayton (S. C.; U. S. dist. court judge), 1782-86 (4 vols.); letters to Lewis R. Gibbes (S. C.; physician, college prof., writer on scientific and natural history subjects), 1843-85 (49 items); letters to Benjamin N. Martin (N. J., N. Y.; author, prof. at Univ. of City of N. Y.) and Daniel S. Martin (N. J.; geologist, prof. at Rutgers College) and their family, 1831-1915 (440 items); letters by and to Edmund Ravenel (S. C.; physician, conchologist, prof. at Medical College of S. C.), 1831-61 (139 items); letters by and to Henry W. Ravenel (S. C.; planter, botanist, writer on agricultural subjects), 1850-89 (210 items); and letters to Arthur Trezevant Wayne (S. C.; ornithologist), 1894-1930 (872 items), and his ornithological journal. Included also are small quantities of correspondence of other persons of prominence; the account book of a silversmith, 1703; plantation books, 1757-1859; and some court books, tax books, deeds, and other papers.

CHARLESTON 10

College of Charleston Library. 66 George St. Mary V. Powers, Librarian.

Holdings: Papers of Burnet Rhett Maybank (S. C.; lawyer, Gov., U. S. Sen.), 1931-54 (a large quantity); a few papers each of several persons of prominence, 1667-1885; records of literary societies of the College, 1848-1955; ledger records of a bank, 1843-72 (15 vols.); and a group of uncataloged manuscripts, such as indentures, bonds, letters, deeds, and plantation plans, 1764-1839.

CHARLESTON 5

South Carolina Historical Society. Fireproof Bldg.   Mrs. Granville T. Prior, Archivist.

Holdings: 450 ft. of papers, chiefly of the 18th and 19th centuries, relating to South Carolina and particularly to its coastal region.

Of primary importance among the holdings of the colonial and Revolutionary periods is the Laurens Collection, 1747-96 (38 vols. and 670 items). This contains the papers of Henry Laurens (S. C.; merchant, planter, Pres. of Continental Cong.), including records of transactions with the French minister, the journal of the South Carolina Council of Safety, Army and Navy returns, and correspondence with George Washington (Va.; Rev. War Commander in Chief, U. S. Pres.), Benjamin Franklin (Pa.; printer, scientist, Member Continental Cong., diplomat), and others; and papers of John Laurens (S. C.; Rev. War officer, envoy to France), including his correspondence with military leaders and statesmen, 1777-81 (85 items). Important also for the early period are papers of Barnard Elliott (S. C.; Rev. War officer), 1775-78 (1 orderly book); Isaac Harleston (S. C.; Rev. War officer), 1779-84 (48 items); Arthur Middleton (S. C.; lawyer, planter, Member Continental Cong.), 1767-82 (1 box); the Pinckney family, 1775-1830 (4 vols. and 93 pieces), including correspondence of Elizabeth Lucas Pinckney (S. C.; one of the developers of indigo as a staple crop); and Pelatiah Webster (Pa.; merchant), 1765 (1 vol.), a journal of his visit to Charleston. Also included are papers of the Commissioners of Fortifications, 1751-70

(1 vol.); records of the Court of Ordinary, 1764-71 (1 vol.); and an account book of the Commissioners of Forfeited Estates, 1782-83.

Papers covering the Civil War and Reconstruction periods include those of Henry W. Fielden (S. C.; Confed. Army officer), 1851-1921 (190 items); John Johnson (S. C.; Confed. Army officer, Episcopal clergyman), 1863-65 (7 vols. and 37 items); Hutson Lee (S. C.; Confed. Army officer), 1858-65 (3 boxes); Andrew Gordon Magrath (S. C.; lawyer, Gov.), 1864-65 (3 vols.); Arthur Mazyck (S. C.; lawyer, librarian), 1840-83 (120 items), containing military papers and notes on a rifle club; Augustine T. Smythe (S. C.; lawyer, Confed. Army soldier, State sen.), 1860-71 (2 boxes), chiefly relating to action around Fort Sumter; J. Adger Smythe (S. C.; mayor of Charleston, cotton broker), 1861-64 (90 items), largely descriptive of army camp life in South Carolina and Virginia; and Edward Willis (S. C.; Confed. Army officer), 1858-80 (2,225 items).   Included also are records of the First Military District of the Department of South Carolina, Georgia, and Florida, 1861-65 (1,021 items); and records of the Importing and Exporting Co. of South Carolina, established to trade with Great Britain through the West Indies, 1863-76 (100 items).

Among papers of other individuals are those of Joseph Barnwell (S. C.; lawyer, S. C. Historical Society pres.), 1861-1930 (50 boxes); Nathaniel Bowen (N. Y., S. C.; Episcopal Bishop of S. C.), 1772-1857 (421 items); Langdon Cheves (S. C.; U. S. Rep., pres. of the Bank of the U. S., State supreme court judge) and his family, 1777-1938 (31 vols. and 224 boxes), including papers of his son Langdon (S. C.; planter, soldier) and his grandson Langdon (S. C.; lawyer, historian); Caroline Howard Gilman (S. C.; author, magazine editor),

1810-80 (109 items); DuBose Heyward (S. C.; novelist, poet, playwright), 1880-1940 (20 boxes); the Manigault family, 1751-1873 (5 vols. and 442 items), including papers of Peter Manigault (S. C.; lawyer, planter, speaker of the Colonial Assembly) and Gabriel E. Manigault (S. C.; physician, Confed. Army officer, prof. of science at the College of Charleston); Thomas Pinckney (S. C.; Rev. War officer, Gov., Minister to Great Britain, U. S. Rep.), 1790-1813 (7 vols.); Joel R. Poinsett (S. C.; U. S. Rep., Minister to Mexico, Sec. War) and James B. Campbell (S. C.; lawyer), 1833-47 (60 items); Daniel Elliot Huger Smith (S. C.; author, curator of S. C. Historical Society), 1680-1917 (24 vols.), consisting of notes on Charleston and the South Carolina coastal area; and John Blake White (S. C.; painter, dramatist, lawyer), 1800-48 (14 vols.).

Important in the Society's holdings are its plantation records, which include the papers of Robert F. W. Allston (S. C.; planter, civil engineer, Gov.) and his family, 1757-1926 (12 vols. and 9,000 items); Theodore Gourdin (S. C.; planter and owner of extensive lands), 1694-1873 (1 vol. and 15 boxes); John Stoney Porcher (S. C.; planter), 1771-1883 (3 vols. and 88 pieces); and Plowden Weston (S. C.; planter), 1786-1869 (216 items). There are also records of plantations in St. Helena's Parish, 1800-21 (3 vols. and 2 items); records, journals, and workbooks of several other plantations, 1817-89 (13 vols. and 67 items); and minutes and meteorological records of an agricultural society, 1842-1925 (7 vols.).

Other holdings of the Society include business and professional papers of James Conner (S. C.; U. S. dist. attorney, Confed. Army officer) and of his father and son, both lawyers, 1843-1938 (87 vols. and 94 boxes); family and business papers of

Daniel Elliott Huger (S. C.; rice planter and broker, State judge, U. S. Sen.) and of his son-in-law, a cotton broker; merchants' daybooks or ledgers, 1764-91 (4 vols.); a report on the Santee Canal, 1800; records of two rice mills, 1860-1925 (5 boxes); and a large number of unprocessed papers of 19th-century Charleston business firms. There are also a collection of medical records, 1775-1856 (15 vols.), including notes on lectures, account books, and prescription books; and a number of diaries, including one of Abiel Abbott (Mass.; Congregational minister), 1818-19, kept in Charleston; a travel journal, 1832, from Charleston to Philadelphia; and the diary of Jacob Sass Schirmer (S. C.; merchant), 1826-80 (9 vols.), a detailed chronicle of Charleston life. There are also some hundred volumes of records of South Carolina Congregational and Episcopal churches and of various church societies, 1732-1954, including an Episcopal "female domestic missionary society," 1857-63 (2 vols.); and records of the Charleston Chamber of Commerce, 1784-1863 (4 vols.); the Community Club of Charleston, 1917-35 (186 items); the New England Society, 1819-1933 (6 vols.); and hunting and jockey clubs, 1785-1833. Included too are a collection of muniments, 1690-1900, and one of land grants and other land papers dating from the Proprietary Government to 1860, assembled by Henry A. Middleton Smith (S. C.; planter, U. S. dist. court judge, S. C. Historical Society pres.); and a large quantity of miscellaneous records of South Carolina families, chiefly genealogical, among them collections assembled by Motte Alston Read (S. C.; geologist, Harvard prof.) and Mabel L. Webber (S. C.; sec. of the S. C. Historical Society).

Records of local governments include those of the highroad commis-

sioners of St. John's Parish, Berkeley
County, 1760-1853 (4 vols.) and of the
police association of the same parish,
1823-40 (2 vols.); and papers of the
Charleston County auditor's office,
1868-1905 (12 vols. and 3,280 items).
There are also some records of the
city of Charleston, on deposit; these
include records of the almshouse, 1801-
1916 (35 vols.); the "orphan house,"
1809-82 (18 vols.); street commissioners, 1806-16 (2 vols.); school commissioners, 1812-1913 (7 vols.); and the
Board of Fire Masters, 1848-1914
(16 vols.).

See Helen G. McCormack, "A Provisional Guide to Manuscripts in the
South Carolina Historical Society," in
10 installments in S. C. Hist. and Genealogical Magazine, beginning 45:111-
115 (Apr. 1944) and ending 48:177-180
(July 1947).

CLEMSON

Clemson Agricultural College Library.
J. W. G. Gourlay, Director of the Library.

Holdings: 94 vols. and 278 boxes,
1805-1940, relating chiefly to South
Carolina and to agriculture. Papers
of individuals include those of John C.
Calhoun (S. C.; U. S. Rep. and Sen.,
Sec. War, U. S. Vice Pres., Sec.
State), 1805-50 (2,500 pieces); Thomas Green Clemson (Pa., Md., S. C.;
mining engineer, founder of Clemson
College), 1833-88 (1,000 pieces); Asbury Francis Lever (S. C.; U. S. Rep.),
1901-40 (30 boxes); and Benjamin Ryan Tillman (S. C.; Gov., U. S. Sen.),
1877-1919 (85 vols. and 215 boxes).
Included also are records of the Pendleton Farmers' Society, 1815-1915
(5 vols.); South Carolina State Agricultural Society, 1855-61 (1 vol.);
Farmers' State Alliance of South Carolina, 1888-99 (2 vols. and 2 boxes);
and South Carolina State Grange, 1872-

95 (1 vol. and 10 boxes). There are
also some account books, particularly plantation account books, diaries,
land grants, and school records.

COLUMBIA 1

South Carolina Archives Department.
1430 Senate St. J. H. Easterby, Director.

Holdings: Noncurrent official records of the colony and State of South
Carolina and its county divisions,
1670 to date, held by the Department
as the State's archival agency. Ef-
fective controls will not be established
over a large number of these records
until after they have been assembled
in the fall of 1959 in the new archives
building. The listing below is there-
fore incomplete and probably, in some
details, inaccurate.

Manuscript originals and file copies include (1) State constitutions,
1776-1868, and journals of constitutional and other conventions, 1788-
1852; (2) legislative records, consisting of journals, 1671-1889, acts,
1691-1946, and other papers, 1783-
1880; (3) executive records, consisting of journals and letter books, 1800-
10, 1867-92, and miscellaneous papers, 1671-1958, of the Governor's
office; journals of the Governor's
council, 1734-89; quit-rent returns
of the auditor general's office, 1731-
75; warrants and other land records
of the surveyor general's office, 1671-
1840; Revolutionary War claims,
1780-83, and ledgers and other documents of the treasury, 1725-1935;
and records of undetermined date of
the adjutant general, agent in Great
Britain, attorney general, board of
agriculture, board of public works,
church commissioners, commissioners of forfeited estates, commissioners of the Indian trade, commissioners
of the navy, comptroller general, rail-

road commission, secretary of state, State dispensary, statehouse commission, and superintendent of education; (4) judicial records, consisting of miscellaneous records of the colony and State courts of chancery, common pleas, general sessions, and probate, 1700-85; and (5) miscellaneous records of Charleston County, 1785-1890. There are also the South Carolina schedules of the U. S. censuses of agriculture, industry, mortality, and social statistics, 1850-80.

Copied documents include manuscript transcripts of records in the British Public Record Office relating to South Carolina, 1663-1782 (36 vols.); typescripts of wills and other probate records, 1671-1868 (119 vols.); photostats of the rolls in the National Archives of South Carolina troops in the Confederate States Army, 1860-65 (18,500 pieces); and microfilms (3,500 rolls) of selected records of approximately 25 of the 46 counties of the State, 1785-1950, vestry minutes and other parish records, 1725-1825, and schedules of the U. S. population censuses, 1800-80.

See R. H. Woody, "The Public Records of South Carolina," in Am. Archivist, 2:244-263 (Oct. 1931).

—oOo—

South Caroliniana Library, University of South Carolina.   E. L. Inabinett, Director.

Holdings: 4,825 vols. and 1,005,000 pieces, 1683-1959, relating chiefly to South Carolina.

Papers of political leaders and holders of public office include those of Milledge Luke Bonham (S.C.; U.S. Rep., Gov., Confed. Army officer), 1860-64 (225 pieces); Pierce Mason Butler (S. C.; U. S. Army officer, Indian agent, Gov.), 1819-83 (1,350 items); John C. Calhoun (S. C.; U. S. Rep. and Sen., Sec. War, U. S. Vice Pres., Sec. State), and members of his immediate family, 1801-99 (3,500 pieces); John Ewing Colhoun (S. C.; planter, lawyer, State legislator, U. S. Sen.), 1769-1822 (405 pieces); John Gary Evans (S. C.; lawyer, Gov.), 1882-1933 (7,259 pieces); James H. Hammond (S. C.; Gov., U. S. Rep. and Sen.) and his family, 1823-1910 (106 vols. and 3,000 pieces); Wade Hampton 3d (S. C.; Confed. Army officer, Gov., U. S. Sen.), 1843-1937 (226 pieces); Hugh Swinton Legare (S. C.; U. S. Attorney Gen.), 1814-90 (244 pieces); Andrew Gordon Magrath (S. C.; lawyer, Gov.), 1872-79 (51 letters); Richard I. Manning (S. C.; planter, Gov.), 1896-1932 (59 vols. and 6,000 pieces); Patrick Noble (S. C.; Gov.) and his family, 1761-1878 (89 items); William C. Preston (S. C.; lawyer, U. S. Sen., pres. of S. C. College), 1823-60 (75 letters); Edward Rutledge (S. C.; Member Continental Cong., Gov.), 1789-99 (41 pieces); William Dunlap Simpson (S. C.; Confed. Army officer, Gov., State chief justice), 1816-94 (3,131 pieces); Hugh S. Thomson (S. C.; State supt. of education, Gov.), 1861-1904 (150 pieces); and Strom Thurmond (S. C.; Gov., U. S. Sen.), 1947-51 (65,000 pieces).

Papers of other men include those of Louis Judson Bristow (S.C., La.; Baptist minister, hospital official), 1910-52 (410 pieces); James Edward Calhoun (U. S. naval officer), 1806-89 (597 pieces); Robert Means Davis (S. C.; educator), 1851-1904 (1,715 pieces); Martin Witherspoon Gary (S. C.; Confed. Army officer, lawyer), 1851-1927 (504 pieces); Oliver Hart (S. C.; Baptist minister) and his family, 1754-1886 (6 vols. and 178 pieces); John Jenkins (S. C.; Confed. Army officer, planter), 1775-1945 (870 pieces); Francis Lieber (Mass., S. C., N.Y.; political scientist, prof. at Univ. of S. C. and Columbia Univ.), 1833-79 (134 pieces); John McLaren McBryde (Va., S.C.,

Tenn.; agriculturist, pres. of S. C. College, and Va. Polytechnic Institute), 1883-1945 (12 vols.); John Joseph McMahon (S. C.; lawyer, planter, State legislator), 1847-1921 (35 vols.); Wyndham M. Manning (S. C.; U. S. Army officer, 1931-42 (12,000 pieces); Samuel C. Mitchell (S. C., Del., Va.; pres. of Univ. of S. C. and Del. College, history prof. at Richmond Univ.), 1908-13 (117 vols.); Henry W. Ravenel (S. C.; planter, botanist), 1859-87 (13 vols. of diary); William Gilmore Simms (S. C.; novelist, poet), 1857-77 (43 pieces); James H. Thornwell (S. C.; Presbyterian clergyman, pres. of S. C. College), 1830-72 (235 pieces); Henry Timrod (S. C.; poet), 1851-1937 (84 pieces); and James Woodrow (S. C.; Presbyterian minister, pres. of Univ. of S. C.), 1874-92 (57 pieces).

There are also papers of the Kincaid-Anderson family (S. C.; planters and merchants), 1767-1926 (9 vols. and 2,575 pieces); the Maverick and Van Wyck families, 1772-1891 (185 pieces); the Middleton family (S. C.; planters and educators), 1844-1921 (810 pieces); and the Thomas family, 1824-1900 (36 vols. and 78 pieces), which contain materials on planting, the Civil War, and the professions of medicine, teaching, and the ministry; other smaller groups of family papers; many small groups of papers of individuals; and papers of church, civic, political, educational, and agricultural organizations, and of business and legal firms. There are also typed copies of county and church records throughout the State, 1691-1935 (902 vols.); and archives of the University of South Carolina, 1800-1952 (524 vols. and 410 pieces).

See annual reports of the Secretary and Treasurer of the University South Caroliniana Society (1937-44), and information about accessions published in the programs for the Society's annual meetings.

GREENVILLE

Furman University Library. Robert C. Tucker, Librarian.

Holdings: A small collection, relating chiefly to Baptists in South Carolina. Included are papers of the Furman family, 1780-1900 (1,200 items); James Clement Furman (S.C.; Baptist clergyman, first pres. of Furman Univ.), 1828-91 (1,500 items); Richard Furman (S. C.; Baptist clergyman, leader in establishment of first national Baptist convention), 1774-1825 (420 items); William Bullein Johnson (S. C.; Baptist clergyman, first pres. of Southern Baptist Convention), 1831-62 (250 items); Basil Manly, Sr. (S. C., Ala.; Baptist clergyman, Univ. of Ala. pres.), 1829-60 (75 items); William Joseph McGlothlin (S. C.; Baptist clergyman, pres. of Furman Univ. and Southern Baptist Convention), 1930-33 (1,200 items); and other South Carolina Baptist leaders, 1759 to date (500 items). There are also papers pertaining to various South Carolina Baptist churches (500 items), Baptist associations (50 items), and Baptist institutions and agencies (2,000 items), all largely 19th century; and papers pertaining to Furman University faculty members and their families.

SPARTANBURG

Spartanburg Public Library. 224 Magnolia St.

Holdings: Notes by John Henry Logan (S. C.; historian) on the history of South Carolina.

—oOo—

Wofford College Library. Herbert Hucks, Jr., Librarian.

<u>Holdings</u>: Archives of the South Carolina Conference Historical Society of the Methodist Church, consisting of minutes, reports, letters, and other Conference papers, since 1795; and records of a few churches.

SOUTH DAKOTA

PIERRE

South Dakota State Historical Society.
Soldiers Memorial.   Will G. Robinson, Secretary.

Holdings: A considerable quantity
of papers consisting of (1) some official records held by the Society as the
archival agency of the State, and (2)
other papers relating chiefly to South
Dakota and Dakota Territory.

Papers of individuals include those
of William Henry Harrison Beadle
(S. Dak.; Dakota Terr. surveyor-gen.,
Supt. of Public Instruction), 1869-1912
(many items); William Maxwell Black-
burn (S. Dak.; Presbyterian clergyman,
historian, pres. of Pierre Univ.), 1885-
98 (a large quantity); Frank M. Byrne
(S. Dak.; farmer, real estate dealer,
Gov.), 1912-20 (a small quantity); Coe
I. Crawford (S. Dak.; lawyer, Gov., U.S.
Sen.), 1890-1910 (a considerable quantity); Samuel H. Elrod (S. Dak.; lawyer,
Gov.), 1905-7 (a small quantity); William Hobart Hare (S. Dak.; Episcopal
bishop, missionary to the Sioux Indians), 1878-1909 (a small quantity);
Charles N. Herreid (S. Dak.; lawyer,
Gov.), 1900-4 (a large quantity); Robert F. Kerr (Nebr., S. Dak.; prof. of
history and economics at S. Dak. Agricultural College, editor of a farm
journal), 1883-1907 (a small amount);
Jefferson P. Kidder (Minn., S. Dak.;
Delegate to Cong. and supreme court
justice for Dakota Terr.), 1859-83 (a
small amount); Andrew E. Lee (S. Dak.;
farmer, Gov.), 1897-1900 (a small
quantity); Arthur C. Mellette (S.Dak.;
Terr. and State Gov.), 1881-94 (a
large quantity); Peter Norbeck (S.Dak.;
Gov., U. S. Sen.), a fair quantity; John
Blair Smith Todd (S. Dak.; U. S. Army
officer, Terr. Delegate to Cong.),
1855-68 (a small quantity); and Robert
S. Vessey (S. Dak.; farmer, merchant,
Gov.), 1909-12 (a large quantity).

Also included are some school records; letters of Indian agents and
other papers relating to Indians; diaries of South Dakota pioneers, Civil War soldiers, and others; and microfilm copies of the original survey
maps covering the public surveys in
South Dakota.

VERMILLION

University of South Dakota Library.
Ruth Bergman, Librarian.

Holdings: Papers of Peter Norbeck
(S. Dak.; Gov., U. S. Sen.), 1898-1936
(16 trunks).

CHATTANOOGA 3

Chattanooga Public Library. 601 McCallie Ave. Elizabeth Edwards, Librarian.

Holdings: 4,872 pieces, relating chiefly to Chattanooga and Tennessee. Papers of persons include those of Henry Clay Evans (Tenn.; Civil War officer, U.S. Rep., U.S. Commissioner of Pensions, consul gen. at London), 1888-1908 (51 pieces); Tomlinson Fort (Ga.; lawyer) and his family, 1839-1910 (400 pieces); Jesse T. Hill (Tenn.; mining engineer), 1880-1905 (50 pieces), about mining and manufacturing of coal and iron products in the Southern States; David M. Key (Tenn.; Confed. Army officer, U.S. Sen., Postmaster-Gen., U.S. dist. court judge), 1834-1901 (381 pieces); Albert S. Lenoir (N.C.; surveyor), 1831-1921 (100 pieces), mainly about rations issued Cherokee and Creek Indians during their removal west; C. L. Loop (Tenn.; Southern Express Co. executive), 1834-1915 (200 pieces); Francis Lynde (N.Y., Tenn.; novelist), 1891-1930 (77 pieces); Emma Bell Miles (Ind.; author, artist), 1907-24 (60 pieces); Zeboim C. Patten (Tenn., N.Y.; Civil War officer, capitalist, insurance underwriter) and his family, 1860-1912 (500 pieces); and William B. Swaney (Tenn.; lawyer, prof. at Chattanooga College of Law, author), 1921-35 (1,700 pieces), on law enforcement and taxation in the United States. Also included are official records of the City of Chattanooga, 1859-1932 (40 pieces); records of the Society of the Army of the Cumberland, 1902-6 (400 pieces), consisting mainly of correspondence concerning the Battle of Shiloh; and records of

the Federated Missionary Societies of Chattanooga, 1911-45 (200 pieces). The Library is the depository for materials collected by the Chattanooga Area Historical Association.

See Hist. Records Survey, Guide to Collections of Manuscripts in Tennessee, pp. 1-3.

GATLINBURG

Great Smoky Mountains National Park. Superintendent.

Holdings: Records of several companies, 1895-1930, engaged chiefly in logging operations in the present park area.

HARROGATE

Lincoln Memorial University. Wayne C. Temple, Director, Department of Lincolniana.

Holdings: In the Hall of Holography, an autograph collection of 2,500 pieces. In the Lincoln Room, 2,000 pieces, 1793-1938, including diplomatic and political correspondence of Cassius Marcellus Clay (Ky.; abolitionist, Minister to Russia), 1840-98 (600 pieces); papers of John L. Worden (N.Y.; U.S. naval officer, commander of the Monitor, Supt. of U.S. Naval Academy), 1835-86 (64 pieces); papers of Abraham Lincoln (Ill.; lawyer, U.S. Rep. and Pres.), 1838-64 (50 pieces), and miscellaneous papers, documents, and letters of vice presidents, cabinet officers, generals, and other contemporaries of Abraham Lincoln,

among them some papers of Oliver
Otis Howard (U. S. Army officer,
Commissioner of Freedman's Bureau,
pres. of Howard Univ.); and a collection of papers pertaining to the migration of the Lincoln family (1,000 pieces), including minutes and reports of
the Lincoln Migration Commission,
1932-35.

See Hist. Records Survey, Guide
to Depositories of Manuscript Collections in Tennessee, pp. 2-4, and its
Guide to Collections of Manuscripts in
Tennessee, pp. 3-5.

HERMITAGE

Ladies' Hermitage Association. The
Hermitage. Martha Lindsey, Regent.

Holdings: A considerable collection of letters and other documents
signed by, addressed to, or concerning Andrew Jackson (Tenn.; U. S. Rep.
and Sen., U. S. Army officer and Pres.),
1803-42.

KNOXVILLE 2

McClung Historical Collection, Lawson McGhee Library. Pollyanna
Creekmore, Librarian.

Holdings: 250 vols. and 70,000
pieces, relating chiefly to Tennessee
and the Old Southwest. Included are
papers of William Blount (N. C., Tenn.;
Member Continental Cong., Terr. Gov.,
U. S. Sen. from Tenn.), 1777-97 (85 letters); Leonidas C. Houk and John C.
Houk (Tenn.; U. S. Reps.), 1870-1923
(31,000 pieces); Will A. McTeer (Tenn.;
U. S. Commissioner for Eastern Tenn.),
1855-1918 (12,500 pieces), pertaining
to his political, commercial, legal,
religious, educational, temperance,
and other interests; and Thomas A. R.
Nelson (Tenn.; U. S. Rep., State supreme court judge) and members of

his family, 1782-1922 (6,000 pieces).
There are also account books and other records of merchants, physicians,
and real estate dealers; records of
various Baptist, Methodist, and
Presbyterian churches, 1785-1955;
many diaries and journals, including
those of Charles Coffin (Tenn.; college president), 1800-22; and a number of miscellaneous autograph letters. There are extensive groups of
typed and photographic copies of papers in the Spanish archives, the British Public Record Office, the South
Carolina archives, the Library of
Congress, the National Archives, and
elsewhere.

See Hist. Records Survey, Guide
to Depositories of Manuscript Collections in Tennessee, pp. 4-7, and its
Guide to Collections of Manuscripts
in Tennessee, pp. 5-8; and a list in
Calvin Morgan McClung Historical
Collection, pp. 168-80 (1921).

KNOXVILLE

Tennessee Valley Authority. Bernard L. Foy, Technical Librarian.

Holdings: A large quantity of the
Authority's records, 1934-57, of
which some are scheduled for permanent preservation. The records
in Knoxville include minutes of the
TVA Board; working agreements
(with Federal, State, and local agencies, land-grant colleges, and private organizations) concerning the
execution of the TVA program; records documenting the development
of policy in accounting, personnel
administration, and public relations;
and records concerning the management of reservoir properties and the
design and construction of TVA's
physical plant. Other important records, in decentralized locations,
are the following: at Chattanooga,
Tenn., records on the generation

and sale of electric energy, the acquisition and sale of real and personal property, the TVA health and safety program, and mapping techniques developed and applied by the Authority; at Norris, Tenn., records concerning forestry and the control of soil erosion; and at Wilson Dam, Ala., records of TVA's chemical and engineering activities, its fertilizer and munitions production, and the development and operation of its malaria control program.

—oOo—

University of Tennessee Library. William H. Jesse, Director of Libraries; John Dobson, Special Collections Librarian.

Holdings: 900 vols. and 108,000 other items, 1783-1958, relating chiefly to Tennessee. Personal papers include those of Philander P. Claxton (N.C., Tenn.; U.S. Commission of Education), 1902-46 (10,000 pieces); John Eaton (Ohio, Tenn.; State Supt. of Education, U.S. Commissioner of Education), 1865-85 (2,500 pieces); Ben W. Hooper (Tenn.; lawyer, Gov., member of U.S. Railroad Labor Board), 1911-26 (35,000 pieces); Absalom A. Kyle (Tenn.; lawyer, State supervisor of banks, U.S. direct tax commissioner for Tenn.), 1847-1902 (100 pieces); William B. Lenoir (Tenn.; merchant), 1787-1913 (2,500 pieces), family and business correspondence; the Rhea family of Tennessee, 1835-1931 (3,700 pieces); Edward J. Sanford (Tenn.; U.S. Supreme Court Justice), 1879-1930 (75 pieces); Mary B. Temple (Tenn.; Daughters of the American Revolution leader), 1876-1920 (2,500 pieces); Oliver P. Temple (Tenn.; lawyer, author), 1832-1909 (9,400 pieces); Laura Thornburg (Tenn.; author), 1926-40 (1,000 pieces), dealing with the Great Smoky Mountains; and Campbell

Wallace (Ga., Tenn.; bank and railroad official), 1840-1946 (5,000 pieces).

Included also is a collection of Rhea County, Tenn., archives, 1785-1875 (18,000 pieces); records of the Ruskin Cooperative Association, in Tennessee and Georgia, 1894-99 (500 pieces); U.S. Food Administration records for Knoxville and Tennessee, 1917-18 (1,800 items); records of the West Tennessee Flood Control and Soil Conservation District, 1949-52 (2,500 pieces); records of graves removed by the Tennessee Valley Authority from the Norris Reservoir area (4,383 items); Historical Records Survey transcriptions of county records in Tennessee (500 vols.); and 180 smaller collections relating chiefly to Tennessee but also to other areas. In addition there are ledgers of firms engaged in leather, laundry, livery stable, hotel, coal mining, printing, merchandising, public utility, and other businesses, 1813-1927 (250 vols.).

See Hist. Records Survey, Guide to Collections of Manuscripts in Tennessee, pp. 8-10.

MEMPHIS 12

Burrow Library, Southwestern at Memphis. Albert M. Johnson, Librarian.

Holdings: (1) 500 vols. and 700 pieces, 1725-1954, consisting of correspondence, diaries, and other historical documents relating to local and State matters, and (2) 200 vols. and 1,200 pieces, 1825-1954, relating to the Presbyterian Church in the United States and to Protestantism.

MEMPHIS 3

Memphis Public Library. 33 South

Front St.   C. Moffett Moore, Chief
Reference Librarian.

Holdings: In the Cossitt Library,
which is the reference library of the
Memphis Public Library, the largest
group consists of the personal papers
of Kenneth D. McKellar (Tenn.; U.S.
Rep. and Sen.), 1911-52 (400 packing
crates in storage). The papers of
Henry A. Montgomery (Tenn.; telegraph promoter, civic leader) and his
family, 1856-1928 (a considerable
quantity), include materials on early
telegraph companies in Alabama, Arkansas, Mississippi, and Tennessee,
among them letters by Amos Kendall
as agent of Samuel F. B. Morse, and
on various business activities in
Memphis. Other papers include the
diary of Josiah Hinds (Tenn.; Methodist minister), 1839-62; papers of a
Memphis firm of cotton factors and
merchants, 1848-74 (300 pieces); papers of Colton Greene (Tenn.; Confed. Army officer), 1861-64 (50 pieces); papers of George C. Harris (Tenn.;
dean of St. Mary's Cathedral in Memphis), 1873-79 (400 pieces), many
concerning contributions for yellow
fever sufferers in 1878; papers relating to Mardi Gras festivals in Memphis, 1873-81; papers concerning the
Illinois Central and other railroads,
1893-1935; and some genealogical
compilations.
See Hist. Records Survey, Guide
to Collections of Manuscripts in Tennessee, p. 10.

—oOo—

Goodwyn Institute Library. Madison
Ave. and Third St.

Holdings: 5 vols. and 200 pieces,
1716-1915, consisting chiefly of genealogical and miscellaneous papers
relating to a few families in Tennessee and Mississippi.
See Hist. Records Survey, Guide

to Collections of Manuscripts in Tennessee, p. 11.

NASHVILLE 12

Disciples of Christ Historical Society. 1101 Nineteenth Ave., South.
Claude E. Spencer, Curator.

Holdings: Correspondence and
other manuscripts relating chiefly to
the history of the Disciples of Christ.

NASHVILLE 8

Fisk University Library. Arna Bontemps, Librarian.

Holdings: 32 vols. and 209,313
pieces, 1698-1948, relating chiefly
to the Negro. Personal papers include correspondence, literary manuscripts, journals and notebooks, and
other papers of Charles Waddell
Chesnutt (Ohio; lawyer, author),
1880-1930 (6,168 pieces), among
them 49 letters by George Washington Cable (La., Mass.; author), 1889-
1921, and 104 by Booker T. Washington (Ala.; founder of Tuskegee Institute), 1900-16. There are also
papers of John Mercer Langston
(Ohio, D.C., Va.; lawyer, educator,
Freedmen's Bureau official, minister
to Haiti, U.S. Rep.), 1827-97 (1,244
pieces); and James Carroll Napier
(Tenn.; lawyer, banker, registrar of
U.S. Treas.), 1868-1939 (285 pieces).
Other holdings include an Anti-Slavery
Collection, 1698-1865 (425 items),
containing bills of sale, free papers,
and the like; a collection relating to
Fisk University, 1865-1945 (675 pieces), among them letters of Erastus
Milo Cravath, its first president; the
archives of the American Missionary
Association, 1839-79 (150,000 pieces), containing letters of many prominent abolitionists and leaders in the

movement for Negro education; the archives of the Julius Rosenwald Fund, 1917-48 (50,000 pieces), relating largely to rural schools for Negroes; and musical manuscripts and letters (516 pieces) in the George Gershwin Memorial Collection of Music and Musical Literature (which does not contain Gershwin's manuscripts).

See American Missionary Association Archives in Fisk University Library (1947. [12] p.), by Arna Bontemps; A List of Manuscripts, Published Works and Related Items in the Charles Waddell Chesnutt Collection of the Erastus Milo Cravath Memorial Library, Fisk University (1954. 32 p.), prepared by Mildred Freeney and Mary T. Henry, with introduction by Arna Bontemps; and Selected Items from the George Gershwin Memorial Collection of Music and Musical Literature ([1947.] 32 p.), with foreword by Arna Bontemps.

NASHVILLE 5

Joint University Libraries.   A. F. Kuhlman, Director.

Holdings: 160 vols., 7,000 pieces, and 125 rolls of microfilmed manuscripts, 1742-1941, relating chiefly to Tennessee and the South and held in the three units described in the paragraphs below.

Manuscripts in the Central Division, formerly the General Library of Vanderbilt University, include astronomical observations and calculations of Edward E. Barnard (Tenn.; astronomer), 1883-92 (395 pieces). There is also an extensive collection of microfilm copies of manuscripts relating chiefly to Tennessee in the period before 1865. These film copies include unpublished schedules of agricultural, slave, and population census schedules for a number of the southern States, 1810-60; various

groups of papers in the Library of Congress, Duke University Library, University of the South Library, and the State Historical Society of Wisconsin; papers of and relating to Thomas Hughes (England; author) and the English settlement at Rugby, Tenn., 1840-1938 (3 reels); papers of James Winchester (Tenn.; War of 1812 officer) and his family, 1785-1868; and a quantity of privately owned letters, diaries, miscellaneous family papers, account books, and church records.

Papers in the Vanderbilt University School of Medicine Library, 19th and 20th centuries, include letters relating chiefly to medical subjects such as yellow fever and malaria epidemics in the South, 1849-94; and material on Crawford W. Long (Ga.; physician, pioneer in the surgical use of anesthesia) and relating to medical education in the United States, particularly to the Vanderbilt University School of Medicine and the University of Nashville Medical Department.

Papers in the Peabody College Division Library, 160 vols. and 6,200 pieces, 1784-1931, include essays, lectures, sermons, and other papers of Philip Lindsley (N. J., Tenn.; Presbyterian minister, Cumberland College pres.), 1810-31; papers of William Harold Payne (Mich., Tenn.; pedagogy prof. at Univ. of Mich., Univ. of Nashville chancellor, Peabody Normal School pres.), 1850-1908 (17 vols. and 2,600 pieces); and correspondence of James Robertson (N. C., Tenn.; frontiersman, founder of Nashville, Indian agent), 1784-1814 (376 pieces), pertaining largely to relations of the frontier settlers with the Cherokee and Chickasaw Indians. There are also various records of Cumberland College, the University of Nashville, and George Peabody College; papers of literary and other student societies of several Tennessee colleges, 1825-1926

(97 vols. and 200 pieces); and a collection of letters and other papers of
trustees of the Peabody Educational
Fund, 1868-1931 (3,000 pieces).

See Hist. Records Survey, Guide
to Depositories of Manuscript Collections in Tennessee, pp. 19-21, and
its Guide to Collections of Manuscripts
in Tennessee, pp. 14-17; and Manuscripts and Other Historical Materials
on Microfilm in Joint University Libraries, Nashville, Tennessee (1954.
21 p. Processed).

NASHVILLE 3

Methodist Publishing House Library.
201 Eighth Ave., South.   Elizabeth
Hughey, Librarian.

   Holdings: Records of the Methodist Church, the Methodist Episcopal
Church, and the Methodist Episcopal
Church, South. These include journals and daily Christian advocates of
the general conferences and jurisdic-
tional conferences, general minutes
of annual conferences, disciplines,
annual conference histories, and general board and commission reports.

NASHVILLE

Tennessee Historical Society. State
Library and Archives Bldg. Robert
T. Quarles, President.

   Holdings: 10,000 items, 1770-1932,
relating chiefly to Tennessee. Included
are papers of Andrew Jackson (Tenn.;
U. S. Army officer and Pres.); John
Overton (Tenn.; State supreme court
justice, political leader), 1782-1834
(1,330 items); John Rhea (Tenn.; U. S.
Rep.) and his family, 1752-1865
(294 pieces); and James Winchester
(Tenn.; War of 1812 officer), 1812-25
(275 pieces). The papers of John P.
Heiss (Tenn.; newspaper editor), 1843-

65 (250 items), contain correspondence with James K. Polk (Tenn.; U.S.
Rep., Gov., U. S. Pres.) on politics
and with William Walker (La., Calif.;
leader of filibustering expeditions)
on Nicaragua. There are also official records of the U. S. Quartermaster Corps, 1862-65 (17 vols.), pertaining to the transportation of supplies for the Union Army; and other
papers that provide information about
Indian relations, plantation operations, the establishment of Memphis,
the Memphis and Charleston Railroad, the War of 1812, the Civil War,
a female academy in Nashville, and
the cotton business and other business
activities. Included also are a number of sermons and church records.

See Hist. Records Survey, Guide
to Collections of Manuscripts in Tennessee, pp. 18-22.

NASHVILLE 3

Tennessee State Library and Archives.   Dan M. Robison, State Librarian and Archivist.

   Holdings: In the Archives Division over 400 tons of papers, comprising (1) noncurrent official records of Tennessee—legislative, judicial, and executive—dating from
1792, and (2) other papers of historical value, especially in relation
to Tennessee.

The latter group includes papers
of R. E. Barclay (Tenn.; mining company official, author), 1857-1945
(2,000 items), among them diaries
and other papers of Julius Eckhardt
Raht (Tenn.; superintendent of Polk
County, Tenn., copper mines), 1857-
78; Godfrey Barnsley (Ga.; English
consul, cotton merchant) and his
children, 1825-1908 (850 items);
George Pearson Buell (Ind.; Civil
War officer) and his father-in-law,
John S. Brien (Tenn.; Davidson

County circuit court judge), 1808-1943
(10,000 items); Jacob McGavock Dickinson (Tenn., Ill.; Tenn. supreme
court justice, specialist in railroad
law, Sec. War), 1851-1928 (40,000
items); Walter W. Faw (Tenn.; State
asst. attorney gen., State court of appeals judge), 1867-1956 (40,000
items); the law firm of Foster and
Woods, 1808-66 (200 items), containing correspondence of Ephraim
Hubbard Foster (Tenn.; U. S. Sen.)
and Robert C. Foster (Tenn.; Mexican War and Confed. Army officer);
Edmund Pendleton Gaines (U. S. Army officer), 1777-1849, and John
Wesley Gaines (Tenn.; lawyer, politician), 1860-1926 (100 items); David
Henley (Mass., Tenn.; Rev. War officer, military agent for War Dept.
in Tenn.), 1784-1800 (50 items);
Andrew Jackson (Tenn.; U. S. Army
officer and Pres.) and his family,
1797-1871 (1,500 items); James
Buckner Killebrew (Tenn.; State
legislator and sec. state), 1831-1906
(2 diaries, 2 scrapbooks, and 500
items); John Overton (Tenn.; State
supreme court justice, political leader), 1766-1833 (500 items); Albert
H. Roberts (Tenn.; lawyer, Gov.),
1918-40 (28 transfer cases); and
Robert Whyte (Scotland, Va., N. C.,
Tenn.; judge of Tenn. supreme court
of errors and appeals), 1767-1844
(1,000 items).

There are letters, diaries, and
other records of soldiers of the Civil War, Mexican War, and World
Wars I and II. The Confederate
Collection includes papers and diaries of several Confederate officers,
among them Richard Stoddert Ewell,
Benjamin Franklin Cheatham, James
E. Raines, and Randal W. McGavock.
Also included are a large number of
account books, turnpike records,
church records, county records, diaries and memoirs for non-war periods, school records, land records,
wills, speeches, and some literary

manuscripts of Tennessee and other
Southern authors. A group of papers
dealing with Rugby, Tenn., 1892-
1938 (200 items), contains information about Thomas Hughes (England;
author).

See Hist. Records Survey, <u>Guide
to Depositories of Manuscript Collections in Tennessee</u>, pp. 16-18.

PITTSBURG LANDING

Shiloh National Military Park.
The Superintendent.

<u>Holdings</u>: 27 vols. and 39 boxes, relating chiefly to the establishment and development of Shiloh
National Military Park. Included
are letters, diaries, and memoirs
of soldiers who fought at Shiloh
(2 boxes); the diary of daily events
for the park, 1900-13 (2 vols.); and
business and historical records of
the park and Shiloh National Cemetery, 1866-1933 (25 vols. and 37
boxes). Scattered among these records are letters and reports on
the Battle of Shiloh and on the historical marking of the battlefield.

SEWANEE

Archive Department, University of
the South Library. Mrs. O. N. Torian, Archivist.

<u>Holdings</u>: 1,200 items, 1767-
1907, relating chiefly to the Episcopal Church in the United States and
Canada and to the University of the
South. Included are papers of Leonidas Polk (Tenn., La.; Episcopal
bishop, Confed. Army officer) and
family, 1823-1928 (769 items); papers of Charles Todd Quintard
(Tenn.; physician, Episcopal bishop,

Confed. Chaplain), 1858-78 (200 pieces, including a 32-vol. diary); and a
collection of letters of American bishops of the Episcopal Church, 1767-

1907 (600 pieces).

See Hist. Records Survey, Guide
to Collections of Manuscripts in Tennessee, pp. 23-25.

TEXAS

AUSTIN 3

Archives Division, Texas State Library. Camp Hubbard. Dorman H. Winfrey, State Archivist.

Holdings: 3,000,000 pieces, 1733-1955, consisting of (1) noncurrent official records held by the Library as the State's archival agency, and (2) other papers relating chiefly to Texas.

In the first category are records of the Governor's office, 1846-1920 (150 cu. ft.); the Adjutant General's Department, 1836-1920 (300 cu. ft.); the Comptroller's Department, 1835-1920 (750 cu. ft.); the Treasury, 1835-46 (50 cu. ft.); the Department of Education, 1866-1914 (130 cu. ft.); the General Land Office, 1836-1900 (400 cu. ft.); and the State Department, 1835-1900 (925 cu. ft.). Records of the State Department include the archives of the provisional government of Texas as a state of the Mexican Republic, 1835-36 (20 cu. ft.); and the archives of the Republic of Texas (papers of the nine congresses, treaties with foreign nations and Indian tribes, customs papers, and other records), 1836-45 (150 cu. ft.). Included also are the Nacogdoches archives, 1733-1836 (8,000 pieces); transcripts of the Laredo Archives, 1755-1846 (8,000 documents), covering official, church, and social affairs in Laredo, Tex.; and transcripts of Mexican, British, and Spanish archives relating to Texas, 1800-36 (10 cu. ft.).

Personal papers include those of Anthony Butler (U. S. Chargé d'Affaires in Mexico), 1830-45 (50 pieces); Alexander Ewing (Tex.; surgeon gen. of the Tex. Army), 1835-38 (50 pieces); George Fisher (Tex.; collector of customs at Galveston),

1829-43 (50 pieces); Memucan Hunt (Tex.; Texas Army officer), 1838-48 (100 pieces); James R. Kerr (Tex.; early settler, Indian fighter, physician), 1790-1850 (100 pieces); Mirabeau Buonaparte Lamar (Ga., Tex.; Pres. of Tex., U. S. Minister to Nicaragua), 1789-1859 (2,815 pieces); Washington D. Miller (Tex.; Sam Houston's private sec., Sec. State of the Republic of Tex.), 1832-66 (100 pieces); John H. Reagan (Tex.; U. S. Rep. and Sen., Confed. Postmaster Gen., chairman of the Tex. Railroad Commission), 1847-1905 (4,000 pieces); and George W. Smyth (Tex.; U. S. Rep., Tex. boundary commissioner), 1830-54 (50 pieces).

Other papers include the journal of a Baptist church, 1851-67; ledgers of a general store at Webberville, 1859-60 (2 vols.); records of a local grange, 1874-83 (1 vol.); and documents on Texas soldiers in World War I (2 cu. ft.).

See Elizabeth H. West, Calendar of the Papers of Mirabeau Buonaparte Lamar (1914. 355 p.); the Library's Biennial Reports, 1909-36; Harriet Smither, "The Archives of Texas," in Am. Archivist, 3:187-200 (July 1940); and Seymour V. Connor, A Preliminary Guide to the Archives of Texas (1956. 91 p.).

AUSTIN

Austin Public Library. 401 West 9th St.

Holdings: In the Austin-Travis County Collection, which relates mainly to the history of Austin and Travis County, manuscript materials include business records, deeds, diaries, letters, organization minutes, and school records.

—oOo—

Church Historical Society. Theological Seminary of the Southwest. 606 Rathervue Pl. Virginia Nelle Bellamy, Archivist.

Holdings: Included are several collections of letters of Episcopal bishops, 1750-1950; and the archives of the Domestic and Foreign Missionary Society, 1820-1900. (The Church Historical Society, which was located in Philadelphia, Pa., until 1956, is the successor of the Church Missions House Library, New York, N.Y., as the official custodian of general Episcopal Church archives, but many of the papers once in that Library are on deposit in the New-York Historical Society.)

—oOo—

Texas Catholic Historical Society. Catholic Chancery, 16th and Congress Sts.

Holdings: A collection known as the Catholic Archives of Texas. Some of the material was formerly in the St. Edward's University Library, Austin, Tex.

AUSTIN 12

University of Texas Library. Alexander Moffit, Librarian.

Holdings: More than 3,200,000 pieces, 12th century to the present, relating chiefly to Texas and Latin America, especially Mexico, and to American and English literature. These include papers acquired through the efforts of the Texas State Historical Society.

Papers of American literary figures include those of Gelett Burgess (Calif.; author), 19th century (112 items); Witter Bynner (Calif., N.Mex.; poet, literary editor), 20th century (422 items); James Branch Cabell (Va.; novelist, essayist), 20th century (48 items); Theodore Dreiser (Mo., N.Y.; editor, novelist), 19th and 20th centuries (53 items); Thomas Stearns Eliot (Mass., England; poet), 20th century (490 items); William Falkner (Miss.; novelist), 20th century (385 items); Eugene Field (Mo., Ill.; journalist, poet), 19th century (663 items); Joseph Hergesheimer (Pa., N.J.; novelist), 20th century (a very extensive collection); Henry James (Mass., England; novelist), 182 letters; Robinson Jeffers (Calif.; poet), 20th century (87 items); James Russell Lowell (Mass.; poet, essayist, Harvard College prof., Minister to Spain and to Great Britain), 19th century (73 items); Christopher Morley (Pa., N.Y.; author, editor), 20th century (a very extensive collection); Ezra Pound (N.Y., Europe; poet), 20th century (93 items); Idella Purnell, Mrs. Remington Stone (Mexico, Calif.; poet, editor), 20th century (1,890 items), relating to Palms magazine; and Walt Whitman (N.Y., D.C., N.J.; poet), 20th century (287 manuscripts).

Papers of other Americans include those of Moses Austin (Va., Mo.; merchant, mine owner), 1761-1821, and Stephen F. Austin (Mo., Tex.; leader in the settlement of Tex.), 1793-1836 (7,600 documents, 15,000 pages); Guy M. Bryan (Tex.; U.S. Rep., Confed. Army officer), 1844-97 (944 documents); Anthony Butler (U.S. Chargé d'Affaires in Mexico), 1814-40 (408 documents); Oscar B. Colquitt (Tex.; Gov., oil businessman), 96,297 pieces; William Eaton (Mass.; U.S. Army officer, consul at Tunis, naval agent to Barbary States), late 18th and early 19th centuries (33 items); Powhatan Ellis (Miss.; U. S. Sen., U. S. dist. court judge, Minister to Mexico), 1811-34 (1,000 pieces); James Stephen Hogg (Tex.; lawyer, Gov.), 1851-1906 (9,830 documents); Sam Houston (Tenn., Tex.; U. S. Rep. and Sen., Gov.), 1793-1863 (600 documents, chiefly photostatic); Thomas Jefferson (Va.; Member Continental Cong., Gov., Minister to France, Sec. State, U. S. Pres.), 68 letters; Anson Jones (Tex.; physician, pres. of the Republic of Tex.), 1,000 pieces; Rufus King (Mass., N.Y.; Member Continental Cong., U. S. Sen. from N.Y., Minister to Great Britain), 101 letters and other papers; William Mahl (N.Y.; railway official), concerning the Southern Railway; Oran Milo Roberts (Tex.; Civil War officer, chief justice of Tex., Gov.), 1840-96 (20 vols. and 400 pages); Thomas J. Rusk (Tex.; U.S. Sen., chief justice of Tex.), 1823-57 (620 pages); George Santayana (Mass., Italy; poet, philosopher); Ashbel Smith (N. C., Tex.; physician, sec. state of the Republic of Tex., Civil War officer), 1823-86 (6,369 documents); Justin H. Smith (Mass., N.H.; historian, Dartmouth College prof.), consisting chiefly of notes and transcripts brought together while writing The War With Mexico; Joseph Story (Mass.; U.S. Rep., U.S. Supreme Court Justice) and his son William Wetmore Story (Mass., Italy; sculptor, essayist, poet), 19th century (1,474 family papers); Alexander W. Terrell (Tex.; lawyer, Confed. Army officer); and Waddy Thompson (S. C., Fla.; U. S. Rep. from S. C., Minister to Mexico), 1824-48 (66 documents).

Also included are papers relating to German, French, and English immigration to Texas; plantation life in Texas; the Texas Navy; and the rise of the Granger movement. The Library has also the Parsons Collection of papers of Governors and other officials of Louisiana, 1660-1880 (1,042

manuscripts); records of veterans of the Texas War for Independence, 1836 (18 documents); some Union Army letters and other communications, 1862-64 (68 items); and records of the S. M. S. Ranch, 1908-22 (34,943 pages), and other organizations in the cattle industry.

Holdings relating to Latin America, including the former provinces of Spain and Mexico now within the United States, number over a million pages of original manuscripts, transcripts, and photographic copies. Included are the Bexar Archives, consisting of civil, religious, and military records of the Spanish province and Mexican state of Coahuila and of Texas, 1699-1836 (80,795 pieces); and papers of the Sanchez-Navarro family, which once owned one-half of the present state of Coahuila, 1650-1826 (75,000 pages). Extensive collections of transcripts and photostats of archives in Spain, France, England, Mexico, and elsewhere include archives of Matamoros, 1720-1880 (12,781 pages); Nacogdoches, 1729-1836 (23,305 pages); and Saltillo, 1688-1834 (12,500 pages). The Genaro García Collection contains papers of Valentín Gómez Farias (Mexico; Pres.), 1820-55 (14,075 leaves); Vicente Guerrero (Mexico; Pres.), 1822-39 (2,276 folios); Servando de Mier (Mexico; politician, writer), 1820-23 (2,173 folios); J. M. L. Mora (Mexico; historian), 1794-1856 (1,802 folios); Mariano Riva Palacio (Mexico; military and political figure), 1830-80 (20,400 folios); and Vicente Riva Palacio (Mexico; statesman, historian, author), 1858-96 (34,088 folios). There are also the Juan E. Hérnández y Dávalos Manuscript Collection, dealing with Mexican history, 1760-1880 (20,000 folios); the W. B. Stephens Manuscript Collection, dealing with the Spanish Southwest, 1488-1860 (20,000 pages); the Alejandro Prieto

Manuscript Collection, dealing with the Spanish Southwest, principally the Mexican state of Tamaulipas, 1823-80 (3,000 pages); and the Manuel Gondra Manuscript Collection, containing papers relating to Paraguay and the eastern coastal region of South America, 1531-1921 (20,000 pages).

Non-American manuscripts include the Brudenell-Cardigan manuscript of Chaucer's works, 1450, and other medieval and Renaissance manuscripts. For later periods, chiefly the 19th and 20th centuries, there are papers of James M. Barrie (Scotland; novelist, dramatist), late 19th and early 20th centuries (43 items); Elizabeth Barrett Browning and Robert Browning (England; poets), 19th century (62 items of the former and 205 of the latter); George Gordon, Lord Byron (England; poet), early 19th century (198 items), and his wife, Anne Isabella Milbanke Byron (England; mathematician), 19th century (53 items); Joseph Conrad (England; novelist), late 19th and early 20th centuries (70 letters); Alfred Edgar Coppard (England; author), 19th and 20th centuries (2,421 items); Robert Bontine Cunninghame Graham (Scotland; writer), 19th and 20th centuries (415 items); Walter John De la Mare (England; poet, novelist), 19th and 20th centuries (68 items); Emile Deschamps (France; poet, dramatist), 19th century (291 letters); Charles Dickens (England; novelist), 19th century (129 items); Charles Montagu Doughty (England; poet), 19th and early 20th centuries (59 items); Alfred Bruce, Lord Douglas (England; author, editor), 19th and 20th centuries (362 items); Havelock Ellis (England; psychologist), late 19th and early 20th centuries (376 items); Oliver Sylvain Baliol Brett Esher, 3d viscount (England; statesman, author), 20th century (110 letters); Reginold Baliol Brett Esher, 2d viscount (England; statesman, author), 19th and 20th centuries (79 letters); Gilbert Frankau (England;

writer), 20th century (180 items); John Galsworthy (England; novelist), 19th and 20th centuries (45 items); David Garnett (England; author), 20th century (78 items); Edward Garnett (England; author), 19th and 20th centuries (1,975 letters); Thomas Hardy (England; novelist, poet), 19th and 20th centuries (126 items); Frank Harris (Ireland, U.S.; author, editor), 19th and 20th centuries (929 items); Maurice Henry Hewlett (England; essayist, novelist, poet), 19th and 20th centuries (204 items); Katharine Tynan Hinkson (Ireland; poet, novelist), 19th and 20th centuries (53 items); and Joseph Maunsell Hone (Ireland; writer), 20th century (208 items).

Other non-American manuscripts include the papers of William Jerdan (England; journalist), 19th century (85 letters); James Joyce (Ireland; author), 20th century (26 manuscripts); Charles Lamb (England; essayist, poet, critic), late 18th and early 19th centuries (56 items); D. H. Lawrence (England; poet, novelist), 20th century (a very extensive collection); Thomas Edward Lawrence, known as Lawrence of Arabia (England; archeologist, soldier, writer), 20th century (239 items); Richard Le Gallienne (England; poet, critic), 19th and 20th centuries (61 items); Edward Verrall Lucas (England; publisher, writer), 19th and 20th centuries (578 items); Arthur Machen (England; novelist, essayist), 19th and 20th centuries (531 items); Alfred Edward Woodley Mason (England; novelist, playwright), 19th and 20th centuries (138 items); George Meredith (England; novelist, poet), 19th century (294 items); George Moore (England; novelist), 19th and 20th centuries (243 items); Liam O'Flaherty (Ireland; novelist), 20th century (163 items); Claude Houghton Oldfield (England; author, civil servant), 20th century (293 items);

John Ruskin (England; critic, author, reformer), 19th century (392 items); George Bernard Shaw (England; playwright, novelist, critic), 19th and 20th centuries (a very extensive collection); Matthew Phipps Shiel (England; journalist, writer), 19th and 20th centuries (1,056 items); Ernest Bramah Smith (England; writer of detective fiction), 19th and 20th centuries (1,128 items); Algernon Charles Swinburne (England; poet), 19th century (109 items); Philip Edward Thomas, known as Edward Thomas (England; poet, critic), 20th century (81 manuscripts); Henry Tonks (England; painter), 19th and 20th centuries (434 items); Denton Welch (China, England; poet, artist), 20th century (159 manuscripts); Oscar Wilde (England; poet, novelist, playwright), 19th century (108 items); Thomas James Wise (England; bibliographer, book collector), 19th and 20th centuries (1,901 letters); and William Butler Yeats (Ireland; poet), 19th and 20th centuries (328 items).

See Eugene C. Barker, "Report on the Bexar Archives," in Am. Hist. Assn., Annual Report for 1902, vol. 1, pp. 357-363, and "Private Papers of Anthony Butler," in The Nation, 92:600 (June 15, 1911); William A. Whatley, "The Historical Manuscript Collections of the University of Texas," in the Texas History Teachers' Bulletin, 9:19-25 (Nov. 1920); Lota M. Spell, "The Mier Archives," in Hispanic Am. Hist. Review, 12:359-375 (Aug. 1932); Carlos E. Castañeda and Jack Autrey Dabbs, Guide to the Latin American Manuscripts in the University of Texas Library (1939. 217 p.), and Calendar of the Manuel E. Gondra Manuscript Collection; the University of Texas Library (1952. 467 p.); Malcolm D. McLean, "The Bexar Archives," in Southwestern Hist. Quarterly, 50:493-496 (Apr. 1947); Winnie Allen and Helen Hunnicutt, "A New Center for Southwestern Historical Studies: IV. The Archives Collection," in the Texas University's Library Chronicle, 4:11-18 (fall 1950); Pablo Max Ynsfran, "Catálogo del Archivo de Don Lucas Alamán que se conserva en la Universidad de Texas, Austin," in Historia Mexicana, 4:281-316 (Oct.-Dec. 1954) and 4:431-476 (Jan.-Mar. 1955); and Lota M. Spell, Research Materials for the Study of Latin America at the University of Texas (1954. 107 p.).

BONHAM

Sam Rayburn Library. H. G. Dulaney, Director.

Holdings: Eighteen 4-drawer filing cabinets and several binders and volumes, containing papers, 1911-57 but chiefly 1942-54, of Sam Rayburn (Tex.; U.S. Rep., Speaker of the House). The papers include correspondence, speeches, memoranda, and reports, filed chiefly in two main series: (1) case files, containing correspondence with Mr. Rayburn's Texas constituents; and (2) general subject files, containing papers relating to specific Federal legislation, Congressional organization and administration, national and international problems, and political campaigns and conventions in which Mr. Rayburn played a part. Segregated from the regularly filed papers are letters, chiefly 1933-56, to Mr. Rayburn from Presidents with whom he served (2 binders); congratulatory messages received on his first election to the Speakership, 1940 (4 vols.); letters from his mother, ca. 1913-24 (1 binder); excerpts from the Congressional Record recording chronologically all his actions and statements on the floor of the House, 1913-57 (4 vols.); several scrapbooks of clippings concerning his public life and service; and a few sound recordings and 16-mm. motion-picture films.

CANYON

Panhandle-Plains Historical Museum. Box 366, W. T. Station.   C. Boone McClure, Museum Director.

Holdings: Papers relating chiefly to the Texas Panhandle. Included are papers of Charles Goodnight (Tex.; cattleman); voluminous records of several ranches and pioneer grocery firms; and 5,000 typed copies of interviews with pioneers.

DALLAS 1

Dallas Historical Society. Hall of State. Mrs. Herbert Gambrell, Director.

Holdings: 750,000 pieces, 17th to 20th century, relating chiefly to Texas and particularly Dallas. Included are papers of Joseph Weldon Bailey (Miss., Tex.; lawyer, U. S. Rep. and Sen.), 1880-1930 (21,463 pieces); William Lewis Cabell (Va., Tex.; U. S. and Confed. Army officer, mayor of Dallas, railroad executive), 1849-1910 (1,401 pieces); Franklin Chase (N. Y.; U. S. consul at Tampico) and his wife, 1840-80 (431 pieces); J. J. Faulk (Tex.; State legislator), 1849-1935 (14,932 pieces); Alexander C. Garrett (Canada, Tex.; Episcopal clergyman, missionary bishop of Dallas), 1872-1924 (150 pieces); Thomas B. Love (Tex.; Democratic leader, State Banking Commissioner, Asst. Sec. U. S. Treas.), 1907-35 (over 100,000 pieces); and Roger Q. Mills (Tex.; U. S. Rep. and Sen.), 1850-1929 (185 pieces). There are also papers of an official of the Texas Emigration and Land Co., 1834-55

(50 pieces); extensive groups of the papers of two pioneer Texas families; a manuscript journal of the Texas convention of 1836; and the Howard Collection of letters and documents relating to Texas and Mexican history, largely before 1845 (2,500 pieces).

—oOo—

Dallas Public Library.   James D. Meeks, Library Director.

Holdings: One of the two official registers of the veterans attending the United Confederate Veterans Reunion, held in Dallas in 1902, showing the name of the soldier, his company and regiment, the State troops with which he fought, and his home post office in 1902. (The missing volume contained the names of the soldiers who fought with the North Carolina, South Carolina, Georgia, Alabama, Mississippi, and Louisiana troops.) The Library also has a collection of data from early wills, from marriage, cemetery, and church membership records, and from other types of records pertaining to Dallas County and other counties in Texas.

DALLAS 5

Southern Methodist University Libraries. Robert M. Trent, Director of Libraries.

Holdings: Scattered manuscripts in the 3 depositories indicated below.

A. V. Lane Museum.   Mrs. John H. Warnick, Curator.

Holdings: Fragments of 12 Oxyrhynchus papyri, and 12 Babylonian cones and tablets.

Bridwell Library of Theology. Decherd H. Turner, Librarian.

Holdings: Papers of Georg Steindorff (Germany, Calif.; Egyptologist, author), consisting of several hundred letters.

Methodist Historical Library. Mrs. John H. Warnick, Librarian.

Holdings: Papers of Littleton Fowler (Tex.; missionary to Republic of Tex.), several hundred items; Selina Hastings, Countess of Huntingdon (England; religious leader, founder of a sect of Calvinistic Methodists), 18th century (60 letters); John Monroe Moore (Tenn., Tex.; Methodist bishop), 2,000 letters; Edwin DuBose Mouzon (Tex.; Methodist bishop), 18,500 letters; Charles C. Selecman (Calif., Tex.; Methodist bishop, pres. Southern Methodist Univ.), several hundred letters; and John Wesley (England; founder of Methodism), 18th century (81 letters). There are also minutes of Soule University, Chappell Hill, Tex., 1856-87.

DENTON

North Texas State College Library. David A. Webb, Librarian.

Holdings: 676 pieces, 1830-1945, including diaries, letters, ledgers, and muster rolls of the Texas War for Independence, the Civil War, and World Wars I and II.

EL PASO

El Paso Centennial Museum, Texas Western College. Rex E. Gerald, Curator.

Holdings: Microfilm negatives of municipal and church archives of Janos, Chihuahua, Mexico, 1760-1800 (3,000 pages), relating to Spanish-Indian contacts; and papers of an estate in Madison Parish, La., 1869-80 (174 items).

FORT WORTH

Federal Records Center, GSA. 424 West Vickery St. Chief.

Holdings: A large quantity of noncurrent or semicurrent records, chiefly of recent date, of nonmilitary agencies of the U.S. Government in Arkansas, Oklahoma, and Texas. Most of these records have been appraised for disposal after specified periods of time, but some will be preserved because of their enduring value. Records in the latter category include records of U.S. district courts and predecessor circuit courts, from 1845; U.S. Circuit Court of Appeals, from 1891; Bureau of Customs, from 1872, chiefly of World War II period; Coast Guard, from 1872; and Bureau of Indian Affairs, from 1852.

FORT WORTH 15

Fleming Library, Southwestern Baptist Theological Seminary. Charles P. Johnson, Director of Libraries.

Holdings: Included are papers of George W. Baines (Tex.; Baptist clergyman, pres. of Baylor Univ.); Benajah H. Carroll (Tex.; Baptist clergyman, Bible School dean at Baylor Univ., pres. of Southwestern Baptist Theological Seminary) and James M. Carroll (Tex.; Baptist clergyman, pres. of Howard Payne College), before 1886 (4 file drawers), relating to the Baptist General Convention of Texas and its prede-

cessors and containing 3 vols. of unpublished sermons; Isham E. Reynolds
(Tex.; dean of School of Sacred Music
at Southwestern Baptist Theological
Seminary); George W. Truett (Tex.;
Baptist clergyman, pres. of Southwestern Baptist Theological Seminary); and
J. Howard Williams (Tex.; Baptist
clergyman, pres. of Southwestern Baptist Theological Seminary). There are
microfilm copies of letters, addresses,
and administrative documents of Lee R.
Scarborough (Tex.; Baptist clergyman,
pres. of Southwestern Baptist Theological Seminary), 1912-42 (109 reels).
There are also miscellaneous Texas
Baptist Church records, dating from
the early 1800's.

FORT WORTH 2

Fort Worth Public Library.
(Mrs.) Abby Moran, Head of Southwest History and Genealogy Department.

Holdings: A substantial quantity
relating chiefly to the early history of
Fort Worth and Tarrant County. The
papers of Mary Daggett Lake (Tex.;
horticultural expert, pioneer garden
club organizer, writer), 1897-1955,
include 3,000 letters, 6,000 holograph
and typed manuscripts, and some diaries. A collection of 4,500 ink drawings constitutes the cartoon collection
named for Hal Coffman (Tex.; Fort
Worth newspaper cartoonist). There
are miscellaneous groups of letters,
account books, club minutes, reminiscences of early residents, and cemetery records. In the Library also are
200 photographs of early Fort Worth
and some other holdings of the Tarrant County Historical Society; and a
collection of autographed photographs
of famous musicians and singers
assembled by a Fort Worth concert
manager.

GALVESTON

Rosenberg Library. Corner
Twenty-Third and Avenue I.
W. R. Holman, Librarian.

Holdings: 39,500 pieces, 1492-
1954, relating to Texas as a colony,
an independent republic, and a State
of the Union.

Of first importance are the papers of Samuel May Williams (Tex.;
pioneer, merchant, banker, sec. of
Austin's colony), 1822-64 (4,100 pieces). These include correspondence
with prominent Texas pioneers and
public figures in Mexico and contain
57 letters of Stephen F. Austin (Mo.,
Tex.; leader in the settlement of
Tex.). Second in size and importance are the papers of James Morgan (Tex.; commandant of Galveston
Island during the Texas Revolution),
1809-80 (1,095 pieces). Papers of
other individuals include those of Gail
Borden, Jr. (Tex.; pioneer, survey-
or, inventor, newspaper publisher,
collector of customs at Galveston),
1832-82 (2 vols. and 290 pieces);
Braxton Bragg (La., Tex.; U. S. and
Confed. Army officer, chief engineer of Gulf, Colorado, and Santa Fe
Railroad), 1849-78 (104 pieces);
David G. Burnet (Tex.; Sec. State and
Pres. ad interim of the Texas Republic), 1834-69 (365 pieces); Walter Q.
Gresham (Tex.; lawyer, State legislator), 1834-97 (41 vols. and 190
pieces); John D. Lockhart (Tex.;
businessman, agriculturist, Confed.
Army surgeon), 1830-1918 (15 diaries and 655 pieces); Henry Rosenberg (Tex.; Swiss consul, merchant,
banker, philanthropist), 1845-1907
(4,600 pieces); Ben C. Stuart (Tex.;
journalist, historian), 1870-1921
(10 vols. and 4,025 pieces); Charles
W. Trueheart (Tex.; Confed. soldier,
physician) and Henry M. Trueheart
(Tex.; realtor), 1839-1905 (746 pieces

and business record books aggregating 350,000 pages); and Zebulon L. White (N.Y., R.I.; newspaper editor), 1860-89 (21 vols. and 365 pieces).

There are other papers concerning the colonization of Texas by North Americans, the relations of early Texas with Mexico, the war for Texas independence, the Republic and its presidents, pioneers of Texas, the flow of German immigration, the beginnings of Free Masonry in Texas, land operations, journalism in Texas, the plantation life and slavery. Materials of Galveston interest include some relating to Bernardo de Gálvez (La.; Spanish Gov. of La.); Jean Laffite (La.; pirate, smuggler) and his sojourn on Galveston Island; the founding of Galveston and the Galveston City Co.; the development of the port and the Galveston Wharf Co.; Galveston in the Civil War, particularly the Battle of Galveston and blockade running; yellow fever epidemics; hurricanes, especially the storm and tidal wave of 1900; seawall construction and grade raising in Galveston; and Galveston's commission form of government.

See news note in Miss. Valley Hist. Review, 10:340-344 (Dec. 1923).

HOUSTON 1

Fondren Library, Rice Institute. Hardin Craig, Jr., Librarian.

Holdings: A collection of miscellaneous manuscripts, among them papers of George Cranfield Berkeley (British naval officer), 1808-13 (1,000 pieces); papers of James Stephen Hogg (Tex.; lawyer, Gov.), 1887-1905 (60 vols., typescript copy); and the journal by Mirabeau Buonaparte Lamar (Ga., Tex.; Pres. of Tex.) of his trip from Georgia to Texas in 1835.

HOUSTON 2

Houston Public Library. (Mrs.) Harriet Dickson Reynolds, Librarian.

Holdings: 27 medieval and Oriental manuscripts, 12th-17th centuries; letters and other papers of prominent Texans, 1826-99 (40 pieces); and diaries of John Milsaps (Tex.; Salvation Army major, editor of the War Cry), 1852-1930 (73 vols.), together with several hundred manuscript sermons delivered in England, 1820-65, and a number of miscellaneous Philippine documents acquired by him while serving in the Spanish-American War. There is also a copy of the R. B. Blake Collection of typescripts of official documents, personal letters, and diaries of prominent individuals, and translations from the Nacogdoches and Bexar archives (more than 100 volumes).

See De Ricci, Census, p. 2164.

LUBBOCK

Southwest Collection, Texas Technological College. Seymour V. Connor, Director; Roy Sylvan Dunn, Archivist.

Holdings: A substantial quantity of manuscripts, 35,000 feet of microfilm, and 10,000 feet of tape recordings, 19th and 20th centuries, relating chiefly to Texas and the American Southwest, with emphasis on local history materials. Personal papers include those of Amon G. Carter (Tex.; oilman, newspaper publisher); William Curry Holden (Tex.; historian, archeologist, prof. at Tex. Tech. Coll.); Clifford B. Jones (Mo., Tex.; banker, pres. of Tex. Tech. Coll.); Elijah P. Lovejoy (Mo., Ill.; editor, abolitionist) and his family, 1804-91; and Carl Coke Rister (Okla., Tex.;

historian, prof. at Univ. of Okla. and Tex. Tech. Coll.). Business records include those of the Yellow House Land Co.; Texas Land and Development Co.; Spur Ranch, 1881-1912; Double U Ranch, including records of Post City; Espuela Land and Cattle Co., 1885-1907; and the Matador Land and Cattle Co., 1882-1952, probably the most extensive single ranch record collection in existence, totaling 260,000 pieces. Other business records pertain to banks, land companies, railroads, and retail and wholesale organizations. Biographical data files have been collected on hundreds of prominent West Texans and a number of collections of family papers have been established. There are also records of Texas Technological College, 1923 to date.

NACOGDOCHES

Stephen F. Austin State College Library. (Mrs.) Lois F. Blount, Director of the East Texas Room.

Holdings: A considerable quantity, relating chiefly to East Texas. Included are biographical and autobiographical accounts of East Texans (5,802 pages); accounts of historical events from the time of the early settlements through the Texas Revolution, the Civil War, and the Reconstruction periods (3,699 pages); correspondence of Samuel E. Asbury, George L. Crocket, and other prominent East Texans (2,202 pages); notes on art and education in Texas, particularly in Nacogdoches County (243 pages); legal papers and accounts of lawsuits (562 pages); land grants, deeds, and land transfers (1,231 pages); notes on religious and ecclesiastical matters in East Texas (910 pages); East Texas census reports (418 pages); original writings of East Texans, historical and literary, including some poems (1,124 pages); and the records

of East Texas lumber, industrial, and railroad companies (500,000 items).

SAN ANTONIO

Spanish Archives of San Antonio. Office of the County Clerk.

Holdings: 2,000 pieces, 1736-1836, consisting chiefly of archives of the Spanish and Mexican governments in Texas. These are a part of the Bexar Archives and include land grants, deeds, transfers, wills, and other documents of legal value. The records not considered to be of legal value were transferred to the University of Texas in 1896. Included also are some records of Franciscan missions, 1793-1834 (171 pieces).
See Carlos E. Castañeda, A Report on the Spanish Archives in San Antonio (1937. 167 p.).

SAN JACINTO MONUMENT

San Jacinto Museum of History Association. Mrs. David W. Knepper, Director.

Holdings: 500,000 pages of manuscripts, including documents relating to Spanish Mexico; the Mexican revolution and its leaders; Texas under the Mexican Republic; Mexican patriots Hidalgo, Morelos, Iturbide, Santa Anna, and others; the Republic of Texas; the Texas navy and the Texas frontier; Stephen F. Austin, Sam Houston, Mirabeau B. Lamar, Andrew and Mary Jane Briscoe, Commander John G. Tod of the Texas navy, Governor Francis R. Lubbock, Thomas Jefferson Chamber, and many other early Texas patriots; and the political, social, and economic growth of the region, including early statehood and the Civil War.

WACO

Baylor University Library. Roscoe Rouse, Librarian.

Holdings: Extensive holdings in Texas history and culture, Baptist history, Baylor University, and Robert Browning.

The Browning Collection contains literary manuscripts and letters of Elizabeth Barrett Browning (England; poet), 101 pieces, and Robert Browning (England; poet), 422 pieces. Included also are 1,032 related letters and manuscripts, and approximately 300 related letters not yet processed.

The Texas History Collection includes papers of James P. Alexander (Tex.; chief justice State supreme court), 2,000 pieces; George W. Baines (Tex.; Baptist clergyman, pres. of Baylor Univ.), 1,200 pieces; William Cowper Brann (Tex.; journalist), 2,000 pages; Samuel Palmer Brooks (Tex.; pres. of Baylor Univ.), 100,000 pages; Rufus C. Burleson (Tex.; Baptist clergyman, pres. of Baylor Univ.), 10,000 pieces; Benajah H. Carroll (Tex.; Baptist clergyman, dean of Bible School at Baylor Univ., pres. of Southwestern Baptist Theological Seminary) and James M.

Carroll (Tex.; Baptist clergyman, pres. of Howard Payne College), 2,000 pages; Oscar H. Cooper (Tex.; pres. of Baylor Univ. and of Simmons College), 2,000 pages; William C. Crane (Tex.; pres. of Baylor Univ.), 200,000 pieces; Joseph Martin Dawson (Tex.; Baptist clergyman, writer), 500 pages; Sam Houston (Tenn., Tex.; U.S. Rep. and Sen., Gov.), 50 pieces; Pat M. Neff (Tex.; lawyer, Gov., pres. of Baylor Univ.), 750,000 pieces; John Franklyn Norris (Tex.; Baptist clergyman), 8,000 pages; Lawrence Sullivan Ross (Tex.; Confed. Army officer, Gov.), 5 folios; and Dorothy Scarborough (Tex., N.Y.; prof. of English at Baylor and Columbia Univs., author of short stories and verse), 20,000 pieces.

The Library also has a number of sermons, journals, and other papers relating to the Baptists; some letters and other papers pertaining to the Civil War and World War I; records of a medical association; records of the American Studies Association of Texas (200 pieces); and Baylor University records (500,000 pieces).

See Ruth Budd, "Baylor University's Browning Collection," in Library Journal, 60:789 (Oct. 15, 1935); and Guy Bryan Harrison, Jr., "The Texas Collection of Baylor University," in Baylor Bulletin, vol. 44, no. 4 (Dec. 1940).

UTAH

CLEARFIELD

Federal Records Center Annex, GSA. Chief.

Holdings: A large quantity of non-current records of Navy overseas bases in the Pacific islands and the Far East, since 1941.

PROVO

Brigham Young University Library. S. Lyman Tyler, Director of Libraries.

Holdings: 250 vols., from 1830 to the present, relating chiefly to Mormon pioneers and later settlers of Utah but including also material on Ohio, Illinois, and the trans-Mississippi West. Included are journals of settlers and several diaries kept by members of the Mormon Battalion during the Mexican War.

ST. GEORGE

Washington County Library. 55 West Tabernacle St. Roxey S. Romney, Librarian.

Holdings: 55 vols., chiefly diaries, journals, and reminiscences that relate to the development of the Church of Jesus Christ of Latter-day Saints and the growth of Utah.

SALT LAKE CITY 16

Daughters of Utah Pioneers. 300 North Main St. Kate B. Carter, President.

Holdings: Hundreds of pieces, 19th and 20th centuries, relating chiefly to the early settlement of Utah. Included are many reminiscent papers on aspects of Utah history, and nearly 200 original journals and diaries of immigrant pioneers.

SALT LAKE CITY 1

Genealogical Society of the Church of Jesus Christ of Latter Day Saints. 80 North Main St. Ellen Hill, Library Supervisor.

Holdings: A quantity of manuscript books and other records and 190,900 rolls of microfilm, consisting of copies of local archives and other genealogical records in the United States and in Europe, especially northern Europe, 17th-19th centuries. Materials reproduced on microfilm include census returns, wills and probate records, other court records, tax and military records, marriage bonds and licenses, and church records of baptisms, marriages, and deaths. Although the primary purpose of the microfilming project is to assemble genealogical information for members of the Church, all series containing genealogical data are being microfilmed in their entirety. The project is not yet completed, and the total will eventually be considerably more than the number of rolls given above.

See Archibald F. Bennett, "The Record Copying Program of the Utah Genealogical Society," in Am. Archivist, 16:227-232 (July 1953).

Historian's Office Library, Church of Jesus Christ of Latter-day Saints. 47 East South Temple St. Joseph Fielding Smith, Church Historian.

Holdings: 142,000 volumes and thousands of items, 1830-1956, comprising the archives of the church. Included are church membership records, minute books, diaries, manuscript histories, and letters. These papers are available by permission of the church historian.

SALT LAKE CITY 12

University of Utah Library. L. H. Kirkpatrick, Librarian.

Holdings: A small collection relating to the University and the Church of Jesus Christ of Latter-day Saints. Included are papers of Esther Nelson (Utah; Univ. of Utah librarian), 1898-1941 (6 filing drawers); and John M. Whitaker (Utah; clerk of the First Presidency of the church), 1870-1956 (7 filing drawers).

SALT LAKE CITY 2

Utah State Archives. 603 East South Temple. Everett L. Cooley, State Archivist.

Holdings: 218 vols., 437 cu. ft. of records, 217 microfilm rolls of county records, 6 microfilm rolls of legislative records, and 10 microfilm rolls of State and territorial records, 1849-1959, consisting of the official records of the Territory and State of Utah.
Territorial Archives include the executive record books, 1850-95 (5 vols.); papers of various territorial executive officials, 1851-94 (17 cu. ft.); reports from the Governor to the

U. S. Secretary of the Interior, 1878-96 (1 cu. ft.); minute book of the Deseret Agricultural and Manufacturing Society, 1856-72 (1 vol.); records of the Nauvoo Legion and Utah Territorial Militia, 1849-72 (5 cu. ft.); papers relating to Indian wars, 1849-53 (11 vols. and 4 cu. ft.); journals of the house of representatives, 1858-78 (2 vols.); journals of the council, 1858-78 (2 vols.); and original and engrossed bills of the legislature, 1851-94 (22 cu. ft.). (Important papers for the early territorial period, including letter books of Governor Brigham Young, are among the archives of the Church of Jesus Christ of Latter-day Saints, described above.)
State records include the Governors' messages to the legislature, 1896-1959 (1 cu. ft.); biennial budgets, 1923-59 (1 cu. ft.); and correspondence of the following Governors: Simon Bamberger, 1917-21 (1 cu. ft.); Henry H. Blood, 1933-40 (41 cu. ft.); John C. Cutler, 1905-8 (6 letter books and 3 cu. ft.); George D. Clyde, 1957-58 (1 cu. ft.); George H. Dern, 1925-32 (30 cu. ft.); J. Bracken Lee, 1949-56 (39 cu. ft.); Charles R. Mabey, 1921-25 (1 cu. ft.); Herbert B. Maw, 1941-48 (30 cu. ft.); William Spry, 1909-16 (10 letter books and 22 cu. ft.); and Heber M. Wells, 1896-1904 (6 letter books and 7 cu. ft.). The correspondence of the governors includes both general and state department correspondence. There are also reports and correspondence of committees appointed or authorized by various governors. Other State records include correspondence of the secretary of state, 1896-1954 (97 letter books and 3 cu. ft.); and records of numerous commissions and boards. There are also reports, minutes, correspondence, and other records of the legislature and the Legislative Council, 1896-1956 (7 cu. ft.); and

legislative original and engrossed bills, 1917-31 (11 cu. ft.).

—oOo—

Utah State Historical Society. 603 East South Temple St. A. R. Mortensen, Director.

Holdings: Some 40 ft. of manuscript materials, including microfilms, 1776-1900, relating chiefly to the discovery, exploration, settlement, and development of Utah, and to the history of the Mormon Church. Included are diaries, journals, letters, and reminiscences of travelers and emigrants. In addition, the files of the WPA Writers' Project and the Historical Records Survey are deposited with the Society, and these files contain hundreds of typescript copies of diaries, journals, and other manuscripts.

VERMONT

BENNINGTON

Bennington Museum, Inc. Richard C. Barret, Director-Curator; Allen D. Hill, Genealogical Consultant.

Holdings: A collection of diaries, letters, business records, church records, early proprietor's and town records, and other manuscripts, dated from the early Revolutionary War through the Spanish-American War, and relating chiefly to Bennington County, Vt., but containing also materials on neighboring counties in Vermont, New York, Massachusetts, and New Hampshire. Among the holdings are many papers on the Battle of Bennington and documents signed by famous Revolutionary personages and by the early Governors of Vermont.

BURLINGTON

University of Vermont Library. Morrison Chandler Haviland, Director; T. D. Seymour Bassett, Wilbur Librarian.

Holdings: The Wilbur Library contains a quantity of papers chiefly of Vermonters or relating to Vermont. Included are papers of Ethan Allen (Vt.; Rev. War officer) and Heman Allen (Vt.; U.S. Rep., Minister to Chile) and their brothers (3,000 pieces), relating to land speculation and early Vermont history; Ira Allen (Vt., Pa.; Rev. War officer, political leader), 1772-1813 (1,021 pieces); Sarah Norcliffe Cleghorn (Vt.; poet, reformer), 1895-1945 (4 ft.), including literary drafts; Samuel Chandler Crafts (Vt.; Gov., U.S. Rep. and Sen.) and his family, 1799-1881 (4 ft.); Dorothea

Frances Canfield Fisher (Vt.; author, educational leader) and her family, 1860-1958 (32 ft.), including correspondence and literary drafts; and Thomas Macdonough (U.S. naval officer), 1813-24, account books. The Stevens Collection (6,000 pieces) contains papers of Henry Stevens, Sr. (Vt.; farmer, businessman, historian), Henry Stevens, Jr. (Vt., England; bookdealer, bibliographer), and Benjamin Franklin Stevens (Vt., England; bookdealer, antiquarian). There are also papers of a Vermont sheep breeder and Civil War soldier, 1840-65 (300 letters); papers of the Champlain Transportation Co. and other shippers on Lake Champlain, 1800-1937 (21 ft.); miscellaneous account books (40 ft.); and letters, deeds, and correspondence relating to the University of Vermont, 1791 to date (50 ft.).

See Hist. Records Survey, Calendar of Ira Allen Papers in the Wilbur Library, University of Vermont (1939. 149 p. Processed).

MIDDLEBURY

Middlebury College Library. Margaret W. Fayer, Librarian.

Holdings: Several hundred manuscripts in the Julian W. Abernethy Library of American Literature, 19th and 20th centuries, consisting chiefly of letters and some literary manuscripts of more than 250 American authors. For each the number of items is usually small, but there are 19 items by Julia Caroline Ripley Dorr (N.Y., Vt.; poet, novelist), 1852-1907, and a larger number of letters to her; 27 letters by Oliver

Wendell Holmes (Mass.; essayist, poet, physician), 1877-92; 29 letters by Edmund Clarence Stedman (N.Y.; poet, anthologist, stockbroker), 1877-1908; 32 letters by Elizabeth Drew Barstow Stoddard (N.Y.; poet, novelist), 1879-1900; and 130 items by or about Henry David Thoreau (Mass.; essayist, poet).

See Viola C. White, A Check List; Abernethy Library of American Literature, pp. 217-220 and 269-291 (1940).

MONTPELIER

Public Records Commission. Olney W. Hill, Director.

Holdings: Chiefly scattered official records of the State. Included are military records for the Revolutionary War, the War of 1812, the Civil War, and the Spanish-American War (48 cu. ft.); working papers and other records of the Eugenics Survey, 1925-31, and of the Commission on Country Life, 1925-31 (60 linear ft.); 1860 and 1880 census enumeration records for Chittenden County (24 vols.); records of the Missisquoi Bay Bridge Commission, 1935-45 (8 cu. ft.), of the Vermont Industrial Agricultural Products Commission, 1940-56 (3 linear ft.), and of the Commission Appointed to Investigate the Subject of Taxation of Public Utilities, 1932 (1 cu. ft.); financial statistics of State, county, and local government in Vermont, 1932-48 (7 cu. ft.); and records of claims under an act providing for the payment and expenses of sick soldiers of the First Vermont Volunteer Infantry of the Spanish-American War (2 boxes). There are also microfilm copies of 3,094 vols. of land and vital records of the State's cities and towns, prior to 1850 (1,500 reels); 331 vols. of probate records, before 1850 (30 reels); and closed

probation and parole case records, 1916-49 (45 reels, restricted).

—oOo—

Secretary of State's Office. Howard E. Armstrong, Secretary of State.

Holdings: Official records of the State, including the following series: Vermont State Papers, 1777-1884 (82 vols. and 10 boxes of loose papers), including petitions, county court records, public letters, reports of officers and institutions, and reports of committees of the assembly; legislative records, 1778-1955 (305 vols.); Surveyors-General papers, 1763-1820 (58 vols.), including records of early surveys, abstracts of vendues, proprietors' records, and maps and town plans; laws of Vermont, 1779 to date (59 vols.); certificates and canvasses of votes for Federal, State, and county offices, 1800 to date with gaps before 1860 (200 vertical files and some boxes and packages); correspondence and papers of the Governors, 1859 to date (120 boxes, 64 files); corporation records, 1860 to date, including articles of incorporation and reports; and records of births, marriages, divorces, and deaths, 1760 to date (3,000,000 cards).

See Augustus Hunt Shearer, "Report on the Archives of the State of Vermont," in Am. Hist. Assn. Annual Report for 1915, pp. 311-355.

—oOo—

Vermont Historical Society. Supreme Court Bldg. Richard G. Wood, Director; Clara E. Follette, Librarian and Museum Director.

Holdings: 700 journals, account books, and other manuscript record books, 61 filing case drawers, 49 manuscript boxes, 134 document boxes, and 65 cartons, containing documents dating from 1740 to 1950, and relating chiefly to Vermont.

Personal papers include those of Jonathan H. Hubbard (Vt.; lawyer, U.S. Rep.), 1809-51 (314 pieces); Oliver Johnson (N.Y., Pa.; antislavery leader, newspaper editor), 1861-89 (95 pieces); Justin S. Morrill (Vt.; U.S. Rep. and Sen.), 1828-96 (270 pieces); Zadock Thompson (Vt.; naturalist, mathematician, prof. at Univ. of Vt.), 1845-74 (30 vols.); Royall Tyler (Mass., Vt.; playwright, novelist, Vt. chief justice), 1781-1882 (2 drawers); Peter T. Washburn (Vt.; Gov.), 1799-1886 (10 document boxes); James Whitelaw (Vt.; surveyor-gen., pioneer), 1768-1829 (4 drawers); and Charles W. Willard (Vt.; lawyer, newspaper editor and publisher, U.S. Rep.), 1840-75 (6 document boxes).

Papers relating to business include records of a mill dam company, 1833-66 (30 pieces), and of a furnace company, 1834-99 (56 vols. of accounts); the David Hubbard Sumner papers on land, canal, and lumbering activities on the Connecticut River, 1791-1888 (2,700 pieces); and a considerable number of account books of general stores and other business establishments. The papers of Thomas Hawley Canfield (Vt., Minn.; pres. of Lake Superior and Puget Land Co., director of Northern Pacific Railroad Co.), 1849-76 (3,000 pieces), contain much on business and also some personal papers of John Henry Hopkins (Pa., Vt.; lawyer, Episcopal bishop). The papers of John Gregory Smith (Vt.; railroad promoter, Gov.), 1810-99 (10 boxes), are largely concerned with his business affairs but among them are some personal papers of his father John Smith (Vt.; lawyer, U.S. Rep., railroad builder) and his son Edward Curtis Smith (Vt.; railroad executive, Gov.).

There are also some school records, 1814-93 (5 vols.); records of a Congregational society, 1789-1898 (4 vols.), and other church records; the inventories of church and town records compiled by the Vermont Historical Records Survey (church, 8 drawers; town, 17 drawers); the James P. Taylor Collection of correspondence and printed material relating to the Vermont Chamber of Commerce and various reform movements such as billboard restriction and water pollution, 1920-50 (95 document boxes); records of the constitutional convention of 1793 (1 vol.); records of an internal revenue collection district, 1783-1848 (745 pieces); records of four antislavery societies, 1834-47 (4 vols.), and of a chapter of the Sons of Temperance, 1850-59 (3 vols.); and letters and other papers relating to the Civil War (uncounted).

See annual report of the Librarian in the Society's Proceedings, 1939-42, and in Vt. Quarterly, 1948-50.

NORTHFIELD

Norwich University Library.
Victor H. Johnson, Librarian.

Holdings: Papers of Alden Partridge (N.Y., Vt.; prof. at U.S. Military Academy, founder of American Literary, Scientific, and Military Academy, which became Norwich Univ.), 1820-35 (several hundred items), relating chiefly to the administration of the school.

ST. JOHNSBURY

Fairbanks Museum of Natural Science. Frederick H. Mold, Director.

Holdings: Several documents

relating to Thaddeus Fairbanks (Vt.;
inventor of the platform scale), and a
few miscellaneous manuscripts.

WINOOSKI PARK

St. Michael's College Library.

Rev. V. B. Maloney, Librarian.

Holdings: A day-to-day diary,
with emphasis on matters ecclesiastical, kept by two Catholic Bishops of
the See of Burlington, Louis de Goes-
briand, 1853-99, and John Stephen
Michaud, 1899-1908.

VIRGINIA

ASHLAND

Randolph-Macon College Library.
Mrs. Flavia Reed Owen, Librarian.

Holdings: (1) Papers of William
E. Dodd (Va., Ill.; historian, prof. at
Randolph-Macon College and Univ. of
Chicago, U. S. Ambassador to Germany), 1899-1936 (3 filing cabinet
drawers), including an incomplete file
of incoming and outgoing letters, working drafts and other material for books
and articles, and a 4-vol. journal,
1916-25; and (2) papers relating to
the Methodist Episcopal Church, South.
Included in the latter group are records
of the Baltimore conference of the
church, 1865-1926 (13 vols.); records
of the Trinity Methodist Church, Richmond, 1835-1934 (46 vols.), and 80
items on other Methodist churches in
Virginia; and records of the Methodist
Church Survey Committee on church
organization, 1950-52 (47 vols.). The
papers of John Early (Va.; Methodist
bishop, founder of Randolph-Macon
College) contain 92 letters, 1800-60;
a 4-vol. diary, 1810-14; a 2-vol. day
book, 1822-36; and 4 vols. of minutes
of the Virginia annual conference of
the church, 1800-40.

CHARLOTTESVILLE

Albemarle County Historical Society.
University of Virginia Library.
William H. Runge, Archivist.

Holdings: Papers relating chiefly
to Charlottesville, Albemarle County,
and Virginia. Included are records of
the Monticello Guard, 1857-81 (5 vols.);
the Charlottesville Lyceum, 1937-45
(1 vol.); and the Women's Christian
Temperance Union of Virginia, 1939-
40.
See "Report of the Archivist," in
Albemarle County Hist. Society, Papers, vols. 1-12 (1940-52); and University of Virginia Library's Annual
Report on Historical Collections.

—oOo—

University of Virginia Library.
Francis L. Berkeley, Jr., Curator
of Manuscripts.

Holdings: 5,000,000 items, dated
from the 13th century to the present
and embracing primarily (1) papers
relating to the history of Virginia and
the southeastern United States, (2)
papers on American literature and,
to a lesser degree, English literature, and (3) the deposited archives
of the University of Virginia and of
several other institutions.
Papers of U. S. Presidents and
Cabinet officers include those of
Amos T. Akerman (Ga.; Attorney
Gen.), 1871-76 (2 vols.); James Barbour (Va.; lawyer, Gov., U. S. Sen.,
Sec. War, Minister to England) and
his family, 1760-1895 (2,500 items);
Henry Clay (Ky.; U. S. Rep. and Sen.,
Sec. State), 1798-1851 (170 items);
Hamilton Fish (N. Y.; U. S. Rep. and
Sen., Gov., Sec. State), 184?-61
(55 pieces); Carter Glass (Va.; U. S.
Rep. and Sen., Sec. Treas.), 1879-
1946 (400,000 pieces); Thomas Jef-
ferson (Va.; Member Continental
Cong., Gov., Minister to France, Sec.
State, U. S. Pres.), 1762-1826 (2,500
pieces); James Madison (Va.; Mem-
ber Continental Cong., U. S. Rep.,
Sec. State, U. S. Pres.), 1780-1834
(165 pieces); James Monroe (Va.;
Member Continental Cong., U. S. Sen.,

Gov., diplomat, Sec. State, U.S. Pres.),
1785-1834 (160 items); Edward R.
Stettinius, Jr. (N.Y., Va.; director
U.S. Steel Corp., Sec. State, U.S. Rep.
to United Nations), 1914-49 (750,000
pieces); Alexander H. H. Stuart (Va.;
lawyer, U.S. Rep., Sec. Interior),
1810-91 (200 items); Claude Augustus
Swanson (Va.; U.S. Rep. and Sen., Gov.,
Sec. Navy), 1921-22 (16,000 pieces);
John Tyler (Va.; Gov., U.S. Rep., Sen.,
and Pres.), 1826-61 (131 pieces); Daniel Webster (N.H., Mass.; U.S. Rep.
and Sen., Sec. State), 1800-53 (115
items), chiefly regarding land speculation; and Woodrow Wilson (N.J.; pres.
of Princeton Univ., Gov., U.S. Pres.),
1897-1923 (248 pieces).

Papers of members of the U.S. Con-
gress include those of James Brecken-
ridge (Va.; lawyer, War of 1812 officer,
U.S. Rep.), 1788-1828 (141 pieces);
William Cabell Bruce (Md.; lawyer,
U.S. Sen.), 1918-45 (15 vols. and 500
pieces); John Warwick Daniel (Va.;
lawyer, Confed. Army officer, U.S.
Rep. and Sen.), 1859-1910 (2,000 items);
Charles James Faulkner (Va., W.Va.;
U.S. Rep., Minister to France, Confed.
Army officer), 1829-84 (600 items);
Charles James Faulkner, Jr. (W.Va.;
lawyer, U.S. Sen.), 1865-1929 (3,000
pieces); Robert M. T. Hunter (Va.;
U.S. Rep. and Sen., Confed. Sec. State
and Sen.), 1826-87 (2,700 items);
Richard Henry Lee (Va.; Pres. of
Continental Cong., U.S. Sen.), 1758-93
(450 items); James McDowell, Jr. (Va.;
Gov., U.S. Rep.) and his family, 1792-
1880 (660 pieces); Wilson Cary Nicholas
(Va.; Rev. War officer, U.S. Sen. and
Rep., Gov.), 1779-1824 (2,800 items);
Miles Poindexter (Wash., Va.; lawyer,
U.S. Rep. and Sen., Ambassador to
Peru), 1897-1937 (800,000 pieces);
John A. Quitman (Miss.; Gov., U.S.
Rep.), 1823-58 (44 items); John
Randolph of Roanoke (Va.; U.S. Rep.
and Sen.), 1781-1833 (750 items);
William Cabell Rives (Va.; Minister
to France, U.S. Rep. and Sen.,

Confed. Rep.), 1827-66 (425 pieces);
John F. Rixey (Va.; lawyer, U.S.
Rep.), 1875-1902 (2 vols.); and Samuel Smith (Md.; Rev. War and War of
1812 officer, U.S. Rep. and Sen.) and
his family, 1726-1924 (2,800 pieces).

Papers of Justices of the U.S. Supreme Court and judges of Virginia
courts include those of Philip Pendleton Barbour (Va.; U.S. Rep., U.S.
Supreme Court Justice), 1809-41
(280 pieces); William H. Cabell (Va.;
Gov., Va. supreme court judge),
1800-51 (335 pieces); Dabney Carr
(Va.; chancery dist. court judge),
1794-1830 (60 pieces); Peter V. Daniel (Va.; U.S. Supreme Court Justice),
1824-60 (94 pieces); Duncan Lawrence
Groner (Va., D.C.; judge of U.S.
dist. court for eastern Va. and of U.S.
court of appeals for D.C.), 1930-57
(6,000 items); George Jefferson Hund-
ley (Va.; judge), 1870-1924 (1 vol.);
John L. Ingram (Va.; judge), 1882-
1911 (200 pieces); James Clark Mc-
Reynolds (Tenn., N.Y.; U.S. Attorney
Gen., U.S. Supreme Court Justice),
1884-1944 (500 pieces); Archibald
Stuart (Va.; Rev. War officer, Va.
general court judge), 1783-1832
(300 pieces); Creed Taylor (Va.;
judge, law teacher), 1791-1823
(416 pieces); and Bushrod Washington (Va.; U.S. Supreme Court Justice), 1780-1826 (54 pieces).

Papers of other public officials
include those of Landon Carter (Va.;
burgess, pamphleteer, agronomist),
1734-77 (190 pieces); James Lawson
Kemper (Va.; Confed. Army officer,
Gov.), 1824-1903 (15 vols. and 15,000
pieces); William Jett Lauck (Va.;
economist, labor expert), 1915-42
(50,000 pieces); Henry Laurens (S.C.;
merchant, planter, Pres. of Continental Cong.), 1778-80 (75 pieces);
Arthur Lee (Va.; Member Continental Cong., diplomat), 1760-91
(347 pieces); Francis Lightfoot Lee
(Va.; Member Continental Cong.),
1773-90 (25 pieces); William Lee

(Va.; merchant, diplomat), 1773-82 (77 pieces); and John R. Wingfield (Va.; State legislator, consul in Costa Rica), 1865-1925 (49 vols. and 7,000 pieces).

Papers of military leaders, in addition to those listed above, include papers of John Hartwell Cocke (Va.; planter, War of 1812 officer, publicist, temperance advocate), 1798-1872 (20,000 pieces); Philip St. George Cocke (Va.; U.S. and Confed. Army officer, planter, writer on agriculture), 1777-1861 (67 pieces); James Chatham Duane (N.Y.; Civil War officer, civil engineer), 1864-65 (2 vols.); John Daniel Imboden (Va.; lawyer, Confed. Army officer, mining promoter), 1831 95 (1,000 pieces); Bradley Tyler Johnson (Md., Va.; lawyer, Confed. Army officer), 1829-1903 (2,000 pieces); William Morris (Va.; Chief of Confed. Signal Corps) and his family, 1846-1900 (3,000 pieces); John Singleton Mosby (Va.; Confed. ranger, lawyer), 1849-1914 (35 pieces); and Thomas L. Rosser (Va.; Confed. Army officer, chief engineer of Northern Pacific Railroad, Spanish-American War officer), 1860-1910 (42 pieces).

Papers of authors and editors include those of Ambrose Bierce (Calif.; short-story writer, journalist), 1866-1916 (582 items); Richard Doddridge Blackmore (England; novelist), 1858-99 (415 pieces); Philip Alexander Bruce (Va.; historian, author), 1889-1933 (1,000 pieces); James Branch Cabell (Va.; novelist, essayist), literary manuscripts; John Esten Cooke (Va.; novelist), 1855-86 (70 pieces); Stephen Crane (N.Y.; writer), 1892-1944 (250 items), including manuscripts of novels and short stories; Richard Harding Davis (Pa., N.Y.; journalist, author), 1863-1916 (5,000 items); John Dos Passos (Va.; novelist), 1949-54 (3 vols. and 6 pieces); Walter Prichard Eaton (N.Y., Conn., Mass.; author, dramatic critic, prof. of playwriting at Yale), 1878-1957 (1,500 items); Ellen Anderson Gholson

Glasgow (Va.; novelist), 1881-1945 (1,760 pieces); Claiborne W. Gooch (Va.; newspaper editor and publisher), 1812-47 (400 items); Nancy Hale (Va.; novelist), 1935-55 (1,000 pieces); Francis Bret Harte (Calif.; short-story writer), 1859-1902 (442 items); Lafcadio Hearn (Ohio, La., Japan; author), 1850-1942 (uncounted collection of manuscripts and Hearniana); Oliver Wendell Holmes (Mass.; physician, author), 1839-94 (334 items); William Dean Howells (Mass., N.Y.; novelist, literary critic, editor), 1866-1917 (377 items); and Thomas Lomax Hunter (Va.; critic, poet, lawyer), 1914-48 (7,500 pieces).

Papers of other writers include those of Mary Johnston (Va.; novelist, advocate of woman suffrage), 1898-1936 (4,000 items); Marie Goebel Kimball (Va.; biographer), 1929-55 (5,000 pieces); Henry Louis Mencken (Md.; author, editor, critic), 1935-51 (73 pieces); Thomas Nelson Page (Va., D.C.; lawyer, author, Ambassador to Italy), 1885-1911 (100 pieces); Edgar Allan Poe (Va., Md., Pa., N.Y.; poet, critic, short-story writer), 1800-1900 (20 originals and 10,000 transcripts); Agnes Rothery Pratt (Va.; novelist), 1929-54 (7 vols. and 900 pieces); Seba Smith, known as Maj. Jack Downing (Maine, N.Y.; political satirist, newspaper editor), 1830-68 (200 pieces); George Sterling (Calif.; poet), 1910-26 (116 items); Frank Richard Stockton (Pa.; novelist, story writer), 1876-1900 (50 items); John Reuben Thompson (Va., N.Y.; poet, editor of the Southern Literary Messenger and other periodicals), 1843-1920 (1 vol. and 400 items); H. G. Wells (England; novelist), 1906-14 (340 pieces); and Walt Whitman (N.Y., D.C., N.J.; poet), 1860-90 (200 pieces). There are many other American and British authors represented by one or a small number of literary manuscripts or letters.

Papers of members of the faculty of the University of Virginia and other schools include those of Edwin Anderson Alderman (N.C., La., Va.; pres. of Univ. of N.C., Tulane Univ., and Univ. of Va.), 1881-1931 (20,000 items); Paul Brandon Barringer (Va.; dean of medicine at Univ. of Va.), 1880-1930 (3,500 pieces); Albert T. Bledsoe (Ill., Miss., Md.; lawyer, prof. of mathematics at Univs. of Miss. and Va., author, editor of Southern Review), 1838-94 (120 pieces); James L. Cabell (Va.; physician, prof. at Univ. of Va.), 1829-37 (89 pieces); Noah K. Davis (Va.; prof. of moral philosophy at Univ. of Va.), 1855-86 (4 vols. and 75 pieces); Gessner Harrison (Va.; classicist, prof. at Univ. of Va.), 1825-60 (260 items); Milton W. Humphreys (Tenn., Tex., Va.; prof. of Latin and Greek at Vanderbilt Univ. and Univs. of Tex. and Va.), 1844-1919 (5 vols. and 44 items); John B. Minor (Va.; prof. of law at Univ. of Va.), 1830-95 (850 items); Lucian Minor (Va.; temperance advocate, prof. of law at William and Mary College), 1829-57 (175 items); Charles Alphonso Smith (La., N.C., Va., Md.; prof. of English at La. State Univ., Univs. of N.C. and Va., and U.S. Naval Academy), 1901-24 (15,000 pieces); and Quincy Wright (Mass., Minn., Ill.; prof. international law at Harvard, Minn., and Chicago Univs.), 1935-55 (1,200 pieces).

Papers of clergymen include those of John A. Broadus (Va., N.C., Ky.; Baptist clergyman, pres. of Southern Baptist Theological Seminary), 1870-90 (25 pieces and transcripts from the seminary collection); Robert L. Dabney (Va., Tex.; Presbyterian theologian, prof. at Va. Union Seminary and Univ. of Tex.), 1830-97 (1,000 pieces); Collins Denny (Va., Ala.; Methodist bishop), 1873-1941 (2,000 pieces); and James Maury (Va.; Jefferson's schoolmaster, plaintiff in the "Parsons' Cause"), 1743-71 (58 pieces).

Papers of other persons include those of Joseph C. Cabell (Va.; principal coadjutor of Thomas Jefferson in founding the Univ. of Va.), 1802-57 (10,000 items); Mark Catesby (England, N.C., S.C.; naturalist), 1747-48 (1 vol.); James Westfall Ford (Pa., Va.; portrait painter), 1823-69 (400 items); Francis Walker Gilmer (Va.; lawyer, author), 1811-26 (105 items); Samuel Higginbottom (England; educator, missionary, agricultural economist, founder of Allahabad Agricultural Institute in India), 1874-1958 (20,000 items); Dolley Payne Madison (Va.; James Madison's wife), 1794-1848 (100 pieces); Thomas Jefferson Randolph (Va.; author, financier), 1792-1875 (500 items); Edward L. Stone (Va.; printer, businessman, civic leader), 1890-1938 (500,000 items); and William Stratchey (Va., England; historian, first sec. of the Va. colony), 1615-28 (1 vol.).

Business papers include early 18th-century letter books of the Carters of Virginia; an old tobacco shipment record from the Rappahannock River (early 18th century); and records of a tobacco warehouse in Lynchburg, 1793-1806 (2 vols.); the Pocket Plantation, 1740-1880 (3,000 pieces), and other plantations; the North American Land Co., 1791-1854 (722 pieces); an iron works and grist mill, 1825-78 (80 vols.); Low Moor Iron Co., 1873-1930 (1,065 vols. and 50,000 pieces); a drug company, 1874-1923 (52 vols.); LaGrange Furnace Co. and Southern Iron Co. of Stewart County, Tenn., 1886-93 (275 vols. and 1,000 pieces); Central Alliance Trade Union, 1891-92 (6 vols.); a Norfolk creosoting company, 1896-1951 (500 pieces); and copra plantations in the Solomon Islands, 1923-34 (3 vols.). There are also hundreds of account books of general stores in Virginia.

Church records include those of a Baptist church, 1831-1950 (29 vols.), a Lutheran church, 1870-1954 (16 vols. and 200 pieces), a Presbyterian church, 1836-1947 (53 vols.), and a Methodist church, 1858-1929 (5 vols. and 18 pieces), all in Charlottesville; and the Nanking (China) Union Church, 1916-40 (13 vols.). School records include those of the Charlottesville City School Board, 1890-1940 (30 vols. and 10,000 pieces).

Other records include the administrative, financial, and departmental records of the University of Virginia and records of student activities, 1814-1955 (300 vols. and 100,000 pieces). There are also records of the city of Alexandria, Va., 1801-84 (117 vols.); the Richmond Police Dept., 1834-43 (1 vol.); a chapter of the Sons of Temperance, 1846-92 (12 vols. and 50 pieces); the Women's Christian Temperance Union, 1878-1944 (9 vols. and 250 pieces); the Thomas Jefferson Memorial Commission, 1935-43 (1,000 pieces); the American Philosophical Association's Committee on the Teaching of Philosophy, 1937-43 (300 pieces); and the U. S. Public Health Survey of Roanoke, Va., 1944 (20,250 pieces). There are also papers of numerous governing families of colonial Virginia, among them papers of the Berkeleys of Barn Elms, Middlesex County (12,000 items), covering three centuries of this family in Virginia; family Bibles and Bible transcripts; and letters and diaries of Civil War soldiers. There are papers relating to the British abolition movement, 1821-87 (60 items); to the disposition of public lands in Missouri, Iowa, and Wisconsin, 1855-95 (1,000 pieces); to the Darwinian theory of evolution, 1784-1920 (120 pieces), including letters of Darwin, Charles Lyell, and Herbert Spencer; to slavery in Virginia; and to the Civil War, the Spanish-American War, and World Wars I and II. On deposit in the Manuscripts Division are the ar-chives of the Albemarle County Historical Society and of a number of other central Virginia organizations, most of them open to research.

See Lester J. Cappon and Patricia H. Menk, "The Evolution of Materials for Research in Early American History in the University of Virginia Library," in William and Mary Quarterly, ser. 3, 3:370-382 (July 1946); Constance E. Thurlow and Francis L. Berkeley, Jr., The Jefferson Papers of the University of Virginia: A Calendar (1950. 343 p.); William E. Stokes, Jr., and Francis L. Berkeley, Jr., The Papers of Randolph of Roanoke; a Preliminary Checklist of His Surviving Texts in Manuscript and in Print (1950. 170 p.); Francis L. Berkeley, Jr., "The University of Virginia Library," in Autograph Collectors' Journal, 4 (no. 2): 32-36 (winter 1952); the Library's Annual Report of the Archivist and its successor, Annual Report on Historical Collections, 1930-50; and Forest History Sources, p. 107.

FREDERICKSBURG

Fredericksburg and Spotsylvania National Military Park. The Superintendent.

Holdings: A few records of an iron furnace operated for the Confederacy; muster rolls, correspondence, and other papers of a Confederate paymaster at the Mobile, Ala., naval station (4,000 items); and papers of Daniel Ruggles (Va.; Confed. Army officer), consisting of telegrams and other records relating to the Shiloh Campaign and a copy book of orders and correspondence concerning operations in the Western Theater, 1862-65.

—oOo—

James Monroe Memorial Foundation,

908 Charles St.   (Mrs.) Ingrid W.
Hoes, Executive Secretary (6115
Western Ave., Washington 15, D.C.).

Holdings: A substantial collection,
1727-1896, relating chiefly to James
Monroe (Va.; Member Continental
Cong., U.S. Sen., Gov., Sec. State,
U.S. Pres.), to his relatives and associates, and to families connected
by marriage with Monroe or his descendants.   There is much Monroe correspondence, 1784-1831, including
letters from relatives and important
political contemporaries, microfilms
of which are in the Library of Congress; and there are business papers,
1820-25, relating to the building of
Monroe's mansion, Oak Hill, in Loudoun County, Va., and papers, 1831-
33, concerning the settlement of his
estate.   Included also are papers of
Samuel Lawrence Gouverneur, Sr.
(N.Y.; sec. to Monroe, postmaster of
New York City); and Joseph Jones (Va.;
judge).
    There are also papers of the Cush-
ing family of Rhode Island, 1785-1873;
private and public papers of the Da-
vidge family of Washington, D.C.,
chiefly middle 19th century; materials
of and concerning Charles Eames
(Mass., D.C.; diplomat, attorney for
U.S. Treas. and Navy Depts.) and Josiah Quincy (Mass.; lawyer, U.S. Asst.
Sec. State, mayor of Boston); papers of
five generations of the Hoes family of
the Hudson River Valley; some letters
of Gouverneur Kemble (N.Y.; ordnance manufacturer, U.S. consul at
Cadiz, U.S. Rep.); personal and business papers, 1799-1851, of John
Thomson Mason (Md.; U.S. Rep.,
judge) and Armistead Thomson Mason
(Va.; U.S. Sen.); legal papers of the
Randolph family of Virginia; and letters, 1817-45, of William Wirt (Va.,
Md.; U.S. Attorney Gen.) and his family.
                    —oOo—

Mary Washington College Library.

Carrol H. Quenzel, Librarian.

Holdings: 32 file boxes, 15 large
folders, and 125 pieces, consisting
chiefly of literary manuscripts of
published and unpublished works by
Virginia authors or relating to Virginia. Included are unpublished biographies of Joseph Eggleston Johnston (Va.; Confed. Army officer, U.S.
Rep.) and Horace Greeley (N.Y.; editor of New York Tribune, U.S. Rep.),
both by Hamilton J. Eckenrode (Va.;
State historian).   There are also
some letters written from the Fredericksburg area by U.S. soldiers
during the Civil War; and letters regarding the first Mary Washington
College Exhibition of Modern Painting (1956) from prominent artists.

HAMPDEN-SYDNEY

Hampden-Sydney College Library.
Paul L. Grier, Librarian.

Holdings: 127 vols. and 21 pieces, relating chiefly to the history of
the College and of churches in the
locality. Included are minutes of
the board of trustees, 1776-1942
(6 vols.); literary society records,
1791-1929 (98 vols.); and minute
books of several churches in the general vicinity. There are also a few
account books.
    See Hist. Records Survey, 100
Sample Entries, p. 115.

HOLLINS COLLEGE

Hollins College Library.   Dorothy A.
Doerr, Librarian.

Holdings: Included are 5 manuscript books, 15th century; and 7 manuscript leaves, 12th-16th centuries.

LEXINGTON

George C. Marshall Research Center. P. O. Box 831.   Forrest C. Pogue, Director.

Holdings: A substantial quantity of papers of George C. Marshall (Va. U. S. Army Chief of Staff, pres. Amer ican Red Cross, Sec. State, Sec. Defense), which are at present (1958) in Washington. These and others still to be acquired are expected to be housed eventually in a separate building belonging to the Center on the grounds of the Virginia Military Institute.

—oOo—

Virginia Military Institute Library. Sidney E. Matthews, Librarian.

Holdings: 94 original letters and photostats of 50 other letters by Thomas Jonathan Jackson, known as Stonewall Jackson (Va.; prof. at the Institute, U. S. and Confed. Army officer).   These belong to the Stonewall Jackson Memorial, Inc.

—oOo—

Washington and Lee University Library.   Henry E. Coleman, Jr., Librarian.

Holdings: 17,954 pieces, 1780-1900, relating chiefly to Virginia and the South. Included are papers of William Fleming (Va.; Member Continental Cong., pres. of the supreme court of appeals), 1729-95 (404 pieces); Zachariah Johnston (Va.; Rev. War officer, State legislator, advocate of religious liberty), 1790's (100 political and personal letters); and Robert E. Lee (Va.; U. S. and Confed. Army officer, pres. of Washington College), 1830-70 (5,000 items). There are also 2 groups of Virginia

family papers, 1780-1900 (12,000 items); and papers of 2 students at the college during General Lee's presidency (450 pieces).

LYNCHBURG

Randolph-Macon Woman's College Library.   Martha S. Bell, Librarian.

Holdings: 314 pieces, 1795-1952. Included are papers of John Randolph of Roanoke (Va.; U. S. Rep. and Sen.), 1795-1810 (48 pieces); and some autograph letters and literary manuscripts of English and American authors.

MANASSAS

Manassas National Battlefield Park. The Superintendent.

Holdings: Some papers of Fitz-John Porter (U. S. Army officer) and of James B. Ricketts (U. S. Army officer) and a small collection of miscellaneous papers, 1861-65, containing soldiers' letters that are chiefly concerned with the First and Second Battles of Manassas (Bull Run).

MOUNT VERNON

Mount Vernon Ladies' Association. Charles C. Wall Resident Director.

Holdings: 1,600 pieces, 1677-1860, relating chiefly to the domestic life of George Washington (Va.; planter, Rev. War Commander in Chief, U. S. Pres.) and his wife Martha, their immediate family, and the family's descendants. Included are Washington's diary, 1797; letters to Washington from members of his

family; estate and land title papers; and
letters of Eleanor Parke Lewis, née
Nelly Custis (Va.; Martha Washington's
granddaughter, Washington's adopted
daughter), 1794-1851 (214 pieces).

NEWPORT NEWS

Mariners Museum.   John L. Loch-
head, Librarian.

Holdings: A considerable quantity
of papers, 1776 to date, pertaining to
nautical matters. Included are contracts, specifications, clearance papers, commissions, bills of lading,
pilots' licenses, and ownership and
registry certificates. There are 184
ships' logbooks, 31 account books,
and some 750 letters. A special collection of papers of Collis Potter
Huntington (Calif., N.Y.; railroad
builder, capitalist) consists largely of
303 letters from Huntington to the
president of the Newport News Shipbuilding and Dry Dock Co., 1891-1900.

NORFOLK 10

Norfolk Museum of Arts and Sciences.
D. M. Halley, Jr., Acting Director.

Holdings: Miscellaneous papers
and business records relating chiefly
to Norfolk and Tidewater Virginia,
some of them dating from the pre-
Revolutionary period. Included are
papers of the Myers family, Norfolk
shipping merchants, 1791-1860; and
papers relating to the Shenandoah and
other Confederate raiders.

PETERSBURG

Petersburg National Military Park.
The Superintendent.

Holdings: 1 vol. and 153 pieces,

relating chiefly to the Petersburg
Campaign of 1864-65. Included is
the Cameron autograph book, which
contains letters and contemporary
photographs of Robert E. Lee,
J. E. B. Stuart, A. P. Hill, Richard
Taylor, and other prominent Confederate leaders. There are also 56
wartime letters, written by participants in the fighting at Petersburg,
7 diaries, and the original report of
Gen. Bushrod Johnson, C.S.A., on
the Battle of the Crater.

—oOo—

Virginia State College Library.
Wallace Van Jackson, Librarian.

Holdings: A collection relating
chiefly to Negroes in Virginia. Included are papers of John M. Gandy
(Va.; pres. Va. State College), 1915-
40, dealing with education of Negroes
in Virginia; and of Luther P. Jackson
(Va.; history prof. at Va. State College, authority on the pre-Civil War
free Negro); records of the Virginia
Negro Voters League, 1940-50; and
papers relating to Negro officeholders in Virginia.

RICHMOND 19

Confederate Museum. Clay and
12th Sts.   India W. Thomas,
House Regent.

Holdings: Several thousand items
relating chiefly to the Confederate
States of America but including some
papers of earlier and later interest.
There are numerous official Confederate documents, reports, muster rolls, maps, letters, and diaries.
Among them are records of the Medical Department of the Confederate
States Army; records of a Confederate general concerning his work as
an agent to supply Confederate

prisoners of war, 1864-65 (3 vols. and 195 items); the journal of an assistant surgeon on the C. S. S. Shenandoah, 1864-65; and telegrams relating to military and naval operations of the Richmond Campaign of 1864 (983 items). Papers of individuals include those of John Thompson Brown (Va.; Confed. Army officer), 1861-64 (77 pieces); Jefferson Davis (Miss.; U. S. Rep. and Sen., Sec. War, Confed. Pres.), 1847-89 (several thousand items); Robert E. Lee (Va.; U. S. and Confed. Army officer, pres. of Washington College), 1854-70 (75 items); William Nelson Pendleton (Md., Va.; Episcopal clergyman, U. S. and Confed. Army officer), 2 vols.; George Shea (N. Y.; justice of N. Y., counsel for Jefferson Davis), 1865-67 (82 pieces), relating to the imprisonment and indictment of Jefferson Davis; and William Booth Taliaferro (Va.; Confed. Army officer), 1859-65 (57 items). There are smaller quantities of papers of several other important Confederate leaders.

See A Calendar of Confederate Papers, With a Bibliography of Some Confederate Publications; Preliminary Report of the Southern Historical Manuscripts Commission (1908. 620 p.), prepared under the direction of the Confederate Memorial Literary Society, by Douglas Southall Freeman.

—oOo—

John Marshall House. 9th and Marshall Sts. Marguerite S. Quarles, Secretary-Curator.

Holdings: A few letters of John Marshall (Va.; U. S. Rep., Sec. State, U. S. Chief Justice) to his sons.

RICHMOND 27

Union Theological Seminary Library. H. M. Brimm, Librarian.

Holdings: 600 vols. of the archives of the Presbyterian Church in the United States. These are chiefly from the Synod of Virginia but also from the Synods of North Carolina and West Virginia. They consist of minutes of the synods and their component presbyteries and scattered records (sessional minutes, marriage registers, and baptismal registers) of local churches. In addition there are a few diaries and an uncataloged collection of letters of value for colonial and 19th-century church history for the areas indicated.

RICHMOND 19

Valentine Museum. 1015 East Clay St. Mrs. Ralph Catterall, Curator of Manuscripts.

Holdings: 77 vols. and 10,000 items, 1697-1955, relating chiefly to Virginia and especially to Richmond. Included are account books (2 vols.) kept by Patrick Henry (Va.; Member Continental Cong., Gov.), as shopkeeper, 1758-60, and lawyer, 1760-70; the Poe-Allan papers, 1803-49 (816 items), comprising 29 letters from Edgar Allan Poe (Va., Md., Pa., N. Y.; poet, critic, short-story writer), 125 letters of the family of John Allan (Va.; merchant), and 662 business papers of the latter's firm; and the Valentine papers, 1786-1920 (5,000 items), including personal and business papers of three generations of the Valentine family, especially of Mann Satterwhite Valentine (Va.; merchant), Mann S. Valentine II (Va.; manufacturer, chemist, archeologist, founder of Valentine Museum), and Edward Virginius Valentine (Va.; sculptor). There are also papers of Daniel Call (Va.; lawyer), 567 items, relating to estates administered by him and including personal and legal papers of John Norton and Sons,

London and Virginia merchants, 1768-
1817; typewritten transcripts of records of Quaker meetings in Virginia,
1673-1844 (12 vols.), from originals
held by the Baltimore Orthodox Friends;
Confederate material (500 items), including letters, Quartermaster Department papers, the Railroad Bureau telegraphic file, and postwar correspondence of Confederate leaders; and materials relating to 19th-century artists,
actors, and musicians associated with
Richmond.

Not included in the total holdings
listed above are transcripts from
Richmond court records, tax books,
and insurance records, 1780-1860, relating to social and business life, education, the theater, and architecture.

RICHMOND

Virginia Baptist Historical Society.
University of Richmond. Woodford B.
Hackley, Secretary.

Holdings: 900 vols. of original
manuscript records of Virginia Baptist
churches and organizations, 1762-1959.
Included are diaries, sermons, letters,
minutes of Baptist associations and
conventions, and church and association histories.

—oOo—

Virginia Diocesan Library. 110 West
Franklin St.   Rev. G. MacLaren Bry-
don, Historiographer, Historical Collections Department.

Holdings: A collection of official
records and other papers, 1607-1955,
relating to the Episcopal Church in
Virginia and West Virginia. Included
are typed copies of letters of James
Madison (Va.; Bishop of Va., William
and Mary College pres.), 1790-1812;
William Meade (Va.; Bishop of Va.),
1841-62; and Richard Channing Moore

(N. Y., Va.; Bishop of Va.), 1814-41.
There are also original letters by or
about individual clergymen of Virginia; the complete diocesan journals
of Virginia and West Virginia, 1785-
1955; other manuscript diocesan records; parish records, dating from
1800, of defunct congregations of the
diocese; and minutes and financial
records of Episcopal missionary and
educational institutions in the diocese.

RICHMOND   20

Virginia Historical Society. 428 North
Boulevard.   John Melville Jennings,
Director.

Holdings: 500,000 items, 1607 to
date, relating chiefly to Virginia and
the South.

Papers of prominent colonial
leaders in Virginia include those of
John Blair (Va.; twice Acting Gov.),
1751 (1 vol.); William Byrd (Va.;
planter, merchant, Indian trader),
1663-91 (1 vol.); William Byrd 2d
(Va.; planter, author, colonial official), 1709-41 (15 items); Paul Carrington (Va.; chief justice of the general court), 1755-92 (110 items);
Robert Carter, known as King Carter
(Va.; public official, landholder),
1702-32 (200 items); Robert Din-
widdie (Va., England; Lt. Gov.),
1751-57 (20 items); and Alexander
Spotswood (Va.; Lt. Gov.), 1710-21
(2 vols.).

Papers of political leaders who
served chiefly during the American
Revolution or the early years of the
Federal Government include those of
Philip Pendleton Barbour (Va.; U.S.
Rep., U. S. Supreme Court Justice),
1802-41 (850 items); Thomas Jefferson (Va.; Gov., Sec. State, U. S.
Pres.), 1780-1826 (100 items); Francis Lightfoot Lee (Va.; Member Continental Cong.), 1768-91 (40 items);

Richard Henry Lee (Va.; Pres. of Continental Cong., U.S. Sen.), 1765-93 (200 items); William Lee (Va.; merchant, diplomat), 1768-93 (500 items); James Madison (Va.; U.S. Rep., Sec. State, U.S. Pres.), 1787-1831 (25 items); John Marshall (Va.; U.S. Rep., Sec. State, U.S. Chief Justice), 1784-1826 (50 items); James Monroe (Va.; U.S. Sen., Gov., Sec. State, U.S. Pres.), 35 items; John Randolph of Roanoke (Va.; U.S. Rep. and Sen.), 1807-33 (90 items); and George Washington (Va.; Rev. War Commander in Chief, U.S. Pres.), 1754-99 (225 items).

Papers of other persons include those of George W. Bagby (Va.; author, editor, lecturer), 1875 (75 items); George Washington Parke Custis (Va.; playwright) and family, 1796-1833 (35 items); Hugh B. Grigsby (Va.; newspaper editor, historian, pres. of Va. Hist. Soc.), 1823-81 (2,000 items); William Wirt Henry (Va.; lawyer, historian), 1776-1898 (1,000 items); James Lawson Kemper (Va.; Gov.), 1875-77 (1 vol.); Robert E. Lee (Va.; U.S. and Confed. Army officer, pres. of Washington College), 1826-67 (500 items); Matthew Fontaine Maury (Va.; oceanographer, U.S. and Confed. naval officer, Naval Observatory Supt.), 1846-73 (130 items); Conway Robinson (Va.; lawyer, court reporter, author), 1832-83 (1,500 items); Raphael Semmes (Ala.; U.S. and Confed. naval officer, lawyer), 1862-68 (150 items); Nicholas P. Trist (Va.; U.S. consul at Havana), 1826-36 (1 vol.); and Henry Alexander Wise (Va.; U.S. Rep., Minister to Brazil, Gov., Confed. Army officer), 1819-74 (225 items).

Included also are records of the General Court of Virginia, 1626-1726 (8 vols.); the Council of Virginia, 1674-1742 (400 pages); the House of Burgesses, 1685-1754 (200 pages); the Society of the Cincinnati, 1783-1931 (20 items); the Colonization Society of Virginia, 1823-58 (2 vols.);

the Southern Rights Association, 1850 (1 vol.); and the Confederate States Army, 1861-65 (1,000 items). There are collections of papers relating to the Virginia and North Carolina boundary line, 1705-10 (100 pages); the American Revolution; and the War of 1812. There are also some church records.

See Catalogue of the Manuscripts in the Collection of the Virginia Historical Society (1901. 120 p.).

RICHMOND 12

Virginia State Library. William J. Van Schreeven, State Archivist.

Holdings: 62,802 vols., 11,517,016 items, 6,078 reference reels of microfilm, and 39,358 maps, 1607-1958, consisting of (1) noncurrent public records held as the State's archival agency, and (2) other papers relating to Virginia and the South. Manuscript holdings are in five categories: colonial records, executive records, legislative records, judicial (county) records, and nonarchival papers.

Colonial records, 1607-1776, consist of 38 vols. of transcripts and original journals of the House of Burgesses, 1693-1776 (8 vols.), council journals and minute books, 1697-1775 (19 vols.), and miscellaneous manuscripts, 1697-1775.

Executive records include those of the following agencies: Attorney General's Office, 1898-1914 (15,000 items); Auditor of Public Accounts, 1773-1943 (1,897 vols. and 738,723 items); Board of Public Works, 1816-1902 (455 vols. and 191,858 items), including papers of various railroads, turnpikes, and canal companies; State Comptroller, 1928-50 (836 vols.); Department of Conservation and Development, 1927-50 (71,000 items); State Corporation Commission, 1883-1944 (4,995 vols. and

148,100 items), including tax reports, valuations and assessments of public service companies, 1883-1933, and records dealing with banks and loan associations; State Board of Education, 1870-1947 (172 vols.), including annual reports of superintendents, 1886-1918, and financial records; Governor and Council of the State, 1776-1954 (126 vols. and 1,892,250 items), including Council journals, 1776-1850, executive letter books, Continental Congress papers, 1774-89 (4,000 items), naval officers' returns, 1782-89, papers relating to John Brown's raid, 1859, and correspondence for most of the Governors; Secretary of the Commonwealth, 1832-1934 (141 vols. and 465,500 items), including executive journals, executive minute books, pardons, and miscellaneous papers; State Department of Taxation, 1782-1956 (45,881 vols. and 2,300 items), including land and personal-property tax lists, 1782-1956; State Treasurer, 1774-1952 (1,322 vols. and 2,284,200 items), including journals, ledgers, receipt books, bond registers, warrants, stocks and bonds, vouchers, and account books; and World War I History Commission, 1917-18 (272,000 items).

Among other executive records are census records, 1850-80 (73 vols.); Confederate War records, 1861-1957 (36 vols. and 106,800 items), including State pension documents; convention records (Revolutionary conventions, convention of 1788, and various State constitutional conventions), 1775-1902 (13 vols. and 2,550 items); election returns and certificates, 1776-1933 (147 vols. and 178,000 items), including those for U.S. Presidents, 1800-56; Land Office records, 1632-1954 (404 vols. and 247,510 items), including Northern Neck Proprietary patent and grant books, plats and certificates, military records, and correspondence; militia papers, 1781-1829 (57,975 items); Revolutionary

War records, 1775-1850 (444 vols. and 87,945 items), including service records, bounty-land claims, pension claims, and records relating to public stores, commercial agents, war office, State navy, board of trade, and committee of safety; Spanish-American War records, 1898-1913 (23 vols. and 10,875 items); materials resulting from Works Projects Administration activities (260,000 items), including newspaper clippings and products of the Historical Records Survey of Virginia counties; War of 1812 records (26 vols. and 1,360 items); papers pertaining to the West Virginia debt controversy (3,000 items); and World War II records, 1941-46 (857,000 items), including Office of Civilian Defense materials and separation notices.

Legislative records include House of Delegates journals, minute books, attendance books, rough and engrossed bills, executive communications, petitions, and other records, 1776-1955 (500 vols. and 285,483 items), and the same type of records for the Senate, 1791-1934 (23 vols. and 180,000 items). Of great importance are the petitions of individuals and groups to the General Assembly, 1776-1861 (30,000 items).

Papers of many eminent Virginians of the 18th and 19th centuries will be found in the above groups. Among them are James Barbour (Va.; lawyer, Gov., U.S. Sen., Sec. War, Minister to England), Daniel Boone (N.C., Ky., Mo.; explorer, pioneer settler), William H. Cabell (Va.; Gov., Va. supreme court judge), Arthur Campbell (Va.; Rev. War officer), George Rogers Clark (Va., Ky.; Rev. War officer), John Floyd (Va.; physician, U.S. Rep., Gov.), William Branch Giles (Va.; U.S. Rep. and Sen., Gov.), Thomas Walker Gilmer (Va.; Gov., U.S. Rep., Sec. Navy), Benjamin Harrison (Va.; Member Continental Cong., Gov.), Patrick Henry (Va.; Member Continental Cong., Gov.), Robert M. T. Hunter (Va.; U. S. Rep. and Sen., Confed. Sec. State and Sen.), Thomas Jefferson (Va.; Member Continental Cong., Gov., Minister to France, Sec. State, U. S. Pres.), Robert E. Lee (Va.; U. S. and Confed. Army officer, pres. of Washington College), John Letcher (Va.; lawyer, newspaper editor, U. S. Rep., Gov.), James Madison (Va.; Member Continental Cong., U. S. Rep., Sec. State, U. S. Pres.), John Marshall (Va.; U.S. Rep., Sec. State, U. S. Chief Justice), George Mason (Va.; planter, Rev. War statesman), James Monroe (Va.; Rev. War officer, Member Continental Cong., U. S. Sen., Gov., Sec. State, U. S. Pres.), Andrew J. Montague (Va., Gov., U. S. Rep.), Wilson Cary Nicholas (Va.; Rev. War officer, U. S. Sen. and Rep., Gov.), John Page (Va.; U. S. Rep., Gov.), Edmund Pendleton (Va.; Member Continental Cong., pres. Va. Committee of Safety and State supreme court of appeals), Francis Harrison Pierpont (Va., W. Va.; lawyer, Gov. of Va.), Edgar Allan Poe (Va., Md., Pa., N. Y.; poet, critic, short-story writer), William Preston (Va.; colonial militia and Rev. War officer), Edmund Randolph (Va.; Member Continental Cong., Gov., U. S. Attorney Gen., Sec. State), John Randolph of Roanoke (Va.; U. S. Rep. and Sen.), Thomas Mann Randolph (Va.; U. S. Rep., Gov.), John Taylor (Va.; Rev. War officer, political writer, U. S. Sen.), John Tyler (Va.; Rev. War officer, Gov.) and his son John Tyler (Va.; Gov., U. S. Rep., Sen., and Pres.), George Washington (Va.; Rev. War Commander in Chief, U. S. Pres.), and Henry Alexander Wise (Va.; U. S. Rep., Minister to Brazil, Gov., Confed. Army officer).

Judicial (county) records consist of deed, will, and order books, and masses of suit papers, marriage bonds, and other unbound local re-

cords, 1634-1865 (3,018 vols. and 2,477,317 items). Not all counties are represented.

Nonarchival papers consist of personal papers, church records, Bible records (828 items), business records, genealogical notes and charts (395 items), diaries, and miscellaneous items. Personal papers include those of James Abercrombie (British Commander in Chief in North America), 1746-73 (letter book); Richard Clough Anderson (Va., Ky.; Rev. War officer, surveyor), 1783-1884 (2,500 items); Nathaniel Francis Cabell (Va.; author), 1724-1860 (134 items), relating to agriculture; Francis Walker Gilmer (Va.; lawyer, author), 1813-25 (131 items); Fairfax Harrison (Va.; railroad executive), 18th and 19th centuries (12,500 items), relating to horses, horse racing, and horse breeding in Virginia; Daniel Harvey Hill (Va., N. C., Ark.; U. S. and Confed. Army officer, college prof., Univ. of Ark. pres.), 1860-88 (800 items); Thomas Jonathan Jackson, known as Stonewall Jackson (Va.; prof. at Va. Military Institute, U. S. and Confed. Army officer), 1847-67 (180 items); Samuel M. Janney (Va.; historian, Quaker preacher, Indian supt.), 1815-85 (19 vols. and 135 items); Zachariah Johnston (Va.; Rev. War officer, State legislator, advocate of religious liberty), 1742-1856 (1 vol. and 174 items); Charles Carter Lee (Va.; lawyer, poet), 1780-1871 (1,917 items), including papers of Henry Lee, known as Light Horse Harry Lee (Va.; Rev. War officer, Member Continental Cong., Gov., U. S. Rep.), his son Henry Lee (Va., France; author), and other members of the Lee family; Daniel Morgan (Va.; Rev. War officer, U. S. Rep.), 1763-1800 (26 items); William Barton Rogers (Md., Va., Mass.; geologist, pres. of Mass. Institute of Technology), 1836-41 (66 vols. and

270 items); William H. Ruffner (Va.; Presbyterian clergyman, State supt. of education), 1866-1907 (1 vol. and 102 items); Henry Tazewell (Va.; State judge, U.S. Sen.), Littleton Waller Tazewell (Va.; lawyer, U.S. Rep. and Sen., Gov.), and other members of the Tazewell family, 1740-1867 (14 vols. and 4,700 items); William H. Whitsitt (Tenn., Ky., Va.; pres. of Southern Baptist Theological Seminary), 1896-99 (1,290 items); and William Wirt (Va., Md.; U.S. Attorney Gen.), 1803-31 (69 items). There are papers of the Fairfax Family Northern Neck Proprietary, 1688-1810 (222 items). Personal papers also include diaries and letters of Confederate soldiers, and papers, diaries, journals, and account books for many Virginia families.

Church records cover the period 1648-1898, mostly prior to 1800, and include Baptist, Christian, Episcopal, Friends, Lutheran, German Reformed, and Presbyterian record books, about 250 volumes. Business records range from single volumes for merchants to the extensive collections for William and David Allason (Va.; merchants at Falmouth and Winchester), 1752-1815 (90 vols. and 3,750 items), and the Tredegar Co. (Richmond iron manufacturers), 1836-1957 (1,117 vols. and 507,400 items). Microfilm records consist of copies of bound volumes of Virginia county court records, 1632-1865 (4,200 reels), and copies of Virginiana in other depositories and in private hands. Maps consist of early and contemporary maps of Virginia, and U.S. Geological Survey sheets and Army Map Service maps pertaining to Virginia and to other areas.

See John P. Kennedy, Calendar of Transcripts Including the Annual Report of the Department of Archives and History (1905. 658 p.); William P. Palmer et al., Calendar of Virginia State Papers (1875-93. 11 vols.);

H. J. Eckenrode, A Calendar of Legislative Petitions, Arranged by Counties, Accomac-Bedford (1908. 302 p.); H. R. McIlwaine, "The Revolutionary War Material in the Virginia State Library," in Magazine of History, 10: 143-150 (July-Dec. 1909); and Earl G. Swem, "A List of Manuscripts Relating to the History of Agriculture in Virginia . . . Now in the Virginia State Library," and "A List of Manuscripts Recently Deposited in the Virginia State Library by the State Auditor," in Va. State Library, Bulletin, 6:5-20 (Jan. 1913) and 7:3-32 (Jan. 1914) respectively, and his "Newly Discovered George Rogers Clark Material," in Miss. Valley Hist. Review, 1:95-97 (June 1914). The Va. State Library Bulletins and Annual Reports contain lists of manuscripts, calendars, indexes, and accession notes.

WILLIAMSBURG

Colonial Williamsburg, Inc. Edward M. Riley, Director of Research; Lester J. Cappon, Archival Consultant.

Holdings: (1) Official records of Colonial Williamsburg, 1924 to date (456 file drawers and 2,448 file boxes), and (2) collections of manuscripts, 1680-1870 (37,500 pieces), relating chiefly to Virginia but containing also a considerable quantity of papers of wider interest. Some of the collections of manuscripts are noted specifically below.

Papers of individuals include those of William Blathwayt (England; Sec. of the Lords of Trade and Plantations, Sec. at War), 1674-1715 (2,568 pieces), pertaining to the British colonies in the West Indies and on the North American continent; William Byrd 2d (Va.; planter, colonial official), 1728-29 (a letter book and 2 other items); Robert Carter of Nomini Hall (Va.; planter, councillor), 1761-69 (3 vols.); Richard Corbin (Va.; colonial receiver-gen.) and his family, 1746-1818 (3 vols. and 350 pieces); John Minson Galt (Va.; physician, Rev. War surgeon) and John Minson Galt 2d (Va.; medical supt. of hospital for the insane) and their family, 1756-1894 (10 vols. and 5,743 pieces); Sir William Gooch (Va.; Lt. Gov.), 1727-51 (65 letters, copies); Benjamin Huntington (Conn.; Member Continental Cong., U. S. Rep., judge of Conn. superior court) and his family, 1761-99 (60 pieces); Thomas Jefferson (Va.; Member Continental Cong., Gov., Minister to France, Sec. State, U. S. Pres.), 1779-1826 (608 pieces); Francis Nicholson (England; Gov. of Va. and Md.), 1680-1720 (1 vol. and 83 pieces); John Norton and Sons (merchants of London and Va.), 1750-95 (2,491 pieces); Alexander Spotswood (Va.; Lt. Gov.), 1696-1740 (49 pieces); and members of the Tucker family, 1768-1860 (24,000 pieces), including extensive correspondence of St. George Tucker (Va.; prof. of law at William and Mary College, U. S. dist. court judge), Nathaniel Beverley Tucker (Va.; prof. of law at William and Mary College), and Henry St. George Tucker (Va.; U. S. Rep., prof. of law at Univ. of Va.). There are several account books and diaries, a few scattered records of Virginia counties, and other miscellaneous papers.

In addition, the files of the Research Department contain microfilm or typescript copies of manuscripts, not readily available in the United States, that relate to the history of Williamsburg and Tidewater Virginia during the 18th century. Included also are photographic copies of records of the British Headquarters in America during the Revolutionary War, 1776-83 (10,434 pieces), consisting chiefly of the correspondence of Sir Guy Carleton (British commander in chief in America in 1782-83) but containing copies of some correspondence of previous commanders in chief.

See A Brief Guide to the Record Groups in the Archives Department of Colonial Williamsburg (1951. 8 p. Processed); and Lynette Adcock, Guide to the Manuscript Collections of Colonial Williamsburg (1954. 58 p.).

—oOo—

William and Mary College Library. James Servies, Librarian.

Holdings: 450,000 pieces relating chiefly to Virginia and the South.

Papers of or relating to men who served as President of the United States or as a Cabinet officer include those of Thomas Jefferson (Va.; Gov., Member Continental Cong., Minister to France, Sec. State, U. S. Pres.), 1761-1931 (267 pieces); Horatio King (Maine, D. C.; editor, lawyer, Postmaster Gen.) and his family, 1879 (69 pieces); James Madison (Va.; U. S. Rep., Sec. State, U. S. Pres.), 1744-1931 (17 pieces); John Marshall (Va.; U. S. Rep., Sec. State, U. S. Chief Justice), 1780-1916 (143 pieces); James Monroe (Va.; U. S. Sen., Gov., Sec. State, U. S. Pres.), 1776-1924 (111 pieces); John Tyler (Va.; Gov., U. S. Rep., Sen., and Pres.) and his family, 1752-1931 (164 pieces); and George Washington (Va.; Rev. War Commander in Chief, U. S. Pres.), 1755-1956 (205 pieces).

Papers of men who served in the U. S. Congress, in addition to some named elsewhere, include those of Thomas Croxton (Va.; lawyer, Confed. Army officer, U. S. Rep.) and his family, 1856-1912 (780 pieces); Alexander M. Davis (Va.; lawyer, Confed. Army officer, U. S. Rep.) and his family, 1850-92 (201 pieces); Francis Burton Harrison (N. Y., Va.; lawyer, U. S. Rep. from N. Y., Gov.

Gen. of the Philippines) and his family, 1777-1927 (570 pieces); Francis Rives Lassiter (Va.; U.S. dist. attorney, U.S. Rep.) and his family, 1861-1928 (7 vols. and 954 pieces); Charles T. O'Ferrall (Va.; lawyer, Confed. Army officer, U.S. Rep., Gov.), 1867-93 (443 pieces); Harrison Holt Riddleberger (Va.; lawyer, newspaper editor, U.S. Sen.), 1874-91 (578 pieces); and John S. Wise (Va., N.Y.; lawyer, Confed. Army officer, U.S. Rep.), 1869-73 (55 pieces).

Papers of other political leaders and public officials include those of Lord John Murray Dunmore (England, N.Y., Va.; colonial Gov.) and his family, 1684-1891 (690 pieces); Patrick Henry (Va.; lawyer, Member Continental Cong., Gov.), 1790-1933 (29 pieces); Robert William Hughes (Va.; newspaper editor, U.S. dist. court judge) and his family, 1725-1933 (432 pieces); George Mason (Va.; planter, Rev. War statesman), 1706-1823 (26 pieces); John Barton Payne (Va., W.Va., Ill.; pres. of the Chicago Law Institute, Cook County superior court judge), 1893-1930 (640 pieces); and William Short (Va., Pa.; diplomat), 1783-1847 (64 pieces).

Papers of military leaders, in addition to those listed elsewhere, include those of Samuel Barron (Va.; U.S. and Confed. naval officer), 1798-1891 (1,758 pieces); William Campbell (Va.; Rev. War officer) and his family, 1726-1920 (1,732 pieces); Joseph Eggleston Johnston (Va.; U.S. and Confed. Army officer, U.S. Rep.), 1839-65 (87 pieces); Robert E. Lee (Va.; U.S. and Confed. Army officer, pres. of Washington College), 1829-1925 (66 pieces); and William Booth Taliaferro (Va.; U.S. and Confed. Army officer, State legislator), 1705-1929 (6,546 pieces).

Papers of members of the faculty of William and Mary College include those of Thomas R. Dew (Va.; economist, pres. of William and Mary) and his family, 1794-1895 (161 pieces); Benjamin S. Ewell (Va.; U.S. and Confed. Army officer, pres. of William and Mary) and his family, 1784-1934 (1,238 pieces); George Frederick Holmes (Va.; prof. of history and literature at Univ. of Va.) and his family, 1790-1898 (64 pieces); James Madison (Va.; Episcopal bishop, pres. of William and Mary), a considerable quantity in the College archives; Nathaniel Beverley Tucker (Va.; prof. of law), 1811-56 (288 pieces); St. George Tucker (Va.; prof. of law, jurist), 1775-1869 (1,368 pieces); Lyon Gardiner Tyler (Va.; pres. of William and Mary, author, editor), 1856-1949 (46,089 pieces); and George Wythe (Va.; Member Continental Cong., prof. of law), 56 pieces and some others in the College archives.

Papers of authors and editors include those of Alexander Brown (Va.; historian) and his family, 1815-1906 (2,500 pieces); Charles Campbell (Va.; historian, antiquarian) and his family, 1807-76 (5,144 pieces); George Washington Parke Custis (Va.; playwright) and his family, 1844-56 (52 pieces); James Barron Hope (Va.; lawyer, poet, Confed. Army officer) and his family, 1850-87 (138 pieces); John B. Minor (Va.; prof. of law at Univ. of Va.), 1876 (4 vols.); Thomas Ritchie (Va., D.C.; newspaper editor) and his family, 1830-1932 (1,068 pieces); and Molly Elliott Seawell (Va., D.C.; novelist, short-story writer), 1900-14 (2 vols.).

Papers of other persons include those of Richard Blow (Va.; merchant, shipowner) and his family, 1760-1938 (26,000 pieces); John Thompson Brown (Va.; lawyer, State legislator), 1788-1919 (4,276 pieces); Robert Wormeley Carter (Va.; planter, State legislator), 1667-1862 (8,226 pieces); John Hartwell Cocke (Va.; planter, publicist, pres. of the

American Temperance Union), 1866-69 (5 vols.); Flora Adams Darling (D. C.; founder of patriotic societies) and her family, 1862-1908 (4,537 pieces); Francis Jerdone (Va.; merchant), 1720-1918 (2,137 pieces); Deborah Norris Logan (Pa.; historian) and her family, 1829-85 (75 pieces); Francis Murphy (N. Y., Maine, Pa.; temperance reformer, lecturer) and his family, 1886-98 (54 pieces); Moncure Robinson (Pa.; civil engineer) and his family, 1788-1888 (1,326 pieces); Peyton Skipwith (Va.; planter), 1760-1912 (6,580 pieces); and George Washington Southall (Va.; lawyer), 1792-1889 (23,510 pieces).

Papers relating to William and Mary College, in addition to those of individuals mentioned above, include notes of classroom lectures, diaries, letters, and other papers of students and professors; records of the Alpha Chapter of Phi Beta Kappa, 1776-81; and archives of the College. Records of other organizations include those of several Virginia mills, 1804-6, 1840-99 (8 vols.); a tavern in Louisa County, 1816-38 (9 vols.); the Chesapeake and Ohio Canal, 1821-29 (2 vols.); a turnpike, 1831-94 (2 vols.); and temperance organizations in Augusta County, 1849-83 (5 vols.). Included also are collections relating to military activities in the United States, 1814-79 (937 pieces); to the Confederate States of America, 1861-1937 (584 pieces); and to Virginia bar examinations, 1910-23 (1,306 pieces).

See Jane Carson, "Historical Manuscripts in Williamsburg," in Manuscripts, 5 (no. 4):9-15 (summer 1953).

CHEHALIS

Chehalis Public Library. Oscar W. J. Smaalders, Librarian.

Holdings: 17 scrapbooks and 17 pieces, chiefly 19th century, relating to pioneer settlers in Washington and the Pacific Northwest. There are also 82 photographs.

OLYMPIA

State Capitol Historical Museum. 211 Twenty-first Ave. West. (Mrs.) Ida N. Burford, Curator-Director.

Holdings: A small quantity of manuscripts, from 1846, relating chiefly to the settlement and development of Washington. Included are centennial materials, personal narratives, and photographs of pioneers and buildings; papers relating to schools and churches; papers of pioneers; and some records of stores and lodges.

—oOo—

Washington State Archives. Department of General Administration. Ralph Burcham, Archivist.

Holdings: 60 file drawers, 1854-1920, consisting chiefly of the official correspondence of the Governors of the Territory and State of Washington. The records are very incomplete for the period 1854-72 but fairly complete for the period 1890-1920.

—oOo—

Washington State Library. Maryan E. Reynolds, State Librarian.

Holdings: 2,150 pieces, 1853-1955, relating chiefly to Washington Territory. Included are correspondence of the Secretary of Washington Territory, 1853-63; Governor's letter books, Dec. 1853—June 1855, May—Nov. 1889, and Jan. 1897—Jan. 1898; Governor's official record books, 1870-89 (2 vols.); records of the Superintendent of Indian Affairs, 1862-74 (390 letters), and letter books of the Puyallup-Nisqually Agency, 1874-80 (2 vols.); incomplete county assessors' census and assessment rolls, 1857-92; original schedules of the Federal census for 1860, 1870, and 1880; and miscellaneous papers primarily relating to military history. There are also about 1,200 unpublished interviews with pioneers, many letters and autobiographical sketches, and several book manuscripts written by State of Washington authors.

PORT ANGELES

Olympic National Park. The Superintendent.

Holdings: Minutes of the Mount Olympus National Park Association, letters, telegrams, and other papers relating to efforts to establish Olympic National Park, 1935-38 (1 vol.).

PULLMAN

Washington State University Library. G. Donald Smith, Director of Libraries.

Holdings: 344,744 pieces, 1534-

1955, relating chiefly to Washington and the Pacific Northwest.

Papers of persons who served as professors or administrators at the State College of Washington (now Washington State University) include those of John Fred Bohler (Wash.; athletic director), 1914-49 (8,000 items); Enoch Albert Bryan (Wash.; author, pres.), 1892-1915 (17,000 items); Wilson Martindale Compton (Wash.; economist, pres.), 1944-52 (1,275 items); Ernest O. Holland (Wash.; pres.), 1883-1936 (20,000 items); Claudius O. Johnson (Wash.; prof. of political science), 1932-36 (2,000 items); Edward C. Johnson (Wash.; plant pathologist, Dean of College of Agriculture), 1914-47 (50,000 items); and Osmar Lysander Waller (Wash.; civil engineer, mathematician, prof.), 1897-1928 (4,000 items).

Papers of other persons include those of Lyndon K. Armstrong (Wash.; mining engineer), 1906-41 (2,500 items); William E. Borah (Idaho; U. S. Sen.), 1911-39 (4,395 items); Clifford M. Drury (Calif., Idaho; Presbyterian clergyman, prof. at San Francisco Theological Seminary), 1832-1941 (100 items), relating to Pacific Northwest missionaries; Cushing Eells (Oreg.; missionary, pioneer), 1834-1904 (50 items); Annie H. Abel Henderson (Md., Mass., Wash.; historian), 1492-1939 (1,000 items), including notes; Henry Harmon Spalding (Wash., Oreg.; missionary, pioneer), 1836-1936 (1,000 items); Thomas Redding Tannatt (N. Y., Wash.; Civil War officer, mining engineer, railroad businessman), 1854-1919 (2,000 items); Elkanah Walker (Oreg.; missionary, pioneer), 1826-1938 (1,000 items); Marcus Whitman (N. Y., Oreg.; missionary, pioneer), 1825-1938 (150 items), including material about him; and Francis Josef Wilmer (Wash.; banker, State legislator), 1898-1933

(1,250 items).

There are records of U. S. Indian agents to the Colville Indians, 1850-1917 (2,750 items), and of Fort Simcoe and the Yakima Indian Agency; archives of Columbia County, 1876-1946 (4,000 items), and of Walla Walla County, 1861-1920 (10,000 items); records of two breweries, 1890-1904 (100 vols.); papers kept by the Secretary of the Washington State Holstein-Friesian Association, 1895-1940 (5,000 items); records of a Spokane bank, 1897-1928 (500 items); papers relating to irrigation in the Columbia Basin, 1905-34 (200 items); files of a fire insurance company of Spokane, 1907-10 (5,000 items); and some documents of the Farmers Educational and Cooperative Union of America (Washington-Idaho Division), 1927-39 (150 items).

Included also are the Conda de Regla Collection relating to many aspects of Mexican history, 16th-19th centuries (25,000 pages); a collection of autograph letters and cards of U. S. Presidents and of U. S. and European military officials, musicians, political leaders, writers, and other persons of prominence, 1774-1942 (1,654 items); a collection of 54 musical manuscripts; miscellaneous papers on the North American Indians (1,500 items); letters and diaries of Civil War soldiers, 1850-64 (120 items); and several groups containing information about mining in the West and especially in the Pacific Northwest.

Other collections, recently acquired, include the McWhorter Collection, consisting of photographs, notes, and correspondence in regard to the Nez Percé and other Pacific Northwest Indian tribes, 1855-1944 (48,000 items); the Kuykendall Collection, consisting of correspondence and unpublished articles regarding southeastern Washington, including material on the Yakima and Nez

Percé Indians, 1856-1950 (4,500 items);
the McGregor Collection, consisting of
correspondence and business accounts
for the McGregor Land and Livestock
Co., a pioneer cattle ranching business, 1897-1940 (3,000 items); the
Banks Collection, consisting of the
unpublished surveys and reports of
Frank A. Banks, Chief Engineer for
Grand Coulee Dam, 1934-55 (50 items);
the Howard Collection, consisting of
photographs, diaries, correspondence,
and business records for the Alaskan
Gold Rush from 1897 to 1905 (300
items); and the Crandall Collection,
consisting of correspondence, clippings, and notes concerning northern
Oregon, 1838-1951 (380 items).

SEATTLE 15

Federal Records Center, GSA, Bldg.
5-D, U.S. Naval Air Station. Chief.

Holdings: A large quantity of
noncurrent or semicurrent records,
chiefly of recent date, of nonmilitary
agencies of the U.S. Government in
Washington, Oregon, Idaho, Montana,
and Alaska. Most of these records
have been appraised for disposal after specified periods of time, but
some will be preserved because of
their enduring value. Records in the
latter category include those of U.S.
district courts, from 1855; Bureau of
Indian Affairs, from 1858; Forest
Service, from 1893; Bureau of Customs, from 1851; and General Land
Office, from 1851.

SEATTLE

Seattle Public Library. Madison and
Fourth Aves. W. O. Youngs, Assistant Librarian..

Holdings: A small collection,
1850-1956, chiefly of local interest.

Included are papers concerning Washington families and literary manuscripts of Pacific Northwest authors.
See Hist. Records Survey, Guide
for Oreg.-Wash., p. 26.

—oOo—

University of Washington Law Library. Condon Hall. Marion G.
Gallagher, Librarian.

Holdings: 500 pieces, 1853 to
date, relating chiefly to the judicial
history of the Pacific Northwest.

SEATTLE 5

University of Washington Library.
Richard C. Berner, Curator of Manuscripts.

Holdings: A growing collection
of manuscripts, 1812-1958, relating
chiefly to the Pacific Northwest.
They are rich in materials for studies in economic history and special
economic problems, for studies in
politics, and for sociological studies, with smaller representation of
data for cultural studies and for intellectual studies per se. The holdings of the Law Library are described separately in the preceding
entry.
    Manuscript groups that coincide
chiefly with the pre-statehood period
of Washington (i.e., before 1889) include papers of Clarence Booth Bagley (Oreg., Wash.; newspaper publisher, Seattle city official, deputy
collector of Internal Revenue), 1861-
1932 (6 cartons), with his collection
of materials relating to frontier life
in Washington Territory, 1854-89
(200 items); David Edwards Blaine
(Wash., Oreg.; Methodist minister),
1849-62 (150 letters); Elisha Peyre
Ferry (Ill., Wash.; lawyer, surveyor-
gen. of Wash. Terr., Gov. of Wash.),

1868-95 (2 cartons); Manning Ferguson Force (Ohio; Civil War officer, jurist) and his family, 1835-74 (2 cartons), among them some correspondence of Peter Force (D. C.; historian, editor) and John Fitch (N. J., Pa.; inventor); Benjamin Freeman Kendall (Wash.; Supt. of Indian Affairs for Wash. Terr.), 1812-70 (300 items); Robert Huston Milroy (Ind., Wash.; lawyer, Supt. of Indian Affairs in Wash.), 1877-78 (1 letterpress book); Isaac I. Stevens (Wash.; U. S. Army officer, Terr. Gov., Terr. Delegate to Cong.), 1835-62 (2 cartons); James G. Swan (Wash.; Govt. official, student of Northwest Indians), 1859-98 (2 cartons), including extensive diaries; and William Henson Wallace (Iowa, Wash., Idaho; lawyer, Terr. Delegate to Cong. from Wash. and Idaho), 1841-79 (1 case).
In some of the above-mentioned groups and others there are diaries and correspondence relating to Indian affairs and Indian wars in Washington Territory and Oregon, diaries and other papers providing information about overland crossings to the Pacific Northwest, and reminiscences and memoirs on frontier and pioneer life in the Puget Sound area. There is also a collection concerned largely with Alaska and British Columbia, 1866-1948 (2 cartons), including 3 diaries of members of a Western Union Telegraph Co. surveying expedition in Alaska, 1866-67; and some Hudson's Bay Co. papers, 1834-70 (4 cartons).

Manuscript groups that coincide largely with the period of statehood include papers of Thomas McArthur Anderson (Ohio, Wash.; lawyer, U.S. Army officer) and his family, 1836-1942 (1/2 carton); Richard Achilles Ballinger (Wash.; lawyer, Sec. Interior), 1907-12 (10 cartons); Erastus Brainerd (Mass., Pa., Wash.; newspaper editor), 1880-1919 (2 cartons); Thomas Burke (Mich., Wash.; lawyer, railroad organizer and counsel), 1876-1925 (27 cartons); Stephen Fowler Chadwick (Wash.; lawyer, political leader, civilian aide to Sec. War), 1919-45 (10 cartons); Stephen James Chadwick (Wash.; State supreme court justice), 1926-31 (205 letters and 3 folders); George Fletcher Cotterill (N. J., Wash.; civil engineer, State legislator, Seattle port commissioner), 1900-58 (27 cartons); Asahel Curtis (Wash.; news and commercial photographer), 1908-41 (4 cartons); William F. Devin (Wash.; lawyer, Mayor of Seattle), 1937-51 (4 cartons); Miller Freeman (Wash.; publisher of trade journals), 1911-46 (2 cartons); and Joseph Maunsell Hone (Ireland; writer), 159 letters relating to his biography of George Moore (England; novelist).

Other manuscript groups largely of the statehood period include papers of Arthur Bernard Langlie (Wash.; lawyer, Mayor of Seattle, Gov.), 1938-57 (28 cartons); Edmond Stephen Meany (Wash.; prof. of history at Univ. of Wash., State legislator), 1889-1935 (40 cartons); David Hunter Miller (N. Y., D. C.; international lawyer, author, special asst. to State Dept.), 9 cartons, relating to the Northwest boundary; Frederick Morgan Padelford (Idaho, Wash.; English prof., dean of Graduate School at Univ. of Wash.), 1901-42 (5 cartons); John Francis Pratt (D. C., Wash.; U. S. Coast and Geodetic Survey official), 1879-1920 (7 cartons); James Delmage Ross (Wash.; electrical engineer, member Security and Exchange Commission), 1903-38 (60 cartons); Eugene Semple (Wash.; Gov.), 1884-1907; Henry Suzzallo (N. Y., Wash.; educator, pres. Univ. of Wash.), 1910-33 (23 cartons); and Reginald Heber Thomson (Wash.; Seattle's city engineer), 1884-1918 (14 vols. of letterpress books). There are also annual reports of a mining company in Juneau, Alaska, 1916-20 (5 vols.); records of a lumber company at Hoquiam, Wash., 1884-1929

(21 vols. and 8 cartons), one at Pysht, Wash., 1920-40 (55 cartons), and one at Seattle, 1889-1956 (15 vols. and 26 cartons); papers of the Seattle Repertory Playhouse (a community theater), 1929-52 (39 cartons); and business records and other papers relating to the University of Washington, since 1862 (37 cartons).

Musical compositions of the following composers are located at the American Music Center in the Music Library: James Beale, Henry Leland Clarke, Dorothy Cadzow Hokanson, Lockrem Johnson, Gerald Kechley, George Frederick McKay, John Verrall, and Carl Paige Wood.

See the Library's The Stevens Collection, Manuscript Series No. 1 (1958. 15 p.); Charles W. Smith, A Union List of Manuscripts in Libraries of the Pacific Northwest, passim (1931. 57 p.), and "The Bagley Collection of Pacific Northwest History," in Wash. Hist. Quarterly, 10:83-87 (Apr. 1919); Keith Murray, "The Wesley L. Jones Papers," in Pacific Northwest Quarterly, 36:65-68 (Jan. 1945); Hist. Records Survey, Guide for Oreg.-Wash., p. 28; John Van Male, Resources of Pacific Northwest Libraries, pp. 161-163 (1943); and Forest History Sources, pp. 110-112.

SPOKANE 43

Eastern Washington State Historical Society. 2316 West First St. (Mrs.) Florence D. Reed, Director; Edna Reinbach, Librarian.

Holdings: Several collections relating chiefly to the Spokane region. Included are reminiscences and letters of early residents; copies of diaries in private possession; records of pioneer families, compiled by the Daughters of the American Revolution; and some business records. There is information about Indian

disturbances, railroad building, pioneer travels from the East, and other phases of the development of Washington. The Society also has a collection of early photographs pertaining to the area.

Papers of individuals include those of William S. Clarke (Wash.; Spokane businessman, author), late 19th and early 20th centuries (3 boxes), containing records of a mining company and of real estate transactions; Marion E. Hay (Wash.; businessman, Gov.), late 19th and early 20th centuries (36 boxes), containing political correspondence and records of real estate activities; William Stanley Lewis (Wash., Calif.; lawyer, writer), 3 boxes, manuscripts of published articles; and James Z. Moore (Wash.; Spokane lawyer, member State constitutional convention of 1889), 2 boxes.

See Hist. Records Survey, Guide for Oreg.-Wash., p. 29.

SPOKANE 2

Oregon Province Archives. Crosby Library. Gonzaga University. Rev. W. P. Schoenberg, Director.

Holdings: 70,000 items, 1843-1947, relating chiefly to Jesuit missionary activities in Alaska, Idaho, Montana, Oregon, Washington, and Wyoming. In addition to these papers there are several thousand items on microfilm, and 15,000 photographs relating to the same areas.

The Northwest Mission papers, 1845-1928 (400 boxes and 35,000 items), contain correspondence between missionaries and Catholic Church and U.S. Government officials, diaries and reports of missions, and personal diaries and notes. They include papers of Pierre-Jean De Smet (Jesuit missionary), 1845-73 (20 pieces); and of successive superiors general of the Rocky Mountain Missions: Joseph Joset, 1846-1900 (329 pieces); Joseph Giorda, 1863-82 (218 pieces); and Joseph Cataldo (also founder of Gonzaga Univ. in Spokane), 1870-1928 (563 pieces).

The Alaska Mission papers, 1869-1947 (10,000 items), contain material similar to that in the Northwest Mission papers. They include papers of Francis Barnum (Alaska; priest, linguist), 1891-1921 (80 pieces); Joseph Raphael Crimont (Wash., Alaska; missionary, Gonzaga College pres., Bishop of Alaska), 1892-1945 (1,301 pieces); Walter James Fitzgerald (Wash., Alaska; educator, Bishop of Alaska), 1883-1947 (390 pieces); Jules Jetté (Alaska; priest, ethnologist, linguist), 1898-1927 (325 pieces); Charles Jean Seghers (Canada, Oreg.; Bishop of Vancouver, Archbishop of Oregon City, i.e., Portland, Oreg.), 1869-86 (40 pieces); and Pascal Tosi (Alaska; Prefect Apostolic of Alaska, Superior General of the Alaska Mission), 1886-98 (93 pieces).

The Indian language collection (50,000 pages) consists of manuscript dictionaries, grammars, catechisms, Gospels, prayers, hymns, and sermons in the Indian languages of the Rocky Mountain region and the Eskimo languages of Alaska. Among the languages included are Assiniboine, Blackfoot, Chinook, Columbia, Colville, Crow, Gros Ventre, Innuit, Kalispel, Nez Percé, Okanagan, Sioux, Tena, Tlingit, and Yakima.

There are also in the archives papers of laymen, including those of a Spokane pioneer, 1883-1916 (5 boxes); and a Salem, Oreg., judge, 1854-1933 (41 vols. and 22 boxes).

SPOKANE 4

Spokane Public Library. Cedar and Riverside Sts. (Mrs.) Gladys S.

Puckett, Librarian.

Holdings: Some letters, journals, and other papers relating chiefly to Washington and the Pacific Northwest. Included are a few letters of Pierre-Jean De Smet (Jesuit missionary).

See Hist. Records Survey, Guide for Oreg.-Wash., p. 31.

TACOMA 3

Washington State Historical Society. 315 North Stadium Way. Bruce Le Roy, Director.

Holdings: 5,000 pieces, 1790-1959, relating chiefly to Washington and the Pacific Northwest. Included are some U.S. court, county, and city archives; various early church, school, and business records; diaries and papers relating to overland crossings and pioneer settlement, Indians, Indian wars, and the Hudson's Bay Co.; and correspondence of missionaries. Papers of individuals include those of Hiram Martin Chittenden (Wash.; U.S. Army officer, military engineer, author); William Hunter (R. I., D. C.; lawyer, second assistant Sec. State); Harold Slater (Wash.; AFL-CIO official), 1935-58; and Isaac I. Stevens (Wash.; Terr. Gov., Terr. Delegate to Cong., U.S. Army officer).

WALLA WALLA

Penrose Memorial Library, Whitman College. Ruth S. Reynolds, Librarian.

Holdings: 3,500 pieces (letters, journals, accounts, and maps), 19th century, relating to the Indians, early missionaries, pioneers of eastern Washington, and other as-

pects of the history of the Pacific Northwest. Included are some papers of
Cushing Eells (Oreg.; missionary) and
his family, 1838-93; John Mullan (U. S.
Army engineer, explorer, road-build-
er); Henry Harmon Spalding (Wash.,
(Oreg.; missionary) and his family,
1836-74; and Marcus and Narcissa
Whitman (Oreg.; missionaries),
1836-47.

See Hist. Records Survey, Guide
for Oreg.-Wash., p. 34.

CHARLESTON 5

West Virginia Department of Archives and History. State Capitol. Kyle McCormick, Director.

Holdings: (1) Noncurrent official records held by the Department as the State's archival agency, and (2) other papers relating to West Virginia and the trans-Allegheny region. In the first category are records of the Governors, 1863-1921; the legislature and other agencies of the State government; and the State constitutional convention, 1872. In the second category are papers of Arthur I. Boreman (W. Va.; U. S. Sen., Gov.), 1861-77 (355 pieces); Henry Mason Mathews (W. Va.; Confed. Army officer, Gov.), 1877-81 (1,106 pieces); Francis Harrison Pierpont (Va., W. Va.; lawyer, Gov. of Va.), 1836-91 (1,569 pieces); and William E. Stevenson (W. Va.; Gov.), 1869-71 (329 pieces). Included also are records of a temperance society, 1839-41; and several Baptist and Methodist churches.

See Hist. Records Survey's Calendars (processed), of the Arthur I. Boreman letters (1939. 91 p.), the Henry Mason Mathews letters and papers (1941. 327 p.), and the William E. Stevenson letters (1939. 105 p.); and the W. Va. Department of Archives and History, Biennial Reports, 1935-52.

MORGANTOWN

West Virginia Collection, West Virginia University Library. Charles Shetler, Curator.

Holdings: 2,500,000 items, 1736-1954, relating chiefly to West Virginia and the upper Ohio Valley.

Papers of governors include those of Arthur I. Boreman (W. Va.; lawyer, Gov., U. S. Sen.), 1830-1905 (10,000 pieces); John J. Cornwell (W. Va.; lawyer, State legislator, Gov.), 1917-21 (31,328 pieces); Aretas Brooks Fleming (W. Va.; circuit court judge, Gov., coal operator), 1784-1924 (50,000 pieces); William E. Glasscock (W. Va.; lawyer, Gov.), 1906-25 (15,000 pieces); Howard M. Gore (W. Va.; U. S. Sec. Agriculture, Gov.), 1917-47 (50 vols. and 26,200 pieces); John J. Jacob (W. Va.; Gov.), 1866-78 (97 pieces); Ephraim F. Morgan (W. Va.; Gov.), 1920-25 (19,430 pieces); Francis Harrison Pierpont (Va., W. Va.; lawyer, Gov. of Va.), 1839-99 (4,000 pieces); and A. B. White (W. Va.; Gov., collector of internal revenue), 1894-1929 (40 boxes).

Papers of other political leaders include those of Johnson N. Camden (Va., W. Va.; banker, railroad capitalist, U. S. Sen.), 1845-1908 (36 vols. and 96 boxes); Henry G. Davis (W. Va.; coal and railroad capitalist, U. S. Sen.), 1865-1916 (134 vols. and 200 boxes); Alston G. Dayton (W. Va.; U.S. Rep., U. S. dist. judge), 1848-1920 (183 boxes); Stephen B. Elkins (N. Mex., N. Y., W. Va.; Civil War officer, Terr. Delegate to Cong., Sec. War, U. S. Sen. from W. Va.), 1861-1946 (3,214 pieces); Guy D. Goff (Wis., W. Va.; lawyer, U. S. Sen.), 1918-31 (211 pieces); Nathan Goff (W. Va.; Civil War officer, Sec. Navy, U. S. Rep. and Sen., U. S. circuit court judge), 1859-94 (9,432 pieces); John T. McGraw (W. Va.; lawyer, State legislator), 1858-1948 (10 boxes); Peter G. Van Winkle (W. Va.;

lawyer, U.S. Sen.), 1827-72 (2 boxes); and Waitman T. Willey (W. Va.; lawyer, U.S. Sen.), 1830-1900 (2 vols. and 7,500 pieces).

Papers of other individuals include those of Charles Henry Ambler (W. Va.; historian), 1834-1945 (12 boxes); Jonathan M. Bennett (Va.; lawyer, banker), 1785-1899 (68,000 pieces); Archibald W. Campbell (W. Va.; newspaper editor), 1855-99 (128 pieces); Harrison Hagans (W. Va.; merchant, iron manufacturer, inventor), 1818-67 (3,000 pieces); Chester D. Hubbard (Va., W. Va.; lawyer, U.S. Rep.), 1814-91 (5,000 pieces); Thomas Jonathan Jackson, known as Stonewall Jackson (Va.; prof. at Va. Military Institute, U.S. and Confed. Army officer, 1845-60 (109 pieces); Melville Davisson Post (W. Va.; lawyer, writer), 1842-1926 (3,000 pieces); Ira E. Robinson (W. Va.; State legislator, State supreme court justice, chairman of Federal Radio Commission), 1832-1951 (28,000 pieces); and Israel C. White (W. Va.; geologist, prof. at W. Va. Univ.), 1870-1927 (30,000 pieces).

Business records include those of the Salt Sulphur Springs Co. (general store, hotel, stage line, telegraph company, and farm), 1819-1932 (88 vols.); Kanawha Saline Co., 1833-35 (16 vols.); Exchange Bank of Virginia, Weston Branch, 1852-68 (39 vols. and 1,200 pieces); Baltimore and Ohio Railroad, 1853-64 (50 pieces); Sweet Springs (W. Va.) Hotel, 1860-1927 (36 vols.); West Virginia Firebrick Co., and other firebrick works; Relief Tow Boat Co., 1870-1909 (55 boxes); and a lumber company, 1889-1926 (56 account books).

Other papers include records of various churches and schools; chapters of the Daughters of the American Revolution, 1892-1947 (1,674 pieces); West Virginia University, 1867-1954 (150,000 pieces); West Virginia State Dental Society, 1900-52 (1,443 pieces); the American Legion, 1945-53 (1 box); and West Virginia War History Commission, World War II (136 boxes). Also included are some Civil War papers; and papers relating to the Virginia–West Virginia debt question; and extensive holdings of county records, 1736-1949.

See the Library's Guide to Manuscripts and Archives in the West Virginia Collection (1958. 160 p.); Hist. Records Survey, Calendar of the J. J. Jacob Letters in West Virginia Depositories (1940. 251 p. Processed), and Calendar of the Francis Harrison Pierpont Letters and Papers in West Virginia Depositories (1940. 387 p. Processed); and Forest History Sources, p. 112.

WISCONSIN

ANTIGO

Langlade County Historical Society.
Antigo Public Library.

Holdings: 300 vols., 10 book-type
files, 15 bundles, and 65 envelopes,
1836-1935, relating chiefly to Langlade County. Included are papers of
Gabriel Bouck (Wis.; lawyer, U.S.
Rep.), 1875-95; a collection on Stockbridge and Muncee Indian affairs; papers pertaining to Czechs in Langlade
County, 1878-1933; a Civil War diary,
1863-65, covering Sherman's march
to Savannah and northward; and 75
World War I letters.
See Hist. Records Survey, Guide
for Wis., p. 1.

APPLETON

Lawrence College Library. H. A. Bru-
baker, Librarian.

Holdings: 186 pieces, 1846-1900,
of which 140 relate chiefly to Lawrence
College. Included are 797 letters of
Amos Adams Lawrence (Mass.; merchant, philanthropist, founder of Lawrence College), 1844-83 (mounted in 3
scrapbooks).

BARABOO

Sauk County Historical Society.
(Mrs.) Dorothy F. Allison, President.

Holdings: Letters, account books,
and various other papers relating to
Sauk County. Included are some papers pertaining to the Civil War and
World War I; various items dealing
with area circuses, particularly

Ringling's; and maps showing nearby
Indian mounds.
See Hist. Records Survey, Guide
for Wis., p. 3.

BURLINGTON

Burlington Historical Society.

Holdings: 4 filing drawers, 1815-
1928, relating chiefly to Burlington
and nearby communities. Included
are papers of two lawyers, 1836-68;
and letters and a diary of the Civil
War period.
See Hist. Records Survey, Guide
for Wis., p. 5.

GREEN BAY

Neville Public Museum. 129 South
Jefferson St. James L. Quinn,
Director.

Holdings: Some 2,000 pieces,
dating from 1760, consisting of letters, legal documents, and other
papers pertaining chiefly to local
and Indian history. Included are
some records of general stores,
1835-50; and minutes of a local
street railway, 1908-27.
See Hist. Records Survey, Guide
for Wis., p. 6.

KENOSHA

Kenosha County Historical Society.
Sheridan Rd. and 56th St.

Holdings: Over 2,000 pieces,
1820 to date, relating chiefly to Kenosha County. Included are account

books, diaries, maps, Civil War letters, and papers pertaining to shipping
on the Great Lakes, manufacturing,
real estate, and other matters.

LA CROSSE

La Crosse County Historical Society.
119 South 17th St.   Eleanor R. Sanford, President.

Holdings: 275 pieces, 1842-1940,
relating chiefly to La Crosse County.
Included are political correspondence,
business papers, family papers, early
town records, and records of fraternal
and other organizations.
See Hist. Records Survey, Guide
for Wis., p. 8.

—oOo—

Wisconsin State College Library.
Martha O. Skaar, Librarian.

Holdings: 300 pieces, 1844-1919,
relating chiefly to La Crosse County.
Included are diaries, letters, and
other papers pertaining to the Civil
War and World War I.

MADISON 6

American Institute of the History of
Pharmacy.   356 Chemistry Bldg.,
University of Wisconsin School of
Pharmacy.   Glenn Sonnedecker,
Director.

Holdings: Manuscript material
dispersed among printed and pictor-
ial material in 110 file drawers,
mostly since 1875.   Included are
correspondence of some important
pharmacists and pharmaceutical scientists; a few business and professional records of old drugstores;
some unpublished association re-

ports and minutes; and student
notebooks.

—oOo—

State Historical Society of Wisconsin.   Leslie H. Fishel, Jr., Director; Josephine L. Harper, Manuscript
Section Head.

Holdings: (1) Archives of the
State of Wisconsin, 1836-1950 (13,500
cu. ft.), in the custody of the Archives
Division, J. E. Boell, Archivist; (2)
the McCormick Collection, 1739-
1954 (2,000,000 items), in the care
of (Mrs.) Lucile Kellar, Coordinator;
and (3) other papers, 1755-1958
(6,866 vols. and 2,911,000 organized
pieces), relating especially to Wisconsin but containing much of value
for the history of other parts of the
United States.   The Society also oper-
ates the Mass Communications History Center, which is collecting
scripts, correspondence, and other
materials resulting from or associated with the operation of radio and
other mass communications media.

State Archives

The State archives consist of 42
record groups (one for each State
agency) and 678 record series.   The
material relates generally to Wisconsin but contains much of value for
the history of other parts of the United States.   Included are the files of
the Executive Department, State
Treasurer, Public Service Commission, Insurance Department, State
Department of Public Welfare, Attorney General, Secretary of State,
Board of Health, Department of Taxation, Conservation Commission, and
Industrial Commission.   The Division
also has in its files in the State Historical Society Building and in regional depositories elsewhere in the

State 362 series of local records. Among them are such series as the proceedings of county, village, and town boards and city councils; correspondence and letter books of administrative officials; reports of county and city officers; tax rolls; treasurers' ledgers and journals; election records; property appraisal records; circuit court files; probate files; records of school, road, and drainage districts; and a few business records.

McCormick Collection

The McCormick Collection was formerly known as the Collections of the McCormick Historical Association of Chicago, Ill. It is based on the papers of Cyrus Hall McCormick (Va., Ill.; inventor and manufacturer of the reaper, philanthropist) and consists of the following groups: (1) The C. H. McCormick family papers, (2) the Nancy (Nettie) Fowler McCormick papers, (3) the Anita McCormick Blaine papers, (4) the Harold Fowler McCormick Collection, (5) records of McCormick reaper companies, (6) records of other reaper companies, (7) papers of collateral McCormick families, (8) the James D. Davidson Collection, (9) other Virginia collections, (10) miscellaneous collections, and (11) the Everett E. Edwards Collection.

The C. H. McCormick family papers, 1790-1940 (117,342 items), provide information about such matters as the charcoal iron furnace business, the invention and development of the reaper, the Presbyterian Church and the Presbyterian Theological Seminary of the Northwest, the Democratic Party, the Civil War, philanthropy, and investments in gold, real estate, railroads, and mines. Included are letters from Daniel Cameron (Ill.; Civil War officer, political leader), 1866-76 (67 items); Edward N. Dicker-

son (N. Y.; patent lawyer, mechanical engineer), 1858-78 (78 items); Charles Richards Dodge (D. C.; textile fiber expert), 1899-1901 (50 items); George Esterley (Wis.; inventor and manufacturer of agricultural machinery), 1882-84 (33 items); George Harding (Pa.; patent lawyer involved in farm machinery litigation), 1862-94 (134 items); Herrick Johnson (Ill.; Presbyterian clergyman, prof. at McCormick Theological Seminary), 1880-1910 (41 items); Daniel Lord and Daniel Lord, Jr. (N. Y.; lawyers), 1866-84 (110 items); Leander J. McCormick (Va., Ill.; Cyrus' brother, reaper manufacturer, inventor), 1856-98 (258 items); William S. McCormick (Va., Ill.; Cyrus' brother, reaper manufacturer, financier), 1832-65 (646 items); Charles W. Marsh and William W. Marsh (Ill.; inventors and manufacturers of agricultural machinery), 1869-1900 (62 items); Junius S. Morgan (England; international banker), 1864-1900 (55 items); William S. Plumer (Va., Pa., S. C.; Presbyterian clergyman, prof. at Columbia [S. C.] Theological Seminary), 1855-80 (64 items); and Benjamin Mosby Smith (Va.; Presbyterian clergyman, prof. of Oriental literature at Union Theological Seminary), 1865-84 (117 items).

The collection of Nancy (Nettie) Fowler McCormick (N. Y., Ill.; wife of C. H. McCormick, educator, philanthropist), 1800-1927 (96,380 pieces), contains genealogical records of the Fowler, Esseltyn, and Spicer families, and materials on social welfare in the United S.ates, health and hygiene, domestic and foreign missions, education particularly in small denominational schools throughout the world, World War I, and the McCormick Harvesting Machine Co. and the consolidation. Included is correspondence of Dwight L. Moody (Mass., Ill.; evangelist), 1873-1901 (69 items);

Richard Cary Morse (N.Y.; Presbyterian clergyman, Y.M.C.A. international official), 1902-23 (161 items); John R. Mott (N.Y.; Y.M.C.A. official), 1898-1923 (449 items); Francis Landrey Patton (N.Y., N.J.; Presbyterian clergyman, pres. of Princeton College and Princeton Theological Seminary), 1873-1921 (61 items); Sara A. Pryor (Va., N.Y.; author), 1869-1911 (230 items); John D. Rockefeller and John D. Rockefeller, Jr. (N.Y.; capitalists, philanthropists), 1902-22 (79 items); C. A. Spring, Sr. (Ill.; manager of the McCormick companies), 1865-88 (63 items); and Woodrow Wilson (N.J.; U.S. Pres.), 1915-22 (30 items). There are also papers of Cyrus H. McCormick, Jr. (Ill.; son of the inventor, manufacturer, philanthropist), 1871-1930 (200 file drawers); and Cyrus McCormick (Ill., N.Mex., N.Y.; son of Cyrus H., Jr., manufacturer, author), 1895-1923 (60 items).

The papers of Anita McCormick Blaine (Ill.; daughter of the inventor, philanthropist, founder of School of Education at Univ. of Chicago), 1876-1954 (1,008,000 items), contain records of humanitarian activities in education, health, housing, all levels of government, and the world peace movement. The collection of Harold Fowler McCormick (Ill.; son of the inventor, manufacturer, philanthropist), 1899-1936 (100,000 items), deals with World War I peace movements, the harvesting machine industry, civic betterment, and the opera and symphonic music in Chicago.

Records of the McCormick reaper companies, 1848-1902 (495 ledgers and account books, 471 vols. containing 446,900 letterpress copies of letters sent, and 347,850 letters received), relate to the reaper business in the United States and foreign countries and deal with inventions, patents, manufacturing, advertising, sales, labor, and other matters. Records of other reaper companies, 1877-1902

(213 vols.), pertain to four competing companies.

Papers of collateral McCormick families, 1831-1905 (10 vols.), include letters and accounts of Stephen McCormick (Va.; inventor and manufacturer of cast-iron plow), 1819-42; and a diary of John H. Simpson (S.C.; Confed. Army chaplain), 1857-71.

The James D. Davidson Collection consists of the papers of James McDowell (Va.; militia officer, planter, capitalist), 1739-1838 (6,801 items), concerned largely with land holdings and land speculations in Virginia and Kentucky; and James D. Davidson (Va.; lawyer, political leader, educator), 1826-1908 (43 vols. and 40,546 items). Included in this collection is correspondence with James B. Dorman (Va.; Confed. Army officer, clerk of State supreme court of appeals), 1848-85 (56 items); John Echols (Va.; lawyer, Confed. Army officer, Chesapeake and Ohio Railway executive), 1843-67 (67 items); John Letcher (Va.; lawyer, newspaper editor, U.S. Rep., Gov.), 1848-66 (55 items); and Alexander H. H. Stewart (Va.; lawyer, U.S. Rep., Sec. Interior), 1838-67 (34 items).

Other Virginia collections, 1767-1910 (146 vols. and 10,964 items), contain papers of a number of families engaged in farming in the Piedmont section and the Valley of Virginia; records of charcoal iron furnaces; and account books of merchants in Rockbridge County. In the miscellaneous collections, 1782-1936 (2 vols. and 1,440 items), are papers of James Chesnut (S.C.; lawyer, U.S. Sen., Confed. Army officer) and his family, 1782-1896 (866 items); Horace S. Oakley (Ill.; lawyer, philanthropist), 1879-1936 (2 vols. and 300 items); and Joseph H. Spencer (Minn.; Civil War officer), 1861-65 (196 pieces).

The Everett E. Edwards Collection, 1920-51 (60,996 manuscripts), is composed of correspondence of Edwards (Minn., D.C.; editor, agricultural historian) with agriculturists, historians, and economists, 19 boxes of lectures and notes, and 44 boxes of notes taken by Lewis C. Gray (Wis., Tenn., D.C.; college prof., agricultural economist) for his History of Agriculture in the South to 1860.

Other Papers

The Society's most famous papers are the Draper Manuscripts (many thousands of items in 486 vols.). They relate chiefly to the area between the Mississippi River on the west and the Hudson River and the Atlantic Ocean on the east, especially the frontier region, during the period 1755-1815, and consist of original papers collected by Lyman C. Draper (N.Y., Wis.; historian, first supt. of State Hist. Soc. of Wis.) and transcripts and notes made by him. The Society also has 28 boxes of Draper's unbound correspondence, memorandum books, and other papers, 1833-93. The bound materials include Draper's partially completed life of Daniel Boone, 5 vols., and his unpublished histories of "Border Forays," 5 vols., and "Mecklenburg Declaration," 3 vols. There are series of papers of or relating to Daniel Boone (N.C., Ky., Mo.; explorer, pioneer settler), 32 vols.; Joseph Brant (Mohawk chief), 22 vols.; Daniel Brodhead (Pa.; Rev. War officer), 3 vols.; George Rogers Clark (Va., Ky.; Rev. War officer), 65 vols.; William Clark (Ky., Mo.; explorer, Gov. of Mo. Terr., Indian agent), 5 vols.; Thomas Forsyth (Ill.; fur trader, Indian agent), 9 vols.; Josiah Harmar (Pa.; Rev. War and Indian wars officer), 2 vols. of transcripts; William Irvine (Pa.; Rev. War officer, U.S. Rep.), 2 vols. of transcripts; Simon Kenton (Ky., Ohio; frontiersman, Rev. War scout, War of 1812 officer), 13 vols.; William Preston (Va.; colonial militia and Rev. War

officer), 6 vols.; Thomas Sumter (S.C.; Rev. War officer, U.S. Rep. and Sen.), 23 vols.; and Tecumseh (Shawnee chief), 13 vols. Other series bear the names of the following events or areas: Frontier Wars, 23 vols.; Kentucky, 30 vols.; King's Mountain, 18 vols.; Pittsburgh and Northwest Virginia, 10 vols.; Tennessee, 7 vols.; and Virginia, 14 vols.

Papers of administrative and diplomatic officials of the U.S. Government include those of Rasmus B. Anderson (Wis.; Minister to Denmark, editor, student of Scandinavian life and literature), 1841-1936 (13 vols. and 53 boxes); Edward S. Bragg (Wis.; Civil War officer, U.S. Rep., Minister to Mexico), 1853-1912 (3 vols. and 1 box); Lucius Fairchild (Wis.; Civil War officer, Gov., U.S. consul general in Paris and Minister to Spain), 1830-1923 (116 vols. and 85 boxes); Timothy O. Howe (Wis.; U.S. Sen., Postmaster Gen.), 1846-82 (2 boxes, transcripts); Henry C. Payne (Wis.; utilities executive, Postmaster Gen.), 1885-1908 (4 vols.); DeWitt C. Poole (N.J.; diplomat, educator), 1918-52 (12 boxes); Jeremiah M. Rusk (Wis.; Civil War officer, Gov., U.S. Rep., Sec. Agriculture), 1862-98 (14 vols. and 4 boxes); and William F. Vilas (Wis.; U.S. Sen., Postmaster Gen., Sec. Interior), 1827-1919 (10 vols. and 57 boxes).

Papers of Members of Congress include, in addition to those mentioned above, papers of Henry C. Adams (Wis.; agriculturist, U.S. Rep.), 1870-1906 (5 boxes); Joseph W. Babcock (Wis.; businessman, U.S. Rep.), 1864-1916 (1 vol. and 1 box); Joseph D. Beck (Wis.; member Wis. Industrial Commission, U.S. Rep., State commissioner of agriculture and markets), 1901-37 (2 boxes); Charles S. Benton (N.Y., Wis.; U.S. Rep. from N.Y.), 1835-73 (1 box); John J. Blaine (Wis.; Gov., U.S. Sen.), 1894-

1934 (8 vols. and 69 boxes); Stephen
Bolles (Wis.; newspaper editor, U.S.
Rep.), 1930-40 (3 boxes); Henry Allen
Cooper (Wis.; lawyer, U.S. Rep.),
1843-1931 (7 boxes); James H. Davidson (Wis.; U.S. Rep.), 1900-10 (1 box);
James Rood Doolittle (N.Y., Wis., Ill.;
lawyer, U.S. Sen.), 1831-1935 (15 boxes); James D. Doty (Wis., Utah; U.S.
Rep., Gov. of Wis. and Utah Terrs.),
1779-1879 (3 boxes); John Jacob Esch
(Wis.; U.S. Rep.), 1891-1921 (33 vols.
and 62 boxes); James A. Frear (Wis.;
lawyer, U.S. Rep.), 1906-40 (6 vols.
and 3 boxes); Nils P. Haugen (Wis.;
lawyer, U.S. Rep.), 1875-1931 (17 vols.
and 66 boxes); and George C. Hazelton
(Wis.; lawyer, U.S. Rep.), 1861-1910
(3 boxes).

Papers of other Members of Congress include those of Merlin Hull
(Wis.; lawyer, U.S. Rep.), 1895-1953
(400 boxes); Paul O. Husting (Wis.;
U.S. Sen.), 1909-18 (27 vols. and 25
boxes); Robert M. La Follette (Wis.;
Gov., U.S. Rep. and Sen.), 1879-1910
(35 vols. and 185 boxes), dealing chiefly with his years as Governor; Morgan
L. Martin (Wis.; lawyer, Terr. Delegate to Cong.), 1747-1888 (27 vols. and
14 boxes); Alexander Mitchell (Wis.;
banker, U.S. Rep.), and his son, John
L. (Wis.; U.S. Sen.), 1859-1906 (2 box-
es); Adolphus P. Nelson (Wis.; banker,
U.S. Rep.), 1908-26 (10 boxes); John
M. Nelson (Wis.; lawyer, U.S. Rep.),
3 boxes; John Fox Potter (Wis.; U.S.
Rep.), 1810-1900 (1 vol. and 5 boxes);
E. William Proxmire (Wis.; State
legislator, U.S. Sen.), 7 cartons;
Lawrence H. Smith (Wis.; U.S. Rep.),
2 large crates; William Sulzer (N.Y.;
U.S. Rep., Gov.), 1899-1923 (1 vol.);
Nathaniel P. Tallmadge (N.Y., Wis.;
U.S. Sen., Gov. of Wis. Terr.), 1812-
60 (2 boxes and 4 reels of microfilm);
John H. Tweedy (Wis.; lawyer, Terr.
Delegate to Cong.), 1832-90 (8 boxes);
Aaron Vanderpoel (N.Y.; U.S. Rep.),
1836-56 (1 box); Cadwallader C. Wash-
burn (Wis.; U.S. Rep., Civil War offi-

cer, Gov.), 1844-77 (3 boxes); and
Luman H. Weller (Iowa; U.S. Rep.),
1828-1912 (11 boxes).

Among papers of other political
leaders are those of George Clinton
(N.Y.; Gov., U.S. Vice Pres.), 1777-
98 (1 box); James O. Davidson (Wis.;
Gov.), 1885-1919 (13 vols. and 36
boxes); Nelson Dewey (Wis.; lawyer,
Gov.), 1836-89 (2 vols. and 10 boxes); Herman Ekern (Wis.; insurance
expert, Progressive leader), 1889-
1938 (60 boxes); William D. Hoard
(Wis.; diary farmer, Gov.), 1900-18
(1 box); Jessie A. Jack Hooper (Wis.;
pres. of Wis. League of Women Voters, officer of General Federation of
Women's Clubs), 1909-34 (5 vols.
and 21 boxes); Elisha W. Keyes (Wis.;
Republican leader), 1833-1910
(41 vols. and 109 boxes); Philip La
Follette (Wis.; Gov., Progressive
leader), 1930-40 (225 boxes); Orland
Loomis (Wis.; lawyer, Progressive
leader), 1929-40 (50 boxes); Francis
E. McGovern (Wis.; Gov.), 1909-15
(47 boxes); Emanuel L. Philipp (Wis.;
Gov.), 1887-1925 (11 vols. and 20
boxes); James A. Stone (Wis.; lawyer, Progressive leader), 1892-1945
(12 vols. and 29 boxes); Horace A.
Tenney (Wis.; newspaper editor, Republican leader) and his family, 1797-
1929 (2 vols. and 5 boxes); and Ellis
B. Usher (Wis.; newspaper editor,
Democratic leader), 1847-1912
(42 vols. and 19 boxes).

Papers of other persons include
those of Cecil Brown (N.Y.; World
War II radio news reporter and commentator, journalist), 55 boxes;
Thomas C. Chamberlain (Wis., Ill.;
geologist), 1878-88 (3 vols. of survey notes); August W. Derleth (Wis.;
novelist, poet), 1867-1946 (26 boxes); Jason Downer (Wis.; State supreme court justice), 1853-83
(7 vols. and 21 boxes); John M. Evans
(Ind., Ill.; physician), 2 boxes; Zona
Gale (Wis.; author), 1875-1930 (1 vol.
and 32 boxes); George Gibbs (N.Y.,

Oreg.; geologist and ethnologist) and his family, 1796-1903 (2 vols. and 4 boxes), including many letters by Oliver Wolcott, Jr. (Conn.; banker, Sec. Treas., Gov.); Joseph C. Harsch (D. C.; newspaper correspondent and news commentator), 19 boxes; Ada L. James (Wis.; social reformer, woman suffrage leader), 1816-1952 (39 vols. and 52 boxes); Charles Jonas (Wis.; U. S. consul, Bohemian newspaper editor), 1853-94 (3 boxes); Hans V. Kaltenborn (Wis., N. Y.; journalist, radio news analyst, traveler), 1923-42 (95 boxes); Increase A. Lapham (Ohio, Wis.; civil engineer, scientist), 1825-1930 (25 vols. and 26 boxes); Henry D. Lloyd (N. Y., Ill.; journalist, author), 1840-1937 (10 vols. and 69 boxes); Louis P. Lochner (Wis., D. C.; newspaper correspondent, radio commentator, Chief of Berlin Bureau of Associated Press), 38 boxes; Charles McCarthy (Wis.; political scientist, legislative reference librarian), 1906-31 (46 boxes); Balthasar H. Meyer (Wis., D. C.; railroad economist), 1877-1944 (5 vols. and 15 boxes); Raymond Robins (Ill., Fla.; social economist, Red Cross worker in Russia), 1888-1951 (35 boxes); Marvin B. Rosenberry (Wis.; chief justice of State supreme court), 1914-49 (75 boxes); Edward G. Ryan (Wis.; chief justice of State supreme court), 1815-1902 (1 box); Moses M. Strong (Vt., Wis.; surveyor, lawyer, dealing with lands, railroads, lumbering, and mining), 1774-1894 (27 vols. and 42 boxes); Henry C. Taylor (Wis., D. C.; agricultural economist), 1893-1951 (4 file cases); Reuben G. Thwaites (Wis.; editor, sec. of State Hist. Soc. of Wis.), 1823-1929 (5 vols. and 6 boxes); Ella Wheeler Wilcox (Wis., N. Y., Conn.; poet), 1917-20 (73 letters); and Cyrus Woodman (Wis.; banker, dealer in lumber, lands, and railroads), 1832-1900 (206 vols. and 2 boxes).

Among papers relating to religious history are those of Samuel Fallows (Wis., Ill.; Reformed Episcopal bishop), 1856-1922 (32 boxes); Jackson Kemper (Pa., Mo., Wis.; Episcopal missionary bishop), 1787-1884 (175 vols. and 3 boxes); and John G. Müller (Wis., Ill.; Evangelical pioneer missionary), 1843-88 (47 vols.). There are also records pertaining to Jesuit activities in North America, 1612-1865 (10 boxes); records of various Catholic officials and churches in Wisconsin, 1695-1867 (3 vols.); and records of several Congregational churches and conventions in Wisconsin, 1839-1944 (96 vols. and 2 boxes).

Papers relating to Indians (in Wis. unless otherwise noted) include papers of John C. Adams (agent for the Stockbridge Indians), 1792-99 (6 boxes); George Boyd (U. S. Indian agent at Mackinac and at Green Bay), 1797-1858 (8 vols.); Edmund Franklin Ely (missionary to the Chippewa of Wis. and Minn.), 1833-1904 (2 boxes of typed copies); Cutting Marsh (missionary to the Stockbridge Indians), 1802-60 (2 boxes); George Morgan (Pa.; U. S. Indian agent at Fort Pitt), 1774-79 (1 box of copies of letter books); Joseph A. Paxson (physician to the Winnebago Indian agency in Nebraska), 1869-71 (2 vols.); and Eleazer Williams (Episcopal missionary), 1789-1858 (6 boxes). There are also vocabularies of several Indian tribes in Wisconsin (5 vols. and 1 box), and extensive copies of documents from the records, in the National Archives, of the Bureau of Indian Affairs, 1804-60 (68 boxes).

Papers relating to military history, in addition to others mentioned elsewhere, include those of Elias Boudinot (N. J.; Rev. War officer, Pres. of Continental Cong.), 1777-78 (1 letter book); Carl R. Gray, Jr. (Wis.; railroad executive, World Wars I and II Army officer), 6 cartons; William G. Haan (U. S. Army officer), 1898-1925 (1 vol. and 12 boxes); Charles King (Wis.; Spanish-American War and World War I officer), 1840-1932 (3 boxes); William D. Leahy (U. S. naval officer, Ambassador to France, Chief of Staff to the Commander in Chief), 1897-1931, 1941-45 (7 vols. and 11 reels of microfilm); and Charles Wilkes (U. S. naval officer, explorer), 1801-80 (1 box). There are two Revolutionary War diaries and many Civil War letters and diaries. A collection of World War I papers includes records of Wisconsin's War History Commission (50 boxes), the State's Council of Defense (21 file drawers), and other organizations.

Among many business and professional records are some American Fur Co. papers, 1816-47 (9 vols. and 42 reels of microfilm), and many other papers relating to the fur trade; records of the National Broadcasting Co. concerning advertising, promotion, and programming in radio and television (203 boxes); records of lumber companies, 1850-1945 (700 vols. and 55 boxes); records relating to the construction of railroads in Minnesota, Nebraska, and South Carolina as well as in Wisconsin; many papers relating to real estate operations; miscellaneous records of one or more canning companies, hotels and taverns, telephone companies, insurance companies, meat packing companies, fire underwriting companies, and banks; and papers on the history of medicine and fluoridation in the United States, 1836-1954 (34 boxes). Also included are records of the Associated Gas and Electric Corp. of New York City (99 cartons).

Papers relating importantly to the University of Wisconsin or members of its faculty include those of Charles K. Adams (pres.), 1872-1902 (1 box); William F. Allen (classical scholar, prof.), 1824-1920 (25 vols.); Edward A. Birge (biologist, pres.), 1897-1948 (15 boxes); James D. Butler (prof. of

ancient languages), 1776-1905 (6 vols. and 14 boxes), containing information about Indian languages and archeology in Wisconsin; Richard T. Ely (prof. of economics), 1850-1938 (280 boxes); Carl Russell Fish (prof. of history), 1891-1932 (17 boxes); Louis Kahlenberg (prof. of chemistry), 1900-39 (12 boxes); Edward Kremers (head of School of Pharmacy), 1835-1941 (21 boxes); William H. Lighty (chairman of Extension Division), 1887-1949 (97 boxes); Daniel Webster Mead (prof. of hydraulic and sanitary engineering), 1875-1903, 1931 (1 box); Edward A. Ross (prof. of sociology), 1870-1921; Frederick J. Turner (prof. of history) and his father, 1863-1926 (3 boxes); and Charles R. Van Hise (geologist, pres.), 1875-1918 (9 boxes).

The Society also has a collection of papers on labor and socialism, 1830-1954 (635 vols. and 305 boxes), that was begun by the University of Wisconsin's American Bureau of Industrial Research, under the direction of John R. Commons. Included are records of the International Workingmen's Association, 1871-76 (5 vols. and 2 boxes), with which Friedrich A. Sorge (N. Y., N. J.; socialist, labor leader) was importantly associated; the Workingmen's Party of the United States, 1876-78 (1 box); the Socialist Labor Party, 1866-1907 (46 vols. and 52 boxes); the Sovereigns of Industry, 1874-79 (7 vols. and 1 box); the Wisconsin State Federation of Labor, 1911-53 (5 boxes); numerous Wisconsin local unions, 1875-1954 (550 vols. and 175 boxes), and small collections of records of various other labor organizations. Included also are an unorganized collection (107 cartons) transferred from the headquarters of the American Federation of Labor, consisting of correspondence, reports, and records of the director of research and the president; and a collection of the American Labor

Education Service, 1927-51 (20 file cases), consisting of records of the Barnard, the Vineyard Shore, and Hudson Shore schools for workers, and affiliated schools. There are also papers of Stephen Pearl Andrews (Tex., Mass., N. Y.; abolitionist, reformer), 1869-1925 (4 boxes); Daniel DeLeon (N. Y.; socialist leader), 1889-1907 (7 boxes); Morris Millquit (N.Y.; socialist leader), 1899-1933 (18 vols. and 11 boxes); William Morris Leiserson (Wis., D. C.; economist, Chairman National Mediation Board, Member National Labor Relations Board), 36 file drawers; Thomas W. Phillips (Pa.; U.S. Rep., philanthropist), 1863-1909 (1 box); Algie M. and May Wood Simons (Wis., Ill.; socialist leaders), 1902-51 (6 vols. and 6 boxes); and other labor leaders.

Other holdings of the Society include records of many organizations, among them the American Home Missionary Society, 1827-48 (2 boxes of photostats of letters and reports from Wisconsin missionaries); the American League for Peace and Democracy, Madison branch, 1937-40 (3 boxes); the American Society of Equity, Wisconsin Union, 1916-34 (5 vols. and 2 boxes); the Wisconsin Lodge of the Independent Order of Good Templars, an international temperance society (57 vols. and 21 boxes); the Madison branch of the Woman's Peace Party, 1915-17 (1 box); the Madison Horticultural Society, 1874-1919 (1 box); the Wisconsin branch of the National Association of Audubon Societies, 1898-1917 (1 box); the Wisconsin Academy of Sciences, Arts, and Letters, 1869-1930 (5 vols. and 1 box); the Wisconsin Archaeological Society, 1857-1943 (5 vols. and 25 boxes); the Wisconsin Daughters of the American Revolution, 1914-42 (9 boxes); the Wisconsin State Horticultural Society, 1854-1910 (1 vol. and 2 boxes); the Wisconsin Woman's Suffrage Association, 1892-1925 (26 boxes);

Works Projects Administration's Federal Music Project in Wisconsin 1936-41 (1 reel of microfilm), and Federal Writers' Project in Wisconsin, 1936-42 (10 vertical file drawers).

There are also several autograph collections, including complete sets of papers by signers of the Declaration of Independence, by signers of the Constitution, and by U. S. Presidents; a collection of papers relating to German emigrants in Wisconsin and other parts of the United States, 1835-1937 (6 boxes); original U. S. census schedules of agriculture in Wisconsin, 1850-80; and many photostat and other copies of U. S. Government records, the originals of which are in the National Archives.

See Reuben G. Thwaites, Descriptive List of Manuscript Collections of the State Historical Society of Wisconsin (1906. 197 p.); Alice E. Smith, Guide to the Manuscripts of the Wisconsin Historical Society (1944. 290 p.); Josephine L. Harper and Sharon C. Smith, Guide to the Manuscripts of the State Historical Society of Wisconsin; Supplement Number One, covering acquisitions from 1941 through May 1956 (1957. 222 p.); and Forest History Sources, pp. 115-122. Three Bulletins of Information (1915-16) provide special descriptions of the Strong, Woodman, Keyes, Civil War, and Labor and Socialism collections. Periodic notes on accessions are printed in the Society's quarterly, Wis. Magazine of History. On the McCormick Collection, see the Hist. Records Survey, Guide for Ill., pp. 10-14; and Lucile Kellar's article in Autograph Collectors' Journal, 4 (no. 3):40-43 (spring 1952).

—oOo—

University of Wisconsin Memorial Library. Louis Kaplan, Director.

Holdings: Included are papers of
Sir Joseph Banks (England; scientist),
1772-1818 (140 items); notes of lectures by Joseph Black (Scotland; chemist, prof. of anatomy at Glasgow Univ.,
chemistry prof. at Univ. of Edinburgh),
1776-78; letters by Louis Blanc
(France; Socialist leader, journalist),
43 items; letters by Peter Collier (Vt.,
D. C., N. Y.; prof. of chemistry at
Univ. of Vt., chief chemist in U. S.
Dept. Agriculture), 58 items; letters
by Prosper Enfentin (France; Socialist, Saint-Simonianism leader), 36
items; notes, drafts, and correspondence of Edna Ferber (Wis., N. Y.; writer) pertaining to her novel Giant; a
large collection of data for study of
the pronunciation of the English language, by Miles L. Hanley (Conn.,
Mass., Wis.; prof. of linguistics at
Yale, Harvard, and Wisconsin); letters
by Samuel L. Clemens, better known
as Mark Twain (Mo., Calif., Conn.,
N. Y.; novelist, humorist), 1867-1910
(161 items); and papers of William
English Walling (N. Y., Conn.; author),
1900-36 (10 folders and 1 carton),
containing family letters, literary
manuscripts, and correspondence with
labor leaders. There are also some
English manor rolls, 14th and 15th
centuries (16 items).

MENOMONIE

Mabel Tainter Memorial Free Library.

Holdings: 50 items, mainly 19th
century, among them 41 account books
of a local lumber company, 1847-68.
See Hist. Records Survey, Guide
for Wis., p. 13.

MILWAUKEE 3

Milwaukee Academy of Medicine.

561 North 15th St.   The Librarian.

Holdings: Minutes, correspondence, and other records of the Milwaukee Academy of Medicine and its
predecessors, 1837-1956; and the
minute book of the Verein Deutscher
Aerzte in Milwaukee, 1883-1906.

—oOo—

Milwaukee County Historical Society.
County Court House. Theodore
Mueller, Curator.

Holdings: Manuscripts relating
chiefly to the Milwaukee community
and to natives or residents of Milwaukee. The largest groups of papers include those of Victor L. Ber-
ger (Wis.; editor, publisher, Socialist leader, U. S. Rep.), 1909-19;
Frederic Heath (Wis.; journalist,
Socialist leader), 1897-1954; Lizzie
Kander (Wis.; social worker), 1874-
1940; Stella Mathews (Wis.; nurse),
1918-49; Mary Callaway Spence
(Wis.; pres. of National Gold Star
Mothers), 1921-33; and Daniel
Wells, Jr. (Maine, Wis.; lumber
magnate, railroad developer, U.S.
Rep.), 1835-1902. There are also
papers of several mayors of Milwaukee, among them Gerhard Adolph
Bading (Wis.; physician, World
War I officer, Minister to Ecuador),
1896-1929; Daniel W. Hoan (Wis.;
lawyer, Socialist and Democratic
leader), 1911-52; Solomon Juneau
(Wis.; fur trader, agent of the American Fur Co., Milwaukee's first may-
or), 1830-36; and Emil Seidel (Wis.;
labor union organizer, Socialist
leader), 1910-47. Besides a number
of diaries, scattered public records
and business records, and brief biographical sketches of 500 members
of a Milwaukee post of the Grand Army of the Republic, the holdings include official records of the Socialist

Party of Milwaukee and Wisconsin, 1897-1940.

See reports on accessions in a mimeographed Newsletter, which is issued irregularly seven times a year.

—oOo—

Milwaukee Public Library. 814 West Wisconsin Ave. Richard E. Krug, City Librarian.

Holdings: A considerable quantity of manuscripts, 1842-1959, relating chiefly to Milwaukee and Wisconsin. Papers of individuals include those of Elizabeth Corbett (Wis., N.Y.; novelist), from 1887 (25 boxes); August Derleth (Wis.; novelist, poet), from 1909 (12 boxes); James T. Farrell (N.Y.; author), 1955-59 (5 boxes); Herbert Kubly (Wis.; author, educator), 1955-58 (4 boxes); Louis P. Lochner (Wis., D.C.; newspaper correspondent, radio commentator, chief of Berlin Bureau of Associated Press), from 1931 (8 boxes); Anne Powers (Wis.; author), 1947-53 (5 boxes); and Charles D. Stewart (Wis.; author), from 1868 (26 boxes), including material he gathered about August Willich (Ohio; newspaper editor, Civil War officer). Also included are Milwaukee County property title records, 1842-1909 (2 boxes); business records and other papers of a German theater in Milwaukee, 1865-1930 (93 boxes); records of an insurance company, 1885-1920 (15 boxes), and of a lumber company, 1903-54 (800 pounds); papers relating to the participation of Milwaukee County in the Civil War and World Wars I and II (11 vols., 6 boxes, and 29 file drawers); records of the Republican County Committee (Milwaukee County), 1893-1904 (12 vols.); and examples of the printing and art work done by a lithographic company, 1893-1955 (55 vols. and 1 box).

Milwaukee Public Museum. Robert G. Lietz, Assistant in History.

Holdings: Papers of Solomon Juneau (Wis.; fur trader, agent of the American Fur Co., Milwaukee's first mayor), 1830-56 (600 items); business papers of an early Wisconsin settler, 1836-67 (2,075 items); and various account books and other business records, chiefly local, 1812-69 (15 vols.).

OSHKOSH

Oshkosh Public Museum. 1331 Algoma Blvd. Richard William Horton, Curator of Anthropology.

Holdings: Several thousand pieces, 1831-1959, relating chiefly to Wisconsin. There are some papers of Richard William Guenther (Wis.; pharmacist, U.S. Rep. and consul general); J. H. Osborn (Wis.; head of the State Grange, State railroad commissioner), 1866-83; and Philetus Sawyer (Wis.; mayor of Oshkosh, U.S. Rep. and Sen.) and his family. Included also are reminiscences of local inhabitants, 1831-1953; records of early trading posts; and a considerable collection of papers on lumbering, 1847-1930.

PRAIRIE DU CHIEN

Joyce Kilmer Memorial Library. Campion Jesuit High School. Gilbert C. Peterson, Librarian.

Holdings: A miscellaneous collection of manuscripts, 1817-1956, consisting chiefly of (1) 52 letters and some other papers of Joyce Kilmer (N.Y.; poet, essayist), and (2) papers relating to Prairie du Chien. In the latter group are records of a Catholic church, 1817-1956, and some Prairie du Chien court records, 1867-69.

RACINE

Racine County Courthouse Historical Room.   Wisconsin and Seventh Sts. (Mrs.) Jessie D. Baillie, Racine County Historian.

Holdings: 3,000 pieces, 1834-1954, relating chiefly to Racine County. Included are papers pertaining to railroads, bridges and harbors, pioneer industries, agriculture, schools and churches, and World War I activities.
See Hist. Records Survey, Guide for Wis., p. 20.

SHEBOYGAN

Sheboygan County Historical Society. Courthouse.

Holdings: 100 pieces and 8 bundles, 1750-1900, relating chiefly to Sheboygan County. Included are a few county archives; and papers of a plank road company, 1856-1900.
See Hist. Records Survey, Guide for Wis., p. 22.

SUPERIOR

Douglas County Historical Museum. 1827 John Ave.   James E. Lundsted, Curator.

Holdings: 250 pieces, 1854-1929, relating chiefly to the Head of the Lakes Region.   Included are papers relating to fur trading, mining, Indian lore, and the Civil War; and a few Douglas County court records, 1860-73.
See Hist. Records Survey, Guide for Wis., p. 23.

WATERTOWN

Watertown Historical Society.   Octagon House.   Gladys Mollart, Curator.

Holdings: 1,425 pieces, 1851-1960, relating chiefly to Watertown and Wisconsin.   Included are some letters of Ralph D. Blumenfeld (N.Y., England; newspaperman, editor, London Daily Express), 1904-38; and material on Joseph Edward Davies (D.C.; lawyer, U.S. Ambassador to U.S.S.R.), and on Carl Schurz (Wis., Mo., N.Y.; Civil War officer, U.S. Sen. from Mo., Sec. Interior) and his wife.   There are some miscellaneous business records and letters about the early kindergarten in Wisconsin.
See Hist. Records Survey, Guide for Wis., p. 25.

WAUKESHA

Waukesha County Historical Society Museum.   County Courthouse. (Mrs.) Edith W. Tallmadge, County Historian and Custodian.

Holdings: Several hundred pieces, 1840-1900, relating chiefly to Waukesha County.   Among the holdings are some Civil War diaries, rosters, and other papers, including pencil sketches of war scenes; account books of a local merchant, 1851-69, and other business records; a few church records; genealogical records of a number of Waukesha families and copies of tombstone inscriptions in 50 cemeteries; and a compilation of medical biographical records, covering 100 years (20 vols.).
See Hist. Records Survey, Guide for Wis., p. 26.

WAUSAU

Marathon County Historical Society. John L. Stoutenburgh, Jr., Executive Director.

Holdings: 6,000 pieces, 1834-1939, relating chiefly to Marathon County. Included are accounts of a general merchandise store, 1862-77, and records of other local businesses; minutes of meetings of agricultural and other local organizations; records of World War I activities; the logbook of the U. S. frigate Brandywine, 1834-37; and recollections of pioneers.

See Hist. Records Survey, Guide for Wis., p. 27.

WYOMING

CHEYENNE

Wyoming State Archives and Historical Department. Lola M. Homsher, Director.

Holdings: (1) 3,200 cu. ft. of original records of State and county governments of Wyoming, 1869-1958, and microfilm copies of 12,466,240 State documents and 1,200,804 county documents; and (2) 1,000 cu. ft. of historical materials relating chiefly to Wyoming, 1865-1960, including diaries, narratives of pioneers, collections of private papers, and pictures; and microfilm copies (121,000 images) of a number of collections of private papers that have been borrowed for filming.

CODY

Buffalo Bill Museum. (Mrs.) Mary Jester Allen, Director.

Holdings: A small collection of letters and other manuscripts by and about William Frederick Cody, known as Buffalo Bill (Kans., Wyo.; scout, showman, U.S. Army officer), relating to his life and scouting activities in the West.

FORT LARAMIE

Fort Laramie National Monument. Superintendent.

Holdings: 2 vols. and 9 boxes, 1850-90, consisting of some sutler's records, 1881-90, and other papers relating to Fort Laramie.

LARAMIE

Archives and Western History Department, University of Wyoming Library. James Ranz, Director of the Library; Gene M. Gressley, Archivist.

Holdings: A considerable quantity of manuscripts relating to the development of the Rocky Mountain region. Papers of individuals include those of Thurman Arnold (Wyo., Conn., D. C.; prof. of law at Yale Univ., Asst. U. S. Attorney Gen.), 1935-59; Frank A. Barrett (Wyo.; Gov., U. S. Rep. and Sen.), 1842-59; Lester C. Hunt (Wyo.; Gov., U. S. Sen.), 1948-54; John B. Kendrick (Wyo.; rancher, Gov., U. S. Sen.), 1917-33; Joseph C. O'Mahoney (Wyo.; U. S. Sen.), 1933-54; Edgar Wilson Nye, known as Bill Nye (Wyo., N. Y.; journalist, humorist, lecturer), 90 letters; Francis E. Warren (Wyo.; Gov., U. S. Sen.), 1873-1929; and Owen Wister (Pa.; novelist), including original journals and notebooks. Included also are records of Carter and Sweetwater Counties, 1868-93 (21 vols.); a Fort Laramie collection, 1868-1900; records of the Wyoming Stock Growers' Association, 1873-1921 (200,000 items); a Union Pacific Railroad collection (1,000 items); a collection on barbed wire (500,000 items); a livestock history collection (3,000 items); a collection on Indians, woman's suffrage, and western transportation (100,000 items); and a frontier justice collection. In the Petroleum History and Research Center there are manuscripts, corporate records, photographs, and recorded interviews providing information about the history of the petroleum industry in the Rocky Mountain region (100,000 items).

MOOSE

Grand Teton National Park. Superintendent.

Holdings: A small quantity of manuscripts relating to the Rocky Mountain region. Included is a diary of Thomas Moran (Pa., N.Y.; landscape painter, etcher), Aug. 1879 (1 vol.), kept on a camping and sketching trip from Fort Hall, Idaho, to the Teton Range.

YELLOWSTONE PARK

Yellowstone National Park. Superintendent.

Holdings: 50 vols. and 800 pieces, 1824-1951, relating to the park and the surrounding region. Materials concerning the Hayden Survey include a copy of a diary, 1872, of William Blackmore (England; financier, member of the Survey); copies of letters, 1872, of his 17-year-old nephew, Sidford F. Hamp (England, Colo.; author); excerpts from diaries, 1872 and 1878, kept by William Henry Holmes (Ohio, D. C.; archeologist, anthropologist, artist with the Survey); and a diary of Albert C. Peale, 1871-72 (Pa., D. C.; physician, mineralogist with the Survey, geologist). Other papers relating to Yellowstone Park include some of Nathaniel P. Langford (Mont.; explorer, park supt.), 1872 and later (2 vols. and 1 piece), and letters and a journal kept by other park officials, 1903-21; letters by Stephen Tyng Mather (ill., D. C.; organizer and director of the National Park Service), 1917-19; and letters and legal papers of John W. Meldrum (Ark., Colo., Wyo.; Sec. and acting Gov. of Wyo. Terr., U. S. Commissioner of Yellowstone National Park), 1894-1933 (480 pieces). There are also official diaries of park scouts, 1872-1912 (46 vols.); a record of burials at Fort Yellowstone, 1886-1914 (2 vols.); and scattered letters and diaries of travelers to and through the park region, 1824-1908.

INDEX

Numbers in parentheses following page numbers indicate two or more occurrences of a name on a page. All proper names and subjects are indexed except those in parenthetical identifications of individuals and in the citations to books and articles. Names of heads of depositories or collections do not appear. The user is warned that subject entries do not constitute a complete analysis of subjects in the manuscripts; only when a subject has been specifically mentioned in the text above does it appear in the index.

UNITED STATES GOVERNMENT